CONCRETE SOLUTIONS

PROCEEDINGS OF CONCRETE SOLUTIONS, 4TH INTERNATIONAL CONFERENCE ON CONCRETE REPAIR, DRESDEN, GERMANY, 26–28 SEPTEMBER 2011

Concrete Solutions

Editors

Michael Grantham
Concrete Solutions, Margate, Kent, UK
Sandberg LLP, London UK

Viktor Mechtcherine
Institute of Construction Materials, Faculty of Civil Engineering, Technische Universität Dresden, Dresden, Germany

Ulrich Schneck
CITec GmbH, Concrete Improvement Technologies, Dresden OT Cossebaude, Germany

CRC Press
Taylor & Francis Group
Boca Raton   London   New York   Leiden

CRC Press is an imprint of the
Taylor & Francis Group, an **informa** business

A BALKEMA BOOK

Cover photo credits: The ASR photo by Eric R. Giannini of the University of Texas at Austin and the repair of the cooling tower by Mieczyslaw Kaminski of Wroclaw University.

CRC Press/Balkema is an imprint of the Taylor & Francis Group, an informa business

© 2012 Taylor & Francis Group, London, UK

Typeset by Vikatan Publishing Solutions (P) Ltd., Chennai, India
Printed and bound in Great Britain by Antony Rowe (a CPI Group Company), Chippenham, Wiltshire

Published by: CRC Press/Balkema
  P.O. Box 447, 2300 AK Leiden, The Netherlands
  e-mail: Pub.NL@taylorandfrancis.com
  www.crcpress.com – www.taylorandfrancis.co.uk – www.balkema.nl

ISBN: 978-0-415-61622-5 (Hbk)
ISBN: 978-0-203-13468-9 (eBook)

Concrete Solutions – Grantham, Mechtcherine & Schneck (eds)
© *2012 Taylor & Francis Group, London, ISBN 978-0-415-61622-5*

Table of contents

Preface	xi
Core sponsor	xiii

Case studies

Case study for the construction repair of destructive skeleton concrete building by lateral forces *A.S.A. Al-Ameeri*	3
Analysis of damage and repair techniques of cracked structural elements in an underground part of a high RC building *G. Dmochowski, J. Dudkiewicz & P. Berkowski*	9
The refurbishment of Bideford Longbridge *J. Drewett & N. Bott*	15
Concept of concrete slab repairs of a flood water dry reservoir *A. Duber & A. Pawlowski*	19
An innovative repair and refurbishment of an underground car park in Dresden, Germany *H. Esteves, U. Hammer, S. Mayer & P. Chess*	25
Damage evaluation and repair proposals for reinforced concrete foundations with corrosion damage, and power line towers on a lagoon, Colima, Mexico *A. Garduno & A. Reyes*	31
Diagnosis and repair of cracking to an old 1880's concrete house for Channel 4 Television, UK *M.G. Grantham, S. Pitchers & S. Jones*	39
Vulnerability assessment of the concrete tanks storage at natural hazards *H. Hammoum, K. Bouzelha, N.E. Hannachi & D. Serre*	45
From concrete repair to concrete conservation: How to preserve the heritage values of historic concrete *H.A. Heinemann, H. Zijlstra, R.P.J. van Hees & T.G. Nijland*	55
Stitching the past—"The strengthening of two heritage marine structures in Jersey with needling technology" *S. Hold*	69
Strengthening and rehabilitation of two damaged bridges in the motorway M-410 in Madrid *C. Jurado Cabañes*	79
Extent of condition assessment of concrete building—practical experiences *J. Lahdensivu & S. Varjonen*	85
Fabrication technology-related cracking of prestressed concrete elements *A.-T. Mircea*	91
Proposal for the retrofit of the world heritage site of Arge Bam after earthquake damage *J. Motamed & A.M. Alani*	95
Corrosion damage of centrifuged reinforced concrete elements *I. Pepenar*	101

Investigation of a repair system in a concrete jetty in the Persian Gulf 105
R. Rashetnia, A. Dousti, F. Moradi-Marani & M. Shekarchi

Non-destructive diagnosis and repair of 300 concrete columns beneath a shopping
mall under full operation 113
U. Schneck

Electrochemical repair

Use of electrochemical migration to mitigate alkali-silica reaction in large scale concrete structures 123
A.F. Bentivegna, E.R. Giannini & K.J. Folliard

Maintenance of transport structures using electrochemical solutions 133
R. Brueckner, C. Atkins, A. Foster, R. Merola & P. Lambert

A new approach for the patch repair of car parks using galvanic anodes 141
C. Christodoulou, J. Webb, G. Glass, S. Austin & C. Goodier

Short-term benefits of cathodic protection of steel in concrete 147
J. Pacheco, R.B. Polder, A.L.A. Fraaij & J.M.C. Mol

Performance and working life of cathodic protection systems for concrete structures 157
R.B. Polder, D. Worm, W. Courage & G. Leegwater

Galvanic corrosion protection of steel in concrete with a zinc mesh anode embedded
into a solid electrolyte (EZA) 163
W. Schwarz, F. Müllner & A. van den Hondel

General repair

Punching strengthening of two-way slabs using a prestressing technique 177
T.F. El-Shafiey & A.M. Atta

Preconditioning concrete for better freeze-thaw durability 187
A. Badr

Effect of using corrosion inhibitors on concrete properties and their activity 195
H.M. Al-Baghdadi & A.M.A. Amir

The use of performance-based specifications to prevent repair of reinforced concrete structures 205
H. Beushausen

An experimental study on the inhibition of calcium nitrite, amino alcohol and sodium
fluorophosphate as reinforced concrete protection 215
A. El shami, M. Choinska, S. Bonnet, P. Mounanga & A. Khelidj

Hybrid connections—the sustainable approach for prefabricated frame structures 227
A. Faur & C. Mircea

Pumping influence on fresh properties of self-consolidating concrete 233
N. Ghafoori, H. Diawara, D. Nyknahad, M. Barfield & M.S. Islam

A comparative study of anti-corrosion products for the protection of reinforcement in monuments 237
A. Gralińska-Grubecka & J.W. Łukaszewicz

Comparison of concrete expansion and stiffness due to alkali-silica reactivity 243
M.S. Islam & N. Ghafoori

Evaluation of restrained shrinkage of repair materials under the local environment of Riyadh 251
M.I. Khan, T.H. Almusallam, S.H. Alsayed, Y.A. Al-Salloum & A.A. Almosa

Experimental research of the intensity of corrosion processes influence by tensile stress
for reinforcing steel covered with polymer sulphur composites 257
M. Książek

Corrosion analysis of reinforced geopolymer concretes 267
K. Kupwade-Patil, E.N. Allouche, S. Vaidya & E.I. Diaz-Loya

The role of ascorbic acid on the adsorption to passive iron surface 279
H. Tian, W. Li, B. Hou & D. Wang

Geopolymer concrete: A concrete of the next decade 287
D.B. Raijiwala & H.S. Patil

Numerical investigation on the effect of concrete-FRP bond on the flexural behavior of RC beams 293
S. Sajedi, F. Ghassemzadeh, M. Shekarchi, F. Faraji & M. Soleimani

Evaluation of the hydration of concrete mixtures by ultrasonic testing 299
A.A. Shah & Y. Ribakov

Self crack healing of strain hardening cementitious composite incorporating expansive agent and
crystalline additive
K. Sisomphon, O. Copuroglu & E.A.B. Koenders 307

Properties of fine cement concretes with carbonaceous nanoparticles 313
S.N. Tolmachev & O.A. Belichenko

The search for alternative reinforcement materials for concrete 325
H.G. Wheat & S. Dale

Determination of the crack self-healing capacity of bacterial concrete 331
V. Wiktor & H.M. Jonkers

Degradation mechanism and repair technology of a concrete structure of a railway
ballastless track
Z. Yi, H. Li, Y. Xie & Y. Tan 335

Non destructive testing and diagnosis of problems

Computerized assessment of the moisture and thermal originated deterioration of concrete facades 343
F. Al-Neshawy, J. Piironen & J. Puttonen

Non-destructive electrical resistivity measurement technique: Evaluation of concrete strengths 349
N.H. El-Ashkar

Applicability of an electromagnetic wave method for estimation of chloride content
of coastal structures
J. Nojima & T. Mizobuchi 359

A fundamental study on quantitative assessment of steel corrosion by a new NDT method
with induction heating
K. Kobayashi, R. Nakamura, K. Rokugo & S. Nakazawa 369

Comparative study of techniques to evaluate the corrosion activity of rebars embedded
in concrete
E. Marie-Victoire, A. Proust, V. L'Hostis & F. Vallot 377

Evaluation of mechanical parameters in repair concrete with impact-echo test method 387
S.R. Moghadam, M.H. Eftekhar, M. Shekarchi, S. Javidmehr, A. Dousti & M. Valipour

Wireless localization of areas with a high corrosion risk on reinforced concrete structures 391
K. Reichling & M. Raupach

Automated multi-sensor systems in civil engineering for condition assessment of concrete structures 397
M. Stoppel, A. Taffe, H. Wiggenhauser, J.H. Kurz & C. Boller

A study on non-destructive measurement using Prompt Gamma-ray Analysis of chloride
profile in concrete
I. Ujike, S. Okazaki, M. Yamate & H. Matsue 405

NDT based evaluation of rubber modified self-compacting concrete 413
M. Usman, M. Rahman & A. Al-Ghalib

Evaluation of bridge decks using Ground Probing Radar (GPR) 419
V. Utsi & A. Birtwisle

Structural life management system of box culverts for power transmission lines   423
S.K. Woo, Y.C. Song, J.H. Jo, J.H. Park & Y. Lee

Modular Corrosion Measurement System (CMS) for electrochemical NDT   427
K. Ahlborn, F. Berthold, W. Vonau, H. Grünzig, U. Schneck, H. Jahn & J. Köhler

Patch repair

Application of polymer concrete in repair of concrete structures: A literature review   435
R. Allahvirdizadeh, R. Rashetnia, A. Dousti & M. Shekarchi

Benchmarking laboratory investigated locally available repair materials against their
manufacturer's data sheets   445
M.I. Khan, T.H. Almusallam, S.H. Alsayed, Y.A. Al-Salloum & A.A. Almosa

Influence of selected aspects of the mixture proportioning on the performance
of repair mortars   451
P. Ramge, H.-C. Kühnen & B. Meng

A rational method for calculation of restrained shrinkage stresses in repaired concrete members   461
S. Sajedi, A. Razavizadeh, Z. Minaii, F. Ghassemzadeh & M. Shekarchi

Discussion on crack path of interface between concrete and polymer cement mortar   467
K. Yamada, A. Satoh, T. Homma, S. Ishiyama & Y. Shinohara

Scaling resistance and application of cementitious repair mortars for concrete barriers   479
W. Yang, Y. Ge, X. Cai & X. Chen

Repair of fire damage

Basic techniques for the damage assessment of concrete members after fire   487
E. Annerel & L. Taerwe

Behaviour of concrete containing lightweight expanded clay aggregates under high temperatures   491
H. Kew, T. Donchev & N. Petkune

Fire damaged concrete—the potential for on-going deterioration post-fire in concrete heated
to temperatures of less than 300°C   497
M.A. Eden

Flexural behavior of partially restrained beams of self compacting concrete exposed to fire flame   503
G. Habeeb & A. Al-Juborry

Assessment of fire damage of an old RC structure   511
Gh. Petrovay & C. Mircea

Assessing concrete repair after thermal exposure: Effect of aggregates on 3D response   517
G. Xotta, V.A. Salomoni & C.E. Majorana

Service life modelling

The application of simple modeling techniques to corrosion induced deterioration
of reinforced concrete   527
J.P. Broomfield

A critical examination of the chloride migration test to assess the resistance of concrete
against chloride ingress   535
J.J.W. Gulikers

Calculating the need for repair of concrete facades in the Finnish climate   541
A. Köliö & J. Lahdensivu

Prediction of reliability of utility tunnel structures subject to dynamic loads   547
M. Kurgansky, V. Gaponov & S. Pavlov

Service life prediction of underground concrete pipes subjected to corrosion   551
M. Mahmoodian & C.Q. Li

Repairing structures for nuclear facilities: A numerical approach by means of FEM
and Monte Carlo techniques 557
B. Pomaro, V.A. Salomoni, C.E. Majorana, F. Gramegna & G. Prete

Multi-physics numerical model for the repair of concrete structures 565
G. Sciumè & B.A. Schrefler

Strengthening materials and techniques/repair with composites

Damage and repair quantification in reinforced concrete beams using vibration data 575
A. Al-Ghalib, F. Mohammad, M. Rahman & J. Chilton

Flexural behaviour of concrete beams reinforced with CFRP composites 585
M.K. Ali, D.B. Tann & A.I. Abu-Tair

Safety of RC highway bridges strengthened with CFRP; flexural and shear limit states 593
O. Ali & D. Bigaud

Strengthening of rectangular reinforced concrete columns using fiber glass reinforced polymers 607
A.H. Elzanaty, H.M. Allam & A. Fawzi

FRP strengthening of shear walls with openings 615
K. Behfarnia, A. Sayah & Sh. Eghtesadi

Using mineral based composites for shear strengthening concrete members 623
T. Blanksvärd & B. Täljsten

Behaviour of RC elements internally reinforced with BFRP at elevated temperatures 631
T. Donchev, P.L. Blanco & P.S. Shah

Rehabilitation of reinforced concrete beams with insufficient longitudinal reinforcement
lap-splice length using FRP sheets
639
M.M. Sayed & T.M. Elrakib

Strengthening of T section RC beams in shear using CFRP 649
E.E. Etman

Concrete repair and strengthening with ultra ductile micro-mesh reinforced mortar 661
C. Flohrer, M. Tschötschel & S. Hauser

Applied research and recent developments on composite material technology
for structural strengthening
667
E. Fyfe, M. Karantzikis & C. Kolyvas

Flexural behavior of CFRP-strengthened and corroded reinforced concrete beams 673
M. Hussein

Using steel fibred high strength concrete for repairing normal strength concrete beams and slabs 681
I. Iskhakov, Y. Ribakov, K. Holschemacher & T. Mueller

Improving the flexural performance of reinforced concrete one-way slabs 689
K.K. Shadhan, A.S.A. Al-Ameeri & N.H. Ali

Time-dependent behaviour of CFRP-strengthened reinforced concrete beams 697
M. Kaminski, E. Kusa & D. Demski

Behaviour of damaged RC beams repaired with NSM CFRP rods 705
A. Kreit, A. Castel, R. Francois & F. Al-Mahmoud

Strengthening of reinforced concrete beam-column joints using ferrocement 717
B. Li & E.S.S. Lam

Engineered Cementitious Composite as a durability protective layer for concrete 727
Y. Lin, L. Wotherspoon, J.M. Ingham, A. Scott & D. Lawley

Three-dimensional modeling of externally repaired beams using FRP sheets during short
and long term loading
735
G. Mazzucco, V.A. Salomoni & C.E. Majorana

Strengthening/retrofitting of masonry by using thin layers of Sprayed Strain-Hardening
Cement-Based Composites (SSHCC)   741
V. Mechtcherine, A.-E. Bruedern & T. Urbonas

A comparative study for shear strengthening techniques of reinforced concrete beams using FRP   749
A.M. Morsy, N.H. El-Ashkar & K.M. Helmi

Repairing reinforced concrete rectangular columns using ferrocement laminates   757
S.M. Mourad & M.J. Shannag

Residual strength of CFRP strengthened beams after heating and cooling   765
D. Petkova & T. Donchev

Strain hardening cement-based composites for repair layers on cracked concrete surfaces   775
C. Wagner & V. Slowik

Flexural strengthening of RC-structures by textile reinforced concrete in practical application   783
S. Weiland, E. Lorenz, Ch. Hankers & D. Matzdorff

Restoring the bearing capacity of circular tunnel linings with the help of high-strength
carbon fibre mesh   789
A.A. Shilin, V. Gaponov, E.Z. Axelrod & S.S. Zalomov

UHPFRC composition optimization for application in rehabilitation of RC structures   795
M. Skazlić, K. Ille & M. Ille

Surface protection methods and materials

Quality control of hydrophobic coatings with an integrated marker element by Laser-Induced
Breakdown Spectroscopy (LIBS)   805
K. Bienert, H. Schalk, A. Molkenthin, G. Wilsch, S. Goldschmidt & E. Niederleithinger

Surface protection of high performance architectural concrete   813
V.R. Falikman, Yu. V. Sorokin & V.V. Deniskin

Coatings and overlays for concrete affected by alkali-silica reaction   823
E.R. Giannini, A.F. Bentivegna & K.J. Folliard

Whole life costing

Life cycle cost analysis of reinforced concrete structures cast with self-compacting concrete
and normally vibrated concrete   835
K.K. Sideris, A. Georgiadis, N. Anagnostopoulos, P. Manita & E. Skarlatos

Epoxy-coated reinforcement—life cycle cost considerations   841
M. Zintel, C. Gehlen & B. Prust

Author index   855

Concrete Solutions – Grantham, Mechtcherine & Schneck (eds)
© 2012 Taylor & Francis Group, London, ISBN 978-0-415-61622-5

Preface

The Concrete Solutions series of International Conferences on Concrete Repair began in 2003, with a conference held in St. Malo, France in association with INSA Rennes. The second conference in 2006 was also held with INSA again, at St. Malo. In 2009, the event was held in Padova and Venice, in association with the University of Padova, with Taylor and Francis publishing the Proceedings for the first time. Now in 2011, the event is being held in Dresden in Germany and has brought together some 112 papers from 33 countries.

Whereas electrochemical repair tended to dominate the papers in earlier years, new developments in structural strengthening with composites have been an increasingly important topic, with a quarter of the papers now focusing on this area. New techniques involving Near Surface Mounted (NSM) carbon fibre rods, strain hardening composites, and new techniques involving the well established carbon fibre and polyimide wrapping and strengthening systems are presented. Seventeen papers concentrate on case studies which are all-important in such conferences, to learn about what works (and what doesn't work!) on real structures. 13 papers are devoted to new developments in NDT. Other topics include service life modelling, fire damage, surface protection methods and coatings, patch repair, general repair techniques and whole life costing.

This book is essential reading for anyone engaged in the concrete repair field, from Engineers, to academics and students and also to clients, who, as the end user, are ultimately responsible for funding these projects and making those difficult decisions about which system or method to use.

Concrete Solutions – Grantham, Mechtcherine & Schneck (eds)
© 2012 Taylor & Francis Group, London, ISBN 978-0-415-61622-5

Core sponsor

Innovative Systems for professional Building Materials Testing

Toni Technik provides a comprehensive range of equipment for quality control of building materials:
From automatic systems up to versatile solutions for specific applications.
Complete service from planning, delivery up to installation, training and after sales service.

The program:

- Servohydraulic compression and flexure testing machines
- Automated sample preparation machines and units
- Instruments for the manual and automatic determination of material characteristics
- Complete test laboratories incl. planning
- Modernisation and upgrading of testing machines
- International sales and service network including calibration

Case studies

Concrete Solutions – Grantham, Mechtcherine & Schneck (eds)
© 2012 Taylor & Francis Group, London, ISBN 978-0-415-61622-5

Case study for the construction repair of destructive skeleton concrete building by lateral forces

A.S.A. Al-Ameeri

Department of Civil Engineering, College of Engineering, University of Babylon, Iraq

ABSTRACT: The study deals with construction repair for destructive members in a skeleton concrete building which had been affected by lateral loads (explosive forces). The explosive forces came from the destruction of neighboring buildings by using explosive materials. This lead to breaking of a group of columns and cracking of the beams and slabs in this building. The failure of columns caused vertical displacement in levels of beams and slabs at different floors, the lower limit of deflection was 2.5 cm and the upper limit was 42.5 cm. The degree of destruction of members in the building was different according to the distance of members from the outside of the building, as the range affected lateral loads due to explosive forces.

The aim of the study was the application and evaluation of scientifically sound construction repair on this building, so that the building would be able to carry design loads and architectural requirements could be restored. This treatment was carried out by using Epoxy Adhesive Resin—type I material for crack widths less than 1mm and fixing plates and using epoxy material for crack widths more than 1 mm. The parts of building having vertical displacements were jacked up by using hydraulic jacks having a capacity of 50 tones or 100 tones with jacking applied carefully and in equilibrium to avoid new cracks in the building. Those members (columns, beams, slabs) too severely damaged were removed and recast, and reconnected to the existing old concrete in these members by using expansive cement. The original design parameters and specifications used in the original design were retained.

1 INTRODUCTION

Exposed reinforced concrete structures either through age or to damage caused by errors in design or the manner of implementation or by the use of poor quality materials can cause problems in service. Typically deterioration results from the impact of environmental factors and circumstances surrounding it, such as sulfate salts or chlorides attacking the building (Neville, 2000), or by exposing buildings to forces exceeding the calculated design (Lateral Forces) which can result from impact or blast. These Lateral forces are not taken into account in the design and especially the design of the columns, and can thus lead to additional damage to the columns or can break them in multiple areas. Such destructive forces can also lead to vertical displacement (Deflection) in the levels of beams and slabs of various decks and this difference in vertical deflection can lead to the generation of strong shearing and bending moments in flexure, which generates stresses additional to these members of the construction (Wang—1953). and hence the occurrence of damage, cracks and displacement resulting from the cracking of the columns. The result of either deterioration due to environmental factors or to destruction by explosive forces leads to problems for the construction and service sectors.

The process of demolition of damaged buildings and the impact of brainstorming requires economic costs and expensive waste of effort and time compared with the costs and efforts of repairing structurally when possible, while maintaining the final form of the building and fulfilling the basic requirements to them.

2 STRUCTURAL EVALUATION

The evaluation of the degree of damage to buildings is done through evaluation of the structural parts affected, which is an essential stage before taking the decision on the possibility of repair or even partial reconstruction of the building or whether to resort to demolition, and it should stand on some important details, including:-

2.1 A general description of the building

The building was an industrial building, built at the end of the 1970's. The structure of the building was from reinforced concrete, consisting of two parts, each part consisted of seven portals, each containing part on two floors and the ground floor as well as shown in Figure (1).

The buildings adjacent to the building in this study were destroyed as a result of bombardment with explosives, and this led to the failure of a set of columns which failed completely, and also to cracking of another set of columns, beams, and slabs which caused vertical displacement (Deflection) in the levels of beams and ceilings with different values for the various decks and beyond—in one of the areas to causing it to offset by 42.5 cm from the original level of the slab in the region of the column (X7-Y3), as shown in Figure (2) and Picture (1).

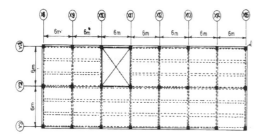

Figure 1. The structural plan of the one part of the building.

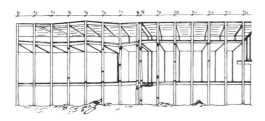

Figure 2. Graphic illustration of the building at the stage of the survey and pre-treatment.

Picture 1. The state of the building during the initial pre-treatment (evaluation) stage.

2.2 Structural members were damaged

The evaluation was based on the amount of exposure to the destructive structural forces and stresses that impacted on the assessment of the structural efficiency of the affected members and this can be summarized as follows:-

2.2.1 Columns

The initial survey of the columns showed that the damage occurred could be divided into two types:-

A—Columns affected by substantial damage (total failure), any breakup of the three areas of the end, the upper and the lower, middle and thus pushing the column from the end, or the upper to the bottom of the inside beams, as in the Picture (2), which generates a displacement in the level of beam and the slab for that area of various values, as shown in Table (1), and therefore require

Picture 2. Samples of the columns affected by the substantial damage.

Table 1. Columns damaged and the amount of deflection generated as a result of this damage in the slabs level.

Floor	Column position	Deflection (cm)
Ground floor	X8–Y3	2.5
Ground floor	X8/–Y3	8
First floor	X4–Y3	7.5
First floor	X6–Y3	23.5
First floor	X7–Y3	42.5
First floor	X8–Y3	35.5
First floor	X8/–Y3	3
First floor	X9–Y3	0
First floor	X10–Y3	0

treatment to remove the broken columns, and to be near to the point of lift of the building.

B-Columns less affected (with cracks in that could be treated: they were on the ground floor columns on the axes (X6-Y2), (X7-Y2) or on the first floor columns on the axes (X5-Y3), (X11-Y3), (X12-Y3), (X13-Y3).

2.2.2 Beams

Because of the differences for vertical deflection, shear forces and bending moments caused stresses in the beams which thus got cracks in the most confined beams between the affected columns and the size of this damage depended on the amount of damage to adjacent columns, as shown in Figure (3). Although inspection of the slab showed some areas where there was minor damage, some areas such as those located between grids (Y2-Y3, X8-X9), were much more damaged as in Picture (3), which required removal and re-casting.

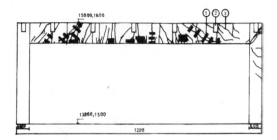

Figure 3. Section in a sample of beam described by the types of cracks occurring and methods of Repair.

1: The use of Epoxy with the installation of sheet steel width 5 cm and thickness of 0.5 cm to deal with crack widths larger than 1 mm.
2: Lintel secondary beam.
3: Use the Epoxy only to treat the crack widths less than 1 mm.

Picture 3. Damage occurring from the slab and secondary beams in the slab, located between grids (Y2-Y3/X8-X9).

3 STAGES FOR CONSTRUCTION TREATMENT

The Stages were included the following:-

3.1 Soil investigations

The purpose of the investigation was to know the possibility of the soil to carry the foundations of the building, especially after the forces of a seismic impact on the soil, through a change in some of the engineering properties. After conducting these investigations (by the National Center for construction Laboratories, NCCL) the results were positive, so the effect was limited, and this stimulate the decision-making resulting in repair and partial reconstruction of the building.

3.2 Stages of repairs

In the light of the positive results of the soil investigations the decision was made to address the building problems and not to resort to destroy it. In other words to address the members affected and to perform the functions required in terms of construction, service and the procedures for treatment in stages, as follows:-

3.2.1 The stage of engineering surveys for levels of columns, beams and slabs

Surveys were completed of the building as illustrated in table (1), which showed the largest group of vertical displacement (42.5 cm) and horizontal displacement (25 cm) in the axis (X7-Y3).

3.2.2 The stage of temporary supporting (Initial) of the building

This phase required calculating the existing loads as shown in Table (3), by using Mechanical Jacks see Picture (4), because the building wasn't able to carry any vibrations' result removal the finishes

Table 2. Properties of epoxy adhesive resin—Type I used in the treatment of cracks.

Test	Result test	(ASTM C881-90) limits
Viscosity (pa.s) grade 1	2	Not more than 2
Consistency (mm)	7	–
Setting time (sec.)	35	Not less than 30
Bonding strength at age (4 days) N/mm^2	12	Not less than 10.3
Absorption (24 hours) Upper limit %	1	Not more than 1
Tensile strength at age (7 days) N/mm^2	36	Not less than 34.5
Elongation at failure %	2	Not less than 1

Table 3. The actual load at each point of the floors.

Floor	Amount of load during the supporting stage (Ton)	Amount of load during the lifting stage (Ton)
Ground floor	80	50
First floor	60	42
Second floor	27	27

Picture 4. Building during the initial phase of the supporting by Mechanical Jacks.

floors of the work, especially the group of columns were had large damage, to provide safety work.

3.2.3 Removal of finishes and restoring flatness for the all floors

In order to reduce loads and to facilitate the process of lifting by hydraulic jacks, as well as damage to a section of the layers some materials were removed, ranging from a layer of concrete with waterproofing (15 cm), and with the removal of a flat layer, consisting of tiling by pre cast concrete units with a layer of tar and moisture-proofing materials.

3.2.4 Stage of treatment of cracks in roofs and main beams

Treatment is classified into two categories namely:

A. Injection (Epoxy Adhesive Resin-Type I) with low viscosity, and properties as in Table (2). The resin was selected to satisfy the American Society for Testing and Materials (ASTM C881-02) for shear and flexural cracks with width (0.5–1) mm (U.S. Army Corps Engineers-2001) as shown in Figure (3).
B. Injection (Epoxy Adhesive Resin-Type I) with fixed sheets of steel Plate width 5 cm and a thickness 0.5 cm, and a length depending on the location of cracks, by screws (Anchor Bolts), and perpendicular to the direction of cracks. This treatment was used for cracks greater than 1 mm (Minour-2001), as is shown both in Figures (3) and (4), in beams at ground

and first floor beams on the axes (X4, X6, X7, X8, X8/, X9, X10).

3.2.5 The stage of main supporting of the building

During this phase the building was supported by using steel columns section. The section of this columns is consist of (HP14 *17) installed on base plates at upper and lower ends with a dimension (50*50*3 cm), and then insert in between the HP and the girder a built-up section in I—shape . This built-up I shape is consist of (W8X67) in web and welding to it two steel plates at the open sides and the same composite section will be used at flange as shown in Figure (5, 6), where the choice of these sections was not solely to prop up the building (AISC-Manual Steel-2003), but to provide greater space for freedom of action to the movement of hydraulic jacks on these sections to make it possible to break down and remove columns in damaged areas by lifting of the building as a whole in the areas of the columns of the ground floor on the axes (X8-Y3), (X8 /-Y3), and columns on the first floor on the axes (X4-Y3), (X6-Y3), (X7-Y3), (X8-Y3), (X8/-Y3), (X9-Y3) and (X10-Y3), taking care not to damage or generate shear forces at the beams on the ground floor.

3.2.6 Stage crushing and removal of damaged columns

The stage was of the process of crushing and removal of columns damaged completely (Full Failure) and where there was a vertical displacement and failure in the areas of connectivity with the beams with the plan to restore them later, as well as facilitating the process of lifting of the building, taking into account leaving the dowel bars from all ends of the top and bottom of the column where it been crushed and removed from its position, as shown in Picture (2) and Figure (6).

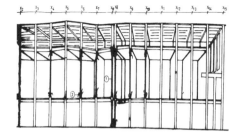

Figure 5. Graphic illustration of the building in the main supporting phase by the steel sections and lifting stage.

1: A section of a steel column (HP 14 * 17) with a base of sheet thickness 3 cm, 2: (Dowels Bar).

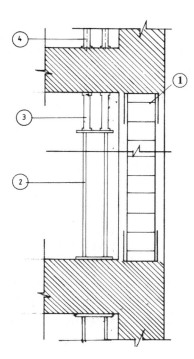

Figure 6. Graphic illustration for the side view of damaged columns during the supporting stage by steel sections, lifting and re-casting stage.

1: The part that has been treated using expanded cement with link connection with dowel bars, 2: A column of steel section (HP14 * 117) with the base plate thickness 3 cm., 3: The supports from steel built up section (W8*87) with plate thickness 1 cm., 4: Mechanical jacks.

3.2.7 *The stage of raising the building*

The lifting of the building was from the focal points (areas of broken column) as shown in Table (1) by two hydraulic jacks, with a capacity of 50 tons and the other 100 tons, to be equivalent to the loads that were actually present in the building in those points as shown in Table (4). Lifting was performed in a series of stages and parallel extent at sites lifted for the maintenance of the building, because the concrete is a brittle material (Neville-2000), where the amount of phase raised one (2.5 cm), and then supported and then directing the second phase so as to ensure beams and slabs were maintained level without the emergence of new cracks as a result of lifting, Table (5) illustrates the sequence and the amount of lifting at each point in the axes of the columns.

3.2.8 *Stage of treatment and repairs of the dam aged members of the building*

This stage was made after the process of lifting the building and included the repairs of each of the columns, the beams and ceilings as follows:

Table 4. The sequence and the amount of lift at each point of the columns.

Floor	Axes position	Amount of lift at each point (cm)
Ground floor	X8–Y3	8
First floor	X8–Y3	3
First floor	X7–Y3	10
First floor	X8–Y3	7.5
First floor	X7–Y3	7
First floor	X6–Y3	10
First floor	X8–Y3	7
Ground floor	X7–Y3	5
First floor	X8–Y3	2.5
First floor	X7–Y3	7
First floor	X8–Y3	7.5
First floor	X8–Y3	5
First floor	X7–Y3	7.5
First floor	X6–Y3	13.5
First floor	X7–Y3	6
First floor	X8–Y3	8.5
First floor	X4–Y3	7.5

A-Beams and Slabs: this included treatment of cracks in the beams that had emerged after lifting by the same method in paragraph (3.2.4). The treatment of failure in secondary beams for the slab in the confined region (X8-X9/Y2-Y3) as shown in Picture (3), had been broken and re-cast with reinforced concrete with a compressive strength of grade 25 N/mm² and the distribution of the same reinforcement as was originally used in the structural design of the building, taking into account the interdependence between the treatment of old concrete and modern concrete mixes by using Expansive Cement (Orchard—1979).

B—Treatment of columns: this consisted of two types:

1. Columns that were damaged completely by breaking down the columns shown in the Table (1), using the master plans of the building, the columns were replaced by columns of the same design, connected by dowel bars during treatment, as in paragraph (3.2.6), and then re-casting the concrete for the column with a compressive strength of grade (25 N/mm²) with processing of the last half meter of the length of the column by using a mixture of concrete where it been contained expansive cement to connect between new and old concrete (Orchard—1979), and also shown in Figure (6).

2. Columns with cracks: the ground floor columns, and columns on the first floor where it was processed by adding a casing (Ali—1998), (Kadhim—1992), by adding a layer to the

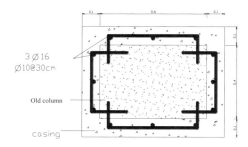

3 ∅ 16
∅10@30cm

Old column

casing

Figure 7. Treatment of damage columns (simple) by using a casing of concrete.

dimensions of the reinforced concrete column from all directions, with rebars added to the annular and longitudinal steel, reinforcing the old concrete through punching the old concrete and rebar and drilling new holes in the treated areas to insert the new reinforcement in the floor, slab and columns, followed by grouting with Epoxy Adhesive as shown in Figure (7).

3.2.9 *Final stage procedure to remove the supports and complete the work*

After the full maturation of the recast concrete to get the desired compressive strength of the concrete used in the new columns to remove:

A. Mechanical supports in all floors.
B. Columns—sections of steel.

Re-layer surfacing of the upper floor with the same specifications prepared with re-laying flooring to the first and second floors using a dehumidifier to remove moisture, to ensure that damaged concrete was free from dampness.

4 CONCLUSIONS AND RECOMMENDATION

Through the review of the building before, during and after treatment we reached the following conclusions:-

1. The larger deflection observed in the column on the axis (X7-Y3) was 42.5 cm, prompting the process of lifting the building by hydraulic jacks in phases and each phase not exceeding 2.5 cm. This did not affect the nature of the building.
2. column damage on the ground floor on the axes (X8-Y3), (X8/-Y3), and the first floor on the axes (X4-Y3), (X6-Y3), (X7-Y3), (X8-Y3), (X8/-Y3), (X9-Y3) and (X10-Y3), prompting the need to remove them before lifting the building by hydraulic jacks with the same method mentioned previously in paragraph (1), and then re-casting them with the approved design specifications of the building.
3. damage to a few columns on the ground floor and on the axes (X6-Y2), and the first floor on the axes (X5-Y3), (X11-Y3), (X12-Y3) and (X13-Y3), which was handled by the encasing with reinforced concrete of thickness 10 cm on the perimeter columns.
4. Treating the beams along the damaged column axes by using Epoxy resin for cracks less than 1 mm, with the use and installation of steel sheet width (5 cm) and thickness (0.5 mm) by anchor bolts for cracks larger than (1 mm).
5. Removing the damaged portions of the slab in the area bounded by axes (X8-X9/Y2-Y3) and re-casting with concrete with the same specifications and approved plans for the building design.
6. Working to open new horizons for the treatment of buildings that deserve treatment and returned to service, and on a scientific basis and to achieve the basic requirements depending on the scientific and practical experiences in this field.

REFERENCES

Ali, Ammar Yasser. "Construction Treatment of a Building Affected by the Exposure of Fire Flame", *Journal of the University of Babylon*/Applied Science/ Volume 3/No. 5/1998.
American Institute of Steel Construction, *Manual of Steel Construction, Allowable Stress Design*, Ninth Edition, 2003, Part 3, (5–20).
ASTM C881-02. "Standard Specification for Epoxy-Resin Based Bonding Systems for Concrete".
Kadhim, Haider. "Evaluation of Reinforced Concrete Parts by Using Reinforced Mortar "Master's thesis/ Faculty of Engineering /University of Baghdad, 1992.
Minour A., Toshiro K., Yuichi U. and Keitetsu R. "Evaluation of Bond Properties in Concrete Repair Material", *Jounal of Material in Civil Engineering*, 2001–March–April, pp. (98–105).
Nevill A.M. 2000. Properties of Concrete, Fifth Edition, pitman press, London, Ch. 9(415) & Ch. 10 (509–514).
Orchard, D.F. 1979. Concrete Technology, Vol. I, Fourth Edition, Applied Science Publisher, Ltd., London., Ch. 1 (59).
U.S., Army Corps of Engineers, Engineering and Design-Standard Practice for Concrete for Civil Works Structure, CECW-EG, March-2001.
Wang, Chu–Kia. 1953. Statically Indeterminate Structures, Tosho—Printing comp. LTB, Tokyo, Ch. 4 (102).

Concrete Solutions – Grantham, Mechtcherine & Schneck (eds)
© 2012 Taylor & Francis Group, London, ISBN 978-0-415-61622-5

Analysis of damage and repair techniques of cracked structural elements in an underground part of a high RC building

G. Dmochowski, J. Dudkiewicz & P. Berkowski
Wrocław University of Technology, Wrocław, Poland

ABSTRACT: The aim of the paper is to present results of an investigation on the general technical condition of the underground structure that forms the foundation platform for a 200 metre high reinforced concrete building. After inspection of that bearing part of the building there were detected multiple cracks in its structural elements, i.e., slabs, walls and columns. In order to complete all the requirements necessary for evaluation of the technical condition of the building the following procedures were carried out: analysis of the structural design, examination of concrete and steel used for construction (material strength tests), and checking of the class of environmental concrete exposure (according to corrosion caused by carbonation and chlorides). After all these examinations were completed, causes of the damage and the technology of the concrete structural repair and protection were defined.

1 GENERAL DESCRIPTION OF THE BUILDING

The object under consideration was a complex of residential and office buildings with two underground storeys. It had a diversified structure over ground level with the dominant feature in the form of the high tower. The main parts of the building were: 51 storeys, 200 m high tower building with offices, 20 storeys, 84 m high residential and office building, adjacent to the tower, and the so-called "podium" building with 4 storeys, situated above the ground level. Shopping malls and technical areas were located at the first three floors and in the fourth floor, in addition to technical rooms, a car-park was located. The underground floors were designed for service rooms and a parking lot. The construction of the complex started in 2007. In 2008 and partly in 2009 two basement levels were constructed which are the subject of this paper.

The complex of the buildings is situated about 10 m below the ground level on a continuous foundation slab of varying thickness, depending on the acting loads. Because the soil strata were diverse, the tower was placed on a composite foundation that consisted of a slab situated on piles. The slab thickness was about 4.0 m under the building core and about 3.0 m under the bearing columns. In addition, in the areas under the columns and under the core, the foundation slab was reinforced with drilled piles of 1500 mm diameter. The length of the piles was adjusted to the soil conditions under the foundation slab. In order to reduce the settlement of the slab, piles with compressed bases were used. Other high parts of the buildings were situated on the foundation slab that had a thickness of 2.4 m. The foundation slab below the peripheral buildings had a thickness that varied from 1.5 to 1.8 metres and, in the central part of the complex, foundation slab thickness varied from 1.2 to 1.5 m.

The foundation slab was designed from C25/30 concrete with the reinforcement steel AIIIN. Exterior basement walls that had a thickness from 40 to 50 cm, and were the elements of the foundation box, were made from the C30/37 concrete. Slabs over the −2 and −1 floors were made as monolithic, reinforced concrete slabs, working mainly in the slab-column system. Locally, there were main and secondary structural beams, further increasing the rigidity of the structure. The underground part of the so-called "podium" was divided into several smaller parts, separated with expansion joints. Those joints were situated due to the structural conditions, i.e., the required distance between them for reinforced concrete structures and the variety of building height. The construction of this part of the building was based on the basic structural grid of 7.9 × 7.9 m, and the floor slabs were generally flat, without main beams, with a thickness from 24 to 40 cm, depending on load conditions. In addition, there was incorporated reinforcement to deal with punching shear. The main monolithic skeleton of the structure, made as a slab-column system, was stiffened by the reinforced concrete walls of elevator shafts and staircases. These elements provide the spatial stability of the specific building segment. The sections' dimensions and the height of columns were taken depending on the height of the building, values of internal forces, and work conditions. The minimum width of columns was 40 cm. Columns were rigidly mounted in the foundation slab. Vertical load bearing structural elements, i.e., columns, reinforced concrete walls and shields, were made as monolithic structures, from different classes of concrete and reinforced with #16 to #32 AIIIN bars. The slanted entrances and exits to the parking lot were made as reinforced concrete slabs with a thickness of 30 cm from the C30/C37 concrete, reinforced with AIIIN steel. In order to reduce the stresses resulting from thermal influences, some structural elements such as beams at the dilatations, were based on pin supports, using special pads.

2 SURVEY OF DAMAGE OF RC ELEMENTS AT UNDERGROUND FLOORS

As a result of the observed significant number of cracks and other damage of the reinforced concrete underground walls and slabs, a survey of cracks was conducted. Visual inspection was carried out of the upper surface of the foundation slab, the upper and lower surfaces of the floors above the −1 and −2 levels, and the walls and columns on both floors.

On the bottom side of both floors, and especially in the plate over the level −2, numerous cracks were noticed with variable widths from capillary up to about 1 mm. Some of those cracks passed through the entire thickness of the slabs (Fig. 1).

Areas with the highest number of cracks were two floors within the tower. At the columns of the building there were no cracks observed, however there were traces of the filling of local concrete defects at the edges of the columns.

Figure 1. Layout of cracks in the underground floor slab.

Figure 2. Roughness of the top surface of the slab—visible layout of reinforcement bars.

At all the walls of that part of the building there were multiple, vertical cracks. According to the information received from the contractor, in the walls of more than 20 m of length, bays of 3 m length were used in strips, resulting in the formation of forced cracks. However, the system of cracks did not copy the layout of the strips and also the cracks were not vertical. This is not consistent with the principles of implementation and operation of such strips. There was also uncertainty as to the correctness of their implementation or even their existence, because placements of those elements were not described in the so-called post-erection design. On the upper surface of the foundation slab and on the upper surface of the floor slabs there were no visible cracks. Those surfaces, however, were mostly flooded by rain water and dirt, while the upper surface of the floor over the −1 level was additionally often brushed and cleaned, so the cracks could be covered. Therefore, a detailed visual inspection was conducted on the lower surfaces of the slabs. In addition, on the upper surface of the ceiling over the −1 level, a layout of reinforcement was seen, which indicated the low thickness of reinforcement cover (Fig. 2).

3 TECHNICAL STUDIES OF REINFORCED CONCRETE STRUCTURAL ELEMENTS

3.1 Analysis of geodesic measurements of foundation slab and underground storey floors

Documentation presented by the investor included results of surveying the upper surface of the foundation slab, the bottom surface of the floors at −1 and −2 levels and the measurements of the location of the vertical concrete elements on the two underground floors. After analyzing the surveys it was found that the upper surface of the slab was very uneven. Measured height differences ranged from 60 up to 70 mm, which far exceeds the permissible value of 20 mm. Measured inclination deviations of reinforced concrete elements on both underground floors, in most cases, did not exceed the limit of 20 mm. However, in several places, the values were higher. Although there were no measurements for floors of the tower, in those areas places where the deflections of the floor slab exceeded the permissible value of 20 mm were visible, already at the stage of the construction, without influence of service load. Those places were considered as being in the state of possible structural failure when working under service load.

3.2 Analysis of concrete strength tests

Tests of concrete strength were conducted by the Accredited Research Laboratory of Building Structures, in accordance with the provisions set out in the design specification. Samples for testing the compressive strength of concrete were taken during the concreting phase. They were taken at random, evenly during the concreting period, then stored and tested. Compressive strength tests were performed after 28 days of concrete maturation. In addition, tests were also performed after 56 days. It was found for many elements that a lower class of concrete than was established in the design (C30/C37) had been used. Statistically, about 30% of samples had a reduced class of concrete in relation to the assumed one.

3.3 Analysis of thickness of reinforcement cover

Generally, required structural protection, including corrosion protection, should be, according to Eurocode 2, determined by taking into account "the way of use, the proposed period of service, maintenance, and actions." Thus, the thickness of the reinforcement cover must be determined in detail with the user, because the durability of the structure is understood as fulfillment of the serviceability conditions during "the entire service lifetime, with no significant decrease in the values or the excessive and unexpected cost of maintenance" (Eurocode 2 2008).

The thickness of the reinforcement cover must be chosen in a way that provides:

- safe transmission of traction forces,
- proper compaction of concrete,
- protection of steel from corrosion,
- appropriate structural fire resistance.

At the stage of the realization of the design the service life of the object was not established. For the building under consideration it was recommended to adopt an S4 structure class, which means a lifetime of 50 years. Investigations of the thickness of steel bar cover were realized using a FERROSCAN PS 200 system. Those tests allowed specifying the size of the cover of the top layer of reinforcement. The accuracy of the measurements was 3 mm. Tests were conducted on site by a licensed testing laboratory.

3.3.1 Analysis of cover of structural elements in terms of technological and structural conditions

The results obtained were verified in terms of the technological and structural conditions, tied to the safety-related transmission of the bond forces and proper concrete compaction. In the tested columns there was #25 and #32 mm reinforcement. The minimum, standard cover for such reinforcement is respectively 25 and 32 mm. Over 50% of the columns did not meet this criterion.

3.3.2 Analysis of thickness of reinforcement cover in terms of anti-corrosion protection

An analysis comparing the size of the proposed reinforcement cover with the requirements of the minimum values resulting from the accepted exposure classes was carried out. According to Eurocode 2, for the concrete columns working in the exposure class XD1, provided for parking lots, and for the S4 class of structure (where the minimum cover for column reinforcement is 35 mm), it was found that the columns did not have adequate cover. For the adopted class of exposure, for the slabs over −2 and −1 floor, on both sides of the slab, the cover should have been 40 mm.

The measured size of the cover, up to 30 mm, did not comply with the code requirements for the exposure class XD1 for the bottom and XD3 for the top surface of the slabs.

Therefore, the slabs should be properly strengthened and protected. The same was the situation with the reinforced concrete bearing walls.

3.3.3 Analysis of thickness of cover in terms of the fire resistance

For all reinforced concrete elements of the designed fire resistance R240, located under the tower, the size of reinforcement cover should not be less than 40 mm, as required by Eurocode 2. Therefore, it was assumed that the cover size of 30 mm, provided in the design, and then executed on the site, was incorrect. So, it was necessary to make an additional fire protection design. In other areas of the investigated part of the building fire protection terms were considered to be met.

4 DESCRIPTION OF THE METHODS OF STRENGTHENING AND PROTECTION OF REINFORCED STRUCTURAL ELEMENTS

Problems of the durability of reinforced concrete construction in various conditions of exploitation are well known and widely discussed subjects in Polish (for ex. Czarnecki et al., 2002, Ściślewski 1999) and foreign literature (e.g., Fagerlund 1997, Broomfield 2009). All significant aspects related to the exploitation of such constructions, starting from the design (e.g., Łapko 2003) and construction issues, through to the appropriate protection of the construction elements during exposure to environmental influences, are well known. Finally, they consider works related to the diagnosis of technical condition in cases of the appearance of damage (Drobiec et al., 2010) and also renovation and strengthening of construction damaged as a result of the influence and activity of various conditions and poor construction practice.

On the basis of the visual examinations, test results of concrete strength and reinforcement cover, analysis of the current technical condition of the construction and the results of geodesic surveying, it was stated that the technical condition of the building structural elements varied from bad to good. Therefore, it was necessary to carry out repair and reinforcement in some areas with the aim of restoring structural elements to good status and meeting the minimum required standard conditions.

On both underground floors a complete survey of cracks and other damage visible on the concrete elements was conducted. There were numerous cracks, sometimes even up to 1 mm width on both floors. In particular, there were many cracks in the area of both floors of the tower. The floors of the tower were reinforced with steel framework, supported by additional reinforced concrete elements (Fig. 3).

The analysis of the surveying documentation provided by the investor that included measurements of the upper surface of the slab, the bottom surface of the ceiling above the −2 and −1 floors, and measurements of the position of the vertical concrete elements on the two underground floors, were made. Numerous deviations were found that exceeded the limits specified in the General Conditions of Technical Performance and Acceptance of concrete and reinforced concrete works and built elements.

For the excessively deflected cracked floors, it was necessary to strengthen them with injection using epoxy resin grout followed by installation of carbon fiber strips (Fig. 4).

Depending on the type of surface and crack widths resin injection was carried out using a gravity

Figure 3. Strengthening of slab with reinforcing steel grid.

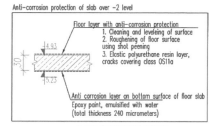

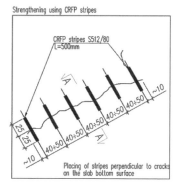

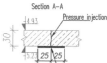

Figure 4. Reinforcement of deflected and cracked slab using carbon strips and injection technique.

method or by pressure techniques—through screwed packers.

Insufficient strength of concrete in slabs over the parking lot was also found, when compared to the classification of the structure basing on the existing, relevant exposure classes. It was necessary to reinforce slabs throughout the car park to protect them from corrosion. An application of epoxy paint emulsified with water was proposed, with a total thickness of 300 μm (Fig. 5).

In case of walls in which excessive deviations from perpendicularity were measured, it was decided to expand their thickness, for example through shotcrete or by strengthening them with a reinforced concrete jacket, not allowing the formation of eccentricity of loads (Figs. 6–7).

In connection with the observed, lower than expected, class of concrete in bearing columns, some of them required strengthening. Strengthening was proposed to be done using two systems. For the columns in which the difference between the results of test strength in relation to the requirements was not more than 5 to 6% (up to 3 MPa), the use of carbon fibers (bands in the upper and lower zones—where there are bending moments), was designed. For the remaining cases, because of the reduced concrete strength parameters, strengthening was done through the use of reinforced concrete jackets of 10 to 12 cm of thickness, using a flowable structural repair mortar and carried out by glue bonding and shotcrete methods (Figs. 8–9).

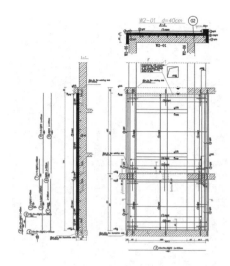

Figure 6. Strengthening of wall using RC jacket.

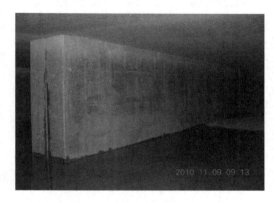

Figure 7. Bearing wall after strengthening using RC jacket.

Figure 5. Anti-corrosion protection of slab and column.

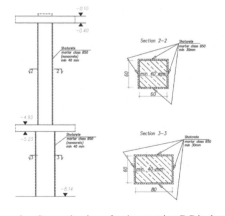

Figure 8. Strengthening of column using RC jacket.

Figure 9.   Strengthening of column using RC jacket.

Figure 10.   Strengthening of column using nanocrete materials.

Basing on the analysis of standard structural and technological terms, corrosion protection (due to the exposure classes) and the conditions of protection against fire, it was found that:

– design assumptions about the thickness of reinforcement cover in columns in many cases
– did not take into account the technological requirements and did not meet the requirements of corrosion protection of concrete;
– in most of the examined columns the reinforcement cover did not meet the conditions proposed in the design, which proved the negligence in their construction.

For such situations, it was necessary to increase the size of cover to the appropriate dimension.

Since the deviation in size in the construction of the columns was very high (in the case of covers up to 12–14 mm), it was recommended as a necessity to perform the protection through the use of appropriate reinforcement mortar—for example, shotcrete, with a minimum thickness of sprayed concrete of 30 mm. It was proposed the technology using flowable structural repair mortars (Fig. 10).

From the standpoint of the fire protection for structural elements in the fire resistance zone defined as R240, columns, walls and ceilings reinforcement covers were too thin. It appeared necessary to additionally protect those elements by spraying of protection mortar.

REFERENCES

Broomfield, J.P. 2009. Application of the new European concrete repair standards BS EN1504 parts 1–10 to a range of reinforced concrete structures. In: *Proc. of the 3rd Int. Conf. on Concrete Repair, Venice/Padua, 29 June-2 July 2009.* CRC Press.
Czarnecki, L. & Emmons, P.H. 2002. Repair and protection of concrete structures. In: Polski Cement. Kraków (in Polish).
Drobiec, Ł., Jasiński, R. & Piekarczyk, A. 2010. Diagnostics of RC structures. Vol. 1. Warszawa: PWN (in Polish).
Eurocode 2: Design of concrete structures—Part 1-1: General rules and rules for buildings. PN-EN 1992-1-1, September 2008 (in Polish).
Fagerlud, G. 1997. Durability of concrete structures. Warszawa: Arkady (in Polish).
Łapko, A. 2003. Design of RC structures. Warszawa: Arkady (in Polish).
Ściślewski, Z. 1999. Protection of reinforced concrete structures. Warszawa: Arkady (in Polish).

Concrete Solutions – Grantham, Mechtcherine & Schneck (eds)
© 2012 Taylor & Francis Group, London, ISBN 978-0-415-61622-5

The refurbishment of Bideford Longbridge

J. Drewett
Concrete Repairs Ltd., UK

N. Bott
Devon County Council, UK

ABSTRACT: Bideford Bridge is a Grade One listed bridge of historic and strategic importance. The owner, Devon County Council, identified a need for significant structural maintenance to the concrete cantilever sections. Various repair options were considered including full replacement but the preferred solution was the repair of the concrete structure and installation of an impressed current cathodic protection (ICCP) system to enhance durability. This was one of the most complex repair and ICCP schemes ever undertaken in the UK over a tidal estuary with traffic continuing to use the bridge.

1 INTRODUCTION

The original Bideford Longbridge connecting the East and West of Bideford town across the River Torridge in Devon, is a Grade One listed mediaeval masonry arch bridge. It has 24 spans ranging from 6.5 m to 11 m and was constructed of timber in 1286. It is believed that the variation in span was dictated by either the length of timber available or the financial support of individual local sponsors. A multi-span masonry bridge was subsequently built around the timber structure in 1460. The bridge has been widened a number of times over its life to accommodate the changing nature and density of traffic flows. The latest widening of the bridge was in 1928 when reinforced concrete cantilever sections were added to each side of the masonry arches to carry footpaths and services. In 1968 three of the west arches were replaced following a partial collapse and in the early 1970's

Figure 1. Bideford longbridge during restoration.

significant strengthening work was undertaken to the remaining 21 spans.

As bridge owner Devon County Council has inspected and maintained this historic structure over the years and after carrying out a structural assessment in 2001, a 3 tonne weight restriction was applied to the bridge. This was required because the cantilevers carrying the footpaths were weak and the steel reinforcement was beginning to corrode due to high chloride levels and lack of concrete cover.

2 REPAIR OPTIONS

Various options were considered, in discussion with key stakeholders, to provide a long term solution to safeguard the bridge. These included complete replacement of the existing reinforced concrete cantilevers with new lightweight steel footways to expose the original masonry bridge and replacement with modern high strength materials to maintain the appearance of the bridge as it is now.

Due to spiralling construction cost inflation, a technical review was carried out in 2007 to identify potentially less expensive but effective solutions to protect the bridge. The option selected was to carry out repairs together with the installation of an impressed current cathodic protection (ICCP) system, which would extend the life of repairs to provide an effective long term solution.

Devon County Council engaged the services of corrosion consultant Brian Wyatt of Corrosion Control, to advise on the most effective corrosion control system. The brief was for a 50 year design life (with a factor of safety of 2 for embedded cathodic protection components) and 25 years to first maintenance.

The cantilevers comprise reinforced concrete corbels which project from the piers and carry pairs of 'in-span' beams. Each pair of beams is connected over the top to form a reinforced concrete slab which carries the footpaths and forms an inverted U under which a number of services are carried. The outer beam of the pair is the original reinforced concrete beam from the 1920's widening and the inner beam, against the masonry arch, is a steel I beam encased in concrete installed in the early 1970's when significant repair works were carried out following a partial collapse of the bridge.

The services on the bridge are medium and low pressure gas mains, a water main, BT services in the cantilever and buried in the footpath and electrical services for the under bridge lighting and street lighting.

The Impressed Current Cathodic Protection (ICCP) system was designed by Corrosion Control using a combination of mixed metal oxide coated titanium mesh and discrete mixed metal oxide coated titanium tubular anodes to ensure a uniform current distribution. A cross section and anode layout is shown in Fig. 2 & Fig. 3.

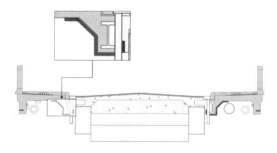

Figure 2.   Cross section showing the mesh layout & discrete tubular anodes.

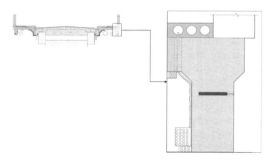

Figure 3.   Cross section showing the anode layout.

Following a further Principal Inspection structural assessment carried out by Devon County Council, two of the spans required urgent structural repairs and this opportunity was used to carry out a trial repair and cathodic protection installation to provide information for the final design and construction of the proposed main scheme. Completion of this work led to the full scheme being tendered and awarded to Concrete Repairs Ltd (CRL) in September 2008 for the contract sum of £1.8 M with a start on site in late September 2008.

One lesson learnt from the trial scheme was that the high standard of surface finish required on the outside beam could not be consistently achieved using sprayed concrete. This was changed to a cast concrete repair for the outside beam although a sprayed finish was considered acceptable for the concealed inner line of beams.

Only 21 spans of the bridge needed to be repaired as the three western most spans had been rebuilt in 1970 following the partial collapse. Devon County Council had, in discussion with the Environment Agency, developed a temporary works envelope to be provided to tenderers which would enable the repairs to be carried out without imposing traffic restrictions on the carriageway. This also enabled tenderers to accurately and confidently price this element of the work in the tender period.

3   SITE OPERATIONS

While the scaffold was being erected, a full scale trial mock up of the cantilever, required by the contract, was constructed in the site compound to demonstrate and prove the methods and materials CRL proposed to use in the contract. The demonstration repairs carried out on this mock up were cored to determine full compaction and bond to the original concrete. Also the resistivity of the repairs was measured to ensure compatibility with the original concrete and the ICCP system.

After erection of scaffolding, the inner and outer beams and the underside of the deck were visually inspected and hammer tested to identify the areas of spalling and delaminated concrete which were to be repaired. There was no requirement to identify or remove carbonated or chloride contaminated concrete because the ICCP system would control future corrosion activity. This is one of the major benefits of cathodic protection, minimizing the amount of concrete repairs needed, reducing the costs and minimising the structural impact of concrete removal.

To retain the structural integrity of the bridge spans and eliminate the need for propping, a sequential repair of the concrete was specified by Devon CC. The maximum volume of concrete removal was limited and therefore the defective concrete was removed in stages by saw cutting the repair perimeter and using hydro demolition to expose the corroding steel. The steel was cleaned to SA2 standard (ISO 8501-1, 1988) using a combination of hydro demolition and grit blasting to remove chlorides and meet the specification requirements.

During the work a problem was identified with black magnetite rust (Fe_3O_4) on the inside steel beam which was not encountered during the trials. This is an unusual corrosion product to be found on steel encased in concrete and it required additional intensive grit blasting to remove.

After cutting out the spalled concrete, new link steel was added to replace badly corroded sections on the inner beams. The new reinforcement was welded into position and electrical continuity checked across the reinforcement prior to reinstatement. The outside beams were shuttered and cast using Fosroc LA55 flowable concrete and the internal beams reformed with sprayed concrete (gunite) using Fosroc Dry Spray.

Figure 4. Mock up trial section.

After reinstatement of the concrete, the anode system was installed. The inside I beam was protected with a mixed metal oxide coated titanium mesh anode (MMO/Ti) fixed to the concrete surface and encapsulated in a sprayed concrete overlay with long discrete mixed metal oxide coated titanium tubular anodes in drilled holes to protect the faces of the beam that were remote from the mesh anode. The outside beam was protected by discrete tubular anodes in holes drilled above the main reinforcement bars. The reinforced concrete corbels were also protected using discrete anodes. In total 4300 discrete anodes were installed and 475 m² of MMO/Ti mesh anode to protect the concrete cantilevered footpaths of the bridge.

The footpath above consisted of a 130 mm thick mass concrete which encapsulated live electric and telecommunication cables and was overlaid with mastic asphalt. This was removed using pneumatic hand breakers to expose the services and reinforced concrete deck below. The exposed deck was cathodically protected using MMO/Ti mesh in a concrete overlay and the surface was reinstated incorporating additional ducting for the ICCP cabling system and the other utilities.

The existing 12 lighting columns which were integral with the footpath parapet were all replaced with new units in galvanized painted steel 2.5 m high with lantern lights. The bases were bolted through to the top of the outer beam and the masonry parapet rebuilt with stainless steel reinforcement to strengthen the detail.

New under bridge lighting was installed to replace the existing inefficient and deteriorating lighting system. This helped to make the bridge an iconic feature of the night landscape emphasising the original brick arches constructed in 1460 which were so important to the Grade One listing.

The cathodic protection system was designed and installed in accordance with the European Standard BS EN12696 (2000). It was divided into 74 zones and monitored using a combination of

Figure 5. Broken out area with the steel prepared ready for reinstatement.

Figure 6. Tubular anodes during installation.

Figure 7. New lighting column installed by CRL Image by John Morton of Devon Country Council.

silver/silver chloride/potassium chloride reference electrodes and MMO/Ti decay probes buried in the concrete alongside the reinforcement. There were 20 multicore armoured cables (18 miles in total) in each footpath for power and data transmission to the two control units situated at each end of the bridge. Telecommunication links with the control units allowed remote monitoring and control of the system. CRL successfully commissioned the ICCP system in November 2009, and in late November 2010 completed the 12 month post installation monitoring programme.

This has been one of the most complex ICCP system design and installations ever undertaken in the UK. Refurbishing a bridge which is Grade One listed over an environmentally sensitive tidal estuary whilst maintaining vehicle and pedestrian access was a huge task for CRL and Devon County Council. Devon County Council's Chief Bridge Engineer, Nick Bott commented that a high level of liaison throughout the design, consultation and procurement processes was required to successfully deliver this highly complex project, with the minimum disruption to the public.

4 CONCLUSION

The highway asset management programme is essential for the UK economy to succeed. It requires timely intervention with the consideration of all options including the latest technological advances. The requirement for sustainable solutions minimising the environmental impact has lead to more emphasis on maintenance and repair rather than replacement. This scheme has used the latest advances in corrosion control to address durability issues which has allowed Devon CC to repair the existing structure rather than replace. This has produced considerable cost savings and allowed the bridge to remain open during the course of the works.

REFERENCES

BS EN12696:2000. *Cathodic Protection of Steel in Concrete.* British Standards Institution, 2000.
ISO 8501-1: 1988. *Preparation of steel substrates before application of paints and related products—Visual assessment of surface cleanliness—Part 1: Rust grades and preparation grades of uncoated steel substrates and of steel substrates after overall removal of previous coatings,* ISO, 1988.

Concrete Solutions – Grantham, Mechtcherine & Schneck (eds)
© 2012 Taylor & Francis Group, London, ISBN 978-0-415-61622-5

Concept of concrete slab repairs of a flood water dry reservoir

A. Duber

Institute of Civil Engineering, Wroclaw University of Nature and Life Sciences, Poland

A. Pawlowski

Institute of Environmental Engineering, Wroclaw University of Nature and Life Sciences, Poland

ABSTRACT: An earth dam dry reservoir was built in 1930 as a part of the Jelenia Gora Valley (Lower Silesia) flood protection system. In 1955 its function was extended and constant water storage for industrial purposes started. This exploitation against the designed "occasional using during flood threat" has caused, after several years, intensive leakage through the dam, which could have been dangerous for the construction stability. That is why in, 1978, a decision to rebuild the dam was made. Works were finished in 1982. The up-stream slope was covered by a reinforced concrete screen, which was connected with a steel diaphragm wall installed at the toe of the dam. The exploitation of the object as an industrial water reservoir lasted till 1989, when it came back to its primary function as a dry reservoir for flood protection. During a condition survey of the reservoir's technical state, made in 2004, a significant degree of deterioration of the screen concrete slab surfaces and joints was found. The degree of deterioration was evaluated on the basis of alkali reaction and sclerometric (hardness) tests. After analysis of gathered data, 3 types of repair technologies were proposed, matching the different degree of slab deterioration and repair procedures for the slabs joints. The concrete layer and the edges of the most damaged elements were to be reconstructed. For the less deteriorated slabs, repairs were limited to filling of local concrete defects. Slabs with minor surface damage were covered with a thin layer of protective mortar.

1 INTRODUCTION

1.1 *Problem statement*

Changes of exploitation mode of a structure should be carefully analyzed during the design stage and performed under strict quality control. It is very risky to exploit structures under new loads and environmental conditions without the correct preparation of a structure for the new tasks. An example of such a case is given in the paper. A dry reservoir with an earth dam, which was filled occasionally only during flood periods, after 50 years of service started to be used for permanent storage of industrial water. The quality of adaptation works—by covering of the upstream dam slope with concrete slabs has proven to be insufficient. After several, years the reservoir has come back to its primary function as a dry reservoir and the concrete screen has to be repaired.

1.2 *History of the reservoir and its exploitation*

The dry reservoir for flood water described in the paper was built in years 1929–1930 as a result of closing 150 m bright valley with an earth dam. Till 1955, according to its design tasks, the reservoir

was used only for short time retention connected with flood protection of the neighboring area. In 1955 on the right bank, in the left entrance to the bottom outlet, a water uptake for local industry needs was constructed. This made it necessary to maintain a constant water level in the reservoir 7 meters below the level of the dam's surface overflow. No adaptation works were done before changing the exploitation mode. Exploitation, which was not in accordance with the primary aims, had a negative influence on the dam's technical condition. In many places of the dam and in the outflow shaft leakage appeared. Areas situated underneath and the base of the downstream part of the dam were drowned. In August 1977, the reservoir, in spite of its poor technical state, was filled up to the level only 0,34 m below the overflow and the increased intensity of leakage indicated the possibility of a dam failure. That is why a decision to renew (rebuild) the dam was made. The works were done in the years 1979–82. Within the works the dam's upstream slope was insulated by placing a reinforced concrete screen and connecting it with the existing sheet pile wall installed at the toe of the dam. During exploitation of the modernized reservoir, a constant retention water level was maintained during the next 7 years. After that, in 1989, the dam returned to its previous function as a flood protection, dry water reservoir.

1.3 *Characteristics of the dam's reinforced concrete screen*

Before 1979 there was 1:2,5 inclination of the lower part of the upstream slope (between levels 391 and 398 m above sea level) and 1:2 in the upper one. Between levels 398,00 and 403,00 m above sea the (crown) slope was protected by a layer of cobbles 0,30 m thick. The lower part of the slope was covered only by grass. At the toe there was a sheet pile wall made of Larsen type III section, about 6 m long (Fig. 1).

The dam slopes, the construction of which had been changed in years 1979–1982, were protected by a screen consisted of 71 reinforced concrete slabs made of R_w 170 concrete (concrete with average compressive strength equal to 17 MPa). Plates, 11,5 m long, 6,0 m high and 0,20 m thick were placed in two layers of 0,15 and 0,23 m thickness and 0,10 m bedding concrete. The plates were reinforced with grids made of #14 steel bars located in the half thickness. The lower slope part was made less steep—the inclination was decreased from 1:2,5 to 1:3,5 (Fig. 1). The lowest part of the slabs was covered with soil of 0,1 to ca. 0,5 m thickness. In the middle and left part of the dam soil was almost fully covering the lowest slabs row, so it was spread to the maximum width of ca. 11,0 m. A small bulge was found in the middle of the row. It was probably caused by slippage of the dam slope during quick emptying of the reservoir.

Archive documentation did not contain any description of the joint's filling method and the only information on the way the slabs joints were insulated was the remnants of bituminous filling with unknown composition. The expansion joints were 30–40 mm width. In the places, where the bituminous filling did not exist anymore, the slab edges, where durability was not sufficient, were usually cut back so the joints were wider. During *in situ* inspection, a decrease of the expansion joint width between the upper and lower slabs row, was found too. Its width was not bigger, then 10 mm. Bituminous filling had been squeezed from or had flown out of the joints during high temperature weather, forming bulging caused by slippage of the upper slabs row downwards. The investigation of some joints revealed, that a special PVC band was placed there and its technical condition was quite good, and was supposed to be the same in other places, too. But most of the joints were exposed and their interior was slowly being filled with small soil particles delivered by wind, forming favorable conditions for plant growth. The rest of the bituminous filling was conserved only on a small part of the joint's length.

The long years of reservoir exploitation, in spite of only occasional water retention, have led to significant deterioration of the slabs (Figs. 1 and 2). From a visual judgment of their state, it was apparent that the worst technical state concerned slabs in the middle part of the screen. Probably they were made with poor quality concrete and exposed for long time to thermal heating by the sun i.e., quite unsheltered, in contrary to both dam's abutments, which were sheltered by trees, so undergoing in winter many thawing (during day) and freezing (in the night) cycles accelerating destruction effects. The smallest extent of destruction can be seen in the upper row of the slabs and the most intensive destructive process was observed in the middle row and upper part of the lower row of slabs. Slabs protecting right abutment, particularly theirs lower parts, demonstrated large surface scaling, with the depth of concrete loosening reaching usually several centimeters and occasionally to half of the slab's thickness, exposing reinforcement.

Figure 1.   Concrete screen on up-stream dam slope.

Figure 2.   Surface damage of concrete slabs.

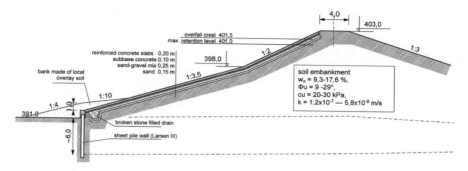

Figure 3. Cross-section of the dam.

However, developed corrosive processes on reinforcement bars were not seen.

Bulging of several slab's surface layer was noticed, too. A dull sound could be heard after hammer rapping indicating its separation from the rest of the slab.

2 INVESTIGATION OF THE CONCRETE SCREEN SLAB'S TECHNICAL STATE

2.1 Evaluation of environmental influence on the concrete

To determine the methodology and scope of concrete investigations firstly the environmental influence was judged. It is essential that the chosen repairs systems should selected according to the environmental parameters, which can be determined with Polish standard PN—EN 206-1:20 03. According to that Standard, the analyzed slabs are subjected to influences, which can be classified to the following exposure classes:

1. Class of exposure to aggressive freezing/thawing influence: XF3.
2. Class of exposure to the aggressive influence of soils and ground water: no threat was determined.
3. Class of exposure to corrosion caused by carbonation: XC4.

2.2 Evaluation of concrete strength with sclerometric method

To determine the concrete strength three slabs were chosen from the screen zone, where over a large area surface peeling (delamination) had occurred as well as two slabs on the slope with a southerly exposure direction which were treated as typical for the rest of the screen. Nondestructive tests with N type Schmidt hammer were conducted according to the standard methodology (e.g., ITB 1977,

Runkiewicz 1983, Proceq 2006). Strength evaluation was based on Schmidt hammer regression curve (correlation curve) expressed with the formula given below adapted for concrete compressive strength of $150 \times 150 \times 150$ mm cube samples.

$$R = 0{,}02128\ L^2 + 0{,}1817\ L - 1{,}44$$

where:

R—concrete compressive strength in MPa,
L—average rebound value of N type Schmidt hammer

This form of regression curve was chosen because it was worked out to control the quality of hydrotechnical concretes made of similar cements and according to similar technology.

As a result of the use of this statistical procedure as well as coefficients resulting from impact direction and concrete age it was determined, that the estimated guaranteed concrete strength of the tested slabs was in the range between 15,9 MPa to 19,0 MPa. These values allowed us to treat this concrete, in places where no frost damage had occurred, as C12/15 class (before B15) and described as Rw170 at the time of placing. It is the concrete base lowest strength value given for most of the materials used for old concrete reprofiling or protection. The strength determined this way concerns only "sound" part of the slabs. Slabs or their fragments, where the surface zone of the concrete had undergone considerable degradation, peels off and is only loosely connected with the remaining parts of element. Such concrete cannot form a base for repair layers without adequate surface preparation.

2.3 Chemical investigations

The aim of investigations was to determine the degree of chemical change to the concrete screen slab which had occurred during exploitation.

To do this various indicator solutions were applied for evaluation. The method allowed us to determine, on a fresh fracture surface of the concrete, the range and the intensity of its changes at different depths measured from the surface. Five indicators were used to make a clear distinction between concrete layers showing different degree of chemical changes:

1. 0.5 percent solution of phenolphthalein—in 70—percent ethyl alcohol,
2. 0.5 percent solution of thymolophthalein—in 90—percent ethyl alcohol,
3. 0.5 percent solution of tropeolin 0 in distilled water,
4. 0.1—percent solution of alizarin yellow in distilled water,
5. 0.5—percent solution of alizarin in distilled water.

Tests were carried out in 5 chosen places: three of them concerned the western concrete screen and the remaining two were the southerly exposed slabs. Analyzing the indicators color reactions on fresh fractures of concrete it was found, that in places, where the largest freezing damage had occurred, the range of concrete zone with alkalinity not high enough to secure reinforcement passivation reached $80 \div 90$ mm below the original slab surface level (actually no longer existing because of concrete peeling). In places, where concrete had resisted freeze-thaw action, the zone thickness was only just $10 \div 12$ mm.

Beginning with the 100 mm depth in slabs with freeze-thaw damage and 20 mm in other slabs the alkalinity of concrete was higher than pH 11. Because the slab reinforcement was placed at the half thickness, even in the most deteriorated slabs there were no conditions to enable reinforcement corrosion, so no more serious slab destruction had occurred. Slab observations confirmed the lack of concrete cracks and spalling characteristic for reinforcement corrosion. However, that did not exclude the possibility that, if appropriate protection was not made, this type of corrosion would appear in deeper zones of unrepaired slabs in the near future following the progress of carbonation and further development of concrete destruction. Considering local condition (non-aggressive environment) it can be supposed, that beyond carbonation there were no other factors having significant influence on the chemical structure of the concrete Taking into account the initial concrete quality as well the intensive freeze-thaw action, the progress of carbonation was typical for this type of construction. Because the reinforcement was placed in half of slabs' depth, it was protected by a comparatively thick (ca. 100 mm) concrete layer, which, even in the case of carbonation of the external parts, should assure effective reinforcement protection for some time.

2.4 State of the concrete screen slabs expansion joints

Tightness of expansion joints between slabs depends mainly on the presence and technical state of a strip seal, whose effectiveness depends on the correctness of their installation. On the basis of general site inspection and from available working plans it was found that expansion joints were protected by a strip joint seal, probably made of PVC, which were correctly concreted in the half thickness of the slabs. However it could not be excluded, that there are some defective places in the screen—e.g., strip fastening only at one side, poor concrete compaction under or over the strip and the like. In the case of the required screen function, i.e., assurance of water tightness in the period of short-term reservoir filling, the dam stability should not be threatened. Risk of stability loss could happen only in the case of a considerable loss of filtration protection tightness and a longer period of maintaining high level of retained water (ITB, 1977). Yet, the existing state resulting from redevelopment/adaptation works aimed to long term water retention should be fully kept e.g., protected against progressing corrosion and degradation of the sealant and joints. In this regard the state of slab edges was especially important (they should form rectangular cross-section of the joints), as well as the fulfillment of the space between the surface and the PVC strip joint seal with a suitably tight and constantly plastic protective material. Expansion joints are not protected from above, because existing bituminous filling in most places had flowed down in periods of higher temperatures or was detached with mechanically damaged slabs edges. The bituminous filling was gradually being replaced by organic substances and small soil particles creating conditions for the plants growth, which favoured further destruction of these parts of the screen.

3 REPAIR CONCEPT

3.1 Methods and scope of slabs repairs

The scope of the concrete screen slab repairs depends on their technical state. In case of serious destructions it is necessary to break slabs' upper part to such a depth, that peeled off and weathered concrete layers will be removed and then a new refilling layer will be made on the existing concrete sub base. New material applied should be characterized by good vapor permeability to avoid detachment of the newly placed layer as a result of the growth of water vapour pressure in the contact zone between the old and the new concrete as well as a not too high elasticity modulus (possibly not bigger then ca. 20 GPa). A similar scope of repairs will be necessary in case of larger concrete losses in the upper and central left row of the screen slabs. System solutions on the basis of cements modified with polymers and fibers should be taken into consideration. In the remaining elements, whose surfaces demonstrate a smaller degree of deterioration, concrete surface cleaning and covering by thin-layer protective mortar after refilling of cavities and larger unevenness, has been proposed. The applied material should show the ability of penetration and crystallization in internal concrete pores to decrease water infiltration by the elements. It is necessary to check, if the agent chosen for superficial protection can be used together with the concrete repair system of another manufacturer. A slabs' surface impregnation with hydrophobic materials based on silicones has been proposed. However one should take into consideration only several years estimated durability of such coatings (Czarnecki, Emmons, 2002). Adequate surface preparation is of key importance for the whole repair success independently from the materials which have been chosen to use in particular project. Slabs have to be cleaned into such a degree, that the external, damaged layer is completely removed and an intact concrete structure is reached. The most often applied methods of cleaning are an abrasive blasting method or a hydro blasting method, which uses an action of a water stream under high, controllable pressure. Pneumatic tools (jackhammers) are used, too, particularly when thicker layers have to be removed. It is essential to get thoroughly acquainted with manufacturer instructions on protective and repair materials and follow exactly all the recommendations.

In the described case the following was recommended for the preparation scope of slab surfaces and of expansion joint edges, which are to be repaired:

- Removal of damaged concrete with use of light pneumatic hammers, abrasive blasting cleaning or hydro blasting methods. It is necessary to get rid of all contamination—oils, fat, epoxies as well as lichens and other biological forms of life. When hollow areas and spalling are found, remove this deteriorated concrete, too. The extent of the thickness of the layer to be removed depends on the extent of the slabs' deterioration.
- In case of technology based on mineral materials concrete should be moisturized to avoid quick loss of water in repair material.

- A bonding layer should be applied in the contact zone between old and new concrete, if the system solution does not recommend differently.

3.2 Repairs variants description

Three variants of main repair were chosen according to the degree of deterioration of the slabs:

I. reconstruction of deteriorated layers of large thickness ≥ 50 mm
II. filling of local concrete losses
III. surface protection of less deteriorated slabs— concerns with all the slabs except ones repaired according to variant I.

3.2.1 Repairs using Variant I

For repairs qualified to be done according to variant I, the following technology was recommended:

Weathered concrete should be removed only from damaged places and adjacent areas if at least 30% of the slab surface has been preserved after action by freeze-thaw damage.

The uncovered part of the slab should have a regular shape e.g., rectangular.

When repairs are more extensive, the upper layer of concrete should be removed from the whole area.

On new exposed slab surface a reinforcement net made of 6 mm ribbed bars (SA-III steel 30 mm A-III steel, with 150×150 mm placed ca. 30 mm below upper surface of slab. To secure full connection between the concrete sub base of the old slab and its new upper part, vertical anchors made of short steel rods should be fixed in a square pattern $0,6 \times 0,6$ m before reconstruction concreting.

As filling material a class C16/20 (former class B20), low water/cement ratio concrete mix with admixtures to increase frost resistance and reduce concrete shrinkage should be used. The concrete should not be too high a strength, to avoid big differences between the old and new modulus of elasticity.

Before placing new concrete, the old concrete surface has to be saturated but surface dry. If repairs do not cover the whole slab's surface, a 10 mm vertical gap should be left between old and new concrete and then filled with a material used for filling regular expansion joints between slabs, with a correct joint design.

3.2.2 Variant II—reprofilation of slabs edges and filling of local damage

For variant II repairs a system of refilling mortar was proposed together with suitable bonding layer. Both should be adjusted to the environmental conditions to which the slabs will be exposed.

3.2.3 *Variant III—superficial protection of slabs not showing concrete peeling*

It was recommended, that after removing dirt from the slab surfaces, the concrete should be strengthened/protected by covering by thin layer of protective mortar.

3.3 *Repair of expansion joints*

Tightness of expansion joints between screen elements was assured by concreting a synthetic insulation band in adjacent slabs. The material filling the joint has an important function to protect the band. To restore this function it was recommended to clean thoroughly the existing gaps, to remove the fragments of concrete loosely connected with remaining part of element and to remove weathered material filling the space between slabs. There are places, where slabs edge reprofiling will be necessary, too. In case of a lack of previous bituminous filling, or if it does not reach sufficiently high, free space to a level equal to ca. 2/3 width measured from the top should be tightly stuffed with a suitableelastic material. Finally the joints will be closed with a durable plastic mass.

4 FINAL REMARKS AND CONCLUSIONS

In the 1960s and 70 s it was the opinion that concrete equivalent to contemporary strength class C12/15 was suitable and sufficient for environmental characteristics for hydrotechnical structures, also for such small thickness elements as the slabs described in this paper. This has proved to be false. Concrete with such strength properties demonstrates inadequate resistance against influences of atmospheric conditions during the expected service life. The present strict requirements to apply higher classes of concretes in such conditions is validated (justified).

It is very probable, that concrete mixes prepared in field concrete production plants, as often happened in the past, where it was difficult to obtain concrete prepared precisely according to the laboratory composed recipe, had a negative influence on the quality of some slabs. That is why, near slabs with good quality concrete there were some slabs made of concrete with lowered quality. The current practice of ordering concrete produced by specialized companies with proper certification systems avoids this insecure part of the building process concerning quality. For hydrotechnical works usually more strict concrete parameters have to be taken into account, particularly additional requirements concerning freeze-thaw resistance and water tightness, which are not sufficient in general standard regulating concrete quality (PN-EN 206-1:20 03).

REFERENCES

Czarnecki, L. & Emmons, P.L. The repair and the Protection of Concrete Constructions. Polish Cement, Kraków 2002 (in polish).

Decree of Environment Protection, Natural Sources and Forestry Minister on requirements on water management structures and their localization. (in polish) Dz. U. Nr 21/1997 r poz. 111.

ITB: Manual for the use of Schmidt hammers in the non-destructive control of the quality of concrete in structures (in Polish), Warsaw, 1977.

Mailvaganam, N.P., Pye, G.B. & Arnott, M.R. Surface Preparation of the Concrete Substrate. Construction Technology Update Just.24. National Research Council of Canada, Institute for Research in Construction, December 1998.

Proceq, S.A. Concrete Test Hammer. Operating Instructions, 2006.

Runkiewicz, L. Evaluation of concrete strength in construction with Schmidt hammer (in polish) ITB, Warsaw, 1983.

Standard PN—EN 206-1:2003 Concrete. Part 1: Requirements, propriety, production and conformity.

Concrete Solutions – Grantham, Mechtcherine & Schneck (eds)
© 2012 Taylor & Francis Group, London, ISBN 978-0-415-61622-5

An innovative repair and refurbishment of an underground car park in Dresden, Germany

H. Esteves, U. Hammer & S. Mayer
Ed. Züblin AG, Germany

P. Chess
C.P. International, Denmark

ABSTRACT: In 1998, an underground car park was built in the city center of Dresden, near the Frauenkirche church. After eleven years of service, cracking in many places was observed and on further investigation it was found that there was significant chloride ingress at several locations.

Several possibilities for repair were considered with their associated costs, potential problems and benefits. After a thorough consideration of the options, an electrochemically based rehabilitation system was considered to be the best option. In this project 13,000 discrete anodes were placed in ceilings and 4,200 m² of coated titanium mesh anode was installed onto the floors. After the cathodic protection was installed, a special colour coating system was applied and all the existing support systems to the car parks were replaced. This included the sprinkler system, fire alarms, video surveillance, electrical system, lighting and air conditioning. The entire project was completed in 5 months and the garage returned to use.

The Cathodic protection system is working well and further chloride induced damage has not been observed or indicated by corrosion sensors.

1 INTRODUCTION

In 1998, near to the Frauenkirche in the city center of Dresden, an underground car park close to the Frauenkirche was built. The two story underground car park can accommodate approximately 150 vehicles on an area of 4,200 m² in total. The underground car park is adjacent to the historic structure "Albertinum" and right above is the main feeder route to the Frauenkirche adjacent to the Salt Lane hotel.

Figure 2. Construction of the car park in 1998.

Eleven years later, the first damage was observed in the garage. On the floor slab in the 2nd basement, numerous cracks were visible, the existing coating had flaked off, the underlying epoxy resin mortar was cracking and the chloride levels were elevated.

The basement ceiling in the 1st basement showed several cracks, but with higher chloride levels along the sides of the cracks and the first signs of chloride induced corrosion cracking and weeping in the walls.

Furthermore, moist cracks, paint peeling and chlorides were present in the ceiling above the 1st basement.

Figure 1. Frauenkirche in the center of Dresden illuminated at night.

Figure 3.   Cracks on the floor slabs in the car park.

Figure 4.   Damage and signs of moisture on the ceiling above 1st basement floor.

To determine the state of the topside of the ceiling above the first basement, trial pits were dug in the soil in Salt Lane road. It was found that there was no waterproofing on the ceiling. With the aid of preliminary investigations, a careful determination of costs and feasibility to provide rehabilitation of the garage was made.

One approach was to seal the topside with a waterproofing membrane. In coordination with urban issues and the adjacent Albertinum it was realized that it would be possible but complex, associated with a very long repair period and would be very expensive. A major challenge would have been to tackle the numerous cables and urban water supplies on top of the garage ceiling along with telecom, gas, electricity lines and road drainage.

Furthermore, there were many unknown facts like the connection situation of the garage ceiling to the existing retaining wall to the Albertinum.

Another approach was the idea to repair the garage applying the protection principle "K" according to the German Committee for Reinforced Concrete. The repair principle K means "Cathodic Protection" (CP).

Figure 5.   Investigation of the ceiling from the top.

2   CATHODIC PROTECTION

The use of Cathodic Protection "CP" is to pass an electrical current from an external anode on to the steel reinforcement to gain a cathodic polarization of the reinforcement. One method is impressed current cathodic protection (ICCP) with an external power unit between anode and steel. Alternatively, sacrificial systems use reactive anode materials to polarize the steel.

2.1   *Protective effects*

The major effect is the polarization of the reinforcement due to the impressed protection current. A sufficient current density significantly reduces or even stops corrosion completely. The protective effects may be subdivided into two categories:

2.1.1   *Primary effects*

– Electron overflow in the reinforcement directly hinders the anodic dissolution, pushing the equilibrium of the reaction into the cathodic reaction direction (oxygen reduction).
– Lowering the steel potential reduces the likelihood of allowing pitting corrosion in presence of chlorides.

2.1.2   *Secondary effects*

– Formation of hydroxyl ions leads to increasing pH level at the reinforcement surface.
– In the long term, reduction of chloride content at the reinforcement surface occurs due to migration.

2.2   *Advantages*

– Chloride contaminated/carbonated concrete does not need to be removed and corroding reinforcement does not need to be uncovered.
– Chlorides inside the concrete matrix move away from the reinforcement.

- Realkalisation of the concrete in the vicinity of the steel.
- Integrated control systems give information about the structure's condition at any time.
- Repair works can mostly be executed when the object is in use thus taking significantly less time.
- No formation of macro-cells.

2.3 CP design and layout

- In accordance with DIN EN 12696: Targets, protection criteria and lifetime of a CP system must be clearly defined in the contract.
- A CP system may never cause or accelerate reactions which jeopardize the structure's safety and use.
- The CP system needs to be adjusted to the structure, its properties and the environment.
- The layout must ensure a homogenous current distribution.
- Definition of which part of the reinforcement needs to be protected, calculation of steel surface, selection of anode type.
- Type, number and position of the monitoring sensors should be chosen in a way that the protective effect can be displayed with sufficient accuracy at any time.

2.4 CP pre investigations

- Continuity of the reinforcement
- Potential mapping
- Concrete resistance measurements
- Concrete cover measurements.

2.5 CP layout

- Definition of protection zones
- Making of execution plans
- Voltage drop calculation of anode system and global cabling
- Set up a quality handbook according to DIN EN 12696
- Set up a service book.

Here, specifically for the garage ceiling, a system with titanium rod anodes (durAnode 3) with different lengths from 150 mm up to 700 mm was selected and a special inactive length was developed to prevent current spread to the lower rebar layer.

Cracks in the ceiling were permanently sealed by injection. The concept therefore constituted protection of the reinforcement and sealing from the inside of the garage, since, without sealing, the ongoing penetration of water and chlorides from the top would make it impossible to prevented reinforcement corrosion. All observed cracks were filled.

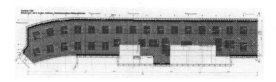

Figure 6. Layout of the cathodic protection system for the ceiling based on discrete anodes.

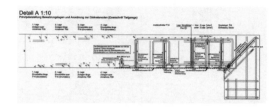

Figure 7. Installation of discrete anodes in hammer-drilled holes in the ceiling and adjacent bored pile walls.

Along with this measure came the entire repair of the garage. Besides the ceiling above the 1st basement, both the floor in the 1st and 2nd basement were treated with cathodic protection. Clear advantages in this project by applying CP were: the fast construction time, the avoidance of deep concrete removals in the building by water jetting or demolition and reconstruction, and the chance to actively monitor the condition of the reinforcement and to adjust the system to individual needs.

As a result of this extensive monitoring, repair intervals can be extended for up to 50 years. In a construction time of only 5 months, the garage was repaired by Ed. Züblin AG, Division Building Maintenance. At the end, more than 13,000 durAnode 3 discrete anodes, made by CPI Limited, were mounted on the garage ceiling, each anode installed into a hole made by hammer drilling up to depths of 750 mm.

Each hole was individually checked prior to the installation of discrete anodes to prevent possible electrical shorts.

After the installation of these discrete anodes, the anodes were connected by titanium wire to a number of different anode areas. More than 8,000 m of coated titanium wire were installed. The titanium wires were applied in slots and immediately covered. Furthermore, sensors, reference electrodes and cathode connections were made in the ceiling.

The floor areas are protected by titanium mesh. The titanium mesh was applied to a total area of 3,900 m² on the two basement levels. After the installation of the leads, reference electrodes and cathode terminals, the entire surfaces were covered

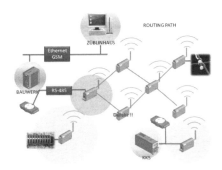

Figure 8. Routing path of the monitoring system.

Figure 9. Anode installation on the 1st basement level.

Figure 10. Casting of the PCC onto the floors to embed the anode mesh.

Figure 11. Entrance of the car park after the repair works were completed.

Figure 12. Parking area with new colour concept after completion and media channel after conclusion.

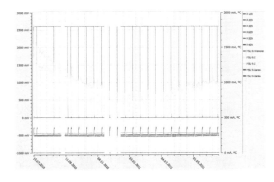

Figure 13. Supervision of the cp system and monitoring of all relevant data.

with a polymer cement concrete overlay (PCC). For this purpose, 421 tons of PCC were used!

Finally, a surface protection system called OS8 was applied onto the bottom slab and to the ramp connecting the 2nd and the 1st basement floor. On the 1st basement floor, a surface protection system called OS11a was applied. All rising components such as columns, walls and ceiling soffits were coated with a surface protection system called OS4. (OS4, OS8 and OS11a are coating systems complying with the German DAfStb Standard).

The surface protection systems were in accordance with a color concept developed especially for the car park. As part of the overall project, Züblin replaced the entire car park ancillary equipment.

Thus, the sprinkler system, fire alarm system, video surveillance, the entire electrical system, lighting, air conditioning, and the fire alarm system were modernised.

The electric lines, the warning systems and the supply lines for the cathodic corrosion protection system were set up in a specially designed media channel in the soffit, for the underground garage. At the same time, the media channel is used to contain the luminaires for the lighting of the parking garage.

3 CONCLUSION

The Cathodic protection system was commissioned in April 2010 and since that time all protection areas are fulfilling the DIN EN12696 protection criteria.

Based on good cooperation with the client, the local team and the expert planners, the project was completed successfully and in time.

LITERATURE

Bazzoni A., B.L. (1996). "Field application of cathodic prevention on reinforced concrete structures". Houston: Corrosion/96, paper 312, NACE.

Broomfield, J. (2007). Corrosion of Steel in concrete, understanding, investigation and repair. London: E & FN Spon.

Broomfield, J.L. (1987). Cathodic protection for reinforced concrete—its application to buildings and marine structures. Houston TX, USA: National Association of Corrosion Engineers.

Chess, P. Gronvold and Karnov, Cathodic Protection International, Copenhagen, Denmark "Cathodic Protection of Steel in Concrete" (1998) London: E & FN Spon.

DIN EN 12696 Cathodic Protectection of Steel in Concrete. Force Technology. (www.forcetechnology.com. http://www.force.dk/NR/rdonlyres/6A6873F7-1A84-426B-B078-C4EF284D2ACE/1805/19192en.pdf. Accessed 8th July 2011.

Muhsau, Frank, Ingenieurgesellschaft der Bauwerkserhaltung mbH, "BE_BP055-01_Untersuchungsbericht.pdf", TG Coselpalais Dresden, 2009.

Sensortec GmbH. www.Sensortec.de, http://www.sensortec.de/images/stories/pdf/Data_Sheet_Multiring_electrode_eng.pdf. Accessed 8th July 2011.

Stratfull, R.F. "Progress Report on Inhibiting the Corrosion of Steel in a Reinforced Concrete Bridge," Corrosion 15, 6 (1959): pp. 331t to 334t.

Concrete Solutions – Grantham, Mechtcherine & Schneck (eds)
© 2012 Taylor & Francis Group, London, ISBN 978-0-415-61622-5

Damage evaluation and repair proposals for reinforced concrete foundations with corrosion damage, and power line towers on a lagoon, Colima, Mexico

A. Garduno & A. Reyes
Comision Federal de Electricidad, Mexico D.F., Mexico

ABSTRACT: This is an example of damage due to severe exposure conditions: four power lines with ten towers each, crossing a lagoon next to the sea from the power plant to land, in Colima, have been studied. The reinforced concrete foundations of the towers were cast in place about 30 years ago. An evaluation was required to know the severity and extent of the damage on the concrete due to corrosion on the reinforcement of piles and beams. Visual inspection, NDTs (pulse velocity measurement, carbonation indicator and an unsuccessful attempt to measure corrosion rate by polarization resistance technique), sampling concrete cores to verify compressive strength and elasticity modulus, sampling concrete powder for determining pH and chloride contents, were carried out. With the results, repair procedures were proposed, considering the operation of the towers during the repair process. In this paper the results of the study and the repair proposals are shared.

1 INTRODUCTION

The power plants Manzanillo I and II in Colima, are located on a strip of land just between the Cuyutlan lagoon and the Pacific Ocean coast, at the Southeast of Mexico (Fig. 1). They have 4 units for a total capacity of 1200 MW; two of them started operating in 1982, the third one in 1983, and the latest one in 1984. Since 2010, the capacity of the plants is being increased by changing units to generate with natural gas instead of fuel oil, improving significantly their efficiency, as well as reducing pollutants. By 2014 their capacity will be 1716 MW. The energy generated is transmitted by 4 power lines that cross Cuyutlan lagoon to the states of Jalisco, Colima and Michoacán. Three of the power lines were built by 1978 and 1980, the latest in 1986 (Fig. 2).

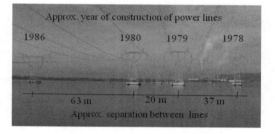

Figure 2. Overview of towers and power plant in the back of the picture.

The power lines must be in good condition to give service once the capacity of the plants have been increased, but the age and exposure conditions have affected the concrete foundations of the towers located in the lagoon. Thus, an evaluation of the concrete structures was required to know the severity and extent of the damage and to establish repair procedures.

2 DESCRIPTION OF THE STRUCTURES

There are 10 towers on each power line crossing the brackish lagoon. The exposure conditions are considered as severe exposure for the reinforcement of the concrete structural elements (ACI 318). The total length of the crossing is about 3 km, and the separation between lines varies from 20 to 60 m (Fig. 2).

Figure 1. Location of power lines on Cuyutlan lagoon.

The foundations of the power lines built up to 1980 were cast in place. They consist of 4 reinforced concrete piers of 2 m diameter, joined in the head by concrete beams. For the construction of these piers, steel permanent formwork was used, and it remains until now. For some time, the steel form protected the concrete, but nowadays it is severely corroded and it is lost in some places. The beams of the towers built by 1978 have 3.5 m length and a 0.8 × 1.2 m section, and the towers built by 1979 and 1980 have 2 parallel beams of 8.5 m length and 0.4 × 1.2 m section each.

The foundation piles of the latest power line were precast and driven in place. These towers have 3 piles of 0.4 × 0.4 m section on each of the four vertices, joined by a concrete capital of 2.4 × 2.4 m, with 5.8 m length beams of 0.6 × 0.8 m section.

There was no further information about the reinforcement of the structural elements or the characteristics of the concrete used for their construction.

The depth of the lagoon on the power lines trajectory is less than 1.0 m, and under the water there is about 0.5 m of soft sediment. The water of the lagoon is being monitored and it has chloride contents from 18,000 to 20,000 ppm and sulfate contents from 3700 to 4500 ppm.

During sampling and site testing, temperature ranged from 18°C (at night) to 32°C.

3 EVALUATION OF THE CONCRETE STRUCTURES

The works for the evaluation began in April 2010 with a detailed inspection of the structures above sea level: piers, piles, heads and beams. The concrete structures that were permanently submerged were not inspected, considering that the corrosion process can not progress without oxygen (García, 2002). The evaluation was focused on the three oldest power line towers because it was apparent that the more recent line was in better condition. Nevertheless the recent towers presented minimal defects in the located areas, related to bad practice during construction, such as segregation and improper consolidation. The following comments refer to the oldest power lines.

There was no need to measure the concrete cover with a magnetic cover meter because spalling allowed us to observe exposed reinforcement and concrete cover on the structural elements. The concrete cover on beams was about 5 cm on the upper and lower sides, and only 2 cm on the laterals. For the piers the concrete cover was about 6 cm. The concrete covers did not meet the minimum indicated on ACI 318 considering the severe exposure conditions.

The reinforcement of the structural elements was also observed. This was done with a rebar locator that helped to establish the separation between bars and to get information about the steel section of rebars and stirrups, and was calibrated in zones with exposed bars.

Damage to the concrete structures was recorded in detail. Most of the beams and piers were affected by corrosion of the reinforcing steel bars and stirrups. Figure 3 presents the most frequent defects found on the structures. Except where there were problems associated with corrosion, the concrete appeared to have good quality: homogeneity, no pores nor segregation.

Beams showed cracks following the reinforcement (from 0.3 to 15.0 mm wide), delamination, spalling, rebar exposure, loss of stirrups and reduction of steel section in some places.

The corrosion on the steel formwork of the piers, about 0.6 m length in the zone of wetting-drying cycles, was the beginning of the problem for the piers. The steel plate was severely corroded and holed in the mentioned zone where stirrups and reinforcement were being corroded as well. In addition, concrete spalling in some places had caused exposure of the steel bars and increased the problem.

3.1 Non destructive tests

In order to avoid an extensive exploration based on coring and removing concrete, representative structures and locations to test with non destructive techniques were chosen.

The carbonation indicator (phenolphthalein) was used only in a few beams to check the level of carbonation at the reinforcement or stirrup depths. The results showed that the carbonation front had reached the stirrups on laterals of beams (Fig. 4) but were not that apparent at the rebar depth.

Ultrasonic pulse velocity was measured according to ASTM C597 to verify, qualitatively, the density and homogeneity, and thus the quality of concrete inside the structures and not only on the cover. This was done on beams because the sensors (PUNDIT) are not suitable for the round piers (Fig. 5).

DEFECTS

A) Longitudinal crack

B) Corroded steel form

C) Spalling

D) Loss of steel section on rebars

Figure 3. View of concrete structures with typical defects related to corrosion.

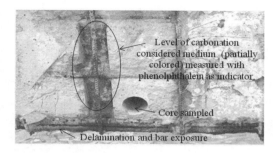

Figure 4. Carbonation indicator on beam.

Figure 5. Pulse velocity measurements on beam.

Table 1. Representative results of ultrasonic pulse velocity measurements.

Location of sensors	Pulse velocity (m/s)	Damage
	1750	cracking around rebars
	4390	sound concrete
	1270	lateral plane of weakness
	1080	cracking and plane of weakness

Table 1 shows representative results of the measurements. The obtained pulse velocities had considerable variations. The lower data, less than 2000 m/s, were associated with cracking inside the concrete due to the expansion of the reinforcement and in many cases, to the plane of weakness induced by the corrosion of the stirrups and lateral bars, as shown in Table 1. Higher results, more than 4000 m/s, were expected in sound concrete with compressive strength above 20 MPa (Neville, 1995). The results in between were dependent on the development of damage.

Measurement of corrosion rate based on the linear polarization resistance technique was done on two occasions. The first one was done on April 2010, at the same time as the other non destructive measurements and sampling of concrete. In that time, a GECOR 6 was used with no results. Apparently there were problems with the electrical contact and the required confinement could not be achieved. Later, in March 2011, the second attempt was done. This time, 2 systems, GECOR 6 and GECOR 8 were used. Improvements were tried for preparing bars, basically an exhaustive cleaning: including sanding, brushing, applying phosphoric acid (1:3), and washing with freshwater. Also, special attention was given to keeping the concrete humid as well as the sponge (contact between the concrete surface and the sensors). Measurements were done on rebars and on stirrups. Figure 6 illustrates the measurement process. Unfortunately the readings were not repeatable with both systems in all cases, and it was difficult to identify the accurate ones. The results are presented in Figure 7.

Corrosion rate results, between 0.05 and 0.43 $\mu A/cm^2$, were indicative of a passive condition

Figure 6. Corrosion measurements on beam.

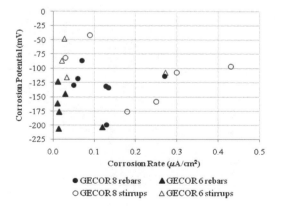

Figure 7. Results obtained with Gecor systems.

up to moderate corrosion (Broomfield 2007). These results should be analyzed considering the high chloride contents that will be discussed later.

Corrosion potential results, from −42.28 to −203.03 mV, were indicative of a low risk of corrosion occurring at the time of measurement for a copper/copper sulfate electrode (ASTM C 876). The results presented a lower risk of corrosion on stirrups than on rebars.

3.2 Core and concrete powder sampling

Concrete coring was done on representative beams, piers (Fig. 8) and heads. This allowed us to verify concrete soundness below the surface of the structures and to obtain some information about the concrete such as the maximum size aggregate (msa) of 25 mm and particle size distribution, which was adequate, as well as mechanical properties when tested in laboratory. The core holes were refilled with commercial grout (Sikagrout).

Samples of concrete powder were taken with an electric drill (Fig. 9) at 2 depths, superficial, about 5 cm depth, and close to the reinforcement depth, from 5 to 10 cm. Care was taken to recover all the powder while drilling.

Cores and concrete powder samples were identified, packed in plastic bags and transported to the laboratory in Mexico City.

3.3 Laboratory testing

Concrete cores were tested in accordance with ASTM C42, C469 and C642 and the compressive strength, modulus of elasticity, as well as density, were determined. Results are shown in Table 2.

The compressive strength results, representative of 30 year old concrete, may indicate a higher water/cement ratio used for the construction of the structures, (Neville, 1995), than that required for

Figure 8. Coring on pier and view of a core representative of sound concrete.

Figure 9. Concrete powder sampling.

Table 2. Average results of laboratory tests on samples of each structural element.

Structural element	Compressive strength MPa	Modulus of elasticity GPa	Density kg/m³
Beams	39.0	24.1	2330
Piers	38.2	24.9	2259
Heads	44.7	25.7	2393
Average*	40.3	24.49	2338

*The average was calculated with all the results and not with the averages of each structural element.

Table 3. Average pH and chloride content on each structural element at superficial and deep measurements.

Structural element	Potencial hydrogen pH		Chloride content% by mass of concrete	
	0–5 cm	5–10 cm	0–5 cm	5–10 cm
Beams	10.7	11.1	0.41	0.41
Piers	11.1	11.1	0.37	0.42
Heads	11.1	11.2	0.32	0.31
Average*	10.9	11.1	0.39	0.40

*The average was calculated with all the results and not with the averages of each structural element.

this exposure condition, by modern standards, of 0.4 (ACI 318).

The modulus of elasticity was measured but it was not a parameter related to the durability of concrete structures. The relation between average compressive strange (fc = 40.3 MPa) and average modulus of elasticity (Ec = 24.49 GPa) can be expressed as, Ec = 3860 (fc)$^{0.5}$. This seems a low value if compared with the expression recommended by ACI 318 for a normal density concrete,

Table 4. Classification of damage for the concrete structures of the power lines towers.

| Damage levels/repairing | Visible defects | Crack width | Chloride (*) | |
		mm	%	pH
Low/Patching	Segregation, no cracks	0	<0.2	>12
Medium/replace concrete, cathodic protection	Several cracking, located spalling, loss in steel section <20%	0–6	0.2–0.4	10–12
Severe/replace concrete and barscathodic protection	Extensive cracking and spalling, loss in steel section >20%	>6	>0.4	10

(*) % by mass of sample (concrete).

Table 5. Estimated damage for the concrete structures of the power lines towers.

| Structural element | Percentage of elements with damage | | |
	Low	Medium	Severe
Beams	7	50	43
Piers	0	60	40
Heads	10	0	0

but it is may be related to the nature of the aggregates used for the construction of the structures.

The density of the cores was representative of normal weight concrete (Neville, 1995), and this is consistent with the pulse velocities obtained on sound concrete. It also showed homogeneity on structural concrete elements.

It should be mentioned that the carbonation indicator was not applied on concrete cores and the information from site was not enough to establish the carbonation front.

Chloride content (% by mass of concrete) and pH were determined for the dust samples in accordance with ASTM C1218 and D1293. Table 3 shows average results for superficial and deep (at rebar depth) measurements. With both parameters, results do not show a differentiation related to the depth up to the rebars.

The maximum chloride content by mass of concrete admissible for these concrete structures was estimated (Mena, 2005). It was considered from the compressive strength results, for a water/cement ratio about 0.5, a cement content of 350 kg/m^3, a density of 2330 kg/m^3 that a maximum of 0.15% chloride of weight of cement was permissible (ACI 318). This meant 0.02% by mass of concrete, and it was greatly exceeded in all cases. From this, it is considered that chloride contents represented a high corrosion risk for the structures (Broomfield, 2007). And, as mentioned, the high levels were found in the surface of the concrete structures as well as at the rebars level, which is an issue to consider for the rehabilitation of the structures.

Although pH results were not lower than 10, they were on the borderline of the limits necessary to passivate the reinforcement (Broomfield, 2007).

4 CLASSIFICATION OF DAMAGES ON CONCRETE TOWER FOUNDATIONS

Considering the defects found on the concrete elements, as well as width of cracks, chloride contents and pH found on samples, the damages were classified on 3 levels, low, medium and severe, as presented in Table 4. This classification was also associated to the repairs required.

With the inspection data, results of NDT and laboratory tests, the conditions of all the concrete structures of the towers were rated. This was necessary in order to plan repairing processes and to estimate the quantities of materials required to rehabilitate the concrete foundations. Table 5 presents the summary of damage.

Results showed great affectations on beams and piers due to chloride contamination, but the approach of patching and sealing may not be enough because of the high chloride levels found inside the structures, and it will be necessary to include a cathodic protection system.

5 REPAIRING PROCEDURES PROPOSAL

The stability and safety of the foundation, considering the current status of the structures and simulating the repairing of one pier at a time, was verified with a simplified static analysis of the towers. For this, it was considered a rigid structure for the steel tower inducing the transmission of all load applications to the concrete foundation. The weight of the tower is about 12,020 kg, the cables weight is about 3619 kg. It was verified an adequate behavior under accidental conditions such as seismic and wind. Also the torsion on piers was checked.

The cathodic protection system is not designed yet, but for these concrete foundations, in the middle of a lagoon, it would not be practical to use impressed current cathodic protection, so it is recommended to use galvanic cathodic protection. The anodes should be embedded in the concrete after removing the concrete cover and cleaning rebars. This should be done for the medium and severe damage repairs.

The repairing procedures for patching and sealing are related to the damage level of the structures, as follows.

5.1 *Low level damage repairs*

These repairs must be done on a few beams and heads. It was required to remove concrete with segregation, to apply anti-corrosive treatment (such as Sika-Top Armatec 110 EpoCem) on bars and to replace concrete with grout (Sikagrout, e.g.). If the depth of concrete replacement was more than 10 cm, the grout could be mixed with 30% gravel (msa 9.5 mm). Finally, curing with membrane was recommended.

5.2 *Medium level damage repairs*

These are the most extensive repairs, half of the beams and more than half of the piers. It was recommended to remove the concrete cover, 25 mm behind rebars (Emmons, 1993), to remove rust on bars, to apply anti-corrosive protection to bars, and to replace concrete (w/c ratio = 0.4, minimum cement content 400 kg/m^3, msa 9.5 mm, pozzolan cement, superplasticizer admixture) but increasing the cover of bars in order to provide enough protection, as required by ACI 318. Vibration can be done by immersion or with form vibrators. Curing with membrane is recommended.

Figure 10 shows a scheme of the beam with the engrossment of the section, including the chimney form (ACI 311) for pouring concrete.

For piers, before removing the concrete cover, the affected steel form had to be cut and removed in all the perimeter in the zone of splash and wetting-drying cycles, about 0.6 m length. Below that, the steel form had to be cleaned about 1.2 m. The rehabilitated section of the pier, from

the original diameter of 2.0 m will be enlarged to 2.30 m, and should enter in the soft sediments.

5.3 *Severe level damage repairs*

About 40% of beams and piers had lost more than 20% steel section, more commonly stirrups, but main reinforcement should be considered. A similar procedure to the repairs for medium damage should be followed, but should also contemplate.

For beams, restitution of stirrups requires removing concrete cover in all the section, and the new stirrup must be tied to sound rebars. Rebars for restitution should be tied to the original rebar, at least the development length in tension indicated on ACI 318, where sound, or anchored with an epoxy resin on piers if necessary.

For piers, rebars for restitution have to be welded to the cleaned steel from below the tide change zone and they should end bended at top of the head at least 12 d_b, as recommended on ACI 318 (Fig. 11). It is recommended to clean the original rebars and not to cut them. The new rebars should be tied to them. New stirrups should be placed around the new rebars, welded where the steel form remains.

Because the humidity on the lagoon is high, the use of a vapor barrier (Sikaguard 62, e.g.) in the zone of splash and wetting-drying cycles in the concrete structures was recommended, once the repairs are concluded, including concrete structures without apparent defects (Bertolini, 2003) to enhance concrete durability.

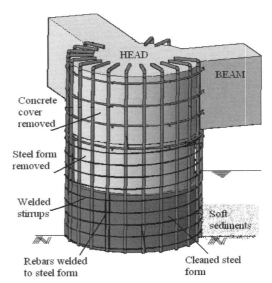

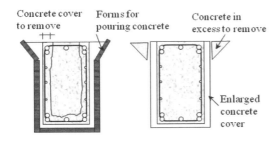

Figure 10. Repairs on beams with medium level damage.

Figure 11. Preparations for repairs on piers with severe level damage.

Environmental restrictions do not allow the pollution of the lagoon with any waste or trash, so special attention must be paid during the removal and replacement of concrete.

During the repairs some difficulties may come because work has to be done on boats and rafts, and there will not be much space for materials and equipment. This must be considered in their planning, as well as the sequence of the repairs.

6 CONCLUSIONS

During the inspection of the concrete foundations it became apparent that the structures from 1986 were in much better condition than the oldest ones. This is attributed to the construction procedure (precast piles) and age. In the other hand, the damage on the three oldest power line tower foundations were associated with scarce concrete cover and to the high chloride and humidity exposure. The concrete quality did not jeopardize the protection of bars against corrosion.

Results of pulse velocity, compressive strength and density, are representative of a good quality concrete. But pulse velocity also shows extensive defects on beams such as delamination and cracking.

pH is a parameter that shows vulnerability. Carbonation measurements were not enough to establish the carbonation front, measurements on cores would have brought more information.

The main problem for the reinforcement is the chloride contamination of the structures. The chloride level at the rebar determines the present extent of corrosion, but the profile would help to determine the future rate. Concrete powder was not sampled in small depth increments, so the profile could not be established.

In this study, corrosion rates and corrosion potentials represent a condition which is not congruent to the observed defects on the structures. The results were not completely reliable. But this could be partially explained when the high chloride contents were found.

NDT was useful to establish the extent of damage and with laboratory results helping to estimate the complexity of the rehabilitation required.

The proposed repair procedures can be a guide to the contractor, who must decide the sequence for works considering structural safety as well as environmental restrictions. The contractor will also design the cathodic protection system in accordance to the patching and sealing procedure, as well as the location of the power lines towers foundations.

The rehabilitation of the towers will be complex. Works have to be done partially on each tower, changing to the next one and coming back, because of the stability and safety issues.

In case the concrete structures are not rehabilitated soon, the corrosion problems will grow and the percentage of severe damage will increase. At this moment there is not enough information to estimate how fast the medium damage will become severe, but it would be desirable to conduct better tests to verify corrosion rate, corrosion potential and measuring concrete resistivity, as well as air permeability, and complementary chloride and carbonation measurements. The new data would help to model and estimate service life.

ACKNOWLEDGEMENTS

The authors are grateful to Comision Federal de Electricidad for permitting the use of the information, and to Mario Montero Catalan for his support.

REFERENCES

American Concrete Institute, 2007, *Manual of Concrete Inspection,* Reported by ACI Committee. ACI 311., Farmington Hills, Michigan.

American Concrete Institute, 2008, *Building code requirements for structural concrete.* Reported by ACI Committee. ACI 318M, Farmington Hills, Michigan.

ASTM C42. 2010. *Standard Test Method for Obtaining and Testing Drilled Cores and Sawed Beams of Concrete.* American Society of Testing and Materials, West Conshohocken, PA.

ASTM C469. 2010. Standard Test Method for Static Modulus of Elasticity and Poisson's Ratio of Concrete in Compression. American Society of Testing and Materials, West Conshohocken, PA.

ASTM C597. 2009. *Standard Test Method for Pulse Velocity through Concrete.* American Society of Testing and Materials, West Conshohocken, PA.

ASTM C642. 2006. *Standard Test Method for Density, Absorption, and Voids in Hardened Concrete.* American Society of Testing and Materials, West Conshohocken, PA.

ASTM C876. 2009. *Standard Test Method for Half-Cell Potentials of Uncoated Reinforcing Steel in Concrete.* American Society of Testing and Materials, West Conshohocken, PA.

ASTM C1218. 2008. *Standard Test Method for Water-Soluble Chloride in Mortar and Concrete.* American Society of Testing and Materials, West Conshohocken, PA.

ASTM D1293. 2005. *Standard Test Method for pH of Water.* American Society of Testing and Materials, West Conshohocken, PA.

Bertolini, L., 2003, *Corrosion of Steel in Concrete, Prevention, Diagnosis, Repair,* Wiley-Vch.

Broomfield J.P., 2007, *Corrosion of Steel in Concrete, Understanding, Investigation and Repair,* Taylor & Francis.

García-Rodríguez F., 2002. *Evaluación de estructuras, Técnicas y materiales para su reparación,* México D.F., IMCYC.

Emmons, P.H., 1993. *Concrete Repair and Maintenance Illustrated.* RSMeans, USA.

Mena-Ferrer, M. 2005, *Durabilidad de estructuras de concreto en México,* México D.F., IMCYC.

Neville, A.M. 1995. *Properties of concrete 4th edition.* Publ. Longman.

Concrete Solutions – Grantham, Mechtcherine & Schneck (eds)
© 2012 Taylor & Francis Group, London, ISBN 978-0-415-61622-5

Diagnosis and repair of cracking to an old 1880's concrete house for Channel 4 Television, UK

M.G. Grantham
Sandberg LLP, London & Queen's University, Belfast, UK

S. Pitchers
Craddy Pitchers Davidson, Bristol, UK

S. Jones
Concrete Repairs Ltd, Bristol, UK

ABSTRACT: Michael Grantham was initially approached in October 2010 by the owner of an old concrete house which was suffering from severe cracking. The house was due to feature on national television in a programme called "Help my House is Falling Down!" which is broadcast at prime time on Channel 4, one of the main UK TV channels. Subsequently, we were asked to appear on the programme and to conduct insitu and laboratory tests to determine the cause(s) of cracking and to help with remedial suggestions. The cause of cracking was very unusual and quite complex, resulting from a combination of expansion due to the use of old foundry waste as an aggregate and also due to cracking due to a lack of restraint in the walls.

This paper details the diagnostic work and also the remedial measures which were undertaken.

1   INTRODUCTION

Concrete is a fundamentally durable material, and has a good track record of successful use in building, provided it is of adequate quality, adequate protection of any reinforcement present has been provided and the structure is adequately designed to withstand the structural loads imposed on it, from either self weight (including the roof) and wind loading.

Occasionally, problems with concrete houses occur, in particular with some of the system built houses built before and after the second world war, including Laing Easiform, Airey Houses, Cornish Houses, Woolaway Houses and Wimpey No-Fines Concrete Houses. These, amongst other system built homes, were the subject of a report by the UK's Building Research Establishment (BRE, 2002) and each type of house was the subject of an individual report on appraisal and repair (Refs listed in BRE, 2002).

Other unusual problems have occurred in houses built with concrete blocks, where the aggregate used in the blocks was unsound. Materials which have caused problems in this respect include unburned coal, hard burned lime, iron pyrites (BRE, 1992 & 1997, RICS, 1997) and slag. The lead author has been involved in a number of such cases over the years, including a failure of houses at Snowdown in Kent and also a major problem involving failure of houses in Northern Ireland and the Isle of Man (both in the 1980's), which were due to the use of clinker aggregate in blocks where the coal contained limestone, which, when fired, became hard burned, slow reacting quicklime. This material was moisture expansive and the result was massive cracking in the blocks resulting in cracking and expansion of the walls of the properties.

With this background, spotting one of the significant causes of problems at the house in the UK's Midlands, was made more easy. Other aspects of the failure were determined by the Chartered Engineer, Simon Pitchers, and also by a second structural engineer involved in the design of the remedial works, Frank Haywood Associates.

This paper discusses the investigation on site, performed while the programme was being filmed for television, the subsequent laboratory work and the remedial measures that have been adopted.

2   SITE INSPECTION

The visit to the property was made in November 2010. Inspection of the house externally revealed cracks up to 8 mm in width, notably between the gable end wall and both the front and rear walls, where the gable end wall appeared to be moving outwards at the top and splitting away from the front and rear walls, more seriously so at the front (Fig. 1).

Internally, the plaster had been removed from the upper rooms but was still present on those downstairs, rendering inspection of the hidden surfaces impossible. Upstairs, a band of severe cracking was present on the front and gable walls, about 1 m deep at mid height in the wall (extending approximately from top to bottom of the window right round the wall (Fig. 2). Inspection of the rear

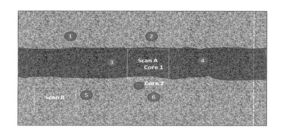

Figure 3.   Schematic showing core sample and PUNDIT and Schmidt Hammer test locations.

Figure 1.   House showing crack (inked over) between gable wall and front elevation.

Figure 2.   Internal cracking in concrete in upper wall.

Figure 4.   Three Ferroscan surveys (600 mm × 600 mm) one above the other on front elevation internal wall. Note the possible reinforcing mesh in the upper part and the apparent presence of iron fragments in the lower part.

40

bedroom showed a similar problem. It was possible to see daylight through some cracks!

Further inspection in the loft of the property revealed similar cracking too, in the upper part of the gable end wall. More detailed inspection revealed an unusual fragment in one wall, apparently comprising a large lump (100 mm or so wide) of what appeared to be "pig iron," which was corroding. This was the first clue as to the cause of the unusual cracking.

In order to investigate further and to establish the comparative condition of the wall in the widely cracked central band and the less fractured concrete above and below the more damaged zone, a series of tests was carried out. Initially we wanted to establish whether any reinforcement was present in the wall, so tests were performed using a Hilti Ferroscan® PS200 scanning covermeter (Fig. 4). The procedures recommended in BS1881 Part 204 (BSI, 1988) were used for this testing. Six tests were then carried out with a Digital Schmidt Hammer (a Proceq Silver Schmidt®), following the procedures recommended in BS EN 12504-2 (BSI, 2001) and six tests were carried out in similar positions using a PUNDIT 6 Ultrasonic Pulse Velocity Testing machine. The procedures recommended in BS EN 12504-4 (BSI, 2004) were followed except that

tests were conducted in indirect mode, owing to the difficulty of getting a path through the walls, because of the uneven surface of the external rendering. These tests were carried out at locations above, in the centre of and below the band of deteriorated concrete in the gable wall at 1st floor level, in the front bedroom. Figure 3 shows the arrangement of test locations.

Two 100 mm diameter core samples were then removed by diamond drilling to enable samples to be sent to the laboratory for petrographic examination.

The test results were very interesting. It was not entirely clear whether some form of reinforcement was present in the walls, as was suggested by the Ferroscan® survey, and lack of time and the poor condition of the walls prevented exploratory cutting out to determine whether any was present. What the covermeter survey did reveal was the presence of numerous metallic lumps in the concrete, similar to that observed in one part of the wall in some areas.

The Schmidt Hammer values showed low results for positions 3 and 4 in the centre, deteriorated, band and interestingly also at Position 5, in the visually better concrete nearer to floor level.

Table 1.   Results of Schmidt hammer tests.

	Test position					
	No 1	No 2	No 3	No 4	No 5	No 6
Schmidt Hammer	43	55	30	13	25	35
rebound number	33	31	20	21	35	35
	53	30	24	20	16	36
	43	17	29	20	34	36
	49	53	25	19	14	28
	40	44	21	24	25	29
	45	58	15	33	38	58
	46	52	31	7	46	37
	55	44	23	27	43	31
	39	64	28	29	31	44
	38	58	28	28	29	32
	50	52	21	59	29	33
Mean	**45**	**47**	**25**	**25**	**30**	**36**

Table 2.   Results of indirect UPV tests.

UPV	Path length (mm)	Transit time 1 us	Transit time 2 us	Mean	UPV km/s
No 1	300	126.5	126.5	126.5	2.4
No 2	300	200.9	200.9	200.9	1.5
No 3	150	86.2	88.2	87.2	1.7
No 4	150	112.1	114.3	113.2	1.3
No 5	300	161.9	162.1	162.0	1.9
No 6	200	78.5	79.1	78.8	2.5

Figure 5. Tensile crack (arrowed) in concrete below centre deteriorated band—the crack did not extend into the centre band.

The ultrasound results all showed rather poor quality concrete (good concrete would be expected to show values in the 4 km/s region, or better). All tests were undertaken using indirect transmission (from the same side of the wall, rather than through it, as the rough surface of the pebbledash rendering made it impossible to take readings through the wall). The reliability of indirect readings is poorer than those using direct transmission.

Of special interest was the presence of several vertical cracks in the concrete underneath the heavily deteriorated band. These were a clear implication of expansive movement of the concrete in the deteriorated band, causing a tensile stress in the zone of concrete underneath (Fig. 5).

3 LABORATORY TESTS

The two core samples were taken in the centre zone of the deteriorated concrete and in the better condition concrete beneath. The former was difficult to remove intact whereas the latter core showed good integrity. The petrographic testing was carried out in accordance with APG SR2 (Eden, 2010) and ASTM C856-04 (ASTM, 2004). In brief, the following work was carried out.

- The samples were examined as received and photographed.
- A longitudinal polished plate was prepared from each core selected for petrographic examination. The polished plates represented the full depths of the samples and were orientated normal to the external surfaces.
- The volume proportions of aggregate, paste and void were determined by point counting of the polished plates using the stereo binocular microscope. The measured volume proportions were used in the calculation of the compositions of the samples using the method given in APG SR2 (2010).

- A longitudinal fluorescent resin impregnated thin section was prepared from the outer end of each sample selected for petrographic examination. The thin sections represented the samples between their external surfaces and maximum depths of about 70 mm.
- The thin sections were examined with a Zeiss petrological photomicroscope and the distribution of porosity and microcracking was assessed from an examination of the thin sections in fluorescent light using the petrological microscope.

3.1 Core 1, deteriorated concrete in centre band

This had coarse aggregate that contained a very wide range of materials that included siliceous gravel, carbonaceous aggregate particles (coal/part-burnt coal/coke) and particles resembling slag. There were also metallic iron fragments and siliceous gravel. The iron particles were commonly corroded around their surfaces and corrosion-stained cracks sometimes appeared to originate from the metallic iron particles many of the aggregate particles in this sample were porous and weak.

3.2 Core 2, lower, intact concrete

The coarse aggregate was a siliceous gravel, together with some brick. The gravel contained abundant quartzite and vein quartz and was composed of dense and robust lithologies that were of low porosity. No evidence was found for the presence of slag, coal or coke in this sample. This sample had very few cracks.

3.3 Chemical tests

Chemical tests were also performed to determine total acid soluble chloride and sulphate using the procedures given in BS1881 Part 124 (BSI, 1988). The chloride levels were low in both samples at

Figure 6. Corroding iron particle and associated cracking in deteriorated core.

0.004% of sample and low to normal sulphate contents were found, 0.09% and 0.31% respectively for deteriorated concrete in the centre band and the sound concrete underneath, respectively.

The overall conclusion on the causes of cracking in the deteriorated concrete core was

- The weak and friable nature of the cement paste: This is regarded as being a result of a high water/cement ratio and also high void content/poor compaction.
- Metallic iron: The expansion associated with the corrosion of metallic iron accounted for some of the cracking in Core 1 (Fig. 7). The observed large iron fragments seen at site were also considered to be a factor in more extensive cracking elsewhere in the structure.
- Coal/part burnt coal: The deteriorated core contained small amounts of coal and part-burnt coal particles. Coal particles are potentially capable of giving rise to expansive cracking when subjected to cycles of wetting and drying.

Overall, and following discussion with the consulting Engineers, Simon Pitchers and Frank

Figure 9. Carbon fibre strips glued in place with epoxy resin to provide additional strength to gable wall.

Figure 7. Rendering removed and insulated cladding being installed.

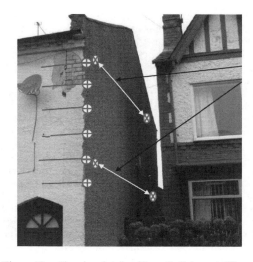

Figure 10. Showing details of bow tie fixings at 600 mm vertical centres (black arrows) tied into joists. 1200 mm long CemTies installed through gable wall into both front and rear walls, generally at 450 mm centres.

Figure 8. Helical stainless steel fixings to restrain gable wall.

Haywood, we concluded that the most likely cause of the cracking seen between the gable wall and front and rear elevations was most probably corrosion of the metal fragments in the concrete that had been placed in the lifts that were visibly damaged, causing a general expansion of these lifts in both a horizontal and vertical sense. The expansive action, that had occurred over a period in excess of 100 years, had caused the expanded sections to force the other elements of the fabric apart, which was entirely consistent with the cracking observed. More structural movement had followed caused by a lack of lateral restraint between the gable wall and the front and rear walls. The method of construction was partly responsible for this, where brick piers had been constructed in the corners to support the shuttering for the concrete, which had then been infilled afterwards, forming planes of weakness between the dissimilar materials that were subsequently exploited by the expanding lifts of concrete.

4 REMEDIAL WORK

A considerable discussion on the best approach for repairing this structure was held, with the possibility of resin injecting the deteriorating cracked band of concrete, and hoping that would sufficiently restrict moisture and oxygen from fuelling further corrosion and expansion. This idea was rejected as there was not sufficient confidence that the moisture could not still find a way in. Furthermore it was evident that the extent of corrosion and expansion was slow (the house was 130 years old) and that keeping the structure dry plus dealing with the existing cracking and restraint issues would be the most appropriate method to prolong the life of the perimeter walls. These decisions were taken by the Consulting Engineers.

The final solution chosen involved providing additional lateral restraint using a combination of bow tie and helical stainless steel fixings between the gable wall and front and rear walls. These were installed in and around the positions of the most serious fractures in the external wall fabric.

In addition to this, cracks in the walls were sealed with resin injection, the walls were stripped of render and insulated cladding applied, followed by reinstatement of the rendering. Internally, the weak defective band of concrete on the first floor and also the weak material on the gable wall in the loft was removed to about 75 mm depth in sections and replaced with a hand applied concrete repair mortar, allowing each insertion of repair material to set and harden, before proceeding with the next part. Finally, carbon fibre strips were added to walls to provide additional tensile strength to supplement the capability of the external wall to withstand wind pressures, prior to replastering.

5 CONCLUSIONS

This project provided an extremely interesting challenge. Rarely do we get to work with concrete in such old structures, and the challenge of finding the causes of the defects was very interesting. Subsequent research showed that an iron foundry was operating quite near to the site, and it is likely that the opportunity for some easily available cheap infill material for the concrete was taken. Fortunately it appeared to have been used in selective lifts of the concrete, which rendered the problem containable, for the most part. Had it been used

throughout the structure, the picture might have been very different. At that time, of course, the consequences of corrosion of the iron fragments had probably not been thought through by the contractor and concrete supplier. Modern engineers and contractors are only too well aware of the damage that corroding iron and steel can do to a structure.

The chosen remedial solution will extend the erviceable life of the building, by reducing the rate of corrosion of the embedded metal fragments that are the principle source of disruption to parts of the external leaf. The rendered insulation on the outside of the perimeter walling will prevent the ingress of rain from the outside and will increase the temperature of the concrete walling during cold spells, moving the dew point and reducing the tendency for condensation to form within the perimeter walling. The addition of a vapour check to the internal face of the perimeter walling would also control migration of water vapour into the perimeter concrete walls. Controlling water migration into the perimeter walling will reduce the rate of corrosion of the embedded metal fragments and will result in an extended serviceable life for the structure, further harnessing the intrinsic thermal mass of the perimeter walling.

These improvements, together with the structural strengthening will improve matters considerably for the structure.

REFERENCES

ASTM C856—04, 2004 Standard Practice for Petrographic Examination of Hardened Concrete, ASTM, (Now superseded by 2011standard).
BRE Report, 1992 Taking care of 'mundic' concrete houses. BRE—Royal Institution of Chartered Surveyors.
BRE Report 325, 1997 Sulfide-related degradation of concrete in southwest England (the mundic problem), BRE.
BS 1881-124:1988, Testing concrete. Methods for analysis of hardened concrete, BSI.
BS1881: Part 204:1988 Testing Concrete—Recommendations on the Use of Electromagnetic Covermeters, BSI.
BS EN 12504-2:2001 Testing concrete in structures. Non-destructive testing. Determination of rebound number BSI.
BS EN 12504-4:2004 BS EN 12504-4 "Testing concrete. Determination of ultrasonic pulse velocity. BSI.
Building Research Establishment, 2002 Non Traditional Housing in the UK—A Brief Review, A report for the Council of Mortgage Lenders, BRE.
Eden, M.A. A code of practice for the petrographic examination of concrete. Applied Petrography Group, SR2, July 2010.
Royal Institute of Chartered Surveyors The Mundic problem—a guidance note. Recommended sampling, examination and classification procedure for suspect concrete building materials in Cornwall and parts of Devon, London, 1997.

Concrete Solutions – Grantham, Mechtcherine & Schneck (eds)
© 2012 Taylor & Francis Group, London, ISBN 978-0-415-61622-5

Vulnerability assessment of the concrete tanks storage at natural hazards

H. Hammoum, K. Bouzelha & N.E. Hannachi
Département de génie civil, Université Mouloud Mammeri, Tizi Ouzou, Algeria

D. Serre
Université Paris Est, Ecole des Ingénieurs de la Ville de Paris, Paris, France

ABSTRACT: In this paper, the concept of vulnerability to natural hazards is used to predict the average level of damage and aging that may occur on a large scale in a water storage tank. To estimate the state of these storage tanks, we develop in this study a ciagnosis method based on the vulnerability index (I_v), taking into account all affecting; environmental, structural and functional factors. From this index, we propose a classification scale of the tanks in three levels of behaviour, which are associated with different colours. The first level includes tanks with good behaviour (green), the second includes tanks with average behaviour (orange) and the third concerns the tanks with bad behaviour (red).

1 INTRODUCTION

The Algerian storage tank park of drinking water has almost 40,000 tanks and is mostly built of reinforced concrete. The feedback from nearly half a century of management has highlighted a great disparity in behavior of these structures, manifested by several pathologies (Hammoum et al., 2010). Lack of maintenance of these tanks, directly exposed to natural threats (snow, cyclones, earthquakes, winds, fires etc.) can accelerate the aging process.

The diagnosis and evaluation of these tanks with various pathologies are complex. An experienced engineer can, at the first visit, know the problem origin, but for a less experienced engineer the same task can become difficult. The diagnosis is always an exercise with a relatively high difficulty level. Confronted with the same exposed problem, the solutions proposed by experts are not of course always the same. Each expert interprets the problem from his own knowledge, because there is no law named diagnosis, but there is knowhow for diagnosis, based on experience. In some emergency situations (like after a major earthquake), the task of diagnosis requires at the same time quick and efficient action. In front these exceptional situations, there are always not enough experts, so we are obliged to engage less experienced engineers in the diagnosis task.

Thus we propose, through our paper, a simple and practical method to a professional (engineer or technician) of civil engineering to evaluate quickly the vulnerability presumption to natural hazards (snow, wind, earthquake etc.) of a storage tank, guiding them in their diagnosis.

2 METHODOLOGY FOR EVALUATING A STORAGE TANK

Many assessment methods for the state of hydraulic structures were developed by the park managers for diagnosis, risk analysis or programming maintenance actions. We can enumerate mainly physical models approach, the expert approach, methods of dependability in the civil engineering and the probabilistic approach.

2.1 Physical models

In the field of storage tanks for fluids, the best known physical model is that of Housner (Housner, 1963). To analyze the tank stability and its hydrodynamic behavior (the liquid effect on the walls under seismic action), Housner breaks the liquid into a passive action causing impulse loads and active action causing oscillation loads.

By applying this model to hydrodynamic tanks calculations, (Hammoum and al., 2010) two highlighted phenomena during a seismic excitation are apparent:

– Horizontal tensile stresses in the circular wall, which would cause a vertical crack in the band.
– The appearance of vertical tensile stresses in the wall, which would cause horizontal cracks.

These two phenomena can also act simultaneously, causing inclined cracks, allowing seepage manifested by the presence of moisture sometimes loaded with salts after percolation through the concrete. This pathology was observed over a wide tank farm appraised in Algeria.

Through a previous study (Hammoum et al., 2010) we showed that the negligence or omission of the hydrodynamic phenomenon, underestimated considerably the tensile stresses (vertical and horizontal) acting in the wall, causing the crack's appearance.

We note however that this approach is reserved for the diagnosis and analysis, risk-depth or a specific mechanism study. However, it cannot be applied for an entire park and for all the aging mechanisms.

2.2 *Probabilistic approach*

The probabilistic approach is reserved for processing data auscultation. It constitutes a powerful method for the diagnosis and analysis of risk assessment (Buyle-Bodin, 2002). For the case of tanks, we may have no information about auscultation and data on incidents or aging are not enough. This approach is not a great contribution. Maintenance strategies must be based on forecasting of the structure's evolution, depending on their environment and stresses to which they will be submitted. These strategies depend on the type of park structures (Cremona, 2002). A park of structures is particularly characterized by the number of structures on component (for structures which can be pinpointed on a map e.g. parks: bridges, dams … or for linear structures (which can be represented by a line): underground networks, roads, linear dams ...) and their homogeneity or heterogeneity.

In the context of a large park of pinpointable structures and homogeneous or homogeneous linear structures, where statistics are available and where the mechanisms are well understood, the maintenance based on reliability is an interesting method. It is based among other things on knowledge of the reliability rate of the elements of the system (Zwingelstein, 1996):

- Identification of parameters falling within the limit state conditions;
- Statistical characterization of these parameters (laws and moments);
- Search the probability of no respect of the limit state.

This approach is commonly applied in the offshore and nuclear industry, but also to distribution networks. We refer the reader interested to (Zwingelstein, 1996).

Maintenance based on reliability has its limits when the data is insufficient: difficult experimental data, few data statistics ... The probability calculations become then quickly complex, even impossible, and their validity is difficult to demonstrate.

As part of an heterogeneous park of pinpointable or linear structures, in unfamiliar structural situations, available data are of poor quality or insufficient and make it difficult to predict the evolution of degradations. In this context, the simplest way to assess future changes and degradation is to examine the laws of evolution of existing structures of the same design and which have similar mechanisms based on feedback (Cremona, 2002).

2.3 *Methods of dependability*

Techniques for Dependability, such as FMEA (Failure Modes of Effetcs Analysis) and FMECA (Failure Modes of Effects and Criticality Analysis) emerged in the sixties in the aviation sector in the USA; they took off in Europe during the seventies in the automobile, chemical and nuclear sectors. It was recently introduced in the civil engineering field, particularly in dams (Peyras, 2002) and (Serre, 2008), in maritime structures (Boero et al., 2006). These techniques are powerful approaches for diagnosis and risk analysis. They show, for a given structure, the aging scenarios and for a park of structures the critical one. However, the cost of these studies is important and this approach remains reserved for large or important structures where we want to know the security and prioritize actions. We cannot consider applying this approach in rapid assessment of a tank.

Currently, research is being conducted within the framework of a PhD at Tizi Ouzou University (Algeria) by Hammoum, and aims to provide an evaluation method for storage tanks taking into account the aging mechanisms by the FMEA method.

2.4 *Expertise approach*

The diagnosis and risk analysis can be realised by pure expertise as a preliminary part of studies or rapid diagnosis. This approach requires that visual inspection is performed by the experts when they have insufficient data on the structure. It is based on knowledge and feedback from experts. Among these expert methods, we can cite the Italian method GNDT (Gruppo Nazionale per la dai Terremoti) used to evaluate a buildings park in Italy. It has also been modified and adapted to evaluate the seismic vulnerability of buildings with reinforced concrete frames in the north of Morocco (Bezzazi et al., 2008). The GNDT method involves eleven structural, architectural and situation parameters that can calculate the vulnerability index of earthquake I_v:

$$I_v = 12,5 + 2,5 \cdot \sum_{i=1}^{11} K_i \cdot W_i \qquad (1)$$

K_i means the assigned qualification to each parameter and Wi the associated weights.

This (I_v) index is normalized so that its values are between 0 and 100 and three qualification levels are selected A, B and C.

In the storage tanks field, (Mathieu, 2003) has conducted research since 1990 in Cemagref (Aix en Provence, France) and has proposed structural, functional and environmental assessment methods which have intended to indicate which tanks have a sensitive environment or important strategic character and those with or without structural disorders and visual deterioration of varying severity.

The structural assessment takes into account various aspects of the hydraulic concrete structure's problems, either by the behaviour of the foundations or the structure, as well as the various materials used. The environmental analysis is done under the five inputs of geological context, seismic, water, snow, wind and architectural criteria. The functional analysis is made under the triple input of use level, water users and structure security. This is the category of approach which we can use to classify our diagnosis method by determining the vulnerability index, which is the object of this paper.

3 PRINCIPLE OF TANK ASSESSMENT BY THE VULNERABILITY INDEX

Based on the approach of (Mathieu, 2003), we are interested in vulnerability assessment of a given concrete tank to natural hazards (earthquakes, wind, snow ...), by determining an index I_v. Thirteen (13) parameters (Table 1) are used to calculate this index.

Each of the thirteen parameters will be penalized by an elementary score (N_{ei}). The principal score selected corresponding to the criteria amplification notes based on the increase of vulnerability risk. Each elementary score is assigned by a weighting coefficient (P_i).

The elementary notation (N_{ei}) of each parameter is between 1 and 4: 1 is the ideal situation and 4 is the critical situation with intermediate scores representing increasing concern or risk. The same approach is used for weighting (P_i) whose values vary from 1 to 4: 1 for a minimum penalty parameter and 4 for a Maximum penalty, also considering intermediate situations.

Table 1. List of analysis parameters.

Type analysis	N°	Parameters definition
Environmental analysis	1	Tank location
	2	Seismic zones
	3	Soil type
	4	Snow zones
	5	Wind zones
Structural analysis	6	Type of structure
	7	Foundation type
	8	Sealing walls
	9	Sealing cover
	10	Apparent defects
Functional analysis	11	Tank role
	12	Importance of tank
	13	Maintenance frequency

A large assessment range would require more finesse in the analysis, which may give rise to controversy within the same group of experts who would have to analyze the same defect or pathology. Therefore, an analysis of an important number of values poses problems of overlapping qualitative classes and avoids a divergence between analytical experts. The Cemagref experience in hydraulic structure damage assessment showed that an analysis on 4 values is well adapted to rapid diagnosis. For these listed reasons, we have adopted a qualitative analysis of states based on four values for defects and degradation. The partial score of a parameter is then obtained by the product ($N_{ei} \cdot P_i$) and vulnerability index "I_v" is expressed as the sum of partial scores of the various parameters:

$$I_v = \sum_{i=1}^{13} N_{ei} \cdot P_i = N_e + N_s + N_f \qquad (2)$$

We denote by (N_e, N_s, N_f), respectively, the overall scores of the environmental analysis, structural analysis and functional analysis.

The choice of parameters 1, 2, 3, 4 and 5 of the environmental analysis is dictated by topographical location and hydraulic consideration at the design of the study. Therefore, the overall score of environmental analysis (N_e) remains constant over time.

The parameters 6, 7, 8, 9 and 10 characterize the state of various structural elements of the tank at the moment of the visual inspection by the expert engineer. It results from cumulative damage and aging following natural attack (snow, wind, earthquake, frost ...). To this end, the overall score of structural analysis (N_s) varies over time.

The vulnerability index concept is related to the moment when the tank is inspected. A single tank may have several vulnerability indices during its life cycle. If we consider that I_{vo} is the vulnerability index at the initial moment when the tank is entering service, after a period of operation, this index will increase to I_{V1} ($I_{V1} > I_{vo}$). Its degradation state and its reached aging state in that time will make it more vulnerable to natural hazards than its initial state. Therefore, to reduce the vulnerability index, it is necessary to act directly on the parameters of the structural analysis overall score (N_s), and this can be achieved through a rehabilitation or repair of the tank.

3.1 Environmental assessment

3.1.1 Structure location

A tank is exposed to various hazards of its supporting natural environment, such as, variations of temperature, humidity, presence and attack by the chlorides, the effect of freezing and thawing and the sea air. The location of the structure is discussed here under the double aspect of climatology and hydrology. Our country is divided into five climatic areas. For each area, we propose a basic note, as illustrated in Table 2.

The weights P_i are determined from the hydrologic parameter (Table 3). Three laws govern the distribution of rainfall in Algeria and were defined by Seltzer in 1946, as follows:

- the rainfall increases with altitude. It is higher on slopes exposed to moist winds than on the other,
- the rainfall increase from West to East,
- the rainfall diminishes with distance from the Mediterranean coast to the south.

3.1.2 Seismic zone

The Algerian seismic code (DTR BC 2-48, 2003), divides the country into four seismic zones. We propose, for different areas, the elementary grades given in Table 4.

Moreover, the weights P_i depends on the major risk that the tank represents for human lives and social and economic consequences as has been observed during earthquakes in Algeria (El Asnam 1980, Oued Djer 1988, Tipaza 1989, Mascara 1994 and Boumerdes 2003). These coefficients are determined by the nature of the implementation site (Table 5).

3.1.3 Soil type

The geological aspect is taken into account in analyzing the implementation category site which is based on the mechanical properties of the soil (Table 6). The sites are classified into four categories by the Algerian seismic code (DTR BC 2-48, 2003) according to the average velocity of the shear wave V_s.

Table 2. Elementary score of structure location.

N°	Structure location	N_{ei}
1	Mountain: Important rainfall with several consecutive snow months.	1
2	Valley of Tell: cold and wet climate with low thermal amplitudes and with heavy snowfall.	2
3	Highlands and North of the Saharan Atlas: cold and dry climate in winter and hot, dry summer with high temperature differences.	2
4	Large tracts of the Sahara: cold and dry climate in winter with strong temperature differences, hot and dry summer.	3
5	Coastal Region: humid climate with the sea spray in aggressive environments by the presence of water, more or less saline.	4

Table 3. Weights depending on the geographic location.

N°	Geographic location	P_i
1	Tank located in the north—Eastern Algeria	4
2	Tank located in the north in central Algeria	3
3	Tank located in the north—West Algeria	2
4	Tank located in south of Algeria	1

Table 4. Elementary notes on the seismic zone.

N°	Zone	Seismicity	N_{ei}
1	Zone 0	Negligible	1
2	Zone I	Low	1
3	Zone IIa	Average	2
4	Zone IIb	Average	3
5	Zone III	High	4

Table 5. Weights depending on the site of the tank.

N°	Implantation site of the work	P_i
1	Greenfield	1
2	Rural area	2
3	In an industrial area	3
4	Urban area	4

Table 6. Elementary score based on ground conditions.

N°	Soil type	Nature of soil	N_{ei}
1	Category S_1	Bedrock	1
2	Category S_2	Firm ground	2
3	Category S_3	Loose soil	3
4	Category S_4	Very loose soil	4

The weights (P_i) are determined by some effects of the implantation site (Liquefaction of sands, landslides, presence of surface faults and rock-falls) that can significantly amplify oscillations of the soil and cause the ruin of all civil engineering structures, even paraseismic. The structures in that area can sometimes undergo seismic loads up to five times higher than similar buildings located in an area less dangerous (Zacek, 2004). It is therefore imperative to take this into account in a vulnerability study and resort to a geotechnical engineer or geologist is desirable. In summary, we can define the weights as indicated (P_i) in Table 7.

3.1.4 *Snow zone*

The Algerian Snow and wind code 99 (DTR C 2-4.7., 2000) drew a map of snow by splitting the Algerian territory into four zones. The snow load S_k on the ground per unit area depends on the location (zone) and the altitude H compared to sea level (Table 8).

Note that for the zone D in the Algerian desert, we observe sand on roofs of buildings.

The weighting parameter (P_i) of snow zone is determined by the roof form, as it favours the accumulation of snow on it or not (Table 9).

3.1.5 *Wind action*

The Algerian Snow and wind code 99 (DTR C 2-4.7., 2000) uses the notion of reference wind speed V_{ref} for splitting the Algerian territory into three wind zones. V_{ref} is defined as the average speed in ten minutes measured in conventional conditions with a return period of 50 years. Table 10 gives the elementary scores corresponding to the wind.

The weighting parameter (P_i) will be determined by reference to the Algerian Snow and wind code to take account of site factors that can amplify the effect of wind on the tank:

Height of tank

– Underground tank $P_h = 0.25$,
– Semi-underground tank: $P_h = 0.50$,
– Tank placed on the ground: $P_h = 0.75$,
– Elevated tank: $P_h = 1.00$.

Table 7. Weights depending on the site effects.

N°	Effect of site	P_i
1	Risk of soil liquefaction in alluvial environment	1
2	Presence of surface fault	2
3	Risk of rocky landslide	3
4	Risk of landslide	4

Table 8. Elementary scores based on the snow zone.

N°	Snow zone	N_{ei}
1	Zone A	4
2	Zone B	3
3	Zone C	2
4	Zone D	1

Table 9. Weights depending on roof cover.

N°	Roof cover	P_i
1	Vault form	1
2	Sloping roof with one or two sides	2
3	Sloping roof with multiple sides	3
4	horizontal roof	4

Table 10. Elementary scores based on wind zones.

N°	Wind zones	Reference speed V_{ref}	N_{ei}
1	No action of wind	--------------	1
2	Zone I	25 m/s	2
3	Zone II	28 m/s	3
4	Zone III	31 m/s	4

Category of the field

– Seaside, beside a lake with at least 5 km in length wind, smooth regions and without obstacles: Pc = 0.25,
– Growing areas with hedges and with small farms, houses or trees. Pc = 0.50,
– Suburban or industrial areas, forests: Pc = 0.75,
– Urban areas with at least 15% of the surface is occupied by buildings average height above 15 m: Pc = 1,00.

Topographic factor

– Site 1: flat
  Sites around valleys and wadis without funneling effect: Pt = 0.25,
– Site 2: Site around the valleys and wadis with funnel effect: Pt = 0.50,
– Site 3: Site on the plateaus: Pt = 0.75,
– Site 4: mountain site or nearby hills: Pt = 1.00.

State of surface of the tank

– Smooth (smooth, smooth paint, wall coated well): Ps = 0.25,
– Few rough (concrete moderately rough, poorly coated wall): Ps = 0.50,
– Rough (rough concrete, uncoated wall): Ps = 0.75,
– Very rough (ripples, ridges, folds): Ps = 1.00.

The weighting coefficient P_i is given by the sum of the partial weights of four factors:

$$P_i = P_h + P_c + P_t + P_s \qquad (3)$$

3.2 Structural evaluation

3.2.1 Type of structure

Knowledge of the structural system and the nature of the materials used in the structural elements is essential for understand the behavior of the tank towards a seismic excitation in order to explain the observed damage. The elementary scores corresponding to types of structures are illustrated in Table 11.

The coefficients P_i are determined by the type of materials used for the realization of the structural elements of the tank (Table 12).

3.2.2 Type of foundation

The peculiarity of the tanks is that they are under great variation in operating loads (water in the tank), some changing daily and for some 3 to 4 times a day throughout their long operating period (Mathieu, 2003). The type of foundation provides information on the global behavior of the reservoir towards these cyclic loads. A score is then associated with each type of foundation (Table 13).

As the soil beneath the foundation is subjected to cyclic loading (several times day), the physical mechanism involved is the settlement of the foundation. This phenomenon frequently encountered, generates cracks in the structure and important disorders or localized disorders in structural elements which may result in limiting or prohibiting the operation of the tank. It is for this reason that the weights (P_i) are determined in view of possible settlements suffered by the foundation (Table 14).

3.2.3 Sealing walls

Tanks are classified according to their mode of sealing (Ducrot et al, 1999) as follows:

- Class A: structures in which the sealing is ensured by the structure alone,
- Class B: structures whose sealing is ensured by the structure, supplemented by a waterproofing coating,
- Class C: Tank sealed by a coating sealing, adhering and self-supporting, the structure takes only a mechanical function,
- Class D: Tank built using prefabricated components.

This leads us to propose the elementary scores of Table 15. The weights P_i are determined by the degree of satisfaction of the sealer (Table 16).

3.2.4 Sealing cover

This elementary score is allocated according to the type of sealing cover (Table 17). The weights P_i are determined by the degree of satisfaction of this sealing cover (Table 18).

Table 11. Elementary scores depending on the type of structure.

N°	Type of structure	N_{ei}
1	Underground tank	1
2	Semi-underground tank	2
3	Tank placed on the ground	3
4	Elevated tank	4

Table 12. Weights depending on the type of materials.

N°	Type of materials used	P_i
1	Steel	1
2	Prestressed concrete	2
3	Reinforced concrete	3
4	Masonry	4

Table 13. Elementary score depending on the type of foundation.

N°	Foundation type	N_{ei}
1	Wells and piles	1
2	General raft	2
3	Continuous soles	3
4	Isolated soles	4

Table 14. Weights based on the settlement of foundation.

N°	Settlements state	P_i
1	No apparent settlement	1
2	Early evolution of the settlement	2
3	Settlement indicating advanced evolution	3
4	Settlement which reflects a change in the behavior of the tank	4

Table 15. Elementary score depending on type of wall sealing.

N°	Type of sealing wall	N_{ei}
1	Class A	1
2	Class B	2
3	Class C	3
4	Class D	4

Table 16. Weights according the satisfaction of the sealing wall.

N°	State of the sealing wall	P_i
1	Satisfactory	1
2	Reasonably satisfactory	2
3	Moderately satisfactory	3
4	Unsatisfactory	4

Table 17. Elementary scores based on the sealing cover.

N°	Type of sealing cover	N_{ei}
1	Sealing by surface impregnation	1
2	Sealing by coating	2
3	Sealing by synthetic resin	3
4	Sealing by membrane	4

Table 18. Weights according to degree of satisfaction of the sealing cover.

N°	State of the sealing cover	P_i
1	New, no visible disorders, satisfactory	1
2	Few disorders seen, reasonably satisfactory	2
3	Dilapidated, moderately satisfactory	3
4	Degraded, unsatisfactory	4

3.2.5 Apparent defects

For encountered defects, the support for this study is the experts knowledge, contained in the technical documentation concerning the tank's pathology. Nearly a hundred defects in reinforced concrete, pre-stressed concrete and masonry tanks were recorded by Mathieu (Cemagref, Aix en Provence, France, 1996). He associates for each defect a gravity index and offers a way of repairing the defect and also establishes a scale for evaluating disorders which consist of four levels (Mathieu et al., 1996).

– Gravity level 1: Little or no visible disorders. Nothing to report in particular. Normal monitoring and maintenance of the tank (annual or biannual, depending on destination).
– Gravity level 2: Some defects. Tank to be monitored.
– Gravity level 3: Specific defects of variable gravity. Needs monitoring and investigations.
– Gravity level 4: The structure cannot fill its function with reliability. The risk of failure is important. Consider possible comfortable solution in emergency or demolition of the tank.

This leads us to propose the elementary score of Table 19. That apparent defects make sense only if we associate them with the age of the structure. This leads us to propose the following weighting coefficients P_i (Table 20).

3.3 Functional evaluation

3.3.1 The tank role

The interest in a tank by the manager of the storage tank park depends on the role it occupies in the drinking water system. The elementary score given to this parameter depends on the position of the tank in the drinking water system (Table 21).

The weights P_i are determined according to the state of accessibility for maintenance or repair work.

3.3.2 Tank importance

The interest of a tank depends also on the security of water distribution to the buildings housing the users. Inspired by the Algerian seismic code (RPA 2003), buildings can be classified into four customary groups, depending on their importance to the protection of persons sheltered, or the economic and cultural property of the community they represent.

– Group 1A: Buildings of vital importance that must remain operational after a major earthquake for the needs of the survival of the region, public safety, national defense building and those housing strategic decisions centers.

Table 19. Elementary score depending on the gravity index of the defect.

N°	Gravity index of defect	N_{ei}
1	Gravity level 1	1
2	Gravity level 2	2
3	Gravity level 3	3
4	Gravity level 4	4

Table 20. Weights according to the age of a tank.

N°	Age of tank	P_i
1	Aged less than 10 years	1
2	Aged between 11 and 20 years	2
3	Aged between 21 and 30 years	3
4	Aged more than 30 years	4

Table 21. Elementary score based on tank role.

N°	The tank role in the drinking water network	N_{ei}
1	Transit tank or break pressure	1
2	Distribution tank	2
3	Head tank	3
4	Tank of pump station	4

– Group 1B: Buildings of great importance that frequently host large gatherings of people, like a large mosque, buildings for offices, industrial and commercial buildings, schools, universities, sporting and cultural buildings, prisons, large hotels, libraries, archives and health buildings and production centers or energy distribution.
– Group 2: Current structures or medium importance buildings such as collective living, buildings that can accommodate less than 300 people simultaneously, such as, buildings for use as offices, industrial buildings, car parks in public parking ...
– Group 3: Small structures such as industrial and agricultural buildings housing goods of low value, buildings with limited risk for individuals and temporary buildings.

This leads us to propose the elementary scores of Table 23.

The second aspect that needs to be addressed for complete safety and security distribution of subscribers is the storage capacity. It is in this mind, we offer a weight P_i according to the storage capacity tank (Table 24).

3.3.3 Maintenance frequency

Control of aging tanks in service can be assured only by maintenance and repair. This operation directly affects the vulnerability level of the tanks, which brings us to propose the elementary score of Table 25. The weighting to be considered for this parameter is the role of the tank in a drinking water network and its importance in the distribution to subscribers. But these parameters have already been discussed above. Which brings us to consider a weighting equal to 1 for all frequencies of maintenance.

Table 22. Weights by the state of accessibility for maintenance.

N°	Accessibility state of the tank	P_i
1	Accessible by paved road	1
2	Accessible by tracks suitable for cars	2
3	Accessible by foot path	3
4	Inaccessible tank	4

Table 23. Elementary scores based on the importance of structure.

N°	Tank importance	N_{ei}
1	The tank supplies buildings of Group 3	1
2	The tank supplies buildings Group 2	2
3	The tank supplies building Group 1B	3
4	The tank supplies Building Group 1A	4

Table 24. Weighting of the storage tank.

N°	Tank capacity	P_i
1	From 0 to 500 m³	1
2	Between 500 m³ and 1000 m³	2
3	Between 1000 m³ and 2000 m³	3
4	Higher than 2 000 m³	4

Table 25. Elementary scores depending on the frequency maintenance of tank.

N°	Frequency maintenance	N_{ei}
1	Monthly	1
2	Quarterly	2
3	Biannual	3
4	Annual	4

Table 26. Evaluation matrix of a partial score of a parameter.

	Elementary score N_{ei}			
Weights P_i	1	2	3	4
1	1	2	3	4
2	2	4	6	8
3	3	6	9	12
4	4	8	12	16

4 CLASSIFICATION

For a given criterion, we can construct a grid of evolution of partial score ($N_{ei} \cdot P_i$), taking into account all possible scenarios. The results are shown in Table 26.

Considering all the thirteen analysis criteria listed above, we propose the following classification, divided into four levels of vulnerability.

– The green level, $13 \leq I_v \leq 39$: The tank is not appraised vulnerable. The structure presents a good behavior to natural hazards and it doesn't require special attention after its commissioning. Only regular interventions are needed.
– The orange level 1: $39 \leq I_v \leq 87$: The behavior of tanks to natural hazards is good enough. The tank is moderately vulnerable.
– The orange level 2: $87 \leq I_v \leq 135$: The tank has a low behavior to natural hazards. It is fairly highly vulnerable.
– The red level: $135 \leq I_v \leq 196$: The tank has a very low behavior to natural hazards therefore very high vulnerability. Therefore, the tank must be decommissioned or otherwise in circumstances of restricting use immediately.

5 CONCLUSION

The methodology based on indices, presented in this paper, allows quick and easy evaluation of the vulnerability of reinforced concrete tanks. It presents an excellent tool for decision at the preliminary stage of expertise in the hands of expert engineers, who will decide solutions to be adopted for the rehabilitation or restoration of the structure.

In the hands of managers, it helps to have an intervention priority in its program of rehabilitation or repair. They are even able to decide on the restriction of service or demolition of the tank. Moreover, in the hands of designer engineers of the studies office, the method can be used in the design stage of the structure. The vulnerability index can predict at this time the political management of the tank during its operation and the maintenance frequency. In other words, it tells us when to pay attention to a tank.

This method is still open to future developments and improvements. With this in mind we developed the survey forms to incorporate the geographic coordinates, in order to geocode tanks and their future implementation in a GIS. The final product will be a considerable contribution and efficient decision tool for expert engineers and managers that are in charge of a wide tank park.

REFERENCES

Bezzazi, M. & Khamlichi, A. & Gonzalez, J.R.A. 2008. Vulnérabilité sismique des constructions de type béton armé aux Nord du Maroc, revue canadienne de génie civil, volume 35.

Boéro, J. & Capra, B. & Schoefs F. & Bernard, O. & Lasne, M. 2006. Analyse de risques pour la maintenance des structures portuaires: exemple de quais gabions soumis à de la corrosion, IXèmes Journées Nationales Génie Côtier-Génie Civil, Brest.

Buyle-Bodin, F. & Blanpain, O. 2002. *Analyse du cycle* de vie des ouvrages en béton, Annales du BTP N° 6, Editions ESKA.

Cremona, C. 2002. Application des notions de fiabilité à la gestion des ouvrages existants. Association Française de Génie Civil, 451 p.

DTR B-C 2-48. 2003. Règles parasismiques algériennes (addenda 2003), CGS, Alger.

DTR C 2-4.7. 2000. Règlement neige et vent 1999, CNERIB, Alger.

Ducrot, B. & Fargeot, B. & Mathieu, G. 1999. L'étanchéité des ouvrages en béton de stockage et de transport de l'eau, partie 1, Annales du BTP, N° 02, Editions ESKA.

Ducrot, B. & Fargeot, B. & Mathieu, G. 1999. L'étanchéité des ouvrages en béton de stockage et de transport de l'eau, partie 2, Annales du BTP, N° 04, Editions ESKA.

Fascicule 74. 1998. Construction des réservoirs en béton—cahier des clauses techniques générales, Ministère de l'équipement des transports et du logement, Paris, France.

Hammoum, H. & Bouzelha, K. & Abdesselem, M. 2010. Expertise d'un réservoir de capacité 2000 m3 à Jijel par la détermination de l'indice de vulnérabilité », International Symposium of Aircraft Materials, ACMA 2010, Marrakech, Maroc.

Hammoum, H. & Bouzelha, K. & Hannachi, N.E. 2010. Analyse hydrodynamique d'un réservoir circulaire en béton arme, posé au sol, Annales du BTP, Eska, N° 2–3.

Housner, G.W. 1963. Dynamic analysis of fluids in containers subjected to acceleration, in Nuclear Reactors and Earthquakes, Report No. TID 7024, U.S. Atomic Energy Commission, Washington DC.

Mathieu, G. & al. 1990. Recommandations professionnelles pour le calcul, la réalisation et l'étanchéité de réservoirs, cuves, bassins, châteaux d'eau enterrés, semi-enterrés, aériens, ouverts ou fermés, Annales ITBTP N° 486.

Mathieu, G & al. 1996. Pathologie et réparation des ouvrages en béton de stockage et de transport des liquide, Annales BTP, numéro spécial.

Mathieu, G. 2003. Méthodologie d'évaluation des ouvrages hydrauliques en béton appliquée un patrimoine, Annales du BTP, N° 5–6, Editions ESKA.

Peyras, L. 2002. Diagnostique et analyse de risques liés au vieillissement des barrages—développement de méthodes d'aide à l'expertise, thèse de doctorat, Université Blaise Pascal, Clermont II.

Serre, D. & Peyras, L. & Curt, C. & Boissier, D. & Diab, Y. 2007. Evaluation des ouvrages hydrauliques de génie civil, Revue canadienne de géotechnique, volume 44.

Serre, D. & Peyras, L. & Tourment, R. & Diab, Y. 2008. Levee performance assessment: development of a GIS tool to support planning maintenance actions, Journal of Infrastructure System, ASCE, Vol. 14, Issue 3, pp. 201–213.

Zacek, M. 2004. Guide d'évaluation de la présomption de vulnérabilité aux séismes des bâtiments existants, collection conception parasismique, France.

Zwingelstein, G. 1996. La maintenance basée sur la fiabilité. Guide pratique d'application de la RCM. Paris: Hermès Editions, 666 p.

Concrete Solutions – Grantham, Mechtcherine & Schneck (eds)
© 2012 Taylor & Francis Group, London, ISBN 978-0-415-61622-5

From concrete repair to concrete conservation: How to preserve the heritage values of historic concrete

H.A. Heinemann, H. Zijlstra & R.P.J. van Hees
Faculty of Architecture, Delft University of Technology, Delft, The Netherlands

T.G. Nijland
TNO, Conservation Technology Team, Delft, The Netherlands

ABSTRACT: The conservation of historic concrete is an increasing task, challenging both concrete repair specialists and conservation specialists. In practice, too often repair strategies are followed where conservation strategies would have been necessary. The application of repair techniques poses two threats towards the historic concrete: using incompatible techniques as too little is known about the specific properties of historic concrete, and endangering its heritage values, which preservation is the main aim of conservation. To achieve a transition from concrete repair to concrete conservation, the preservation of the heritage values must become an inherent part of the process. In this paper, the successive steps from determining the material relationship of the heritage values to the evaluation of different conservation strategies based on the preservation of the values are presented. Dilemmas when balancing the preservation of the heritage values and of the original material, while being forced to treat degradation are illustrated by means of some Dutch examples.

1 INTRODUCTION

With the reviewing of our 20th century built heritage, a continuously increasing number of historic concrete buildings are being listed as monuments. These buildings are listed because of their significance to society, which means that the monument should be protected together with its heritage values for future generations. Due to a poor state of conservation, historic concrete buildings may require future intervention.

In practice, several historic concrete buildings are being repaired according to a conventional repair approach, mainly focusing on preserving functionality by treating a damage cause or a symptom. However, specific requirements of conservation, such as the preservation of heritage values and of the original material as historic evidence, are not taken into account. Additionally, the specific material properties of historic concrete, which can challenge the compatibility of some repair techniques, are often not fully investigated and understood. Choosing inappropriate repair strategies and materials may lead to poor performance of a repair, resulting in even more risks for the monument itself and its heritage values.

In this paper, it is shown that by analysing the relationship between the historic concrete, its state of conservation and its heritage values, the conservation of historic concrete can be improved. By understanding how the heritage values are related to the material, something that is seldom done in case of historic concrete, the impact of deterioration and possible interventions can be evaluated systematically. Different conservation strategies can be evaluated not only for their technical long-term performance but also their impact on the development of the heritage values during time. Additionally, such an analysis points out which combinations of material properties, values and deterioration mechanism we cannot treat with current methods or techniques, without endangering heritage values or the building. Two cases of Dutch historic concrete structures, a plain concrete fort dating from 1901 from the Defence Line of Amsterdam and the earth-retaining walls of H. van der Velde's unfinished Great Museum from 1922, will be used to illustrate the potential of such an analysis and outline some dilemmas and current knowledge gaps.

2 CONSERVATION OR REPAIR?

The aims of concrete repair can be summarized as to maintain the function of a concrete structure for a specific, often limited, period. Criteria for choosing a repair strategy are the function of the structure, the type of damage present in relationship with the desired remaining service life, and technical and economic aspects. The limited time-span of a remaining service life, usually a couple of years or decades, can be a realistic goal achievable with standard repair strategies and techniques.

However, the aims and criteria valid for concrete repair are not *a priori* valid for concrete conservation. When challenged with the conservation of a listed historic concrete building, it is necessary to understand the differences between concrete repair and concrete conservation (Heinemann et al. 2010). That conservation of heritage structures requires extra attention is mentioned in several works on concrete repair, yet what the demands are in detail, and how to implement these in the repair process is not explained (see for example fib CEB FIP 2002; Matthews et al. 2007).

Common assumptions and prejudices are that concrete conservation is about retrofitting older concrete structures with a poor performance to modern standards, working with constraints such as preserving even very poor and deteriorated concrete under all circumstances, or that repairs have to be mainly aesthetically compatible. Published case studies of repairs or interventions of historic concrete usually only discuss these challenges. Implicitly, it seems that aims and challenges of concrete conservation are either to make a repair aesthetically compatible or to improve a 'poor' structural capacity. These demands can be true in some cases, yet they are not the general rules and the only options for conservation.

Several international guidelines and charters discuss the aims and framework of conservation in general (for example ICOMOS 1964, 2003). The main aim of all charters is to safeguard our heritage for future generations together with their heritage values. Heritage values express which aspects of a building are significant and outline why a building should be preserved for a society and listed as a monument. The types of values differ, depending on the cultural context of a society. In the Netherlands, for example, the following categories of heritage values are handled: aesthetical and architectural values, scientific and cultural historical significance, integrity, and uniqueness (Ministerie voor Onderwijs Cultuur en Wetenschap 1988; Rijksdienst voor de Monumentenzorg 1991). The heritage values of a building are determined by a value assessment which is based on historical surveys (Rijksdienst voor het Cultureel Erfgoed et al. 2009).

It is a common misconception that values are mainly related to aesthetics, as outlined by the ICOMOS Charter *Principles for the Analysis, Conservation and Structural Restoration of Architectural Heritage* (2003 art. 1.3), where it is stated that the *"value of architectural heritage is not only in its appearance, but also in the integrity of all its components as a unique product of the specific building technology of its time."*

Concluding, it is not only the state of conservation and function, but especially the type of heritage value ascribed to the historic concrete and the building as a whole that determine the criteria for planning and evaluating a conservation strategy. As values vary from building, context and culture, there is no fixed rule of what the most suitable conservation strategy for a group of values or types of historic concrete is, instead case based decisions have to be made.

To be able to determine the criteria for a specific concrete conservation project, it is essential not only to understand the state of conservation and material properties but also to understand in detail the values of the historic concrete. Yet to be able to do so requires a sound understanding of the construction history and properties of the historic concrete.

3 PROPERTIES OF HISTORIC CONCRETE

Prior to any intervention, whether repair or conservation, it is necessary to understand the properties of the historic concrete and its state of conservation. Technical surveys carried out in a repair process investigate mainly the presence of damage, the possible damage cause and the structural capacity. The properties of the concrete (e.g. strength, composition) are investigated and evaluated to determine the damage cause and the performance of the structure. The results of such surveys are an overview of present damage and its cause, an evaluation of its impact on the structure, and suggestions for suitable repair strategies.

Yet there are more dimensions to the properties of historic concrete relevant for conservation than only those related to durability and strength. The original concrete is a witness of former historic periods and a bearer of heritage values of a society. Therefore, it is important to understand the properties of the historic concrete relevant for construction history and heritage values as well.

The historical dimensions are investigated during a construction historical survey. In such a survey, former periods of the building are studied as its construction period and the different periods during the building's life. The scale of historical surveys can vary from the scale of the urban area, of the building to the scale of the component (Rijksdienst voor het Cultureel Erfgoed, et al. 2009). From an analysis, conclusions are drawn if a building is of historical significance, the types of heritage values encountered and hence decision are made if the building should be listed and preserved.

Based on a historical survey, the historic concrete can be assessed for example as significant due to its aesthetical qualities or as an example for early concrete technology. However, these assessments remain on the level of keywords and only indicate if the building and its elements are of a high, positive or indifferent heritage value, and outline how far they can be modified during an intervention (Rijksdienst voor het Cultureel Erfgoed, et al. 2009).

A more detailed research on how the heritage values manifest themselves in the historic material is not carried out in concrete conservation practice. An obstacle is that the construction history of historic concrete is not sufficiently understood yet and the existing knowledge not well disseminated neither amongst construction historians nor concrete specialists. Historical knowledge on the level of the component is even scarcer, both amongst academics and practitioners, and not discussed in construction historical surveys. However, this level of detail is relevant as on this level many threats occur for the historic concrete and its ascribed heritage values either due to degradation or due to interventions. Therefore, the first main challenge in achieving the conservation of concrete is a better understanding of the properties of historic concrete.

3.1 Construction history of historic concrete

In recent years, the number of publications on the history of concrete slightly increased. However, most publications either focus on key moments and key figures, early proprietary reinforcement systems and major concrete construction companies, such as the invention of Portland cement, the first reinforcement systems by Lambot, Monier or Hennebique, or the theories and experiments of Mörsch, Considère or Abrams (see for example Addis 2007; Curbach et al. 2007; Hassler & Schmidt 2004; Huberti 1964; Newby 2001; Oosterhoff et al. 1988). However, what is seldom discussed is when and how the new techniques, materials and theories were disseminated and applied in practice. This includes as well the changing properties of the concrete and of the raw materials due to improved construction methods, new materials and changing theories of concrete mix design.

Knowledge of construction history is relevant to be able to recognise and evaluate the significance of the historic concrete. In practice, the knowledge of the construction history of historic concrete often remains on the level of the social, economic or architectural history of the construction period. In historical surveys the concrete related information is often restricted to either reinforcement systems on a typological level or general, not object-related anecdotes of construction history.

For construction historians, concrete is often a too modern material and its history is not commonly taught or studied. Support during research by concrete specialists is difficult as they are educated and trained for modern concrete and not construction history.

When evaluating historic concrete, both in terms of quality and of significance, it is important to consider the historical context of the historic concrete. The quality, composition and execution of historic concrete cannot be compared to modern concrete, instead it has to be evaluated if the historic concrete is of a high, normal or poor quality for its construction period. It has to be known which properties, material and construction techniques were state-of-the-art, experimental, or consciously chosen and hence might be significant, or already poorly chosen and executed at the time of construction. This also requires a detailed understanding of the different development phases of historic concrete.

The three main phases of the historic concrete are first, the exploring and empiric phase in the second half of the 19th century, secondly the emergence of a scientific approach in the late 19th and early 20th century, and thirdly the wide scale adoption phase starting before the Second World War and emerging in the following reconstruction period. These phases are not uniform for all aspects of historic concrete and for all countries. For example, research on cements and structural theories preceded research on concrete technology and construction methods. Additionally, the appreciation of historic concrete as a structural and aesthetical material changed during time and should be known to understand why concrete was chosen as construction material.

National characteristics of historic concrete are not often considered as concrete is seen as a universal material, and already early on materials, concrete technology, and construction methods were internationally exchanged. Nevertheless, national variations can be encountered due to local available raw materials, the period of first application, the national level of sophistication of research and construction, and introduction of codes of practices.

In the Netherlands, for example, reinforced concrete was only used from the late 19th century on and the required knowledge and main raw material, Portland cement, had to be imported. Most imports, both material and knowledge, came from Germany, the UK, and Belgium. A local variation in material use was for example the use of trass-bearing cements for early (plain) concrete structures. The Dutch had a strong tradition of using trass for hydraulic engineering works and the Netherlands was one of the few European countries, beside Germany and Belgium, which used trass in cement (for example Hambloch 1918; Probst 1917; van der Kloes 1908).

The original concrete itself is a main source of historical information for the different phases and variations encountered in the history of concrete. The historic concretes can vary as the changes and developments of concrete technology influenced the choice of materials and the quality of the concrete. The following material aspects, which are relevant for both heritage values and durability, varied during time and can be investigated during historical surveys (Heinemann in prep.):

- preferred or available binder types (Portland cement, different types of slag-bearing cements, trass-bearing cements, etc.) and their chemical composition
- type of aggregate (gravel, crushed stone, broken bricks, slags and pumice etc.) and their size and grading (none, continuous, gap-grading)
- quality and origin of the raw material
- the concrete mix design (prior to the introduction of design rules, use of water-cement factor, etc.) and the use of additives and admixtures
- the surface finish of the historic concrete (plastered, exposed, board marked, tooled, coloured concrete etc.).

Such a description of the historic concrete, which can require detailed material research, allows an analysis of the materialisation of the heritage values.

3.2 The materialisation of the heritage values of historic concrete

In Dutch practice, no uniform methods are applied to carry out value assessments and the level of detail of historical surveys strongly depends on the individual historian and the type of assignment. For historic concrete, the level of detail of historic surveys and value assessments usually does not go to the level of the material. However, this information is later relevant as reference for evaluation of different conservation strategies and their impact on the heritage values.

To analyse the materialisation of the abstract heritage values, they first have to be broken down into material-related attributes. For example, aesthetical values can be related to the appearance of the historic concrete, the proportions of the concrete element, and especially its surface finish, including colour and texture. In a second step, it has to be determined how these material properties were achieved and which aspects were

consciously modified or then commonly applied. These research questions can be answered by further material and historical research.

For example, if the aesthetical values are related to the surface finish of a historic concrete, the following variables can be determined: the colour of the concrete, either due to the binder, aggregates, pigments, or painting and the texture achieved by tooling, formwork imprints, or plastering. Not only the original surface finish has to be considered, but also the signs of aging and weathering, and previous interventions (see for example Fig. 1). These should be evaluated to see if they are a part of the aesthetical values, have no impact or are rather a threat.

For the scientific and cultural historical values, the original historic concrete itself can be important; for example, as evidence of a historical relevant period or event, or as a representative of a former level of sophistication of concrete technology. For this, it should be understood which constituents, techniques and theories were commonly applied in a specific period and how different theories of concrete technology were applied in practice. In case the concrete is evidence of a historic event, it might not be the concrete itself which is of high value but the traces of the historic event recognisable on the concrete. For example, the damage caused during a bombardment in the Second World War to the concrete casemates of the Dutch defence line in Kornwerderzand are considered a valuable artefact of an important battle (see Fig. 2).

More difficult is the interpretation of values related to authenticity as the definition of authenticity is heavily discussed and can have many dimensions as shown by the *Nara Document on Authenticity* (ICOMOS 1994). Two common interpretations of authenticity are the presence of the original material or the original appearance of the building (for example Figs. 3, 4). Whereas for the first interpretation, changes during time such

Figure 1. Coloured concrete figures with traces of biological growth (Zoo Rotterdam, van Ravensteyn, 1938–1940).

Figure 2. Damages caused during the Second World War still visible at the casemate VI, Kornwerderzand (1932).

Figure 3. Fort Vijfhuizen (1899), one of the first plain concrete forts of the Defense Line of Amsterdam.

Figure 4. Dresselhuys pavilion, Sanatorium Zonnestraal (Duiker, Bijvoet & Wiebenga, built 1928–31), restored to the original appearance in 2008.

as aging or modifications to the building are often accepted or appreciated as long as the original material can be perceived, for the second interpretation the original material is often considered less relevant as long as the original perception of the building is preserved or even reconstructed.

Yet only once it is understood and determined which variables of the historic concrete are relevant for the heritage values, is it possible to determine any threats towards the conservation of historic concrete.

4 DURABILITY AND THREATS

It is common knowledge that concrete structures can be threatened by degradation and several methods of investigation and repair exist. The degradation mechanisms for modern and historic concrete are the same, yet historic concrete can be more prone to some degradation mechanisms than modern concrete. Therefore, a more thorough investigation of the state of conservation and material properties of historic concrete might be required, independent if a repair or conservation is planned.

Yet for conservation, it is not sufficient only to investigate threats to the structure but also threats to the heritage values. The encountered damages have to be investigated and reported more holistically. This should also be done for normal concrete structures, but for conservation it is even more crucial. In surveys, not only the damage cause and mapping where damage occurred should be mentioned, but also a description of possible and present damage symptoms, and which material aspects will be affected by the damage. Such a survey should include possible threats which might only affect the heritage value but not the structure, as their endangerment should require action too.

4.1 Durability of historic concrete

The damage assessment of historic concrete itself does not differ in principle from the assessment of modern concrete structures, besides having to be more careful when using destructive testing techniques when the building is listed. Yet what can differ are the properties of the concrete itself, and experience is required when it comes to identifying and interpreting the historic concrete and damage cause.

Concrete was initially considered to be a very durable material, yet the first signs of degradation initiated research on the durability of concrete. The poor durability of Portland cement in seawater led to the investigation of other cements, which led to the acceptance of slag-bearing cements in the 1910s. The risk of corrosion of the reinforcement was another early question, which was empirically negated at the beginning of the 20th century (for example Boon 1908).

Concrete durability was addressed more commonly from the 1920s on in concrete textbooks, but research was still in its infancy. The influence of the quality and thickness of the concrete cover and of the environment (e.g. exposure to sea water) was, for example, only considered in the 1930 edition of the Netherlands Code for Reinforced Concrete (van der Vooren 1931), and compared to modern standards still rather simplified.

As most degradation mechanisms show symptoms only years or even decades after construction, potentially deleterious concrete constituents could have been used for a longer period. The possibilities of new damage mechanisms had to be considered, for example that some cracking was not caused by shrinkage but a different, until then unknown mechanism such as an alkali-silica-reaction (ASR) (Bosschart 1957). Before excluding the use of deleterious aggregates, the damage cause of ASR had first to be discovered. Chlorides were considered as beneficial accelerators for prefabricated concrete elements to increase the production speed, or used on-site when carrying out works during low temperatures. The properties of the concrete could also be affected by an arbitrary concrete mix, with a too high water content, or poor distribution of coarse and fine aggregates, leading to a higher porosity of the concrete. A review of the constituents and design theories used for historic concrete can help to identify potential degradation risks for different phases of historic concrete (Heinemann in prep.).

However, many historic concrete buildings are in a reasonable state of conservation, which shows that the properties and durability of historic concrete are not always less than those of modern concrete and do not always lead to severe damage. As the durability of (historic) concrete is not influenced by only one parameter alone, the context of the building has to be studied as well (Marie-Victoire et al. 2006).

4.2 Threats to the heritage values of the historic concrete

One of the main conservation aims is to preserve the listed building together with its heritage values. Therefore it is necessary to know when and in which degree the values are endangered. The threats can be external, and sometimes obvious such as the threat of demolition, yet they can be also inherent in the concrete, e.g. a too high amount of calcium sulfate in early concretes, added to control setting.

Whereas threats to the historic concrete as a material can be identified by common assessment techniques and by broadening our knowledge of historic concrete, an evaluation of the threats to the heritage values of the historic concrete requires a different approach. To analyse the threats to the heritage values, it is necessary to know in which

way the values are related to the material and construction method (see section 3.2) and the symptoms and causes of the different degradation mechanisms.

For example, most damage mechanism symptoms affect the surface of the concrete, either due to cracking, spalling, staining or leaching. Therefore, any damage mechanism leading to these symptoms is a potential threat to heritage values associated to the surface such as it is in the case of exposed concrete (see Fig. 5).

However, deterioration does not automatically pose a threat to values related to the original material. Although the historic concrete might show deterioration, it can still be in a sufficient sound condition to bear witness of the ascribed heritage value if it can remain unaltered onsite and it can be demonstrated that future development of damage is sufficiently slow. Such cases show that a good evaluation of the severity of the damage and its progress is necessary to determine the safety of both values and structure. Listed buildings are not museum objects and should have a function, therefore a careful balance between safety and preservation of values has to be made.

Other possibilities are that only heritage values are endangered without posing a threat to either the structural integrity or the safety of the structure. For example, the erosion of a valuable surface texture of an exposed concrete can affect the appearance of the historic concrete but does not necessarily affect the functionality and integrity of the structure.

Besides threats due to degradation, the heritage values can also be threatened by interventions and repairs. Often small scale standard repairs such as local patching, or application of painting or coatings are carried out without consideration of the impact on heritage values (see Fig. 6).

Figure 5. Cracking, leaching and formation of stalactites, and biological growth affecting the appearance of exposed concrete elements (Zoo Rotterdam, van Ravensteyn, 1938–1940).

Figure 6. Local gray patching and application of a white paint on a red, textured plaster on an early reinforced concrete viaduct (Hofplein viaduct, Rotterdam, 1904–1908).

5 CONSERVATION OF CONCRETE

In the case of concrete repair, the planning of a repair strategy focuses on the questions of how to treat the damage cause or at least the damage symptoms, and how to maintain the functionality and safety of the structure. Strategies would be evaluated, amongst others, on (cost) effectiveness of the intervention, and, ideally, the durability of the intervention in relationship with the remaining service life of the structure.

As concrete repair specialists are commonly in charge of choosing techniques for a concrete conservation project, the above mentioned strategies and criteria are applied, maybe unconsciously or out of habit, for concrete conservation. A discussion of which heritage values should be preserved and how they are affected by a repair is often not done. The additional requirements of conservation, such as the theoretically perpetual service life of a listed building and reversibility or retreatability of the intervention are not discussed either (Heinemann, et al. 2010). In the conservation process, an additional step should be introduced, before discussing the technically and financial feasibility of a possible conservation strategy: a discussion of the conservation aim, independent of the state of conservation.

5.1 Conservation aim

The conservation aim is a formulation of the state in which the historic concrete and the building or structure would preserve the heritage values the best. It should be based on an analysis of the previously gained information on the construction history and of the heritage values. Appelbaum (2009) calls the conservation aim the ideal state, and uses it as a reference when it comes to planning a realistic treatment goal for the conservation of objects.

The formulation of a conservation aim is not an academic mind game, but is a serious discussion of what to preserve before discussing how to do it. A standardised list of which conservation technique to use for each combination of heritage value, type of historic concrete and encountered damage cannot be made as the combinations are too manifold. However, the underlying question for all combinations is the same: in which state does the material preserve the heritage values the best. The answers can vary from the historic concrete's present state of conservation, or a previous, modified or new state; the emphasis can either be placed on the original material or on the appearance of the building (which do not necessarily exclude each other). Similar degrees are defined in conservation charters: preservation (maintain the object in its present condition), restoration (returning existing fabric into an earlier state), reconstruction (using new fabric to return into a former state) or adaption, with preservation as the preferred option (Australia ICOMOS 1997).

It is not demanded that the chosen conservation aim is technically or economically feasible. Its main purpose is to function as a point of orientation when discussing and evaluating different conservation strategies on their impact on both heritage values and material. Practical obstacles making it unable to achieve the conservation aim can, for example, be a too poor state of conservation of the historic concrete, a (new) function required, time or financial limits, or no suitable repair technique existing yet. Yet, especially in such cases, a previously formulated conservation aim can help to find alternatives and to articulate advantages and disadvantages of different conservation strategies.

5.2 Requirements for concrete conservation

Once the aim of conservation has been formulated in mutual discussions with all parties involved, such as heritage care authorities, restoration architects, construction historians and concrete repair specialists, and has been outlined which remaining 'monumental' service life is aspired, criteria for possible conservation strategies can be formulated.

Some criteria are similar to those of conventional concrete repair, such as safety and functionality of the structure and costs; some other criteria are more demanding. These depend on the heritage values, the type of historic concrete, the structure and function, and type of degradation, and will usually vary for each conservation project. Criteria have to be formulated for the appearance of the intervention (colour, texture, invisible, covering etc., see Fig. 7), the acceptable degree of material loss (surface, bulk, reinforcement, elements, see Fig. 8) during consecutive intervention cycles,

Figure 7. Attempts to adapt a patch repair in colour and texture to the surrounding concrete.

Figure 8. Large scale material loss due to hydrodemolition (circumambulation passageway, Pilgrimage church, Brielle, 1912).

the treatment or slowing down damage causes and symptoms, or, contrary, accepting the latter as signs of age or because they reflect the once state-of-the-art concrete technology better than any repair would do.

A characteristic of the repair of monolithic concrete structures is that the damaged historic concrete cannot be simply locally replaced with the same type of concrete as one can replace a deteriorated block of natural stone with a new one. Instead, repair materials, especially repair mortars, often have a different material composition than the parent concrete to be able to achieve a durable repair. The choice of a suitable material has to be based on chemical, physical, dimensional, permeability and electrochemical compatibility (Vaysburd 2006).

When working with historic concrete, the technical compatibility of common repair techniques, which were developed for modern concrete, should be verified as composition and properties of historic concrete differ from modern concrete. The compatibility of a conservation technique should

not only be evaluated in a technical and aesthetical sense, but also with respect to the heritage values.

As it is intended to preserve the historic concrete together with its heritage values for as long as possible, the aging and possible future failure of a repair technique has to be considered. For conservation, the demands of reversibility and re-treatability, meaning that either an intervention can be undone or that its application does not exclude future treatment, respectively, are to be dealt with. In case of a failure of a repair, it should be indicated in which degree and how the historic concrete will be affected, including the impact and possible loss of historic material associated with of the removal of the repair material.

The proven service life of repair techniques is a couple of decades at best in most cases, with repairs surviving for a few years only not being an exception at all (see for example Tilly 2011; Tilly & Jacobs 2007). Therefore, it becomes clear that frequency, extent and impact of future interventions that will inevitably occur over the 'monumental' service life of a historic building have to be taken into consideration. This may be complicated by the fact that heritage values themselves are not static but will also develop over time. In an ideal case, these would increase with time. As a reference, it is helpful to estimate the development of the heritage values without intervention. This might show, considering the assessed degradation and material properties, that heritage values would diminish with time, indicating the need of intervention, or contrary that the values would not be affected or even increase during time.

5.3 Evaluation of conservation strategies

Due to the diversity of repair techniques and manifold combination of heritage values, material properties and degradation, it will usually be necessary to compare different conservation strategies (Heinemann, et al. 2010). A choice must be made of which strategy would be the most suitable, balancing technical demands and preservation of the heritage values. In an ideal case, no conflicts arise; the repair technique treats the damage cause and symptoms, preserves the heritage values, and with a reasonable number of repair cycles, the listed building can stay forever: the 'monumental' service life is realized.

In practice, however, conflicts arise and choices have to be made, either in favour of preserving the values or the functionality of a building or structure. In this case, the heritage values of the historic concrete can give guidance. As the core of conservation is to preserve the heritage values, a strategy which preserves these values as long as possible should be favoured.

A quantitative approach, determining which strategy would preserve the most values, is not yet possible as heritage values are usually expressed qualitatively. A threshold for what area of facade can be altered or what volume of concrete bulk can be removed cannot be given. In case the historic material is of a very high value, the rule of the thumb 'the less on the long-term the better' can be an orientation. For the appearance of the building, the overall impact of different interventions should be evaluated, possibly by different groups, including ordinary persons and specialists. In this, the conservation aim and the development of the heritage values and building without intervention can be used as reference points.

If these reference points are nearly identical, the solution might be no intervention at all; in this case, any intervention might even cause harm to the heritage values. To carry out no intervention might also be the solution for very extreme cases where the degradation might be very severe or when the immediate impact of a repair on the values would be too high (see Fig. 2). In such cases, it might be an option to accept further degradation and appreciate the heritage values as long as possible. When a threshold, for example for safety, has been reached, radical intervention can still be chosen. Yet what has to be kept in mind is to document the historic concrete as part of our history prior to its loss.

More debateable are situations in between these two extremes. A direct solution can be difficult either due to currently lacking concrete conservation techniques, insufficient knowledge, the properties of the historic concrete or the specific combination of heritage values and encountered degradation. If it is not possible to treat the damage, maintain functionality and preserve all heritage values, the different criteria have to be prioritized for each conservation project individually. Demands of functionality might be modified, requiring less intervention; the environment might be changed, diminishing further deterioration; or it might have to be accepted that by sacrificing one value, other values or historic fabric can be preserved.

A higher frequency of intervention and maintenance might have to be accepted compared to common maintenance, as only a less durable repair technique might preserve the heritage values in the long-term. On the other hand, an initially high loss of deteriorated original material might be accepted if it improves the effectiveness and causes less material loss in the long-term.

If no suitable conservation techniques exist yet, it should be tried to at least decelerate future degradation and to document the listed building and the historic material. The use of new and unapproved techniques and materials we have little experience with should be only done carefully, as well as the application of common 'modern concrete' techniques for historic concrete. In conservation charters, the use of traditional techniques is preferred; the application of new techniques is not excluded when their *"efficacy of which has been shown by scientific data and proved by experience"* (ICOMOS 1964).

6 DILEMMAS

Despite accurate investigations, situations can occur when the preservation of the heritage values or the original material cannot be achieved without losses of heritage values or by choosing technically less effective repair techniques. A common dilemma is when the degradation of the concrete and the heritage value have the same origin. Some causes of dilemmas and possibilities for solutions will be discussed in the following two examples.

6.1 *Fort Bezuiden Spaarndam*

Fort Bezuiden Spaarndam (1901, see Fig. 9) is a plain concrete structure that is part of the Defence Line of Amsterdam, built between 1883 and 1920. The Defence line is inscribed as a UNESCO World Heritage Site, amongst other aspects, for its significance in the development of concrete technology in the Netherlands; the forts are an example of the transition from brick construction to plain concrete structures to reinforced concrete (UNESCO).

However, which specific properties of the concrete represent these values is not mentioned and no guidance is given if and how far the original material should be preserved to maintain the heritage values. But determining the relationship between the abstract heritage values to the existing historical material is a crucial prerequisite for the preservation of the heritage values.

Figure 9. Casemate of the fort Bezuiden Spaarndam.

The question is which material aspects are characteristic for an early plain concrete military structure and how does it stand in relationship with concrete technology of that specific period. The historic context concerning concrete technology is that no codes of practice existed yet, most knowledge was empirical, and theories for good concrete differed from modern concepts. Portland cement was expensive and the use of cheaper lime-based cements, sometimes with trass, was not excluded (Minister van Oorlog 1906). Crushed stone as aggregate was preferred over gravel as its rough surface and sharp edges allowed in theory a better bond between aggregate and cement, yet required a higher cement content, thus was also more expensive.

This led to the choice of strong yet expensive concrete with Portland cement and crushed stone (porphyry from Quenast, Belgium) for the important exposed elements such as the casemates and exterior walls. For secondary elements, such as interior walls, locally available gravel was used as aggregate, for minor elements broken bricks. Comparing the concrete mix of Fort Bezuiden Spaarndam with earlier forts, one can notice that previous concrete was sometimes made with a trass-Portland cement or trass-lime cement in combination with broken bricks as coarse aggregate. Later forts are usually made with Portland cement and gravel, and are sometimes reinforced. So in this case the specific concrete mix design is a relevant representative of the heritage values.

Nowadays, the important elements made with porphyry show signs of ASR due the combination of used raw materials. When analysing the state-of-conservation together with the materialisation of the heritage values, dilemmas suddenly become obvious as in this case when the heritage values and degradation have the same material origin. The former intention to use a very high quality concrete for the crucial concrete members is the cause for the presence of damage today.

There are two options for interpretation of the present damage: it is the direct result of misconceptions of former concrete technology from an experimental phase and hence the damage is acceptable; or despite the fact that the original concrete mix is the damage cause, the ASR is a threat to the original material.

A dilemma is that ASR cannot be cured yet and only the degradation can be delayed; a common approach would be to demolish the concrete if the damage is too severe. Yet it would mean an immediate loss of the heritage values ascribed to the concrete and loss of evidence of previous concrete technology. From other forts with similar problems try-outs were made to treat the symptoms and to decelerate degradation by injecting the concrete and applying a coating (Bakker 1996), yet on the long-term they were ineffective (see Fig. 10).

The conservation aim in such a case would be to preserve the different concrete mixes on-site so that the different forts of the Defence Line together can document the development of concrete technology in the Netherlands. Without intervention, the damage might still continue, yet due to the nature of ASR in a much slower pace. Secondary damage such as freeze-thaw damage could occur through the ingress of water in the cracks.

As ASR cannot be treated yet, and other degradation mechanisms are present, it is relevant to known if and how far the damage will increase, and if it is possible not to intervene as long the safety is not endangered. The risk of further degradation and secondary damages should be tried to be minimized, for example by preventing moisture ingress through the earth-covered roofs. By choosing such an approach, the historic concrete would still be exposed to further deterioration yet would be preserved in a sound state to transmit its heritage values.

6.2 Earth retaining walls of the unfinished groot museum

The earth retaining walls are the only tangible remains of the unfinished *Groot Museum* by the famous Belgian architect *Henry van de Velde* for the art collectors Kröller-Müller (see Figs. 11, 12). The construction works for the huge museum project were abruptly ceased in 1922 due to the economic crisis. Although continuation of the works was intended, the original plan was never finished. Instead, a smaller museum was built nearby by the same architect and opened in 1938.

The walls are listed as a national monument due to their architectural historical values. Yet, they also bear witness to former construction methods as the abrupt ceasing of the works preserved many traces

Figure 10. Casemate of Fort Aalsmeer, 10 years after intervention.

Figure 11. Overview of the earth retaining walls of the unfinished Great Museum (van de Velde, 1922).

Figure 12. Detail of an earth retaining wall, showing exposed starter bars were the works were abruptly ceased.

on-site. As the walls have no function, no maintenance and repair was carried out. The walls merged slowly into the landscape of the surrounding national park. The national park and the museum have always belonged together and several sculptures can be found in the proximity of the walls, which could easily be mistaken for a sculpture as well.

The walls show signs of degradation, such as rebar corrosion with cracks and spalling, and biological growth. The question arose whether the corrosion-related damage should be treated and if so, how. Three different strategies—dog nothing, cathodic protection, and local concrete replacement (either repair mortars or shotcrete)—were evaluated on their impact on the heritage values (Heinemann 2008). As the walls have no function, the performance of the repaired structure was secondary.

The main criterion was the preservation of the appearance of the surface, including the signs of aging and the biological growth, and of the traces of the workmanship such as locally still present formwork and formwork imprints.

Both, the cathodic protection and the local concrete replacement were considered to have a too strong impact on the heritage values as both would alter the appearance too strongly. The surfaces would have to be cleaned, destroying the signs of weathering and removing the biological growth. The newly repaired surfaces would appear too neat in the ruin-like context, where the walls merged with the surroundings.

As any future damage expectations were very low,—the concrete with insufficient cover had already been affected—, a choice of not carrying out any intervention at all was suggested, under the condition that the walls will be regularly inspected. Such an approach can be legitimate and the most appropriate one when it comes to preserving the heritage values of the structure. Limited further degradation of the concrete is acceptable and emphasizes only the function of a ruin; the remains of the walls are still sufficient to witness the former plans of building a large museum.

7 CONCLUSIONS

The conservation of historic concrete is a complex field which shows similarities to concrete repair. Looking closer, however, they are fundamentally different. Conservation aims at preserving heritage values, which is not part of repair. The properties of historic concrete differ from modern concrete as well, which question the technical compatibility of standard repair techniques. The combination of both, different aims and different types of concrete, endangers the heritage values of historic concrete when conventional repair strategies are followed.

Before developing new and more compatible techniques for historic concrete conservation, the strategies applied for the conservation of historic concrete should be reconsidered. A first conclusion is that the preservation of heritage values of the historic concrete must be structurally integrated in the conservation process to enable their preservation.

Due to the manifold combination of historic concretes, heritage values, degradation mechanisms, and conservation aims, no universal advice can be given on which approach is the most suitable for the conservation of historic concrete. Instead, each conservation project requires a tailored, inter- and multidisciplinary approach.

As a starting point, the properties of the historic concrete must be understood better. With this knowledge, the properties which are relevant for the different categories of heritage values can be determined. This can be used to evaluate later the threats toward the heritage values due to deterioration and different possible interventions.

A better understanding is beneficial for the survey of the state-of-conservation, as the different properties of historic concrete can affect its durability and the compatibility of repair techniques. A survey of the state-of-conservation should be extended to the impact of present and expected damage and their symptoms of the heritage values. In practice, both technical and historical surveys should be consulted therefore together to understand better the relationship between the material, the heritage values, and the threats towards both.

To integrate the preservation of the heritage values, consensus has to be reached on the conservation aim. This will allow us to assess which criteria any possible conservation strategy has to fulfill.

When the specific requirements for an individual conservation project are determined, different strategies should be evaluated and judged. This should include the evaluation of the benefits and risks of different conservation strategies on the heritage values and on the material performance. It should not be forgotten to carry out a comparison of the different strategies over several consecutive intervention cycles, as it is intended to preserve the historic material with its heritage values for as long as possible.

In practice, too many small and large obstacles still exist to achieve the transition from repair to conservation. Only a small number of experts exist who understand the conservation of concrete and the related disciplines, such as construction history, conservation philosophy, concrete durability and concrete repair. Conservation campaigns are carried out by parties who understand too little of each other's profession, leading to miscommunication and unawareness of the complexity of the field.

Further research of concrete conservation is desperately needed in all fields and scales. Without profound knowledge of the construction history, it is difficult to characterise the historic concrete as it is not known what the used components could have been. Their deviating properties do not only influence the durability of the historic concrete, but also determine the propertie s of repair materials.

Construction historical knowledge is relevant to determine the heritage values and their materialisation, allowing us to better evaluate the impact of degradation and repair on the values. Currently used repair techniques have to be reviewed for their suitability for conservation and their long-term behaviour during several consecutive intervention cycles.

REFERENCES

Addis, B. 2007. *Building: 3,000 Years of Design, Engineering and Construction London: Phaidon.*
Appelbaum, B. 2009. *Conservation Treatment Methodology* (2nd ed.). Oxford: Butterworth—Heinemann.
Australia ICOMOS. 1997. *The Australia ICOMOS Charter for the Conservation of Places of Cultural Significance (the Burra Charter).*
Bakker, M. 1996. Ongewapend beton beschermd. *Bouw Wereld* (18), 3.
Boon, A.A. 1908. *Gewapend Beton. Een handleiding voor de studie van materialen, constructie en statische berekening (1st ed.).* Leiden: A.W. Sijthoff's Uitgeverij—Maatschappij.
Bosschart, R.A.J. 1957. Alkali-reacties van de toeslag in beton. *Cement,* 9(11–12), 7.
Curbach, M., van Stripriaan, U., Wachtendorf, U., & Wiens, U. (Eds.). 2007. *Gebaute Visionen 100 Jahre Deutscher Ausschuss für Stahlbeton* Berlin: Beuth Verlag GmbH.
fib CEB FIP. 2002. *Management, maintenance and strengthening of concrete structures: International Federation for Structural Concrete (fib).*
Hambloch, A. 1918. Tras en zijn praktisch gebruik in het Bouwbedrijf (Drees, E., Trans.).
Hassler, U., & Schmidt, H. (Eds.). 2004. *Häuser aus Beton—Vom Stampfbeton zum Grosstafelbau.* Berlin, Dortmund: Ernst Wasmuth Verlag Tübingen, Lehrstuhl Denkmalpflege und Bauforschung der Universität Dortmund.
Heinemann, H.A. 2008. Betonmuren van Henry van de Velde's Grote Museum in het Nationaal Park De Hoge Veluwe. Report. Delft: Technical University of Delft.
Heinemann, H.A. in prep. From Concrete Repair to Concrete Conservation: how to preserve the heritage values of historic concrete (Working title). Unpublished Doctoral thesis, Technical University of Delft, Delft.
Heinemann, H.A., van Hees, R.P.J., Nijland, T.G., & Zijlstra, H. 2010. *The Challenge of a Perpetual Service Life: The Conservation of Concrete Heritage.* Paper presented at the Service Life Design for Infrastructures.
Huberti, G. (Ed.). 1964. *Vom Caementum zum Spannbeton* Wiesbaden and Berlin: Bauverlag GmbH.
ICOMOS International Council on Monuments and Sites. 1964. International Charter for the Conservation and Restoration of Monuments and Sites (The Venice Charter 1964).
ICOMOS International Council on Monuments and Sites. 1994. The Nara Document on Authenticity.
ICOMOS International Council on Monuments and Sites. 2003. ICOMOS Charter- Principles for the analysis, conservation and structural restoration of architectural heritage.
Marie-Victoire, E., Cailleux, E., & Texier, A. 2006. Carbonation and historical buildings made of concrete *Journal de Physique IV*(136), 14.
Matthews, S., Sarkinnen, M., & Morlidge, J. (Eds.). 2007. *Achieving durable repaired concrete structures. Adopting a performance-based intervention strategy.* Bracknell: IHS BRE Press.
Minister van Oorlog. 1906. *Algemeen voorwaarden voor de uitvoering van werken voor den dienst der Genie.* The Hague: De Gebroeders van Cleef.
Ministerie voor Onderwijs Cultuur en Wetenschap. 1988. Monumentenwet 1988.
Newby, F. (Ed.). 2001. *Early reinforced concrete* Aldershot, Great Britain: Ashgate Publishing Limited.

Oosterhoff, J., Arends, G.J., Eldik, C.H.v., & Nieuwmeijer, G.G. 1988. *Constructies van ijzer en beton Gebouwen 1800–1940 Overzicht en typologie* (1st ed.). Delft: Delft University Press, Rijksdienst voor de Monumentenzorg.

Probst, E. 1917. *Vorlesungen über Eisenbeton*. Berlin: Julius Springer.

Rijksdienst voor de Monumentenzorg. 1991. *Handleiding Selectie en registratie Jongere Stedebouw en bouwkunst (1850–1940)* Zeist, The Netherlands: Rijksdienst voor de Monumentenzorg.

Rijksdienst voor het Cultureel Erfgoed, Stichting Bouwhistorie Nederland, Vereniging Nederlandse Gemeenten, Atelier Rijksbouwmeester, & Rijksgebouwendienst. 2009. *Richtlijnen bouwhistorisch onderzoek* (2nd ed.). The Hague, The Netherlands.

Tilly, G. 2011. Durability of Concrete Repairs. In Grantham, M.G. (Ed.), *Concrete Repair. A practcal guide*. London and New York: Routledge Taylor & Francis.

Tilly, G., & Jacobs, J. 2007. *Concrete repairs. Performance in service and current practice.* Watford: IHS BRE Press.

UNESCO United Nations Educational Scientific and Cultural Organsation. State of Conservation of World Heritage Properties in Europe Netherlands Defence Line of Amsterdam. Retrieved 22-10-2010, from http://whc.unesco.org/archive/periodicreporting/EUR/cycle01/section2/759-summary.pdf.

van der Kloes, J.A. 1908. *Mortels en beton* (2nd ed.). Maassluis: J. van der Endt & Zoon.

van der Vooren, A.A. 1931. *Gewapend betonvoorschriften 1930*. Amsterdam: L.J. Veen's uitgevers mij. N.V.

Vaysburd, A.M. 2006. Holistic system approach to design and implementation of concrete repair. *Cement & Concrete Composites, 28*, 8.

Concrete Solutions – Grantham, Mechtcherine & Schneck (eds)
© 2012 Taylor & Francis Group, London, ISBN 978-0-415-61622-5

Stitching the past—"The strengthening of two heritage marine structures in Jersey with needling technology"

S. Hold
Arup, Cardiff, South Wales, UK

ABSTRACT: Two mass granite masonry structures in the St. Aubins Bay on the south coast of Jersey in the Channel Islands have recently been strengthened and rehabilitated using a large number of stainless steel reinforced high strength grout needles and mini-piles.

The 400 years old St. Aubins Fort Breakwater and the nearby North Pier of St. Aubins Harbour which is 160 years old, had in recent years shown serious signs of distress, prompting the need for urgent investigations to find structural strengthening and repair solutions. They have distorted vertical and horizontal geometry which would have been difficult to conventionally survey accurately so LiDAR was used to record and model both the structures and their surroundings. The "virtual" models of the structures in this part of St. Aubins Bay enabled assessments to be made of both the general environment and to apply marine engineering sea state data to the structures. The two structures, although similar in construction, had very different structural difficulties to overcome; significant settlement and rotation of the inner wall of the North Pier in the harbour and four previous 'wedge failure' collapses in the past 40 years of the inner face at the St. Aubins Fort Breakwater.

This paper describes the structures, the sea state investigations, and uses of the 'virtual' LiDAR models that assisted the assessment and analysis. The models also enabled us to arrive at an "engineered" number for the reinforced cementitious grout mini stitching anchors which both support the inner walls as well as tie them back to the main body of the structures. Both projects commenced in the latter part of 2010 and were completed before summer of 2011 in order to avoid the Jersey tourist season.

1 BACKGROUND

1.1 *Project location*

The two structures are located in St. Aubins Bay on the south coast of Jersey. In 2001 problems of inner wall settlement and rotation were identified at the St. Aubin North Pier. In 2007 attention was also focussed upon the recurrence of major masonry movements and loss of pointing mortar at the end of the St. Aubins Fort Breakwater.

1.2 *Heritage structures*

The Heritage of these structures is significant with the St. Aubins Fort being originally constructed to protect boat-building. In 1542 it became the 'playground' of Charles I as a teenager in the 1640s. Eventually in 1740 the quay side at the Fort required a breakwater to shelter the landing wharf. In 1780 the spit of sand, which had also provided ship building (and landing of smuggled goods) at the then small hamlet of St. Aubins on the shore-line, was used to build a pier which is today the South Pier of the harbour. The St. Aubins area then thrived in boat building and commerce and

eventually the north arm of the St. Aubins Harbour was constructed in 1846, thereby providing a tidal but enclosed harbour.

The Pier and Breakwater were originally constructed from two outer walls of dressed granite masonry blocks with secondary rock core fill material. The structures have no foundations as we understand them in the modern sense and were founded upon the beach sands.

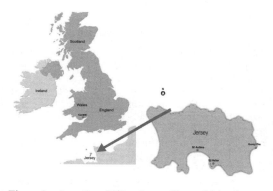

Figure 1.   Location: U.K.—Jersey Channel Island.

Figure 2.   St. Aubins Piers.

Figure 3.   North Pier inner wall LiDAR model.

1.3   Site investigations

Arup initially carried out studies of the North Pier in 2001 followed by an intrusive site investigation and historical data desk studies. The investigations at St. Aubins Fort have only taken place in recent years, prompted by an accelerating risk of damage and a likely further wedge failure collapse at the 'bulge' of the inner face and end of the breakwater (Fig. 8).

1.4   Stitching 'Secret Fix' required

This paper describes the iterative engineering that provided the 'secret fix' reinforced concrete grout solution that was used to arrest the movement of the walls and to provide them with support whilst 'stitching' them together for future generations. The solution used was a reinforced cementitious grout stitching anchor (by Cintec) and the design process was augmented on site by Geomarine Ltd, the successful Jersey based contractor, who developed the practical learning curve techniques for drilling and installing the long slender anchors. This process was aided by having a two stage tender process which allowed for a trial anchor at the North Pier site before the major project commenced.

1.5   LiDAR used for difficult geometry

The fundamental engineering question of "what are the problems" prompted several lines of enquiry and there was a need to establish accurate geometry for these non-uniform and awkwardly shaped structures. LiDAR techniques were used to obtain accurate drawing information so that intrusive site investigations could be carried out and to determine the type and condition of the materials used.

Historical research at Marine Heritage libraries, the British Museum, the Maritime Museum and Societé Jersaisé also provided important further desk study information.

Figure 4.   St. Aubin's Fort 1640.

The combination of the data gathering produced a chronology of how the structures were built and how, over many years, they have been maintained, repaired and added to. A study of the information also helped to understand what was likely to be causing the type of distress seen on the structures in the modern era. In order to understand 'cause and effect' of the distress, it was necessary to try to determine the inherent strength of these loosely bound stone structures so that their current structural integrity could be estimated.

The St. Aubins Harbour North Pier is typically constructed as a free draining structure, i.e. dressed stone outer walls and secondary material core fill that the tide can rise and fall within (Fig. 7). However, the St. Aubins Fort Breakwater (since the pressure filling with cementitious grout in 1973) and with its joints pointed, must now be considered as a 'solid' structure. The North Pier is therefore considered a typical 'soft' core structure which dissipates wave impact energy through the soft core before arriving at the inner harbour wall of the structure.

Figure 5. North Pier deck movements.

Figure 6. St. Aubins Fort Breakwater.

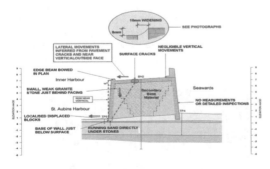

Figure 7. Representation of the North Pier failure mechanism (Wedge failure).

1.6 Long term loading assessment

Once our understanding of the structure's behaviour had formed, an assessment of the long term strength requirements could be made. The consideration of the tides, currents, winds and various

Figure 8. Fort area of 'bulging' and rebuild.

'worst case' combinations of these elements helped to formulate the sea state data that provided the type and magnitude of the principal load cases, i.e. the wave energy impact and overtopping forces that could be applied to the structural models. These forces were significant for the St. Aubins Fort Breakwater but not so onerous for the St. Aubins North Pier as it has a very sheltered orientation and location.

The North Pier however had suffered from washout and overdredging of the harbour in the 1990s, triggering base instability of the inner wall (Fig. 7) but the pier must be able to resist impact from mooring vessels, car parking on the deck and surcharge from boat lifts. The evidence at deck level (Fig. 5) and the geotechnical site investigations led us to predict an imminent wedge failure, Fig. 7 and Fig. 8.

However, for both pier assessments, wave overtopping, with an allowance for future increase in sea levels, was one of the most significant load cases allowed for in the calculations.

1.7 Heritage and Environmental constraints

There are invariably practical considerations and constraints in finding funding for Heritage structure remediation. Heritage structures invariably provide little revenue and are usually treated as custodial assets by the authorities who are responsible for them. Furthermore, environmental and historical heritage constraints were identified at the St. Aubins North Pier for which in 2005 it was proposed to rebuild the 'failed' inner wall of the pier on a new foundation 2 meters inside its present alignment. However, in 2005 the States of

Figure 9. St. Aubins Fort wedge failure 1972.

Jersey Planning Department did not approve this engineering solution and required a 'stitch in place' solution be investigated. To further complicate finding structural solutions, an environmental impact assessment identified two endangered species of molluscs living within the masonry of the North Pier and in 1973, following a partial collapse, the end of the Fort Breakwater was rebuilt and pressure grouted with cementitious grout thus making this structure perform as a 'solid' structure.

The presence of the two endangered mollusc species living in the upper levels of the North Pier also meant that the inner wall rebuild solution was not viable. The St. Aubins Fort Breakwater problems were related to the end of the Breakwater being a 'solid' structure (i.e. the voids and soft core were filled with cementitious grout after one of the several collapses and rebuilds in 1972). It was not thought financially viable to 'take down and rebuild' the end of the Breakwater to remove the cementitious grout to re-establish the original structural 'soft' core.

2 DESIGN CONSIDERATIONS

2.1 Bathymetry

The St. Aubins Bay maritime charts and the States of Jersey P.S.D. (Public Services Department) drawings were used to provide the initial data, following an intrusive site investigation in 2003.

The detailed intrusive site investigation work in 2003 identified that the North Pier was vulnerable to settlement as well as horizontal sliding of the base of the inner wall as a result of overdredging in the late 1990s. The South Pier however, has a larger cross-section, is more stable and the intrusive site investigations showed, it was less likely to suffer vertical settlement of the inner wall. However, the base stones of this pier were also drawn out as a result of the overdredging. The prognosis in 2003 was that there was a strong likelihood of a wedge failure (similar to those at St. Aubins Fort) and the likelihood of this type of failure was increasing with time (Fig. 8).

2.2 'Virtual' model of structures

In 2009 an accurate survey of both the North Pier and St. Aubins Fort was carried out using LiDAR techniques (Light Detection and Ranging—an optical remote sensing system). This process creates a 'virtual' model of the structures and their surroundings to an accuracy of ± 2 or 3 mm (Figs. 3 and 11). The accurate three dimensional models also readily enabled two dimensional engineering drawings to be produced. The model was of the two structures and the surrounding bay which further helped to illustrate the low tide conditions and the sea bed (the seabed of the harbour and the Fort Breakwater are exposed at low tides.).

3 SEA STATE CONDITIONS

To assess the forces that the two structures will have to resist in the future, waves, tides, winds and combinations of these forces were estimated. Various combinations of these and other loadings were considered with a pragmatic safety factor adopted (Fig. 12).

3.1 Scale drawings from model

The Fort Breakwater had a paucity of drawings and engineering data recorded historically so the LiDAR model and drawings for this structure were also used to provide accurate scale drawings for a detailed intrusive site investigation of the troubled end of the structure pier. The data from the intrusive investigation of 2009 enabled the St. Aubins Fort Breakwater to 'catch up' with the engineering information already available for the St. Aubins Harbour North Pier.

The similar solution chosen to strengthen the piers allowed both projects to be considered at the same time. Economy of scale was therefore possible to make the optimum use of the funding made available for strengthen these heritage structures.

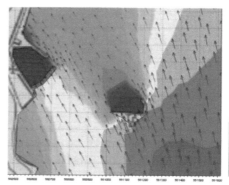

Figure 10. Wave climate from M.I.K.E. model.

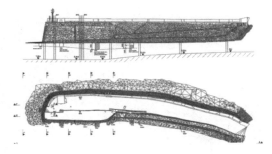

Figure 11. St. Aubin's Fort LiDAR model and 2D drawings for Site Investigation.

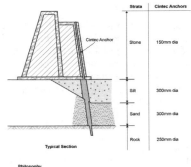

3.2 Summary of physical effects to design against

The North Pier experiences very low wave loading and impact forces. It was built commercially to enclose a harbour. By comparison mooring forces are negligible. However, car parking, boat lifts and occasional over topping need to be considered. This pier acts as a free draining structure, is subject to wash out, settlement due to soft strata beneath the sand and a rotation of the inner wall due to over-dredging.

The Fort Breakwater on the other hand is subject to large wave impact forces and was built to shelter the Fort Wharf. Mooring forces are negligible but the lower deck is regularly over topped. This pier is not free draining because it has been pressure grouted and the inner wall rebuilt several times because of settlement and wedge failures.

3.3 Forces to resist

The design solution was therefore required to; support the existing inner walls vertically, prevent further base sliding and tie the masonry both vertically and horizontally i.e. 'stitching'.

3.4 Principles of the Cintec anchor

The principles of the Cintec stitching anchor are that a steel reinforcement cage of small diameter is contained within a cementitious grout circular column. The high strength, high bond grout is pumped in the drilled circular hole under pressure (5 bar) so that the grout seeps through a fabric material 'sock' and inflates. The high strength grout inflates the sock under pressure to create a larger diameter than the core drill when it is removed in both voids and softer strata materials. The larger diameter therefore coincides with the location of weaker strata where more capacity of cross section is required. The sock also prevents grout loss and grout spread elsewhere other than

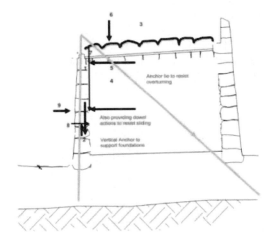

No	Load
1	Wall dead load
3	Surcharge from vehicles
4	Active soil pressure
5	Wave load
6	Wave overtopping load
	Resistance
2	Wall buoyancy
7	Vertical soil-wall friction
8	Horizontal soil-wall friction
9	Passive soil pressure

Figure 12. Forces to resist.

just on the surface of the sock. Therefore the grout is contained and does not pose an environmental threat. (In the case of the North Pier, to the molluscs that an Environmental Impact Assessment revealed inhabit the voids in the pier wall above the high water mark). (Fig. 18).

3.5 Base design assumptions

The base design assumptions by the Cintec/Arup team were that the 100 mm diameter cross section filled with 60 N/mm^2 cementitious grout and six 8 mm diameter 610 N/mm^2 stainless steel reinforcing rods would provide a tension resistance in the region of 170 KN and a compressive resistance in the region of 210 KN.

3.6 Spacing of anchors

The loading arrangements per linear meter allowed a design for the requisite number of anchors vertically and horizontally to be accommodating these forces i.e. enabled a refined engineering judgment to provide an 'engineered' spacing of the anchors per meter run.

3.7 Public information exercise

The historical and environmental aspects of the project were highlighted by the planning constraints

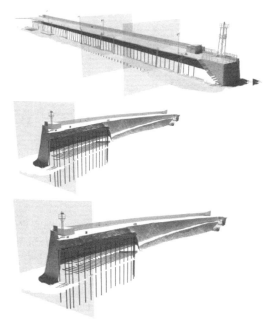

Figure 15. Cut aways of the models showing needle spacings.

of 2005 and the environmental scoping report produced as part of the E.I.A. in 2009. Both of these constraints pointed the way towards the 'stitching anchor' solution for the North Pier. The technique and theory was presented to the relevant authorities and the Jersey public in a graphical way using the LiDAR model. Leaflets and posters were produced to explain the project to the public at large and demonstrate that the project was necessary as well as illustrating the specialised methods to be used (Fig. 15).

3.8 Programmed to miss tourist seasons

Another public awareness consideration was that the project was to commence on site after the summer tourist season in 2010 and would be completed by May 2011 prior to the following tourist season.

4 CONSTRUCTION

4.1 Tidal working

Both structures are tidal, there is an 11 to 12 metre tidal range in Jersey, but the St. Aubins Fort environment is by far the more onerous in as much that it becomes an isolated island at mid tide. The original contract was tendered as the St. Aubins North Pier project to Jersey based contractors who had been trained and approved to use the Cintec system.

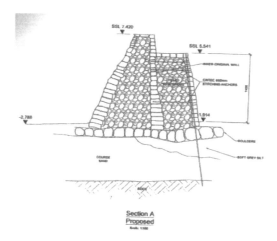

Figure 13. Cintec design philosophy of expanding sock.

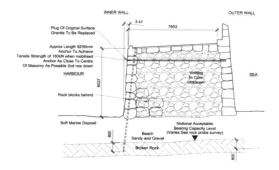

Figure 14. Cross sections of anchor solutions.

Figure 16. Fort horizontal drilling.

Figure 17. Anchors.

Figure 18. Before grout under pressure and after inflation—grout contained.

4.2 Further trial holes

Geomarine Jersey Ltd were the successful tenderer for the contract and they elected to scaffold the inner face of the North Pier for the installation of both the vertical and horizontal anchors. To facilitate the scaffold they placed an apron of crushed, graded rock at the base of the wall on the seabed which not only provided support to the scaffolding but also, when in place, reduced the risk of horizontal sliding of the inner wall base. As part of the trial anchor works, an additional horizontal borehole was driven from the gravel platform. The borehole indicated the wall stone thickness, and the base of the wall was 2 to 3 stones thick. The borehole also allowed the Ø (phi) value of the core material to be established to determine the downward friction loading the material applies to the inner face of the wall.

4.3 Test anchor

The contractor carried out, as part of his tender, a test anchor at one location on the inner face of the North Pier to establish a learning curve. The main practical issue to overcome was the drilling of a casing of 100 mm diameter, extracting the core material, inserting the anchor in the hole, and then retracting the outer drill bit cylinder without snagging or catching the linen fabric sock. After several different options were tried, a practical method was found using simple masking tape to tie back the linen sock around the reinforcement before it

was inserted in to the hole which then allowed the drill bit cylinder to be extracted over the rod and sock without fouling.

4.4 Segmental constructions

The problem of constructing either a 9 or 11 m long mini pile or tie was resolved by providing couplers for unit sections of anchor 2.5 m long. The method of securing the sock safely within the casing with masking tape proved effective as the grout pressure of 5 bar easily burst the masking tape to allow full inflation of the sock in voids and soft strata. An added bonus in terms of the integrity of the anchor was that the inflated sock bulged and increased in diameter in weak or voided strata. However, the void habitat of the molluscs was not contaminated by spillage of grout because it was contained by the linen sock (Fig. 18).

4.5 Load test calibration

Geomarine Ltd carried out a load test of the trial anchor before work commenced which achieved an actual load on an individual anchor of 200 kN which calibrated the engineering judgment design principles used. Design safety factors for modern day marine codes were complied with as much as

Figure 19.   Pointing at the Fort Bridge.

Figure 20.   Secret Fix, cap replaced.

practically possible for heritage structures. Engineering judgement also ignored the positive effects of 'bridging' or 'arching' between mini piles and the existing bearing capacity of the consolidated beach sands beneath the wall.

4.6 *Emergency pointing work*

The St. Aubins Fort Breakwater was issued as a variation order to the North Pier contract and the stabilisation of the very vulnerable bulging masonry at the end of the breakwater was immediately secured with lime pointing mortar to provide a wedge that would restrain the larger stones from 'popping out'. The lime pointing formed a wedge shape in the joints to hold in place both the vertical face and filled the cracks in the masonry joints at deck level. These cracks made the structure vulnerable to overtopping and water penetration downwards into the body of the breakwater at high tides.

4.7 *Work sequencing*

The North Pier works started with vertical anchors working from the seaward end to strengthen the most vulnerable part of the inner wall first. The horizontal ties for the Fort were drilled by placing the rig upon a horizontal machine platform that could safely support it and drill into the original inner wall of the Fort (Fig. 16).

These horizontal anchors, besides stitching the masonry and old grout within the pier together, also by projecting into the inner wall of the original breakwater, provided some measure of cantilever vertical support to the outer wall. The bulge at the end of the breakwater was stitched together with smaller anchors and a smaller, drill arrangement that provided a lattice of further 'secret fix' reinforced cementitious ties to the bulged area.

Figure 21.   Completed project; no visible changes.

4.8 *Additional work to South Pier*

The works to both the St. Aubins Piers and St. Aubins Fort Breakwater were completed before May 2011 and included some additional horizontal anchors for securing a section of the St. Aubins South Pier that was suffering from localised inner wall horizontal shunting as a result of wave impacts on the harbour outside face of the wall.

5   CONCLUSIONS

5.1 *A heritage and environmental solution*

This stitching method rehabilitation and strengthening of the two lose masonry marine heritage structures provided a cost effective and practical site specific solution. The method is environmentally sound, efficient and provides enhanced structural capacity (and life in use of these two unique marine heritage structures) so they are safeguarded for future generations.

ACKNOWLEDGEMENTS

The author acknowledges and thanks contributions from:

Ray Hine—Technical Services Manager, Port of Jersey,

Iain Barkley—Geomarine Ltd,

John Brookes—Cintec Ltd,

Clon Ulrick, Anna Ulanovsky and Sam Issacs—Arup.

REFERENCES

Bezuigen, A., Muller G, Wolters, G. Failure Mechanisms for Blockwork Breakwaters,—*ICE Proceedings Coastlines, Structure and Breakwaters* 2005.

Goda, Y. Ed. Random seas and design of maritime structures, advanced series on ocean engineering—Volume 15,. *World Scientific.*

Hold, S. Repair of St. Catherine's Breakwater Roundhead—ICE 2009 proceedings.

Kortenhaus, A. Voortman, H Eds. Probabilistic design tools for vertical breakwaters, 2001. Sweets and Zeitlinger BV Lisse.

Overtopping Manual—http://www.overtopping-manual.com/calculation_tool.html.

Shore Protection Manual, Coastal Engineering Research Centre, Department of the Arm Core of Engineers, 1984.

Wolters, G, Muller, G, Bruce T et al. Large scale experiments on wave downfall pressures on coastal structures,—*ICE Proceedings Coastlines, Structures and Breakwaters* 2004.

Concrete Solutions – Grantham, Mechtcherine & Schneck (eds)
© 2012 Taylor & Francis Group, London, ISBN 978-0-415-61622-5

Strengthening and rehabilitation of two damaged bridges in the motorway M-410 in Madrid

C. Jurado Cabañes

Polytechnic University of Madrid/Ingecal Ingenieros, S L., Madrid, Spain

ABSTRACT: The new highway M-410 in Madrid was constructed in the year 2007. This motorway near to Parla city crosses the road from Madrid to Toledo. To solve this crossing, three bridges were constructed with deep foundations. On the two lateral bridges, called PS-18 and PS-19, after constructing the piles and the deck-slab resting on the soil, it was necessary to remove the earth under the concrete slab to make two lateral roads, but before this, sonic transparency testing was conducted in each pile and two boreholes which showed that the earth at the level of the bottom of the piles, was sandy and with a great water flow, so it was was impossible to retire the earth under the concrete deck-slab, because the piles were not correctly founded. The solution of this pathology was the construction of two sheets of deep micropiles at each abutment of the bridges.

1 INTRODUCTION

During the year 2007 a new highway called M-410 was constructed in the village of Parla near to Madrid, the capital city of Spain (Fig. 1), which surrounded the city along the south.

The new highway M-410 belongs to the project of construction, of a part of a net of infrastructures along the south zone of Madrid named REDSUR, and this consists of a highway of 25 kilometres, for the connection of the radial highways N-IV and N-V.

REDSUR is the name given to the construction of 81 new kilometres of highways and infrastructures, surrounding Madrid along their south side.

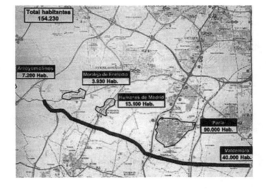

Figure 2. Plan of REDSUR actuation on the South of Madrid.

that connects 16 bedroom cities and the cost of the works was 272 million Euros (Fig. 2).

The project was divided in 10 phases that were finished in 2007 and the phase described in this paper, was phase 2, to connect the villages of Arroyomolinos and Valdemoro.

REDSUR will improve the communications of 1.3 million people going to and from Madrid, who live in the southwest region, which supports a very heavy traffic of vehicles between 20,000 and 60,000 every day and whose roads have remained saturated during recent years. Near to the Parla village this new motorway M-410 crosses the existing one A-42, which connects Madrid with Toledo (Fig. 3).

Figure 1. Situation of Parla near Madrid.

Figure 3. Situation of new the bridges over the motorway A-42 which connects Madrid with Toledo.

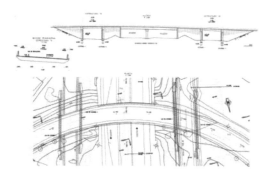

Figure 4. Plan of situation of bridges PS-18 and PS-19.

2 BRIDGES PS-18 AND PS-19

The bridges PS-18 and PS-19 are two symmetrical bridges with respect to the motorway A-42, with abutments constituted with sheet piles of 1.00 meter diameter and 13.00 meters long, separated 1.25 m in order to form one discharge arch between two piles, to permit the excavation under the bridge forming a hollow of 5.50 meter high, that would be covered with a reinforced concrete wall (Fig. 4).

3 THE PATHOLOGY DETECTED

On September 2007, tests of sonic transparency were made in each of the 22 piles of every structure, detecting that important anomalies existed on the bottom of the piles of both bridges. It was recommended that a thorough detailed study of the pathology was conducted, to discover if these anomalies could affect the structural behaviour of the bridges. The bridges were scheduled to be opened to traffic in January 2008.

Figure 5. Sandy material under the bottom of one of the piles.

As a consequence of this, four new boreholes and four penetrometric tests, each one at every abutment of the bridges were made, during which it was discovered that a cap of granular material with a strong flow of water, that had produced a washing of the concrete at the base of the piles existed at the bottom of the piles, (Fig. 5).

In these conditions it was prudent to consider only the friction load of the piles, discarding the tip resistant load, since we could not know what percentage of this last load could be useful. So, for safety, it was decided to design a new system of foundations, that would allow the load at the top of the piles to be resisted, discarding completely the collaboration of them by the tip and considering only the friction resistance of the piles.

4 THE OPTIONS FOR REPAIR

To repair the pathology two options were studied:

A. To perforate the interior of the piles and withdraw the low detritus on the bottom followed by injecting grout that replaced this. This would allow the complete return of the admissible tip load resistance for the piles.
B. To discard totally the capacity of the tip load resistance of the piles, considering only the friction resistance, which had not been affected by the mentioned anomalies in the bottom, and providing a supplementary system that was capable to resist the rest of the load.

The two bridges have at each abutment 11 piles of $\Phi = 1.00$ m. and 13.00 meters long, tied on the top by a concrete tie beam, with a transversal section of 1.30 m width and 2.11 m height.

For the first option, it was necessary to drill three core holes in each of the 44 meters of piles, so this

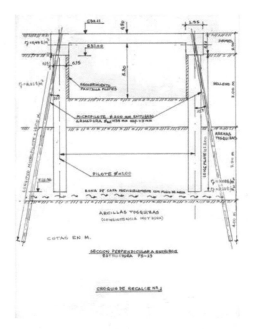

Figure 6. Solution adopted for the rehabilitation of PS-18 and PS-19.

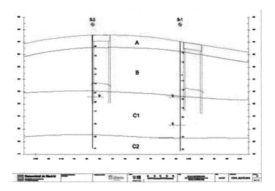

Figure 7. Geotechnical profile of the site.

A. Superficial landfill corresponding to the package of road works with a thickness of 2.00 m.
B. Landfill of terrace with a thickness of 7.00 m. and a friction resistance for piles of $r_f = 3.36$ t/m².
C1. Mioceno Sustratum. Coarse sandy very dense soil with a thickness of 7.00 m., a friction resistance for piles of $r_f = 9.00$ t/m² and tip resistance of $r_p = 900$ t/m².
C2. Substratum Mioceno. Coarse clayey very hard, which correspondents to the low substratum with a thickness until the end of the tested area.

implies the accomplishment of $3 \times 44 = 132$ meters of drilling in concrete! The operative procedure would consist of injecting water for one of them and extracting the detritus for the other two, until the rejection was turning out to be clean water. Later closing two drills, cement mortar would be injected through the third one with pressure, until it was overflowing for the drill of injection, which would indicate that the bottom of the pile and the three drilled holes had been refilled completely. This system presented the uncertainty, that if the bottom of the piles were located in a constant cap of granular material with a significant flow of water, much of the cement injection and mortar could get lost across the above mentioned cap and not return for the other two drills. And there were indications, which showed that an underground flow of water existed at this depth. On the other hand, still supposing that this was not taking place, the accomplishment of 132 meters of drilling and the later operations, would take an extraordinarily long time, not being able to conclude the works, before the scheduled opening time in January 2008.

5 THE GEOTECHNICAL SURVEY

The geotechnical characteristics of site it can be seen in the Figure 7. The geotechnical campaign showed the existence of four layers:

6 THE ADOPTED SOLUTION OF REPAIR

Finally the adopted solution to solve the pathology detected consisted of the construction of two sheet micropiles inclined 15° with the vertical, outside the abutment of each bridge, in order to avoid the area of the bottom of the concrete piles, going 4.00 meters below the zone of the water flow, just to situate the influence zones of the tip of the micropiles away from this, so the active and passive zones of the micropiles were in healthy clays (Fig. 8).

Since the friction resistance load of the existing piles was intact, it was only necessary that each sheet of micropiles must resists the tip load resistance of the piles at every abutment.

Making the necessary calculations and discarding the tip load resistance of the existing piles, each new micropile might absorb $N_{p,Ed} = 736{,}96$ kN.

Discarding as is usual, the tip resistance of micropiles and considering only the friction resistance of these, which is a supplementary security, and using four new micropiles at each abutment, every new micropile could resist $R_{fc,d} = 738{,}43$ kN, that is:

$$R_{fc,d} = 738{,}43 \text{ kN} > N_{p,Ed} = 736{,}96 \text{ kN}$$

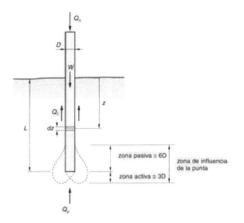

Figure 8.   Zones active and passive of one pile.

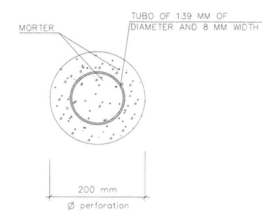

Figure 10.   Transversal section of micropiles.

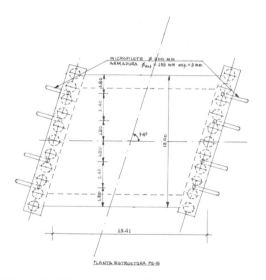

Figure 9.   Plan of the existing piles and the new micropiles.

Figure 11.   Works of micropiling on PS-18.

So the solution was to place four micropiles of $\Phi = 200$ mm with a length of 18 meters, inclined 15° with the vertical at each abutment. In Figure 9 is shown the plan of the disposition of the existing piles and the new micropiles at each bridge.

By this way the existing piles resist part of the loads by friction resistance and the rest of the loads which must support the bridge are resisted by the friction resistance of the micropilotes, avoiding the transmission of loads to the level of the water flow.

In Figure 10 can be seen the transversal section of the micropiles used.

7   CONCLUSIONS

Finally the works were made between December 2007 and January 2008 without any problems and the bridges were inaugurated on time, by the Mayor of the city of Madrid, at the end of January 2008.

In Figure 11 the works of micropiling on bridge PS-18 are shown.

Also it was necessary to design an element of connection between the existing tying beams of each abutment and the new micropiles.

For this, connectors were designed consisting of reinforced bars welded to the tubes of the micropiles (Figs. 12 and 13).

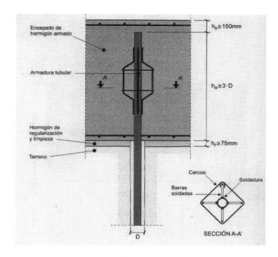

Figure 12. Connection between the existing structure and the new micropiles.

BIBLIOGRAPHY

Eurocode 1. prEN 1991-1-4, 2004 *"Bases of project and actions in structures"*.

Eurocode 2. prEN 1991-1-4, 2004 *"Project of structures of reinforced concrete"*.

Eurocode 3. prEN 1991-1-4, 2004 *"Project of structures of steel"*.

P. Jiménez Montoya, A. García Meseguer. F. Morán Cabré 2009, *Reinforced Concrete*. 15a edición. Ed. Gustavo Gili.

Spanish Ministry of Civil Works. *1998, "Instruction on the actions to consider in the project of bridges of highway. IAP-98"*.

Spanish Ministry of Civil Works. 2002, *"Norm of seismic construction: General part and Building Construction"*. NCSE-O2 (Real Decreto 997/2002).

Spanish Ministry of Civil Works. *"Spanish rules relative to the actions to consider in the project of roadway bridges"*.

V. Escario, 1985, *Geotechnical Synthesis of the Soils in Madrid*. Ministerio de Trasportes y Comunicaciones.

Figure 13. Connectors designed to transmit the loads to the micropiles.

Concrete Solutions – Grantham, Mechtcherine & Schneck (eds)
© 2012 Taylor & Francis Group, London, ISBN 978-0-415-61622-5

Extent of condition assessment of concrete building—practical experiences

J. Lahdensivu & S. Varjonen
Tampere University of Technology, Tampere, Finland

ABSTRACT: Concrete structures exposed to outdoor climate deteriorate due to several different degradation mechanisms, whose progress depends on many factors related to structure type, exposure and materials. The repair need of concrete structures should be determined by systematic condition assessment in every case. The aim of this paper was to evaluate the scope of the condition assessments made on Finnish precast concrete buildings during the last 15 years. The evaluation is based on 262 condition assessment reports on precast concrete buildings built between 1948 and 1993 and interviews of the owners of the buildings, condition investigators, structural designers and inspectors of repairs in 12 cases.

The scopes of the studied condition assessments were compared to the Finnish national guidelines for condition assessment of concrete structures. The average sample size of a condition assessment was 12.1. In 19% of the condition assessments, the sample size was 1–5, in 28% 6–10, and in 23% 11–15. The recommended sample size depends on the number of precast concrete panel and balcony types, but for an average 5-storey block of flats with two stairways, the minimum sample size is 15–21. In general, the realised sample size was only half of the minimum sample size recommended in Finnish guidelines for condition assessment of concrete structures.

The repair method for a concrete structure should be selected on the basis of a condition assessment. According to the interviewees, too extensive repair methods are recommended and selected when the scope of a condition assessment is small leading to unnecessarily heavy repairs in almost half of the cases.

1 INTRODUCTION

1.1 About Finnish building stock

Since the 1960's a total of approximately 44 million square metres of concrete-panel facades have been built in Finland (Vainio et al. 2005). In fact, more than 60% of the Finnish building stock has been built in the 1960's or later. Compared with the rest of Europe, the Finnish building stock is rather young.

Despite the rather young age of the Finnish precast building stock, several problems have been encountered in their maintenance and repair. The structures have deteriorated due to several different mechanisms, whose progress depends on many factors related to structures, exposure and materials. Thus, the service lives of structures vary widely. In some cases structures have required considerable, and often unexpected, costly major repairs, less than 10 years after their completion. Therefore, many new methods have been developed in Finland for maintaining and repairing these concrete structures during the last 20 years. The methods include a condition assessment practice and its extensive utilisation, rational repair methods and

their selection, as well as first-rate repair products and appropriate instructions for managing repair projects.

Development of condition assessment systematics for concrete facades started in Finland at the turn of the 1990's when extensive scientific research on the subject was conducted. As a result of that work, the first national condition assessment manual was prepared for carrying out condition assessments. The manual published in 1997 harmonised the practices of various condition investigators and created common standards and guidelines for the sector as to the contents and sample sizes of assessments. The manual was updated and revised for the new edition that came out in 2002.

A large number of condition assessments of concrete structures have been carried out since the mid-1990's, and they have become a key tool in assessing the repair need of structures.

1.2 The most common deterioration mechanisms

The most common deterioration mechanisms causing the need to repair concrete facades, and concrete structures in general, in Finland are corrosion of reinforcement due to carbonation as

Figure 1. Typical finnish suburban concrete buildings from the 1970's.

well as insufficient frost resistance of concrete which leads to, for instance, frost damage (Pentti et al. 1998).

1.2.1 *Corrosion of reinforcement*

Reinforcing bars encased in concrete are normally well protected from corrosion due to the high alkalinity of concrete pore water. Corrosion may start when the passivity is destroyed, either by chloride penetration or due to a reduction in the pH of carbonated concrete (Page 1988). Carbonation begins at the surface of a newly constructed member and propagates slowly as a front at a decelerating rate deeper into the structure. The speed of propagation is influenced mainly by the quality of concrete (amount of cement and porosity of concrete) as well as moisture exposure. Heavy moisture exposure, for example due to rainfall, slows down carbonation because water blocks CO_2 from entering the pores (Parrott 1987, Tuutti 1982 and Richardsson 1988).

Once the passivity is destroyed either by carbonation or by chloride contamination, active corrosion may start in the presence of moisture and oxygen (Parrott 1987). Corrosion may advance for a long time before it can be noticed on the surface of the structure. Because corrosion products are not water soluble, they accumulate on the surface of steel near the anodic area (Mattila 1995). This generates internal pressure, because the volume of the corrosion products induced by carbonation is four to six times that of the original steel bars (Parrot 1987 and Tuutti 1982).

The internal pressure caused by corrosion products leads to cracking or spalling of the concrete cover. Visible damage appears first in spots where the concrete cover is thinnest and the moisture content of concrete is highest. According to Tuutti (1982), the relative humidity of concrete has a strong influence on the corrosion rate. Significant corrosion occurs only when the relative humidity of concrete exceeds 80%. Between September and April, the relative humidity of concrete facades in Finland is typically between 90 and 95%. That translates into a corrosion rate of 1 to >10 µm/a.

Chloride-induced corrosion is very common in bridges and marine structures, but not in Finnish concrete facades. In only four out of 946 buildings was the chloride content high enough for corrosion (Lahdensivu et al. 2011). There, chlorides had been used as an accelerator in fresh concrete and the facade panels had been produced in winter on the construction site.

1.2.2 *Frost damage of concrete*

Concrete is a porous material whose pore system may, depending on the conditions, hold varying amounts of water. As the water in the pore system freezes, it expands about 9% by volume which creates hydraulic pressure in the system Pigeon & Pleau (1995). If the level of water saturation of the system is high enough, the overpressure cannot escape into air-filled pores and thus damages the internal structure of the concrete, resulting in its degradation (Fagerlund 1977). Advanced frost damage leads to total loss of concrete strength.

The frost resistance of concrete can be ensured by air-entraining which creates a sufficient amount of permanently air-filled so-called protective pores where the pressure from the freezing dilation of water can escape. Finnish guidelines for the air-entraining of facade concrete mixes were issued in 1976 (Anon. 2002).

1.3 *Objective*

The objective of this paper was to study the sample sizes of condition assessments and the impact of visually observable damage on sample size.

The aim of the interview study was to determine which factors contribute to the success of a facade renovation process and how conditions assessments or the repair-related decision-making process need to be developed, and whether renovation processes differ significantly between regions.

2 CONDITION ASSESSMENT

2.1 *General*

Damage to structures, its degree and extent, due to various deterioration phenomena can be determined by a comprehensive systematic condition assessment. A condition assessment involves systematic determination of the condition and performance of a structural element or an aggregate of structural elements (e.g. a facade or balcony) and their repair needs with respect to different deterioration mechanisms. This is achieved by various research methods such as examination of design documents, various field measurements and investigations, sampling and laboratory tests.

The wide variation in the states of deterioration of buildings, and the fact that the most significant deterioration is not visible until it has progressed very far, necessitate thorough condition assessment at most concrete-structure repair sites. Evaluation of reinforcement corrosion and the degree of frost damage suffered by concrete are examples of such assessments.

2.2 *Sample size according to Finnish condition assessment manual*

Concrete facades and balconies are often built of different panel types, and, moreover, the surface materials of panels may differ even by panels. According to the national concrete facade assessment manual, at least three comparison samples are to be taken from each panel type (Anon. 2002). The typical precast blocks of flats erected between the late 1960's and early 1980's contain at least five different types of panels: the windowed panels of the long sides, the solid panels of the ends, balcony slabs, balcony side panels and balcony railings. Moreover, the plinth panels and the uppermost thin-shell panels must generally be inspected separately. Then, sample size ought to be at least 15–21 per assessed building. In case there are many different panel or panel surface types, they must be divided into even smaller categories.

Different materials, manufacturing and working modes as well as the properties of structures cause variation in the propagation of deterioration and damage, and therefore results based on samples from a single panel type cannot be generalised to all panels of a facade section. According to the manual, the sampling and evaluations of a condition assessment must be carried out so that the results can be analysed by structure and panel types.

Condition assessments are a sample surveys which means that the received results are always more or less uncertain. The bigger the sample size, the more reliable the results obtained. But costs also increase in proportion to sample size. The magnitude of the used sample size depends on the importance of the examined degradation mechanism and the importance of its accuracy in drawing conclusions. A condition assessment is successful and reliable when the conclusions drawn from it, especially the estimated repair need and suggested repair method, are appropriate and economical considering the damage.

3 RESEARCH MATERIAL

The research material consists of a database of deterioration and material properties of existing Finnish concrete facade panels built up between 1961 and 1996, condition assessment reports on buildings built up between 1948 and 1993, and interviews of structural designers, condition investigators, owners of buildings and inspectors of repairs.

3.1 *Database*

Condition assessment systematics for concrete facades and balconies have been developed in Finland since the mid-1980's. A large body of data on implemented repair projects has been accumulated in the form of documents prepared in connection with condition assessments. Approximately 1,500 precast concrete blocks of flats have been subjected to a condition assessment, and painstakingly documented material on each one exists, including the buildings' structures and accurate reports on observed damage and the need for repairs based on accurate field surveys and laboratory analyses.

The condition assessment data on 946 buildings has been stored in a database. The condition assessment reports have been collected from companies which have conducted them as well as from rental housing companies owned by cities.

The scope of condition assessments was examined based on implemented samplings. The evaluation used sampling data on such buildings of the database whose panel types and area and volume data could be determined. The database included 262 such buildings built in 1948–1993. Condition assessments on these projects were carried out in 1992–2006.

3.2 *Interviews*

The significance of condition assessments in real estate maintenance, selection of repair method and repair design was determined by interviewing different parties. The material of the interview study consisted of interviews of 12 repair designers, condition investigators, clients and repair supervisors. The 12 buildings in different parts of Finland were 3–8 storey precast concrete blocks of flats completed in 1969–90 whose facade and/or balconies had been repaired within the last two years. The southernmost cases were in the Greater Helsinki area, the northernmost ones in Oulu, the easternmost in Kuopio and the westernmost in Turku.

4 RESULTS AND DISCUSSION

4.1 *Actual sample sizes of condition assessment*

According to the condition assessment reports, the typical Finnish precast concrete block of flats has five storeys, two stair wells and 28 balconies. The average building was completed in 1978 and subjected to a condition assessment in 2002.

The database shows that an average of 12.1 samples are taken from each building in condition assessments of facades and/or balconies. That figure includes samples from facade panels (solid and windowed panels), plinth panels, uppermost thin-shell panels and balcony structures (side panels, slabs and railing panels). The majority of condition assessments took 6–10 samples (28% of the total) or 11–15 samples (23%), but the share of 1–5 samples was also quite large (19%). On average, slightly more samples are taken from facades than balconies. The database indicated that an average of 7.2 concrete core samples had been taken from facades and an average of 6.1 from balconies per building.

In general, considerably fewer samples have been taken in condition assessments than the national condition assessment manual recommends (Anon. 2002), because nearly 50% of all assessments used 1–10 samples while the minimum suggested in the manual is 15–21 depending on the number of panel types in the evaluated building.

The database also reveals that visible damage to structures had no impact on the sampling of assessments, but the planned sampling programme was realised as such in the majority of cases. In buildings where no immediate repair need was detected, 1.8 more samples, on average, were taken than in buildings where repair measures were recommended based on the assessment. There is large deviation in the number of samples which led to different repair recommendations. For instance, patching and coating was recommended as the repair alternative based on 2–23 samples, see Figure 2.

However, it must be taken into account that the above comparison of sample sizes does not fully explain the adequacy of the condition assessment. For instance, in some cases wide-spread and far advanced frost damage may be visible which justifies taking only a few samples to determine the appropriate repair method. Thus, the quality of a condition assessment cannot be evaluated merely on the basis of sample size. It is essential that the assessment is sufficiently inclusive considering the extent of damage to a structure and the aims of the assessment. Comparison of sample sizes does, however, give a rough idea of the coverage of the conducted condition assessment.

The sample size of an assessment should depend largely on the condition of the assessed structure. According to the national condition assessment manual, the evaluation of a structure that visually seems to be in good condition requires thorough and extensive examination since incipient damage is not visible. On the other hand, the damage to a dilapitated structure may be visually observable and extensive and thorough investigations may be unnecessary (Anon. 2002).

Based on performed evaluations, it appears that visually observable advanced deterioration of concrete facades and balconies has not had an impact on the sampling implemented as part of condition assessments in practice, see Figure 3.

4.2 *Real estate management strategies*

The aim of the interview study was to determine the factors that contribute to the success of a facade repair process as well as the need to develop condition assessments or the decision-making process related to facade repairs, and whether regionally significant differences exist between facade repair processes.

Based on the interviews, the most common maintenance method for outdoor concrete structures is need-based maintenance based on

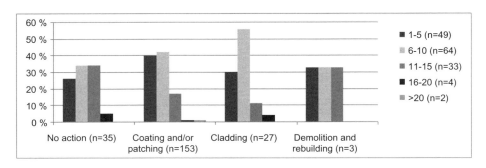

Figure 2. Sample size distribution leading to recommended facade repair methods (n = 218).

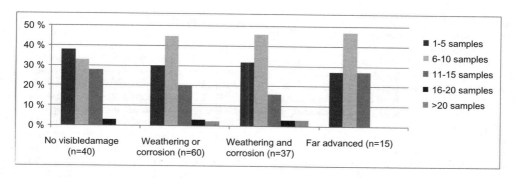

Figure 3. Impact of visible damage on sample size distribution in assessment of condition of facades (n = 152).

condition assessments or investigations. Facilities management based on recommended maintenance periods is also very common with property owners managing large numbers of rental dwellings.

There are large regional and property owner-related differences between maintenance programmes. In the Greater Helsinki area and Turku region, where repair of facades and balconies is busiest in Finland, people are trying to increase the service life of structures through continuous monitoring and light maintenance. Consequently, problems are detected and measures taken already before actual damage occurs, and repair consists primarily of light repairs. In the rest of Finland, actual maintenance of facade and balcony structures has not been done regularly, but thorough repair of facades is primarily done in connection with renovation when the building is about 25 to 40 years old. Then, in most cases, a thorough renovation is required.

The limited resources available for repairing facades and balconies play a major role in repair decisions according to the interviews. The targeting of available resources varies. In most instances an attempt is made to use resources so as to achieve the best overall return. In the growth centres of southern Finland, repairs are made to internal spaces of buildings and their outdoor structures. In other parts of the country, available resources have often been targeted either at repair of internal spaces or outdoor structures.

The factor that mostly explains the differences in renovation strategies is the dissimilar deterioration of concrete structures. The durability properties of the concrete used for old precast concrete blocks of flats are very similar across the nation, but the real stress level of buildings varies significantly. The deterioration rate is fastest in coastal areas where more freeze-thaw cycles occur during the year and precipitation even in winter consists mostly of water or sleet.

4.3 Timing of condition assessment

Condition assessment reports provide repair recommendations for facades and balconies based on the degree of degradation of structures. Generally the reports suggest several repair alternatives that meet different requirements. The lightest alternative is often determined by technical requirements while a heavier alternative may also take into account economical or aesthetic factors.

According to the interviews, a facade or balcony structure repair project is most often launched as a result of visible damage to structures. When the property owner, the building manager, the maintenance men or the occupants notice visible damage in structures, such as corrosion or frost damage, there is need to determine the actual condition of the structure by a condition assessment.

Large rental housing companies use also more systematic condition monitoring methods. The condition of properties is followed regularly through assessments by building managers at about two year intervals, and by visual condition assessments of investigators every 5–10 years. However, the focus of the assessments by building managers is charting damage to internal spaces. More detailed condition assessments are typically commissioned based on the condition investigator's observations, or at the latest when the building is about to reach the age when repair is a must, or at about 15 years. An assessment made then does not necessarily lead to repair measures, but observed damage may be monitored regularly, for instance at five year intervals, or if necessary, by investigations. Renovation measures can be scheduled for a date determined by technical condition.

4.4 Selection of repair method

The repair design of a building starts on the basis of a condition assessment, and generally the first choice recommended by the investigator as a repair method is selected to ensure long service life. The repair method and time suggested by the condition assessment are seldom departed from, and should that happen, there is a good reason for it such as making the repair in connection with other repairs. If much time has passed since the condition assessment was made, generally over five years, further investigations are conducted prior to selecting the final repair method.

Based on the interviews of condition investigators and repair designers, more thorough investigations should often be carried out in support of repair decisions, but the clients are not always willing to pay for them. According to the interviews, too narrow condition assessments lead either to excessive certainty in making a repair recommendation or significant need of further investigations at the repair design phase. Generally further investigations concern detrimental substances such as PCB and lead analyses of elastic joints as well as asbestos surveys, but more comprehensive investigations may also be performed.

A light condition assessment may also lead to surprises at the repair phase causing additional costs. Typical such costs are those of extra chipping and safety attachments of panels.

5 CONCLUSIONS

According to the database, an average of 12.5 samples are taken from each studied building in condition assessments of facades and/or balconies. The majority of the assessments (28%) are done based on 6–10 samples. Condition assessments based on 11–15 samples constitute 22% of the database, but even the share of assessments based on 1–5 samples is quite large (19%). On the whole, the number of samples taken in conditions assessments has been about half of what the current national condition assessment manual recommends.

Analyses based on the database also reveal that extensive occurrence of visible widespread far advanced corrosion or frost damage has not reduced the sample sizes of condition assessments.

The repair strategies of concrete facades differ considerably depending on property owner and locality. The coastal areas, where concrete structures have suffered more damage faster than in the interior, are one of the major factors behind the differences.

The repair need and method of concrete structures is selected on a technical basis according to the recommendation of the condition investigator. Thus, the investigator and the reliability of the condition assessment bear a big technical and economical responsibility for the success of future repairs. The quality of condition assessments cannot thus be evaluated solely on the basis of sample size. It is essential that a condition assessment is sufficiently comprehensive considering the degree of damage to the structure and the goals set for the condition assessment. A condition assessment is always based on sampling and visual inspection. The appropriate sample size depends on the investigated quantity and the significance of its accuracy in drawing conclusions.

REFERENCES

Anon. 2002. *Condition assessment manual for concrete facade panels*. Helsinki. Concrete Association of Finland BY 42, 178 p. (In Finnish).

Fagerlund, G. 1977. The critical degree of saturation method of assessing the freze/thaw resistance of concrete. *Tentative RILEM recommendation.* Prepared on behalf of RILEM Committee 4 CDC. Materiaux et Constructions 1977 no 58, pp. 217–229.

Lahdensivu, J., Tietäväinen, H., Pirinen, P. 2011. Corrosion of reinforcement in existing concrete facades. In Peixoto de Freita, V., Corcacho, H., Lacasse, M. (editors) *Proceedings of 12th International conference on durability of building materials and components*. Porto, Portugal, pp. 1155–1162.

Mattila J. 1995. *Realkalisation of concrete by cement-based coatings*. Tampere, Tampere University of Technology, Structural Engineering. Licentiate's Thesis. 161 p. (In Finnish).

Page C.L. 1988. Basic Principles of Corrosion, In: Schiessl, P. (ed.), *Corrosion of Steel in Concrete*, London, Chapman and Hall, pp. 3–21.

Parrott L.J. 1987. *Review of carbonation in reinforced concrete*. Cement and Concrete Association. Wexham Springs. 42 p.

Pigeon, M., Pleau, R.1995. Durability of concrete in cold climates. Suffolk. E & FN Spon. 244 p.

Pentti, M., Mattila, J., Wahlman, J. 1998. *Repair of concrete facades and balconies. Part 1: Structures, degradation and condition investigation*. Tampere. Tampere University of Technology, Structural Engineering. Publication 87, 156 p. (In Finnish).

Richardson M. 1988. *Carbonation of reinforced concrete*. Dublin, CITIS. 203 p.

Tuutti K. 1982. *Corrosion of Steel in Concrete*. Stockholm. Swedish Cement and Concrete Research Institute. CBI Research 4:82, 304 p.

Vainio, T., Lehtinen, E., Nuuttila, H. 2005. *Building and renovation of facades*. Tampere. VTT 26 p. + app. 13 (In Finnish).

Concrete Solutions – Grantham, Mechtcherine & Schneck (eds)
© *2012 Taylor & Francis Group, London, ISBN 978-0-415-61622-5*

Fabrication technology-related cracking of prestressed concrete elements

A.-T. Mircea

Faculty of Civil Engineering, Technical University of Cluj-Napoca, Romania

ABSTRACT: Unexpected cracking can be a significant problem for precast elements made of reinforced prestressed concrete. The paper refers to the investigations performed upon prestressed concrete roof elements affected by atypical cracking, with the aim of identifying their causes, and to recommend the necessary solutions. Being manufactured by a precast concrete factory, the typified roof units were made of concrete C35/45. After removing the formwork, some uncommon cracks at the soffit near the ends of numerous elements of 18.0 m span were observed. At the request of the producer, a research programme was initiated, with the following investigations: visual examination and geometrical measurements, on-site testing of one unit, as well as an analysis considering the conditions of Limit State Design, composition of concrete and fabrication technology.

1 INTRODUCTION

Over time, building methods involving precast and prestressed concrete elements have produced significant savings in materials, labour, and construction period. The steel forms used for precasting must be robust enough to hold alignment and shape, and have to be supported, anchored and braced in order to withstand vibration. They should also be clean, smooth, tight and leak-free. In addition, the procedures and techniques used by the construction team must ensure that the environmental conditions requested for the fresh concrete are maintained. This implies that high quality engineered casting of concrete needs to be completed at specialized production factories with a superior degree of control in manufacturing of a wide variety of structural and architectural concrete elements—which in turn are meant to be used extensively in commercial, industrial, and residential applications.

Concrete naturally shrinks as it cures, so cracking can be the result of one or a combination of factors, such as drying shrinkage, thermal contraction, external or internal restraint to shortening, subgrade settlement, and applied loads. However, unexpected cracking can be a significant problem for precast elements made of reinforced prestressed concrete. At the request of the producer of typified precast units, research was initiated in order to investigate some large span prestressed curved and ribbed concrete roof elements (Figure 1), suited for industrial halls, affected by atypical cracking, with

Figure 1. The investigated prestressed concrete roof element affected by atypical cracking.

the aim of identifying their causes, and to recommend the necessary solutions.

The major source of concern was that after removing the formwork some uncommon cracks at the soffit near the ends of numerous elements of 18.0 m span were observed (Figure 2), especially in conditions in which with similar elements but with smaller spans (of 12.0 and 15.0 m) the cracks were not present. It has to be mentioned that all these prefabricated units were made of concrete C35/45, cast in metal forms, handled and stored at a specialized precast concrete production factory.

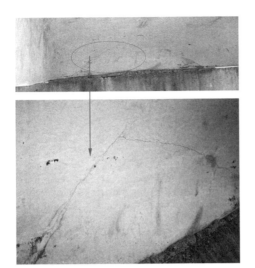

Figure 2. Uncommon cracks occurred at the soffit near the ends of the 18.0 m span roof units.

2 RESEARCH METHODOLOGY OVERVIEW

The investigations carried out enclosed visual examination and geometrical measurements, on-site testing of a precast element (the one considered to show the most cracks), as well as an analysis performed considering the conditions of Limit States Design, the composition of concrete, the fabrication technology and manufacturing circumstances.

2.1 Data relating to the precast roof elements

The investigated precast units are typified, they have constant width of 1.50 m, variable height section (between 30 cm at the extremities and 75 cm in field), and a total length of 17.65 m. The initial stress is induced by 8 prestressing tendons, every 4 in each rib.

Mix design is fundamental in order to ensure a good quality concrete. The composition of concrete C35/45 used for the examined precast elements consists of following ingredients: cement (600 kg/m³), water (240 kg/m³), fine sand 0–3 (515 kg/m³), coarse sand 3–7 (390 kg/m³), and gravel 7–16 (655 kg/m³).

The concrete roof elements were cast in self-supporting metal formworks, and after removing them, no dimensional irregularities were observed. According to the project, the precast units were transported in the storage area. Having a weight of 6554 daN, the on-site handling and transportation was made by lifting device (gantry crane).

2.2 Highlighted aspects

The visual investigation made at the deposit of precast units highlighted following aspects:

- Some of the elements showed cracks at both extremities, as illustrated in the pictures from Figure 2;
- The average opening of these cracks was 0.1 mm, and the maximum opening was 0.2 mm;
- Cracks occurred only between the ribs (except for one rib, at which the crack had penetrated 25% of the width of the rib);
- It was revealed that those roof elements were cast in hot weather, while the metal formwork was heated due to the direct action of the sun.

In agreement with the producer, it was decided to carry out a test upon the most affected element, in accordance with the testing methodology of precast elements in terms of behavior under static loads.

2.3 On-site testing of one unit

The test was performed in order to verify the production and the factory's technological conditions during the manufacturing process. It was carried out upon a unit indicated by the producer, taken from the current batch, considered to show the most cracks. The tested unit was loaded with calibrated weights made of concrete (Figure 3), placed by the lifting device.

As seen in Figure 4a, both ends of the precast unit were sustained (for a length of 9 cm) by cement mortar beds prepared on two concrete beams. Figure 4b presents the loading scheme and the equipment.

The loading and unloading stages were as follows:

- Service load, verification of long-term loading;
- Loading equivalent to a maximum crack width of 0.1 mm, at the level of the prestressed reinforcement, situated nearest to the tension fiber;

Figure 3. Behavior of the investigated prestressed concrete roof element under static loads.

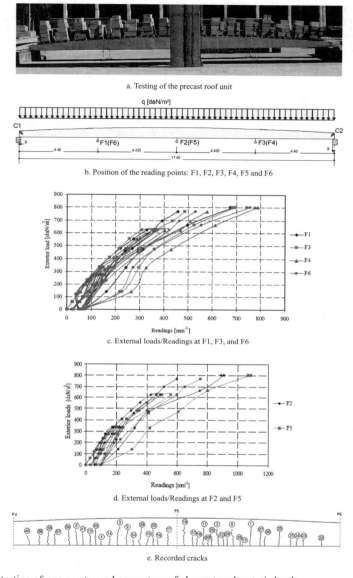

a. Testing of the precast roof unit

b. Position of the reading points: F1, F2, F3, F4, F5 and F6

c. External loads/Readings at F1, F3, and F6

d. External loads/Readings at F2 and F5

e. Recorded cracks

Figure 4.   On-site testing of one prestressed concrete roof element under static loads.

– Design load, corresponding to Ultimate Limit State;
– Overloading with 30% of the design load.

The measurement of displacements was done by equipment fitted on each rib at the midspan, at one third and at the ends. Readings (presented in Figures 4c and d) were made for each stage of loading and unloading by following the indications of the devices. The zero reading was set before loading the tested unit. Appearance and development of cracks was monitored at each stage of loading and unloading, at the level of the prestressed reinforcement, situated nearest to the tension fiber, on one lateral side. The normal cracks have appeared at the design loading of 625 daN/m^2, corresponding to the Ultimate Limit State. The maximum value of crack opening (0.02 mm) was recorded at a load of 805 daN/m^2.

A total number of 41 cracks were recorded (see Figure 4e). No inclined cracking was noticed, on the transmission length of the prestressed reinforcement no cracks were observed, and the atypical cracks detected at the soffit near the ends of the unit did not develop during the tests.

2.4 *Analysis of the fabrication technology*

The investigated cracks, observed after removing the formwork did not have a cleaving stress specific layout. The typified precast units' fabrication technology was kept to rule, the only deviation was recorded by pouring the fresh concrete during hot weather conditions into a metal formwork overheated due to the direct action of the sun, even if after that, excessive evaporation of the concrete mix was tried to be prevented by sealing with plastics foil.

In case of the analyzed units, the high cement content of 600 kg/m^3, w/c = 0.4, associated with uncontrolled temperatures can induce an excessive shrinkage and consequently the cracking of concrete:

- Plastic shrinkage: by pouring fresh concrete into the hot metal casing result a very rapid loss of moisture at the surface of plastic concrete caused by a combination of factors like relative humidity, concrete and environmental temperature. If moisture from the surface of fresh concrete evaporates faster than is replaced by bleed water, the surface of concrete reduces its volume. Thus, within the superficial layer appear cracks with variable length, width and spacing;
- Autogenous shrinkage: water is rapidly drawn into the hydration process and the demand for more water creates very fine capillaries, the surface tension within causes shrinkage which can lead to cracking. Conventional curing by sealing the surface to prevent evaporation is not enough and water curing is essential.

These excessive unit deformations have lead to a secondary stress state, objectified finally by local cracking of the precast units. The cracks have not been generated in the upper layer, situated in the field, being highly reinforced, and more deformable, but in the end zones which are more rigid, with restraint deformations, and lower reinforcement ratio at the soffit.

The preventive methods and measures used during the fabrication process of the precast elements must ensure that the environmental conditions for the fresh concrete (moisture and temperature) are maintained. At the same time additional protection may be needed in order to prevent degradation of fresh and immature concrete due to unfavorable weather conditions such as wind, precipitations and extreme temperatures. It is evidenced by specialized literature that cracking can occur when water is unable to raise to the surface of fresh concrete fast enough to replace that being evaporated,

therefore in hot weather conditions it is important to mix and place the concrete at or below the environmental air temperature.

3 CONCLUSIONS AND RECOMMENDATIONS

The investigation made upon the prestressed concrete roof elements has pointed out following:

The investigated elements satisfy both operational and safety requirements imposed by the legislation and other regulations in force. Crack covering with cement grout before final montage is necessary.

The cause of cracking was found to be plastic and autogenous shrinkage which occurred due to the fabrication technology (pouring of fresh concrete into an overheated steel formwork—the production took place during hot summer weather conditions), along with a low reinforcement ratio at the end zones.

Recommendations to prevent these problems were:

- To protect the casing from direct action of the sun;
- To replace the rebars Ø 3/150 with Ø 4/150 in the end zones of this type of precast elements.

ACKNOWLEDGEMENT

The whole team involved in this research, M. Filip, C. Mircea, and G. Petrovay are greatly acknowledged and appreciated for their contributions.

REFERENCES

C 181-1988: Testing methodology of prototypes and zero series for precast units in terms of behavior under static loads. INCERC 1988, B.C. nr. 11/1987.
Cemex Literature, 2009. Using concrete in hot weather, www. cemex.co.uk/ concrete.
Eurocode 2: Design of Concrete Structures, part. 1 General rules and rules for buildings.
Mircea A.T. 2009. The importance of every detail: Performance analysis of a concrete pavement; *International Conference on Concrete Repair: Concrete Solutions 2009*, Venice-Padova, Italy; CRC Press/ Balkema, Taylor & Francis Group London, UK.
Mircea A.T., Filip M., Mircea C. & Petrovay G. 2005. On-site testing of a precast roof element; *Precast concrete structures—Present and perspectives*, Cluj-Napoca, Romania.
Mircea C., Filip M., Mircea A.T. & Petrovay G. 2005. Research upon a cracking stage of precast roof units; *Precast concrete structures—Present and perspectives*, Cluj-Napoca, Romania.

Concrete Solutions – Grantham, Mechtcherine & Schneck (eds)
© 2012 Taylor & Francis Group, London, ISBN 978-0-415-61622-5

Proposal for the retrofit of the world heritage site of Arge Bam after earthquake damage

J. Motamed & A.M. Alani
University of Greenwich, Chatham Maritime, Kent, UK

ABSTRACT: An earthquake of magnitude 6.5 on the Richter scale, with a maximum intensity value of 9 EMS on 26 December 2003, resulted in almost complete destruction of the ancient town of Bam, Iran, and the surrounding area of Baravat, approximately 800 km south-east of Tehran. Out of a population of 180,000 the official government report on 29 December 2004 announced a loss of more than 30,000 lives with 50,000 injuries. Damage beyond repair was caused to about 18,000 homes and hundreds of businesses. The historical monument of Arge Bam, parts of which date back 2000 years, was severely damaged.

The construction of Arge Bam was based on a traditional method known in the region as chineh, a layer technique, and spread to Arabia and Africa. The materials used were comprised of a mixture of stone, aggregates, clay, lime and pozzolan layered with sun dried blocks of mud clay (khesht).

This paper focuses on the investigation work carried out within the context of proposing a sympathetic restoration method for the historic fabric of Arge Bam (a world heritage site). The proposed method considers the seismic strengthening of the remaining structure with the least possible change within the context of long term maintenance of this historic site.

1 OBJECTIVES

This paper investigates and proposes a sympathetic restoration method for an acceptable seismic strengthening approach with the least possible alteration to the remaining original structure and the historic fabric of Arge Bam.

2 BACKGROUND

The earthquakes recorded during the last 25 years are: 250 km southeast of Bam on 22 February 2005 of magnitude 6.4 Mw with a loss of 600 lives and 125 km southeast of Bam on 11 June and July 28, 1981 of magnitudes 6.6 and 7.3 Mw with a loss of 4500 lives.

The historic monument of Arge Bam which is around 220,000 m², includes 25 distinct monuments, comprising residential, social, educational and commercial buildings, a military camp, mosques, bazaar, school, prison, sports centre, ice house, and the governor's section and is surrounded by 2,000 m of walls, Figure 1.

The height of the walls and towers in the Citadel varies from 6 to 18 m, with the base width ranging

Figure 1. The picture on the left was taken two months before the earthquake of 26 December 2003 (left). The main building of Citadel after 26/12/03 (right).

from 2 to 6 m. Outside and along the walls, there are defensive trenches of 1.4 m. Arge Bam was inhabited until around 1910 when it was used as a Ghajar military camp and is listed as a world heritage site by UNESCO.

The oldest part of the Citadel was built on rock and later areas were built on surrounding lower soft alluvial soil.

Each layer of the chineh is defined and enveloped by a continuous render coat that is taken up and over it (Walls 2003). The height of 40 cm relates to the length of a builder's arm when kneeling on top of a wall and reaching down the sides to apply the render coat. The layers are staggered and are usually about 5 m long. The advantage of the technique is that it does not need scaffolding.

The horizontal joints between the layers are smooth to allow some relative movement between layers horizontally, also dispersing the vertical cracks from earthquakes, settlements and shrinkage through vertical joints at 5 m spacing. This dispersion absorbs the energy from earthquakes, therefore decreasing the damage on the structure.

Each layer of chineh was allowed to dry for a week to complete its shrinkage cycle before placing the above layer. A few courses of khesht were also laid in between every successive, five or so layers. A number of walls or abutments of khesht supported roofs made of domes or arches.

3 DAMAGE FROM EARTHQUAKE

The soil in the lower part of the hill was silt, therefore the monuments located in the southern part of the site, such as the main entrance were more vulnerable to the seismic forces, Figure 2.

The main entrance was coated with heavy clay and lime gypsum render restricting movement joints in the chineh. This rigidity of the rendering resulted in severe compression and external buckling of the earthen walls, Figure 2. In a number of cases the surface rendering separated from the ancient wall in large chunks.

In previous restorations of the Ice House, a stepped dome was built on the existing walls after 1974. The aerial photographs for The National Geographic Magazine in 1974 show that the dome was not reconstructed at the time of that aerial survey (Langenbach 2004). This additional loading may have resulted in increasing the damage to the inner part of the internal wall as well as initiating vertical structural cracks near its entrance, Figure 3.

The layered earth walls were weakened by the presence of termite infestation which also caused hollow narrow tunnels which undermined the strength of the palm tree trunk roof joists. In later restoration, mud clay straw surface render was applied to a number of monuments which also attracted a larger population of termites.

Extensions in later periods during the expansion of the Citadel, and restorations in the second half of the 20th century with little architectural and engineering input were the reason behind the scale of destruction of Arge Bam during the earthquake of 2003, Figures 2 & 3.

4 CONSERVATION CHARTERS

Most international Conservation Charters for cultural heritage strongly recommend minimal structural intervention to preserve the original fabric of the monument while accepting the need to provide long term structural integrity to provide a safe site.

The Venice Charter (1964) is the cornerstone for the conservation intervention of historical

Figure 2. Main chineh entrance to Arge Bam located on the south side of the compound has been restored (left) with mud straw render restricting layered movement joints.

Figure 3.   The Ice House with the reconstructed dome before (left) and after 26/12/03 (right).

monuments, but nevertheless has some ambiguities and contradictions in its statements regarding the future structural safety of monuments.

The Burra Charter (1999) categorized the concepts of preservation, restoration, and reconstruction as follows:

Preservation is to maintain the historic fabric in its actual state while controlling its decay. Any seismic retrofit work should be carried out with the least possible irrevocable alteration to the historic structural system.

Restoration is to return the historic fabric to its previous state without introducing new materials.

Reconstruction is to return a place as much as possible to its previous known stage and its main difference with the above two is the inclusion of new and ancient materials in the historical fabric. Reconstruction is appropriate when a part of the structure is incomplete due to damage and/or modifications and where, through this method, it recovers the cultural value of the monument. It outlines that this may be limited to a place and does not have to constitute the major part of the fabric. This should be restricted to the reproduction of physical or documental evidence and must only be differentiated from the original when closely inspected (Daniel et al., 2006).

5   CONSTRUCTION MATERIAL

The potential benefits of lime mortar in construction are well-known in the field of building conservation technology but have not been adequately explored in terms of its effects on seismic performance (Hami 1967).

Lime, clay and pozzolan mortar mix has successfully been used in Iran for making unfired bricks as well as for mortar bedding over the past two thousand years. Masonry bedded in mortar with low cohesion contributes to a type of "ductile" behaviour.

In Kashmir, a system of interlocking horizontal timber runner beams was used, without vertical wood columns, to hold the rubble, masonry and soft mud mortar buildings together on the silty soil. Historical reports confirm that these buildings withstood earthquakes better than the nearby unreinforced brick palace and government buildings (Langenbach 2004).

It is worth considering Kashmiri experience, which may prove to be an appropriate concept for walls subjected to earthquake forces. In Kashmir, the weak mortar used, combined with the overall flexibility of the building structure and restraint provided by the tie timber beams, may prove to be more resistant to catastrophic fracture and collapse by allowing the cracks to be distributed throughout the wall.

The flexibility and internal damping of the layered and khesht walls can also serve to change the building's response, reducing the out-of-plane forces in the walls while the timber acts to keep the weaker layered units in place when the wall deforms. Use of fired clay brick should be prohibited in the reconstruction of Arge Bam.

Alternative fibre polymer reinforcement may be investigated as a replacement to the traditional use of straw which attracts termites. Termites, found in warm climates, feed on the straw and to a lesser extent on the roof joists, although the needles on the surface of the trunk of palm trees slows their infestation.

6   RESEARCH

The objectives of the research are to establish a sound basis for the preservation of historic layered and unfired brick masonry. The research project would consider

- Providing safe access to each monument with minimal interruption to the existing debris and remaining structure, and method statements and a detailed plan of intervention for each monument.
- Temporary supports, shoring, needling and propping of the remaining structure.
- Management and use of the debris produced by the earthquake at each monument.
- The study of the effects of mortars of varying strength and constituents and the post-elastic in-plane strength and behaviour of layered walls.
- Data collection of the archaeologically important aspect of Arge Bam (material properties, architectural configurations, building technologies,) to determine the original structural configuration.
- Investigation of the seismic behaviour of earthen structures using finite element models including the model stiffness under static and dynamic loading, and the softening and destabilising effect of loads on the earthen walls.
- An overall study of stiffness of the earthen walls.

7 CODES OF PRACTICE

There are disagreements between the historic preservation documents which recommend using the weakest and most lime-rich ASTM formula (K) 1 unit cement to 2.25–4 units lime for restoration work in the Uniform Building Code (ASTM 2006), which prohibits the use of mortar weaker than the three strongest categories, known as ASTM types M, S & N: 1 unit cement to 0.25–1.25 units lime for any mortar used in structural masonry which includes most historic masonry walls (Langenbach 2004).

The Iranian Seismic Code IS2800 generally excludes the use of lime mortar and earth walls. The use of hydraulic lime mortar as well as the use of earth structures which have in certain cases demonstrated durability comparable to cement block walls, needs to be investigated (Hami 1967 & Hydraulic Lime Mortar 2003).

While the Codes are developments based on the performance of the wall under load at its design strength at the construction stage, the preservation documents aim at maximizing the long-term durability of walls with relatively weaker material in responding to the environment. It is worth comparing the long-term performance of ancient masonry and modern masonry to understand the benefit of the softer, high lime mortars.

IS2800 does not cover the behaviour of masonry when it is cracking and yielding in an earthquake. The code is for present-day construction such as steel and reinforced concrete and is based on linear elastic calculations using reduced forces to approximate post-elastic actual behaviour, but designers often give very low values to masonry because of its lack of material ductility. However, as a system, there is substantial remaining capacity in a wall which has begun to crack before it becomes unstable.

The adoption of IS2800 for Building Conservation to allow improvements to existing historical buildings requires a thorough investigation covering the specific needs of historical buildings in relation to the varying period, region and design of the historical building. This development of the code would minimize disagreements over what future strengthening would be necessary for historic buildings.

8 CONCLUSIONS

Understanding both the behaviour of layered (chineh) and unfired brick (khesht) construction can guide us towards those methods which are least destructive for the original fabric. Some of these methods may even be more effective over the long-term, not only because they build on what already exists, but also because they are developed from local social and economical conditions and have been tested by the previous earthquakes.

The objective of historic preservation is to preserve continuity within the slow evolution of building traditions while providing the most effective lasting resistance to movement over time, the gradual settlement of the foundations, the slow erosion of the lime, as well as against future earthquakes.

Local seismic faults are now active and regular earthquakes are reoccurring in this region. The seismic strengthening should also provide safety for the large number of visitors to the monument.

An Italian team of conservationists from the Universities of "Politecnico" of Milan, Parma, Florence and Padua who appreciate the importance of maintaining the historic fabric were approached by the management of the Bam site to develop a project for repair and restoration of a typical building (Mirza Na'him). Meanwhile, this group has been adopting techniques which could provide solutions to more general reconstruction of the whole area of the Bam Citadel (Binda et al., 2006).

Reconstruction of monuments such as Arge Bam may take many years and consume a substantial budget.

REFERENCES

ASTM Standards in Building Codes, 43rd edition, June 2006.

Binda, L., Condoleo, P., Licciardi Marino, L.G. Modena, C. & Petrini, V. 2007. Report on the Intervention to Bam (Iran). www.webjournal.unior.it/Dati/19/75/web%20journal%203,%20news%202.pdf Accessed 6th July 2011.

Daniel, T. & Neumann, J.V. 2006. Structural engineering issues for the reconstruction and restoration of Bam. Pontificia Universidad Católica del Perú. Proceedings of the Getty Seismic Adobe Project 2006 Colloquium.

Hami, A. 1967. Investigation of Material Property of Sarouj and Shefteh Ahak (lime mortar). University of Tehran, Farsi Publication.

Hydraulic Lime Mortar, 2003. Published by Donhead.

Langenbach, R. 2004. Soil Dynamics and the Earthquake Destruction of Earthen Architecture of the Arge Bam. JSEE, Special Issue on Bam Earthquake,.

Motamed, J. 2004. The Bam earthquake of 26 December 2003, Iran'. Earthquake Engineering Field Investigations (EEFIT), Institution of Structural Engineers. http://www.istructe.org/EEFIT/files/Bam.pdf Accessed 6th July 2011.

Standard No, 2800. Iranian Code f Practice for Seismic Resistant Design of Building, Building and Housing Research Centre, Iran (2007).

The Burra Charter 1999. The Australia ICOMOS Charter for Places of Cultural Significance.

The Venice Charter 1964. International charter for the conservation and restoration of monuments and sites. ICOM and UNESCO.

Walls, A.G. 2003. Arabian Mud Brick Technology: Some thoughts after the Bam Earthquake. (available from the authors of this paper).

Concrete Solutions – Grantham, Mechtcherine & Schneck (eds)
© 2012 Taylor & Francis Group, London, ISBN 978-0-415-61622-5

Corrosion damage of centrifuged reinforced concrete elements

I. Pepenar
ICECON GROUP—The Research Centre CERTINCON, Bucharest, Romania

ABSTRACT: The paper presents the results of research on the service behaviour of the centrifuged reinforced concrete elements in the external electric transformer stations of 100 kV and 220 kV, after 30–40 years of service in natural and industrial atmospheric environments, in respect of the damage generated by the corrosive action of aggressive agents. Investigation of the damage state of centrifuged reinforced concrete elements, on site and in the laboratory, showed that many of the examined elements presented damage due to corrosion and defects, occurring more or less extensively. This damage was in various stages of development and had a different influence on the resistance, stability and durability of the elements/structures. In order to assure normal service conditions of electric transformer stations there were proposed intervention measures to remedy existing damage and systematic monitoring of the service behaviour of reinforced concrete elements/structures.

1 INTRODUCTION

In Romania, connecting the units to the power system is generally through external electric transformer stations of 110 kV and 220 kV. These stations are mainly made of centrifuged hollow reinforced concrete elements (columns, beams and supports) with circular cross-section and various dimensions. The electric transformer stations are placed both in industrial platforms (power, chemical and other industries), as well as in all urban centres. Consequently, reinforced concrete elements are exposed to the aggressive action of natural and industrial atmospheric environments, containing a variety of aggressive agents, with different types and classes of aggressivity on the concrete and steel reinforcement. Following long-term service (30–40 years) in aggressive environments some damage occurred due to premature corrosion of centrifuged reinforced concrete inside some electric transformer stations. Factors that caused or partially caused these problems were: initial execution malfunctions, the absence of efficient initial corrosion protection measures, corresponding to type and classes of aggressivity of the environment and insufficient maintenance measures.

This paper presents the results of the research on the service behaviour of centrifuged reinforced concrete precast elements of electric transformer stations, damages caused by the action of aggressive agents and intervention measures proposed in order to assure the resistance, stability and durability of construction elements and the normal conditions of service of electric transformer stations.

2 SERVICE BEHAVIOUR OF ELEMENTS

2.1 Characteristics of reinforced concrete elements

The bearing structure for sustaining technological equipment in the electric transformer stations (flexible electrical conductors/cables, electrical equipments) is composed of reinforced concrete portal frames with different heights, consisting of precast columns and beams. Also, in the stations are disposed centrifuged reinforced concrete supports for sustaining the electrical equipment (Fig. 1).

The columns were elements with variable circular cross-section (truncated cones): the height-8.30 … 19.70 m; the external diameter-Ø 53 … 74 cm (base) and Ø 35 … 48 cm (top); the reinforcement-(10 … 22) Ø 20 … 25 mm steel bars (longitudinal) and Ø 3 mm steel wire spirals

Figure 1. Electric transformer station: general view.

(transversal); the thickness of wall section-7 ... 9 cm (base) and 5 ... 8 cm (top).

The beams were elements with constant circular cross-section: the length-8.00 m ... 16.20 m; the external diameter-Ø 30 ... 45 cm; the reinforcement-(12 ... 20) Ø 16 ... 22 mm steel bars (longitudinal) and Ø 3 mm steel wire spirals (transversal); the thickness of wall section-6 ... 7 cm.

The supports were elements with constant circular cross-section: the height-2.90 ... 6.50 m; the external diameter-Ø 25 ... 36 cm; the reinforcement-(8 ... 13) Ø 16 ... 22 mm steel bars (longitudinal) and Ø 3 mm steel wire (transversal); the thickness of wall section-5 ... 8 cm.

All the elements were designed and manufactured of concrete class C30/37.

The horizontal centrifuged reinforced concrete beams rested on columns of the portal frames. The joining column-beam was entirely welded, being made of metallic parts welded on rings columns, on which rested the ends of the beams (articulated joint type).

The precast centrifuged hollow reinforced concrete elements (columns, beams and supports) were made since the 1960's, according to a project-type developed by the Russian model.

2.2 *Aggressivity of environments*

The centrifuged reinforced concrete elements of electric transformer stations are located outdoors and therefore are exposed to:

- natural-urban atmospheric aggressive environments with low (XA 2b) and moderate (XA 3b) aggressivity classes;
- industrial atmospheric aggressive environments with moderate (XA 3b) and high (XA 4b) aggressivity classes, in accordance with specific technical regulations (CP 012-1 2007).

The main aggressive chemical agents present in the natural-urban and industrial atmosphere are:

- gaseous aggressive agents: sulphur dioxide, nitrogen oxides, ammonia, chlorine, etc.
- liquid or vapour aggressive agents: acids, chlorides, sulphates, etc.
- solid aggressive agents: powders, aerosols, dust, ash, etc.

In addition to the corrosive action generated by aggressive chemicals present in the atmosphere, overlaps the destructive action of the climatic factors, especially the wetting-drying and freezing-thawing repeated phenomena.

2.3 *Damages by corrosion*

To evaluate the damage state of reinforced concrete elements (columns, beams), which form the portal frame structures and supports, on site and laboratory tests using specific investigation techniques were performed (Pepenar 1999).

Investigation of the damage state of reinforced concrete elements, showed that the majority of examined elements presented damage due to corrosion and defects, occurring to various extents. This damage was in various stages of development and had a different influence on durability and safety in service of the construction elements.

The results of investigation on site were registered in the form of surveys of damage/defects and pictures, and are concisely presented as follows:

- cracking, delamination and spalling of concrete cover, with uncovering of longitudinal and transversal steel reinforcements, remaining in contact with aggressive atmospheric agents (Fig. 2);
- advanced corrosion of longitudinal and transversal steel reinforcements, both in the areas along joints formwork components used in the manufacture of precast elements ("stripes"), as well as in the rest of circumference of the elements, having the effect of reducing their diameter and in the case of transversal reinforcement (steel wire spiral), even in disappearance, in some areas, due to corrosion (Fig. 3);
- cracks in concrete cover, with variable lengths and widths, caused mainly by corrosion of steel (Fig. 4);
- segregations and voids in concrete, in some areas, especially along the areas of "stripes" (Fig. 5);
- damage of column-beam joints: corrosion of metallic joints, spalling of concrete and uncovering of reinforcement in the end areas of beams (Fig. 6).

The results of the laboratory tests performed on a large number of concrete samples extracted from the centrifuged reinforced concrete elements of electric transformer stations investigated, showed the following:

a. For the elements exposed in natural-urban atmospheric environments:
- the pH of the aqueous suspension of the samples varied between 10.0 and 11.5, values that indicate a partial removal of alkalinity of the concrete cover;
- the water soluble chloride ion concentration in the concrete samples ranged between 0.007% and 0.11% Cl^- (by weight of concrete); higher values of Cl^- ion concentration may have induced corrosion of steel;
- the water soluble sulphate ion concentration in the concrete samples ranged between 0.005% and 0.19% SO_4^{-2} (by weight of concrete). These values are normal for concrete;

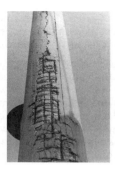

Figure 2. Column: cracking, delamination and spalling of concrete cover, uncovering of steel reinforcement.

Figure 3. Column: advanced corrosion of steel, reduction of diameter and fracture of steel wire spirals, in some areas, due to corrosion.

Figure 4. Beam: longitudinal crack in concrete cover induced by corrosion of reinforcement steel.

b. For the elements exposed in industrial atmospheric environments:
  • the pH of the aqueous suspension of the samples varied between 6.5 and 10.5, values that indicate a total or partial removal of alkalinity of the concrete cover under the action of atmospheric aggressive agents with acid character;
  • the water soluble chloride ion concentration in the concrete samples ranged between 0.014% and 0.42% Cl^- (by weight of concrete); higher values of Cl^- ion concentration would certainly have induced corrosion of steel;

Figure 5. Columns: segregation and voids/holes in concrete, especially along the "stripes" of elements, corrosion of reinforcement, fracture of steel wire spirals.

(a)   (b)

Figure 6. Columns, beams: damage of column-beam joints: corrosion of metallic joints (a), damage of concrete and uncovering of reinforcing steel in the end areas of beam (b).

  • the water soluble sulphate ion concentration in the concrete samples ranged between 0.019% and 0.98% SO_4^{-2} (by weight of concrete); higher values of SO_4^{-2} ion concentration may have induced sulphate corrosion of concrete and corrosion of steel.

The results of studies on the effects of corrosion on mechanical behaviour of concrete elements centrifuged showed a reduction of up to 20% of projected bearing capacity of elements.

2.4 *Causes of damage*

The observed damage was due to different causes, with direct or indirect action. Often complex factors contribute to the appearance and development of damage processes. Mainly, damage was due to the actions of physical, chemical and electrochemical processes of aggressive agents on concrete and steel reinforcement.

The nature and rate of corrosion processes of the centrifuged reinforced concrete elements depends on many factors, among which can be mentioned: the degree of contamination of the atmosphere with gaseous, liquid/vapour and solid aggressive agents (sulfur dioxide, chlorine, sulphates, chlorides, etc.), relative humidity and air temperature, frequency and duration of rain, and wind velocity, wetting-drying and freeze-thawing repeated phenomena, etc.

The corrosion-induced damage of the reinforced concrete elements had been favoured and accentuated by the existence of initial execution defects (segregation and voids in concrete, especially along the areas of "stripes", non-uniformity of thickness of concrete cover on the circumference of elements, cracks in the concrete cover, etc.), some mechanical damage probably appeared during the storage, transport or montage of the elements and the absence of efficient intervention measures (repair, corrosion protection) of these elements.

3 INTERVENTION MEASURES

Taking under consideration the advanced corrosion damage state of some structural elements of the electric transformer stations, the accelerated evolution of corrosion processes once initiated (which affects the resistance, the stability and the durability of the investigated elements/structures) intervention measures were proposed, regarding the repair, strengthening or replacement of the damaged elements.

The proposed intervention measures were applied differently, depending on the nature and degree of the damage of the elements/structures and the possibility of interruption of electricity to the station.

The intervention measures consisted of:

- repair of local damage and defects and corrosion protection by protective paint systems of the centrifuged reinforced concrete elements, in accordance with specific technical regulations (C 170 1987);
- strengthening of strongly damaged elements by jacketing with reinforced concrete and corrosion protection by protective paint systems of the concrete jacket, in accordance with specific technical regulations (C 170 1987);
- replacement of strongly damaged elements with new elements: galvanized steel elements, corrosion protection by protective paint systems, in accordance with specific technical regulations (GP 111 2005); centrifuged elements with polymeric composite reinforcement (Taranu et al., 2009);
- replacement of current bearing structure for the support of technological equipment with another structure, similar but designed according to environmental conditions;

- replacement of external transformer station type with an internal station type, in the case of modernization of existing power units.

In the case of existing electrical transformer stations, along with the intervention measures aimed at the replacement/rehabilitation of elements damaged by corrosion (repair, strengthening, corrosion protection), there are proposed actions aiming maintenance measures that were recommended as a result of the monitoring of the service behaviour of reinforced concrete elements/structures.

4 CONCLUSIONS

The results of the research on the service behaviour of the precast centrifuged reinforced concrete elements for the support of electrical equipment in the electric transformer stations of 110 and 220 kV, after 30–40 years of service in aggressive environments, revealed the existence of advanced corrosion-induced damage, which could affect the resistance, stability and durability of the structures.

Damage due to corrosion had been favoured or accentuated by the existence of initial defects of execution of the precast reinforced concrete elements, mechanical damage that appeared during the storage, transport or montage of the elements and the absence of efficient intervention measures (repair, corrosion protection) of these elements.

In order to assure normal service conditions of these electric transformer stations intervention measures to remedy existing damages and systematic monitoring of the service behaviour of reinforced concrete elements/structures was required.

REFERENCES

C 170 1987. Instructiuni tehnice pentru protectia elementelor din beton armat si beton precomprimat supraterane in medii agresive naturale si industriale, C170-87. *Buletinul Constructiilor* 6: 58–103. Bucharest: INCERC.

CP 012-1 2007. Cod de practica pentru producerea betonului. *ASRO*: 1–92. Bucharest: ASRO.

GP 111 2005. Ghid de proiectare privind protectia impotriva coroziunii a constructiilor din otel, GP 111-04, *Buletinul Constructiilor* 8–9: 479–570. Bucharest: INCERC.

Pepenar, I. 1999. In M.A. Lacasse & D.J. Vanier (eds), Investigation and diagnosis of concrete structures in aggressive environments, *Durability of Building Materials and Components 8; Proc. intern. conf., Vancouver, May 30—June 3 1999.* Ottawa: NRC-IRC.

Taranu, N., Oprisan, G., Budescu, M. & Gosav, I. 2009. Hollow Concrete Poles with Polymeric Composite Reinforcement. *Journal of Applied Sciences* 9(14): 2584–2591.

Concrete Solutions – Grantham, Mechtcherine & Schneck (eds)
© 2012 Taylor & Francis Group, London, ISBN 978-0-415-61622-5

Investigation of a repair system in a concrete jetty in the Persian Gulf

R. Rashetnia & A. Dousti
Construction Materials Institute, University of Tehran, Tehran, Iran

F. Moradi-Marani
PHD student of L'Université de Sherbrooke, Quebec, Sherbrooke

M. Shekarchi
Construction Materials Institute, University of Tehran, Iran

ABSTRACT: The Persian Gulf region is known to be one of the most aggressive environments for reinforced concrete constructions. Chloride induced corrosion is believed to be the main reason for premature deterioration and sometimes failure, of reinforced concrete structures constructed in this region. Due to these environmental problems, repair is a significant resort. The durability of a concrete repair can depend on many factors. In fact, failure of a concrete repair material is more likely to occur due to incompatibility between the repair and concrete or high shrinkage levels. Either of these factors can lead to cracking and debonding. This in turn allows chloride and carbon dioxide to penetrate again. The purpose of this study is the diagnostic investigation of a repair system related to a reinforced concrete jetty. No sign of steel corrosion appeared on the repaired areas; but shrinkage cracking and incipient corrosion around the repaired areas were indications of dimensional and electrochemical incompatibility between repair concrete and substrate. The repair strategy was re-evaluated by the repair index method (RIM) proposed by Andrade and Izquierdo. The results showed that the patching repair method was more suitable and feasible in comparison with other techniques.

1 INTRODUCTION

The Persian Gulf region is known to be one of themost aggressive environments for reinforced concrete constructions. Chloride induced corrosion is believed to be the main reason for premature deterioration, and sometimes failure, of reinforced concrete structures constructed in this region (Guettala A, Abibesi A, 2006) (Marseguerra M, Zio E, 2000) (Al-Bahar S, Attiogbe E M, Kamal H, 1998). The harsh climate of the Persian Gulf region can be described as having high temperatures, high evaporation rates and consequently high salinity of water, which increases chloride induced reinforcement corrosion rates (Cusson D, Qian S, Hoogeveen T, 2006) (Fookes P G, Simm J D, Barr Jm, 1989). Despite the fact that concrete is a reliable structural material with good durability performance, exposure to severe environments makes it vulnerable (Guettala A, Abibesi A, 2006). Therefore a regular schedule for maintenance and repair protocol is fundamentally important in controlling the safe and efficient operation of a structure (Marseguerra M, Zio E, 2000). Once a detailed investigation to determine the extent and cause of degradation has been conducted, corrosion damage assessment can lead to selection of effective repair schemes (Al-Bahar S, Attiogbe E M, Kamal H, 1998). Regular inspections after repair work are necessary to ensure the satisfactory performance of repair systems. In addition, field investigations of repaired concrete structures are necessary to develop guidelines for adequate selection of concrete repair systems, improved repair procedures, extended durability of rehabilitated structures, and evaluation of discrepancies between laboratory results and field performance (Cusson D, Qian S, Hoogeveen T, 2006). This paper presents a case study where a concrete jetty structure is exposed to the severe marine environment of Persian Gulf. The structure showed early age corrosion of reinforcing bars and prestressing tendons. The principal causes of this accelerated deterioration are highlighted and analyzed. In consideration to the properties of the substrate concrete, a patch repair system was used for extending the service life. A second condition assessment was conducted and the performance of the repair work after seven years in service was measured. It was concluded that one of the main reasons for the continued deterioration which resulted was incompatibility between the repair concrete and substrate.

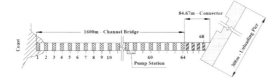

Figure 1. The structural layout of the jetty.

2 JETTY STRUCTURE

The jetty is located on the northern coast of the Persian Gulf, north of the Strait of Hormuz, near the port of Bandar-Abbas. This structure is located in a region classified as hot and wet according to climatic classifications of Fookes et al. (Fookes P G, Simm J D, Barr Jm, 1989). The structural layout is shown in Fig. 1 and consists of two main parts of Unloading Pier and Channel Bridge. The unloading pier is made from cast-in-place reinforced concrete cross girders along with a steel-concrete composite deck, and the channel bridge consists of a 64-span-bridge with length of 1600 m which connects the Unloading Pier and the coast. Every span is composed of three prestressed box girders and two steel cross girder-pile systems.

The concrete elements were designed for a nominal compressive strength of 40 MPa. The strength of the concrete was tested using a non-destructive Schmidt hammer. The measured strength ranged from 48.5 ± 6.5 to 65.0 ± 5.0 MPa, reflecting good compressive strength. According to ACI 350-01[10], corrosion protection of reinforced concrete exposed to seawater, requires a minimum compressive strength of 34.5 Mpa.

3 CAUSES OF DEGRADATION

A few years after construction, the first degradation in the RC elements was reported. Investigations showed evidence of rust staining and, minor cracking to spalling, and delamination of concrete cover due to chloride-induced steel corrosion. In the splash and spray condition zones, severe degradation was observed in both prestressing tendons and reinforcing bars of the box girders. In steel anchorage points and box girder-bearings, stress concentration was impressively responsible for intensified micro cracks at these regions. These micro cracks were a direct reason for ingress of chloride and other aggressive ions into the concrete. In some elements of the prestressed box-girders which were buried in coast regions, significant corrosion effects were observed. Due to high evaporation rates, chloride ions from spray or splash of seawater have a concentration of 21.6 gr/dm^3 (Table 1) and present a significant source of marine salts

Table 1. Chemical analyses of the Gulf and potable water of Bandar-Abbas.

Components (g/lit)	The Gulf water			Potable water
	Sample 1	Sample 2	Sample 2	
Cl$^-$	21.30	21.55	21.16	0.16
SO$_4{}^{2-}$	3.09	3.54	2.96	0.04
Na$^+$	12.13	11.49	11.87	0.04
K$^+$	0.41	0.40	0.41	Negligible
Ca^{2+}	0.80	0.75	0.80	0.003
Mg^{2+}	1.34	1.34	1.49	0.002
pH	7.96	8.12	8.03	8.05

in the atmosphere (Novokshchenov V, 1995). The specified depth of concrete cover was 40 mm and even in some regions it was decreased to 20 mm which was inadequate to meet service-life criteria in the Persian Gulf region. The reason for this problem probably was caused by poor site practice or poor manufacture. There was a concentration of deterioration in the east part of the jetty structure significantly more than other parts. The reason was probably the dominant wind which caused more splashing. The chloride threshold for active corrosion of the reinforcing steel is not a unique value as it depends on several factors (Alonso C, Andrade C, Castellote M and Castro P, 2000). A negligible depth of carbonation was observed which led to the exclusion of carbonation as a contributing factor to the corrosion process. It worthy of mention that high humidity and salt crystallization on the surface of concrete elements in marine structures usually prevents CO2 diffusion and acts as a protection against carbonation (Castro P, sanjuan M A and Genesca J, 2000) (Al-Khaiat H and Haque M N, 1997) (Castroa P, Moreno E I and genesca J, 2000).

4 REPAIR METHOD

The durability of a concrete repair is dependent on many factors. In fact, failure of a concrete repair material is more likely to occur due to incompatibility between the repair material and concrete or to high shrinkage levels. Moreover, other factors can lead to cracking and debonding, which allows chloride, carbon dioxide or detoriative agents penetrate. A patch repair method was selected for the repair of this structure. Table 2 shows the mix design of the repair material. All of the deteriorated concrete layers were removed, corrosion products were removed from the reinforcement bars and the reinforcement was exposed at least 2 cm beyond the cover. The corroded rebars were replaced with new ones and all reinforcement was

Table 2. Mix design for repair concrete.

Components	Weight (kg/m³)	Description
Cement	380	ASTM Type II
Silica-fume	35	–
Total water	187	–
Free water	158	–
W/C	0.380	–
Gravel (15 mm)	670	Absorption = 1.52% (SSD)
Sand	1123	Absorption = 2.10% (SSD)
Superplastisizer	6	Melcrit
Additive	1.80–2.25	Conbax
Total Weight	2375	–

Table 3. Loss of steel cross-section due to reinforcement corrosion.

Locations	Orginal diameter of bar, d (mm)	Mass of corroded bar, m_s (kg/m)	Average reduction in bar diameter, Δ_d (µm)	Cross-section area loss (%)
Channel bridge	8	0.247	1674	37.5
	8	0.312	891	21.0
	8	0.346	513	12.4
	8	0.277	1301	29.9
	10	0.316	2845	48.8
	10	0.279	3277	54.8
Unloading pier	16	1.029	3089	34.9
	16	0.869	4135	45.0
	16	1.258	1724	20.4
	16	1.130	2470	28.5
	16	1.338	1278	15.3

painted by a zinc-rich coating in the form of an anodic coat for corrosion protection. The depth of concrete cover was increased to 80 mm. This repair method was according to Raupach's classification (Raupach M, 2006), aimed at restoring passivity, and creating chemical conditions in which the reinforcement surface was returned to, or maintained at a passive condition while controlling anodic areas.

5 POST-REPAIR ASSESSMENT

The jetty was re-examined seven years after the repair was carried out. In this part of the study, the jetty structure condition is assessed. Steel corrosion had progressed in both reinforcing bars and prestressing tendons, ranging from negligible to very severe conditions. Average steel cross-section loss ranged from 12.4% to 54.8%, representing a significant corrosion state (Table 3).

The measured potentials by half-cell test method indicate active corrosion in some elements and incipient corrosion around repaired areas, the results are presented in Fig. 2. While no signs of damage were observed during the initial post repair period, the chloride concentration increased at the level of reinforcement after seven years in which active corrosion set off and cracks propagated in the concrete cover. Variations in chloride concentration were also studied during the seven-year post repair evaluation and results are presents in Fig. 3. According to Fig. 3, the chloride concentration at the depth corresponding to concrete cover of 40 mm, increased from 0.035% in 2000 to 0.091% by weight of concrete in 2007, well above the 0.070% estimated threshold value. Assuming a linear regression as a function of time, the chloride concentration at 40 mm, reached the threshold value within four years after the repair. Repaired surfaces did not perform as well as expected and cracks with various sizes in the repaired areas

as well as progressive corrosion in the boundary of substrate concrete and repaired areas were observed. Compatibility of the repair material with the existing substrate is an important aspect of the repair methodology. Stress is induced by processes such as volume change, stiffness mismatch, thermal coefficients of expansion is match, and electrochemical effects, etc. Emmons et al. (Emmons E H, Vaysburd A M and Mcdonald J E, 1993) defined compatibility as a balance of physical, chemical, and electrochemical properties and also dimensional changes between a repair material and the substrate concrete. Accordingly, repair materials should withstand induced stresses without distress and deterioration over the designated period of time. Early age cracking of repaired areas due to shrinkage or early age corrosion due to imbalanced electrochemical conditions between repaired and substrate concrete (electrochemical incompatibility) are two main types of incompatibility (Vaysburd A M and Emmons P H, 2000). The measured potentials by half-cell test method indicate active corrosion in some elements and incipient corrosion around repaired areas (Fig. 2). To locate ongoing corrosion, potential gradients between active and passive areas were used (Elsener B 2001). These gradients indicated electrochemical incompatibility between repair concrete and substrate in early ages. Fig. 2 shows that the potential difference between the patch repair and substrate was around −50 mV for undamaged areas, while for incipient anodes or susceptible areas it was at least −100 mV. In situ half-cell potential methods depends mainly on the moisture level, which may result in erroneous results (Ann K Y and song H, 2007). Results may not necessarily be associated with a high or low probability of steel corrosion. Potential values for

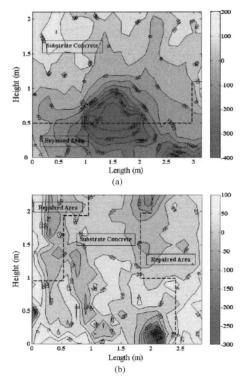

Figure 2. (a) & (b) The measured potentials by half-cell test.

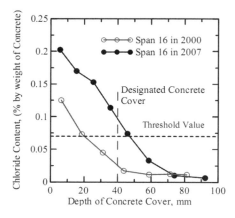

Figure 3. Chloride ion profile.

concrete elements in splash and atmospheric zones with normal moisture level are most likely close to real corrosion conditions. Half-cell potential mapping in Fig. 2 shows a range of potential values from +200 mV to −400 mV, with a clear delineation of anodic and cathodic areas. Boundary areas between repaired surfaces and substrate concrete are susceptible to corrosion with more negative and imbalanced potential, whereas cathodic areas show positive and balanced potential. In addition to half-cell potential maps which confirm activation of incipient corrosion in the boundary areas, the chloride profile of the substrate concrete in the boundary areas showed high concentrations at the level of the reinforcement. Fig. 8 shows variations in the chloride content of a repaired area, the substrate concrete, and a boundary area in a repaired section similar to that presented in Fig. 7. Formation of parallel cracks at 40–60 cm spacing was observed which was attributed to dimensional incompatibility between the old and repair materials. Crack widths varied from hairline sized to nearly 1 mm depending on their location and order of formation. It is possible that the use of a mortar mixture with silica-fume in the repair material could have intensified shrinkage cracking. The early age and long-term deformation properties of repair concrete and mortar have been studied considering the effect of maximum size of aggregate and using silica-fume (Momayez A, Ehsani M R, Rajaie H and Ramezanianpour A, 2005) (Browon M D, smith C A, Sellers J G, Folliard K J and Breen J E, 2007). While the use of silica fume enhances the transport properties of the repair material, it may adversely cause mismatch of shrinkage, stiffness, and strength.

6 EVALUATION OF REPAIR STRATEGY

The Repair Index method (RIM) is based on a predominantly economical criterion and it is an approach for selecting a repair system. The repair strategy was evaluated using the RIM due to the incompatibility of the repair system with the base material (Andrade C and Izquierdo D, 2005). Patch repair and cathodic protection as two common options were compared by the RIM method. This method is based on defining a set of safety, serviceability, environmental impact, durability, and economy requirements. Table 4 describes the proposed ranking for the set of requirements with durability and economy among the areas of highest importance in this type of structure.

The structure was classified by levels of importance into its components and was ranked according to a range of 1 through 4 weight criteria proposed by Andrade and Izquierdo (Andrade C and Izquierdo D, 2005). Table 5 shows the component ranking of the reinforcement corrosion repair. Ranking for the set of requirements (Table 4) can be varied depending on the priority criteria used by the owner, contractor, or the maintenance staff considering particular conditions, budgetary, and management constrains. The partial values assigned in Table 5 for this jetty structure are described as the following:

6.1 *Safety*

The consequences of structural failure are very important (rank 1). A ductile failure for both repair methods was used (rank 3). Execution controlling wise, quality control for both repair methods is important (rank 4). Feasibility of post-repair monitoring is one of the important factors. Cathodic protection is monitored with sensors (rank 4), while patching is monitored with visual observation (rank 2). In the other point of view, safety of workers is very important. Both cathodic

protection and patching present similar safety risks during concrete removal or cleaning of the bars (rank 3). Moreover cathodic protection needs instrumentation and monitoring of a permanent electrical current (rank 3) but patching has little or no risk for users after being applied (rank 4).

6.2 *Serviceability*

For cathodic protection, the structure is modified by the permanent application of electrical instruments (rank 1). The disturbance of the removal of damaged concrete is comparatively small for patching (rank 3). Fitness for use is one of the serviceability factors. Cathodic protection is not suitable for repairing small areas within a larger structure (rank 1), but patching is technically suitable for the problem studied (rank 4).

Table 4.   Proposed ranking of importance.

Requirement	Importance
Safety economy	10%
Serviceability	10%
Environmental impact	10%
Durability	35%
Economy	35%

6.3 *Environmental impact*

Emission of pollutants to the environment was assessed for each method. Cathodic protection releases no pollutants to the environment (rank 4). For patching, usually some organic or polymeric based materials are used (rank 2). (b) Sustainability

Table 5.   Requirements of the repaired structure classified by levels of importance.

Requirement	Repair performance index	Cathodic protection	Patching
Safety	a. Structural failure	Very severe 1	Very severe 1
	a. Failure type	Ductile 3	Ductile 3
	b. execution control	Guarantee 4	Guarantee 4
	c. Feasibility of post repair	Sensors 4	Visual 2
	d. Safety of workers	moderate 3	moderate 3
	e. Safety of users	moderate 3	High 4
	Average	3.0	2.8
Serviceability functionality	a. Disturbance	High 1	moderate 3
	b. Fitness for use	Very low 1	High 4
	Average	1.0	3.5
Environmental impacts	a. Emission pollutants	negligible 4	Low 2
	b. Sustainability	Low 2	Low 2
	Average	3.0	2.0
Durability	a. Service life (year)	>50	<15
	b. Number of types of attack	Two types 3	One type 4
	c. Exposure class	Splash 1	Splash 1
	Average	2.0	2.5
Economy	a. Direct cost/m² (dollar)	>200	100–200
	b. Extension of damage	<%20	<%20
	c. Period of disturbance (days)	7–15	1–7
	d. Maintenance coast (dollar)	>70	<30
	e. Preparation of substance	Low 3	High 1
	Average	1.6	2.2

wise, both cathodic protection and patching use a relatively high amount of materials and energy (rank 2).

6.4 *Durability*

Service life for cathodic protection is expected to perform longer than 50 years without needing replacement (rank 4). Given the prior experiences with patching materials in similar conditions in Iran, patching usually performs less than 15 years (rank 1). Corrosion and alkali silica reaction (Golam Ali M, 1993) usually affects cathodic protection (rank 3) but corrosion most likely impacts the performance of patching (rank 4). Damaged concrete elements are in the splash zone. A classification of rank 1 was assigned for this repair performance.

6.5 *Economy*

The economical factors depend very much on the local and regional conditions and the initial and long term costs of systems used. It is however expected that cathodic protection will be costlier than the patch technique both for initial and long term costs.

Finally the repair index (RI) was computed for the two repair methods by multiplying the average values for each requirement from Table 4 by the importance factor from Table 5, and presented as:

Cathodic protection:
$$RI = (3 \times 0.10) + (1 \times 0.10) + (3 \times 0.10) + (2 \times 0.35) + (1.6 \times 0.35) = 1.96 \quad (1)$$

Patching:
$$RI = (2.8 \times 0.10) + (2 \times 0.10) + (2.5 \times 0.10) + (3.5 \times 0.35) + (2.2 \times 0.35) = 2.73 \quad (2)$$

These values indicate that patching, with higher RI, is the most feasible and economical repair method for this structure as compared to cathodic protection. To decrease the opportunity for incipient corrosion, it was recommended that the repair size should not be restricted to visible cracking, spalling and delaminated areas. The adjacent areas were checked by hammer test and chloride profiles. If the results showed any sign of deterioration or a critical amount of chlorides, the deteriorated or contaminated concrete were removed by the patch repair work. To control dimensional incompatibility, it was recommended that silica-fume be eliminated from the mix design and replaced with slag blended cements and fibers to increase the concrete ductility. Moreover, a higher volume of coarse aggregate was recommended to reduce opportunity for restrained shrinkage cracking in repair system. Recent studies at CMI (CMI 8708304, 2007) showed that application of blended cement, with 25% slag, as well as polypropylene fibers, at least 1.0% weight of cementitious materials, significantly decreased the early age and long term deformations of concrete in comparison with the mix design in Table 2.

7 CONCLUSION

Dimensional and electrochemical incompatibility between the repair and substrate concrete led to further corrosion in repaired areas. Incipient anodes near to the boundary zone of repaired and unrepaired areas were the sign of electrochemical incompatibility and transversal cracks were the sign of dimensional incompatibility. These cracks were noticeable within a distance of 40–60 cm. Use of a high percentage of silica-fume and a high volume of fine aggregate in the repair concrete may have contributed to the cracking potential. Due to these incompatibilities, the Repair Index Method (RIM) was used to differentiate between the two methods. A detailed analysis of the data, according to Tables 4 and 5, by this method confirmed that it was not necessary to replace patch repair with another system but it required some modifications to decrease dimensional incompatibility and to postpone electrochemical incompatibility in form of incipient anodes.

REFERENCES

Al-Bahar, S., Attiogbe, E.M. & Kamal, H. 1998. Investigation of corrosion damage in reinforced concrete structure in Kuwait. *ACI Material Journal,* 95(3): 226–231.
Alonso, C., Andrade, C., Castellote, M. & Castro, P. 2000, Chloride threshold values to depassivate reinforcing bars embedded in a standardized OPC mortar. Cem Concr Res 30(7): 1047–1055.
Al-Khaiat, H., Haque, M.N. 1997, Carbonation of some coastal concrete structures in Kuwait. *ACI Material journal,* 94(6): 602–607.
Andrade, C., Izquierdo, D. 2005, Benchmarking through an algorithm of repair methods of rei forcement corrosion: the repair index method. *Cement & Concrete Composite.* 27(6): 727–733.
Ann, K.Y., Song, H. 2007, Chloride threshold level for corrosion of steel in concrete. *Corrosion Science.* 49(11): 4113–4133.
Brown, M.D., Smith, C.A., Sellers, J.G., Folliard, K.J. & Breen, J.E. 2007, Use of alternative materials to reduce shrinkage cracking in bridge decks. *ACI Material Journal* 104(6): 629–637.
Castroa, P., Sanjuan, M.A. & Genesca, J. 2000, Carbonation of concretes in the Mexican Gulf. *journal of building and environment,* 35(2): 145–149.
Castroa, P., Moreno, E.I. & Genesca, J. 2000, Influence of marine micro-climate on carbonation of reinforced concrete buildings. *Cement & Concrete Research,* 30(10): 565–1571.

Cusson, D., Qian, S. & Hoogeveen, T. 2006, Field performance of concrete repair systems on highway bridge. *ACI Material Journal*, 103(5): 366–373.

Elsener, B. 2001, Half-cell potential mapping to assess repair work on RC structures. *Construction & Building Materials*, 14(2–3): 133–139.

Emmons, E.H., Vaysburd, A.M. & McDonald, J.E. 1993, A rational approach to durable concrete repairs. *Concrete International*, 15(9): 40–45.

Fookes, P.G., Simm, J.D. & Barr, J.M. 1986, Marine concrete performance in different climatic environments. *Proceeding of international conference on concrete in the marine environment, The Concrete Society*, London, 1986.

Golam, A.M. 1993, Cathodic protection current accelerates the alkali-silica reaction. *ACI Material journal*, 90(3): 247–252.

Guettala, A. & Abibsi, A. 2006, Corrosion degradation and repair of a concrete bridge. *Material & Structures*, 39(4): 471–478.

Marseguerra, M. & Zio, E. 2000, Optimizing maintenance and repair policies via a combination of Genetic Algorithms and Monte Carlo simulation. Reliabil Eng Sys Saf 68(1): 69–83.

Momayez, A., Ehsani, M.R., Rajaie, H. & Ramezanianpour, A. 2005, Cylindrical specimen for measuring shrinkage in repaired concrete members. *Construction & Building Materials*, 19(2): 107–116.

Novokshchenov, V. 1995, Deterioration of reinforced concrete in the marine industrial environment of the Gulf- A case study. *Material & Structures*, 28(7): 392–400.

Raupach, M. 2006, Patch repairs on reinforced concrete structures—model investigations on the required size and practical consequences. *Cement & Concrete Composite*, 28(8): 679–684.

Vaysburd, A.M. & Emmons, P.H. 2000, How to make today's repairs durable for tomorrow—corrosion protection in concrete repair. *Construction & Building Materials*, 14(4): 189–197.

Concrete Solutions – Grantham, Mechtcherine & Schneck (eds)
© 2012 Taylor & Francis Group, London, ISBN 978-0-415-61622-5

Non-destructive diagnosis and repair of 300 concrete columns beneath a shopping mall under full operation

U. Schneck

CITec Concrete Improvement Technologies GmbH, Germany

ABSTRACT: Deicing salt had accumulated in groundwater bearing soil under the asphalt of an underground car park. With the steep moisture gradient between the soil and the elevated reinforced concrete columns, chloride could migrate into the columns and had concentrated on the concrete surface at values up to 6%, related to cement mass. Coincidentally, a significant number of columns showed spalling that was not caused by corrosion, but obviously because of load. After a thorough corrosion survey on 30 columns and identifying the corrosion mechanism, the other 90% of the car park could be tested non-destructively in an accelerated way and be evaluated according to patterns that allowed conclusions from potential and resistivity readings only on the chloride situation. Conventional repair was no durable solution because of the continued chloride migration from the soil and foundations. So a galvanic Cathodic Protection (CP) with discrete anodes was chosen as the main repair strategy. It was supported by a short-term chloride extraction (ECE) prior to installation in "heavy" cases to enhance the lifetime of the CP, which was proven with at least 28 years.

1 INTRODUCTION

An underground car park was situated underneath a multi-story shopping mall. It was open and half buried into ground level. 300 single founded columns with a diameter of $300 \times 60 \times 60$ cm were bearing the building in a grid of 8.40 m. They were pre-cast reinforced concrete elements, and their foundations were covered by an asphalt layer. The columns had no rebar connectivity to each other or to ceilings and beams they supported. The ground water level was up to some cm below the asphalt surface.

Spalling and delamination, which was observed on some columns, had been a patch repaired in 2003, and the splash zone of all columns had got a surface protection.

Continued spalling and delamination some years later caused a corrosion survey in several steps, which is described next. In some cases heavily corroded reinforcement was visible (see Fig. 2), and chloride values up to 6%, related to cement mass, were determined. As an additional information by the facility management, the stock of de-icing salt for the mall, that had been stored in a compartment within the car park, got dissolved during a flood and had penetrated into the asphalt and soil.

Figure 1. View into the underground car park.

Figure 2. Chloride induced corrosion after spalling of top concrete.

2 QUALIFIED CORROSION SURVEY

The client was convinced that a thorough diagnosis of the entire situation was needed in order to develop a durable maintenance and repair concept at a reasonable cost.

2.1 Approach

It was agreed to run an intensive condition survey first on 10% of the columns within an area of accumulated visible damage. The scope of measurements comprised the following data:

- rest potentials and surface resistivity in a grid of 30 × 15 cm and 24 sampling points per column (CITec Multi-Electrode see Fig. 3).
- minimum concrete cover per grid cell.
- chloride and concrete moisture profiles in at least 4 layers of 2 cm thickness each on data points of interest.
- surface rebound values.
- concrete damage (delamination, spalls).
- previously repaired areas.
- state of reinforcement.

With a complex evaluation of these data (Schneck 2005) efforts were made to find a general damage mechanism and a pattern of detection of the state of damage for each column by a simplified scope of measurement, that could be applied to the remaining number of columns and help to accelerate the condition survey.

2.2 Results of the initial measurements

A first finding was that the columns had no rebar connectivity to other concrete members. This made the interpretation of the potential mapping more difficult, because chloride induced corrosion activity and the interactions between anode and cathode were limited to relatively small (cathode) areas.

Furthermore, the following, general results were found:

- the concrete cover was on average quite high (50 mm) and did not deviate much.
- rest potentials ranged between –550 and 50 mV vs. CSE and were mostly negative close to the asphalt surface.
- layers with high chloride content (4 to 7%) were situated usually well above the reinforcement, but not all columns had such high chloride accumulation (see Fig. 4).
- the concrete moisture content was increasing from the surface to inner parts, were it got very high—up to 8%.

Figure 3. Multi-Electrode for simultaneous potential and resistivity measurement.

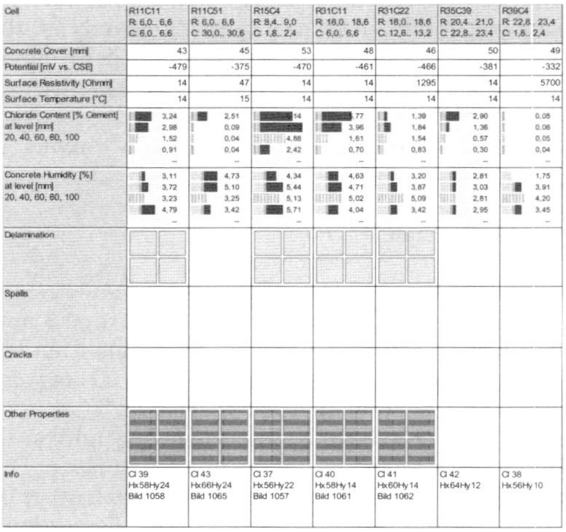

Cell	R11C11 R 6,0..6,6 C 6,0..6,6	R11CS1 R 6,0..6,6 C 30,0..30,6	R15C4 R 8,4..9,0 C 1,6..2,4	R31C11 R 18,0..18,6 C 6,0..6,6	R31C22 R 18,0..18,6 C 12,8..13,2	R35C39 R 20,4..21,0 C 22,8..23,4	R39C4 R 22,8..23,4 C 1,6..2,4
Concrete Cover [mm]	43	45	53	48	46	50	49
Potential [mV vs. CSE]	-479	-375	-470	-461	-466	-381	-332
Surface Resistivity [Ohm]	14	47	14	14	1295	14	5700
Surface Temperature [°C]	14	15	14	14	14	14	14
Chloride Content [% Cement] at level [mm] 20, 40, 60, 80, 100	3,24 / 2,98 / 1,52 / 0,91	2,51 / 0,09 / 0,04 / 0,04	14 / 4,88 / 2,42	77 / 3,96 / 1,61 / 0,70	1,39 / 1,84 / 1,54 / 0,83	2,90 / 1,36 / 0,57 / 0,30	0,08 / 0,06 / 0,05 / 0,04
Concrete Humidity [%] at level [mm] 20, 40, 60, 80, 100	3,11 / 3,72 / 3,23 / 4,79	4,73 / 5,10 / 3,25 / 3,42	4,34 / 5,44 / 5,13 / 5,71	4,63 / 4,71 / 5,02 / 4,04	3,20 / 3,87 / 5,09 / 3,42	2,81 / 3,03 / 2,81 / 2,95	1,75 / 3,91 / 4,20 / 3,45
Delamination							
Spalls							
Cracks							
Other Properties							
Info	CI 39 Hx58Hy24 Bld 1058	CI 43 Hx56Hy24 Bld 1065	CI 37 Hx58Hy22 Bld 1057	CI 40 Hx58Hy14 Bld 1061	CI 41 Hx60Hy14 Bld 1062	CI 42 Hx64Hy12	CI 38 Hx56Hy10

Figure 4. Comparative list of all data per grid cell.

- spalls and delaminated areas were often well situated within the concrete cover zone and did not touch reinforcement—only in few cases damage as seen in Fig. 2 appeared
- 85% of the concrete area repaired in 2003 did show delamination again; the total amount of delaminated area had increased by 40% since.

2.3 Evaluation of the results and observations

From the condition survey the following damage scenario could be concluded: Deicing salt has accumulated in groundwater bearing soil under the asphalt. With the steep moisture gradient between the soil and the embedded single foundations of the columns on the wet side and the elevated reinforced concrete columns on the dry side, chloride has been migrating into the columns aided by capillary suction and did concentrate on the concrete surface at values up to 6%, related to cement mas.

Coincidentally, a significant number of columns showed spalling that was not caused by corrosion, but obviously because of longitudinal load. The reinforcement was covered by at least 50 mm of concrete in a very wet environment, so that the chloride migration itself would not cause corrosion problems. But the combination of load triggered spalling and chloride migration started to cause an avalanche effect, when in spalled areas—at now reduced concrete cover—the reinforcement got in high chloride and semi-wet, corrosive conditions.

2.4 *Results of the continued, accelerated survey*

For the remaining 290 columns it was the task to identify columns bearing some chloride or high chloride securely as well as columns having concrete damage in principle. So the general concrete cover measurement and the detailed concrete damage recording were skipped.

Here, the surface resistivity was a helpful parameter. The intensive comparison of all NDT data, damage, chloride and moisture content allowed us to create the following evaluation pattern which divided into 4 criteria:

a. no action required at max. chloride content of 0.8%—corresponding to a min. rest potential of > −250 mV vs. CSE per column.
b. initial chloride extraction (followed by CP) at chloride content exceeding 4%—corresponding to a min rest potential of <−450 mV vs. CSE.
c. CP installation on columns where the rest potentials ranged between the above cases a) and b) (E between −250 mV and −450 mV).
d. additional columns with no action required, when E was between −250 mV and −450 mV and the surface resistivity was >1,500 Ωm.

In total dust samples were taken on 33 columns, and for the patterns b), c) und d) the NDT data and chloride data were correlating better than 90%. Pattern a) seemed to be chosen too restrictive, and with the help of surface resistivity data according to pattern d), some more columns ware classified into "no action" status.

3 RECOMMENDED REPAIR CONCEPT

Conventional repair was no durable solution because of the continued chloride migration from the soil and the foundations into the columns. Depending on the weather conditions, on the blank concrete a water suction horizon was clearly visible (see Fig. 5). An impressed current system

Figure 5. Water suction horizon on a column.

Table 1. Summary of recommended repair actions.

Repair action	Columns	Percentage of total
Not required	53	19
Concrete repair	127	45
Galvanic CP	221	78
Initial ECE	83	29

would have caused very high installation effort, since the columns did not have reinforcement interconnection.

So a galvanic CP system with discrete zinc anodes was chosen as main repair strategy. In order to extend the lifetime of the CP and to avoid possible acidification of the mortar/concrete around the anodes, it was supported by a short-term ECE prior to installation in 37% of the CP cases, where very high chloride contents were to be reduced to less than 2% within 2 weeks of application.

The damaged columns had to be repaired conventionally. A structural engineer was consulted about possible strengthening actions due to the damage observations (which is not part of the publication).

4 CHLORIDE EXTRACTION (ECE)

The aim of the ECE was to reduce the chloride content from initially very high values >4% (by cement mass) down to less than 2%. According to long-term experience, such a target can be realized within only 2 weeks. The application could be done with the car park in use, and the pre-manufactured ECE-tools allowed their quick assembly and removal. Fig. 6 shows the layout on widely distributed columns.

Figure 6. ECE installation while the car park stayed in use.

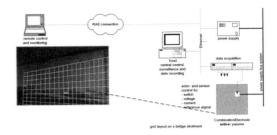

Figure 7. Schematic layout of the CITec ECE system.

4.1 Principle

The technical solution (Schneck 2009), which was developed in 2001 by CITec is designed for the focussed treatment of smaller corrosion "hot spots". Up to 2011, this patented technology has been used successfully on 19 structures, treating a total surface of ca. 2,100 m² and removing more than 84 kg of chloride—which equals an amount of 132 kg of NaCl. The basic layout is to be seen in Fig. 7 and has the following key features:

- The electrodes used for the ECE have a size of 60×60 cm, are pre-manufactured, re-usable and have an ion exchanger for binding chloride.
- According to the configuration (rebar spacing, concrete cover, chloride content, concrete permeability etc.) the electrodes can be combined in groups (max 10 m²).
- A chloride measuring unit (Schneck, Gruenzig, Vonau, Herrmann & Berthold 2006) signals the ion exchanger saturation and switches off the related electrodes (and prevents unwanted chlorine evolution).
- The control of the ECE is based on a uniformly provided voltage of 40 V and a pulse width modulation (PWR, Schneck, Mucke & Gruenzig 2001) that switches the electrodes or groups of electrodes in intervals—normally 12 hours. The on-time is reduced when defined parameters such as current or potential readings are exceeded.
- Chloride saturated electrodes are regenerated in a solution at pH = 14. So the bound chloride is replaced by OH-, can be analysed, and the electrodes get a fresh alkaline buffer capacity, and waste from the ECE application can be avoided.

4.2 Results

All treated 83 columns were grouped into 3 sub-applications, which had 3 groups of electrodes

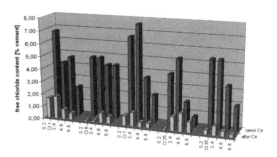

Figure 8. Chloride profiles 2–4–6–8 cm before and after ECE.

each—corresponding ca. 9 columns/ 36 electrodes per group. The following data were recorded:

- driving voltage per group
- current/current density per group
- impressed charge per group
- temperature
- chloride profiles on selected locations
- chloride collected in the ion exchanger of the electrodes.

Due to the high degree of reinforcement, the impressed charge of between 670 and 1,415 Ah corresponded to a charge density of between only 70 and 105 Ah/m², related to the reinforcement. But having mostly uncorroded rebar surfaces, such a result is within a common range.

The maximum current per group—in the first minutes after switching on—was about 19 A, which corresponded to 3.75 A/m² rebar surface. During the 12-hour-operation time, it dropped down to 8–10 A. In other groups the current density did not exceed 1 A/m² (all at a constant voltage of 40 V).

The chloride content could be reduced substantially, as Fig. 8 shows. The specified target could be reached. From the regeneration of the electrodes after use 1.3 kg Chloride was analyzed in total, which corresponds to 2 kg of Sodium Chloride and in average 33 g Chloride per m² concrete surface.

5 CATHODIC PROTECTION (CP)

It was planned to place 2 zinc rods of 45 mm length and 28 mm diameter in each column, as shown in Fig. 9. So it was intended to establish a protection height of about 30 cm and to cover 20 cm of visible columns and 10 cm of buried area, because this was the most affected part of the columns.

The zinc rods had a star-shaped surface in order to increase the zinc surface (see Fig. 10). They were mounted with cement mortar. Because every column represented a separate, very small anode zone, no permanent data recording was

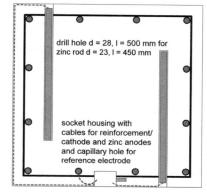
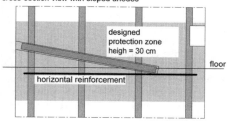

Figure 9. Principle array of the zinc anodes within the column.

Figure 10. View on the anode positioned in a drill hole.

planned to be installed. For a verification of the correct working of the CP, the anode and cathode wiring could be disconnected in an empty socket housing. For monitoring potentials, a luggin probe hole towards the reinforcement was left accessible there.

The feasibility of the planned CP design was verified by a test installation. Within that, a minimum lifetime of 20 years has been specified. The basic layout is to be seen in Fig. 9.

5.1 Trial installation on one column

On a column without concrete damage and 3.75% chloride maximum/1.25% chloride in rebar vicinity the installation was verified on the intended protection height, the relation between potentials measured on the concrete surface and inside the luggin probe hole. The lifetime specification was verified, too. The test installation was controlled over 3 weeks with several switch-off measurements. The following measurements were made:

- resistance between anode(s) and reinforcement.
- active-, instant-off- and off-potentials on the column surface.
- active-, instant-off- and off-potentials in the capillary hole.
- protection current as voltage drop over a precision resistance.

The IR drop was with ca. 3 mV almost negligible. The on-polarization could be verified on the whole intended area, as it can be seen in Fig. 11. Fig. 12 shows the measurement setup with a special reference electrode that has a length of 100 cm and can be inserted in small drill holes.

In Fig. 13 the development of the potential in the luggin probe hole and the protection current over a period of time can be seen, including some "off"-measurements, that show a behavior of the CP installation within an expected range for a galvanic system. The average current density, related to the assumed reinforcement surface, was about 1 mA/m².

5.2 Lifetime evaluation

With the Faraday equation a lifetime evaluation can be made from the measured protection currents. Since they are expected to drop during the time of operation, the calculation should be on the "safe side". The following data are given:

- zinc mass/rod: m = 896 g.
- zinc density: $\rho = 7.13$ g/cm³.
- molar mass of zinc: M = 65.38 g/mol.
- surface area of a zinc rod: A = 0.025 m².

117

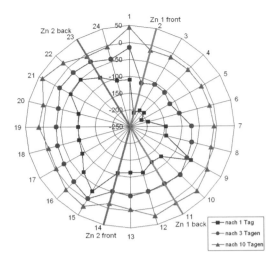

Figure 11. On-potentials around the cross-section of the column.

Figure 12. Measurement setup for the trial CP.

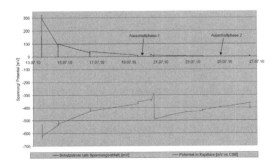

Figure 13. Development of protection currents (top curve) and on-potentials (bottom curve) over a period of 2 weeks with 2 extended switch-off measurements.

Table 2. Lifetime evaluation for the zinc anodes.

| | 1 anode/rod | | 2 anodes/rods | |
	min	max	min	max
Current [mA]	0.09	0.75	0.25	3.00
Corresponds to current density of zinc [mA/m²]	3.58	29.84	4.97	59.68
Lifetime [years]	934.3	112.1	672.7	56.1
Including safety deduction of 50% [years]		56.0		28.0

From this, the number of molecules of zinc can be calculated with n = m/M = 13,70 mol for one rod or 27.41 mol for two rods. According to Faraday is

$$t = \frac{n \cdot z \cdot F}{i}$$

with the following parameters:

i: current [A]
t: time [s]
z: charge number of ion; for $Zn \rightarrow Zn^{2+}+2e^-$ $z = 2$
F: Faraday constant F = 9.6484 ∗ 104 As/mol
n: number of molecules of element.

Table 2 is a case evaluation for the observed minimum and maximum currents, related to a CP with one and with two zinc rods. By calculation with the above equation, this results in the said lifetime of the anodes until their total consumption. With a safety deduction of 50%, a minimum lifetime of 28 years can be expected, and the CP design with sacrificial anodes could be applied for the other columns.

5.3 Installation on 220 columns

Now all other columns could be equipped with the CP system as planned. A short switch-on measurement was done and written in the 220 protocol sheets. It could be proven that all installations were correctly done, although on 5 columns short circuits between anode and reinforcement could not be avoided. For a galvanic CP this is no problem—only switch-off measurements cannot be made and no protection current can be recorded. Fig. 14 shows the appearance of the columns after finishing the installation.

Generally, a shift of on-potentials into the negative direction was measured (except for the short circuits), and the average values, taken ca 15 to 45 s after connecting the electrodes with the reinforcement, are to be seen in Table 3.

118

Figure 14. View on a column after closing the cable slots and the switch housing.

Table 3. Summary of the switch-on measurements.

	Change of potential within 15 to 45 s after switching on [mV]			Resistance between anodes and rein-forcement	Protection current ca 15 s after switch-ing on
	$E_{capillary}$	$E_{surface\,1}$	$E_{surface\,2}$	$[\Omega]$	$[mA/m^2]$
min	−189	−248	−153	0	0.0
max	8	7	2	28,000	43.1
avg	−27	−38	−34	1,070	8.4

6 CONCLUSIONS

Although the concrete damage seemed to be primarily caused by chloride, which was supposed to come from splash water, a thorough condition survey resulted in 2 obviously different, but overlaying processes: spalling because of load and chloride ingress by capillary movement from the soil/foundation into the columns.

Because further chloride ingress could not be stopped, concrete replacement was not able to provide a long-term repair effect.

The combination of ECE and galvanic CP have been offering a durable solution at a reasonable effort. During the site works the car park could remain fully under service.

REFERENCES

Schneck, U. 2005. Qualifizierte Korrosionsuntersuchungen an Stahlbetonbauwerken. *Bautechnik 82 (2005), 443–448.*

Schneck, U. 2009. Long term behaviour of box girder sections with residual chloride after the application of ECE. In M. Grantham (ed): *3rd International Concrete Solutions Conference, Proc., Padova, 2009.* Rotterdam: Balkema.

Schneck, U., Mucke, S. & Gruenzig, H. 2001. Pulse Width Modulation (PWR)—Investigations for raising the efficiency of an electrochemical chloride extraction from reinforced concrete. In P.L. Bonora (ed): *EUROCORR 2001, Proc., Riva del Garda, 2001.* Milano: Associazione Italiana di Metallurgia.

Schneck, U., Winkler, T. & Mucke, S. 2001. Integrated system for the inspection and the corrosion monitoring of reinforced concrete structures. In: *1st Quality Control and Quality Assurance of Construction Materials Conference, Proc., Dubai, 2001.* Dubai: Dubai Municipality.

Electrochemical repair

Concrete Solutions – Grantham, Mechtcherine & Schneck (eds)
© 2012 Taylor & Francis Group, London, ISBN 978-0-415-61622-5

Use of electrochemical migration to mitigate alkali-silica reaction in large scale concrete structures

A.F. Bentivegna, E.R. Giannini & K.J. Folliard
The University of Texas at Austin, Austin, USA

ABSTRACT: In 2009, the American Society of Civil Engineers (ASCE) issued a "D-" or a poor evaluation of America's bridges (ASCE, 2009). With an aging infrastructure and limited funding, the need exists for the development and implementation of new repair techniques. In many regions, deterioration of concrete infrastructure is due to the destructive chemical interaction known as alkali-silica reaction (ASR). This reaction occurs between hydroxyl ions from the cement paste and certain siliceous aggregates. The reaction leads to the formation of a gel that absorbs water and expands, eventually leading to cracking of the concrete. Research funded by the United States Federal Highway Administration (FHWA) investigated the use of electrochemical migration of lithium compounds to nullify the expansion of the gel and to extend the service of existing-infected structures. The research in this project implemented electrochemical techniques on in-situ structures as well as on large-scale laboratory specimens. The research is aimed at the long-term monitoring and evaluation of the effectiveness to mitigate expansion.

1 INTRODUCTION

1.1 Background

"Alkali-Silica Reaction is major durability problem that has resulted in premature deterioration of various types of concrete structure in the United States and throughout the world" (Folliard, 2006) Alkali-silica reaction (ASR) was first discovered by Thomas Stanton in California in the late 1930's. He determined certain reactive minerals in aggregates combined with high alkali cements can result in expansion in concrete that can lead to increased stresses, which could lead to failure (Stanton, 1940).

1.2 ASR mechanism

There are three components necessary for ASR to occur in concrete structures. They are: reactive siliceous aggregates, alkalis, and moisture. The majority of the alkalis present in concrete structures come from portland cement, but other sources of alkali may include supplementary cementing materials, aggregates, chemical admixtures and external sources (i.e., saltwater and deicing salts). The presence of high amounts of alkalis in the pore solution of cement requires an equal number of hydroxyl ions (OH-) to be present in order to maintain charge equilibrium. Hydroxyl ions raise the pH of the solution, which dissolves the reactive silica components in aggregates.

Cement alkalis, sodium (Na+) and potassium (K+), then attack the aggregates and combine with the remaining silica to form a gel product. This gel product swells as it absorbs water from the surrounding cement paste. The expanded gel induces pressure within the concrete, which leads to cracking (Folliard, 2006). The process of concrete ASR expansion and cracking can be split into three separate periods:

1. Incubation Period—ASR gel absorbs water and begins to expand in the concrete structure and the gel moves into available adjacent voids. The internal pressure is limited at this stage due to the freedom to expand. The chemical reaction is "incubated" at this stage while the reaction is still occurring (Fan, 1998).
2. Cracking Stage—Upon filling all of the available voids, the ASR reaction continues to produce gel which causes further expansion. Internal pressures increase as the gel swells. The pressures from the swelling can lead to tensile forces in the exterior concrete and lead to cracking. The cracking occurs because the gel is forced out due to the internal pressures trying to reach the surface (Fan, 1998).
3. Stabilization Stage—ASR occurs for a long time, but the rate decreases until the reaction forming gel and the rate that the gel is extruded from the cracks reaches equilibrium. The reaction may be completed upon the depletion of the available alkalis in cement (Fan, 1998).

1.3 Preventing ASR

The risk of premature deterioration of concrete structures due to ASR can be reduced by using one of the following techniques in fresh concrete:

- Avoid using expansive reacting aggregates
- Use low alkali concrete
- Use of supplementary cement materials (SCMs)
- Use of lithium-based admixtures.

Using aggregates that are not found to be expansive in standardized laboratory testing and minimizing alkali content of the concrete are the simplest techniques for mitigating damage. Another common technique for prevention is the use of SCMs (e.g., fly ash, silica fume, ground-granulated blast furnace slag, and calcined clays). The SCM amount required to suppress expansion generally depends on the reactivity of the aggregates, alkali content of the concrete and other properties (Thomas, 2007).

Another technique used to suppress expansion in fresh concrete is the addition of lithium-based admixtures, which was discovered in 1951 by McCoy and Caldwell (1951). Today, the primary form of lithium used to mitigate expansion due to ASR is $LiNO_3$. This chemical combination has prevailed as the primary chemical for mitigating ASR due to the neutral pH of the solution which does not affect the pore solution of the concrete (Stokes, 1997).

1.4 Mitigating expansion due to ASR

When precautions are not taken to prevent deterioration of concrete made with reactive aggregates and highly alkaline cements, techniques are needed to mitigate deterioration of structures in-situ. The two approaches for repairing structures which display damage due to ASR are: (1) mitigation of the symptoms and (2) mitigation of the cause (Thomas, 2007).

Techniques for mitigating the symptoms include: cracking filling to restrict water ingress, slot cutting (stress relieve) to allow for the continued expansion, and additional external restraint to prevent continued expansion (Thomas, 2007).

The techniques available for mitigating the cause are to dry the concrete and to use lithium compounds. Concrete can be dried by using breathable sealers which lower the relative humidity of the concrete and prevent the absorption of water, which leads to the swelling and cracking of the concrete. The other technique is through the use of lithium based compounds (Thomas, 2007). Research has shown that lithium is an effective admixture for suppressing expansion due to ASR (McCoy, 1951). The challenge in exsisting strucutres is to find techniques for driving lithium into the concrete to effective depths to prevent the expansion.

1.5 Electrochemical migration

A variety of techniques have been investigated to determine the most effective technique for penetrating lithium into hardened concrete including topical spray, vacuum impregnation, and electrochemical migration (Thomas, 2007). This paper will focus on the use of electrochemical migration on field structures and large-scale laboratory specimens.

Electrochemical migration of lithium into hardened concrete has been adapted from the technique used to remove chloride ions from concrete structures, known as electrochemical chloride extraction (ECE). ECE is a temporary treatment that removes salt (chloride) ions from concrete through the application of a low voltage DC electric potential. With a few modifications, the system can be altered to drive lithium ions into a concrete structure (Whitmore, 2000). The treatment requires four main components:

1. Anode
2. Cathode
3. Power source
4. Source of lithium ions.

The typical anode used is a titanium mesh wrapped on the concrete surface. The mesh is made of an inert material to prevent the deterioration/consumption of the anode during the treatment (Whitmore, 2000).

The anode is then coupled with a cathode; for this process, the reinforcement steel inside the concrete is used. Prior to treatment, the steel has to be checked for continuity throughout the concrete to ensure even distribution of the lithium ions (Whitmore, 2000).

The other two components of the treatment are the power supply and the lithium treatment. The power supply must be capable of converting high voltage AC power to low voltage DC output. A typical power supply can treat approximately 100 m^2 of concrete surface. The lithium solution used will serve as an electrolyte solution providing continuity between the anode mesh and the cathode reinforcement (Whitmore, 2000). A schematic of the electrochemical treatment can be seen in Figure 1.

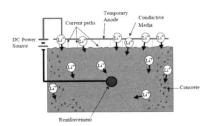

Figure 1. Schematic showing lithium ion migration during electrochemical treatment (Whitmore, 2000).

2 FIELD INVESTIGATION AND RESULTS

2.1 *Field trial introduction*

The first phase of the field trial investigated the use of electrochemical treatment on bridge columns in Houston, Texas, USA. The columns under investigation were part of a high occupancy vehicle (HOV) flyover bridge in the metropolitan Houston area. A photograph of the bridge and columns can be seen in Figure 2. The roadway opened for traffic in 2000 and developed significant cracking in the columns over first six years of service. Figure 3 illustrates the severity of cracking prior to treatment.

Cores were extracted from the columns to validate the damage was due to ASR. The petrographic evaluation completed by Dr. Grattan-Bellew at Laval University found siliceous aggregate with dissolution and the formation of ASR gel around the aggregates. A combined effort of the Texas Department of Transportation and the The United States Federal Highway Administration (FHWA) investigated the use of various techniques to mitigate future damage on these columns. This paper will only present data on a control column (column without any mitigation treatment) and two columns treated with electrochemical migration of lithium.

2.2 *Instrumentation and monitoring*

The instrumentation and monitoring of the bridge columns focused on two different types of data to assess the effectiveness of the treatment:

- Measuring expansion of the column caused by ASR
- Measuring the propagation of cracking in the structure.

The expansions measurements were obtained by embedding stainless steel gage studs in the concrete column over a gage length of 500 mm and measuring the distance between them using a digital Mayes Gage (Fig. 4). Two vertical and horizontal measurements are taken on each of the columns. The digital gauge is accurate to 0.001 mm and expansion values are reported to the nearest 0.0001%.

The monitoring of the cracking propagation was completed on two adjacent surfaces of the columns with a modified crack mapping technique from Ministere de l' equipment, de stransports et du logement in France. The technique establishes six axes, two transverse, two horizontal and two 45° axes, graduated in 0.1 m increments drawn on the concrete surface for classifying the degree of cracking. Cracks were evaluated along these axes and recorded if the width was greater than 0.10 mm and smaller than 2 mm. A crackmeter with a scale ranging from 0.05 mm to 2 mm (0.08 in.) and a magnifying glass (magnifying

Figure 2. Houston, texas, USA field trial investigation concrete bridge.

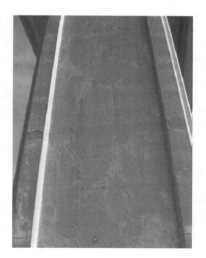

Figure 3. Column cracking prior to treatment.

Figure 4. Mayes gage.

power 10 X) were used to measure the widths of openings at the concrete surface. A quantitative cracking index (CI) was calculated by as the total open crack width in mm divided by the total length of the six axes in m. The cracking mapping technique allows for the quantitative review of the number of cracks as well the change in crack opening (Godart et al., 1992).

The monitoring of the expansion measurements and crack propagation monitoring are completed three times a year. Initial monitoring prior to treatments was completed in 2006, six years after placement.

2.3 Electrochemical treatment

The electrochemical migration of lithium was performed over 8 weeks in 2006 by Vector Corrosion Technologies. The treatments required two weeks for preparation of the columns, five weeks for treatments, and one week for demobilization (Giannini, 2009).

A description of the treatment follows: Holes were drilled from the surface of the concrete to the reinforcement in several locations. Electrical wire was fused to the reinforcement at one end and a regulated power supply at the other; the hole was then sealed with grout. Additional larger holes were drilled into the concrete between the rebar to a depth of several inches past the rebar. Titanium mesh anode strips and irrigation tubes were inserted into these holes in order to help impregnate the concrete with lithium from inside the rebar cage, as well as from the surface. Paint was removed from the surface of the concrete by blasting, and a layer of cellulose was sprayed onto the vertical surface of the column to hold the electrolyte solution. A titanium mesh anode was embedded in the cellulose. Electrical wires were connected to the titanium anodes at one end and the power supply at the other. An irrigation system was connected to an inline pump to circulate a large supply of lithium nitrate solution. Finally, a collection system at the bottom of the treatment area returned the electrolyte to the pump for recirculation. The entire installation was then sealed with plastic sheeting to ensure that the lithium nitrate electrolyte was directed to the collection system (Giannini, 2009).

The treatment duration was five weeks; the power supply set a constant current to the anodes throughout the application. Figure 5 illustrates the columns during the treatments. The current passed throughout the hardened concrete via the electrolyte solution drawing the Li$^+$ ions from the surface and holes between the reinforcement to the cathode. A noncorrosive titanium mesh anode was used on the surface. Lithium hydroxide was added to the electrolyte solution throughout the testing

Figure 5. Electrochemical treatment.

to prevent the solution from becoming acidic and etching the concrete surface (Giannini, 2009).

2.4 Monitoring and results

After the treatments in early 2006, subsequent site visits have occurred to monitor the expansion and crack propagation.

Figure 6 presents the horizontal expansion data of the two columns treated with electrochemical migration of lithium and the control with no treatment applied; the vertical measurements are not presented due to the negligible expansion due to the restraint provided by the weight of the structure. The columns electrochemically treated columns experience more or similar expansion levels as the control columns that were not treated.

Figure 7 presents the quantitative crack mapping data from the control column and the two electrochemically treated columns. No clear trend or cracking behavior can be drawn from this form of monitoring at this time. The authors believe that the variability between operators during the cracking monitoring may lead to error in the testing.

In addition to quantitative measurements a visual inspection of the structure was performed. Observations of the structure found etching of the concrete surface, typical of chemical attack. Figures 8 and 9 demonstrates the surface deterioration found on all faces of the two columns

126

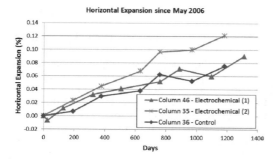

Figure 6. Horizontal expansion of Houston bridge columns.

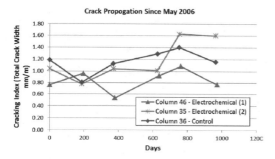

Figure 7. Quantitative crack indices (CI) of Houston bridge columns.

Figure 8. Concrete surface ~5 years after electrochemical treatment.

Figure 9. Close-up of concrete surface deterioration ~5 years after electrochemical treatment.

electrochemically treated approximately 5 years later. The darker colored circles are the mortar repairs used to fill the holes where connections to the reinforcement were made after the treatment. The largest crack widths found on the column measured nearly 0.5 mm.

The field trial in Houston, Texas, USA allowed for a rare opportunity to experiment with a technique to mitigate ASR on a large scale hardened concrete structure. However, the project did present some limitations, which include the lack of a true control and the history of the structure. The variability of concrete mixtures between columns and within the same column cannot be completely accounted for. The amount of monitoring visits to the site is limited due to the travel cost. Also, a true baseline value of the expansion history of the column is not known due to the initiation of measurements approximately 6–8 years after placement.

Due to the shortcomings of the field trial the development of a large-scale exposure site testing at the University of Texas at Austin was initiated. The outdoor exposure site allowed for the monitoring of concrete elements with identical mixture design immediately after the time of construction.

3 UT AUSTIN LARGE-SCALE INVESTIGATION AND RESULTS

3.1 UT Austin large-scale introduction

The second phase of this project created large-scale concrete columns at the Concrete Durability Center research laboratory at The University of Texas at Austin. Four circular reinforced columns (0.61 m diameter × 1.22 m height) were created with a highly reactive fine aggregate from El Paso,

Texas, USA and a non-reactive coarse aggregate from Austin, Texas, USA. Three columns were cast with materials intent to be expansive and result in cracking and the other cast with the same aggregates but with a sufficient dosage of $LiNO_3$ to suppress expansion. The latter column is designed to be a non-reactive control. Two of the three expansive columns will receive an electrochemical treatment identical to the treatment performed in the Houston Field Trial and the other column will serve as an expansive control to compare the effectiveness of the technique.

The columns were cast in August of 2008 in two layers with internal vibration performed after each layer. The columns were moist cured for 7 days on the top surface and formwork was removed at the end of this time.

3.2 Instrumentation and monitoring

The instrumentation and monitoring of the columns focused mainly on the expansion due to ASR and the depth of penetration of lithium. The three techniques for monitoring the expansion of the columns were:

- Mayes Gage
- Concrete Embedment Strain Gages
- Circumferential Measurements.

The same technique as the field columns was used to measure the surface expansion in the vertical direction only. Due to the curvature of the column, the gage could not be used in the horizontal direction.

Two concrete embedment strain gauges were placed at the mid-depth of the columns: one in the horizontal direction and one in the vertical direction. Figure 10 shows the gauges suspended

inside the reinforcement steel prior to concrete placement.

The other technique implemented to monitor the concrete expansion was the use of a circumferential pi tape. This measuring device measures the circumferential expansion of the concrete. The measurements were precise to ±0.03 mm. In order to measure the circumference from the same location every time, a builders square was placed on top of the column and measured down 508 mm. This measurement was marked on the four cardinal directions of the columns. With the marks around the column, an assistant holds the tape just below the marks at two of the locations and the other operator holds the tape at the two other locations on the column. The measurements were read on a vernier scale and circumference was calculated by multiplying the pi tape reading by pi (π). Figure 11 illustrates the technique used to monitor the circumferential expansion of the columns.

The baseline measurement, zero measurement, for each of the elements was taken at approximately seven days after placement. The measurements for the concrete embedment gages are taken four times daily. The measurements are taken at 12:00 AM, 6:00 AM, 12:00 PM and at 6:00 PM. The measurements are recorded in the data logger storage unit for approximately 28 days. At that time the measurements are downloaded and analyzed. The demountable mechanical strain gages and circumference measurements were taken under specific climatic conditions. The ambient temperature must be 23 ± 1.5°C. The weather must be cloudy to mostly cloudy and not raining so as to not impart the thermal effects of direct sunlight or moisture effects on the measurements. Due to the high summer temperatures and an average of

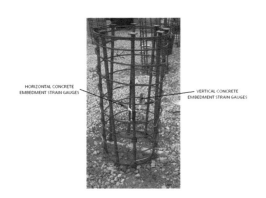

Figure 10. Concrete embedment strain gauges suspended at mid-depth of the column in the vertical and horizontal direction (Bentivegna, 2009).

Figure 11. Monitoring circumferential expansion using a pi tape.

300 days a year of sun in Austin, Texas, expansion measuring is sporadic throughout the year and often limited to only a few hours in the early morning during summer months. The expansion measurements were taken several times in the first year, with less frequent monitoring intervals thereafter (Bentivegna, 2009).

3.3 Electrochemical treatment

The two reactive columns were treated with electrochemical treatment when the average expansion of the columns reached 0.1 percent. The same treatment procedure and duration was used as described for the Houston field trial.

3.4 Monitoring and results

Figure 12 illustrates the vertical surface expansion values of the columns. The non-reactive column (Column 13) was cast approximately one year after placement of the other three columns; therefore, there is less data available. The column has shown no signs of cracking and has no noticeable expansion using the surface expansion measurements. The reactive column (Column 5), no mitigation treatment performed, displayed similar expansion values to the columns 4 and 5, which were treated with the electrochemical treatment.

The initial baseline recording of the column was taken 7 days after placement when the formwork and burlap were removed. Only the reactive control (Column 2) and one electrochemically treated column (Column 5) are presented in Figure 13. Similar amounts of expansion are evident, resulting in similar cracking and deterioration between the two columns.

The circumferential measurements were not initiated until approximately 180 days after placement. The measurements are taken under the same environmental conditions as the surface expansion measurement conditions described

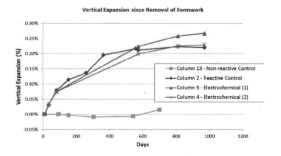

Figure 12. Vertical surface expansion of UT Austin large-scale field columns.

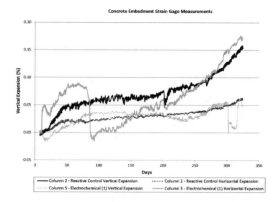

Figure 13. Concrete embedment strain gage expansion of UT Austin large-scale field columns.

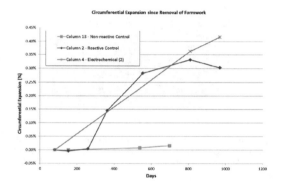

Figure 14. Circumferential expansion of UT Austin large-scale field columns.

above. Figure 14 summarizes the circumferential expansion measurements of the columns. The reactive control (Column 2) and the electrochemically treated (Column 4) had similar values of expansion with the treated column display slightly more with the most recent measurements. The non-reactive control (Column 13) cast with $LiNO_3$ did show any signs of expansion.

In addition to expansion monitoring, cores were extracted from the concrete columns to determine the depth of penetration of the Li^+ ions. The cores were ground at 4 mm increments where the samples of each depth segment were collected and tested using inductively coupled plasma (ICP) mass spectrometry. Figure 15 displays the concentration of the Li^+ ions and alkali ions (Na^+ and K^+) as a function of depth of an electrochemically treated column. The necessary concentration of Li^+ ions to suppress ASR expansion has

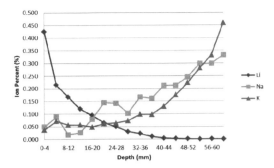

Figure 15. Ion concentration from the concrete surface depth.

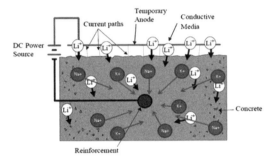

Figure 16. Schematic showing lithium ion and alkali ion migration during electrochemical treatment, modified from (Whitmore, 2000).

been shown to be around 100 ppm or 0.01% (Thomas, 2007). The percentage of Li^+ ions in the concentration drastically reduces after the first 20 mm to a level that is insufficient to mitigate ASR beyond a depth of 40 mm. The reinforcement is located at approximately 50 mm from the concrete surface where the levels of alkali ions appear to be increasing to significant levels. The increased alkali ion concentration at depths near the reinforcement may be the possible cause of the expansion. Figure 16 illustrates the mechanism for the increased concentration of the alkali ions at depths near the reinforcement. The electric current passes through the concrete surface via electrolyte solution. The current not only draws the Li^+ cations, it draws the alkali (Na^+ and K^+) cations, therefore increasing the severity of ASR gel formation near the reinforcement.

The exposure site at UT Austin allowed for a more thorough understanding of the concrete history and regimented monitoring schedule. The expansion values of the electrochemically treated columns are equivalent or greater than that seen of the control columns without any treatment.

4 CONCLUSIONS

From the field trial in Houston, Texas, USA the following conclusions can be made:

1. Monitoring of a large scale field structure can be challenging due to the many uncontrollable variables including: variability in monitoring temperature, lack of history of mixture materials, lack of structure history, lack of true baseline data points, and lack of a true control.
2. Electrochemical treatment is a costly and time-consuming mitigation technique that resulted in equivalent or slightly more expansion than the concrete columns that remained untreated.
3. The electrochemical treatment left the concrete surface etched and severely deteriorated possibly allowing for the potential for other durability related problems.

From the large-scale columns cast at UT Austin the following conclusions can be made:

1. The electrochemical treated columns experienced similar or greater expansion levels than the reactive controls.
2. The non-reactive control validated that lithium can be used in large scale structures to prevent ASR deterioration.

From the experimental investigations summarized in this paper, electrochemical migration of lithium compounds into hardened concrete does not appear to be a valid technique for mitigating alkali-silica reaction in hardened concrete. The potential for worsening the reaction and further deteriorating the concrete surface is a likely possibility. Future testing is needed to evaluate if the technique can potentially harm the structural integrity of the concrete surrounding the reinforcement due to the additional alkali ion concentration.

ACKNOWLEDGEMENTS

The authors would like to acknowledge the combined financial support of the United States Federal Highway Administration (FHWA) (FHWA Project DTFH61-02-C-0097) and the Texas Department of Transportation (TxDOT).

REFERENCES

ASCE. (2009). Report Card for America's Infastructure. *American Society of Civil Engineers*.
Bentivegna, A. (2009). *Development and Monitoring of an Outdoor Exposure Site to Mitigate Alkali-Silica Reaction in Hardened Concrete*. Austin, Texas, USA: The University of Texas at Austin.

Fan, S. a. (1998). Length Expansion and Cracking of Plain and Reinforced Concrete Prisms Due to Alkali-Silica Reaction. *ACI Materials Journal*, 480.

Folliard, K.T. (2006). *Interim Recommendations for the Use of LIthium to Mitigate or Prevent Alkali-Silica Reaction* (ASR). McLean, VA: FHWA.

Giannini, E. (2009). *Field Studies of Mitigation Strategies for Alkali-Silica Reaction in Hardened Concrete.* Austin, Texas: The University of Texas at Austin.

Godart, B.F. (1992). Diagnosis and Monitoring of Concrete Bridges Damaged by AAR in Northern France. *Proceedings of the 9th International Conference on Alkali-Aggregate Reaction*, (pp. 368–375). London, United Kingdom.

McCoy, W. a. (1951). A New Approach to Inhibiting Alkali-Aggreagate Expansion. *Journal of the American Concrete Institute*, 693–706.

Stanton, T.E. (1940). Expansion of Concrete through Reaction between Cement and Aggregate. *American Society of Civil Engineers.*

Stokes, D.W. (1997). A Lithium-Based Admixture for ASR Control That Does Not Increase the Pore Solution pH. *Fifth CANMET/ACI International Conference on Superplasticizers and Other Chemical Admixture in Concrete* (pp. 855–868). Farmingoong Hills: American Concrete Institute.

Thomas, M.F. (2007). *The Use of Lithium to Prevent or Mitigate Alkali-Silica Reaction in Concrete Pavements and Structures.* McLean, VA: FHWA.

Whitmore, D. a. (2000). Use of an Applied Electric Field to Drive Lithium Ions into Alkali-Silica Reactive Structures. *International Conference on Alkali-Aggregate Reaction*, (pp. 1089–1098). Quebec City, Canada.

Concrete Solutions – Grantham, Mechtcherine & Schneck (eds)
© 2012 Taylor & Francis Group, London, ISBN 978-0-415-61622-5

Maintenance of transport structures using electrochemical solutions

R. Brueckner, C. Atkins, A. Foster, R. Merola & P. Lambert
Mott MacDonald, Altrincham, UK

ABSTRACT: The service life of highway structures is largely governed by the durability of the structural elements. Deterioration of these elements is dominated by the effects of corrosion of the steel. Reinforcement corrosion is generally caused by carbonation or chloride ingress from de-icing salts or marine environments.

Corrosion can be prevented or reduced to a tolerable level by using electro-chemical techniques such as Cathodic Protection (CP), corrosion inhibitors, realkalisation, chloride extraction and electro-osmotic methods. CP can be a particularly effective repair technique for chloride contaminated concrete.

This paper gives an overview of the different repair strategies available for transport structures such as road and rail bridges, elevated highways and canals. Cathodic protection systems have developed during the years and these different solutions are described based on a bridge structure. All repair strategies have their advantages and disadvantages and these are also highlighted.

1 INTRODUCTION

Steel in concrete normally does not corrode. Despite being embedded in a moist environment within a porous material, the steel is protected. When concrete hydrates it produces a highly alkaline solution with a pH in excess of 13. When steel is exposed to an alkaline solution it forms a stable oxide film over its surface that protects the steel from corrosion. However, the protective nature of this passive film can be compromised due to two commonly encountered mechanisms, those of chloride ion attack and carbonation.

Chloride ion attack is widely considered to be the most significant cause of concrete deterioration for transport structures. When chlorides reach the steel in sufficient quantities they disrupt the passive film and form localised areas of intense corrosion. Chlorides are a common species and are readily available from a range of sources. In 1888 a patent was filed for adding calcium chloride to concrete to speed up the rate of strength gain. This practice continued in the UK until 1972 when its use was banned due to concerns regarding reinforcement corrosion. In addition to this marine dredged aggregates were widely used in coastal areas. Chlorides from such sources are commonly termed 'internal' as they originate within the original mix. When cement hydrates it chemically combines some of the chlorides, dependant upon the composition of the binder, and stops them participating in the corrosion process.

The major source of chloride ions for most transport structures, other than those close to marine environments, is de-icing salt which has continuously contaminated structures since its effect was discovered in the 1930's resulting in its widespread use since the 1960's. Such external sources of chlorides continuously increase the total chloride content to beyond the critical level at which corrosion of embedded steel is initiated.

The primary effect of carbonation is the reduction of alkalinity which forms the protective layer at the steel surface. The atmosphere contains a small proportion of carbon dioxide. This can dissolve in moisture to form a mild acid. The carbonic acid produced reacts with the alkalinity in the concrete and can reduce it to a level where corrosion can occur.

For a given concrete, the rate of carbonation is largely dependant on the moisture content. In a dry environment the pores in the concrete are open and the atmosphere can penetrate the concrete more rapidly. This leads to a higher rate of carbonation. However corrosion needs moisture to occur and so a drier environment may carbonate rapidly but may not result in corrosion. In a very humid environment the pore structure of concrete is blocked with moisture and carbonation takes place more slowly. In addition, as concrete carbonates some of the chemically combined chlorides are released and are then free to promote corrosion.

2 CORROSION PREVENTION

Over the past two decades Mott MacDonald's Materials and Corrosion team have been involved with protecting a large number of varying transport structures. The application and development of different electrochemical repair options can be largely illustrated though the experience gained on the Silver Jubilee Bridge in the North West of England.

The Silver Jubilee Bridge was constructed in the 1960's and is a Grade II listed structure (Figure 1). It is part of a major regional highway route that carries over 90.000 vehicles per day on four lanes over the River Mersey. Any closure would result in a diversion of at least 40 miles (65 km). Even partial closure results in heavy congestion, requiring the need for night time maintenance adjacent to live traffic so it is crucial to maintain the integrity and durability of the structure.

The main central span of the bridge is a 330 m long steel arch structure with two 76 m side spans and is believed to be the largest of its type in Europe. The deck is reinforced concrete supported on structural steelwork. The approach viaducts have four main beams supported by reinforced concrete piers. The ends of the beams were precast, and the central spans were cast in place at the same time as the deck. The approach spans are a total of 522 m in length.

The highways in this part of England are subjected to chloride-based de-icing salts during the winter months. The original waterproofing system of the bridge deck, unlike that used on the approach viaducts, could not prevent extensive chloride contamination and degradation. However, the viaducts have joints over every third pier that have degraded with time, allowing chloride-contaminated water to leak onto the substructure. Chlorides have penetrated the concrete cover, and levels at the reinforcement have reached 2% by mass of cement—more than sufficient to initiate and sustain corrosion.

During the repair history it was necessary to develop effective methods of stopping or controlling corrosion that suited the individual circumstances and requirements of the local council. This has required extending the boundaries of corrosion engineering to achieve a durable and reliable repair at the lowest practical cost, Lambert (2007). Most of the areas protected to date have been accessible from underneath the bridge, see Figure 2. This has meant that although access has sometimes been extensive, it has been relatively straightforward. Unfortunately the ultimate element to protect was the main bridge deck. Being 40 m above the River Mersey and adjacent Manchester Ship Canal, this was always going to be somewhat challenging to repair.

2.1 *Holding repairs with corrosion inhibitors*

Patch repairs are often mis-applied as the initial repair method for locally delaminated concrete.

a) before rapair

b) 10 years after rapair

Figure 2. Original approach viaduct pier located beneath a deck joint.

Figure 1. Silver jubilee bridge.

Such repairs are often little more than aesthetic. They involve simply removing damaged material, cleaning the steel, and reinstating the concrete. Where significant levels of chlorides are present patch repairs are only effective in the short term, and problems can often be experienced with incipient anode effects where the repaired areas become cathodic to the adjacent areas causing enhanced corrosion of the surrounding steel.

The patch repairs carried out in the early stages at the Silver Jubilee Bridge were mainly performed to ensure public safety. While reinforcement section loss was not significant enough to warrant structural concerns, the public was at risk from falling delaminated concrete from under the approach viaducts. Loose and delaminated concrete was removed and the steel and exposed concrete over-coated using a polymer-modified cementitious mortar containing an amino alcohol corrosion inhibitor. The coating minimized any further corrosion of the reinforcement, prevented significant further ingress of the contaminants and minimised significantly the formation of incipient anodes.

This repair method was the subject of a government-funded research project, (Baldwin, 2003) which concluded that the repairs were all performing adequately and had prevented significant section loss over the previous 10 years. Minor issues such as discoloration of repair areas, which is an anticipated side effect due to UV exposure, and slight degradation of the coating were observed.

2.2 Corrosion inhibitors

Corrosion inhibitors are used in the protection of metal in a variety of industrial applications. Inhibitors can be introduced to new build reinforced concrete structures, for example, in the form of calcium nitrite admixtures. More recently, vapour phase inhibitor chemicals have been developed which can be applied to the surface of reinforced concrete. Due to their high vapour pressure these chemicals can migrate through the concrete and provide a protective film on the steel. This form of protection method is most successful on structures which are not already excessively damaged, are carbonated or do not have high concentrations of chloride ions. Because of this, the application on the Silver Jubilee Bridge has been limited to the holding repairs as discussed above. Additionally, elements of the structural steel work of the bridge have been treated with inhibitors.

Inhibitors are commonly used during the rehabilitation of car parks where a cathodic protection may not be necessary for the entire structure. Parking bays are mostly less contaminated than access ramps and drive ways. Heritage structures, whether metal reinforced concrete or steel framed masonry, may also benefit from the application of inhibitors providing a non-intrusive, low impact treatment with little or no change in appearance. Force Crag Mine in Cumbria (Figure 3), a National Trust industrial heritage site, was protected using an inhibitor containing wax 10 years ago. The wax still provides good protection of the exposed steelwork and the appearance of the structure was not altered during application. There is also particular interest in the use of penetrating inhibitors with pre-stressed and other sensitive or susceptible structures where the use of active electrochemical techniques may not be desirable.

2.3 Cathodic Protection (CP)

Concrete can be cathodically protected using various methods by means of an impressed current cathodic protection (ICCP) or galvanic (sacrificial) system. Both systems work by polarising the reinforcement in an electrical circuit so the anodic, iron-dissolving mechanism is forced to take place at an installed anode. ICCP systems generally use inert long-life electrode such as mixed metal oxide coated titanium. The reinforcement is polarised using an external DC power source. Galvanic systems use less noble metal electrodes, commonly zinc, aluminium or magnesium, which corrode preferentially to the steel and thereby provide the required protection.

2.3.1 Conservative CP systems

The first cathodic protection system at the Silver Jubilee Bridge was installed in 1993 and represented the first major use of coated titanium mesh with a dry-mix sprayed concrete or gunite overlay for CP systems in England. The basic mesh and overlay system was also used on the next two repair schemes, but in 1998, another innovative approach, a hybrid system, was employed. This combined

Figure 3.   Force Crag Mine 10 years after inhibitor wax application.

discrete anodes with mesh and overlay. In an unusual step, dry-mix gunite was used for the concrete repairs, while wet-mix gunite was used for the overlay to minimize dust and noise disruption to a neighbouring school. In 2000 a CP system and patch repairs were used during a repair contract which included extensively contaminated areas next to the abutment and locally affected areas at the highest sections of the approach viaducts. To reduce costs, locally affected areas with difficult access were patch repaired using hand-applied mortar containing corrosion inhibitor to protect against the incipient anode effect.

The systems installed after 2000 were re-designed by reviewing the operating criteria of the existing systems. By employing this technique it was possible to reduce the quantity of anodes used, in some cases by a factor of 3. In addition, the lower current demand meant larger zones could be used, which reduces the number of monitoring probes and power supplies. As an example, one system installed in 1995 used 7 zones to protect one 30 m long beam. Four of these zones had multiple layers of anode mesh. There were 24 reference electrodes and 6 graphite potential probes installed. In 2005 four similar beams were protected as a single zone, with a single layer of mesh anode and 4 reference electrodes.

2.3.2 *Innovative deck solution*

The remaining heavily chloride contaminated bridge element to be protected was the deck. There were, however, limitations in respect of the suitability of the existing systems and accessibility. The bridge deck is 40 m above the River Mersey and Manchester Ship Canal and traffic management is restricted. A mesh and overlay system would certainly be able to provide the current, but the vibrations in the deck caused by traffic would mean there was a risk that the sprayed concrete overlay would debond. Discrete anodes could be installed by roped access, but would require drilling holes into the deck at depth. If the holes were drilled marginally too deep there was a risk of drilling into live traffic. A galvanic system, as previously installed in hybrid systems, would fall under the same restriction. The application of corrosion inhibitors could provide a time limited protection but a more durable solution was required. What was needed was an anode system that could be surface mounted and securely fixed but did not require an overlay. Such a system did not exist in the UK market.

The only other current solution would involve the removal and replacement of the bridge deck. Aside from the traffic chaos associated with its closure, the environmental consequences of this could not be tolerated. The deck contains approximately 1000 m^3 of concrete. The embodied energy in the deck concrete is around 6 TerraJoules, equivalent to the energy produced by 1200 barrels of oil, (Atkins 2010). The diversion of the traffic over the 65 km long alternative route would cause the release of an additional 1000 tons CO_2 per day based on 20% HGV's for the total 90.000 vehicles crossing the bridge per day. This does not take account of the associated disruption to the local economy and population.

After extensive research, a cassette system originally designed for installation on jetties and harbours was identified. The anode sits in a glass fibre filled FRP tray which can be mounted on a concrete surface using sleeved bolts, see Figure 4. In the environment of jetties and harbours the foam never dries out as it is wetted by the tide but on the bridge this would not happen. Moisture is necessary to act as transport medium for the current to the reinforcement protected. An alternative approach was developed using calcium nitrate impregnated glass fibre foam which is able to remain moist simply by being in contact with the atmosphere.

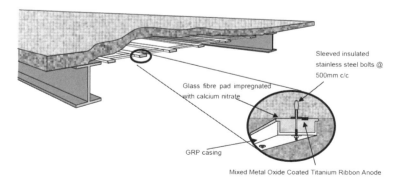

Figure 4.   Cassette system installed on deck soffit.

2.4 Electro-osmosis

An electro-osmosis system has been specifically developed to control moisture levels in a pier of the bridge by the application of controlled low voltage DC pulses. The electronically-controlled system is designed to operate at maximum efficiency while avoiding problems of stray-current corrosion to buried steel. The system is capable of reducing moisture levels in concrete to between 60% and 70% RH, and maintaining this level irrespective of external weather conditions. According to Vernon (1935) corrosion of steel commences at a slow rate at approximately 60% RH and significantly increase at 75–80% RH. These thresholds may be affected by the level of chloride contamination. However, an additional benefit to the removal of excess free moisture is the associated reduction in dissolved salts, particularly chloride, present within the pore solution of the concrete, with the overall effect of reducing chloride ions to below critical levels with respect to chloride-induced corrosion.

The system is also designed to negatively polarise the reinforcement resulting in a degree of cathodic protection, helping to reduce the corrosion risk of embedded steel during the transition period from high to low relative humidity (typically several months), and providing additional protection throughout the life of the installation, Lambert (1997).

The system has been specifically assessed for possible side effects resulting from its operation.

No evidence has been found to indicate significant risks of bond strength reduction, excess alkali generation, hydrogen evolution or stray current corrosion of adjacent discontinuous steel. This was the first such system in the UK. It was installed in 2002 and has sufficiently protected the trial pier.

2.5 Electrochemical chloride extraction and realkalisation

The use of CP can result in a number of potentially beneficial side effects. The ferrous component, being the cathode in a corrosion cell, generates hydroxyl ions which helps maintain a passive oxide film on the surface of the steel and protects it from further corrosion. In addition, because the cathode is negatively charged, ions such as chloride are repelled from the steel and attracted to the anodes.

While these processes occur naturally as a consequence of CP, they can also be optimised as remediation treatments in their own right. The claimed benefit of such techniques is that they can be applied temporarily in order to increase the alkalinity or reduce chloride levels and then be removed. Commercially these techniques are referred to as electrochemical chloride extraction (ECE) and realkalisation, although the former is sometimes confusingly referred to as 'desalination', McFarland (1999).

2.5.1 Realkalisation of concrete

Steel reinforcement is passivated (protected) by the alkaline environment created by the surrounding concrete. Carbonation of the concrete by the acidic reaction with atmospheric carbon dioxide results in the conversion of the normal concrete constituents, calcium hydroxide and calcium silicate hydrates, to calcium carbonate.

This is accompanied by a reduction in alkalinity and loss of protection to the reinforcement, which can then corrode in the presence of oxygen and water. In the past the only remedy for this type of deterioration would be to remove and replace the effected concrete to restore the alkaline environment and in the majority of cases this will continue to be true.

The electrochemical technique of realkalisation restores the alkaline environment around the reinforcement without removal of the carbonated cover concrete. The target pH value is greater than 10.5 which is sufficient to restore and maintain the protective oxide layer. Typically in the realkalisation process a temporary mesh electrode contained within a reservoir of alkaline sodium carbonate solution is attached to the surface of the concrete. An electrical connection is made between the surface mesh and the reinforcement and a current is applied, such that the reinforcement becomes cathodic and the mesh anodic.

The alkaline sodium carbonate ions from the reservoir are transported to the cathode via electro-osmosis. Electrolysis at the cathode simultaneously results in the generation of hydroxyl ions which additionally increase the alkalinity around the reinforcement and so restores the repassivation layer on the steel surface. When the cover zone is saturated (confirmed by testing) the current is disconnected and the external electrode and reservoir are removed. In the case of AAR susceptible concrete it is possible to vary the treatment so that repassivation solely relies on the electrolysis. The concrete surface is then generally coated with a conventional anti-carbonation coating to prevent re-carbonation of the now alkaline pore solutions.

This technique can have advantages where disruption to the normal operation of a structure has to be kept to a minimum.

2.5.2 Chloride extraction

Chloride extraction (desalination) makes use of the same electrochemical principles as realkalisation, see Section 2.5.1 above, except that the primary aim is to remove negatively charged chloride ions from within the concrete, by ion migration, to the surface anode.

The current density required for chloride extraction to be effective is generally much greater than that required for realkalisation. The time period required to reduce the chloride concentration at the reinforcement to acceptable levels is dependent on a number of factors. The application of this technique may be restricted because the required duration to achieve an acceptable chloride level is difficult to estimate. This can create problems with budget and programme.

3 COMPARISON OF ELECTRO-CHEMICAL REPAIR METHODS

The electrochemical repair methods discussed above provide advantages and disadvantages and the suitability of each method should be assessed for each individual structure under consideration

Table 1. Advantages and disadvantages of conventional repair options.

Method	Advantage	Disadvantage
Patch repairs	Quick repair strategy; Small areas; No additional dead load; Can be used with inhibitors or galvanic anodes; Simple access.	Short term solution, <5 years; Ring anode effect—can be controlled with galvanic anodes/ inhibitors; Discoloration.
Inhibitors	No alteration in appearance; Reapplication possible; Good for carbonated structures; Simples access; Simple application.	Short—Medium term solution <10 years Not applicable for excessively damaged structures and chloride content >1% Cl⁻ Must be able to penetrate to the steel.

Table 2. Advantages and disadvantages of Cathodic Protection Systems.

Method	Advantage	Disadvantage
Cathodic protection—ICCP	Long term solution >25 years; Larger structures; Large current; Installation as preventive method feasible; Hydroxyl generation at cathode; Movement of salt ions towards anode; Inert anode (MMO).	Operation and maintenance requirements; Possibility of stray current; Power source required; Hydrogen embrittlement; Increased AAR reaction possible; Full access required.
Mesh & Overlay	Long term solution 25–50 years; Large current output; Robust system.	Additional dead load to structure; Not possible for vibrating structures (bridge decks); Scaffolding required; Surface preparation required; Surface tie wire can cause short circuits; Dust containment from overlay; Reduced headroom; Difficult to repair in case of defect.
Discrete	Long term solution 20–25 years; Protection at depth or remote from accessible face; Anode can be drilled out in case of defect.	Limited to thicker elements; Bore holes—risk of short-circuit; Scaffolding required.
Cassette system	Simple installation; No surface preparation required; Vibrating structures; Installation via roped access.	Vulnerable to theft or damage; Chemicals are irritants.
Cathodic protection—galvanic	Flexibility in application; No power source required; Minimal maintenance; No hydrogen risk.	Medium term solution approx. 10 years; Anode get consumed; Limited protection current; Difficult to demonstrate performance to standards.

Table 3. Advantages and disadvantages of electrochemical repair options.

Method	Advantage	Disadvantage
Electro-osmosis	Removal of excess moisture in structure; Reduction in dissolved salts.	Needs to be on to work.
Realkalisation	Temporarily application; Less disruption to operating structure; No alteration to appearance; Reapplication possible.	Application time difficult to define; Handling large volumes of liquid can be difficult; Greater current, risk of stray current corrosion.
Chloride extraction	Temporary application; No alteration to appearance; Reapplication possible.	Application time difficult to define, it depends on a number of factors—budget estimation difficult; Target level needs to be destructively determined; Greater current, risk of stray current corrosion.

of being repaired. Repair methods should be selected based on the following parameters:

– The intended service life extension;
– Access restrictions;
– Maintenance/monitoring requirements and their budget;
– Structural restrictions—dead load and headroom;
– Noise, dust and environmental impact;
– Time and budget restrictions.

Structures may also be repaired using a combination of several methods. To prevent health and safety risks to the public in the first instance it is possible to remove all delaminated/spalled concrete. In addition to this netting can be installed or regular delamination surveys may be carried out if it is considered necessary to delay the final repair. Table 1 shows the advantages and disadvantages of conventional repair options.

Table 2 shows the advantages and disadvantages of the various CP systems available.

To identify the appropriate system it is important to take all restrictions which may be imposed by the structure into account. In the example of the protection of the deck of the Silver Jubilee Bridge, it was not feasible to install a mesh and overlay CP system or discrete anodes because of the vibrations and limited depth of the deck, respectively. Both options would have, however, easily fulfilled the service life requirements.

Other more conventional repair options were already excluded based on the extended service life requirements and access restrictions which prohibited the closure of the bridge to avoid significant disruption to the regional traffic flows and the local economy. Table 3 gives the advantages and disadvantages of the alternative electrochemical repair options to CP.

4 CONCLUSIONS

There are a variety of electrochemical repair solutions which can be implemented to significantly extend the service life of transport structures affected by reinforcement corrosion. The options discussed in this paper are all appropriate for specific requirements as governed by their respective advantages and disadvantages. Repair strategies are often dominated by budget and lifetime requirements and access restrictions at the structures.

The various corrosion control systems installed at the Silver Jubilee Bridge were carefully selected for their suitability at each repair stage. The holding repairs significantly reduced the risk to health and safety of the public. Corrosion inhibitors were used in patch repairs to provide a more durable solution. The cathodic protection systems installed at the bridge were the most appropriate systems at the time of installation but were under constant review and development to take advantage of technological improvements and to suit the individual requirements. The Intranode Cassette system was chosen as to be the most appropriate to withstand bridge vibrations, reducing installation time and avoiding long-term traffic management.

Every structure and each individual element need to be assessed for their requirements and the most appropriate system needs to be identified by the engineer. Conventional CP systems such as mesh and overlay and discrete anodes can be used in most cases. It is, however, clearly desirable to be able to develop new systems with reduced environmental footprints and improved health and safety considerations for those carrying out the installation. Through relatively modest research and development it is possible to design innovative CP systems that are able to reduce installation time, employing reduced amount of material and capable of significantly extending the life of critical transport structures.

REFERENCES

Atkins, C., Lambert, P., Brueckner, R., Merola, R. & Foster, A. 2010. Sustainable and cost effective solutions to life extension of bridges. In Frangopol, Sause & Kusko (eds.), Bridge Maintenance, Safety, Management and Life-Cycle Optimization; Proc. 5th IABMAS, Philadelphia, USA, Taylor & Francis Group.

Baldwin, N.J.R. & King, E.S. 2003. Field Studies of the Effectiveness of Concrete Repairs, Phase 4 Report: Analysis of the Effectiveness of Concrete Repairs and Project Findings. Research Report 186, Health and Safety Executive, Sudbury, UK.

Lambert, P. 1997. Controlling Moisture, Construction Repair: Concrete Repairs 6.

Lambert, P. & Atkins, C. 2007. Maintaining the Silver Jubilee Bridge—Cathodic protection for a critical causeway. Concrete International.

McFarland, B. 1999. Electrochemical repair using realkalisation and chloride extraction techniques. Concrete Repair Association Guidance Note.

Vernon, W.H.J. 1935. A Laboratory Study of the Atmospheric Corrosion of Metals. Trans. Faraday Society, 31, UK.

Concrete Solutions – Grantham, Mechtcherine & Schneck (eds)
© 2012 Taylor & Francis Group, London, ISBN 978-0-415-61622-5

A new approach for the patch repair of car parks using galvanic anodes

C. Christodoulou & J. Webb
AECOM Europe, UK

G. Glass
Concrete Preservation Technologies, University of Nottingham Innovation Lab, Nottingham, UK

S. Austin & C. Goodier
Loughborough University, UK

ABSTRACT: Car parks constructed with in-situ concrete are generally characterised by very shallow (typically wafer type) slabs which enables fast construction and keeps the self-weight of the structure to a minimum. However, many of these car parks are now displaying signs of significant structural deterioration, mainly due to corrosion damage of the reinforcement leading to spalling of the concrete cover. This paper reviews the corrosion management strategy that was utilised for the concrete repairs of a corrosion damaged car park in the UK. The new approach on this particular scheme has been the positioning of the galvanic anodes. Traditionally they are positioned within the concrete patch repair however, the reinforcement that will be most at risk will be immediately outside this patch repair, and hence in this structure the anodes were placed immediately outside of the patch repair. This paper reviews the performance of these galvanic anodes based on this new approach. The findings help to improve our understanding of the corrosion protection mechanisms and provide a method of assessing performance.

1 INTRODUCTION

Multi storey car parking structures are a common part of our infrastructure, many of which were built in the construction boom of 1970s using reinforced concrete. The typical structural arrangement was one-way spanning ribbed or two-way spanning waffle floor slabs. These particular structural arrangements offer shallow slab depths throughout the structure as opposed to a traditional one or two way spanning slab with deep beams. The load is distributed between the numerous narrower and shallower ribs and is cost effective for larger spans.

Deterioration of concrete structures can be simplified to the deterioration of the concrete itself and deterioration due to corrosion of the reinforcement (which consequently also has an impact upon the concrete). Under normal circumstances concrete offers a highly alkaline environment with a pH in excess of 13. Under these conditions, the steel reinforcement develops a protective and passive oxide layer (Page & Tradeaway 1982).

However, the presence of chlorides (due to the spreading of de-icing salts during winter maintenance) and carbon dioxide (CO_2) in the atmosphere are some of the major factors responsible for corrosion damage. The former will affect mainly road surfaces and vertical surfaces close to the road, whereas the latter tends to affect all the atmospherically exposed elements. However, carbonation is a much slower process and usually affects areas where there is low cover to the reinforcement. Chloride induced corrosion, once initiated, can propagate and quickly reach very high intensities.

Patch repairs are commonly used to restore the concrete profile. For concrete deterioration relating to carbonation, patch repairs can be very effective as the freshly alkaline mortar will restore the passivity to the reinforcement. However, when the corrosion damage is chloride induced significant quantities of contaminated but sound concrete need to be removed. Bridge Advice Note 35 (BA 1990) suggests that areas which show chloride concentrations greater than 0.3% by weight of cement and half-cell potential measurements are higher than −350 mV should be removed. This approach often makes patch repairs uneconomic for chloride contaminated structures (Christodoulou 2008).

Galvanic anodes have been employed in association with patch repairs to repair reinforced concrete structures. Galvanic anodes are based on the principle that different metals produce different potentials (Broomfield 2000). Therefore, particular metals can be used which will corrode sacrificially to protect the steel reinforcement and offer a protective effect. Compared with a traditional Impressed Current Cathodic Protection system their main advantage is their lack of need for a power supply. In addition, there is no associated complex wiring installation and performance monitoring is less complicated. However, it is acknowledged that galvanic anodes have a lower protective current output and as a result might be ineffective in concrete with high corrosion rates (Christodoulou et al., 2009).

Galvanic anodes are traditionally installed within the patch repair. However, these anodes can suffer from poor current distribution. This can be due to the resistivity of the concrete, the arrangement and density of the reinforcement, the concentration of chlorides etc. In general, when patch repairs are to be combined with galvanic anodes, the resistivity of the repair material should be limited to ensure that the protective current from the anodes is delivered to the reinforcement outside the patch repair, which is recognised as an area of high risk (Page & Sergi 2000).

Half-cell potential mapping is routinely used to assess the corrosion risk. However, the same technique is also utilised to assess the presence of anodes within the patch repair. The work by Elsener (2001) suggests that although it is not currently a requirement by a code of practice to monitor the galvanic anodes, it can be a very effective approach to provide to the client the re-assurance that the rehabilitation design is successful. Also this data can be utilised to revise the original design if necessary.

The objective of this work was to develop a new design approach for concrete patch repairs in association with the use of galvanic anodes. This design approach was used on the concrete repairs of a multi storey concrete car park (MSCP) in the UK where the galvanic anodes were installed within the parent concrete rather than in the patch repair. The anodes were then monitored to assess their performance, thus improving our understanding of the corrosion protection mechanisms.

2 INITIAL SURVEY

The MSCP was built in the early 1970s and it has a concrete one-way spanning ribbed type deck arrangement. The structure is receiving high amounts of daily vehicular traffic as it is serving a major shopping centre. The structure received waterproofing to its ground and top floors in the approximate late 1990s in order to minimise the ingress of chlorides to the originally unprotected deck.

During the preliminary inspection of the structure it was identified that it suffered significant structural damage to the corrosion of the reinforcement (Fig. 1). This was evident on the decks where the reinforcement was exposed but also on the soffits where there was significant spalling of concrete. In addition, it was apparent that the structure suffered from a significant degree of dynamic cracking and water dripping from one level to the other was observed in a large proportion of the structure. The original construction joints were of poor construction quality and water dripping was again evident. Finally, the majority of the expansion joints had failed allowing water to pass through them and damage the soffits of individual levels.

Following the preliminary investigation to identify and record the defects and the analysis of historical data made available by the client, additional testing was undertaken to verify the cause of corrosion of the reinforcement. Intrusive investigations were undertaken in 1997, 1999 and 2008 to determine the depths of carbonation and chloride levels while at the same time assessing the probability of corrosion activity with potential mapping.

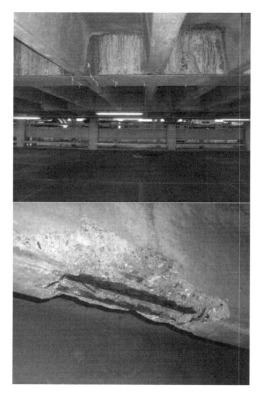

Figure 1. General condition of the soffit.

Carbonation was identified to be an issue for the parapets as they exhibited a very low cover to the reinforcement. However, the decks appeared to have high levels of chloride concentration at the depth of reinforcement and based on BA 35 (BA 1990) there was a significantly high risk of corrosion. By 2008, there were locations where the chloride levels were up to 2.92% by weight of cement even at a depth of 30 to 55 millimetres. Furthermore, the overall depth of the slab spanning between the ribs was at best found to be around 80 mm. Coupled with the low cover to the deck's reinforcing mesh, there were several delaminated areas.

From the profile of the chloride levels their concentration reduced with depth and they were also reduced as higher levels of the structure were tested. This suggests that chlorides were brought to the unprotected surface of the decks by cars and penetrated the concrete surface, rather than being cast within the concrete. However, on the roof decks, de-icing salt was spread routinely to prevent ponding water from freezing. The ribs of the car park were in general in good condition. However, corrosion damage was observed in areas where the dynamic cracks on the deck were leaking.

3 DESIGN

The client's brief called for essential repairs to the car park in order to restore the structural integrity and limit the need for major concrete repairs within the next 10 year period. The client did not favour electrochemical treatment with a complex monitoring system as they did not have the technical expertise to monitor and maintain the system. In addition, they had negative previous experience with Impressed Current Cathodic Protection (ICCP) which was in line with similar experiences published by the Virginia Department of Transportation. Brown & Sharp (2008) published a survey of cathodic protection systems on Virginia bridges which identified that a number of ICCP systems were no longer operational. The report concluded that there was inadequate transfer of responsibilities for maintenance and operation of the ICCP systems and they do require specialist involvement.

For this particular project the most suitable corrosion management strategy was that of concrete patch repairs in conjunction with the use of galvanic anodes. Other rehabilitation methods such as impressed current cathodic protection, chloride extraction and re-alkalisation were also considered but not pursued due to their associated technical implications, cost issues and traffic management on a fully live car park.

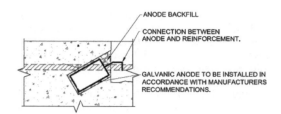

Figure 2. Galvanic anode design.

Galvanic anodes are traditionally installed within the patch repair (British Standards, 2000; Broomfield, 2000; Sergi, 2009). In addition, it is a requirement that the repair material should have a resistivity limited in the range of 50% to 200% of that of the parent concrete (British Standards, 2000, CPA 2011). This approach enforces a limitation to the quality of the repair material in order to ensure that the protective current will be able to flow to steel reinforcement.

With concrete patch repairs it is recognised that the reinforcement adjacent to the patch will be at the greatest risk due to the "incipient anode" effect (Raupach, 2006; Broomfield, 2000; Page & Sergi, 2000). However, it is acknowledged that the protective effect afforded by the galvanic anode will be dependent on resistivity of the concrete, moisture levels and steel density. The design of the repairs aimed to bypass the above issues by installing the galvanic anodes in parent concrete adjacent to the patch repair. Figure 2 illustrates the design approach and the anode installation.

4 INSTALLATION AND RESULTS

Following identification of defects, breaking out of the concrete and cleaning of the reinforcement, galvanic anodes containing approximately 65grams of zinc were installed in drilled holes in the parent concrete at the periphery of the patch (Fig. 3) and filled with proprietary putty to physically separate them from the repair concrete. The steel connection was then made with the steel present within the repair area. The original design required the anodes to be placed at a spacing of not greater than 350 mm.

The anodes were monitored during the repair contract in order to assess their performance. The monitoring was undertaken by means of half-cell potential measurements. It aimed to assess that installed anodes were active and also quantify the range of the protective effect afforded from the anodes in this particular structure. During the initial testing of the anodes no steel connections to the reinforcement were available. A connection was made to the adjacent steel fencing and therefore all measurements will be relative to the steel fencing and are not absolute values. The data shows changes in potential as a function of distance that result from the electric field produced by installed anodes and steel cathode in the concrete at the time of the measurement.

Figure 4 illustrates patch repair no. 10 which was undertaken as a trial during November 2010. In total 9 anodes were installed in a 1.1 m² area of repair. The first test undertaken aimed to identify that all the anodes were indeed active by undertaking potential mapping around the periphery of the patch. Measurements were obtained at approximately 50 mm intervals around the periphery of the patch, which assisted to locate the anodes with high accuracy.

Figure 5 illustrates the results of the potential measurements. As discussed previously, the potential values are relative to the steel fencing connection and not those of the reinforcement.

From the results it can be observed that all 9 anodes installed were active and offered a protective effect.

The anodes on the patch repair were checked for activity at approximately 15 days after placement of the concrete (24/11/2010) and again after 2 months in-service to determine their performance over time. However, the second time not all the faces of the patch repair could be surveyed due to the presence of vehicles.

Following, a second test was undertaken in order to assess the polarisation effect afforded by the anodes. The reference electrode was moved away from faces 1 and 4 of the patch repair at intervals of 50 mm. Figure 6 illustrates the results of the potential mapping. It can be observed that in both cases the anodes polarised the reinforcement up to approximately 700 mm away from the edge of the patch. The test was repeated on several other patches protected with sacrificial anodes two

Figure 3. Typical patch repair showing three installed galvanic anodes, before the application of the patch repair material.

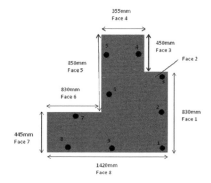

Figure 4. Positions of anodes in patch repair no. 10 (all dimensions in mm).

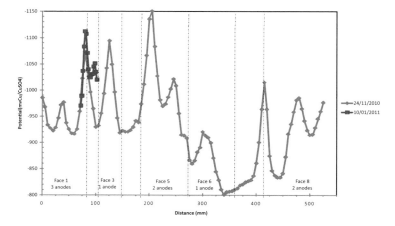

Figure 5. Potentials around patch repair no. 10.

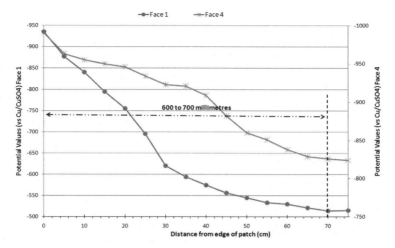

Figure 6. Relative polarisation effect from anodes installed on patch no. 10 after 15 days (Face 1) and after 2 months (Face 4).

months after installation. The anodes influenced the potential in the parent concrete to a distance of between 400 and 800 mm from the edge of the patch. The distance of 400 mm was measured in the case of a patch containing one anode only and was measured away from the patch on the far side to the face containing the anode.

5   DISCUSSION

A correctly-installed high quality repair material will ensure that the repair will not suffer from any substantial cracking, the concrete matrix will not be as porous and the resultant resistivity will be high. All the above will assist to ensure the longevity of the repair and in this particular case achieving a repair with higher resistivity than the parent concrete will have a favourable effect. The repair, due to its higher resistivity, will be shielded from chloride ingress and protective current from the galvanic anodes will flow preferentially to the lower resistivity parent concrete where the reinforcement is at a higher risk of corrosion.

Following installation and testing of the galvanic anodes it was identified that they were very effective for the particular structure and the given environmental conditions. In particular the polarisation distance was considerable, indicating that the anodes offered a protective effect at a significant distance from the repair.

The findings formed the basis for an increase in the anode spacing in this structure from a maximum of 350 mm to 600 mm. This increase in anode spacing offered significant cost savings to the overall costs of the project. Furthermore, in locations where multiple small patches were to be undertaken, the galvanic anodes were placed strategically in order to achieve the desired protective effect whilst at the same time keeping the number of the anodes installed at a minimum.

The findings of the study suggest that potential mapping is an effective technique for the assessment of the performance of galvanic anodes. It does not require the use of highly sophisticated equipment and it can be undertaken by non-specialised Engineers. The potential mapping can assess whether the anodes are active or not and also identify their polarisation effect to the adjacent reinforcement. This suggestion is in line with the work undertaken by Elsener (2001) who also used potential mapping to assess the effectiveness of concrete repairs in reinforced concrete structures.

Traditionally, half-cell potential mapping in the UK is undertaken based on a 500 mm grid. ASTM C-876 (2009) suggests that, for decks with a large surface area, a grid up to 1.2 m may be employed for rapid corrosion assessment of the structure although it is recognised that localised corrosion spots might not be identified. In these localised areas of corrosion the potential measurements might change by several hundred millivolts in less than 300 mm. Undertaking potential mapping at a small grid (50 mm) has the advantage that any potential localised corroding spots will be identified. In addition, the polarisation effect of the anodes can be better determined.

It is suggested that a new criterion is adopted when assessing the performance of the galvanic anodes through the use of half-cell potential mapping. The patch repairs receiving the galvanic anodes should be mapped around their perimeter to assess whether the galvanic anodes installed are active and provide a protective effect. In addition, the polarisation effect offered by the anodes should be checked in order to assess the adequacy of the original design. Anode spacing can then be revised depending on the measured polarisation effect and the required design life of the repairs.

6 CONCLUSIONS

The results of this work suggest that the following can be established:

- Galvanic anodes installed in cavities within the parent concrete can be successfully installed in order to protect the steel reinforcement in the parent concrete without compromising the quality of the patch repair.
- The protective current is delivered to the steel outside the patch which is at greatest future corrosion risk as opposed to clean steel within the patch repair. Materials used for the concrete repairs do not affect the flow of the protective current from the galvanic anodes to the steel in the parent concrete. High quality repair materials and bond coats can be used to prevent future deterioration and prevent chloride ingress down the interface between the repair and parent concrete.
- Close interval potential mapping (50 mm spacing) is an effective technique to assess the performance of galvanic anodes. Close spacing of the measurements has the advantage that localised corrosion spots can be detected if present.
- A new criterion for the assessment of the performance of galvanic anodes is proposed. The anodes should illustrate a measurable influence on the steel potentials away from the area of patch repair that is preferably at least 400 mm from the edge of the patched area.

ACKNOWLEDGEMENTS

The authors would like to thank the CICE of Loughborough University and the EPSRC for supporting the lead author throughout the duration of this project.

REFERENCES

ASTM 2009. *Standard Test Method for Corrosion Potentials of Uncoated Reinforcing Steel in Concrete*, American Society for Testing and Materials, West Conshohocken, Pennsylvania, USA.
BA 35/1990. *Inspection and Repair of Concrete Highway Structures*, Departmental Standard, UK.
British Standards Institution (2000). BS EN:12696, *Cathodic Protection of Steel in Concrete*, London.
Broomfield, J.P. 2000. *The principles and practice of galvanic cathodic protection for reinforced concrete structures*. Monograph No: 6. Corrosion Prevention Association, Bordon, UK.
Brown, M.C. & Sharp, S.R. 2008. "Survey of Cathodic Protection Systems on Virginia Bridges" Report VTRC 07-R35, Virginia Transportation Research Council (www.virginiadot.org/vtrc/main/online_reports/pdf/07-r35.pdf)
Christodoulou, C. (2008). Electrochemical treatment methods of corroded reinforcement in concrete, 2nd International Conference on Concrete Repair, Rehabilitation and Retrofitting, Cape Town, South Africa.
Christodoulou, C., Glass, G. & Webb, J. 2009. Corrosion management of concrete structures, *The Structural Engineer*, Volume 87, 23/24, December 2009.
Corrosion Prevention Association 2011. Technical Note 19, Acceptable electrical resistivities of concrete repairs for cathodic protection systems.
Elsener, B. 2001. Half-cell potential mapping to assess repair work on RC structures, *Construction and Building Materials*, 15, 133–139.
Page, C.L. & Sergi, G. 2000. Developments in cathodic protection applied to reinforced concrete, *Journal of Materials in Civil Engineering*, (1), 8–15, month??? 2000.
Page, C.L. & Treadaway, K.W.J. 1982. Aspects of the electrochemistry of steel in concrete. *Nature*, 297, No. 5862, 109–115.
Raupach, M. 2006. Patch repairs on reinforced concrete structures—Model investigations on the required size and practical consequences, *Cement and Concrete Composites*, 28, 679–684.
Sergi, G. 2009. Ten year results of galvanic sacrificial anodes in steel reinforced concrete, EUROCORR, Nice, France.

Concrete Solutions – Grantham, Mechtcherine & Schneck (eds)
© 2012 Taylor & Francis Group, London, ISBN 978-0-415-61622-5

Short-term benefits of cathodic protection of steel in concrete

J. Pacheco
Materials & Environment, Delft University of Technology, CiTG, Delft, The Netherlands

R.B. Polder
Materials & Environment, Delft University of Technology, CiTG, Delft, The Netherlands
TNO Built Environment and Geosciences, Delft, The Netherlands

A.L.A. Fraaij
Materials & Environment, Delft University of Technology, CiTG, Delft, The Netherlands

J.M.C. Mol
Materials Science and Engineering, Delft University of Technology, 3ME, Delft, The Netherlands

ABSTRACT: Cathodic Protection (CP) of steel in concrete has been used over the past decades in order to increase the remaining service life of concrete infrastructure. CP involves the application of an electrical current to the corroding reinforcing bars, thus stopping and preventing further corrosion. The application of current on the reinforcing steel involves an alteration of the conditions inside corrosion pits that need further investigation. In this study, CP was applied to four concrete specimens, exposed separately to salt/dry cycles, carbonation or mixed-in chlorides, with actively corroding bars. Afterwards, such specimens were exposed to outdoor (unsheltered) environment until 2010. The four of them were subjected to CP at fixed voltage and the current density was monitored for 18 days. Significant changes were found during the first 24 hours of CP. It was found that the immediate current density was related to the corrosion rate before CP. Then, a steep decrease was observed during the first 4 to 8 hours, remaining stable afterwards. Destructive analysis and assessment of the deterioration of reinforcement was carried out once the CP period was finished. This included measurements of the size in pits and estimations of the volume loss. With the use of a previously proposed model, approximations of the pH inside corrosion pits were carried out, by relating the electrical charge, the neutralization of hydrogen and volume pit with results of pH $\approx$ 2–3.

Keywords: Corrosion, cathodic protection, pitting, repair

1 INTRODUCTION

An oxide film known as 'passive' layer protects reinforcing steel embedded in concrete. This layer is produced by the action of the pore solution (pH $\approx$ 13) and oxygen, remaining thermodynamically stable under certain conditions. However, passivation is destroyed when the chloride concentration is high enough or when the pH of the pore solution is reduced to near-neutral values. Under chloride attack, localized corrosion deterioration, in the form of pitting corrosion, takes place. Furthermore, the effect of reduced pH dissolves the passive layer over the whole surface of the steel bars. When pitting corrosion is affecting the reinforcing steel, the pH inside such pits is believed to be acidic (Arup 1983), even to significantly low values if enough oxygen is available

(pH~1–2) (Gonzalez 1996). Yet, quantitative studies regarding the magnitude of such pH have not been reported in literature. Cathodic protection (CP) has been applied successfully to concrete infrastructure in order to increase its remaining service life. One of the primary aims of CP is to stop and prevent further corrosion deterioration (Pedeferri 1995). Also, the neutralization of pH inside corrosion pits may be considered as a secondary effect (Polder 2011).

In 1998, concrete specimens were cast and exposed to either chlorides (salt/dry cycles or mixed-in during casting) or accelerated carbonation, which resulted in different corrosion conditions for embedded steel bars. The behavior of electrochemical parameters (corrosion potential, concrete resistivity, corrosion rate and chloride content) was studied over a period of 2.5 years testing (Polder 2002). In 2010, four specimens were selected and subjected to CP current.

In this paper, the short-term development of CP current in concrete specimens with different degrees of corrosion deterioration will be described.

2 EXPERIMENTAL DESIGN

In 1998, reinforced concrete prisms of $100 \times 100 \times 300$ mm were cast with two groups of smooth steel bars of 8 mm in diameter: the first group at 10 mm and the other at 30 mm cover depth, as shown in Figure 1. The steel bars were previously treated with sand paper polishing and cleaned with acetone. Four stainless steel screws (grade 316) of 5 mm diameter were placed in pairs at 10 and 50 mm cover depth, respectively. Activated titanium (Ti*) wires of 10 mm length with insulated copper wires were used as embedded reference electrodes. At the beginning, the potential of the Ti* electrodes was close to that of Ag/AgCl (saturated KCl). From four weeks after casting, one face of each specimen was exposed to salt/dry cycles of 24h in 3% NaCl solution and 6 days in 20°C and 50% RH for 26 weeks. Specimens exposed to accelerated carbonation were stored in conditions of 5% CO_2, 20°C and 50% RH for 26 weeks. Mixed-in chloride specimens were cast and stored in a room with 20°C and 80% RH for the same period. After that, the specimens were stored in an unsheltered environment in The Netherlands for 10 years.

Four concrete specimens were selected in order to study the short-term effects of CP of steel in concrete according to their concrete mixture and exposure conditions: CEM I with 0.45 w/b ratio (1450-SD) and CEM III 0.55 w/b ratio (3550-SD) specimens exposed to salt/dry cycles, CEM I with 0.55 w/b ratio (1550-C) carbonated concrete and CEM I with 0.55 w/b ratio (1552-MC) with mixed-in chloride at 2% of cement weight.

Two separated carbon fiber strip anodes were attached to the exposed face of the specimen with a layer of cementitious mortar and kept in a fog room (20°C, >90% RH) for 24 hours. Then, bars to be protected were connected to a resistance of 10Ω in order to measure electrical current density to each bar by Ohm's Law.

In all four specimens, two bars out of three for each cover depth were subjected to CP, leaving the central bar unprotected (10C and 30C). Reference bars were kept unprotected in order to monitor changes in their potential before and during CP and during depolarization.

The electrical resistance (R) of the cell was measured between the carbon anode and each bar at 10 or 30 mm of cover. These measurements were carried out with an ESCORT resistance-meter at 120 Hz AC. The corrosion potential (E) values were measured with the use of a high impedance voltmeter HP-972 A, between each mild steel bar and the closest activated titanium (Ti*) reference electrode. Linear polarization resistance (Rp) measurements were carried out with a CorrOcean Multicorr MKII device. The Rp test involved the (three) bars of the same cover depth as alternatively working, reference and counter electrodes, without correction for ohmic drop (Polder 2001). The exposed area of the bar (0.0011 m²) and B value (B = 26) were given as input for the test. As a result, the outcome of the Rp was reported as corrosion rate (CR).

Before any CP current density was applied to the bars, each specimen was stored inside a plastic box with a 10 mm water level at the bottom, and separated from the others in order to avoid electrolytic contact. After 24 hours, values of corrosion potential of anodes and bars with the embedded Ti* reference electrodes, corrosion rate by LPR and cell electrical resistance were measured.

The protected bars were subjected to 1.4V for 18 days and the CP current was monitored. Afterwards, depolarization measurements were carried out and another period of CP at 1.2V was applied for 15 days, which are not presented in this paper. Next, the specimens were split and the steel bars removed. Visual inspection of the bars was carried out and the size and volume of corrosion pits were measured. Corrosion pits were considered to have a half-spherical shape, in order to measure the diameter and the depth of the pit and estimate the volume. Modeling of pH inside corrosion pits considered that the whole pit was filled with liquid. A previously proposed model (Polder 2009; Polder 2011), estimates the pH in liquids inside pits by relating the electrical current density flow and OH^- production during CP. According to this model, the CP current has an effect on the neutralization of acid inside corrosion pits; and when the

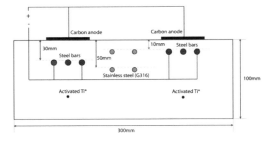

Figure 1. Schematic figure of CP in concrete specimens.

liquid is neutralized, the CP current decreased due to the increase in the polarization resistance of the system. Therefore, when the current became stable, it was concluded that the acid must have been neutralized. In this study, the first 24 hours of CP were investigated and the estimation of pH inside corrosion pits carried out. The estimations of pH were carried out with the use of Equations 1, 2 and 3, as follows:

$$M_{H^+} = \frac{Q}{F} \qquad (1)$$

$$a_{H^+} = \frac{M_{H^+}}{V_{H^+}} \qquad (2)$$

$$pH = -\log(a_{H^+}) \qquad (3)$$

where M_{H^+} is the amount of hydrogen ions in mole, Q is the charge in A·s (Coulomb) over the period of acid neutralization, F is Faraday's constant (96500 A·s/mole), a_{H^+} is the activity of H^+ in moles/litre and V_{H^+} is the volume of acid liquid in litres.

The measurements of the volume of corrosion pits were carried out assuming a regular half-spherical shape of the pit, therefore, diameter and depth of the pits were measured using a caliper for pit sizes >0.1 mm. For smaller pits, the estimated volume assumed a diameter of 0.1 mm.

3 RESULTS AND DISCUSSION

3.1 Electrochemical measurements

The results of electrochemical parameters: corrosion potential (E), corrosion rate (CR) and electrical resistance (R) before CP are shown in Table 1.

In this table, the reinforcing bars were labeled according to their cover depth and relative position. In this sense, according to Figure 1, the bar at 10 mm cover depth in the left side of a group was named 10 L. This labeling system was applied to the rest of the bars with C referring to central and R to right positions. A10 is related to the anode strip in front of the group of bars at 10 mm depth, while A30 refers to the anode close to the group of 30 mm. 10R and 50R are related to the stainless steel bars used for resistivity measurements at 10 and 50 mm cover depth.

The table shows significant differences among the concrete specimens. First, corrosion potentials of the steel bars show that the most negative potentials were observed in the bars embedded in the 1550-C specimen. This tendency was also found when measuring the potential of the anode. Such behavior is probably caused by changes in the pH and chemical composition of pore solution and pore structure. The most positive values of potential were found in the 3550-SD specimen; also, the highest values of electrical resistance were found in this specimen. In this case, the slag content slowed down the deterioration of steel bars. For specimens cast with Portland cement, the highest corrosion rate value was found in 1450-SD followed by 1552-MC. In these two specimens, values of electrical resistance were found to be the lowest of the four. The potential of carbon anodes, one at 10 mm and the other at 30 mm from the steel bars, showed considerable differences before any current was applied. These variations may be attributed to changes in the chemical composition of the pore solution (RILEM TC 154-EMC 2003).

In order to check the Ti* potential, an additional set of tests against an external Ag/AgCl 3M KCl

Table 1. Electrochemical parameters of concrete specimens before CP, after 24 hr in contact with water.

Bars	1450-SD E vs Ti* (mV)	CR (μm/y)	R (kΩ)	3550-SD E vs Ti* (mV)	CR (μm/y)	R (kΩ)	1550-C E vs Ti* (mV)	CR (μm/y)	R (kΩ)	1552-MC E vs Ti* (mV)	CR (μm/y)	R (kΩ)
10L	−429	20.8	1.5	−409	2.5	8.3	−622	3.3	2.1	−428	12.8	2.7
10C	−452	47.5	1.2	−393	2.8	8.3	−623	3.3	2.1	−330	12.2	2.5
10R	−429	21.1	1.4	−394	2.7	7.3	−622	3.4	2.0	−325	5.9	2.5
A10	−72	–	–	−120	–	–	−274	–	–	−102	–	–
30L	−414	10.9	2.6	−277	1.2	14.5	−547	2.8	3.2	−407	18.2	2.1
30C	−348	32.5	2.6	−273	1.2	15.3	−626	2.9	3.2	−448	20.5	2.2
30R	−328	10.5	3.5	−276	1.9	17.4	−627	2.6	3.2	−422	8.2	2.5
A30	−58	–	–	−138	–	–	−235	–	–	−109	–	–
10R	–	–	5.8	–	–	15.3	–	–	3.5	–	–	1.6
50R	–	–	2.5	–	–	18.4	–	–	4.9	–	–	1.3

*Note: shadowed cells are bars subject to CP.

Table 2. Ep of steel bars, carbon (Anode) and Ti* electrodes vs. Ag/AgCl 3M KCl electrode.

Electrode	1450-SD	3550-SD	1550-C	1552-MC
10L	−114	+26	+31	−74
10C	−214	+5	−56	−239
10R	−191	−31	−23	−112
Anode	+90	+131	+153	+86
Ti*−a	+69	+224	+378	+117
30L	−226	+71	−199	+57
30C	−133	+94	−148	−205
30R	−94	+74	0	−263
Anode	+92	+134	+153	+78
Ti*−b	+58	+223	+376	+127

Note: Ti*−a is near bars at 10 mm depth; Ti*−b is near bars at 30 mm.

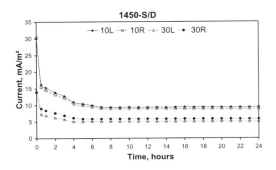

Figure 2. Current density of CP bars in specimen 1450-S/D, mA/m^2 over 24 h.

electrode were carried out. The results of these measurements are shown in Table 2. The potential of bars and anodes vs Ag/AgCl electrode was influenced by the particular conditions of the specimens. The potential difference between Ag/AgCl and Ti* electrodes should be about 50 mV in ordinary conditions. However, similar values were only found in the 1450-SD. In the case of specimen 3550-SD, the slag content reduced the pH of the pore solution. Obviously, the carbonated specimen reported the highest difference between Ti* and Ag/AgCl electrodes which is most probably due to drop of the pH in the pore solution by carbonation. Finally, 1552-MC reported values that are in between those of 1450-SD and 3550-SD. It seems that changes in the microstructure and the presence of chlorides in the pore solution may have influenced its pH. This evidence shows the effect of variations of pH on the electrochemical potential of the Ti* electrodes.

In propagation, on the other hand, the values of corrosion rate and electrical resistance are related to the characteristics of the pore structure. Concrete resistivity (which is related to electrical resistance of the pore network) has significant influence on the corrosion rate after initiation (Andrade 1996; Polder 2001).

3.2 Cathodic protection

The values of CP current to each electrode were recorded during 18 days, with a driving voltage of 1.4V over 0.0011 m^2 of steel surface. After 18 days, the current was stopped for depolarization of the system for 48 hours.

Figure 2 shows the CP current density of electrodes in specimen 1450-SD over the first 24 hours. In this figure, reinforcement at 10 mm

cover depth showed high values of current density at time (t = 0), which was immediately after starting CP. The current density in electrodes at 30 mm depth was nearly half of that consumed by bars at 10 mm. A gradual reduction of current density on each electrode took place between t = 0 and 7 hours for bars at 10 mm; and 4 hours for those at 30 mm of depth. This period is referred as 'transition' for the rest of this paper. In transition, the neutralization of pH inside corrosion pits takes place (Polder 2011). The point in time at which the gradual reduction is finished (7 hours for bars at 10 mm and 4 hours at 30 mm) is considered as a turning point. After this turning point, the current density remains stable during the rest of the exposure period with almost no variation. The current density of bars at 10 mm remained higher (with a ratio of ca. 2) compared to bars at 30 mm cover depth. Also, the cell resistance between bars at 30 mm is higher than that for bars at 10 mm (also in a ratio of ca. 2) as shown in Table 1. Therefore, the difference between current density demand of bars at 10 mm and 30 mm is influenced by the combined action of corrosion rate before CP and in the cell resistance. Before the turning point has been reached, current demand during the transition period includes the current required to neutralize pH inside corrosion pits and the current required for cathodic protection. After the transition period has ended, the current density of the CP bars is consumed mainly by cathodic reactions.

In the case of specimen 3550-SD, the initial current density at t = 0 was considerably lower than in 1450-SD as shown in Figure 3. Again, bars at 10 mm demanded more current immediately after starting CP while bars at 30 mm required less current density. The ratio between current density requirements of bars at 10 mm and 30 mm and cell resistance was 2:1. The transition period lasted 4 hours for bars at 10 mm, and 2 hours for bars at 30 mm. As in 1450-SD, current density of 10 mm bars remained higher than bars at 30 mm depth in the stable period.

As a summary of specimens exposed to salt/dry cycles, concrete containing Portland cement showed that current density for all protected bars was significantly higher than with blended slag cement. In slag concrete, chloride ingress is delayed due to a denser pore structure (Polder 2002). The influence of slag had increased the required time at which corrosion had started and most probably, the redistribution of chlorides after the salt/dry cycles. Another condition for the lower current density is the higher resistivity of such specimens.

The current to steel bars in specimen 1552-MC is shown in Figure 4. This specimen reported similar values of current density of bars at 10 mm and the bar 30R. However, bar 30L consumed more current than the other three protected bars. Chlorides were added to the fresh mix of this concrete specimen, thus all the bars were exposed to a roughly equal amount of chlorides. In this case, this behavior was attributed to local defects of the steel-concrete interface, which may be related to deficiencies during the fabrication of the specimens. This was confirmed visually when the bars were extracted from the specimens at the end of the testing period. In the transition period, the

decrease of current density in these bars lasts until four hours in all cases. Even the bar 30 L which had higher current density demand stabilized its current density at this time. Still, the current density in the bar 30 L was around twice as much as the rest of the bars.

This behavior gives some important aspects to consider. For instance, an appropriate evaluation of the deterioration of steel bars in concrete structures is important when designing a CP system. An optimized CP system should consider the differences in corrosion of bars, in order to apply sufficient current density such that the bars with higher demands will still be protected, but at the same time, it would be economically efficient to avoid overprotection of the reinforcement. In chloride-contaminated concrete, the time during which the current density is gradually reduced depends on this parameter. Bars with higher corrosion deterioration are expected to have deeper and bigger corrosion pits filled with acidic solutions. Therefore, the volume of acid to be neutralized is higher than in less corroded bars. The time required for acid neutralization inside corrosion pits will depend on this factor.

Results of current to bars embedded in carbonated concrete are shown in Figure 5. Initial values of current were between 8–13 mA/m² for bars at 30 mm and 10 mm respectively with a ratio c.a. 1.6. The gradual reduction of current density in the transition period lasted until 5 hours for bars at 30 mm and 7 hours for bars at 10 mm depth. The length of the transition period in carbonated concrete was longer than in salt/dry concrete, because an overall (general) reduction of pH results in the breakdown of the passive layer over the whole exposed surface of the steel bar. Visual inspection of the bars in this specimen showed that a high number of small pits (diameter <0.1 mm) were covering the exposed steel. This kind of overall pitting deterioration might be the reason for the increased current to bars. The application of current to reinforcement in concrete also leads to additional or

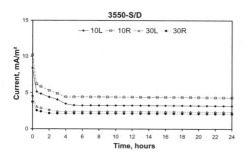

Figure 3. Current density of CP bars in specimen 3550-S/D, mA/m² over 24 h.

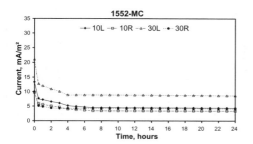

Figure 4. Electrical current density of CP bars in specimen 1552-MC, mA/m² over 24 h.

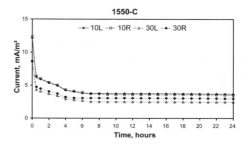

Figure 5. Current density of CP bars in specimen 1550-C, mA/m² over 24 h.

secondary benefits (Pedeferri 1995; Mietz 1998). In the case of carbonated concrete, changes in pore structure and chemical composition of the pore solution prevent the use of the model. The pH of carbonated concrete determines the conditions of either passivation or corrosion. In this study, the application of CP in carbonated concrete is more related to the combined effect of realkalisation of concrete and cathodic protection of steel. The effect of concrete realkalisation must be taken into account for the demand of current. The transition period during early CP application is influenced by the demand of current for production of OH⁻ ions at the surface of reinforcement. This implies that the current becomes stable after the pH in the steel-concrete interface is raised to a certain value. The combined effect of realkalisation and cathodic protection on values of 4-hour depolarization has also been reported (Bertolini 2003). In this research, values of depolarization were not higher than 100 mV at 10 mA/m² until CP had been applied for 4 months.

3.3 Discussion

The relationship between the initial CP current (t = 0), and the corrosion rate is shown in Figure 6. It appears that, the current density immediately after applying CP depends on the state of corrosion in each bar; with high corrosion rates related to higher current density values with a correlation factor of 0.86.

The correlation between the corrosion rate and initial current density after 24 hours of CP is shown in Figure 7. The relationship between these two parameters is as good as the correlation of corrosion rate and initial current density as shown in Figure 8. The slope of the trend line is lower than that of current density at t = 0. This suggests that the success of CP is determined by the corrosion state of the bars, modified by external parameters

(temperature, moisture content, etc.) A model to predict such behavior may have the form:

$$y = ax + b \qquad (4)$$

where y is the CP current density, x is the corrosion rate of bars and parameters: a and b depend on other mechanisms. Factor a should be related to the total volume of acidic liquid in the pit. As the liquid is neutralized, the slope of the trendline will be lower towards and eventually near zero (t = ∞). Factor b is related to concrete properties like electrical resistance (influenced by cement type, water-to-binder ratio, etc.) and the chemical composition of the pore solution (in case of carbonated concrete). The bars that had low corrosion rates still consumed current density when CP was applied due to cathodic reactions on the steel surface.

It should be noted that the slope of the trend line after 24 hours is one order of magnitude lower than that at t = 0. As the neutralization process is achieved, the cathodic reactions will determine the CP current to bars. As for the cell resistance, Figure 8 shows the relationship between the inverse of cell resistance of bars and the initial current density in specimens subject to CP. This figure

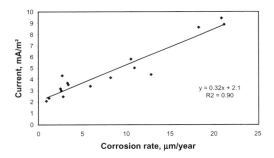

Figure 7. Relationship between initial corrosion rate and CP electric current density in treated bars, t = 24 h.

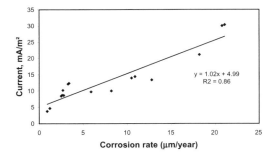

Figure 6. Corrosion rate and CP current of treated bars in all specimens at t = 0 h.

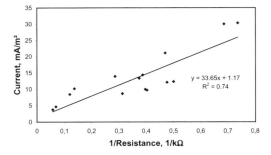

Figure 8. Inverse cell resistance and current density of protected bars at t = 0.

also shows a linear relationship between these two parameters. As the cell resistance increases the current density in the reinforcement is reduced. These results are important when designing CP systems where the cell resistance is expected to be high.

3.4 Depolarization

After 18 days, the CP current was stopped and depolarization measurements were carried out. According to recommendations (Pedeferri 1995; NEN-EN12696 2000; COST 534 2009), the quality of protection offered by a CP system is satisfactory if the potential of steel has depolarized from its value at switch-off by least 100 mV after 24 hours. The values of depolarization of steel bars in specimens subjected to CP at 1.4 V are shown in Table 3.

In this table, it is shown that, for most bars, depolarization did not reach the value of 100 mV. While at first instance this may suggest that CP was not successful, in fact it suggests that the specimens require more than 48 hours for full depolarization. Bars in specimen 1450-SD depolarized less than 50 mV. This behavior may be caused by reduced oxygen content at the surface of steel due to high moisture content in the specimens. Since they were stored inside a box with a 10 mm water level, the moisture inside them may have slowed down the oxygen transport that is needed for depolarizing reactions. If that is true, waiting longer might show higher depolarization. The quite negative potentials (in all specimens) support this

Table 3. Depolarization values vs Ti* of steel bars in concrete specimens after 18 days at 1.4 V.

Specimen		10L	10C	10R	Anode	30L	30C	30R	Anode
1450-SD	Current density, mA/m²*	3.9	–	5.5	–	4.4	–	2.4	–
	E On, mV vs Ti*	−749	−483	−747	724	−761	−426	−762	700
	Off	−714		−703	612	−722		−740	585
	1 hr	−719	−487	−719	349	−731	−431	−731	335
	4 hr	−709	−488	−709	172	−707	−422	−707	173
	24 hr	−687	−497	−686	51	−692	−436	−692	44
Depolarization		+27	−10	+17	−561	+30	−5	+48	−541
3550-SD	Current density, mA/m²*	1.9	–	2.8	–	2.2	–	1.9	–
	E On, mV vs Ti*	−908	−372	−896	545	−828	−294	−829	603
	Off	−772		−750	456	−677		−673	512
	1 hr	−729	−363	−728	326	−657	−278	−656	396
	4 hr	−690	−358	−690	183	−620	−275	−620	252
	24 hr	−638	−353	−637	94	−580	−272	−579	151
Depolarization		+134	+10	+113	−362	+97	+22	+94	−361
1550-C	Current density, mA/m²*	2.2	–	2.0	–	1.6	–	2.0	–
	E On, mV vs Ti*	−1188	−715	−1189	287	−1152	−722	−1145	314
	Off	−1114		−1123	256	−1091		−1073	275
	1 hr	−1080	−715	−1077	−19	−1055	−718	−1050	3
	4 hr	−1076	−718	−1074	−196	−1053	−724	−1052	−174
	24 hr	−1036	−727	−1035	−293	−1011	−723	−1003	−268
Depolarization		+78	−12	+88	−549	+80	−5	+70	−543
1552-MC	Current density, mA/m²*	1.6	–	1.4	–	8.0	–	5.1	–
	E On, mV vs Ti*	−831	−385	−829	645	−799	−503	−797	677
	Off	−822		−820	487	−751		−754	516
	1 hr	−795	−383	−794	262	−758	−501	−758	297
	4 hr	−776	−381	−776	103	−739	−500	−739	140
	24 hr	−728	−382	−727	12	−696	−496	−696	41
Depolarization		+94	−1	+93	−475	+55	−5	+58	−475

*at the end of the 18 day period.

view. In the case of specimen 3550-SD, the bars at 10 mm depth depolarized above 100 mV; however, the bars at 30 mm did not depolarize more than 100 mV, although they were really close. Overall, 18 days is not enough time to say if depolarization was not successful, besides the fact that the current densities were low.

In the carbonated specimen 1550-C, none of the bars depolarized more than 100 mV. At first glance, this may suggest an improper application of CP, however, the depolarization values are closer to the 100 mV shift, than in 1450-SD and changes in the pore structure and pore solution must be taken into account. As described before in Table 1, the potential of carbonated specimens was significantly more negative than −350 mV; and as the specimens were wet, the drop of such potentials may be even higher. Nevertheless, these values are modified by the differences found in the Ti* electrodes when compared to the Ag/AgCl as described in Table 2.

The depolarization in specimen 1552-MC was also near to 100 mV for bars at 10 mm cover depth and around 50 mV for bars at 30 mm. In both cases, the depolarization suggests that more time was required for full depolarization.

For reference bars (without CP) changes in potential are probably attributed to changes in temperature and moisture content inside the specimens. The range of changes fluctuated between −22 to +14 mV. It should be mentioned that the electrical fields of CP protected bars might have influenced such values.

3.5 *Estimation of pH inside corrosion pits*

The model for estimation of pH inside corrosion pits assumes that the current is reduced from t = 0 until stabilization (turning point), because in that period the acid is neutralized. The charge that is required for acid neutralization is shown in Figure 9. As the figure shows, the estimated charge from t = 0 until the turning point, is composed of

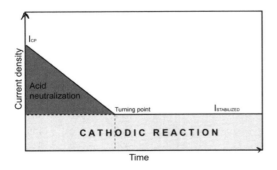

Figure 9. Schematic figure of acid neutralization.

two parts: the acid neutralization charge and the cathodic reaction charge. The exceeding current during transition is required for acid neutralization (dark gray). As the liquid inside pits becomes less acidic, the current is reduced to that necessary only for cathodic reaction purposes (light gray). After the transition period is finished, the required current for maintaining proper protection is obtained.

The visual inspection of extracted bars involved the physical measurement of corrosion pit size and an estimated loss of volume in the steel bars. Then, the assumption is that all liquid inside those pits has a low pH and thus the total amount of acid is proportional to the total pit volume. Next, the amount of charge needed to neutralize that amount of acid is calculated. Then, the total neutralizing charge is used to calculate the pH in the liquid. For this, the considered accumulated charge was determined to be between t = 0 and the time at which the current density flow became (turning point) without considering the current involved in the cathodic reaction. In this sense, values of charge were different for each bar.

A summary of pit size measurements is shown in Table 4. In almost all cases, the central bar reported higher values of corroded surface and volume of iron dissolution. However, there is considerable scatter in the results of pit measurement (surface, volume, mean depth). It must be noted that only the exposed area of steel bars ($0.0011 \ m^2$) was considered when measuring the pit size and volume loss. Nonetheless, visual inspection of bars showed that corrosion pits were found underneath the coating particularly in bars embedded in the 1450-SD specimen. Those pits were not considered for the calculation of the volume loss.

Since the loss of metal volume and the total charge at the time at which the current became stable during the first 24 hours are known, it is possible to estimate the pH inside the corrosion pits of steel bars protected with CP with the use of equations 2, 3 and 4. Results of pH estimations are shown in Table 5. Some very low pH ($\approx$2) values were found in bars where the volume of metal loss is small. On the overall, the results of pH estimations are lower than expected. The range of variation is narrow for all values, even though estimations of pit volume and thus acid were in a wide range. This suggests that the estimations of pH have a good correlation to what is probably expected with direct measurements of pH.

Based on the previous table, the estimations of pH of liquid inside corrosion pits seem valid and suggests that the acidity of liquid inside pits is strong enough to result in a severe attack on the steel surface (Arup 1983; Gonzalez 1996; Bertolini 2004). On the other hand, even though the model

Table 4. Corrosion pit size measurement and estimation of corroded area and volume loss.

Specimen		10L	10C	10R
1450-SD	surface (mm²)	250	720	340
	volume (mm³)	220	1000	140
3550-SD	surface (mm²)	40	30	20
	volume (mm³)	30	40	20
1550-C	surface (mm²)	90	130	60
	volume (mm³)	80	60	40
1552-MC	surface (mm²)	200	220	20
	volume (mm³)	260	220	20
		30L	**30C**	**30R**
1450-SD	surface (mm²)	60	320	70
	volume (mm³)	120	890	130
3550-SD	surface (mm²)	20	10	10
	volume (mm³)	30	20	20
1550-C	surface (mm²)	50	120	60
	volume (mm³)	20	100	40
1552-MC	surface (mm²)	120	190	50
	volume (mm³)	240	290	100

Table 5. Estimation of pH inside corrosion pits by charge values at individual turning points.

	Time, hrs	Bar	Charge mA*s	Vol., mm³	(H⁺), mmol/l	pH
1450-SD	7	10 L	590	220	2.6	2.5
		10R	558	140	3.9	2.4
	4	30 L	234	120	1.9	2.7
		30R	269	130	2.0	2.6
3550-SD	4	10 L	170	30	5.6	2.2
		10R	186	20	9.3	2.0
	2	30 L	87	30	2.9	2.5
		30R	67	20	6.7	2.4
1550-C	7	10 L	218	80	7.2	2.2
		10R	242	40	12.0	2.1
	5	30 L	135	20	4.4	2.3
		30R	170	40	12.1	2.3
1552-MC	4	10 L	265	260	1.3	2.9
		10R	202	20	10.0	2.0
	4	30 L	392	240	1.6	2.7
		30R	147	100	1.4	2.8

is not applicable for specimen 1550-C, results show values that are similar to those found in the rest of the specimens. The realkalisation effect and the cathodic reaction on the steel surface are to be taken into consideration when analyzing these results.

4 CONCLUSION

Corrosion rate, corrosion potential and cell resistance measurements and subsequent application of CP to corroding steel reinforcement embedded in concrete has led to:

- CEM I salt/dry concrete had the highest corrosion rates before CP, consumed higher values of electrical charge during the treatment and higher values of volume loss of steel. CEM III salt/dry reported higher values of resistivity, low corrosion rate, low lost volume of steel and lower consumption of electrical charge. CEM I carbonated concrete, had low corrosion rates, intermediate resistivity, less volume loss of steel and low charge demand. CEM I concrete with mixed-in chlorides had the lowest values of resistivity, high corrosion rates, higher demands of charge and high values of volume loss of steel.
- The initial current density demand and total charge consumption are related to the initial state of corrosion of steel bars subject to CP. The volume of metal lost due to dissolution in chloride environment is related to the corrosion rate of bars before CP. Neutralization of pH inside corrosion pits most likely take place in the first 8 hours of CP.
- Total charge over 18 days at 1.4V depends on the conditions of corrosion deterioration of steel (corrosion rate).
- Evidence obtained during the recording of the current density demand of steel bars suggests that it is possible to estimate the pH inside pits (values between 2 and 3). These estimations suggest results, which may represent actual values of pH inside corrosion pits.

REFERENCES

Andrade, C. & Alonso, C. (1996). Corrosion rate monitoring in the laboratory and on-site. *Construction and Building Materials* 10(5): 315–328.

Angst, U., Elsener, B., Larsen, C.K. & Vennesland, Ø. (2010). Considerations on the effect of sample size for the critical chloride content in concrete. *2nd International Symposium on Service Life Design for Infrastructure, Delft, The Netherlands, RILEM*.

Arup, H. (1983). *The mechanisms of the protection of steel by concrete*, Society of Chemical Industry.

Bertolini, L., Elsener, B., Pedeferri, P. & Polder, R.B. (2004). *Corrosion of steel in concrete*, Wiley-VCH.

Bertolini, L., Pedeferri, P., Redaelli, E. & Pastore, T. (2003). Repassivation of steel in carbonated concrete induced by cathodic protection. *Materials and Corrosion* 54.

COST 534 (2009). *New Materials, Systems, Methods and Concepts for Prestressed Concrete Structures.* R.B. Polder, Alonso, M.C., Cleland, D.J., Elsener, B., Proverbio, E., Vennesland, Ø., Raharinaivo, A. Brussels, BE, COST.

Gonzalez, J.A., Feliu, S., Rodriguez, P., Lopez, W., Ramirez, E., Alonso, M.C. & Andrade, C. (1996). Some questions on the corrosion of steel in concrete. Part II: Corrosion mechanism and monitoring, service life prediction and protection methods. *Materials and Structures* 29.

Mietz, J. (1998). *Electrochemical rehabilitation methods for reinforced concrete structures—A state of the art report.* E.F. o. C. Publications.

NEN-EN12696 (2000). *Cathodic protection for steel in concrete.*

Pedeferri, P. (1995). Cathodic protection and cathodic prevention. *Construction and Building Materials* 10(5).

Polder, R.B. (2001). *Corrosion protection of reinforcement in concrete with fly ash cement and other binders subjected to salt/dry loading, accelerated carbonation and addition of chloride: Results until 2.5 years age and destructive analysis.* Building and Construction Research. Delft, TNO.

Polder, R.B. (2001). Test methods for on site measurement of concrete resistivity of concrete—a RILEM TC-154 technical recommendation. *Construction and Building Materials* 15.

Polder, R.B. & Peelen, W.H.A. (2002). Characterisation of chloride transport and reinforcement corrosion in concrte under cycling wetting and drying by electrical resistivity. *Cement & Concrete Composites* 24.

Polder, R.B., Peelen, W.H.A., Lollini, F., Redaelli, E. & Bertolini, L., (2009). Numerical design of cathodic protection systems for concrete. *Materials and Corrosion* 60(2): 130–136.

Polder, R.B., Stoop, W.H.A. & Neeft, B.J.Th. (2011). Early stage beneficial effects of cathodic protection in concrete structures. *Materials and Corrosion* 62(2): 105–110.

RILEM TC 154-EMC (2003). Half-cell potential measurements—Potential mapping on concrete structures. *Materials and Structures* 36.

Concrete Solutions – Grantham, Mechtcherine & Schneck (eds)
© 2012 Taylor & Francis Group, London, ISBN 978-0-415-61622-5

Performance and working life of cathodic protection systems for concrete structures

R.B. Polder
Delft University of Technology, The Netherlands
TNO, Delft, The Netherlands

D. Worm, W. Courage & G. Leegwater
TNO, Delft, The Netherlands

ABSTRACT: Corrosion of reinforcing steel in concrete structures causes concrete cracking and steel diameter reduction, eventually resulting in loss of safety. Conventional repair means heavy, labour intensive and costly work and the required quality level is under economic pressure. Consequently, conventional repair is short lived in many cases. An alternative repair method is cathodic protection of steel in concrete, where corrosion is prevented by applying a current to the structure. This paper presents results from an inventory of CP systems in the Netherlands installed between 1987 and 2010 to assess their service life. About 150 structures have been protected with CP. Performance and maintenance data are reported. Failure of components as a function of age is quantified by survival analysis. Degradation of components and systems appears to occur in limited numbers. On the average, the time until minor repair of parts is necessary is about 15 years.

1 INTRODUCTION

Corrosion of reinforcing steel in concrete structures may occur, e.g., in bridges due to penetration of chloride ions from de-icing salts or sea water spray [Bertolini et al., 2004]. Reinforcement corrosion causes concrete cracking and steel diameter reduction eventually resulting in loss of safety. Conventional repair means heavy, labour intensive and costly work. Economic pressures (time and money) work against the required quality level (perfect steel cleaning, removal of contaminated concrete). Consequently, conventional repair is short lived in many cases. Corrosion reappears quickly and structures need to be repaired again after a relatively short time, further increasing life-cycle cost. In a European study of the life of repairs (mainly patch repair), it was found that repairs had a short life in practice [Tilly & Jacobs 2007]. A completely different situation comes about with cathodic protection (CP) as a repair method. Cathodic protection of reinforcing steel has been applied to concrete structures with corrosion damage in Europe for about 25 years [Grefstad 2005, Nerland et al., 2007, Polder 1998, Wenk & Oberhänsli 2007]. A recent study reports on long term performance of CP systems in UK motorway structures [Christodoulou et al., 2010].

This paper presents results from a survey of CP systems in The Netherlands. About 150 structures have been provided with CP since 1987. Sufficient documentation of design, performance and maintenance is available for working life analysis of about 105 systems. The large majority provide corrosion protection for a long time. Degradation of components occurs in limited numbers and failure of components as a function of age has been quantified. In a limited number of cases, intervention (repair or replacement of parts) has been necessary with regard to electrical connections, primary anodes, reference electrodes and power units. Failure of parts of the anode system has occurred with a rate that increases with age. Taking CP system life until interventions are necessary as the main criterion, the mean service life is about 15 years. However, complete failure of the anode was rare; and no cases have been reported where corrosion had reappeared.

2 COMPONENTS OF CP SYSTEMS

A CP system for protection of steel in concrete basically consists of a conductor called the anode from which a small direct current flows through the concrete to the reinforcement, see Figure 1. The steel potential becomes more negative and corrosion is suppressed. The anode can be either directly applied to the concrete surface (e.g., a conductive coating) or consists of a mesh of activated titanium

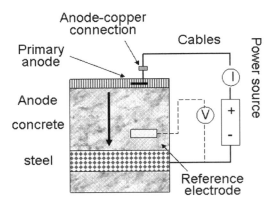

Figure 1. Basic setup of a concrete CP system.

or carbon fibres embedded in a cementitious overlay. Other types comprise titanium strips in boreholes or slots filled with cementitious mortar. The anode material (with or without overlay) is fed by a primary anode (PA, a metal wire, mesh or strip), together they form the anode system. The anode system is linked through anode-copper connections and isolated cop-per cables to the power unit.

Further components are reference electrodes that operate as monitoring sensors for checking protection and a low voltage power source. In order to ensure that the CP system works properly routine monitoring is performed by electrical measurements (depolarisation) at least twice a year; visual inspection is carried out once a year [CEN 2000]. Such monitoring is part of a maintenance contract between the CP company and the owner of the structure, that usually runs for ten years and that includes routine checks and replacement of failing components.

The anode system is the most expensive part of a CP system: it may cost between 60 and 90% of the total cost, depending on the size of the system. Within the anode system, the anode itself (conductive coating, titanium mesh and overlay) is the most expensive part. Primary anodes are the next expensive parts; primary anode-copper connections are third.

3 FAILURE MODES

Failure of a CP system (e.g., current stops flowing) causes loss of protection to a degree that is depend-ant on the type of component that fails. Various failure modes occur: power units may stop working, an-ode-copper connections may corrode, reference electrodes may fail and anode materials or primary anodes may degrade. The effect of

failure of a component will differ: when a part of the central installation fails as a result current will stop flowing and the whole system is unprotected, however it is also possible that only a part of the system fails which will result in local unprotected areas. Failures in the total CP system will be detected during the next (routine) protection check, within half a year or less. Local failures might be unnoticed during a protection check, these will be picked up during the yearly visual inspection. Previous work has shown principles, conceptual models for degradation, strategies to avoid such failures and practical observations [Polder & Peelen 2011]. The most common types of failure and their effect will be explained below.

Power unit failure will occur instantly (e.g., due to lightning strike) and will cause the whole system to shut down. Primary anode or anode-copper connection failure prevents current flowing to at least part of the system. Reference electrode failure hinders protection checks. Anode degradation (due to oxidation of carbon particles or acid formation in the bond plane) increases cell resistance. This in turn will cause the need to increase the driving voltage, further accelerating degradation. After some time it becomes impossible to maintain sufficient current for full protection [Mietz et al., 2001]. Global anode failure means the need for complete replacement of the anode, involving high costs. Medium levels of costs are involved for primary anode failure. The other types of failure can be corrected for less money, like replacing a failed power unit.

However, it should be noted that anode system failure does not cause immediate loss of protection. Some of about 700 conductive coating CP systems in a UK motorway complex have shown significant coating degradation (estimated from a photo up to 50% of the surface), but according to polarization testing, these CP systems were still working properly, i.e., providing corrosion protection [Christodoulou et al., 2010]. Similar cases of coating anode degradation but sufficient protection for several years have been observed in the survey reported here. Apparently, there is no simple and hard criterion for degradation related CP system failure. What looks like system failure does not bring about reactivation of corrosion in the short term. Instead, the need for "non-negligible maintenance" is used here as the criterion for working life.

4 STATISTICAL ANALYSIS

The statistical technique of survival analysis was used for the analysis of service life of concrete CP systems. In general, this field involves modelling time-to-event data. That is, the data consists of objects (e.g., patients, engines, systems) together with a time until a particular event occurs (e.g., death, failure). See [Kalbfleisch & Prentice 2002] for a comprehensive survey of survival analysis. In this case the events are particular types of failure of CP systems, like global or local failure of the anode or failure of primary anodes, connections or reference electrodes. The goal of the analyses is to quantify and be able to predict time until failure. One of the difficulties in analysing failure time data is that for some existing objects the time to failure is not known. Reasons can be:

1. the object is still working now, or
2. after a last known point in time in the past at which the object was still working, there has been no further information on the state of the object, for instance due to lack of monitoring.

This lack of information after a certain point in time is called (right-) censoring. Now, for every object in the group under analysis we can specify a time after which the object has either failed or been censored. There are various techniques that take this censoring into account.

One of the results one would like to obtain from the analysis is the survival function S(t), a function in time describing the probability to survive up to and including time t, or the failure function F(t) = 1−S(t), indicating the probability to have failed at or before time t. In order to estimate the survival function, one can use non-parametric or parametric methods.

The Kaplan-Meier estimator (see [Kalbfleisch & Prentice 2002, Section 1.4]) is called non-parametric because it does not assume a particular distribution type of the survival function (like normal, exponential, etc.). This gives an estimated survival function S(t) or estimated failure function F(t) = 1 − S(t). The variance can be approximated using the so-called Greenwood's formula (see [Kalbfleisch & Prentice 2002, Section 1.4]). Based on this, approximate 95% confidence intervals of the failure function can be calculated, i.e., bounds on the estimated F(t), such that the real failure function is within these bounds with 95% probability. However one must realise that with only a few events of failure, the uncertainty of the estimated failure function will be quite high.

Using a parametric method, the failure function can be estimated by fitting the censored data to a distribution. Here a two-parametric Weibull distribution was used (see [Kalbfleisch & Prentice 2002 Section 2.2.2]), which is one of the most widely used lifetime distributions in reliability engineering. It is a versatile distribution that can take on the characteristics of other types of distributions, based on the value of the shape parameter. Such a parametric method can be useful for obtaining predictions of failure probabilities in the future.

5 FIELD DATA

In 2011 an inventory was carried out amongst companies in The Netherlands that had installed CP to concrete structures, as an update to previous surveys performed in 2006 and 2009 [Polder & Peelen 2011]. The inventory deals with the following aspects of a CP system: object identification, year of installation, type of structure, protected area and anode type; and required or performed maintenance, repairs, failure and replacement of components. It produced the following observations.

Between 1987 and 2010, circa 150 CP systems were installed on various types of concrete structures like bridges, apartment and office buildings, industrial and parking structures with a total protected area of 82,500 m^2 of concrete surface. The number of systems per year is shown in Figure 2, about 105 concerned buildings and circa 45 were bridges. In approximately 65 cases conductive coatings were used for the anode compared to around 40 cases in which titanium anodes were used. This is without counting multiple anode types in different parts of a structure (which occurred in 6 cases). Galvanic anodes have been increasingly applied over the last twelve years, to a total of about 35 structures.

From 105 cases sufficient documentation was received for survival analysis. For 45 systems no or insufficient information was available (apart from having been installed), which in most cases means that they are not checked or maintained. For an increasing number of (older) CP systems, recent information is lacking because their maintenance contract was not renewed after 10 years. Because many galvanic systems are not checked on a regular basis, no systematic performance analysis of galvanic CP is possible. Most of the 105 documented cases have been monitored regularly for a longer period of time and have worked well or are still working well. No corrosion related damage was reported. For the discussion of performance, the assumption is made that each CP system was designed, installed and activated properly.

Up until 2010, there were 56 CP systems dating to 2001 or before, so at least ten years old. In three cases, the concrete structure had been demolished (due to redundancy), five were "unknown", which basically had been neglected. Twelve had been working well but were no longer monitored. Twenty eight required minor or major ("non-negligible") maintenance. Nineteen systems were still operating well, with only routine maintenance (regular checking).

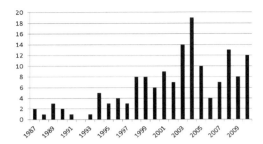

Figure 2. Number of structures with CP in The Netherlands versus time.

In sixteen cases the anode system failed to some extent, reported as:

- Local poor overall condition of the conductive coating, in seven cases at ages between three and ten years; this was mainly due to local water leakage from overlying parts; the need to replace the anode was signalled in two of these cases, at seven or ten years of age; however, anode replacement was not yet carried out and corrosion protection did not seem to be compromised (based on depolarisation testing)
- The anode was replaced, in one case at seven (a coating) and in one case at 17 years age (a non-mesh titanium type)
- Failure of primary anodes, seven cases at ages between five and 16 years, which were disbonding or all replaced.

In five cases, anode-copper connections were failing and had to be replaced. This occurred at ages between five (one case) and 15 years (two identical cases). In eight cases, power units failed and had to be replaced at ages between 3 and 12 years. In five cases, reference electrodes had to be replaced at ages from 10 years. Reference electrodes, connections and power units were failing and had to be replaced in the oldest CP project in the Netherlands. It was installed in 1987, on a bicycle lane of a bridge. These items were repaired for a modest amount of money in 1999 [Schuten et al., 2007]. Since then, it worked properly for at least several years. A few cases were reported suffering from repeated vandalism; others required repairs due to being hit by vehicles. These cases are not further considered.

The total number of systems younger than ten years was circa 95. Out of these, 55 were monitored and most of them showed good performance without interventions. Minor interventions concerned failing connections (1) primary anode (1), reference electrodes (2), power units (2) and 5 cases of local anode degradation. Around 40 CP systems were not monitored, approx. 35 of these are galvanic systems.

Summarising the inventory, in about 65 out of 105 documented cases, the CP system worked well without failures or unforeseen maintenance. Of about 56 systems of ten or more years of age, about 19 (33%) operated without significant interventions. Some 28 older systems required some form of non-negligible maintenance. For a relatively high amount of 17 older and 42 newer systems the present performance was unknown, that is, they were not regularly checked anymore or they had never been checked regularly.

6 DATA ANALYSIS AND DISCUSSION

This section is aimed at analysing the field data for age-dependent failure of CP system parts. Conductive coatings, primary anodes to them and connections (for both coating and titanium systems) have failed over the years in a number of CP systems. Occurrence and correcting these types of failure are called non-negligible maintenance in this discussion. Power units and reference electrodes have failed in low numbers and are less expensive to replace, so these are left out.

The survival analysis carried out as described in section 4 relates the number of failures to the number of CP systems of a particular age; the results are shown in Figure 3. Two types of analysis are used. The solid lines are results of Kaplan-Meier estimates, with the central step-line being the best estimate; upper and lower bounds for 95% confidence are indicated. The smooth hatched lines were produced by fitting a Weibull distribution to the data, again with the central curve as the best fit with upper and lower 95% bounds.

Summarising, the graph shows an increasing probability of the need to carry out maintenance with increasing age of CP systems. The two types of analysis produce similar results. It appears from this analysis that there is a 10% probability that a CP systems needs maintenance at an age of about 7 years or less, with 95% confidence this probability lies between 3 to 17%. Moreover, there is a 50% probability that maintenance is needed at an age of 15 years or less; this probability lies between 35 and 70% with 95% confidence.

It should be stressed that if a CP system meets this "failure criterion", it does not mean the end of its working life. Actually, all of the systems that needed some maintenance, were still working or were working again after maintenance. Maintenance costs were limited in most cases. Only in two cases did the complete anode system need replacing, costing money of the same order

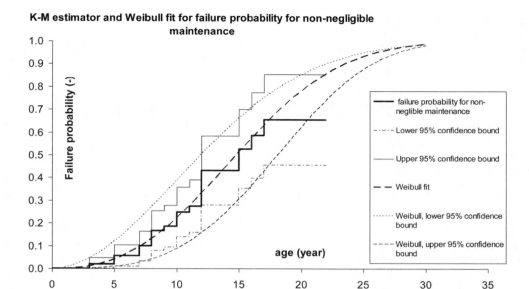

K-M estimator and Weibull fit for failure probability for non-negligible maintenance

- failure probability for non-neglible maintenance
- Lower 95% confidence bound
- Upper 95% confidence bound
- Weibull fit
- Weibull, lower 95% confidence bound
- Weibull, upper 95% confidence bound

age (year)

Failure probability (-)

Figure 3. Failure probabilities for requiring (non-negligible) maintenance of CP system components as a function of age.

as a new system. For example, simple power units are relatively inexpensive today and anticipating replacement after 10 to 15 years may be a good strategy. Reference electrodes have been improved and/or become cheaper and placing redundant numbers may be a good strategy.

In addition, it should be noted that after some time, steel passivation occurs and current demand decreases. In [Christodoulou et al., 2010] it is suggested that such a new (second generation) CP system can be designed for lower current density and thus in general can be installed at lower cost.

In the previous section, older and newer CP systems (installed before and after 2001) have been distinguished; possible failure differences between these two groups will be analysed. It should be noted that populations were of similar size: 51 documented and monitored systems up until the end of 2001 and 55 systems after 2001. In a previous study it was postulated that some failures that occurred on early systems, were not seen on newer systems, as if companies had improved critical details [Polder & Peelen 2011]. Early failures would represent growing pains of a new industry. This seems to be supported by the present data with regard to connections, power units and possibly for primary anodes. Five cases of connection failure were reported of systems installed up until the end of the year 2001; only one for a system later than 2001. Similarly, power units of older dates failed more frequently in older systems: eight from 2001

or before and only one from the period after 2001. Also older primary anodes failed more frequently than newer ones. In particular with primary anodes, it appears that over time, companies have been experimenting with materials and execution details and seem to have improved them. On the other hand, local anode failure was observed more frequently on newer systems. A clear explanation is not at hand; it may have to do with the fact that in the last ten years more bridges have been equipped with CP (as opposed to more buildings before 2001); which might constitute more aggressive exposure.

7 CONCLUSIONS

In order to assess the performance of CP systems in practice, information on 150 concrete structures with Cathodic Protection installed was sought for in an inventory among CP and concrete repair companies in the Netherlands. Statistical techniques from survival analysis were used. Information on performance and maintenance suitable for such analysis was obtained for 105 cases. Out of these, about 51 had been operating for ten years or longer. About two thirds of the older systems required minor interventions. It should be noted that the conclusions below apply only when proper maintenance is carried out, which involves electrical testing for depolarisation at least twice a year and visual inspection once a year, as prescribed by the European CP standard [CEN 2000] and usually as part of a maintenance contract between the owner and the CP contractor.

The main conclusions from this study are:

- Complete replacement of the anode was carried out in only two cases, one conductive coating anode (on a bridge) and one titanium anode (non-mesh type).
- Anodes based on activated titanium have shown long working lives.
- Conductive coatings have shown deterioration in limited numbers, mainly related to local water leakage, that caused the need for local repairs of the coating (ten cases); however, corrosion protection may be provided even if their condition is (visually) poor.
- Replacement of primary anodes and anode-copper connections was necessary in a number of cases, in particular with older systems; possibly critical details have been improved and the service life of these components has gone up.
- Power units and reference electrodes have been replaced in some cases. Simple power units and reference electrodes are relatively inexpensive today, so the cost of these actions is limited.
- Working lives of CP systems without major intervention of ten to twenty years have occurred in practice; corrosion and related damage to concrete has been absent in all documented cases. When intervention was necessary, it was mainly related to defective details such as local leakage and poor electrical isolation.
- Survival analysis of 105 documented cases suggests that (minor) interventions are increasingly necessary with increasing age. It appears that there is a 10% probability that a CP system needs maintenance at an age of about 7 years or less. With 95% confidence this probability lies between 3 to 17%. Moreover, there is a 50% probability that maintenance is needed at an age of 15 years or less; with 95% confidence this probability lies between 35 and 70%.

ACKNOWLEDGMENTS

The authors gratefully acknowledge the CP and repair companies who provided information for the inventory: Care4concrete.nl, CORRPRE, ECORemain, RENDON, Van der Heide and Vogel. The work has been made possible by a grant from the Ministry of Economic Affairs under the TNO-co arrangement, project KB Plus Prestatie Toolbox (CP + Performance Toolbox).

REFERENCES

Bertolini, L., Elsener, B., Pedeferri, P. & Polder, R.B. 2004. *Corrosion of Steel in Concrete: Prevention, Diagnosis, Repair.* Wiley, Weinheim, ISBN 3-527-30800-8.

CEN, 2000. *Cathodic protection of steel in concrete.* EN 12696.

Christodoulou, C., Glass, G., Webb, J., Austin, S. & Goodier, C. 2010. Assessing the long term benefits of impressed current cathodic protection. *Corrosion Science* 52, 2671–2697.

Grefstad, K. 2005. Cathodic protection applied on Norwegian concrete bridges. Experience and recommendations. *Eurocorr05*, Lisboa. (CD-ROM).

Kalbfleisch, J.D. & Prentice, R.L. 2002. *The statistical analysis of failure time data.* Second Edition, New Jersey: John Wiley & Sons.

Mietz, J., Fischer, J. & Isecke, B. 2001. Cathodic protection of steel-reinforced concrete structures—results from 15 years' experience. *Materials Performance* 40 (12): 22–26.

Nerland, O.C.N., Eri, J., Grefstad, K.A. & Vennesland, Ø. 2007. 18 years of Cathodic Protection of Reinforced Concrete Structures in Norway—facts and figures from 162 installations. *Eurocorr07*, Freiburg (CD-ROM).

Polder, R.B. 1998. Cathodic protection of reinforced concrete structures in The Netherlands—experience and developments, *HERON* 43 (1): 3–14.

Polder, R.B., & Peelen, W.H.A. 2011. Service life aspects of cathodic protection of concrete structures. In *Concrete Repair, A practical Guide*, M. Grantham (ed.), Taylor and Francis, Abingdon.

Schuten, G., Leggedoor, J., Polder, R.B. & Peelen, W. 2007. Cost aspects of cathodic protection; a review after 14 years of operation. In Corrosion of reinforcement in concrete, mechanisms, monitoring, inhibitors and rehabilitation techniques, European Federation of Corrosion Publication 38, M. Raupach, B. Elsener, R. Polder, J. Mietz (eds.), Woodhead Publishing Limited, Cambridge, 300–306.

Tilly, G.P. & Jacobs, J. 2007. *Concrete repairs—performance in service and current practice*, IHS BRE Press, Bracknell.

Tinnea, J.S. & Cryer, C.B. 2008. Corrosion control of Pacific coast reinforced concrete structures: A Summary of 25 years experience. In: 1st International Conference on Heritage and Construction in Coastal and Marine Environment MEDACHS08, Portugal (CD-ROM).

Wenk, F. & Oberhänsli, D. 2007. Long-term experience with cathodic protection of reinforced concrete structures, *Eurocorr07*, Freiburg. (CD-ROM).

Concrete Solutions – Grantham, Mechtcherine & Schneck (eds)
© 2012 Taylor & Francis Group, London, ISBN 978-0-415-61622-5

Galvanic corrosion protection of steel in concrete with a zinc mesh anode embedded into a solid electrolyte (EZA)

W. Schwarz & F. Müllner
CAS Composite Anode Systems GmbH, Austria

A. van den Hondel
Eco Remain, Capelle aan den Ijssel, The Netherlands

ABSTRACT: The efficiency of the Galvanic Corrosion Protection (GCP) of the steel reinforcement of a novel Embedded Zinc Anode (EZA) is evaluated on three types of civil structures—a road bridge (cantilevers, part of the underside the bridge deck and an abutment) in the Styrian Alps in Austria, concrete abutments of a steel bridge and support-beams for the bearings of a road bridge in the Netherlands. The EZA is applied to the surface of concrete members whose steel is to be protected from corrosion by embedding a zinc mesh (2–4 kg/m²) into a proprietary mortar that hardens to a solid electrolyte. The efficiency of the GCP was monitored with embedded reference cells, concrete resistivity—and macro cell sensors. The macro cell sensors allow the quantification of the galvanic protection efficiency. Data collected over a period of up to nearly 4 years show that the EZA protects the steel reinforcement efficiently and reliably.

1 INTRODUCTION

Galvanic corrosion protection of steel in concrete is based on the formation of a galvanic element if a metal less noble than cast iron steel, in direct contact with the concrete overlay, is electrically connected to the steel rebars. The reinforcing steel is protected from corrosion as long as sufficient galvanic current flows between the galvanic anode and the steel reinforcement. Most commonly, zinc is used as the sacrificial anode material. The galvanic element formed corresponds to a conventional zinc/air battery that is becoming popular again as an alternative source of energy.

Galvanic corrosion protection was first employed to protect a bridge deck in Illinois in 1977 within the cooperative highway research program, with mixed results (Kepler et al., 2000). A problem with the initially applied sacrificial anodes was that their protection current decreases with time, and they eventually become passive, so most systems have a relatively short useful life (Virmani & Clemena 1998).

In the 1990's, sacrificial anode systems based on sprayed zinc anodes, zinc foil glued to the concrete surface (zinc hydrogel system), zinc mesh pile jackets around bridge columns filled with sea water were starting to be evaluated and used for the protection of bridge structures (Virmani & Clemena 1998, Kessler, Powers & Lasa 2004; Szabo & Bakos 2006, Bullard, Cramer & Covinho 2009).

To a limited extent, zinc anodes embedded into the concrete overlay, are used to protect the steel reinforcement especially accompanying concrete repair.

The efficiency of galvanic corrosion protection depends on the lasting activity of the zinc anode. Deposition and agglomeration of the anodic products like zinc hydroxide and zinc hydroxychlorides or contact with calcium hydroxide in the pore solution may passivate the zinc anode surface. Service time of the zinc anode may be limited by self corrosion that increases with the activation of the zinc anode and may reach up to 70% of the zinc consumed during operation.

The driving voltage is set by the properties of the anode, the interface of the anode to the concrete and by the electrolytic conductivity of the concrete overlay. Sprayed zinc anodes require sufficient humidity and high chloride contents to operate satisfactorily (Bäßler et al.). Galvanic systems are not suitable for the protection of steel in carbonated concrete members.

For the galvanic systems evaluated so far, efficient corrosion protection for steel in concrete has been provided. Expected service times are in the range of 40 years and more.

Experience showed that most failures of galvanic systems occurred due to the failure of the adhesion of the anode to the concrete overlay and due to passivation of the anode exposed to frequent wet dry cycles. Zinc-Hydrogel anodes are especially sensitive to exposure to high humidity with subsequent delamination.

A novel galvanic zinc anode system, composed of a zinc mesh embedded into a proprietary mortar that solidifies into a solid electrolyte, was developed by CAS. The solid electrolyte of the embedded zinc anode system (EZA) is based on a tecto-alumosilicate-binder containing additives that prevent passivation of the zinc anode, assure high and durable galvanic activity of the zinc anode and high and durable adhesion towards the concrete overlay.

The efficiency of the galvanic corrosion protection (GCP) of the steel reinforcement with a novel embedded zinc anode (EZA) is evaluated on three types of civil structures—a road bridge (cantilevers, part of the underside the bridge deck and an abutment) in the Styrian Alps in Austria, concrete abutments of a steel bridge and support-beams for the bearings of a road bridge in the Netherlands. The results of the evaluation of the performance and of the efficiency of the protection of the steel reinforcement against corrosion are presented.

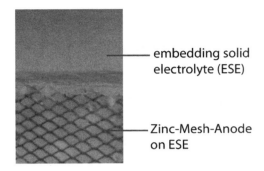

Figure 1. Embedded galvanic zinc anode (EZA): zinc mesh embedded into the TASC mortar from which the embedding solid electrolyte forms.

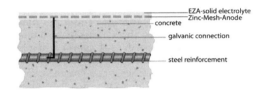

Figure 2. Scheme of the mode of operation of an EZA.

2 DESCRIPTION OF THE SYSTEM

The galvanic EZA system is composed of a zinc mesh (rhomboedric, mesh size 2–4 cm, 2–8 kg/m²) embedded into the proprietary solid electrolyte (Figure 1) that ascertains an optimum electrolytic contact between the zinc anode and the concrete overlay.

The solid electrolyte, based on a tectoalumosilicate cement (TASC), prevents the self passivation of the zinc anode and therefore assures an optimum and reliable protection of steel reinforcement endangered by, or already damaged by chloride induced corrosion.

The zinc anode, a zinc mesh, is embedded into the proprietary solid electrolyte that ascertains an optimum electrolytic contact between the zinc anode and the steel reinforcement.

Unlike impressed current CP systems, hydrogen evolution is not possible on an EZA. The EZA is especially suited for the corrosion protection of prestressed concrete structures.

The EZA is placed on the surface of the concrete member in which the steel reinforcement is to be protected from corrosion (Figure 2).

The concrete surface has to be prepared with the standard procedures for placing coatings on concrete surface (high-pressure water jetting, sand blasting, etc.). The concrete surface has to be clean and electrolytically conductive as specified in EN 12696. Tie wires embedded into the concrete overlay have got to be removed. Prior to the installation

of the EZA, sensors and electrical connections to the steel rebars have to be installed.

The EZA is installed analogous to how tiles are placed: A layer of the TASC-mortar (2–3 mm) is placed on the concrete surface. The zinc mesh is pressed onto the mortar layer. If required, the zinc mesh may be fixed with plastic bolts to the concrete. After hardening (after about 12 hours), the individual zinc sheets are mechanically coupled with a crimping tool and electrical connections are installed if depolarisation measurements are required. Otherwise, the zinc mesh may be directly connected to the steel rebars by shooting steel bolts into drilled holes onto steel rebars.

Subsequently, the zinc mesh is embedded into a second layer of the TASC-mortar. After applying the mortar has to be covered with a plastic sheet or foil for at least three days to prevent evaporation of water.

Adhesion strength after 24 hours is in the range of 0.6–1.0 MPa, after 7 days >2 MPa and after 28 days about 2.5–3.0 MPa.

The EZA shall be put into operation at least three weeks after installation by connecting the anode to the steel rebars.

The efficiency of corrosion protection by the EZA may be evaluated according to the procedure described in EN 12696—the 24 h depolarisation criterion. For that purpose, the installation of into the concrete overlay embedded reference cells and

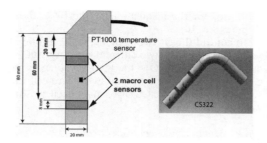

Figure 3. Scheme of a macro-cell sensor (graphic on the left) for the monitoring of the efficiency of galvanic corrosion protection systems. Insert on the right shows a sensor combining two macro cell sensors, three concrete resistivity sensors and three temperature sensors from CorSensys AG (CH).

Figure 4. County road bridge "Alplgrabenbrücke" in the Styrian Alps on the county road B72.

an automated monitoring and control system is required.

Alternatively, the efficiency of the EZA may be monitored and verified by macro cell sensors embedded into the concrete overlay (Figure 3).

The macro cell sensors are inserted into 22 mm holes drilled into the concrete and embedded into a thin layer of anchor mortar containing double the amount of chloride than the adjacent mortar. In this project, the macro cell sensors were embedded without adding chloride to the mortar.

To monitor corrosion rates and the effectiveness of corrosion protection systems, the current flowing between the macro cells and the steel reinforcement is measured resistantless. Anodic currents indicate corrosion, cathodic currents indicate full corrosion protection (Schwarz & Tritthart 2009, Schwarz et al., 2009). Currents are directly measured in $\mu A/cm^2$. A corrosion current of one $\mu A/cm^2$ corresponds to a loss of the cross section of steel rebars of about 12 μm/year.

The verification of the effectiveness of galvanic corrosion protection systems by the 100 mV criterion according to EN 12696 requires the installation of reference cells and insulation of the anode from the rebars in order to be able to disconnect the anode from the rebars, whereas macro cell sensors may be installed anywhere at anytime to verify the efficiency of corrosion protection systems.

3 FIELD INSTALLATIONS

3.1 *Alpine road bridge*

For the evaluation of the efficiency and durability of the EZA system, a road bridge in an alpine region of Styria (Austria) was chosen (Figure 4) for the following reasons:

The bridge is located in the Styrian alps in an altitude of 1000 m above sea level. The climate in that region is characterized by rapid wetting and drying cycles with large temperature differences in the summer including temperature changes crossing the thaw point and by frequent frost-thaw cycles with exposure to deicing salt during winter. The exposure to UV-light is high.

3.1.1 *Description of bridge condition*

The bridge structure shows visible concrete damages—cracks, spalling and corrosion—near the abutment "Birkfeld". The damages originate in part from the bridge deck slipping towards and bumping into girder support (Figure 5) and in part from the corrosion of the steel reinforcement due to soaking of the cantilevers and bridge deck underside with de-icing salt (Figure 6). Water and saltwater during wintertime penetrated the bridge deck through cracks due to the bridge deck bumping against the abutment.

For the evaluation of the state of the bridge condition, corrosion potentials were measured by steel potential mapping with a saturated copper sulphate electrode, chloride profiles were determined on drill dust and on drilled cores, and the carbonation depth was measured. Potential mapping showed very high corrosion risk in the abutment, cantilevers and the underside of the bridge deck near the abutment "Birkfeld".

Chloride contents of 4.0–5.6 wt%/ cement weight down to a depth of 2 cm were measured in the areas that were frequently wetted. In the less frequently wetted areas, the chloride content was significantly lower, ranging from 0.5–0.9 wt.%/ cement weight but the carbonation depth was ≥4 cm.

Therefore one has to assume high corrosion activity of the steel reinforcement of the concrete members with the risk of significant loss of cross section of the steel reinforcement in the

Figure 5. Bridge deck bumping against the girder support causing cracks in the bridge deck.

Figure 6. Damage due to corrosion of the steel reinforcement on the abutment "Birkfeld" at the underside of the bridge.

future, possibly leading to structurally unsafe conditions.

3.1.2 *Installation of the EZA—system*

The EZA system for the galvanic corrosion protection (GCP) of the steel reinforcement in the concrete members of the county road bridge "Alplgrabenbrücke" was installed from 17 to 27 September 2007 on 50 m² of concrete surface. To evaluate the influence of weathering, chloride content and geometry of the concrete members on the efficiency of the GCP, four different protection zones were installed (Figures 7 & 8).

Concrete members were protected that were particularly endangered and/or damaged by the corrosion of the steel reinforcement: abutment "Birkfeld", the bridge deck underside near the abutment and the adjacent cantilevers. A total of 500 kg EZA mortar and 100 kg zinc-mesh

were used for the installation of the EZA anode (Figures 9 & 10).

To control the efficiency of the GCP, a total of seven reference cells (two different types Ag/AgCl—marked A, Mn/MnO_2—marked M), one set of concrete resistivity sensors and two macro-cell sensor sets, embodying each three macro-cell sensors, were installed.

3.1.3 *Monitoring & control system*

The data acquisition and monitoring unit—the Low Energy Data Acquisition and Control Unit (LE-DAC) is especially designed for stand alone operation without an external power source. For the control of and for the data acquisition from GCP systems, the LE-DAC units (power requirement 20 mW) may be operated by alkaline cells for at least two years without replacing them.

The galvanic currents between the EZA anodes and the steel reinforcement were measured resistant less.

The LE-DAC may be programmed to execute depolarization measurements in pre-set intervals.

Depolarization measurements are executed as follows:

1. Interrupt mechanically the connection EZA to the steel reinforcement by a relay.
2. Data acquisition every 0.1 sec during 2 sec for the determination of the instant off potentials
3. Data acquisition every minute for 20 minutes.
4. Data acquisition every 10 minutes up to 24 hours after start of depolarization.
5. Reconnection of the EZA with the steel reinforcement.

The master control unit of the LE-DAC unit may be extended to monitor macro-cell currents. The macro cell currents were measured resistant less. Monitoring the macro-cell currents allows quantifying the efficiency of the corrosion protection of the GCP systems. Macro-cell currents and concrete resistivity were measured using a CS 322 sensor from CorSensys AG (CH).

3.1.4 *Operation of the EZA systems— evaluation and conclusions*

3.1.4.1 Start up of the GCP systems

Data acquisition was started on 3 October 2007. The GCP systems were put into operation on 1 November 2007 by connecting the EZA anodes with the steel reinforcement. The open circuit potentials (driving voltages) ranged from 300 to 800 mV, increasing continuously after installation of the GCP system and rapidly decreasing three weeks after installation (Figure 11, indicating that the EZA systems should be put into operation no later than 3 weeks after installing them on the concrete members. Depolarization measurements were

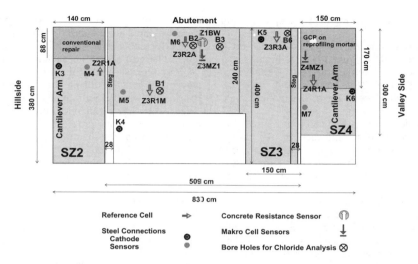

Figure 7. Layout of the GCP zones at the bridge deck underside and cantilevers of the Alplgraben bridge.

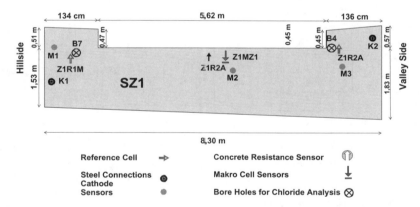

Figure 8. Layout of the GCP zone at abutment "Birkfeld" of the Alplgraben bridge.

Figure 9. View on the GCP zones during installation of the—EZA and sensors.

Figure 10. View on the GCP zones after completion of the installation.

executed once a week during the start-up operation (Figure 11).

The galvanic currents of the different GCP zones vary strongly (Figure 12). The highest currents were measured on the underside of the bridge deck (zone 3—max. 21 mA/m^2) and at the cantilever on the up-hill side of the bridge (zone 2, max. 17 mA/m^2).

The smallest currents were measured on cantilevers on the down-hill side of the bridge (zone 4, max. 8 mA/m^2). The galvanic currents depend strongly on the concrete temperature and drop rapidly at temperatures below freezing (Figure 12).

The results of the 24 hour depolarization measurements show that the steel reinforcement was reliably protected from corrosion after 1 month of operation of the GCP systems (Table 1): The 24 h depolarisation values range from 116 mV to 262 mV at temperatures close to freezing.

3.1.4.2 Data of operation of the GCP systems

The operating data of the GCP systems over a period of nearly four years (1 November 2007—2 July 2011), outlasting four alpine winters, were evaluated and analyzed with respect to stability, performance and durability of the GCP systems: The course of the galvanic current of the GCP systems show that the initially high galvanic currents decreased during the first three months continuously and stabilized after about six month (Figure 13). The mean values of the galvanic currents and environmental parameters (RH, T), measured after stabilization of the galvanic systems, are listed in Table 2.

The data shows that the GCP systems in the protection zones 1–3 were highly active, with the highest activity in zone 1 (bridge deck underside). The GCP system in zone 4 was installed on an area that was refurbished with repair mortar. Galvanic activity was expected to be low due to the repassivation of the steel reinforcement induced by the repair mortar.

During the unusually dry spring time 2011 (Figure 14), galvanic currents were lower in comparison with the same period in 2010 but still above 2 mA/m^2. In the zone 4, currents were close to 0 mA/m^2.

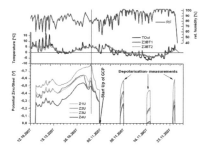

Figure 11. Open-Circuit potentials before and during the operation of the GCP systems in relation to air (Tout) and concrete temperature (BT1, BT2) and the relative humidity's (RH).

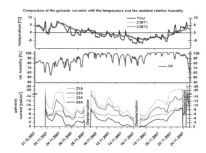

Figure 12. Galvanic currents in the different GCP zones (Z_i) during start-up in relation to the ambient temperature (T_{out}), concrete temperature (BT1, BT2) and the relative humidity of ambient air.

Table 1. 24h depolarization measurements according to En12696 during start-up.

Date	Measurement	Steel Potentials v. Ref. cells normalized to Ag/AgCl (mV)							
		Z1 R1M	Z1 R3A	Z2 RIM	Z3 R2A	Z3 R3A	Z4 R1A	RH%	T°C
16.11.07	Inst Off	−304	−620	−548	−648	−636	−585	92	−3.5
	24h	−163	−385	−416	−493	−497	−535	95	−3.9
	24h Dep	141	235	132	155	139	50		
06.12.07	Inst Off	−484	−675	−740	−813	−761	−847	102	−0.2
	24h	−321	−413	−601	−678	−645	−725	102	0.3
	24h Dep	163	262	139	135	116	122		

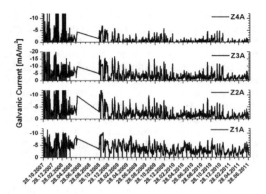

Figure 13. Galvanic currents of the GCP systems measured from 1 November 2007 till 1 July 2011.

Table 2. Galvanic Currents measured from 4 February 2009—27 June 2010.

Zone	Z1 mA/m²	Z2 mA/m²	Z mA/m²	Z4 mA/m²	RH %	T_{air} °C	$T_{concrete}$ °C
Mean	3.80	2.17	3.69	0.77	80.3	4	6.1
Min	0.66	0.00	0.00	0.00	29.2	−14	−11.6
Max	9.04	9.70	16.66	5.82	98.3	25	23.9

Comparison of the course of the galvanic currents with temperature and relative humidity reveals that at temperatures above 0°C relative humidity controls mainly the galvanic currents, at temperatures below 0°C temperature controls mainly the galvanic currents (Figure 14).

The galvanic currents decreased and approached in some zones zero at dry ambient air (RH < 50%) and temperatures below freezing but increased immediately if humidity levels and/or temperature increased again to the values previously measured at the corresponding humidity and/or temperature levels. During the time period of observation the GCP systems passed four alpine winters without measurable loss or decrease in performance. Furthermore, the numerous wet/dry and freeze/thaw cycles did not affect the long-term performance of the GCP systems. Galvanic currents decreased to values averaging at about 2 mA/m² during the exceptionally dry spring/early summer 2011 (February—June 2011). During that period average relative humidity was below 65%, with extended periods with an average humidity in the range of 30–45% in March and April 2011. After the end of the dry period, the end of May 2011, currents increased again.

Calculated from the galvanic currents integrated over time, between 2.7% and 7.0% of the zinc anode (2000 g/m²) were consumed (Table 3) during the period of operation from 1 November

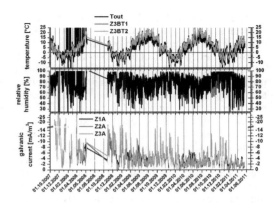

Figure 14. Galvanic currents of the GCP systems in comparison with the ambient relative humidity (RH) and temperature (ambient temperature T_{out}, concrete temperature BT1-1 cm below the concrete surface, BT2-3 cm below the concrete surface). Data from 1 November 2007 till 1 July 2011.

Table 3. Anode material consumed from 1 November 2007 until 27 June 2010 and service time expectancy of the GCP systems.

Zone	Z1	Z2	Z3	Z4
Charge passed in coulombs	366.527	309.981	413.244	158.575
% of zinc anode consumed	6.2%	5.2%	7.0%	2.7%
Calculated service time-expectancy in years at mean current listed below*	31	56	32	164
Mean current (04/2/09–27/06/10)	3.80	2.17	3.69	0.77

* Service time expectancy calculated for 70% (1400 g/m²) zinc as available during service time.

2007—27 June 2010. Using the mean galvanic current values during the time period of stable operation (4 February 2009—27 June 2010) and assuming that a minimum of 70% of zinc will be available for galvanic protection, one obtains life time expectancies of a minimum 30 years. Considering worst cases in self-corrosion and local depletion, one may safely assume a service time expectancy of a minimum 15 years.

3.1.4.3 Steel potentials
To compare the reliability and performance of two different types of reference cells that are frequently used in CP installations, Ag/AgCl cells and Mn/MnO₂ cells were installed. The Mn/MnO₂ cells proved to be more reliable than the Ag/AgCl cells: Ag/AgCl cells, once dried out, do not regenerate

if rewetted. The cell Z3R1 A in zone 3 no longer worked after 3 months of operation and is not considered in the evaluation of the data.

The values of the steel potentials reported relate all to a Ag/AgCl//3M KCl cell. The values measured against the Mn/MnO$_2$ cells were normalized to the Ag/AgCl cells. The observed steel potentials measured before applying CP correlate with the chloride concentrations determined in the concrete overlays ranging from medium corrosion probability up to pitting corrosion. The galvanic corrosion protection results in a significant shift of the 24 h off steel potentials towards more positive values (Figure 15). The potentials measured during the operation of the GCP systems are composed of the steel potential and the strength of the electric field generated by the galvanic current at the location of the tip of the reference cell. After disconnecting the EZA from the steel reinforcement, the electric field vanishes within a short time—0.1 s—and the value of the steel potential may be measured (instant off potential). The steel potentials move towards the rest potential during the subsequent depolarisation. One may assume that the off-potentials, measured after 24 hours of depolarisation, are close to the rest potentials. Galvanic corrosion protection results in a shift of rest potentials towards more positive values and therefore lower corrosion probability.

3.1.4.4 24 h Depolarization Measurements

The efficiency of the corrosion protection of the GCP systems was verified by depolarization measurements according to EN 12696 as described in chapter 3. The results of a depolarization measurement executed on 26 February 2010 are shown for example in Figure 16: The instant off potentials were attained after 0.1 s. The subsequent depolarization within 24 h exceeded 100 mV. The results of the depolarization, among selected and representative 24 depolarization measurements in the time period from 1 November 2007 until 17 June 2011 are listed in table 4—RH denotes relative humidity, CT concrete temperature.

The results of the depolarization measurements show that that the steel reinforcement in the concrete members in the zones Z1–Z3 is fully protected from corrosion by the installed EZA anodes over the full length of observation time—nearly 4 years: The 24 h depolarization values in the galvanic

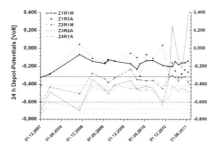

Figure 15. Development of the 24 h off potentials obtained from 24 h depolarisation measurements.

Table 4. Data from 24 hour depolarisation measurements according to EN12696.

Date	Measurement	Z1 R1M	Z1 R2A	Z1 R3A	Z2 R1M	Z3 R2A	Z3 R3A	RH %	CT °C
06.12.07	Inst. Off	−484	−622	−675	−740	−813	−761	89	−0.8
	24h Off	−321	−408	−413	−601	−678	−645	95	0.2
07.12.07	24h Dep.	163	214	262	139	135	116		
26.02.09	Inst. Off	−310	−49	−395	−385	−476	−489	67	−2.2
	24h Off	−146	274	−113	−278	−349	−347	93	−1.9
27.02.09	24h Dep.	164	323	282	107	127	142		
12.08.10	Inst. Off	−246	−138	−330	−479	−591	−553	72	18.4
	24h Off	−138	90	−113	−358	−445	−477	89	8.1
12.08.10	24h Dep.	108	228	217	121	146	76		
30.12.10	Inst. Off	−345	49	−450	−364	−420	6	81	−5.9
	24h Off	−203	264	−294	−319	−328	100	98	−5.5
31.12.10	24h Dep.	142	215	156	45	92	94		
21.04.11	Inst. Off	−243	−187	−332	−386	−255	25	50	11.7
	24h Off	−164	−109	−285	−323	−221	151	45	13.1
22.04.11	24h Dep.	79	78	47	63	34	126		
17.06.11	Inst. Off	−283	−39	−383	−482	129	67	81	15.9
	24h Off	−143	186	−266	−377	373	307	81	15.8
18.06.11	24h Dep.	140	225	117	105	244	240		

protection zones Z1–Z3 are >100 mV at which full corrosion protection is expected according to EN 12696 with the following exceptions: The depolarization value of ≥100 mV may not be attained at very dry weather as during the depolarization measurement on 21 April 2011 (RH 45—50%). However, the subsequent depolarization measurement from 17 June 2011 (RH 81%) showed that the 100 mV criterion was fulfilled again. During winter time (31. 12. 2011) at concrete temperatures of—6°C, the 100 mV criterion was not fulfilled in zone 2 & 3. There will be only negligible corrosion in a dried out or frozen concrete overlay.

The 100 mV criterion was not fulfilled in the protection zone 4: the reference cell and the macro cell sensor were installed in an area in which repair mortar was applied on the steel reinforcement. In that area, the steel reinforcement was exposed to air and was covered with repair mortar. The steel reinforcement should be passive in such an environment. The small currents indicated high resistance between the EZA anode and the steel rebars, eventually due to the repair mortar. Moreover, the cantilever on the downhill side was mostly dry as the bridge deck was inclined uphill.

3.1.4.5 Macro cell currents

The galvanic currents decreased continuously after start-up and reached stable values after about one year of operation. The macro cell currents decreased and stabilized—parallel to the galvanic currents—after about one year (Figure 17). Weak anodic macro-cell currents persisted for sensor MZ3 in zone 3. Sensor 3 was located 6 cm below the concrete surface. These anodic currents were measured despite the fact that 24 depolarization values showed full corrosion protection (Table 4). However, the value of the currents—<0.2 µA/cm²— correspond to corrosion rates resulting in losses of cross section of steel rebars of <3 µm/year. 10% loss of cross section would be reached after 500 years. The macro-cell measurements show that the steel reinforcement is reliably protected from corrosion.

3.1.4.6 Durability and weathering resistance

The EZA system is fully functional after nearly four years of operation enduring four alpine winters. The galvanic zinc anode protects the steel reinforcement reliably and durable from corrosion.

Delamination of the surface layer of the solid EZA electrolyte has been observed in areas which were soaked thoroughly with de-icing salt solution during winter time. However, the zinc anode mesh was not laid open due to the delamination of the surface layers. Cores showed that in areas where the EZA was soaked with deicing salt solution from the inside through cracks across the bridge deck, the compound between the EZA mortar and

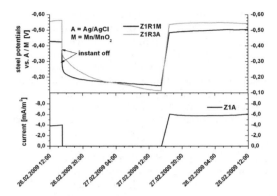

Figure 16. Galvanic currents and steel potentials in zone 1 during the depolarization measurement from 26/2/2010.

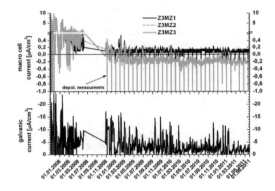

Figure 17. Macro cell currents during the operation of the EZA in protection zone 3.

the concrete remained fully intact. The galvanic corrosion protection was therefore guaranteed in all areas in which the EZA anode is installed.

3.2 De Meernbrug steel bridge

This 2010 project in Utrecht, The Netherlands, was initiated due to reinforcement corrosion in the concrete front wall of both abutments of the steel "De Meernbrug" bridge over the Amsterdam-Rijn canal. Reinforcement corrosion was initiated due to high levels of penetrated chloride readily available from deicing salts from the overlying road. Over 1% mass of chloride by mass of cement was present at the rebar level in the damaged areas. Undamaged concrete showed high levels of chloride as well, but were slightly lower.

During repair works a decision was made to change traditional repair work to cathodic protection. The three main reasons were: reduction of direct costs due to the fact that traditional repair conforming to EN1504-standards would mean excessive removal of chloride contaminated concrete while cathodic protection would mean limited repair of delaminated and disintegrated spots; reduction of risks for future development of concrete damage on the none repaired locations and reduction of overall execution time of the work being done.

In total some 200 m^2 of traditional reinforced concrete was cathodically protected. For the protection, some minor surface repairs were performed, after which a zinc mesh with a total amount of 4 kg zinc per m^2 of concrete surface was applied.

The amount of zinc relative to the amount of steel surface to be protected (relative steel density was well below 1 m^2 steel per m^2 concrete) showed a theoretical lifetime expectancy of more than 15 years.

The zinc mesh was embedded in non-cementitious TASC-mortar which forms the core of the system's performance. The system of cathodic protection as applied was finalized with an aesthetic coating system based on the Sika Decadex system. This is a typical installation of an "install and forget" system as there is no need for a power supply on this remote site and no need for extensive monitoring and control as the system is always "on". Both issues were demands made by the department responsible for the future maintenance of the bridge.

As inspected in 2011 the system's performance is up to the industry's standards.

3.3 'Hubertusviaduct' in den haag

This 2008 project in The Hague was initiated by the municipality. During a damage assessment of a large fly-over junction 'Hubertusviaduct,' with 4 abutment walls, there was a chloride induced reinforcement corrosion problem in the concrete just beneath the expansion joints. During the repair works, all expansion joints were replaced with new, watertight rubber joints. The concrete damage was repaired and the abutment was cathodically protected.

In total 90 m^2 was covered with zinc mesh with a total of 2 kg per m^2 of concrete (Figure 18). Considering the low reinforcement density, a lifetime of over 10 years is expected. A total area of 90 m^2 of concrete was protected on 4 different locations, divided into 5 separate zones. Each zone was installed with a decay-probe (activated titanium Ti*) and a reference-electrode (manganese dioxide MnO_2-type). All connections within a zone to the reinforcement, the zinc-anode, the decay-probe and the reference-electrode were made in a connection box. The entire surface was coated with the Decadex coating system. Figures 20 and 21 show the system in use on site.

Figure 18. De Meerenbrugg steel bridge in Utrecht with concrete abutements.

Figure 19. One of the abutments of the De Meerenbrugg steel bridge in Utrecht protected with the EZA system.

Figure 20. Support for the bearings on one of the abutments of the Hubertus viaduct in The Hague.

Table 5. Verification of the effectiveness of the GCP of the EZA by 24 h depolarisation measurements according to EN 12696. Potential values in mV.

Cell	Type	On-potential	Instant-off	1h off	24 h off	24 h Depolarisation
Re1	MnO_2	547	457	386	288	169
DP2	Ti*	366	278	183	91	187

172

Figure 21. EZA protected with an acrylic coating (Decadex) exposed to de-icing salt solution from a leaking joint of the Hubertus viaduct in The Hague.

Performance of the system has been monitored with respect to the EN12696 standard. Visual inspection showed no signs of aging, deterioration or failure, despite the fact that leakage from the joints above was abundant and water load was permanent on the horizontal parts of the installation. The protective current density was typically 2 mA/m² concrete after 3 years of operation.

The depolarisation of the cathodic protection system in 24 hours was well above the EN12696 criterion of 100 mV, averaging 174 mV depolarisation in 24 hours. A typical depolarisation measurement result from 30 June 2011 is given in Table 5.

Already after a few years, the joints had started to leak again and the EZA was exposed to deicing salt solution during wintertime (Figure 19). The EZA has outlasted three winters, two of which were harsh. The Decadex coating protected the EZA efficiently from damage.

Performance has been above expectation in the first 3 years. The system is capable of withstanding water load, deicing salts, proves to be frost-thaw-resistant and shows no signs of aging.

4 CONCLUSIONS

The performance of the novel EZA galvanic corrosion protection system, consisting of a zinc mesh embedded into a proprietary non-cementitious mortar that hardens to a solid electrolyte, was evaluated on concrete members of three different civil structures—an alpine road bridge in Austria, abutments of a steel bridge in Utrecht, NL and on the abutments of a viaduct in The Hague, NL.

Measurements according to EN12696 and with macro cell sensors over a period of up to nearly 4 years show that the EZA system has protected the steel reinforcement of the concrete members reliably from corrosion.

During very dry seasons (RH < 50%) and under freezing conditions (T < 5°C), galvanic currents decrease towards zero values but return to normal if humidity and/or temperature increase again. Frost-thaw salt resistance may be obtained by covering or impregnating the TAS-EZA with a water impermeable frost thaw salt resistant coating. Calculated from the galvanic currents integrated over time, a maximum of 7 wt.% of the zinc-anode was consumed during the initial three years of operation. Considering self corrosion and local variations of the current flow, a service time expectancy of minimum 15 years may be safely assumed for a EZA containing a zinc mesh with 2 kg/m².

REFERENCES

Bäßler, R., Burkert, A., Eichler, G. & Mietz, J. 2006. Integrated Protection System for Chloride Deteriorated Concrete Structures., In M.G. Grantham, R. Jaubertie, C. Lanos, (Eds.), *Concrete Solutions, Proceedings of the Second International Conference on Concrete Repair,* St. Malo, France, 27–29 June 2006: 220–234. Garston Watford: BRE Press.

Bullard, S.J., Cramer, S. & Covino, B. 2009. *Final Report—Effectiveness of Cathodic Protection* SPR 345. Report No. FHWA-OR-RD-09-18, National Energy Technology Laboratory, Oregon.

Kepler, J.L., Darwin, D. & Locke Jr., C.E. 2000. Evaluation of Corrosion Protection Methods for Reinforced Concrete Highway Structures, *Structural Engineering and Engineering Materials SM Report* No. 58, University of Kansas Center for Research Inc., Lawrence, Kansas, May 2000.

Kessler, R.J.; Powers, R.G. & Lasa, I.R. 2002. Un update on the long-term use of cathodic protection of marine structures, *Corrosion 2002, paper 02254,* NACE International.

Rothman, P.S., Szeliga, M.J. & Nikolakakos, S. 2004. Galvanic Cathodic Protection of Reinforced Concrete Structures in a Marine Environment, *Corrosion 2004, paper 04308,* NACE International.

Schwarz, W. & Tritthart, J. 2009. Effect of cathodic protection: a viable method to monitor and control the efficiency of CP?, *Materials and Corrosion* 60: 138–147.

Schwarz, W., Schauer, M. & Binder, F. 2009. Auswirkung des KKS auf Makrozellenströme: Eine verlässliche Methode zur Überwachung der Wirksamkeit von KKS?, *in 1. Kolloquium 27. und 28. Januar 2009—Erhaltung von Bauwerken,* M. Raupach (Ed.), Technische Akademie Esslingen TAE: 559–568.

Szabo, S. & Bakos, I. 2006. Cathodic Protection with Sacrificial Anodes, *Corrosion Reviews* 24: 231–280.

Virmani, Y.P. & Clemena, G.G. 1998. Corrosion Protection- *Concrete Bridges Report No. FHWA-RD-98-088,* Federal Highway Administration, Washington, D.C.

General repair

Concrete Solutions – Grantham, Mechtcherine & Schneck (eds)
© 2012 Taylor & Francis Group, London, ISBN 978-0-415-61622-5

Punching strengthening of two-way slabs using a prestressing technique

T.F. El-Shafiey & A.M. Atta
Tanta University, Tanta, Egypt

ABSTRACT: Punching shear failure normally occurs in reinforced concrete slabs subjected to concentrated loads and particularly in concrete bridge decks due to development of an internal arching action within the system. This study presents punching shear behavior of two-way slabs strengthened with transverse prestressed bars. The main purpose of this paper is to develop the use of a prestressing technique to repair or strengthen two way slabs due to construction or design errors, poor quality or inadequate materials, overloading and accidents. Eight two-way slabs ($1100 \times 1100 \times 120$ mm) with a steel reinforcement ratio of 0.94% were tested under concentric loading. In addition to a non strengthened slab, the present research was studied in two groups to examine different configuration shapes of prestressing bars around the punching area to study their effectiveness under ultimate limit states. The test results indicated a large efficiency of this method to change the mode of failure from punching shear failure to flexure failure. The strengthened slabs showed an increase of up to approximately 50% in load-carrying capacity and an increase of up to 80% in punching cracking load with respect to the un-strengthened control slab.

1 INTRODUCTION

In flat slabs the force and moments transferred between the slab and the column cause high shear and bending stresses in the slab, near the column. These stresses produce concrete cracking and may lead to slab failure. The punching failure is associated with the formation of a pyramidal plug of concrete which punches through the slab. The punching failure results from the superposition of shear and flexural stresses in the slab. It is a local and brittle failure mechanism. Nowadays, flat slabs are a common solution for buildings because they are economical, easy and fast to build. The need to study suitable strengthening and/or repairing methods is associated with the increased use of this kind of slab. The repair and/or strengthening method (or methods) to be used in any particular situation depends on technical and economical factors, and may be a complex task.

Researchers investigated different methods to strengthen different types of slab-column connections such as; interior, edge, and corner, to avoid failure due to punching shear. Ebead and Marzouk (2002) and Zhang et al. (2001) proposed the use of external bonded steel plates and bolts to increase punching shear capacity. Hassanzadeh and Sundqvist (1998) proposed the use of inserted vertical steel bars around the column. Reinforcing or strengthening slabs using FRP has been conducted

by many researchers. Ospina et al. (2003) proposed the use of internal FRP reinforcing bars to increase the punching shear capacity of two—way slabs. Research by Harajili and Soudki (2003) demonstrated that using flexible CFRP sheets in the tension zone of slabs leads to significant improvements in the flexural stiffness, flexural strength, and shear capacity of interior slab-column connection. Baris and Ogguzhan (2003) proposed the use of CFRP strips in the vertical direction as shear reinforcement around the column to increase punching shear resistance in flat slabs. Punching shear test results reported by Matthys and Taerwe (2002); and EL-Ghandour et al. (1997, 2000); demonstrated the differences between FRP and ordinary steel reinforcement. Hassan and Rizkalla (2004) analyzed concrete bridge decks reinforced with different types and configurations of FRP bars using non-linear finite element formula to study their effectiveness under service and ultimate limit states.

The present work reports the experimental research carried out to study a strengthening method for flat slabs under punching using transversal prestressed bars. Variations of this method have been studied by various authors namely: Ghali et al. (1974), Ramos et al. (2000), El-Sakawy et al. (2000) and Harajli et al. (2006). Eight experimental slabs were produced and tested. The experimental results are compared with a prediction based proposed model.

2 EXPERIMENTAL PROGRAM

2.1 Description of the specimens

A total of eight square slab-column connections (1100 × 1100 × 120 mm) were tested under static loading. Flexural steel reinforcement details were kept the same for all the specimens and detailed as in Figure 1. The main flexural reinforcement was 12 mm diameter bars spaced at 100 mm and arranged to give an average effective depth (d) of 105 mm. The specimens were designed to fail in pure punching shear for specimens before strengthening. The principal variables considered in this research were the number of prestressing layers and distribution of prestressing bars around the column position. Details of the different distribution of bars used in the strengthened slabs are shown in Figure 2. Vertical holes were positioned around the loading area using PVC pipes with 18 mm diameter prior to casting to ease laboratory application as shown in Figure 3. These pipes were pulled out before concrete hardening. The used prestressing bars were of 16 mm diameter. The clearance between the prestressing bars and the holes was filled with Cementitious grout to achieve the bond between prestressing bars and concrete.

2.2 Material properties

To evaluate the test results, concrete cylinder tests were conducted, according to the ASTM C31 and ASTM C39 procedure, to obtain the strength of the materials used to prepare the specimens. To determine the concrete compressive strength,

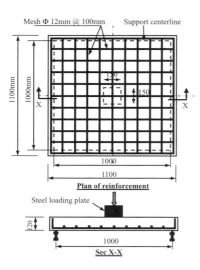

Figure 1. Details of specimens before strengthening and control slab.

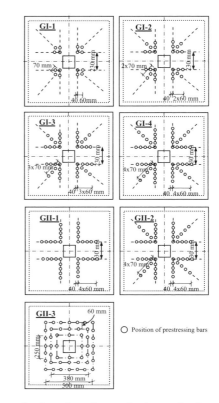

Figure 2. Location of strengthening applications.

Figure 3. Position of pipes placed prior to casting.

150 × 300 mm concrete cylinders were cast at the same time as the slabs. Nine concrete cylinders were tested during the experiment on the slabs to obtain the average compressive strength. The average cylinder compressive strength of concrete used in this study was 30 MPa with difference not more than ±2 MPa for all specimens. The longitudinal reinforcement of the specimens investigated in this study was high tensile steel reinforcement with average yield strength and ultimate strength of 450 MPa and 610 MPa respectively. For the transverse prestressing bolts with a diameter of 16 mm, an average ultimate tensile strength, f_{pu}, of 640 MPa, and average yield stress, f_{py}, of 540 MPa, were used.

2.3 Test setup, test procedure and instrumentation

The specimens were tested as simply supported along all the edges with the effective span 1000 mm length. To prevent crushing of concrete under the loading point, a square steel loading plate (150 mm × 150 mm × 100 mm) was used to resemble the column and guarantee that the punching shear contour lines started outside the column perimeter as presented in Fig. 4. A monotonic load was applied through the stroke control of the testing machine to capture the post-maximum load behavior. The strengthened slabs were subjected to prestressing using prestressing bolts as presented in Fig. 5 bar after bar before loading to 33% of

ultimate bar load. A load cell was placed at selected anchorage locations to monitor the prestressing force during the prestressing process. Strain gauges were mounted to measure the strains of steel bars and prestressing bars to provide additional strain information about steel bars and prestressing bars. The strain gauges were located at a distance of d (70.5 mm) from the column face, assuming a 45-degree punching crack angle, in both directions and at the mid point of the prestressing bars. Deflections were measured at the mid point of the slab using Linear Variable Displacement Transducers.

3 DISCUSSION OF TEST RESULTS

3.1 Crack pattern, cracking loads, modes of failure, and failure load

In the control specimen, GC, the first cracks appeared at a load of around 80 kN. These were flexural cracks on the bottom surface. With the increase of vertical load, radial cracks started to occur and spread out from the loaded area towards the slab edges. Subsequently the inclined cracking within the slab thickness that afterwards developed into the punching failure surface, started to be noticed on the bottom surface. The failure surface had the shape of a pyramidal plug of concrete, starting at the top of the slab around the column perimeter and arriving to the bottom surface at a distance about 2d from the column perimeter at load 210 kN as shown in Figure 6.

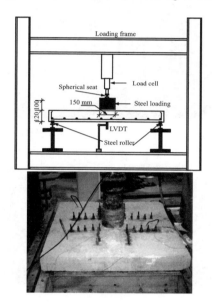

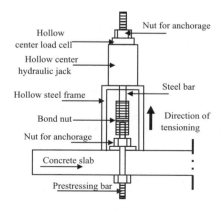

Figure 4.   Test setup and slab details.

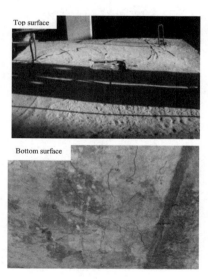

Figure 6.   Crack patterns and mode of failure for control specimens.

Figure 5.   Prestressing process.

179

For all specimens with different layers of transversal prestressing reinforcement, the crack development followed a similar pattern to he control specimen. The first tangential cracks started to be noticed between 70 kN and 90 kN. The radial cracking load for every specimen in the both groups differed according to the distribution of prestressing bars. In specimens of group GI, this load increased gradually with increasing number of transversal prestressing bars layers. That due to the increasing of the strengthened area from two layers, specimen GI-1, up to five layers, specimen GI-4. The punching cracking load ranged between 200 kN to 250 kN. The failure loads for specimens depended on the failure type. The punching failure load ranged between 275 kN and 320 kN for specimens GI-1 and GI-2 respectively. The flexure failure load ranged between 340 kN and 345 kN for specimens GI-3 and GI-4 respectively. The failure modes are shown in Figure 7. In specimens of group GII, the punching cracking load was

GI-1

GI-2

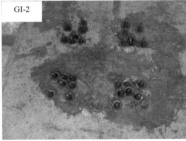

GI-4

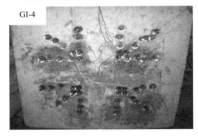

Figure 7.   Crack patterns and mode of failure for group I specimens.

GII-1

GII-2

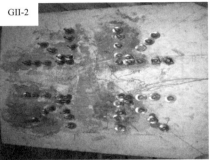

GII-3

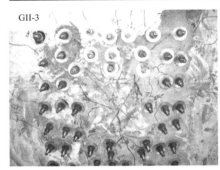

Figure 8.   Crack patterns and mode of failure for group II specimens.

approximately equal for specimens GII-2 and GII-3 and increased by about 20% compared to specimen GII-1 which might a result of decreasing in number of prestressing bars in specimen GII-1 compared to other specimens. The failure modes for all specimens of this group were flexural failure as shown in Figure 8. The comparisons between flexure cracking load, punching cracking load and failure loads are presented in Figures 9 to 11.

3.2   Deflection and ductility

The recorded vertical deflections on the specimens with strengthening prestressing bolts were also smaller than those observed in the control specimen for the same load. It appears that the presence

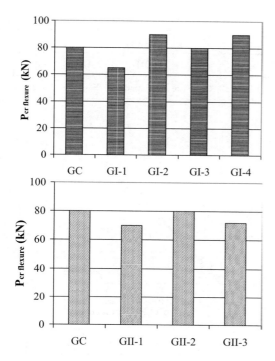

Figure 9.   Flexure cracking loads for tested specimens.

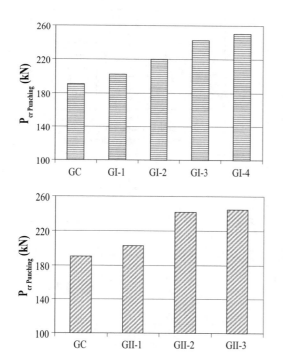

Figure 10. Punching cracking loads for tested specimens.

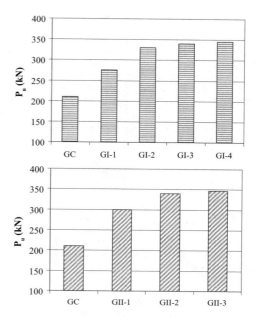

Figure 11.   Ultimate loads for tested specimens.

of the reinforcing bolts lead to an increment of the stiffness of the slab. The deformations of the slabs were approximately rigid body rotations about axes close to the edges of the loaded area, as shown in Figures 12-a and 13-a. On the other hand, the ductility of the slabs seemed to be greatly affected with the number of prestressing bolts as well as the distribution of these bolts. For specimens GI-1 with two layers of strengthening bolts, the toughness increased by about 70% compared to control specimen with the same mode of failure. When three layers of transverse bars were used the toughness increased by 47% compared with GI-1. While, with the use of four and five layers, specimens GI-3 and GI-4, exhibited 115% and 124% increase in ductility compared to GI-1 respectively (see Figure 14). For group GII specimens the increase in ductility ranged between 221% and 333% compared with the control specimen. These large values referred to changing of the failure mode to flexural failure. The specimens GII-3 indicated larger toughness value compared to all specimens due to good confinement of transverse prestressing bars around the "column". Table 1 shows the failure mode for the tested slabs.

3.3   Steel strain results

The strains on the bottom reinforcement bars grew with the increase of the vertical load. On the specimens reinforced with the vertical prestressing

Table 1. Failure mode for tested slabs.

Specimen	Control slab	Group GI				Group GII		
	GC	GI-1	GI-2	GI-3	GI-4	GII-1	GII-2	GII-3
Failure mode	Punching	Punching	Punching	Flexure	Flexure	Flexure	Flexure	Flexure

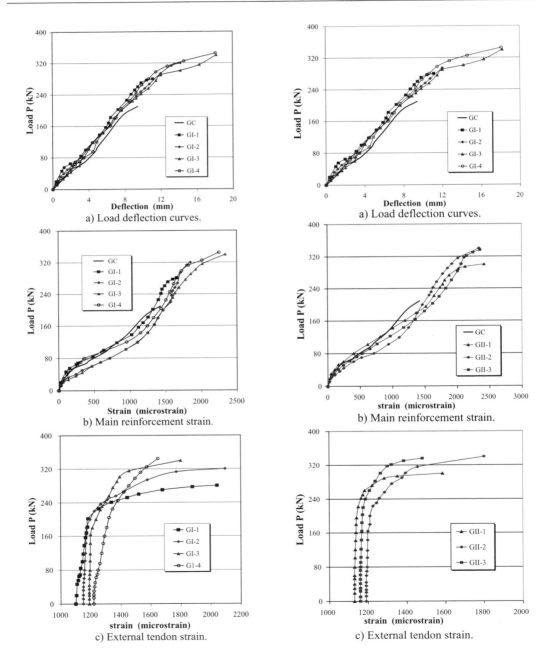

Figure 12.   Experimental results for group I.

Figure 13.   Experimental results for group II.

a) Load deflection curves.

a) Load deflection curves.

b) Main reinforcement strain.

b) Main reinforcement strain.

c) External tendon strain.

c) External tendon strain.

182

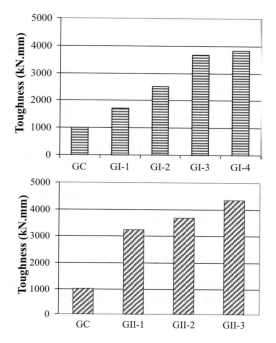

Figure 14. Toughness of tested specimens.

bolts the strains on the bottom reinforcement were approximately the same compared to the control specimen. Figures 12-b and 13-b shows the yielding of steel which took place in specimens GI-3, GI-4 and all specimens of GII compared to other specimens. The strain in the vertical bolts stayed approximately constant until the applied load reached about the slab predicted resistance without shear reinforcement. Then the forces grew quickly with the increase of vertical load. The strains in the bolts of the innermost layer were usually higher than in the outermost layers. Figures 12-c and 13-c presents the average strain distribution for prestressing bolts.

4 THEORETICAL PREDICTIONS FOR PUNCHING SHEAR CAPACITY OF STRENGTHENED SLABS

The punching failure mechanism of reinforced concrete slabs is controlled by the tensile stresses around the punching cracks and by the dowel action of steel reinforcement (Rochdi et al., 2004). To compute the punching load of the control slab, the analytical model developed by Menetry (2002) is considered here. This model is resisted mainly by the vertical component (P_{ct}) of the tensile force of concrete along the inclined punching crack in addition to the force generated by dowel action of

tension reinforcement (P_{dows}). The Menetry model is shown schematically in Figure 15 and expressed as:

$$P_{pun} = P_{ct} + P_{dows} \tag{1}$$

The punching crack is assumed to be a truncated cone in shape developed between two radials r_1, r_2 where:

$$r_1 = r_s + d/(10\tan\theta), r_2 = r_s + d/\tan\theta,$$
$$\text{and } s = \sqrt{(r_2 - r_1)^2 + (0.9d)^2} \tag{2}$$

in which r_s is the radius of the column, θ is the inclination of the punching crack and S is the inclined length of the punching crack.

The vertical component of the concrete tensile, Pet is expressed as follows:

$$P_{ct} = \pi(r_1 + r_2) \cdot S \cdot \sigma_y = \pi(r_1 + r_2) \cdot S \cdot f_{ct}^{2/3} \cdot \xi \cdot \mu \tag{3}$$

where ξ is a parameter taking into account the influence of the percentage of tension steel reinforcement ps on the concrete tensile stress and determined as:

$$\xi = -0.1ps^2 + 0.4ps + 0.35, 0 < ps < 2\% \tag{4}$$

And μ is the parameter take into account the aggregate size-effect and expressed as:

$$\mu = 1.6(1 + d/d_a)^{-1/2} \text{ (with } d \geq 3d_a) \tag{5}$$

where d_a is the aggregate size.

The total shear force which can be transferred by reinforcing bars, of diameter Φs. crossing the punching crack is computed according to Menetry as:

$$P_{dows} = \frac{1}{2} \sum^{bars} \phi^2 \sqrt[3]{f_c f_y (1 - \xi_1^2)} \sin\theta \tag{6}$$

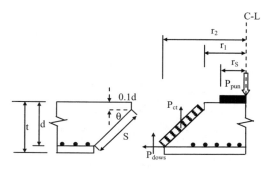

Figur 15. Punching shear capacity of reinforced concrete slab modeled by Menetry.

where $\zeta = \sigma_s/f_y$, σ_s is the axial tensile stress in bar, f_y is the yield strength of steel, and f_c is the compressive concrete strength.

The calculation of punching load of the strengthened slab may differ depending on the strengthening technique. The punching crack causing the punching failure is not formed suddenly, but preceded by the formation of internal microcracks that propagate progressively. Therefore, the external strengthening used in this work using external prestressing bolts is gradually loaded. The expression presented by Menetry may be modified to account for the forces carried by the external strengthening tools and expressed in Eq. 7.

$$P_{pun} = (P_{ct}) \cdot \alpha_c + P_{st} + P_{dows} \qquad (7)$$

where P_{st} is the additional punching load for strengthened slabs due to vertical prestressed bolts and α_c is an incremental factor due to additional normal forces.

$$\text{where } \alpha_c = 1 + 0.07 \, (P_u / A_c) \qquad (8)$$

A_c is describing as the effective concrete area under pressure of prestressing bars.

Experimental study showed that the failure surface for specimens GI-1 and GI-2 occurred outside the strengthened zone. Therefore all prestressing bolts of the strengthened specimens are assumed to contribute in resisting punching shear. The proposed model for strengthened specimens is shown in Figure 16. The vertical component of the tensile force P_{st} for prestressing bolts may be expressed as:

$$P_{st} = 2\pi\phi_1^2 f_y \sum_{i=1}^{i=n} \beta_i \text{ (Elshafiey 2004)} \qquad (9)$$

Based on the experimental work, it was noted that each bolt carries a different load depending

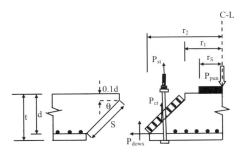

Figure 16. Punching shear capacity of strengthened slab using external prestressing bolts.

Table 2. Comparison between experimental failure punching load and proposed model.

	GC	GI-1	GI-2
(P_{uexp}) Experimental result	210	275	330
(P_{upm}) Proposed model	230	271	325
(P_{uexp})/(P_{upm})	0.91	1.01	1.02

on its position measured from column face. So β_i ranged between 0.055 and 0.09 (Elshafiey 2004) according to bolt position. While angle θ, measured from experimental tests was found to be about 22°. Comparisons are made in Table 2 between the strengthening slabs for group GI and proposed model showed good agreement.

5 CONCLUSIONS

- The use of transverse prestressing bolts is an easy and economical method to apply to flat slabs that need to be retrofitted, aiming to have a better punching behaviour and delaying the punching shear cracks at different levels.
- The increase of length strengthened by using transverse prestressing bolts to 2d or more changes the mode of failure from punching to flexural failure.
- The change in configuration of the prestressing bolts did not affect the failure mode while the distance of strengthened length to more than 2d and the effectiveness only showed in the toughness and deflection.
- All strengthened specimens had a higher ultimate load, (ranging between 30% and 60%), and toughness, (ranging between 70% and 333%), relative to the control specimen. The increases in the previous parameters seem to be related to the strengthening system used.
- A proposed model was carried out for each strengthening method to predict the punching load. These models were verified and validated against selected experimental results.

ACKNOWLEDGEMENT

The tests were carried out in the Reinforced Concrete Laboratory, Faculty of Engineering, Tanta University, Egypt. The authors are grateful for the precious technical assistance of the students of the repair and strengthening of R.C. structures project for academic year 2008/2009. Also great thanks to Prof. Emad Etman for his help during the revision stage.

REFERENCES

Baris, B. and Oguzhan, B. (2003). "Punching shear strengthening of RC flat plate using CFRP", Journal of Struc. Eng., ASCE, Vol. 129, No. 9, September 1, pp. 1173–1182.

Birkle, G. and Dilger, W. (2003). "Performance of slab-column connections with shear studs in radial and orthogonal arrangements", ICPCM-A New Era of Building Cairo, Egypt, pp. 665–674.

Ebead, U. and Marzouk, H. (2002). "Strengthening of two-way slabs using steel plates," ACI Struc. J., Vol. 99, No. 1. pp. 23–31.

El-Ghandour, A.W., Pilakoutas, K. and Waldorn, P. (1997). "Behavior of FRP RC flat slabs", Proc. of the 3rd International Symposium on Non-Metalic (FRP) Reinforcement for Concrete Structures, Sapporo. Vol. 2, pp. 267–574.

El-Ghandour, A.W., Pilakoutas, K. and Waldorn, P. (2000). "Punching shear behavior and design of FRP RC flat slabs", Proc. of the International Workshop on Punching Shear Capacity of RC Slabs. Stokholm, Sweden, pp. 359–366.

El-Salakawy, E., Soudki, K. and Polak, M.A. "Punching Shear Behavior of Flat Slabs Strengthened with Fiber Reinforced Polymer Laminates", Journal of Composites for Construction, ASCE/September/October, 2004.

El-Shafiey, T. (2004). "Strengthening of Reinforced Concrete Flat Slabs Against Punching Shear", Scientific Bulletin, Ain Shams University, Vol. 39 No. 4 pp. 47–74.

European Committee for Standardization. EN 1992-1-1 Eurocode 2: Design of concrete structures—Part 1–1: General rules and rules for buildings. CEN, Dec.. 2004, p. 225.

Ghali, A., Sargious, M.A. and Huizer, A. (1974). "Vertical Prestressing of Flat Plates Around Columns", Shear in Reinforced Concrete, ACI, Special Publication SP 42, Detroit, Vol. 2, pp. 905–920.

Hamza, A.M. (2000). "High volume fraction of fibers as a shear reinforcement in flat slab structures", J. of the Egyptian Society of Engineers. Vol. 39, pp. 35–40.

Harajili, M.H. and Soudki, K.A. (2003). "Shear strengthening of interior slab—column connections using CFRP sheets", Journal of Composites for Construction, ASCE, Vol. 7, No. 2, May, pp. 145–163.

Harajli, M.H., Soudki, K.A. and Kudsi, T. "Strengthening of Interior Slab-Column Connections Using a Combination of FRP sheets and Steel Bolts", Journal of Composites for Construction, ASCE September/October, 2006.

Hassan, T.K. and Rizkalla, S.H. (2004). "Punching shear strength of GFRP reinforced deck slabs girder bridges", conf, of advanced composite material in bridges and structures, Calgary, Alberta, Canada.

Hassanzadeh, G. and Sunqvist, H. (1998). "Strengthening of Bridge slab on Columns". Nordic Conc. Res., Vol. 1, No. 21, pp. 25–36.

Menetry, P.H. (2002). "Synthesis of Punching Failure in Reinforced Concrete Slab", Cement and Concrete Composite. No. 24, pp. 497–507.

Mosallam, A., Kreier, J., Lanccey. T., Haroun, M. and Elsanadedy, H. (2000). "Experimental and Numerical Analysis of Two-way Concrete Salb repaired with polmer Composites", Acun 2 Int. Composites Conf., Univ. of New South Wales Sydney.

Ospina, C.E., Scott, D.B. and Cheng, J.R. (2003). "Punching of Two-way Concrete slabs with FRP reinforcing Bars or Grids", ACI Strue. J., Vol. 100, No. 5, pp. 589–598.

Ramos, A.M.P., Lúcio, V. and e Regan, P.E. (2000). "Repair and Strengthening Methods of Flat Slabs for Punching", International Workshop on Punching Shear Capacity of RC Flat Slabs, Royal Institute of Technology, Department of Structural Engineering, Stockholm, June de.

Rocdi, E.H., Bigaud, D., Ferrier, E. and Hamelin, P. (2004). "Punching Shear strength of RC slabs Externally Strengthened by CFRP laminates". Conf, of Advanced Composite Material in bridges and Structures, Calgary, Alberta. Canada.

Seible, F., Ghali, A. and Dilger, W. H. (1980). "Preassembled shear reinforcing units for flat plates", J. ACI, 77(1), pp. 28–35.

Zaghloul, A.E. and Razaqpur, A.G. (2003). "Punching shear strength of CFRP reinforced concrete flat plates", Conf. of AICSGE 5. Alexandria University, pp. RC-263–276.

Concrete Solutions – Grantham, Mechtcherine & Schneck (eds)
© 2012 Taylor & Francis Group, London, ISBN 978-0-415-61622-5

Preconditioning concrete for better freeze-thaw durability

A. Badr
School of Built Environment & Engineering, University of Bolton, Bolton, UK

ABSTRACT: This paper reports the results of experimental research investigating the effect of pre-conditioning concrete specimens using different drying regimes on the durability of concrete subjected to freeze-thaw cycles. Different types of concrete were investigated. After the initial time of curing, three series of specimens were prepared for freeze-thaw tests. The first series of concrete specimens was subjected to freeze-thaw cycles without any pre-conditioning. The second series of specimens were dried in an environmental chamber at 40°C and a relative humidity of 45% for 48 hours. The rest of the concrete specimens were left to dry in room conditions for 7 days. The mass of deteriorated concrete and the residual strength were assessed after 25, 50 and 100 cycles of freeze-thaw. The results showed that drying concrete specimens before being subjected to freeze-thaw cycles enhanced the resistance to freeze-thaw deterioration. However, the effect of the drying regimes was less pronounced in the air-entrained concrete.

1 INTRODUCTION

In the last two years, numerous concrete structures and concrete pavements have been exposed to very cold weather due to the record low temperatures reported during the winters of 2009/2010 and 2010/2011 in many parts of the world. The UK experienced several spells of severe winter weather with extremely low temperatures and substantial snowfalls. Temperatures generally fell below −10°C on several nights and on occasion below −20°C. Some snowfalls were considered amongst the most significant and widespread since 1965 (Met Office 2011). Concrete structures exposed to cold weather can be susceptible to degradation due to freeze-thaw cycles during such severe conditions.

The deterioration of concrete due to freeze-thaw cycles is a very complex phenomenon. Many theories have been presented to explain the disintegration mechanisms. The prevailing mechanisms are generation of hydraulic pressure due to freezing in capillaries, osmotic pressures resulting from partial freezing in capillaries of solutions with a local salt concentration and differential strains due to localized shrinkage and swelling as well as thermal strains. However, the ease with which water can move within concrete depends on the microstructure and the pore size distribution (Penttala 2006, Basheer et al., 2001, Powers 1975, Fagerlund 1974).

There are many factors that can affect the microstructure characteristics of concrete such as replacing a certain amount of Portland cement with silica fume (Badr & Platten 2006, Poon et al., 2006, Yajun & Cahyadi 2003), using an air entraining agent (Shang et al., 2009, Du & Folliard 2005, Chatterji 2003) and drying of concrete using specific water removal techniques. (Collier et al., 2008, Gallé 2004, Konecny & Naqvi 1993, Zhang & Glasser 2000).

Each of these factors can modify the microstructure in such a way that it may either improve or degrade the ability of the concrete to resist deterioration due to freezing and thawing. For example, it is well established that air entraining agents improve the freeze-thaw durability of almost all types of concretes (Shang et al., 2009, Bassuoni & Nehdi 2005, Harrison et al., 2001, Pigeon et al., 1996). The effect of silica fume is less known and there is contradiction in the literature about the freeze-thaw durability of silica fume concrete (Badr 2010). For example, Sabir & Kouyiali (1991) reported significant increases in the flexural strength of silica fume concretes after 35 cycles of freezing and thawing compared to a control mix without silica fume. However, Pigeon et al. (1986) reported that silica fume concretes are more susceptible to damage caused by freeze-thaw cycles. Toutanji et al. (2004) reported that the freeze-thaw durability of concrete containing silica fume is inversely proportional to the amount of silica fume added.

Exposing concrete to drying conditions at early ages will almost certainly result in coarsening the microstructure of concrete as well as increasing the risk of micro-cracking. Gallé 2004 argued that de-saturation, and dehydration phenomena associated with drying could generate damage to the microstructure due to micro-cracking, capillary porosity evolution and fine pore collapse. Thus, the removal of evaporable pore water could initiate significant degradation in the microstructure of concrete. Gao et al. (2002) suggested that the main reason for the deterioration under freeze-thaw loads could be attributed to the formation of micro-cracks during the hardening of the cement paste of concrete. On the other hand, pre-drying concrete before being exposed to freezing condition will reduce the degree of saturation within the microstructure of concrete. In a saturated or almost saturated microstructure, the moisture will exert internal stress during the freezing cycle. If these stresses exceeded the tensile strength of concrete micro-cracks could be formed and any existing micro-cracks may propagate. Jacobsen et al. (1996) showed that a considerable part of the water existing in the pore structure goes into newly created micro-cracks and contributes to the deterioration by freezing there at −20°C. Therefore, it can be argued that the net effect of pre-drying concrete before being exposed to freezing conditions is not well established and needs further investigation.

2 OBJECTIVES

The main aim of this research was to investigate the effect of preconditioning concrete, before being subjected to freeze-thaw cycles, on its durability.

To achieve this main aim the following objectives have been identified:

- Carry out freeze-thaw tests on moist cured and pre-dried concrete specimens.
- Study the effect of different drying regimes, i.e., controlled conditions using an environmental chamber or uncontrolled in room conditions.
- Investigate the effect of preconditioning on Portland cement and silica fume concrete in the presence and absence of air entraining agent.

3 MATERIALS AND MIXES

3.1 Materials

The Portland cement used was CEM1 conforming to BS EN 197-1. Silica fume (SF) was used as a cement replacement material. The coarse aggregate was well graded limestone natural gravel of 10 mm nominal maximum size. Siliceous sand which complied with zone M of BS EN 12620 was used as a fine aggregate. Superplasticiser (SP) conforming to BS5075 Part 3 was used in all mixes. Air entraining agent (AEA) based on the salt of ether sulphate which complies with BS5075 Part 2 was used in the air-entrained mixes.

3.2 Mixes

Four mixes were initially optimised from laboratory tests. The composition of these four mixes is given in Table 1. The name of every mix consists of two parts indicating the binder type and whether air is entrained. For example, CM-NA is a control mix made with CEM1 as a sole binder and includes no entrained air. Similarly, SF-AE is an air-entrained concrete mix with 10% of the CEM1 replaced by SF on a weight-to-weight basis.

The aggregate-to-binder and water-to-binder ratios were kept constant for all mixes at 4.0 and 0.40, respectively. The limestone was 40% of the total aggregate in all mixes. A target consistence class S2 (between 40 and 110 mm, BS EN13250-Part 1) was achieved for all mixes by changing the SP dosage. As would be expected, mixes with silica fume required higher SP dosages compared to counterpart mixes without silica fume, as can be seen in Table 1.

The dosages of the air-entraining agent (AEA) were determined from trial mixes to achieve an air content of about 6% in the air-entrained mixes. For the Portland cement mix (CM-AE), 0.45 liter was required per cubic meter whereas 0.95 liter was required for the counterpart silica fume mix (SF-AE), as shown in Table 1.

3.3 Mixing

The coarse and fine aggregates were mixed with the binder in a dry state for about one minute in a conventional rotary drum mixer of 50-liter capacity. Half of the mixing water was added and mixed for three minutes before adding the remaining mixing water and SP in addition to AEA where applicable. A further three minutes of mixing were needed to achieve uniform mixture.

3.4 Specimens

Concrete cubes (150 and 100 mm) were cast and a vibrating table was used to achieve full compaction. Thermocouples had been set within one of

Table 1. Mix proportions (per m³) and slump values.

Mixes	CEM1 kg	SF kg	Lime-stone kg	Sand kg	SP liter	AEA liter	Air %	Consistence mm
CM-NA	450	–	720	1080	1.0	–	2.8	70
CM-AE	450	–	720	1080	1.0	0.45	6.1	110
SF-NA	405	45	720	1080	1.2	–	2.2	60
SF-AE	405	45	720	1080	1.2	0.95	5.9	90

the 100 mm cubes during the casting of the in order to monitor the temperature profile inside the core of concrete specimens during the freeze-thaw cycles.

3.5 Curing and preconditioning

All specimens were covered with wet hessian and polyethylene sheets overnight. They were then demolded after 24 hours and submerged in a water curing tank for 7 days. After which, the 150 mm cubes were cut into small cubes of 70 mm nominal dimension. The 100 mm cubes were kept intact.

The 70 mm cubes were then divided into three series as follows:

- Series 1 (Moist): Specimens were stored in room conditions for 1 day to be prepared for the freeze-thaw tests.
- Series 2 (Dry40): Specimens were dried in an environmental chamber at 40°C and a relative humidity of 45% for 48 hours.
- Series 3 (Dry20): Specimens were left to dry in room conditions for 7 days. The average room temperature was 20±5°C and the relative humidity was 70±10%.

4 FREEZE-THAW CYCLES AND TESTING

4.1 Preparation of specimens

Prior to starting the freeze-thaw cycles, control specimens were chosen randomly to be tested for compressive strength at room temperature to establish a control compressive strength for each mix.

Special aluminum adhesive tape was used to create a reservoir on the top surface of each specimen, as shown in Figure 1. In order to reduce the variability in the results, the top surface of each specimen was a cut face. Salt solution was prepared by adding 50 g of deicing salt per liter of

Figure 1. Reservoir on the top surface of each specimen.

distilled water. The salt solution was used to fill the reservoirs on top of each specimen before transferring the specimens to an environmental chamber to start the freeze-thaw test. The level of the salt solution was monitored daily during the thaw cycle and a top up was made if needed.

4.2 Freeze-thaw tests

The freeze-thaw tests were carried out according to RILEM recommendation (RILEM 4-CDC 1977). The specimens were exposed to freeze-thaw cycles inside an environmental chamber running at -20 ± 2. The nominal freezing cycle was 8 hours and the nominal thawing cycle was 16 hours. However, temperature monitored during the tests indicated that the specimens remained in the freezing state for about 16 hours and thawed for 8 hours only, during which the salt was in the solution state.

After certain numbers of freeze-thaw cycles, the weight loss and residual compressive strength were determined to quantify the damage due to freeze-thaw.

5 RESULTS AND DISCUSSION

5.1 Effect of entrained air

Table 2 presents the results obtained for the weight loss for air-entrained and non-air-entrained concrete after 25 cycles. It can be seen that there is a significant reduction in the weight loss of the air-entrained mixes compared to the weight loss in the non-air-entrained concrete. The use of air entraining agent resulted in an average reduction in the weight loss by 91% in the Portland cement concrete (CM mixes) and 84% in silica fume concrete (SF mixes). The reduction was noticed in all cases regardless of the binder type or the method of preconditioning. The reduction in each individual case is shown between brackets in Table 2, where each value is the percentage reduction in weight loss of air-entrained specimens compared to the counterpart non-air-entrained specimens.

The effect of air entrainment was even clearer when comparing the residual compressive strength, as shown in Table 3. On average, the residual

Table 2. Weight loss after 25 cycles.

	Weight loss (mg/mm^2)		
	Moist	Dry40	Dry20
CM-NA	23.6	12.4	13.7
CM-AE	1.7 (−93%)	1.2 (−90%)	1.4 (−90%)
SF-NA	18.5	7.5	9.4
SF-AE	1.8 (−90%)	1.6 (−79%)	1.5 (−84%)

Table 3. Residual compressive strength (MPa) after 25 cycles.

	Control	Residual strength		
	@7 days	Moist	Dry40	Dry20
CM-NA	25.4	5.4	13.7	10.1
CM-AE	22.9	27.5	28.6	27.9
		(+465%)	(+132%)	(+206%)
SF-NA	26.8	8.2	12.4	14.9
SF-AE	23.5	31.9	32.7	28.6
		(+344%)	(+201%)	(+119%)

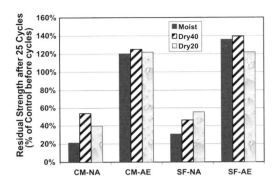

Figure 2. Relative residual strength after 25 cycles.

strength of the air-entrained mixes was increased compared to the counterpart non-air-entrained concretes by 268% and 221% for CM and SF mixes, respectively. The increase in each individual case is shown between brackets in Table 3. The increase was more pronounced in the moist cured specimens.

The enhanced freeze-thaw durability of air-entrained concrete is in agreement with other research (Shang et al., 2009, Bassuoni & Nehdi 2005, Harrison et al., 2001).

The good resistance to deterioration by freeze-thaw cycles of air-entrained concrete used in this study suggests that the hardened concrete with and without silica fume had adequate systems of entrained air voids. This is in agreement with Pigeon et al. (1996) and Hale et al. (2009). It can, therefore, be suggested that the dosages of the air-entraining agent used in this study were adequate for mixes with and without silica fume. However, it should be noticed that the air-entrained silica fume mix (SF-AE) required a much higher dosage of the air-entraining agent compared to the air-entrained control mix (CM-AE), as could be seen from Table 1.

It was interesting to notice that the residual strength of the air-entrained concrete specimens subjected to 25 freeze-thaw cycles was in fact higher than their "start" strength, i.e., the strength of control specimens at the age of 7 days. Figure 2 presents the relative residual strength compared to the strength of counterpart control specimens.

The relative residual strength of the CM-AE and SF-AE specimens were significantly higher than 100% i.e., that of the control specimens, regardless of the preconditioning method. This increase can be attributed to the net effect of two factors. The first is degradation in the strength due to the freeze-thaw cycles and the second is strength development during the time of freeze-thaw cycles due to resuming the hydration process. The net effect was an average increase of about 22% and 32% for CM-AE and SF-AE, respectively. On the other hand, the degradation due to the freeze-thaw

cycles outweighed the development in strength in the non-air-entrained concretes and, therefore, the net result was a reduction in the residual strength. The average reduction was, 62% and 54% for CM-NA and SF-NA, respectively.

5.2 Effect of preconditioning after 25 cycles

Tables 2–3 and Figure 2 also provide information about the effect of the three preconditioning regimes used in this research on the weight loss and residual strength. It can be seen that the pre-dried specimens had better resistance to freeze-thaw degradation after 25 cycles. In non-air-entrained concrete (CM-NA and SF-NA), the weight loss of the pre-dried specimens was almost halved compared to the moist specimens. However, the reduction in the weight loss of the pre-dried specimens was less pronounced in the air-entrained mixes. The effect of the preconditioning method can be made clearer if the weight loss of pre-dried specimens is normalized as a percentage of the weight loss of the counterpart moist specimens, as can be seen in Figure 3. The average weight loss of the pre-dried air-entrained specimens was about 77% and 86% of that of the moist specimens for CM-AE and SF-AE, respectively. The corresponding values for the non-air-entrained specimens were 56% and 46% CM-NE and SF-NE, respectively. The values clearly show that pre-drying resulted in reduced freeze-thaw degradation as manifested by weight loss for all types of concrete although the effect was clearer in the non-air-entrained concrete.

Visual inspection of the specimens after completing 25 freeze-thaw cycles confirmed that the pre-dried specimens performed better than the moist cured specimens. Figures 4–5 show the CM-Moist and CM-Dry20 specimens, respectively. It can be seen that the deterioration on the top surface of the CM-Moist specimens was greater and the coarse aggregate were clearly

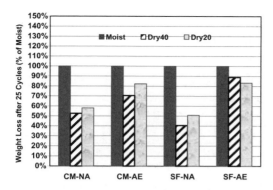

Figure 3. Normalized weight loss after 25 cycles.

Figure 4. CM-Moist specimens after 25 cycles.

Figure 5. CM-Dry20 specimens after 25 cycles.

exposed due to the loss of the cement paste and fine aggregate. In addition, the expansion in one of the CM-Moist specimens resulted in exerting tensile stresses higher than the tensile strength of the aluminum tape used to create the reservoir. The aluminum tape remained intact in all CM-Dry20 and CM-Dry40 specimens.

It might be possible to explain the superior freeze-thaw resistance of the pre-dried specimens in the light of the hydraulic pressure theory. When water within the larger pores freezes, the created ice needs extra space to expand by about 9%. The empty or partially empty pores within the pre-dried specimens seemed to be able to provide this much-needed space. However, during the expansion of ice any excessive water could be pumped away from the freezing sites casing a buildup of hydraulic pressure. Yamashita et al. (1997) showed that the characteristics of the pore system would dictate the extent of the hydraulic pressure. The more the resistance to the movement of the unfrozen water, the higher the extent of the hydraulic pressure. Consequently, the hydraulic pressure could be intensified when the unfrozen water needs to travel for long distance to reach an empty pore. Furthermore, the pumped unfrozen water could find it difficult to move within microstructures that contain large amount of clogged or saturated pores. Thus, it could be suggested that the unfrozen water within the pores of the pre-dried specimens either found it easy to move within the pore structure or, indeed, the next available empty pore was not far from the freezing site. Gallé 2004 stated that the removal of evaporable pore water and dehydration phenomena associated with drying could cause capillary porosity evolution and fine pores collapse. Thus, it is rational to believe that pre-drying concrete resulted in larger and empty pores within the microstructure making it relatively easy for the unfrozen water to move within such microstructure. Therefore, it is likely that the generated hydraulic pressure was lower than the tensile strength of concrete. This is more or less similar to the way air entraining agents work within the microstructure of concrete i.e., by providing empty pores for excessive water and reducing the travel length. This could also explain the reduced effectiveness of pre-drying in the air-entrained specimens observed in this research.

5.3 Effect of preconditioning up to 100 cycles

The analysis of the effect of the three preconditioning regimes after 25 cycles on the weight loss and residual strength showed that the effect was less pronounced in the air-entrained mixes. Therefore, it has been decided to continue testing up to 100 cycles for the non-air-entrained mixes only.

Figures 6–7 show the change in the weight loss of the concrete specimens due to increasing the number of freeze thaw cycles for Portland cement and silica fume mixes. It can be seen that the weight loss in the pre-dried specimens was significantly less than that of the moist specimens regardless of the number of freeze-thaw cycles or the drying method. However, there is a trend in the results suggesting that specimens dried at 40°C for 48 hours

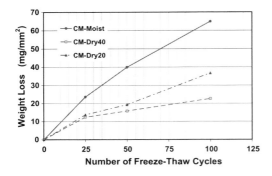

Figure 6.   Weight loss of Portland cement mixes up to 100 cycles.

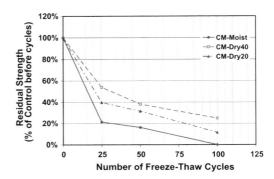

Figure 8.   Relative residual strength of Portland cement mixes.

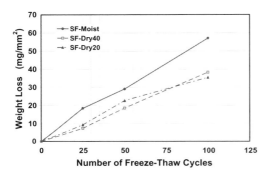

Figure 7.   Weight loss of silica fume mixes up to 100 cycles.

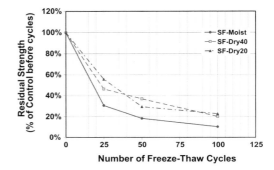

Figure 9.   Relative residual strength of silica fume mixes.

(Dry40) performed better than the specimens dried at 20°C for 7days (Dry20). The superior effect of the Dry40 regime was particularly clearer for the Portland cement specimens, as can be seen in Figure 6. For example, the weight loss of CM-Moist specimens after 50 cycles was 39.9 mg/mm² compared to 19.3 and 15.3 mg/mm² for CM-Dry20 and CM-Dry40, respectively. That represents a reduction in the weight loss of about 62% for the latter compared to a reduction of 52% for the former. The corresponding values for SF-Moist, SF-Dry20 and SF-Dry40 are 29.1, 22.7 and 18.6 mg/mm², respectively. Therefore, the reduction in the weight loss for SF-Dry20 and SF-Dry40 compared to SF-Moist was 28% and 34%, confirming the greater effect of the Dry40 regime.

The residual strength results confirmed the general trends concluded from the weight loss results. Figures 8–9 present the residual strength as a percentage of the strength of the control specimens before starting the freeze-thaw tests. The figures clearly show that the residual strength of the pre-dried CM and SF specimens was significantly higher than that of the counterpart moist

specimens, regardless of the number of test cycles. For example, the relative residual strength after 100 cycles of the CM-Dry40 specimens was 25% compared to nil for the CM-Moist specimens. Similarly, the relative residual strength after 100 cycles of the SF-Dry40 specimens was 23% compared to 10% for the SF-Moist specimens.

Although the residual strength of specimens pre-dried using the Dry40 regime was, in general, higher than the residual strength of specimens pre-dried using the Dry20 regime, the difference was not as significant as in the case of weight loss. However, the effect was, again, clearer in the Portland cement specimens. The residual strength of CM-Dry40 specimens was significantly higher than that of CM-Dry20 specimens. Considering an average value for the relative residual strength over the entire testing range from 25 to 100 cycles, CM-Dry40 would have an average of 40% compared to 27% for CM-Dry20.

The corresponding values for the SF-Dry40 and SF-Dry20 would be 35% and 36%, respectively. These values confirm the finding obtained earlier from the analysis of the weight loss results i.e., the superior effect of the Dry40 regime was particularly clearer for the Portland cement specimens. However, it could be safely stated that both drying regimes lowered the degree of saturation within the pore structure to a value below the so-called "critical degree of saturation". Previous studies showed that below a critical saturation level the damage to concrete would be insignificant even under severe freezing conditions (Fagerlund 1977). This supports the explanation given earlier in section 5.2 of this paper i.e., pre-drying provided the microstructure with large amount of empty pores that were enough to accommodate the excessive unfrozen water as well as reducing the travel length to reach empty pores. It could be argued that ultimately the pores ought to refill with water under normal rainfall and atmospheric exposure. However, the results suggest that pre-dried concretes exposed to water for up to 100 days performed better than the moist cured concretes. During the tests, the top surface of each specimen was exposed to water during the thaw cycle up to 100 days in some cases. Therefore, at least the top surface was anything but dry. In fact, it could be safely stated that it was saturated yet the specimens survived more than 100 days. In practice, it is unlikely that pre-dried concrete will be exposed to moisture continuously for more than 100 days except for dams and underwater structures.

Nonetheless, it could be more plausible to attribute the enhanced freeze-thaw durability of the pre-dried specimens to a modification in the microstructure in such a way that squeezed water found easier routes for quick escape, compared to the moist cured specimens. During the process of ice formation the expansion would pump any excessive water away from the freezing sites casing a buildup of hydraulic pressure. The characteristics of the pore system would dictate the extent of the hydraulic pressure (Yamashita et al., 1997). Obviously, the more the resistance to the movement of the unfrozen water, the higher the extent of the hydraulic pressure. Thus, it could be suggested that the unfrozen water within the pores of the pre-dried specimens found it easy to move within the pore structure. Thus, it is rational to believe that pre-drying the concrete specimens investigated in this research resulted in coarsening of the microstructure. This could have been caused by capillary porosity evolution and fine pores collapse due to the removal of evaporable pore water and dehydration phenomena associated with drying (Gallé 2004). This explanation gains more support from the timing of the pre-drying of concrete investigated in this research. The pre-drying process started ate early age; just after seven days of curing. Effectively this suspended the hydration process and contributed more to the coarsening of the microstructure.

Combining the effect of the preconditioning methods on the weight loss and residual strength it can be stated that pre-drying concrete before being subjected to freeze-thaw cycles enhanced the freeze-thaw resistance of all types of concrete investigated in this research although specimens were ponded during the freeze thaw tests. However, it has been shown that the Dry40 regime was more effective than the Dry20 regime in enhancing the freeze-thaw resistance of Portland cement concrete (CM mixes). The above results could have a significant impact on the concrete industry with regard to curing of freshly placed concrete in places where there is a potential risk of freezing conditions. For example, it might be desirable to stop curing concrete pavements after a short time of curing because the best practice in this case could be allowing the pavement to dry before being exposed to the freezing temperatures. Another example could be planning the construction of concrete structures well ahead of cold winters to allow enough time for drying before the onset of freezing weather. However, if there is no time for natural drying then artificial means could be used to dry concrete. In fact, artificial drying proved to provide better freeze-thaw resistance but, obviously, it has economical and environmental cost. However, for such measures to be implemented in the concrete industry further research is needed in conjunction with field trials.

6 CONCLUSIONS

For the concrete and test conditions used in this investigation, the following conclusions are made:

- Air-entrained specimens showed improved resistance to degradation due to freeze-thaw cycles regardless of the binder type or the method of preconditioning.
- Pre-drying concrete before being exposed to freeze-thaw cycles could be an effective technique in enhancing the freeze-thaw durability of all types of concrete, regardless of the method of drying.
- Specimens dried at 40°C for 48 hours (Dry40) performed better than specimens dried at 20°C for 7 days (Dry20), particularly for Portland cement concrete.
- The results of this research could have a significant impact on concrete practice in areas with potential risk of freezing. For example, it might be desirable to allow concrete pavements and bridge decks to dry rather than being moist cured before the onset of freezing weather.

REFERENCES

Badr, A. 2010. Freeze-thaw durability of Portland cement and silica fume concretes. *Concrete under Severe Conditions,* Costa-Borges et al. (Editors), CRC Press, (1): 559–666.

Badr, A. & Platten, A. 2006. Effect of silica fume and fly ash on fatigue and impact strength of FRC. *Wastes & Secondary Materials in Pavement Engineering, 5th Inter. Conf., Liverpool, UK, 22–23 February,* 1(2): 1–12.

Basheer, L., Kroppb, J. & Clelandc, D.J. 2001. Assessment of the durability of concrete from its permeation properties: a review. *Construction and Building Materials,* 15(1): 93–103.

Bassuoni, M.T. & Nehdi, M.L. 2005. The case for air-entrainment in high-performance concrete. *Structures & Buildings,* ICE, 158(5): 311–319.

Chatterji, C. 2003. Freezing of air-entrained cement-based materials and specific actions of air-entraining agents. *Cement & Concrete Composites,* 25(7): 759–765.

Collier, N., Sharp, J., Hill, J. & Godfrey, I. 2008. The influence of water removal techniques on the composition and microstructure of hardened cement pastes. *Cement and Concrete Research,* 38(6): 737–744.

Du, L. & Folliard, K.J. 2005. Mechanisms of air entrainment in concrete. *Cement and Concrete Research,* 35(8): 1463–1471.

Gallé, C. 2004. Effect of drying on cement-based materials pore structure as identified by mercury intrusion porosimetry: A comparative study between oven-, vacuum-, and freeze-drying. *Cement and Concrete Research,* 31(10): 1467–1477.

Fagerlund, G. 1974. Critical moisture contents at freezing of porous materials. *CIB/RILEM 2nd Symposium on Moisture Problems in Buildings, Rotterdam, Netherlands,* 1(1): 1–17.

Fagerlund, G. 1977. The international cooperative test of the critical degree of saturation method of assessing the freeze/thaw resistance of concrete. *Materials and Structures,* 10 (5), 231–253.

Gao, X.F., Lo, Y.T. & Tam, C.M. 2002. Investigation of micro-cracks and microstructure of high performance lightweight aggregate concrete. *Building and Environment,* 37(5): 485–489.

Hale, W.M., Freyne, S. & Russell, B.W. 2009. Examining the frost resistance of high performance concrete. *Construction and Building Materials,* 23(2): 878–888.

Harrison, T.A., Dewar, J.D. & Brown, B.V. 2001. Freeze-thaw resisting concrete: its achievement in the UK. *Construction Industry Research & Information Association, CIRIA,* C559.

Jacobsen, S., Sellevold, E.J. & Matala, S. 1996. Frost durability of high strength concrete: Effect of internal cracking on ice formation. *Cement and Concrete Research,* 16(6): 919–931.

Konecny, L. & Naqvi, S.J. 1993. The effect of different drying techniques on the pore size distribution of blended cement mortars. *Cement and Concrete Research,* 23(5): 1223–1228.

Met Office. 2011. Snow and low temperatures: December 2010. *UK Climate, Past Weather Events,* 3rd June 2011 at: http://www.metoffice.gov.uk/climate/uk/interesting/dec2010

Penttala, V. 2006. Surface and internal deterioration of concrete due to saline and non-saline freeze–thaw loads. *Cement and Concrete Research,* 36(5): 921–928.

Pigeon, M. Aitcin, P.C. & Pleau, R. 1986. Freeze-thaw durability of concrete with and without silica fume. *Journal of Cement, Concrete and Aggregates,* 10(2): 101–110.

Pigeon, M. Marchand, J. & Pleau, R. 1996. Frost resistant concrete. *Construction and Building Materials,* 10(5): 339–348.

Poon, C.S., Kou, S.C. & Lam, L. 2006. Compressive strength, chloride diffusivity and pore structure of high performance metakaolin and silica fume concrete. *Construction and Building Materials,* 20(10): 858–865.

Powers, T.C. 1975. Freezing effects in concrete, Durability of concrete. *ACI SP-47:* 1–12.

RILEM 4-CDC. 1977. Methods of carrying out and reporting freeze-thaw tests on concrete with de-icing chemicals. *Materials and Structures,* 10 (58): 212–215.

Sabir, B.B. & Kouyiali, K. 1991. Freeze-thaw durability of air-entrained CSF concrete. *Cement and Concrete Composites,* 13(3): 203–208.

Shang, H., Song, Y. & Ou, J. 2009. Behavior of air-entrained concrete after freeze-thaw cycles. *Acta Mechanica Solida Sinica,* 22(3): 261–266.

Toutanji, H., Delattec, N., Aggounb, S. & Dansona, A. 2004. Effect of supplementary cementitious materials on the compressive strength and durability of short-term cured concrete. *Cement and Concrete Research,* 34(2): 311–314.

Yamashita, H., Sakai, K. & Kita, T. 1997. Effect of Pore Structure in Concrete on Frost Resistance. *Durability of Concrete, 4th CANMET/ACI Inter. Conf., Sydney, Australia:* 919–931.

Yajun, J. & Cahyadi, J.H. 2003. Effects of densified silica fume on microstructure and compressive strength of blended cement pastes. *Cement and Concrete Research,* 33(10): 1543–1548.

Zhang, L. & Glasser, F.P. 2000. Critical examination of drying damage to cement pastes. *Advances in Cement Research,* 12(2): 79–88.

Concrete Solutions – Grantham, Mechtcherine & Schneck (eds)
© *2012 Taylor & Francis Group, London, ISBN 978-0-415-61622-5*

Effect of using corrosion inhibitors on concrete properties and their activity

Haider M. Al-Baghdadi & Abeer Mohammed Abdul Amir
College of Engineering—Babylon University, Iraq

ABSTRACT: In this investigation, the effect of using sodium benzoate and potassium dichromate as anodic corrosion inhibitors in concentrations (1%, 2% and 3% by weight of cement) and SBR (Styrene—Butadiene—Rubber) emulsion in three concentrations (10%,15% and 25% by volume of water) are studied on concrete properties; compressive strength, splitting tensile strength, flexural strength and absorption. Also the effect of these additives on corrosion rate was studied. The polarization resistance technique was used to measure the corrosion rate.

The reinforced concrete samples were immersed partially in 3.5% NaCl solution for three months. These samples were loaded with 10% of the design load after 6 weeks of immersion to make micro cracks in the concrete body.

The test results indicate that the use of sodium benzoate and potassium dichromate in 2% conc. by weight of cement cause a considerable reduction in compressive strength of about 15% and 4% at 28 days respectively, but at later ages the specimens increased in compressive strength by about 7% and 11% respectively at 90 days, with increasing in; splitting tensile strength of about 17% for sodium benzoate and 21% for potassium dichromate, flexural strength of about 18% and 20% respectively. They also caused a reduction in the absorption test of about 38% and 42% respectively and an inhibitor efficiency of about 98% for each one. The test results for the SBR emulsion in dosage 10% and15% had a negative effect on all mechanical properties of the concrete but SBR in dosage 25% by volume of water lead to a considerable improvement in all mechanical properties of concrete mixes with an increase in; compressive strength of about 8%, 11% and 7% at ages 28,60 and 90 days respectively, splitting tensile strength and flexural strength of about 37%, and caused a maximum reduction in absorption of about 77% with an inhibitor efficiency of 97%.

1 INTRODUCTION

Reinforced concrete is a versatile, economical and successful construction material. It can be moulded to a variety of shapes and finishes. Usually it is durable and strong, performing well throughout its service life, which typically exceeds 50 years. Sometimes, it does not perform adequately as a result of poor design, poor construction, inadequate materials selection, a more severe environment than anticipated or a combination of these factors (Broomfield, 1997).

Reinforced concrete superstructures along the coast can corrode due to marine atmospheric exposure if not properly designed. Marine atmospheric can be defined as that atmosphere within 300 m (1000 ft) of ocean or tidal water (California Dept of Transportation, 2003).

The cost of repairing or replacing deteriorated structures has become a major liability for highway agencies, estimated to be more than 20 billion$ and to be increasing at 500 million$ per year that's in United States (US Dept of Transportation, 2000).

Reinforcing steel embedded in concrete shows a high resistance to corrosion because the cement paste in good quality concrete provides an alkaline environment with pH (12.5–13.5) that protects the steel from corrosion by forming a protective ferric oxide film that passivates the surface of the steel bar when it is embedded in concrete. This passive film is only a few nanometers thick and is stable in the highly alkaline concrete (pH approx. 11–13.5) (Broomfield, 1997).

The protective action of the passive film is immune to mechanical damage of the steel surface, it can, however, be destroyed by carbonation of concrete or by the presence of chloride ions. The reinforcing steel is depassivated when the pH falls below 10 for any reason then the corrosion may occur (US Dept of Transportation, 2000).

Then carbonation or chloride ions can penetrate through the concrete pores to the oxide layer on the rebar breaking down the passive layer and leaving the steel bar vulnerable against aggressive agents; in the presence of moisture and oxygen the corrosion will occur (Corrosion Guidelines, 2003).

1.1 *The corrosion process*

Once the passive layer breaks down then areas of rust will start appearing on the steel surface. The chemical reactions are the same whether corrosion occurs by chloride attack or carbonation. When steel in concrete corrodes, it dissolves in the pore water and gives up electrons:

The anodic reaction:

$$Fe \rightarrow Fe^{+2} + 2e^{-} \qquad (1)$$

The two electrons ($2e^{-}$) created in the anodic reaction must be consumed elsewhere on the steel surface to preserve electrical neutrality. This is a reaction that consumes water and oxygen (Perez, 2004):

The cathode reaction:

$$2e^{-} + H_2O + \tfrac{1}{2} O_2 \rightarrow 2OH^{-} \qquad (2)$$

Hydroxyl ions ($2OH^{-}$) are generated in the cathodic reaction; These ions increase the local alkalinity and will therefore strengthen the passive layer, warding off the effects of carbonation and chloride ions at the cathode (Broomfield, 1997). If the iron is just to dissolve in the pore water (the ferrous ion Fe^{+2} in equation 2.3 is soluble) cracking and spalling of the concrete cannot be seen. Several more stages must occur for rust to form. This can be expressed in several ways; one of which is shown below where ferrous hydroxide becomes ferric hydroxide and then hydrated ferric oxide or rust (Perez N., 2004):

$$Fe^{+2} + 2OH^{-} \rightarrow Fe(OH)_2 \qquad (3)$$
(Ferrous hydroxide)
$$4Fe(OH)_2 + O_2 + 2H_2O \rightarrow 4\,Fe(OH)_3 \qquad (4)$$
(Ferric hydroxide)
$$2Fe(OH)_3 \rightarrow Fe_2O_3 \cdot H_2O + 2H_2O \qquad (5)$$
(Hydrated ferric oxide or rust)

Most problems with corrosion of steel in concrete are not due to loss of steel but growth of the oxide that has a volume of about twice to six time that of the steel it replaces when fully dense (Bertolini, L. et al., 2004). When it becomes hydrated it swells even more and becomes porous. This leads to the cracking and spalling of the concrete cover that are observed as the usual consequences of corrosion of steel in concrete and the red/brown brittle, flaky rust on the bar and the rust stains are seen at cracks in the concrete (Broomfield, 1997).

1.2 *Corrosion inhibitors*

Corrosion inhibitor technology has been used around since 1960, but has only been available to the construction industry for the past ten years. Corrosion inhibitors are chemical admixtures when added to concrete mix in very small concentration can be able to prevent or delay the corrosion that happens in reinforcement bars (Hussan Baker, 1989).

Corrosion inhibitors are generally used as admixtures in concrete for construction, but they can also be used for repairs by being admixed into concrete for paths, sprayed or painted onto the surface of the concrete or applied by saturation treatment (Roberge P.R., 2000).

There is accomplished behavior for inhibitor molecules to penetrate the concrete through cracks and pores and then react with the cement and reinforcement steel to restore with successfully the passivating film to the steel and extend the useful life of the concrete structure (Broomfield, 1997).

Corrosion inhibitors are organic or inorganic. Inorganic inhibitors like, potassium dichromate, zinc and lead chromate, sodium benzoate, calcium hypophosphite, and calcium nitrite and organic inhibitors like, sodium cinematic, ethanolamine (Bregman J.I., 1963).

In general, they are classified based on their protection mechanism that are added to a water source or other fluids or gases, they can protect by affecting the anodic reaction or the cathodic reaction or both reaction (mixed) [(Broomfield, 1997), (Fontana, 1978)].

They also may:

• Increase the anodic or cathodic polarization behavior;
• Reduce the movement or diffusion of ions to the metallic surface, and;
• Increase the electrical resistance of the metallic surface (Kepler et al., 2000).

R.S. Stephen (Stephen, 2004) investigated the use of penetrating corrosion inhibitors to extend the life of existing reinforced concrete bridge decks. The idea of simply applying inhibitors to the concrete surface is appealing. It is critical that the inhibitor not only penetrates the concrete but also reaches the reinforcing steel in sufficient concentrations to inhibit corrosion.

2 EXPERIMENTAL WORK

2.1 *Materials*

Ordinary Portland cement type I, locally available, was used in this study conforming to the Iraqi specification IQS No.5/1984 (IOS 5:1984, for Portland Cement).

The physical properties and chemical composition of this cement are given in Tables 1 & 2.

Table 1. Physical characteristics of cement.

Physical properties	Test results	Limit of Iraqi specification IQS No. 5/1984
Setting Time, min	105	$> = 45$ min
Initial	220	$< = 600$ min
Final		
Fineness (Blaine Method) in cm^2/gm	2880	$> = 2300$
Compressive strength in MPa:		
	3	4
at 3 days	18.0	$> = 15$
7 days	27.0	$> = 23$

Table 2. Chemical composition and main compounds of ordinary portland cement.

Oxide	Content %	Limits according to IQS No. 5/1984
SiO_2	20.82	–
CaO	62.45	–
MgO	1.53	$< = 5\%$
Fe_2O_3	3.60	–
Al_2O_3	5.46	–
SO_3	2.41	$< = 2.5\%$ if C3A $< 5\%$ $< = 2.8\%$ if C3A $> 5\%$
Free lime	1.23	–
Loss on Ignition	3.05	$< = 4\%$
Insoluble Residue	1.10	$< = 1.5\%$
L. S. F	0.88	0.66–1.02
Main compounds (Bogue's equation)		% by wt. of cement
C3S		42.29
C2S		27.78
C3A		8.38
C4AF		10.95

Respectively as tested in the cement test laboratory at Babylon University.

Graded sand was used in this study. It was brought from Al-Akhader—Karbalaa, washed and left to dry. Table 3 shows the sieve analysis, percentage fines, SO_3% and Fineness modulus according to IQS 45:1984 specification (IQS 45:1984, for Aggregate).

Graded rounded river gravel was used in this study. It was brought from Al-Nibaee—Baghdad with a maximum aggregate size 20 mm. It was washed and left to dry; Table 4 shows the sieve analysis, percentage fines, SO_3% and limits according to the specification for IQS 45:1984 (IQS 45:1984,

Table 3. Sieve analysis and some properties of fine aggregate.

Sieve size (mm)	% Passing	LL Limit of Iraqi specification No. 45/1984 (zone 1)
10	100	100
5	95	90–100
2.36	80	60–95
1.18	67	30–70
0.6	51	34–75
0.3	21	5–10
0.15	4	0–10
0.075	0	$< = 5$

SO_3% = 0.14, Limit of Iraqi specification for SO_3% $< = 0.5$
Fines % = 0, F.M = 2.8.

Table 4. Sieve analysis for coarse aggregate.

Sieve size (mm)	% Passing	Limit of Iraqi specification No. 45/1984, 5–20 mm
37.5	100%	100%
20	100%	95–100%
10	35%	30–60%
5	5%	0–10%
2.36	0%	–

SO_3% = 0.08, Limit of Iraqi Specification for SO_3% = 0.1, Fines % = 0.

for Aggregate). Tap water was used throughout this work for both mixing and curing the specimens.

The steel reinforcement that was used in this work was wires of 0.5 cm in diameter. The three bars of the reinforced concrete samples were arranged as equal triangular legs with 9 cm leg length.

2.2 Corrosion inhibitors

Two types of anodic, inorganic corrosion inhibitors were used.

2.2.1 Sodium Benzoate (SB) (C_6H_5COONa)

(SB) with purity >97%, soft powder material with white color and a approximate density of (572.2) kg /m^3. (SB) was used in three concentrations (1%, 2% and 3% by weight of cement) and added to mixing water then added to the concrete mix. After hardening, the concrete specimens showed on their surfaces a white thin layer which was easy to peel with hand or water as shown in Figure 1.

2.2.2 Potassium Dichromate (PD) ($K_2Cr_2O_7$)

(PD) with purity 99.8, with orange color and approximate density of (1281) kg/m^3, was also used

Figure 1. The white layer on the surface of the concrete specimens due to existence of sodium benzoate admixture.

Figure 2. Steel reinforced wires before and after cleaning.

in three concentrations (1%, 2% and 3% by weight of cement). It was added to water mix then added to the concrete mix. After hardening the concrete specimens had a green color due to adding this admixture.

2.2.3 Styrene—Butadiene—Rubber (SBR) admixture

SBR is used for concrete repair as a bonding additive as well as a waterproofing and adhesion aid. SBR; is a milky white emulsion with 30% solid content, pH = 9.5 and with density 1.018 gm/cm³ in 25°C.

SBR was used in three concentrations (10%, 15% and 25%) by volume of mixing water [by replaced volume of water with SBR, water/cement ratio = (water + SBR)/cement ratio].

Emulsion SBR, according to the manufacturer, has many advantages like: plasticizing action, waterproofing action, improves adhesion, reduces permeability, increases mechanical strength (although see our test results from the lab trials), up-grades chemical resistance, versatile and easy to use, cost effective, improves freeze-thaw resistance and is compatible with many types of cement.

2.3 Concrete mixes

The concrete mixes were designed in accordance with the American mix design method (ACI 211) to have a compressive strength of 25 MPa at age 28

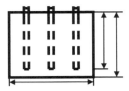

Side View

Figure 3. Details of reinforced concrete specimen.

days. An ordinary Portland cement concrete mix with cement: sand: gravel ratio of 1: 1.8: 2.5 and a water/cement ratio of 0.48 was prepared for casting specimens. The materials were mixed by using an electrically driven batch mixer.

2.4 Concrete testing

2.4.1 Compressive strength test
The concrete compressive strength was measured with 150 mm cube samples. The cubes were removed from the curing water at age of 28, 60 and 90 days. The reported values were the average of three specimens for each age (B.S. 1881: Part 116, 1989).

2.4.2 Splitting tensile strength test
The concrete splitting tensile strength was measured with 100 *200 mm cylinders according to ASTM C 496-86 (ASTM, Standard Test Method for Splitting Tensile Strength of Cylindrical Concrete Specimens 2004).

The reported values were the average of three specimens for each mix.

2.4.3 Flexural strength test
Flexural strength testing was carried out on (100*100*400 mm) simply supported prisms with a clear span of 300 mm. The prisms were tested according to arrangement two—point load. The test was performed according to (B.S. 1881, Part 118, 2000).

The average of three prism specimens was adopted and the specimens were tested at age of 28 days.

2.4.4 Absorption test
The concrete absorption was measured on 100 mm cube specimens after 28 days of curing in tap water, these specimens were dried in oven at 105 ± 5°C for 72 hours then the specimens were immersed in water for 24 hours (Mouad Nory, Hnna, 1984).

The average result of three specimens was adopted.

2.5 Electrochemical tests

2.5.1 Polarization resistance of steel reinforcement wires

2.5.1.1 Instrumentation
The setup used for polarization measurement (Three electrode method) according to ASTM

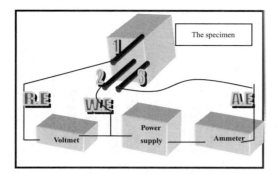

Figure 4. Diagram of polarization resistance test circuit. What is AE in the setup? the counter electrode would be missing (CE).

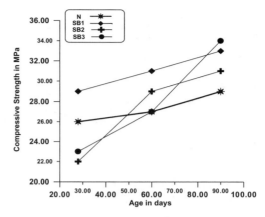

Figure 5. Development of compressive strength with age for mixes with Sodium Benzoate admixture.

STP 908(ASTM Special Technical Publication 908,1984) shown in Fig. 4 includes the following parts:

1. Power supply (EIS CO. Low voltage power supply) D.C Voltage max. 250 v, D.C Amps. Max. 4 Amper.
2. Current measuring instrument (MX 553— Metcix) digital multimeter.
3. Voltage measuring instrument (MX 553— Metcix) digital multimeter.

3 RESULTS AND DISCUSSION

3.1 Compressive strength test

For 1% Sodium Benzoate admixture, the compressive strength at ages 28, 60 and 90 days were higher than the reference mix (C25) by approximate 12%, 15% and 14% respectively.

The Sodium Benzoate in conc. 2% and 3% affected compressive strength at early ages (28 days) with a considerable reduction—15% for 2% addition and 11.5% for 3% addition, but at later ages the specimens showed an increase in compressive strength by about 7% and 17% at age 90 days respectively and that means this admixture may work as a retardar as shown in Fig. 5.

For Potassium Dichromate admixture with conc. of 1% and 2%, compressive strength had a considerable reduction of 8% and 4% respectively at ages 28 days and obtained a development in compressive strength at ages 60 and 90 days, with an increase 49% and 11% at age of 90 days respectively. That again may be due to that admixture working as a retarder, it may retard the action of C3S or C3A which give the compressive strength at the early ages of the concrete.

For the 3% addition of potassium dichromate by weight of cement the compressive strength improved by 15.4%, 15% and 14% for ages 28,

60 and 90 days respectively as shown in Figure 6. These results agree with Limaye & Angal (Limaye et al., 2000) who used two types of corrosion inhibitors in two types of concrete: strong and weak; they stated that "the use of penetrating corrosion inhibitor as admixture to concrete did not impair any mechanical or physical properties also compressive strength and bond strength showed improvement at ambient temperature and even at a higher temperature of 60°c".

Concrete specimens with SBR (Styrene— Butadiene—Rubber) admixture (10% by vol. of water) have exhibited a reduction in compressive strength for all ages and that agrees with Folic and Radonjanin [Folic and Radonjanin,1998] who studied the mechanical properties and determined the optimal curing conditions of styrene butadiene rubber (SBR). The researchers used concrete modified with 2.5%, 5% and 7.5% polymer by weigh of cement. The results showed that the compressive strength was slightly increased with increase of the SBR cement—ratio (1%–7.5% by weight of cement). Also these results contradict with the Products Publication as shown in Fig. 7

The concrete specimens with SBR 15% by vol. of water have shown an insignificant increase of 4%, 4% and 2% for ages 28, 60 and 90 days respectively, this agrees with Folic and Radonjanin [Folic and Radonjanin,1998] that is explained above.

The present work specimens with SBR in 25% conc. by vol. of water have obtained an increase in compressive strength about 8%, 11% and 7% for ages 28, 60, and 90 days respectively.

3.2 Splitting tensile strength test

All the concrete samples with the three different admixtures (Sodium Benzoate, Potassium Dichromate, SBR (Styrene—Butadiene—Rubber)) revealed an increase in splitting tensile strength

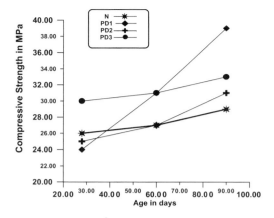

Figure 6. Development of compressive strength with age for mixes with Potassium Dichromate admixture.

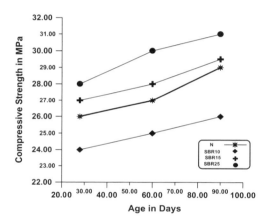

Figure 7. Development of compressive strength with age for mixes with SBR admixture.

with the increase of the percentage added as shown in Fig. 8; and this agrees with Berke (Berke, 1989) who states that: corrosion inhibitor provides corrosion inhibition in the presence of chloride and improves the concrete properties with increasing the percentage of addition.

3.3 Flexural strength test

The concrete mixes with different admixtures in different concentrations recorded an increase in values of modulus of rupture as compared with the reference concrete mix as shown in figure 9.

3.4 Absorption test

Concrete mixes with different admixtures in different concentrations showed a noticeable reduction in water absorption. This reduction increases with

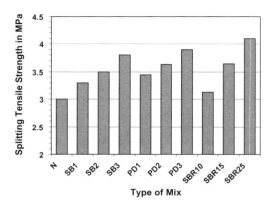

Figure 8. Splitting tensile strength for concrete specimens with different admixtures.

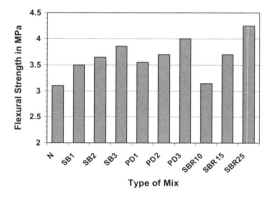

Figure 9. Flexural strength for different concrete mixes.

increasing of the concentrations for all studied admixtures. This finding conforms with properties of corrosion inhibitors which prevent or delay the corrosion of steel reinforcement and SBR emulsion without any effect or with a little effect on concrete properties with decreasing the absorption and porosity of concrete mix (Qian S. and Cusson D., 2004) as shown in Figure 10.

3.5 Corrosion rates of reinforced concrete samples

3.5.1 Sodium Benzoate inhibitor (SB)

The sodium benzoate inhibitor decreased the corrosion rate in the studied concentrations as shown in Figure (11). The corrosion rates are low in the three concentrations (1%, 2% and 3% by weight of cement) and they do not indicate any noticeable increase or decrease with time in (8 to 12 weeks).

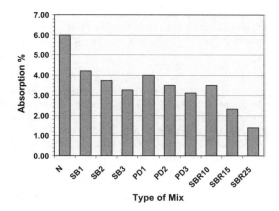

Figure 10. Absorption for different concrete mixes.

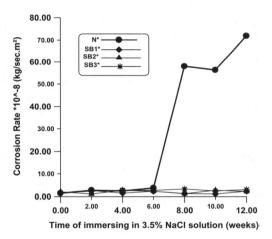

Figure 11. Corrosion rate for reinforced concrete samples with sodium benzoate admixture.

The sodium benzoate inhibitor has good efficiency because it enhances the protection afforded by the alkaline environment. The adhered layer that is produced on the steel bar due to the effect of sodium benzoate will protect in form further attack. The presence of oxygen can form a strong chemical bond (C_6H_5COO Na) with iron and this will reduce the active regions on the surface of the iron and facilitates the passivation of remaining regions (Anton and Norman, 1970).

3.5.2 *Potassium Dichromate inhibitor (PD)*

The corrosion rate of sample (PD1*) increased after 12 weeks of immersion in salt solution. The chromate is an anodic inhibitor. It can, in case of incomplete protection, increase the corrosion rate intensity. There is a critical concentration below which the corrosion intensity steadily increases. When the

inhibitor concentration is increased beyond the critical value, the corrosion intensity begins to drop, as in samples (PD2*) and (PD3*) see Figure (12).

The following explanation was stated by Rozenfeld (Rozenfeld I.L., 1975) and Anton (Anton D.B. and Norman E.H.,1970): "Anodic inhibitor which cause a large shift in the corrosion potential are called passivating inhibitors, they are also called dangerous inhibitors because, if used in sufficient concentrations they cause pitting corrosion and some times an increase in corrosion rate". The corrosion rate is almost equal in sample (PD2*) through 6 weeks to 12 weeks.

3.5.3 *SBR (Styrene—Butadiene—Rubber) admixture*

The corrosion rates of samples (SBR10*) and (SBR15*) increased at 2–12 weeks of partial immersing in 3.5% NaCl solution. On the contrary, the corrosion rate of sample (SBR25*) was decreased. The SBR admixture reduces the porosity and permeability. In (SBR10*) and (SBR15*) samples the amount of SBR admixture is not enough to decrease porosity and prevent the corrosive ions form reaching the iron surface. The opposite action of (SBR10*) and (SBR15*) samples of increased corrosion rate may be due to the fact that emulsion SBR is containing alkyl lithium compounds that's come from manufacture. And because of that fact, the corrosion process happened faster in presence of lithium chloride than in presence of sodium chloride, that may be the cause of the high rate of corrosion in samples (SBR10*) and (SBR15*) as shown in Fig. 13.

3.6 *Inhibitor efficiencies*

The efficiency of the inhibitor is measured by:

Inhibitor Efficiency (%) = 100 * (CR uninhibited—CR inhibited)/ CR uninhibited.
where: CR uninhibited = corrosion rate of the uninhibited system.
CR inhibited = corrosion rate of the inhibited system.

In general, the efficiency of an inhibitor increases with the increase in inhibitor concentration as shown in Table 5.

3.7 *Classification degrees of corrosion current*

Corrosion can be classify as the following degree (Broomfield, 1997).
Passive condition: Icorr <0.1 µA / cm^2
Low corrosion: Icorr (0.1–0.25) µA / cm^2
Moderate corrosion: Icorr (0.25–0.75) µA / cm^2
High corrosion: Icorr (0.75–1) µA / cm^2
Severe corrosion: Icorr >1 µA / cm^2

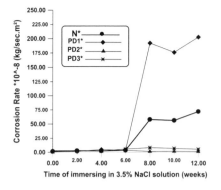

Figure 12. Corrosion rate for reinforced concrete samples with potassium dichromate admixture.

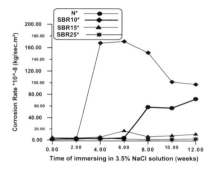

Figure 13. Corrosion rate for reinforced concrete samples with SBR admixture.

Table 5. Inhibitors Efficiency for concrete samples with pre cracking after 12 weeks of immersion in salt solution.

Symbol of the mix	Type and % of admixture	Inhibitor Efficiency %
SB1	Sodium benzoate 1% by weight of cement	97%
SB2	Sodium benzoate 2% by weight of cement	97%
SB3	Sodium benzoate 3% by weight of cement	96%
PD1	Potassium dichromate 1% by weight of cement	(−) adverse effect
PD2	Potassium dichromate 2% by weight of cement	98%
PD3	Potassium dichromate 3% by weight of cement	92%
SBR10	Styrene-Butadiene-Rubber 10% by volume of water	(−) adverse effect
SBR15	Styrene-Butadiene-Rubber 15% by volume of water	(−) adverse effect
SBR25	Styrene-Butadiene-Rubber 25% by volume of water	97%

Classification of the degrees of corrosion current at the end of the 12 weeks of partial immersion in 3.5% NaCl solution are shown in Table 6.

3.7.1 Economical cost

After studding the economical cost of using the corrosion inhibitors in the best dosage; Sodium Benzoate in dosage 2% by weight of cement, Potassium Dichromate in dosage 2% by weight of cement and SBR (Styrene—Butadiene—Rubber) in dosage 25% by vol. of water, and estimating which one of the three is the best economically as shown in Table 7.

From table 7 the three admixtures in the conc. above have improved the economical cost but the

Table 6. Classification degrees of corrosion current.

Symbol of sample	I corr. ($\mu A/cm^2$)	Classification degree
N	0.248	low
SB1	0.009	passive
SB2	0.0076	Passive
SB3	0.0106	Passive
PD1	0.699	Moderate
PD2	0.0047	Passive
PD3	0.0193	Passive
SBR10	0.335	Moderate
SBR15	0.183	Low
SBR25	0.0066	Passive

Table 7. The final calculation of the economical cost study.

Details	Ref. mix	Mix with 2%SB	Mix with 2% PD	Mix with 25% SBR
The cost of the work to cast 1m³ concrete (ID)	150,000	150,000	150,000	150,000
The cost of durability (ID)	100,000	60,000	60,000	60,000
Annual reduction for capitalism value for each mix (ID)	20,000	12,000	9,250	10,100
Benefit over the average of the Exploitation Cost (ID)	10,000	25,800	27,750	24,250
The summation (ID)	280,000	247,800	247,000	244,350

SBR with 25% conc. seems the best one with a reduction of 13% in economical cost.

4 CONCLUSIONS

If the concrete is produced in compressive strength 25 MPa with a cement content (390 Kg), low water/cement ratio, good compaction, good curing and high thickness of concrete cover, the steel reinforcement will have a good protection (pH 12–13.5 and low permeability) against corrosion even in aggressive environment.

Through the use of two anodic, inorganic corrosion inhibitors and SBR admixtures it was observed that:

1. If some kind of anodic corrosion inhibitors (like potassium dichromate) are used in low dosages, they may will act as corrosion accelerators and not as corrosion inhibitors if they are added in low concentrations therefore they are known as dangerous inhibitors (Anton D.B. and Norman E.H.,1970).
2. Corrosion inhibitors work better in concrete with micro cracks than in concrete without micro cracks.
3. The Sodium Benzoate admixture in dosages 2% and 3% by weight of cement has no significant effects on concrete properties it only has an effect on compressive strength at (28 days), but that effect diminishes at later ages (60 and 90 days). Also this admixture is active to protect the steel reinforcement wires against corrosion after initiating cracking for 90 days of immersing in 3.5% NaCl solution. The inhibitor efficiency is 97% and 96% respectively.
4. The potassium dichromate admixture in dosage of 1% by weight of cement acts as corrosion accelerator and not as corrosion inhibitor.
5. The Potassium Dichromate admixture in dosage of 2% and 3% by weight of cement has no detrimental effects on concrete properties. It just has an effect on compressive strength at 28 days, but that effect diminishes at the later ages (60 and 90 days) with increasing; in compressive strength by 12% for dosage 2% and 14% for dosage 3% at age 90 days, in splitting tensile strength of 21% and 30% respectively, in flexural strength by 19% and 29% respectively, and a reduction of 42% and 48% respectively in absorption. Also this admixture is active to protect the steel reinforcement wires against corrosion for 90 days of partial immersion in 3.5% NaCl solution with inhibitor efficiency of 98% and 92% respectively.
6. The SBR (Styrene Butadiene Rubber) admixture in dosages of 10% and 15% by vol. of mixing water has a harmful effect on the corrosion process because it works as a corrosion accelerator and not as corrosion inhibitor.
7. The SBR (Styrene—Butadiene—Rubber) admixture in dosage 25% is superior in enhancing most concrete properties. It increases; compressive strength by about 8%, 11% and 7% for ages 28, 60, and 90 respectively, 37% in splitting tensile strength, 37% in flexural strength and with a maximum reduction of 77% in percentage absorption. It also yields a reduction of 97% in corrosion rate after 12 weeks of partial immersing in 3.5% NaCl solution with a reduction in economical cost of 13%.

REFERENCES

Anton, D.B. and Norman, E.H.,"Nace Basic Corrosion Course", Scope and Language of Corrosion, Graduate Engineering Center, University of Missouri, National Association of Corrosion Engineering, St. Louis, 1970.

ASTM Special Technical Publication 908,"Corrosion Monitoring in Industrial Plants Using Nondestructive Testing and Electrochemical Methods", Canada, 22–24 May 1984.

Berke, N.S. "Review of Corrosion Inhibitors in Concrete", Materials Performance, Vol. 28, No. 10, Oct. 1989, pp. 41–44.

Bertolini, L., Elsener B., Pedeferri, P. and Polder, R. "Corrosion of Steel in Concrete", copyright 2004, printed in Federal Republic of Germany.

Bregman, J.I. "Corrosion Inhibitors", Collier-Macmillan Canada, Toronto, Ontario, 1963.

California Department of Transportation,Division of Engineering Services, Materials Engineering and Testing Services, Corrosion Technology Branch "Corrosion Guidelines", Version 1.0, September 2003.

Folic, R.J. and Radonjanin, V.S. "Experimental Research on polymer Modified Concrete" ACI materials Journal, Vol. 95, No. 44, July–August 1998, pp. 463–496.

Fontana, M.G. "Corrosion Engineering", McGRAW-HILL international book company, 1978.

Broomfield, J.P. "Corrosion of Steel in Concrete" Understanding, Investigation and Repair, 1997, E. & FN Spon an Imprint of Rutledge London & New York.

Baker, H. Corrosion Engineering, Technology University, 1989.

Kepler, J.L., Darwin, D. and Locke, C.E. "Evaluation of Corrosion Protection Methods for Reinforced Concrete High way Structures. University of Kansas, Center for Research, INC, Law Rence, Kansas, May 2000.

Limaye, R.G., Angal, R.D. and Radke, A.S. "Experiment Studies on Penetrating—type Corrosion inhibitor in reinforced conceit", Indian Concrete Journal, Jan. 2000, pp. 22–26.

Mouad Nory, Hnna, "Concrete Technology", Technology University, 1984.

Perez, N."Electrochemistry and Corrosion Science", Department of Mechanical Engineering, University of Puerto Rico, Kluwer Academic Publishers, 2004.

Products Publication of SBR (Styrene—Butadiene—Rubber), www.paco-systems.co.uk, www.fosroc.com, www.tecroc.co.uk. Internet References

Qian, S. and Cusson, D. 2004. "Electrochemical Evaluation of The Performance of Corrosion Inhibiting System in Concrete Bridges", Journal of Cement and Concrete Composites, Vol. 26, No. 4, May–2004, pp. 217–233, (NRC) National Research Council Canada, Ottawa, Ontario, Canada.

Roberge, P.R. "Handbook of Corrosion Engineering", MC Graw–Hill, 2000, Chapter 10.

Rozenfeld, I.L. "Corrosion Inhibitors", Institute of Physical Chemistry USSR Academy of Sciences, Mc GRAW-HILL International Book Company, 1975.

Stephen. R.S. "Evaluation of Two Corrosion Inhibitors Using Two Surface Application Methods For Reinforced Concrete Structures", Virginia Dep. of Transportation, University of Virginia, Des. 2004.

U.S. Dep. Of Transportation, Federal Highway Administration. August, 2000. "Materials and Methods for Corrosion Control of Reinforced and Prestressed concrete structures in New Construction".

Concrete Solutions – Grantham, Mechtcherine & Schneck (eds)
© 2012 Taylor & Francis Group, London, ISBN 978-0-415-61622-5

The use of performance-based specifications to prevent repair of reinforced concrete structures

H. Beushausen

University of Cape Town, Department of Civil Engineering, Cape Town, South Africa

ABSTRACT: As a result of reinforcement corrosion damage, a large portion of existing reinforced concrete structures worldwide is in need of repair and ongoing maintenance, which puts significant constraints on national construction budgets. In the past, one reason for poor performance of existing concrete infrastructure was the absence of adequate specifications for concrete durability. Recently, an increasing number of performance-based design approaches for concrete durability have been developed worldwide, allowing the assessment of the potential durability properties of specific concrete mixes. Performance design may include conformity assessment of the as-built structure, using appropriate test methods for evaluation of durability indicators, such as diffusion coefficients or transport properties. Such quality assessment schemes can be used at an early age to predict deterioration of the structure and design appropriate maintenance schedules in order to prevent damage and eliminate the need for repair. This paper presents an overview on different philosophies, principles, test methods, and practical examples for performance-based design of reinforced concrete structures and proposes a framework for the use of performance assessment for the development of maintenance strategies.

1 INTRODUCTION

In many countries worldwide, a large part of the national concrete infrastructure is deteriorating prematurely and is in need of continuous maintenance and repair. The main reason for premature deterioration of concrete structures is steel reinforcement corrosion due to carbonation or the ingress of chlorides. This situation puts significant pressure on national construction budgets and has in the past decades increasingly raised awareness on durability issues in the design process for concrete structures.

Current design specifications for concrete durability in national standards usually follow the prescriptive approach which sets limiting values for mix design parameters, such as minimum cement contents, maximum water/binder ratios, and cover depths. Although useful for certain applications, this approach is often criticized for its failure to represent a rational design approach for concrete durability. In the past years, an increasing number of research projects dealt with performance-based design concepts for concrete durability, which are based on experimental or analytical assessment of the concrete's resistance against deterioration.

Internationally, the development of performance specifications for concrete is currently receiving considerable attention. The ACI published a report on performance-based requirements for concrete in 2010 (ACI ITG-8R-10). A new fib Task Group (TG 8.10) on performance specifications for concrete was established in January 2011. Further, a number of RILEM Technical Committees has in the past dealt with performance evaluation of concrete and the currently active RILEM TC 230 PSC is dealing with the specific focus on performance based specifications and quality control of reinforced concrete structures and is drawing up a state-of-the-art report on the topic. These efforts (and others not mentioned here) can be expected to change the concrete industry in the next years and decades, hopefully resulting in design and construction of more durable structures.

A range of different approaches to performance-based design have been developed world-wide, some of them based purely on pre-qualification of concrete mixes in the design stage, and others including conformity assessment of the as-built structure. The latter approach allows accounting for the important influences of construction procedures and quality of workmanship with respect to concrete placement, compaction and curing. For conformity assessment and quality control of the as-built structure, the concrete's resistance against carbonation and the ingress of chlorides can be experimentally assessed with appropriate test methods, which allows characterizing the concrete for its potential durability and modelling the potential service life of the structure.

One of the main international guidelines for service life modelling of concrete structures is the fib Model Code on service Life Design (fib, 2006), which proposes an approach to avoid or minimize deterioration caused by environmental action, comparable to present approaches to design for structural loading. Based on quantifiable models for the 'loading' (i.e., the environmental actions) and the 'load-bearing resistance' (i.e., the resistance of the concrete against the considered environmental action), different design options are proposed, including the full probabilistic approach, the semi-probabilistic approach (partial safety factor design), deemed to satisfy rules, and avoidance of deterioration.

Essentially, all of the proposed design approaches above can be linked to performance specifications and performance assessment. Appropriate deterioration models for service life prediction have been developed in various countries worldwide and many of them make use of measurable concrete properties as input parameters. Prominent examples include the European model DuraCrete (2000), the Scandinavian model Clinconc (Tang, 1996), the European Equivalent Durability Concept (CEN/TC 104/SC1/TG17, 2006), and the South African Service life prediction models (Alexander et al., 2008). Other approaches such as the North American Life 365 (Thomas et al., 2000, Ehlen et al., 2009) are based on analytical prediction of concrete deterioration using computer programmes and do not include any material testing.

This paper presents an overview on the principles of performance-based specifications, focussing on approaches that include quality assessment of the as-built structure and discussing recent international developments. In addition, a basic framework is developed that shows how quality assessment of concrete structures within a performance specification theme can be used to develop optimum maintenance plans and thus reduce life-cycle costs and reduce the need for extensive concrete repair.

2 THE LIMITATIONS OF THE TRADITIONAL PRESCRIPTIVE APPROACH FOR SERVICE LIFE DESIGN OF RC STRUCTURES

The traditional prescriptive approach for concrete durability presents limiting values for water/binder ratio, binder content, thickness of the cover and compressive strength for different exposure classes. For example, EN 206 (BS EN 206-1, 2000) distinguishes between 10 environmental classes for reinforcement corrosion depending on whether corrosion is caused by carbonation, chlorides from seawater, or chlorides originating

from other sources than sea water. Compared to previous versions of this approach, the one in the new Eurocode (e.g., the approach stipulated in the British Annex to the Eurocode (BS EN 1992-1-1:2004)) can be considered significantly more advanced as it makes allowance for different standard binder combinations and allows the user to "trade off" cover depth against concrete quality.

For some applications the traditional prescriptive approach may be sufficient, especially for structures where durability is of no major concern. However, the approach was developed for a very limited range of common concretes and does not sufficiently account for the influence that different binder types and mineral components have on concrete durability. In addition, the influence of other mix ingredients such as aggregates, admixtures and mineral additives is ignored.

Modern types of concrete, such as high strength concrete, self compacting concrete, fibre reinforced concrete, concretes containing special additives such as internal curing agents, recycled constituents, durability-enhancing admixtures, etc, can be expected to have different durability characteristics compared to conventional concrete and are not covered in the current prescriptive approach.

More importantly, even for conventional concretes, the prescriptive approach does not take into account the influences of on-site practice during the construction process, such as placement, compaction, and curing, all of which have a significant influence on the quality of the concrete cover and hence the concrete's resistance against the ingress of harmful substances. Prescriptive approaches for concrete durability, although providing some useful basic guidelines for conventional concretes, can therefore not provide a rational service life design for most applications.

3 THE PRINCIPLES OF PERFORMANCE-BASED SPECIFICATIONS FOR RC STRUCTURES

3.1 General

Performance concepts are based on quantitative predictions for durability from exposure conditions and measured material characteristics. The resistance of the structure, measured through durability parameters of the actual concrete used, is compared against the environmental load, similar to the approach for designing and controlling compressive strength for certain loading conditions. On this basis, deterioration of a concrete structure during its lifetime is quantitatively predicted using appropriate deterioration models. The obvious advantage over traditional prescriptive approaches is that the influence of mix design parameters and mix constituents can be individually assessed for different types of concrete, which allows rational, economic and innovative design of concrete mixes that are tailor-made for the specific project requirements and environmental conditions.

In the international research and engineering communities, the move towards performance-based specifications for concrete durability has sped up considerably in recent years. However, presently there are still very few examples of practical applications reported in the literature. To move from prescriptive to performance-based approaches for concrete durability, a framework guide is needed to successfully develop and implement such an approach. One such framework (which has, for example, been adopted in South Africa during the past 15 years) was suggested by Harrison (1995), who recommended seven steps for development:

Define exposure classes related to the mechanism(s) of deterioration
Derive a quantitative design methodology, including definition of end of design life
Develop test methods that relate to the input parameters of the design method
Produce provisional compliance criteria and calibrate against traditional solutions
Establish limitations of test applicability
Ensure production control and acceptance testing
Conduct full-scale trials and long-term monitoring to confirm compliance requirements

On a similar account, Walraven (2008) stressed the need for certain elements in the practical application of a performance approach in durability specifications and for service life assessment, including limit state criteria, a defined service life, deterioration models, compliance tests, a strategy for maintenance and repair, and quality control systems.

Limit state criteria for concrete durability should be quantifiable, i.e., they need to be linked to appropriate test methods, and preferentially have a clear physical meaning. Common deterioration models for concrete structures generally comprise mathematical expressions and should include parameters that are directly or indirectly linked to the performance criteria. With such deterioration models, the durability performance of the structure can be estimated for the required service life duration. For example, based on measured chloride diffusion coefficients, the time-dependent ingress of chlorides can be predicted using Fick's laws of diffusion.

Examples of service-life models that make use of diffusion models to predict chloride ingress or carbonation into concrete include the European performance-based design approach "DuraCrete" (DuraCrete, 2000), the South African chloride prediction model (Alexander et al., 1999) and the Scandinavian model "Clinconc" (Tang, 1996). More recent versions of the Duracrete model were published in the fib Model Code for Service Life Design (fib, 2006).

Most existing service-life models define the end of service life as the beginning of the corrosion propagation period. However, the literature also contains information on recent research that aims at a better understanding of the corrosion propagation period in order to assess if corrosion propagation can be successfully and safely be incorporated in the design service-life duration of concrete structures (Andrade et al., 2009, Otieno et al., 2011).

The required service-life durations will vary from project to project but commonly, a service life of up to 30 years is specified for temporary structures, 50 years for "common" structures such as buildings, and 100 years or more for monumental structures such as dams, large-span bridges, power stations, port structures, etc.

In performance-based design, the estimation of the duration of the corrosion initiation period is linked to the testing of relevant properties of the concrete cover layer, which can be used to assess the potential ingress of harmful substances such as chlorides and carbon dioxide. Such test methods should be able to be applied to both pre-qualification and compliance control of the as-built structure, and should yield relevant durability parameters that can be used in deterioration models and service life models. Various performance-based test methods that meet these criteria have been developed in different parts of the world, as discussed later.

3.2 Exposure conditions

An important aspect for performance-based design of concrete durability is the correct definition of the prevailing exposure conditions. Important environmental aspects include temperature, relative humidity, nature and concentration of aggressive agents such as chlorides, and freeze-thaw cycles. Many of the existing performance-based design approaches for concrete durability make use of the environmental exposure classes of the Eurocode (BS EN 206-1, 2000). The most important environmental classes for reinforcement corrosion link to marine exposure (Exposure class XS), exposure to de-icing salts (XD), and exposure to carbonation (XC), as summarized in Table 1.

A direct application of these classes needs to be done with caution, as environmental aspects may

Table 1. EN 206-1: 2000, Environmental sub-classes relevant to reinforcement corrosion.

Class	Description
XS1	Exposed to airborne salt but not in direct contact with seawater
XS2	Permanently submerged
XS3	Tidal, splash and spray zones
XD1	Moderate humidity,
XD2	Wet, rarely dry
XD3	Cyclic wet and dry
XC1	Permanently dry or permanently wet
XC2	Wet, rarely dry
XC3	Moderate humidity (60–80%)
XC4	Cyclic wet and dry

vary between countries, different regions in a country, or different locations in a city. For example, the marine environmental classes XS may not be applicable to all chloride exposure environments and should be viewed as guidelines only. Factors that may also need to be considered are water temperature, relative ambient humidity, salinity of the ocean, abrasive wave actions, prevailing wind conditions, etc. The aggressiveness of the marine environment for example of the Mediterranean Ocean, the Baltic Sea and the Gulf will be very different from each other.

In addition, environmental exposure conditions may also vary between different parts of the same structure, for example between parts exposed to rain and those that are sheltered. Therefore, the aggressiveness of the environment needs to be clearly understood and only relevant environmental aspects should be considered and quantified for a given reinforced concrete structure.

3.3 Pre-qualification of concrete mixes

The literature contains a range of different definitions of performance-based specifications for concrete durability. One of the principle differences between various approaches is that some of them are based solely on pre-qualification of concrete mixes in the design stage and that others combine pre-qualification with compliance control of the as-built structure. If solely used for the purpose of pre-qualification, performance-based design focuses on the evaluation of a particular concrete mix that is intended to be used later in construction. Based on the measured durability characteristics of the concrete prior to construction it is assumed that the as-built structure too will be inherently durable, but no further tests are performed on the as-built structure to verify the actual in-situ quality.

One such method was proposed by Baroghel-Bouny (2006, 2009), which makes use of "durability

indicators" such as initial calcium hydroxide contents, porosity, ion diffusion coefficients, and permeability to gas or water to predict the potential durability of concrete mixes. In the design phase, these indicators are assessed either through testing or mathematical modelling. In this manner, a class for the "potential durability" is assigned to different concretes. The outcome of the assessment is used as input in deterioration prediction models to give an estimate of the service life of the structure, considering the prevailing environmental conditions.

Another philosophy on performance-based design was recently introduced with the "Equivalent Durability Concept" (CEN/TC 104/SC1/ TG17, 2006). The basic premise of this concept is that "if a concrete has a similar performance in a durability related assessment procedure to one with a known history of satisfactory use, it should perform equally well in the same environment." Equivalent durability for exposure classes XC (exposure to carbonation) and XS/XD (exposure to chlorides) are assessed with an accelerated carbonation test and diffusion tests, respectively. Reference concretes have to be defined for each country, considering locally available materials, and need to have been proven to perform satisfactorily in the field. Important draw-backs of this method include that the approach was developed for standardized materials only, which excludes innovative mix designs with new materials such as chemical or mineral additives, and that it is inherently difficult to select suitable reference concretes for comparison.

The most common "performance simulation" tests applied for the assessment of the concrete quality necessary for reinforcement corrosion resistance are the Bulk Diffusion (NT Build 443, 1995, ASTM C1556, 2004, XP CEN/TS 12390-11, 2010) and accelerated carbonation tests (Kollek, 1989, CEN/ TS 12390-10, 2007, CEN/TS 12390-XXX, 2009). The advantage of these performance simulation test methods is that they attempt to simulate the real deterioration process, exposing concrete to a high concentration of the deleterious species. An important disadvantage of these methods is that they are time-consuming due to long test durations of several weeks or months, which usually limits their application to the pre-qualification stage.

4 QUALITY CONTROL AND CONFORMITY ASSESSMENT OF DURABILITY PARAMETERS

4.1 General considerations

In contrast to the approaches discussed in Section 3.3, performance-based compliance assessment and quality control includes the evaluation of the as-built structure for compliance with design requirements. The actual in-situ quality of the structure can then be compared to the design specifications and appropriate measures can be implemented should the structure not conform to limiting design values for concrete durability. This method allows evaluating not only mix design parameters but also construction-related influences and will therefore give a much better indication of the potential durability of the as-built structure.

The philosophy of performance prediction and quality control involves the understanding that durability will be improved only when measurements of appropriate cover concrete properties can be made on the as-built structure. Such measurements must reflect the in-situ properties of concrete, which are measured either in-situ on the as-built structure or on cores removed from the structure. The traditional "performance simulation tests" discussed earlier, i.e., the bulk diffusion test for chloride penetration or the accelerated carbonation chamber test, are usually not suitable for quality control as they may require several months before meaningful data can be obtained.

Appropriate test methods for the control of in-situ durability properties of concrete have been developed in different parts of the world. An evaluation of the principles, merits and limitations of such methods was presented by RILEM TC 189-NEC (Non-Destructive Evaluation of the Covercrete) (Torrent and Luco, 2007; Romer and Luco, 2005). One important conclusion of the work of TC 189-NEC was that suitable devices exist, with which the quality of the concrete cover can be assessed in-situ or on cores that are removed from the structure. The test procedures investigated included methods to assess transport properties such as gas permeability, capillary suction and electrical conductivity (or alternatively electrical resistivity) of concrete. The results obtained with such test methods reflect the pore structure, pore connectivity and pore chemistry of the concrete and are used to assess the resistance against the ingress of deleterious agents, commonly carbon dioxide and chlorides.

The main advantage that test methods for transport properties have over performance-simulation tests such as bulk diffusion or accelerated carbonation is that test results are obtained in a very short period of time, which makes them suitable for on-site quality control.

4.2 Test methods for carbonation prediction

Gas permeability tests are commonly applied to characterize the concrete's ability to resist carbonation and comprise the measurement of gas flow through a concrete sample under an externally applied pressure gradient. The test results can be linked either to analytical models for the estimation of diffusion coefficients, or empirically related to the rate of carbonation.

Many of the available gas permeability tests that are used in performance evaluation of concrete are based on the principles of the Cembureau method (Kollek, 1989, RILEM TC 116-PCD, 1999) (Fig. 1). In the Cembureau method, unidirectional gas flow between two parallel surfaces of the test specimen (typically 150 mm diameter by 50 mm thick) is caused by a constant absolute pressure difference of the test gas between the two surfaces.

In various recent research projects around the world, test methods for concrete permeability were empirically linked to carbonation in real structures. For example, Immamoto (2008) measured permeability with the test equipment developed by Torrent (Figs. 2 and 3) and a found a good correlation between permeability results and carbonation depth development for Japanese concretes. Similarly, Torrent and Frenzer (1995) and Torrent and Jacobs (2009) established a correlation between permeability and carbonation of existing structures in Switzerland, using the same method.

The distinctive characteristic features of this test are a two-chamber vacuum cell and a regulator that balances the pressure in the inner (measuring)

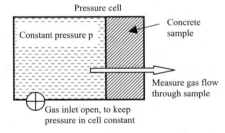

Figure 1. Schematic of the cembureau permeability test.

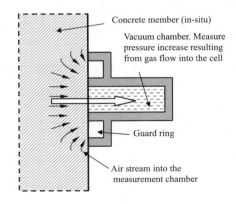

Figure 2. Detail of air-flow into the vacuum cell of the torrent permeability tester.

Figure 3.   Torrent permeability tester.

Table 2.   Classification of permeability of concrete cover, based on kT (Torrent and Jacobs, 2009).

kT (10^{-16} m^2)	Permeability
<0.01	Very low
0.01–0.1	Low
0.1–1.0	Moderate
1.0–10	High
>10	Very high

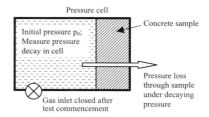

Figure 4.   Schematic of the South African OPI test.

Figure 5.   Permeameter (South African OPI test).

chamber and in the outer (guard-ring) chamber. The outer guard ring prevents air from the surrounding areas from flowing into the pressure measurement chamber, which would influence the test results. During the test, the cell is placed on the concrete surface and a vacuum is produced with the pump. Due to the external atmospheric pressure and the rubber rings the cell is pressed against the surface and thus both chambers are sealed. The rate at which the pressure increases in the inner chamber is recorded and related to the permeability of the underlying concrete.

An important advantage of the Torrent Permeability Tester is that it can be applied in-situ on the as-built structure in a fully non-destructive manner. However, a disadvantage resulting from on-site application is that the test results are influenced by the moisture content of the concrete, which makes it necessary to apply correction factors to the permeability results based on measurements of concrete moisture content, for example using resistivity readings as a reference.

A rating scheme of permeability results obtained with this method and a proposal for its use in performance-based specifications was presented by Torrent and Jacobs (2009), as summarized in Table 2. Note that with this method, permeability (kT) is expressed in the unit [m^2].

In South Africa, oxygen permeability results are used to characterize young concrete for influences such as concrete grade, binder type, initial curing and construction effects such as compaction. In contrast to the Cembureau method, the South African Oxygen Permeability test measures the gas flow through a concrete disk (68 mm diameter, 30 mm thickness) under a falling head pressure gradient. The schematic of the test method is presented in Figure 4. Figure 5 shows a typical test arrangement using the Permeameter. Details on the test equipment and test procedure can be

found in the literature (Alexander et al., 1999, Beushausen et al., 2003).

Based on empirical relationships, the carbonation resistance of concrete was found to be sufficiently related to the early age (28d) oxygen permeability index (OPI) value, so that permeability can be used in a carbonation-type service life model (Mackechnie and Alexander, 2002). A recently updated version of the South African deterioration model for the prediction of carbonation combines the aspects of binder chemistry, mix composition, environmental conditions, and the concrete's diffusivity as characterized by the permeability value, for the prediction of carbonation (Salvoldi et al., 2011).

A rating scheme similar to that developed in Switzerland (see Table 2 above) was originally developed in South Africa, grouping concrete into durability classes 'excellent, 'good', 'poor' and 'very poor', based on permeability results (Alexander et al., 1999). This rating approach was however changed in subsequent years and currently, permeability requirements are linked to environmental exposure classes. Table 3 presents an extract of typical project requirements used by the South African National Roads Agency Limited for durability specifications for concrete infrastructure exposed to environmental classes XC3 and XC4 (compare Table 1). A higher OPI value refers to a lower permeability. Note that the OPI is measured on a log scale and that there is therefore a considerable difference between OPI values of 9.0 and 9.6.

4.3 Test methods for prediction of chloride penetration

The resistance of concrete against chloride ingress can be modelled based on resistivity (or the inverse, conductivity) measurements. Most service life models for RC structures use diffusion characteristics of the concrete to model chloride ingress, as discussed earlier. The fundamental relationship between resistivity or conductivity and ion diffusivity was for example presented by Streicher and Alexander (1995) and Andrade et al. (2009, 2010). Correlations between conductivity results and diffusion coefficients after several years marine exposure have been shown to be good over a wide range of concretes (Mackechnie, 2001, Mackechnie and Alexander, 2002), indicating the usefulness of these test methods for the service life prediction of RC structures exposed to chlorides.

Concrete resistivity is usually measured using the principles of the Wenner Probe. Discussions on the use of electrical resistivity as a method for durability specification and modelling of service life of reinforced concrete structures were presented by Andrade et al. (2009) and Andrade and d'Andrea (2010).

The South African chloride conductivity test involves the measurement of a sample's electric conductivity using a pre-conditioned concrete disk of 68 mm diameter and 25 mm thickness. Further details on this method, the interpretation of test results and the use of conductivity values in service-life prediction of RC structures are presented in the literature (Streicher and Alexander, 1995, Beushausen et al., 2003, Alexander et al., 2008).

Similar to the discussions in Section 4.2 for permeability, the chloride conductivity is used in South Africa in durability specifications for structures in the marine environment (class XS, compare Table 1). Table 4 presents an extract of typical specifications used. As can be seen, limiting conductivity values differ for different binder types to account for the influences of pore chemistry and chloride binding. As already shown in Table 3, a 'trade-off' can be made between concrete quality and cover depth in order to find the most economic and practical solution for the project.

Other methods for quality control of concrete exposed to chloride environments include the North American Rapid Chloride Permeability Test ASTM C 1202 and the Rapid Migration Test AASTHO TP 64. The latter is for example used to characterize the concrete's resistance against chloride ingress in the European model Dura-Crete (2000) and the Scandinavian model Clinconc (Tang, 1996).

4.4 Framework for quality control procedures

A framework for performance-based service life design and quality control is illustrated in Figure 6. The performance-based design done in this way needs to include prescriptive requirements for material parameters (mix proportions and mix constituents) since the interpretation of the measured durability characteristic may depend on the type of material used. For example, concretes made with different binder types may have the same transport properties such as permeability or resistivity but a different resistance against carbonation or chloride ingress, since the latter depends on additional factors such as chloride binding

Table 3. Typical permeability specifications used in South Africa (extract).

Environmental class		XC3		XC4	
Cover depth (mm)		40	50	40	50
OPI (log scale)	recommended	9.4	9.1	9.6	9.3
	minimum	9.0	9.0	9.2	9.0

Table 4. Typical chloride conductivity (CC) specifications used in South Africa (extract).

Environ. class		XS2			XS3		
Cover depth		40	50	60	40	50	60
CC (mS/cm)	FA	1.00	1.40	1.80	0.65	1.10	1.45
	GGBS	1.10	1.60	2.10	0.85	1.35	1.70
	CSF	0.30	0.40	0.50	0.25	0.35	0.40

FA = 70% CEMI, 30% fly ash
GGBS = 50% CEMI, 50% GGBS (slag)
SF = 90% CEMI, 10% silica fume

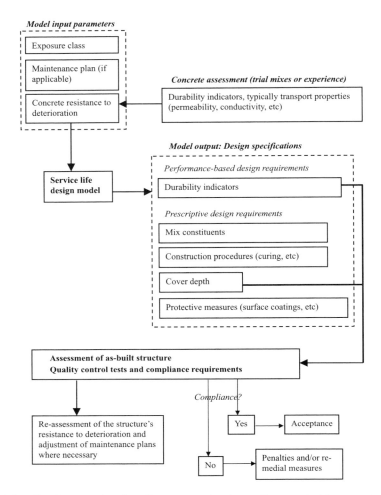

Figure 6. Principles of performance-based quality assessment and compliance control for concrete durability.

mechanisms, amount of carbonatable material in the concrete, etc., and hence on type and amount of constituent materials used. Limiting values for durability characteristics should ideally be based on a comprehensive statistical evaluation of relevant influencing factors (environment, expected scatter in test results, measurement uncertainties, etc), applying relevant service life models.

5 THE USE OF PERFORMANCE-BASED QUALITY CONTROL TO DEVELOP MAINTENANCE PLANS

In the past, most concrete structures were designed by structural engineers who did not consider the aspect of concrete deterioration and hence made little provision for service-life design and maintenance planning. Owners often believed that their structures would last for the required service life

without further costs incurring for maintenance and repair. The increasing number of deteriorating and damaged concrete structures has changed this perception in the past decades and owners and engineers alike are beginning to understand that service-life considerations need to be an integral part of the design process and that proper maintenance plans need to be put into place to ensure effective and economic use of structures.

Ideally, the owner or manager of a structure needs to be given a "manual" by which to best manage the structure for optimum service life. The same approach has for a long time been used, for example, in the automobile industry. Every owner of a motor vehicle accepts that his vehicle has a limited life span and that routine inspections and some repair need to be carried out during the service life of the vehicle. If a similar mindset was developed in the construction industry, it would greatly enhance durability and reduce service-life costs of concrete structures. The difference between a new motor vehicle and a concrete structure is that in most cases the original quality of the former is known, which allows the application of a standard maintenance schedule. The quality of the as-built concrete structure however needs to be assessed and quantified if an effective maintenance plan is to be developed.

In the current context, the maintenance plan should include routine inspection of the structure, which may result in specification of appropriate protective measures or repair. Such remedial measures for concrete structures are most successful if they are carried out early, before significant damage has occurred. Once corrosion of steel reinforcement has commenced and resulted in damage such as cracking, delamination, spalling, loss of rebar cross-section, etc., measures to stop damage progression and reinstate structural integrity become increasingly expensive. The best method to avoid significant damage is deterioration prediction in combination with properly scheduled condition assessments. An important part of maintenance planning is therefore the prediction of deterioration processes during the anticipated life time of the structure. For example, based on the prediction of carbonation development and the ingress of harmful substances such as chlorides, a time plan for maintenance measures can be developed.

The principles of quality assessment on the as-built structure, as discussed earlier, can therefore successfully be applied to plan routine maintenance measures and design a schedule for appropriate remedial measures, as indicated in Figure 6.

6 CONCLUDING REMARKS AND FUTURE OUTLOOK

Worldwide, there is a clear trend towards performance-based specifications for concrete durability. In some countries, such as for example South Africa, performance-based specifications and quality control for reinforced concrete structures are already applied on a large scale (Beushausen et al., 2010). The underlying principles for performance approaches were discussed and examples of appropriate test methods for quality assessment and service life prediction of reinforced concrete structures were presented.

The literature contains a range of different philosophies for performance approaches for concrete durability. The two main schools of thought include those which apply performance evaluation in the design stage only (pre-construction) and those who further include quality assessment of the as-built structure. In some cases it may be sufficient to restrict the performance evaluation to the design stage. However, if the actual quality of the as-built structure is not measured, the important influence of construction procedures on concrete durability cannot directly be assessed, which may result in significant over—or underestimation of the potential service life of the structure. A range of appropriate test methods for the control of in-situ concrete quality have been developed worldwide, allowing an estimate of the service life duration of concrete structures subjected to chloride ingress and carbonation.

Performance specifications can be used to develop appropriate maintenance plans for reinforced concrete structures and thus prevent costly repair measures at a later stage. Again, this can only be successful if appropriate measures are put in place to control concrete durability properties of the as-built structure.

Amongst engineers, concrete suppliers and contractors in many countries, the gradual implementation of performance-based design and quality control methods for concrete is starting to raise awareness on the importance of concrete durability. This shift in mindset can already be expected to have a significant impact on the quality and durability of reinforced concrete structures.

For performance-based approaches to be successful in the long run, a significant amount of future research is required. This includes further research to link durability indicators to the actual long-term performance of the as-built structures, the refinement of appropriate test methods, the development of clearly formulated and rational conformity criteria, as well as the development of guidelines for remedial measures for structures that do not meet the specified performance criteria.

REFERENCES

ACI ITGG-8R-10, 'Report on Performance-Based Requirements for Concrete', American Concrete Institute, December 2010, p. 46

Alexander, M.G., Ballim, Y. and Stanish, K. 'A framework for use of durability indexes in performance-based design and specifications for reinforced concrete structures', Materials & Structures, Vol. 41, No. 5, June 2008, pp. 92v1–936.

Alexander, M.G. and Beushausen, H. 'Performance-based durability testing, design and specification in South Africa: latest developments', Proceedings: International Conference on Excellence in Concrete Construction through Innovation, London, 9–10 September 2008.

Andrade, C. and d'Andrea, R. (2010). 'Electrical resistivity as microstructural parameter for modelling of service life of reinforced concrete structures", 2nd International symposium on Service Life Design.

Andrade, C., D'Andrea, R., Castillo, A. and Castellote, M. 'The Use of Electrical Resistivity as NDT Method for the Specification of the durability of Reinforced Concrete, NDTCE'09, Non-Destructive Testing in Civil Engineering, Nantes, France, June 30th—July 3rd, 2009.

Alexander, M.G., Mackechnie, J.R. and Ballim, Y. 'Guide to the use of durability indexes for achieving durability in concrete structures', Research Monograph No. 2, Universities of Cape Town and the Witwatersrand, 1999, p. 36

ASTM C 1202–1997, Standard Test Method for Electrical Indication of Concrete's Ability to Resist Chloride Ion Penetration. ASTM, USA.

ASTM C1556 (2004), 'Standard Test Method for Determining the Apparent Chloride Diffusion Coefficient of Cementitious Mixtures by Bulk Diffusion', Philadelphia: American Society for Testing and Materials, 2004.

Baroghel-Bouny, V. 'Durability indicators: relevant tools for performance-based evaluation and multi-level prediction of RC durability', Proceedings of International RILEM Workshop on Performance based evaluation and indicators for concrete durability, March 2006, Madrid, Spain, p. 25

Baroghel-Bouny V., Nguyen T.Q. and Dangla P. 'Assessment and Prediction of RC Structure Service Life by Means of Durability Indicators and Physical/chemical Models', Cement and concrete composites, vol. 31, n° 8, 2009, pp. 522–534.

Beushausen, H., Alexander, M.G. and Mackechnie, J. 'Concrete durability aspects in an international context', Concrete Plant and Precast Technology BFT, vol. 7, 2003, Germany, pp. 22–32.

Beushausen, H., Knecht, J., Alexander, M. and Schubert, K. 'Performance-based durability control for precast concrete elements', The 3rd fib International Congress, Washington, USA, May-June 2010.

BS EN 206-1: 2000, Concrete—Part 1: Specification, performance, production and conformity.

BS EN 1992:1-1:2004, UK National Annex to Eurocode 2: Design of concrete structures—Part 1–1: General rules and rules for buildings.

CEN/TC 104/SC1/TG17, 'Equivalent Durability Concept, a discussion document for CEN/TC 104/SC1 to decide upon what is achievable for the 2010 revision of EN 206-1, Draft 8 version 1, May 2008, p. 13

CEN/TS 12390-XXX: Testing hardened concrete—Part XX: Determination of the potential carbonation resistance of concrete: Accelerated carbonation method, Draft version, Nov 2009.

CEN/TS 12390-10: Testing hardened concrete—Part 10: Determination of the relative carbonation resistance of concrete, Sept. 2007.

DuraCrete R17, Final Technical Report, DuraCrete—Probabilistic Performance based Durability Design of Concrete Structures, The European Union—Brite EuRam III, May 2000, Document BE95-1347/R17.

Ehlen, M.A, Thomas, M.D.A. and Bentz, E.C. 'Life-365 Service Life Prediction Model Version 2', Concrete International, May 2009.

fib bulletin 34: Model Code for Service Life Design, Switzerland, 2006, p. 110

Harrison, T.A. 'Framework for Durability Performance Specifications for Concrete Used in Normal Construction', Proceedings: XIth European Ready-Mixed Concrete Congress, Turkey, 1995.

Imamoto, K., Shimozawa K., Nagayama, M., Yamasaki J. and Nimura S. 'Threshold values of air permeability of concrete cover—a case study in Japan', SACoMaTIS 2008, Proc. of Intern. RILEM Confer., Varenna, Italy, Vol. 1, pp. 169–177.

Kollek, J.J. 'The determination of permeability of concrete by the Cembureau Method. A recommendation', Materials and Structures, Vol. 22, 1989, pp. 225–230.

Mackechnie, J.R. 'Predictions of Reinforced Concrete Durability in the Marine Environment', Research Monograph No. 1, Department of Civil Engineering, University of Cape Town, 2001, p. 28

Mackechnie, J.R. and Alexander, M.G. (2002), 'Durability predictions using early age durability index testing', Proceedings, 9th Durability and Building Materials Conference, 2002. Australian Corrosion Association, Brisbane, p. 11

Nordtest, 'Concrete, hardened: Accelerated chloride penetration', NT Build 443, Espoo, Finland, 1995.

Otieno, M.B., Beushausen, H. and Alexander, M.G., 'Modelling corrosion propagation in reinforced concrete structures - a critical review', Cement & Concrete Composites, Vol 33, 2011, pp. 240–245.

Romer, M., Fernández Luco, L. RILEM TC 189-NEC: Non-destructive evaluation of the concrete cover: Comparative test—Part I: Comparative test of 'penetrability' methods—Part II: Comparative test of 'Covermeters', Materials and Structures, v. 38, n. 284, Dec. 2005, pp. 895–911.

RILEM TC 116-PCD, 'Permeability of concrete as a criterion of its durability', Materials and Structures, Vol. 32, April 1999, pp. 174–179.

Salvoldi, B., Beushausen, H. and Alexander, M. (2011), 'Modelling the Carbonation of Concrete using performance based tests: Proposition of a Conceptual Framework', submitted for ICCC, Madrid, June 2011.

Streicher, P.E. and Alexander, M.G. 'A chloride conduction test for concrete', Cement and Concrete Research, 25(6), 1995, pp. 1284–1294.

Tang, L., Chloride Transport in Concrete-Measurement and prediction, Building materials, Chalmers, Gothenburg, 1996.

Thomas, M.D.A. and Bentz, E.C. Manual: Computer Program for Predicting the Service Life and Life Cycle Costs of Reinforced Concrete Exposed to Chlorides, October, 2000.

Torrent, R. and Frenzer, G. 'Studie über Methoden zur Messung und Beurteilung der Kennwerte des Überdeckungsbetons auf der Baustelle', VSS Report, No. 516, Zurich, 1995.

Torrent, R. and Fernández Luco, L. (editors) State of The Art Report (STAR): RILEM TC 189-NEC: Non-Destructive Evaluation of the Covercrete, Zurich, Switzerland, 2007, p. 223

Torrent, R. and Jacobs, F. 'Swiss Standard SIA 262:2003, a step towards performance-based specifications for durability', Proceedings of the international RILEM TC 211-PAE Final Conference "Concrete in Aggressive Aqueous Environments; Performance and Testing", Volume 2, Toulouse, France, 2009, pp. 532–539.

Walraven, J. Design for service life: how should it be implemented in future codes, International Conference on Concrete Repair, Rehabilitation and Retrofitting, Proceedings ICCRRR 2008, Cape Town, 24–26 November 2008, pp. 3–10.

XP CEN/TS 12390-11: Testing Hardened concrete—Part 11: Determination of the chloride resistance of concrete, unidirectional diffusion, Jan. 2010.

Concrete Solutions – Grantham, Mechtcherine & Schneck (eds)
© 2012 Taylor & Francis Group, London, ISBN 978-0-415-61622-5

An experimental study on the inhibition of calcium nitrite, amino alcohol and sodium fluorophosphate as reinforced concrete protection

A. El shami, M. Choinska, S. Bonnet, P. Mounanga & A. Khelidj
University of Nantes-Research Institute of Civil Engineering and Mechanics, France

ABSTRACT: This paper presents two experimental ways to evaluate the efficiency and the durability performances of inhibitors as reinforced concrete protection. The first method is based on study of mechanical and transport properties of concrete specimens and the second method is based on the application of the Nernst equation for the pore concrete simulating solutions which is measured by impedance spectroscopy, rest potential and linear polarization. In the present study, three types of inhibitors (anodic inhibitors (calcium nitrite); cathodic inhibitors (ethanol amine) and sodium fluorophosphate inhibitors) to control rebar corrosion. The measurements carried out in order to characterize the inhibitor's behaviour as repair materials were: compressive strength, permeability, shrinkage, chloride migration and a corrosion resistance test of pore concrete simulating solutions conducted by varying the type and the concentration of inhibitors. The addition of inhibitors not only increased the compressive strength of the concrete but also improved the corrosion resistance properties.

1 INTRODUCTION

Steel in concrete remains in the passive state in alkaline solution but various contaminants have a detrimental effect on passivity. Among them, chloride ions are the most common and localized corrosion triggers when chlorides reach the metal surface (Valcarce and Vàzquez, 2008). The use of corrosion inhibitors is probably more attractive from the point of view of economics and ease of application (Ergun *et al.*, 2008). Reviews of the most commonly used corrosion inhibitor types and the various possible mechanisms of inhibition have been recently published (Fekry and Ameer, 2010; Altaf *et al.*, 2010).

The aim of this work is to test the efficiency of calcium nitrite-based inhibitor, the amino alcohol-based inhibitor and sodium fluorophosphate with the two methods to evaluate the efficiency and the durability performances of inhibitors as reinforced concrete protection in concrete specimens and in pore concrete simulating solutions. The study was performed through the use of electrochemical and analytical techniques to discuss the inhibition mechanism in the presence of chloride ions.

2 EXPERIMENTAL PROGRAMME

2.1 *Materials and compositions of mixtures*

The effect of some corrosion inhibiting admixtures on the rheological and mechanical properties of hardened concrete was investigated experimentally. A cement of type I, CEM I 52.5, was used to prepare ordinary Portland cement concrete (OPCC). The chemical composition of the Ordinary Portland Cement is given in Table 1.

Natural calcareous medium (4/12 mm) and coarse (12/20 mm) aggregates as well as natural calcareous sand (0/4 mm) were employed for concrete preparation.

Three different types of inhibitors were investigated:

• The first inhibitor was a calcium nitrite (CNI). This corrosion inhibitor contains minimum 30% active ingredients by mass. Its density is about 1.90 g/cm^3, and its pH value is 7. The water content of CNI is approximately 30%; this amount was taken into account for the calculation of the water-to-cement ratio (W/C).

The nitrate ions are effective by reacting with defective ferrous ions prior to chloride attack, repairing in this way the passive layer around the steel bar. They reduce the corrosion rate by an increase in the corrosion potential of the steel. According to the behaviour, it is also used as an accelerating additive for cold weather application.

• The second is ethanolamine (amino alcohol), called AMA, and is an aqueous solution. Its density is about 1.01 g/cm^3, and its pH value is 11.2. Mixed inhibitors act on both anodic and cathodic sites and they reduce the corrosion rate without a significant change in the corrosion potential, generally by surface adsorption over the surface of the steel in contact with the inhibitor and consequently forming a thin protective layer. Due to its high affinity to steel, it is also able to displace chloride ions from the metal surface to protect concrete from chloride induced corrosion.

- The third is sodium monoflurophosphate (noted MFP), with 95% of Na_2FPO_3. MFP is a so-called migrating corrosion inhibitor. When incorporated into the concrete mix, it seeks out and forms a corrosion inhibiting protective layer on the metal reinforcement. The basic mechanism of Na-MFP inhibitor is to protect the passive layer of the reinforcement against disruption due to carbonation. It protects both cathodic and anodic areas. It is known to act also as a retarding admixture.

For mechanical tests, one type of concrete has been considered: an Ordinary Portland Cement concrete (OPCC). This type of concrete was admixed with various amounts of inhibitors, dissolved in the mixing water before adding to the dry concrete mix. The mix proportions of the 4 compositions investigated in this study are given in Table 2. The W/C ratio is 0.48.

Table 1. Chemical composition of cement.

Composition (% of mass)	CEM I 52.5
CaO	64.58
SiO_2	21.39
Al_2O_3	3.66
Fe_2O_3	4.25
MgO	0.96
SO_3	2.63
Na_2O	0.10
K_2O	0.28
Loss on ignition	0.92
Insoluble residue	0.09
Activity of alkaline	0.28
CaO free	0.48
Blaine specific surface (cm^2/g)	3820

2.2 Tests on concrete

2.2.1 Rheological properties

A slightly increased workability is obtained using AMA corrosion inhibitor, while the workability is not significantly influenced by addition of (CNI). An increase of the workability is obtained due to the addition of the MFP corrosion inhibitors.

2.2.2 Mechanical properties

- Compressive strength

For each concrete mixture, 22 cylindrical specimens (diameter: 11 cm; height: 22 cm) were prepared from a single batch. After casting, all the specimens were moist-cured at $20 \pm 2°C$ and over 95% of relative humidity (R.H.) for 24 h. They were then de-moulded. The cylindrical specimens were kept in a water tank at $20 \pm 2°C$ until the age of testing. The compressive strength and the Young's modulus were measured at 1, 3, 7, 14, 28 and 90 days on three cylindrical specimens at each test-age (Figure 1). The values given in of this paper are the mean values of three compressive strength or Young's modulus values.

- Shrinkage test

$7 \times 7 \times 28$ cm^3 prismatic concrete specimens were prepared from the same batch required for compressive strength and cured at $20 \pm 2°C$ and over 95% of relative humidity (R.H.) for 24 h. and then de-moulded. The shrinkage was measured at room temperature for 28 days. Drying shrinkage has been measured by using a simple technique, allowing length change measurement by means of dial gauge (with an accuracy of 10 µm/m). Two stainless steel plugs remained gripped to the concrete by means of embedded screw rods and constituted the ends of the mould as well as of the sample. Each end had a recessed stud placed at the centre for length change measurement.

The samples were kept at $T = 20°C$ in their moulds ($\pm 1°C$). From casting up to 28 days, the shrinkage was measured at $T = 20°C$.

Table 2. Compositions of OPCC with or without inhibitors (kg/m^3).

Mix no	Cement	Water	Coarse aggregate	Medium aggregate	Sand	Inhibitor type	Inhibitor content
1	350	168	561	432	868	–	–
2	350	168	561	432	868	AMA	5 L/m^3
3	350	168	561	432	868	CNI	10 L/m^3
4	350	168	561	432	868	MFP	2% by mass. of cement

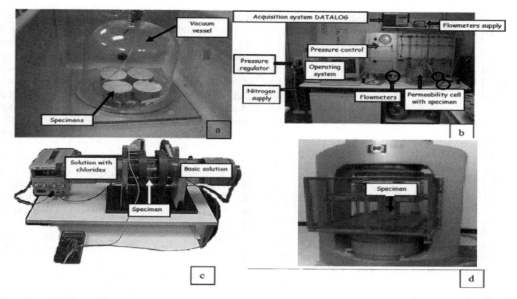

Figure 1. Experimental set-up, a) porosity device, b) permeability device, c) chloride migration device, d) mechanical set-up.

2.2.3 *Transport properties*

• Porosity

Porosity measurements were conducted on 3 cylindrical specimens (diameter: 11 cm; height: 5 cm). The specimens were dried at $80 \pm 5°C$ until constant weight had been achieved and were then placed in a desiccator under vacuum for at least 4 h, where after the desiccator was filled with de-aerated, half saturation with NaOH (0.025 mol/L) and KOH (0.083 mol/L) for 48h. Then the desiccator was filled with NaOH (0.025 mol/L) and KOH (0.083 mol/L) complete saturation (2 cm over the surface) for 24 h (Figure 1). The porosity was calculated using the following formula by Equation 1.

$$P = \left(\frac{W_{sat} - W_{dry}}{W_{sat} - W_{dry}} \right) \times 100 \qquad (1)$$

where: p is vacuum saturation porosity (%); W_{sat} corresponds to weight in air of saturated sample (g);

W_{wat} corresponds to weight in water of saturated sample (g); W_{dry} corresponds to weight of oven-dried sample (g).

• Gas permeability

Gas permeability is determined by measurement of the gas flow rate at a steady-state flow under a gradient of pressure applied to a concrete specimen. In our tests, permeability was measured using a CEMBUREAU permeameter with nitrogen (see Figure 1). For each concrete mixture, 3 cylindrical specimens (diameter: 11 cm; height: 5 cm) were used. The apparent gas permeability (ka in m²) is obtained using the volumetric flow rate (Qv in m³/s) in steady-state conditions (Choinska *et al.*, 2007). It can be determined by Equation 2 which is based on the Hagen–Poiseuille relationship for laminar flow of a compressible fluid through a porous body with small capillaries under steady-state conditions

$$K_a = \left(\frac{2\eta L P_2 Q_v}{A \left[P_1^2 - P_2^2 \right]} \right) \qquad (2)$$

where L is the specimen length in the direction of the flow (m); A is the flow area m²; P_1 and P_2 are the upstream and downstream pressures in (Pa), and μ is the dynamic viscosity of the applied gas (Pa.s).

The intrinsic permeability (k_v in m²) can be determined by the Klinkenberg method which shows that for a given saturation degree, the apparent permeability is generally a linear function of the inverse of the average pressure (Pm). Therefore, the intrinsic permeability may be calculated using Equation 3.

$$K_a = K_V \left(1 + \frac{\beta}{P_m} \right) \qquad (3)$$

where β (Pa) is a constant called Klinkenberg coefficient. The average pressure P_m is determined as $[(P_1+P_2)/2]$.

• Migration test

Two cylinders concrete (110×220 mm) were cast, demoulded after one day and stored in a climate room at $20°C \pm 2°C$ and more than 90% R.H. till the end of the 90 days.

Figure 1. presents the chloride ion migration cell developed by Djerbi (Djerbi *et al.*, 2009) and used in the present study. After the gas permeability and porosity tests, each concrete disc was placed between two chambers containing solutions made with NaOH (0.025 mol/L) and KOH (0.083 mol/L). NaCl (0.513 mol/L) was added in the upstream solution and a 12V current is applied between the sides of the concrete sample. The test was carried out at T = 20 ± 1°C.

As the flow becomes constant, the effective chloride coefficient De (m^2/s) can be calculated using the modified Nernst–Planck's equation, as demonstrated in (Andrade, 1993) by Equation 4. This equation neglects the diffusion and convection flows with respect to the electrical migration flow. Assuming much diluted solutions, it gives:

$$D_e = \left(\frac{R(T+273.15)}{Z.F} \cdot \frac{L.Q(Cl^-)}{\Delta E . C_0 t} \right) \qquad (4)$$

where De is the diffusion coefficient of concrete (m^2/s), C_0 is the chloride concentration (mol/m^3) of the catholyte solution (upstream compartment), assumed to be constant; Q [Cl^-] is the cumulative amount of chloride ions (mol/m^2) arriving in the downstream compartment during the time t (s); L is the thickness of the specimen (m); z is the valence ion (z = 1); F is the Faraday constant (F = 96480 J/V); E is the actual potential drop between the surfaces of specimen (V); R is the gas constant (R = 8.3144 J/mol/K); and T is the temperature (°C). The chloride concentration was determined by means of potentiometric titration with a Metrohm SA CH- 9101 Herisau automatic titrated with 0.05 M silver nitrate ($AgNO_3$) titrant.

2.3 Pore solution tests

The following treatment was applied on the carbon steel (with 0.42 wt.% C, a diameter of 8 mm).

The steel sample dipping in solution contains 184 ml HCl (33%), 2 g/L hexamethylene tetramine and the per litre of aqueous solution during one minute. After treatment, the sample was rinsed several times with deionized water, then samples were immersed in alkaline solutions simulating the concrete interstitial electrolyte at ambient temperature (Table 3). A saturated calcium hydroxide solution (noted S1) has been used to simulate the aqueous alkaline content of the concrete pore solutions, with an approximate pH of 12.7. To simulate the aqueous phase of a concrete contaminated with chloride, 35 g/L NaCl was introduced in the S1 solution to obtain an electrolyte designated by S2. The pH of the solution containing chloride was 12.5. The choice of this solution is found in the literature (Simescu and Idrissi, 2009).

Corrosion inhibitors, CNI, AMA and MFP, were added to the different solutions separately. Since the reaction mechanism of the corrosion inhibitors with the cement has not been studied on a quantitive basis, it is difficult to calculate the exact amount of corrosion inhibitor in the simulated pore solution. In this study, the volume ratio of corrosion inhibitor to the simulated pore solution is taken between the volume ratio of the corrosion inhibitor to the free water content and the volume ratio of the corrosion inhibitor to the total water content (Luo, 2006).

The dosage of CNI is 150 ml/l by ratio equal approximately. It is reported that the maximum ratio of [Cl^-]/ [NO_2^-] ratio to prevent steel corrosion in concrete is about 0.8~1.5 (Hicks, 2004), AMA is 4% (v/v) according to a previous work (Jamil, *et al.*, 2004) it was found that the inhibitor was effective for concentrations 4% (v/v). In this work the dosage of MFP is 2% and demonstrates that good protection is already provided with 2% of inhibitor that is below the recommended amount (5%). The test set up is shown in Figure 2.

2.4 Electrochemical measurement

The fact that concrete itself is not a homogenous material and its properties can vary very widely with the change in its components and their proportions in the mix (such as type and amount of cement, water/cement ratio, method and period of curing and addition of cementious materials)

Table 3. Description of the various electrolytes used.

Solution	Ca(OH)$_2$ (mol/L)	NaOH (mol/L)	KOH (mol/L)	NaCl (g/L)	PH
S1	Saturation	0.001	0.001	0	12.7
S2	Saturation	0.001	0.001	35	12.5

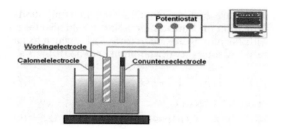

Figure 2. Test set-up for the electro chemical measurements.

precludes the existence of a unique value, particularly when expressing this value as a percentage of cement weight. Thus, many researchers are inclined to use well-controlled synthetic solutions to emulate concrete environment and prefer to use the Cl-/OH parameter as an indication of chloride threshold level. Less scattered results and more repeatable data are obtained when using this parameter (Hurley, 2007). Therefore, the use of a solution is considered more representative. Different electrochemical techniques were used to evaluate the corrosion behaviour of the MFP, AMA and CNI in comparison with S1 (concrete pore solution) and S2 (concrete pore solution contaminated with chloride, 35 g/L NaCl). open circuit potential (noted Ecorr), potentiodynamic polarization and electrochemical impedance spectroscopy (EIS) measurements. Ecorr was monitored during 8 days. Polarization curves (I = f(E)) were plotted with a scan rate of 0.1 mV/s from −100 to 1000 mV vs. Ecorr in the anodic direction. EIS measurements were carried out at corrosion potential with a frequency variation between 100 kHz and 0.05 Hz and a potential sine signal of 10 mV. Impedance data were fitted using software.

3 RESULTS AND DISCUSSION

3.1 Effect of corrosion inhibitor on concrete compressive strength and rheological properties

This part focuses on the compressive strength of concrete samples admixed with 5 L/m³ of AMA, 10 L/m³ of CNI and of 2% by weight of cement of MFP inhibitors and samples free from inhibitors, cured in water at 20°C, up to 90 days. The compressive strength of the concretes is given in Figure 3 as a function of curing age. One may observe that, in most cases, the compressive strength values obtained for concretes admixed with the AMA inhibitor are higher than those obtained for concretes without inhibitor but this tendency is not true in every case (for instance AMA at 90 days).

This shows the accelerating properties of AMA inhibitor at early ages however the final strength (90 days) based on Portland cement, is reduced by 5%. This reduction was also confirmed by another author (De Schutter and Luo, 2004).

The reduction in strength of the OPC admixed with AMA may be attributed to the organic component of the corrosion inhibitor which interferes with the hydration process (Saraswathy and Won Song, 2007). No significant influence is noticed for Young's modulus for OPC concrete admixed with AMA-based inhibitors (Table 4).

It is worth noting that calcium nitrite presence in this concrete has a positive effect on the compressive strength; with content 10 L/m³ of CNI approximately 25% in comparison with the reference concrete. No significant influence is noticed for Young's modulus for OPC concrete admixed with AMA-based inhibitors.

The results indicate that MFP causes higher initial strength development at early ages but slightly reduces the strength at later ages (90 days). MFP might be judged to have a retarding effect on early cement hydration. This slight delay indicates that the apatite products could be calcium apatite (fluoroapatite ($Ca_5 (PO_4)_3F$) or hydroxyl apatite) would be due to the decreased dissolution rates of various ions into the alkaline pore solution. After Na-MFP has hydrolyzed into the pore water, the formation of phosphate and F- would delay the

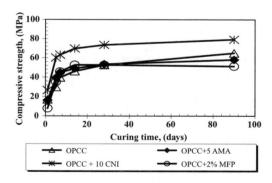

Figure 3. Compressive strength of OPCC concrete with all inhibitors.

Table 4. The Young's modulus was obtained on $7 \times 7 \times 28$ cm³ prismatic concrete specimens.

Mix	3 days	7 days	28 days	90 days
OPCC	27.71	33.88	37.67	44.40
OPCC + 5 AMA	30.10	32.07	38.13	45.16
OPCC + 10CNI	29.20	33.03	37.45	45.20
OPCC + 2% MFP	30.00	37.33	38.54	46.68

dissolution rate of Ca++ and retard the formation of C–S–H (Chaussadent *et al.*, 2006).

For the Young's modulus, corrosion inhibitor CNI also seems to induce higher early age values for all concrete, while the final value is not significantly influenced. No significant influence however is noticed for Young's modulus for concrete admixed with AMA. All the values of the Young's modulus are slightly increased due to the addition of inhibitor MFP.

3.2 *Influence of corrosion inhibitors on gas permeability and porosity*

The intrinsic gas permeability values obtained on dry samples at the ages of 90 days are plotted in Figure 4. The gas permeability of all the mixtures is within the same order of magnitude. AMA inhibitor gave gas permeability about 13% lower than the reference mix. It has been assumed that pore blocking by gel formation of the inorganic component was responsible for these results (Tritthart, 2003). However, for the samples with addition of the nitrite based inhibitor CNI showed significantly higher effective intrinsic permeability in comparison with the reference samples.

The addition of calcium nitrite influences the hydration process of cement paste. Apparently, calcium nitrite has the function of accelerating and stabilising the formation of the crystal phase of calcium hydroxide which leads to an increase in the micropore diameter in the hardened cement paste and thus to an increase in permeability compared to concrete without inhibitor (Kondratova *et al.*, 2003).

With the same trend, the samples with addition of the monofluorophosphate based corrosion inhibitor MFP showed slightly higher intrinsic permeability in comparison with the reference samples. Na_2PO_3F hydrolyses into the pore solution of concrete to form phosphate and F^- (Equation 5). Those anions react with certain components of the cement matrix to form fluorapatite and fluorite,

which are highly insoluble calcium compounds (Equation 6). Furthermore, NaF would also react with calcium hydroxide to form CaF_2, which has a very low solubility (Sisomphon *et al.*, 2010).

$$PO_3F_2 + H_2O \rightarrow F^- + PO_4^- \qquad (5)$$

$$5Ca[OH]_2 + 3Na_2PO_3F$$
$$\rightarrow Ca_5[PO_4]_3[F,OH] + 4NaOH + 2NaF + 3H_2O \qquad (6)$$

Results obtained for porosity tests confirm the general trend. Indeed, no significant influence is noticed for the MFP and AMA (12 and 12.4% respectively) therefore CNI is slightly more porous than the latter (14%).

3.3 *Influence of corrosion inhibitors on chloride migration properties of concrete samples*

The test results of samples with inhibitors are plotted in Figure 5. The chloride migration coefficients of all the mixtures are lower than that obtained from the reference. A higher reduction is noticed with MFP.

The concrete samples treated with 10 L/m³ CNI showed chloride migration coefficients 30% higher in chloride migration testing in comparison to the reference sample. Similar trends are also found for the gas permeation tests, where the concrete samples with AMA have slightly higher chloride migration 32% than the reference because the effects on cement hydration are less relevant and the volatile component evaporated. Thus, according to the literature, amino alcohol-based inhibitor seems to be more effective in simulated pore solution than in concrete (Söylev *et al.*, 2007).

3.4 *Influence of corrosion inhibitors on drying shrinkage of concrete*

The drying shrinkage of OPC concrete is shown in Figure 6. The drying shrinkage of all concrete

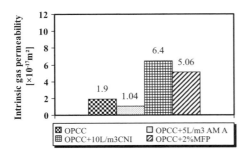

Figure 4. Intrinsic gas permeability (with and without inhibitor, at the age of 90 days).

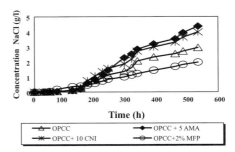

Figure 5. Evolution of cumulative concentration chloride migration as a function of time for OPC concrete.

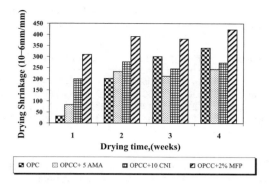

Figure 6. Drying shrinkage of OPC concrete.

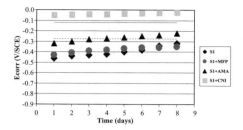

Figure 7. Evolution of the rest potentials for steel immersion in S1.

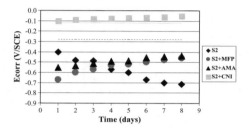

Figure 8. Evolution of the rest potentials for treated in S2.

specimens without inhibitors increased very quickly during the first 2 weeks, but only slightly after that.

Shrinkage values of both control concrete and OPC concrete admixed with AMA inhibitor varied between 339×10^{-6} and 242×10^{-6} mm/mm, it represents a difference of approximately 29%. While at fourth week, concretes with CNI had drying shrinkage values of 253×10^{-6} mm/mm, respectively.

The drying shrinkage values for MFP were 421×10^{-6} mm/mm higher drying shrinkage than OPC concrete by approximately 20% results from water loss, higher porosity and permeability of concrete, this result suggests that the use of MFP to replace by up to 2% by weight of cement cannot reduce the drying shrinkage of concrete.

3.5 Corrosion behaviour in alkaline medium and neutral solution

3.5.1 Corrosion potential evolution
At the start of the addition of inhibitors (Figure 7) the rest potentials are respectively around −100 mV for the S1+CNI and mainly between −430 and −330 mV for all inhibitor added in S1. (ASTM C876) indicates that the corrosion probability of rebars embedded in concrete is less than 10% when the rest potential is above −120 mV (SCE) and it is more than 90% when the rest potential is below −276 mV (SCE). Thus, the rebars in S1+ CNI are probably passive whereas an active corrosion probably takes place on the rebars in S1 without inhibitor.

Eight days after addition of inhibitors Figure. 7, the rest potentials of S1+CNI are respectively between −50 and −20 mV and between −220 and −330 mV for all inhibitor added in S1. The rest potentials for the rebars in S1 without inhibitor shifted slightly towards more negative values. On the contrary, the rest potentials for S1+AMA,

S1+MFP shifted towards more positive values and are more homogeneous (−300 mV ± 100 mV) than the initial ones. This rather indicates a slowdown of the corrosion probability after the inhibitors addition. Indicating adsorption of an inhibitor film on the iron surface. The corrosion current decrease with time starting of addition inhibitors.

Just after addition of inhibitors Figure. 8, the rest potentials for S2+CNI are respectively between −120 and −100 mV and almost equal to −680 mV for S2+MFP and between −600 and −400 mV for respectively S2+AMA and the rebars in S2 without inhibitor. Thus, these rest potentials continue to decrease slightly. Concerning the rest potential values for S2+MFP and S2+AMA are almost the same as those obtained after 4 days (more or less 30 mV). In Figure. 8, after eight days of addition of inhibitors, the rest potential values are always lower than the initial ones indicating an efficiency of the inhibitor (except rebars in S2 without inhibitor). The rest potentials increase with time starting of addition inhibitors then slightly decrease for those obtained after 8 days.

3.5.2 EIS measurements
A proposed R(QR) electric equivalent circuit for non treated steel given in Figure 9a where Re corresponds to the electrolyte resistance, while C_{dl} and R_t present the double layer capacitance and the charge transfer resistance of the steel/solution interface. The proposed electric equivalent circuit

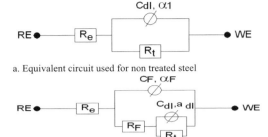

a. Equivalent circuit used for non treated steel

b. Equivalent circuit used for steel treated with inhibitors.

Figure 9. Equivalent circuit used for modelling the EIS data.

Table 5. Corrosion potential, current density for all specimens after 8 days of immersion in S1 solution.

Sample	C_F ($\mu F/cm^2$)	Rt ($k\Omega.cm^2$)	R_F ($k\Omega.cm^2$)	Cdl ($\mu F/cm^2$)
S1	–	106	–	44.8
S1+MFP	2.36	232	1.64	36.3
S1+AMA	14.23	2185	23.17	16.24
S1+CNI	7.11	845	14.45	20.1

Table 6. Corrosion potential, current density for all specimens after 8 days of immersion in S2 solution.

Sample	C_F ($\mu F/cm^2$)	Rt ($k\Omega.cm^2$)	R_F ($k\Omega.cm^2$)	Cdl ($\mu F/cm^2$)
S2	–	9.5	–	80.01
S2+MFP	20.92	56.3	0.58	26.81
S2+AMA	40.29	107	37	74.1
S2+CNI	9.47	207	109	28.06

for steel treated with inhibitors is given in Figure 9b where C_F and R_F represent the capacitance and resistance of the inhibitor film. The electrical parameters (C_{dl}, R_t) obtained through fitting EIS data, using the electric equivalent circuit R(QR), are listed in (Table 5). The Bode representations show two time constants (one at high frequency HF and another at low frequency LF) for treated steel, and thus the capacitive loop observed in the Nyquist plots is consisted of two non-decoupled capacitive loops. From these diagrams low values of C_F and C_{dl} are recorded (Table 6).

Figure 10 shows the main conclusions for all types of inhibitors: S1+CNI always has a lower corrosion rate than S1. The order of inhibition is: S1+AMA > S1+CNI >S1+MFP >S1 according to the values of Rt.

For non-treated-steel, the Nyquist plots and the Bode diagrams are presented in Figure 10. The electrical parameters (C_{dl}, Rt) obtained through fitting EIS data, using the electric equivalent circuit R(QR), are listed in (Table 5).

For the steel film, the double layer capacitance $C_{dl} < 2.5\ \mu F/cm^2$ shows that a small part R_t of the inhibitor steel surface is involved in the electrochemical reactions at the steel/solution interface (Simescu and Idrissi, 2009). These elements R_f and C_f are absent in diagrams corresponding to reference specimens immersed in alkaline solution, during only 8 days. These indicate the inhibitor layer of iron oxides/hydroxides surface film seems to cover the entire surface blocking the active sites and the total impedance of the system increases continuously.

The chloride presence in S2 solution (Figure. 11) containing CNI, AMA and MFP aged 8 days in the same aggressive solution gives simultaneously a competition between the formation and local destruction of the film obtained by the slow inhibitor dissolution. This classical corrosion mechanism leads to the diminution of R_t and R_f to the increase of the double layer capacitance C_{dl}.

This evolution corresponds to the electrolyte diffusion into the film pores. The order of inhibition is: S2+CNI >S2+AMA >S2+MFP >S2 according to the values of R_t.

3.5.3 Polarization curve

Figure 12 represent the potentiodynamic polarization curves of steel in S1 solution without and with different concentrations of inhibitors CNI, AMA and MFP. The data show that, the addition of inhibitor has a beneficial affect on the corrosion potential (E_{corr}) value. It is obvious that the anodic Tafel slope and cathodic Tafel slope do not remain constant upon the addition of each inhibitor.

These results indicate that, these inhibitors decrease the surface area for corrosion, affecting the mechanism of corrosion by blocking the reaction sites of the metal surface and changing the anodic and cathodic reaction mechanisms. For E_{corr} the order of inhibition from high to weak is: S1+MFP > S1> S1+AMA >S1+CNI.

The corrosion currents for S1+CNI, S1+AMA and S1+MFP are illustrated in Figure 13. According to RILEM studies (Andrade et al., 2004), 4 ranges of corrosion activity can be distinguished from negligible, to weak, to moderate and up to high, the corresponding thresholds being 0.1, 0.5 and 1 $\mu A/cm^2$.

After addition of inhibitor, The data show lower corrosion currents with time and after 8 days the corrosion current range is from 0.12 to 0.46 $\mu A/cm^2$ for S1+CNI, S1+AMA respectively. For rebar S1+MFP, where the initial corrosion currents at the start of addition of the inhibitors were in

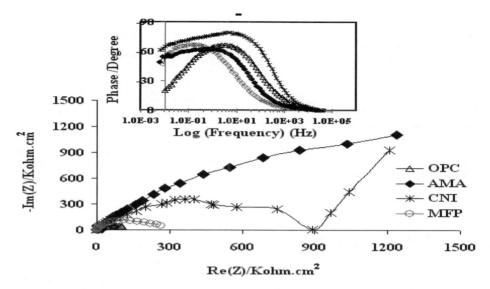

Figure 10. Bode and Nyquist plots for steel without treatment and with compound MFP, AMA and CNI after 8 days in S1.

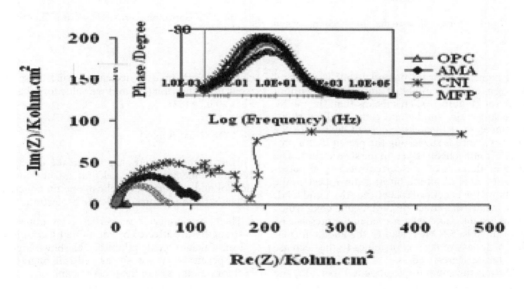

Figure 11. Bode and Nyquist plots for steel without treatment and with compound MFP, AMA and CNI after 8 days of immersion in S2.

the range moderate to weak, subsequently they are in the range of high 3.26 μA/cm^2 corrosion activity after 8 days. The values obtained 8 days after inhibitor treatment are lower than the initial ones. It is to be noticed that this corrosion current decrease tendency, which could be considered as an efficiency indicator for the inhibitor treatment, is more noticeable for rebars showing a high initial corrosion activity. In cases, S1+CNI, S1+AMA, the corrosion activity decreased to a lower range but for S1 was never reached. So the corrosion process is probably slowed down but not stopped. For Icorr the order of inhibition from high to weak is: S1 >S1+MFP> S1+AMA >S1+CNI.

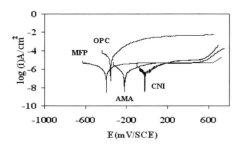

Figure 12. Polarization curves for OPC and MFP, AMA&CNI after 8 days of immersion in S1.

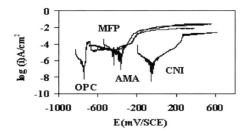

Figure 14. Polarization curves for OPC and MFP, AMA&CNI after 8 days of immersion in S2.

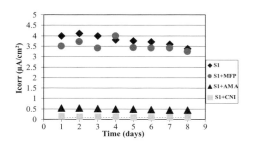

Figure 13. Corrosion currents for steel immersion in S1.

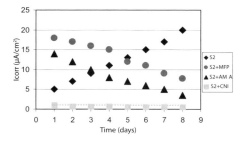

Figure 15. Corrosion currents for steel immersion in S2.

A higher significant potential shift is observed between S2 with inhibitor and the S2 without inhibitor (Figure 14). This means that, the inhibitor changes the anodic and cathodic Tafel slope. The increase of the passive current density for the film resistance is suggesting the presence of a protective homogeneous layer on the steel surface. The drop of decades of the current density at corrosion potential of all inhibitors with respect to the S2 shows the beneficial role of the AMA and CNI. This means the effect of AMA and CNI which forms a stable passive layer even in the presence of chloride ions. S2+MFP lead to the anodic formation of a passive layer contributes to the decrease of chloride aggressiveness.

During the inhibitor treatment Figure 15, the corrosion activity of the rebars in S2+CNI is negligible to weak as the average corrosion current value is equal to 0.22 (±0.04) µA/cm². But S2+AMA show a corrosion current ranging from 2.5 to 5 µA/cm² after 8 days, indicating a higher corrosion activity of the rebars. With time, the corrosion currents for S2+CNI remain low (0.95 ± 0.05 µA/cm², 0.58 ± 0.06 µA/cm² and 0.22 ± 0.05 µA/cm² respectively for 1 day, 4 days and 8 days After addition of inhibitor. Concerning the S2+MFP and S2, the corrosion currents of rebars S2+MFP almost

changing with time to decreased while those for rebar in S2 increase (the average value for rebar in S2 is 20.02 ± 0.23.

4 CONCLUSION

This experimental study has shown the effectiveness of some inhibitors: calcium nitrite, amino alcohol and sodium fluorophosphate on concrete behaviour and reinforced concrete protection.

- The mechanical properties (compressive strengths) are affected by addition of CNI inhibitor. Calcium nitrite inhibitor has shown higher gas permeability, porosity as well as in migration chloride values than the other systems.
- As expected the pore-blocking effect causes a reduction in gas permeability, porosity as well as in drying shrinkage by addition of AMA. This effect is not only mechanically effect, which blocks the pores only but there are other effect which forms a stable passive layer even in the presence of chloride ions
- In alkaline solution with or without chloride, the CNI steel sample is more resistant than mild steel alone and causing passivation of steel in concrete. Thus, a dense and protective layer is formed.

- In spite of the mechanical properties are not affected by addition of MFP and the same trend with pore concrete solutions measured, however, with a chloride ions solution, at very high concentrations exceeding the chloride threshold tolerated for the start of steel corrosion in alkaline media ($[Cl^-]/[OH^-] > 0.6$), Na_2PO_3F hydrolyses into the pore solution simulating the concrete to form phosphate and so anodic formation of passive layer contributes to the decrease of chloride aggressiveness.
- Finally the comparisons between the efficiency of inhibitors with the two methods are in good agreement provided the metrology of the experiments is carefully controlled.

ACKNOWLEDGEMENTS

This work has been financially supported by the European projects DURATINET and CPER (Contrat de Plan Etat Région).

REFERENCES

Altaf F, Qureshi R, Ahmed S, Khan Y. & Naseer A. 2010. Electrochemical adsorption studies of urea on copper surface in alkaline medium. *Electro analytical Chemistry*; vol. 642: n°1: pp. 98–101.

Andrade C. 1993. Calculation of chloride diffusion coefficients in concrete from ionic migration measurements," Cement Concrete Research; vol. 23: pp. 724–42.

Andrade C., Alonso A & Al. 2004. Test method for on-site corrosion rate measurement of steel reinforcement in concrete by means of the polarization resistance method. RILEM TC 154-EMC: Electrochemical Techniques for Measuring Metallic Corrosion—Recommendations, *Materials and Structures*, Vol. 37: n°9, pp. 623–643.

ASTM standards, 04.02 concrete and aggregates, C876, Standard test method for half cell potentials of uncoated reinforcing steel in concrete.

Berke N.S. & Hicks M.C. 2004. Predicting long-term durability of steel reinforced concrete with calcium nitrite corrosion inhibitor. *Cement and Concrete Composites*, vol. 26: pp. 191–198.

Chaussadent T., Nobel-Pujol V., Farcas F., Mabille I. & Fiaud C. 2006. Effectiveness conditions of sodium monofluorophosphates as a corrosion inhibitor for concrete reinforcements. Cement and Concrete Research, vol. 36: pp. 556–561.

Choinska M., Khelidj A., Chatzigeorgiou G. & Pijaudier-Cabotl G. 2007. Effects and interactions of temperature and stress-level related damage on permeability of concrete, *Cement and Concrete Research*, vol. 37: pp. 79–88.

De Schutter G., Luo L. 2004. Effect of corrosion inhibiting admixtures on concrete properties. Construction and Building Materials, vol. 18: pp. 483–9.

Djerbi A., Bonnet S., Khelidj A. & Baroghel-Bouny V. 2008. Influence of traversing crack on chloride diffusion into concrete. *Cement and Concrete Research*, vol. 38: pp. 877–83.

Ergun U¨., Yu¨ zer D, Emregu¨ l KC. 2008. The inhibitory effect of bis- 2,6—(3,5-dimethylpyrazolyl) pyridine on the corrosion behavior of mild steel in HCl solution. *Materials Chemistry and Physics*; vol. 109: n°2–3: pp. 492–499.

Fekry AM. & Ameer M.A. 2010. Corrosion inhibition of mild steel in acidic media using newly synthesized heterocyclic organic molecules. *International Journal of Hydrogen Energy*; vol. 35: p. 7641.

Hurley M.F. (2007). Corrosion initiation and propagation behaviour of corrosion resistant concrete reinforcing materials." PhD thesis, University of Virginia, USA.

Jamil H.E., Shriri A., Boulif R., Bastos C., Montemor M.F. & Ferreira M.G.S. 2004. Electrochemical behaviour of amino alcohol-based inhibitors used to control corrosion of reinforcing steel. *Electrochimica Acta*, vol. 49: pp. 2753–2760.

Kondratova I.L., Montes P. & Bremner T.W. 2003. Natural marine exposure results for reinforced concrete slabs with corrosion inhibitors. *Cement and Concrete Composites*, vol. 25: pp. 483–490.

Luo L. 2006. PhD thesis Influence of corrosion inhibitors on concrete properties: microstructure, transport properties and rebar corrosion. PhD thesis, pp. 83–86, ISBN-1090-8578-114-0, ISBN-13978-90-8578-114-1, Belgium.

Saraswathy V. & Won Song- Ha. 2007. Improving the durability of concrete by using inhibitors Building and Environment vol. 42: pp. 464–472.

Simescu F. & Idrissi H. 2009. Corrosion behaviour in alkaline medium of zinc phosphate coated steel obtained by cathodic electrochemical treatment. *Corrosion Science*. vol. 51: n°4, pp. 833–840.

Sisomphon K, Copuroglu O. & Fraaij A.L.A. 2010. Development of blast furnace slag mixtures against frost salt attack. *Cement & Concrete Composites*, vol. 32: pp. 630–638.

Söylev T.A., McNally C. & Richardson M. 2007. Effectiveness of amino alcohol-based surface-applied corrosion inhibitors in chloride-contaminated. *Cement and Concrete Research* vol. 37: pp. 972–977.

Tritthart J. 2003. Transport of a surface-applied corrosion inhibitor in cement paste and concrete. *Cement and Concrete Research*, vol. 33: pp. 829–834.

Valcarce M.B. & Va´zquez M. 2008. Carbon steel passivity examined in alkaline solutions: the effect of chloride and nitrite ions. *Electrochemica Acta*; vol. 53: n°15: pp. 5007–5015.

Concrete Solutions – Grantham, Mechtcherine & Schneck (eds)
© *2012 Taylor & Francis Group, London, ISBN 978-0-415-61622-5*

Hybrid connections—the sustainable approach for prefabricated frame structures

A. Faur & C. Mircea
Technical University of Cluj-Napoca, Cluj-Napoca, Romania

ABSTRACT: Two tests were performed on hybrid frame connection models, a connecting system of linear reinforced concrete members with a great potential in seismic protection. The aim of the paper is to emphasize the ease of replacement of the mild steel reinforcement, which often yields during frequent earthquakes. Despite a slightly inferior structural performance, revealed by the experimental evidence and numerical analyses, the full unbonded mild steel reinforcement is able to open a new direction in structural rehabilitation and repair, these usually very demanding works being reduced to simple and cost-effective operations.

1 PREAMBLE

1.1 Brief introduction to the hybrid RC frame concept

Hybrid RC frame connections are a special type of precast beam to column connection, with a unique post-elastic behavior, as shown by the flag response given in Figure 1b. The precast concrete frame units are assembled by unbonded post-tensioned strands, while the energy dissipation is ensured by special mild steel reinforcing bars. The main advantage of this type of connection is its self-centering ability, the residual drifts after strong earthquakes being practically insignificant. The concept was developed by Priestley et al. (1999) within the PRESS project, during the last two decades of the previous century.

The layout of the strands runs through linear HDPE ducts placed in the centre of the beams, and passes through the columns too. The post-tensioning force acts to restore the initial displacement state of the frame during and after an earthquake. Besides self-centering, post-tensioning also provides vertical shear resistance through the friction mechanism developed at the beam-column interface, and contributes to the overall bending moment capacity of the connection.

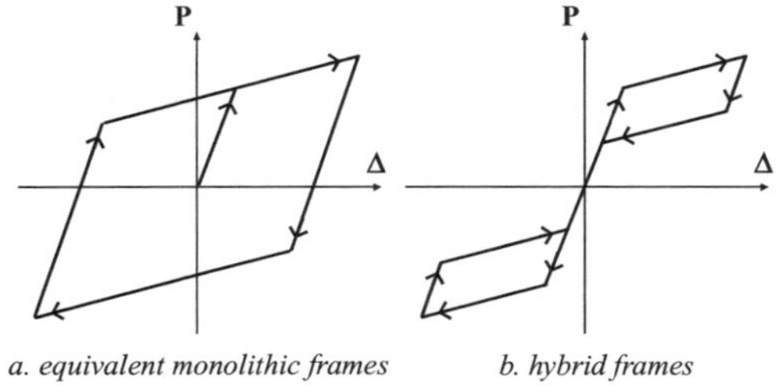

The special mild steel rebars, placed at the top and bottom of the beam, are introduced into ribbed grouted ducts, and partially debonded at the beam-column joint. By plastic incursions, the rebars ensure the post-elastic absorption of the earthquake induced energy.

In order to restore the initial seismic performance of the structure, the special mild steel rebars must be replaced with new ones. However, the replacement is not easy due to their bond to the solid grout, and expensive devices should be designed. Next, the paper focuses on the dismounting feature of these rebars, as a fundamental component of a sustainable structural earthquake resistant design.

1.2 Research significance

Two tests were carried out in order to assess the performance of a hybrid connection designed using two alternatives.

The first was the traditional one, as presented above, while the second introduced fully debonded mild steel rebars. Next, the paper presents comparative experimental results and theoretical analyses, emphasizing the particular problems for each solution.

Research reveals an apparent superior performance for the special mild reinforcement not entirely intentionally debonded, but its superiority in the terms of the mechanical behavior and

a. equivalent monolithic frames   *b. hybrid frames*

Figure 1. Idealized energy dissipation comparative rules for prefab RC frames.

elastic behavior, that is not so large, and might be compensated by the ease of replacement of the second solution.

2 TESTING PROGRAM

2.1 Design approach

Direct Displacement Based Design (Paulay 2000) was applied for a seismic scenario corresponding to a six storey hybrid frame structure placed in a region with the design ground acceleration $a_g = 0.24$ g and the corner period $T_c = 0.1$ s. The method was found more convenient to use than any other traditional seismic force-based design method, because no member rigidity (i.e., beam and column flexural rigidity) is involved in the design process. Moreover, it is a simple procedure, based on a clear and desired failure mechanism, and no sophisticated analysis is needed to determine the structure's real stress state by the time it reaches the imposed displacement. Table 1 presents the deformational, geometrical and gravitational characteristics of the structural model.

The principle of the method consists in finding of the characteristics of an equivalent single degree of freedom structure (SDOF) that has the same secant stiffness and damping properties as the initial multi degree of freedom structure (MDOF) at the design displacement response. After the design drift is established (i.e., the relative storey drift ratio multiplied by the storey height), the yield drift θ_y results from:

$$\theta_y = 0.5 \left(0.5 \; \varepsilon_y \frac{L_b}{h_b} \right) \qquad (1)$$

where ε_y = mild steel yield strain; L_b = beam span; and h_b = beam height. As stated by Priestley (2002), the yield drifts for hybrid frame structures are about $40 \div 50\%$ of those for monolithic ones. This implies a higher ductility ratio with respect to the same design drift. Thus, the system ductility is obtained by dividing the design displacement to the yield displacement:

$$\mu = \frac{\Delta_d}{\Delta_y} \qquad (2)$$

Table 1. Equivalent SDOF structure design characteristics.

Δ_d	H_e	θ_y	Δ_y	μ	m_e
mm	m	–	mm	–	to
263	12.576	0.006	75	3.489	224.3

where μ = system ductility;
Δ_d = design displacement;
and Δ_y = yield displacement. The design and yield displacement refer to the SDOF equivalent structure and are obtained by multiplication of design and yield drifts with the SDOF effective height.

An equivalent viscous damping is needed in order to include the elastic and the hysteretic damping of the system. A reduction factor for the corner displacement corresponding to the known damping can then be used for reducing the elastic displacement spectrum, as shown in Figure 2. After that, the effective period T_e of the equivalent SDOF structure is found directly from the already obtained reduced displacement spectrum. Table 2 shows the damping properties of the structure.

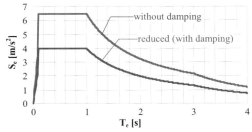

a. elastic acceleration spectrum

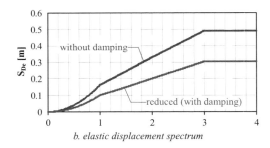

b. elastic displacement spectrum

Figure 2. Design spectrums.

Table 2. Damping characteristics for the equivalent structure.

ξ_{el}[*]	ξ_{hyst}[**]	ξ_{eq}[***]	R_ξ[****]	T_e
–	–	–	–	sec
0.05	0.128	0.149	0.643	2.496

[*]ξ_{el} = elastic damping
[**]ξ_{hyst} = hysteretic damping
[***]ξ_{eq} = equivalent hysteretic damping
[****]R_ξ = corner displacement reduction factor

The secant stiffness of the substitute structure K_e is:

$$K_e = \frac{4\pi^2 m_e}{T_e^2} \qquad (3)$$

where m_e = equivalent mass of the substitute structure; and finally the design base shear force is found with

$$V_{base} = K_e \cdot \Delta_d \qquad (4)$$

The design internal forces in the structural members are found by the distribution of the base shear force to the floor levels and considering the simple equilibrium rules assuming that no bending moments are developed at the members' midspan.

Table 3 presents the main internal forces (see Fig. 3) associated with the secant stiffness of the experimental models.

With the known design bending moment and rotation at the contact interface between the beam and the column, the quantities of special reinforcement and post-tensioned strands are found using the guidlines proposed by ACI T1.2-03 (2003). A contribution of 30% for the special reinforcement (M_s) from the overall design bending moment (M_d), as presented in Figure 3, was considered. According to Priestley et al. (2007), it seems that this is the optimum percentage to minimize the residual drifts and to keep the connection energy-dissipation performance to an acceptable level.

One of the key features of a hybrid connection is the intentionally debonded length of the special mild steel reinforcement, which is located at the beam-to-column interface, as presented in Figure 4 (see also Fig. 6a). One reason for making this adjustment is to delay the fracture of the special reinforcement by minimizing the strains encountered during an earthquake.

During a seismic event, the mild steel rebars will lose adherence in the zones adjacent to the deliberately unbonded length, as a consequence to the inelastic strain penetration developed in the these bonded regions. According to ACI T1.2-03 (2003), this additional unbonded length is taken for design purpose at ultimate conditions only as $5.5d_{bl}$. It should be mentioned that the specified value is considered as the sum of the strain penetration encountered at both sides of the deliberately unbonded length (see Fig. 4).

However, following a series of tests and mathematical analyses, Raynor et al. (2002) stated that a lower value is more reliable than the one proposed by ACI T1.2-03 (2003). They also recommend that the total additional unbonded length should be calculated by

$$l_{uat} = 2 \times \frac{2.1(\sigma_u - \sigma_y)}{(f'_g)^{1.5}} d_{bl} \qquad (5)$$

Table 3. Bending moment design results for the connection.

K_e	V_{base}	M_s	M_p	M_d	M_s/M_d
kN/m	kN	kNm	kNm	kNm	%
1421.2	374.2	48.0	110.8	158.7	30

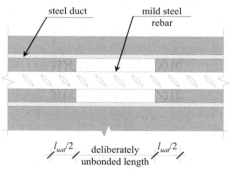

a) strain penetration into the bonded region

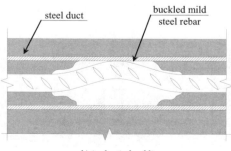

b) inelastic buckling

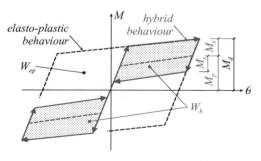

Figure 3.   Idealized moment-rotation response.

Figure 4.   Rebar behavior over the debonded length.

where l_{uat} = the additional unbounded length developed at both sides of the intentionally unbonded length;

σ_u = bar ultimate strength;

σ_y = bar yield strength; f_g = bond grout strength;

and d_{bl} = steel bar diameter.

As recently reported by the authors, nonlinear cyclic analyses revealed that the unbonded length of the special mild reinforcement has a major influence upon the recentering ability of the connection and its energy dissipation capacity. A larger value reduces the residual drifts but provides less performance in terms of the energy dissipation. However, future discussions about larger design values for the design drifts associated with longer debonded lengths should be based on more experimental evidence.

The first tested model followed a conventional hybrid design approach, but with an easier access to the mild reinforcement by placing it beyond the bottom plan of the slab as shown in Figures 6a, b. As observed after the test, the mild steel rebars introduced in grouted corrugated sleeves (Fig. 6b) were practically impossible to be replaced, their withdrawal being very difficult, as emphasized in Figure 5, and any future possibility to introduce new bonded rebars would be unlikely without considerable and very costly efforts.

The second model (see Fig. 6c) was conceived to ensure a much easier replacement of the special mild steel reinforcement that yields during a severe earthquake.

The alternative presumes the lack of bond of the mild steel reinforcement, which is able to have a uniform strain on its full length. A viscous grease injection of the sleeve, as usually used in unbonded post-tensioning, may be adequate to remove the

corrosion vulnerability of the rebars. Post-elastic buckling was prevented by a special device, ensuring discrete and controlled deformable contacts with the rebars.

2.2 *Experimental models*

Figure 6 underlines the dismountability concept for the two experimental models, in relation with a traditional hybrid connection. The full scale experimental models are shown in Figure 7.

The models were built with a C 25/30 concrete strength class, with an effective compressive cylinder strength of 33 MPa. The mild passive steel reinforcement had a yielding tensile strength of 355 MPa and an ultimate strength of 443 MPa, with the corresponding ultimate strain equal to 20%. The post-tensioned unbonded strands, ensuring the self-centering ability, were made of high strength steel of low relaxation class, with a yielding strength of 1636 MPa, a tensile strength of 1860 MPa, and a corresponding ultimate strain of 2%. The control stress in the post-tensioned strands was 790 MPa, about 50% of the yielding strength.

2.3 *Equipment and loading program*

The specimens were gradually loaded with a horizontal enforced displacement at the top of the beam to column subassembly.

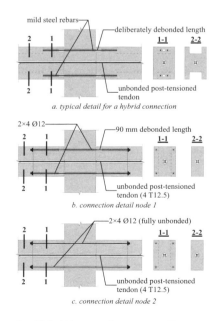

a. typical detail for a hybrid connection

b. connection detail node 1

c. connection detail node 2

Figure 6. Hybrid beam-column connections.

Figure 5. Idealized moment-rotation response.

a. node 1

b. node 2

Figure 7. Experimental models.

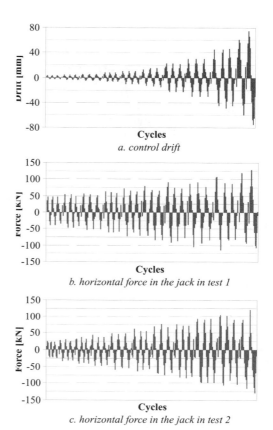

a. control drift

b. horizontal force in the jack in test 1

c. horizontal force in the jack in test 2

Figure 8. Loading programs.

In total, 42 full alternate similar cycles were applied to both tested models. The relative control drift was increased step by step from 0.1% up to 2.5%, which the damage limit control considered.

The alternant drifts were imposed by a hydraulic jack of 3000 kN controlled by a force transducer C6 A/3000 kN. The force transducer was connected to a portable multi-channel electronic PC parallel measurement unit Spider 8. Displacements were measured by inductive transducers HBM-WA/300 mm linked to the same PC unit.

Half-bridge LY 41-6/120A strain gauges were used to measure the strain of the post-tensioned strands and special yielding mild steel rebars, while concrete strains were monitored with dial rigid mechanical devices. Crack and joint openings were measured with portable optical instruments and distance roulettes.

Figure 8 shows the testing program in the terms of the control drift, and the correspondent forces in the jacks, registered for both experimental models considering the same control drift.

3 COMPARATIVE RESULTS

Figure 9 presents a comparative full hysteretic behavior of the two tested models.

In order to emphasize the influence of the dismountability upon the connection behavior, Figure 10 shows the envelope of the maximum drifts registered during the tests.

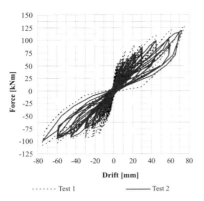

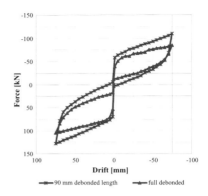

Figure 9. Hysteretic response of the connections.

Figure 11. Theoretical envelope of the loading-unloading cycles.

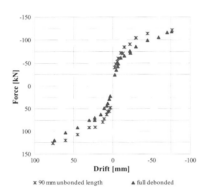

Figure 10. Experimental envelopes for the test maxim displacements.

limit the difference was up to 16%. The numerical analyses (see Fig. 11), showed that the difference in bearing capacity increased approximately linearly up to a 10%. It is clear that the second approach leads to a more flexible connection, but in practical terms the difference is not very significant. A greater deformational potential may be assumed for the second model, as long as local post-elastic buckling is prevented. Thus, the energy dissipation capacity may also be improved.

ACKNOWLEDGEMENTS

This paper was supported by the project "Doctoral studies in engineering sciences for developing the knowledge based society-SIDOC" contract no. POSDRU/88/1.5/S/60078, project co-funded from European Social Fund through Sectorial Operational Program Human Resources 2007–2013.

4 CONCLUSIONS AND COMMENTARIES

In the case of the first specimen, the mild yielded reinforcement was very difficult to be pulled out of its ducts, due to the intense bond caused by the triaxial stress state. A realistic estimation of the additionally unbonded length can minimize the effort of pulling the bars out of their steel ducts and breaking the bond. This also implies the fact that the steel bar is able to maintain its initial straight layout, even at higher drifts. It is known that the reinforcing bars subjected to large cyclic strains are more likely to buckle even for lower values of L/d_{b_L} ration, where L is the unfixed bar length. If this occurs, it is likely for the special reinforcement bar to get stuck in the steel duct.

For the second specimen, the extraction of the rebars was much easier and the conditions for the full replacement were ensured.

However, in terms of the performance up to the damage limit control drift, the first model performed better. Its bearing capacity was greater at the ultimate drift by about 5%, but up to that

REFERENCES

ACI T1.2-03, Special Hybrid Moment Frames Composed of Discretely Jointed Precast and Post-Tensioned Concrete Members.

Paulay, T. 2000. A simple displacement compatibility-based design strategy for reinforced concrete buildings, *Proceedings of the 12 World Conference on Earthquake Engineering* Paper No. 0062.

Priestly, M.J.N. 2002. Direct Displacement-Based Design of Precast/Prestressed Concrete Buildings. *PCI Journal* November-December: 66–80.

Priestley, M.J.N., Calvi, G.M. & Kowalsky, M.J. 2007. *Displacement-Based Seismic Design of Structures.* Pavia: IUSS Press.

Priestley, M.J.N., Sritharan, S., Conley, J.R. & Pampanin, S. 1999. Preliminary results and conclusions from the PRESSS five-storey precast concrete test building, *Journal of the Precast/Prestressed Concrete Institute* 44 (6): 42–67.

Raynor, D.J., Lehman, D.E. & Stanton, J.F. 2002. Bond-Slip Response of Reinforcing Bars Grouted in Ducts. *ACI Structural Journal* 99(5): 568–576.

Concrete Solutions – Grantham, Mechtcherine & Schneck (eds)
© 2012 Taylor & Francis Group, London, ISBN 978-0-415-61622-5

Pumping influence on fresh properties of self-consolidating concrete

N. Ghafoori, H. Diawara, D. Nyknahad, M. Barfield & M.S. Islam
Civil and Environmental Engineering, University of Nevada Las Vegas, Las Vegas, USA

ABSTRACT: Pumped concrete has been widely used for repair and rehabilitation of many concrete structures. The flow ability, passing ability, and self densification of Self-Consolidating concrete are beneficial when repair is needed for tight and heavily-reinforced situations. The research investigation presented herein was intended to study the influence of pumping on the fresh properties of self-consolidating Concretes (SCC). The selected SCCs were made with a constant water-to-cementitious materials ratio of 0.40, a uniform cement content of 390.38 kg/m^3 and a constant coarse-to-fine aggregate ratio of 1.083. Both polycarboxylate-based High Range Water-Reducing Admixture (HRWRA) and Viscosity Modifying Admixture (VMA) were used to produce self-consolidating concretes with a slump flow of 635 ± 25 mm, VSI of 0, and T$_{50}$ of 2 to 5 seconds. A pumping distances of 60 m was used to evaluate the flow ability, passing ability, stability, rheology (yield stress and plastic viscosity), air content and air void characteristics of the selected self-consolidating concretes. Test results revealed that the pumping adversely affected the fresh performance of the self-consolidating concrete by decreasing the unconfined workability, flow rate, and passing ability; and by increasing the dynamic segregation resistance. The impact of pumping on the rheological properties of self-consolidating concrete was manifested by a moderate increase in relative yield stress and a significant decrease in relative plastic viscosity. The air content remained unaffected by the pumping action, whereas the air voids characteristic was altered through size increases of the air bubbles.

1 INTRODUCTION

Pumping concrete through pipeline is considered nowadays as one of the most convenient methods of transporting concrete from the mixer to the place of deposit. The use of pumps and associated pipelines as a means of transporting and placing concrete in civil engineering and building construction started in the early 1930s and has increased considerably recently. The main advantage of pumping resides in its placement of large volumes of concrete in congested sites. The cost of a pumping installation may be cheaper than that of alternative methods of concrete placement. However, the circumstances of each particular case should be considered in choosing the appropriate method of placement (Orchard, 1973).

In order to be pumpable, concrete must satisfy certain conditions regarding its matrix constituents, its fresh properties, and the site condition. These conditions can be summarized as: raw material (aggregate, water content, cement and additives), workability, air content, and temperatures (Neville, 1987).

The gradation of the used aggregate should be smooth. The correct quantity and grading of the fine aggregate is of more importance than the grading of the coarse aggregate. As mentioned by Orchard (1973), it is important that the fine aggregate should have 15 to 20% passing a No. 52 ASTM (0.3 mm) sieve and 3% passing a No.100 ASTM (0.15 mm) sieve.

The water content is very important in pumpable concrete. With lower water content, the solid particles, instead of moving longitudinally in a coherent mass in suspension, would exert pressure on the walls of the pipe. When the water content is optimum, as Neville (1987) stated, friction develops only at the surface of the pipe and in a thin layer of lubricating mortar (1 to 2.5 mm).

The concrete suitable for pumping should not be too dry, too wet, or harsh and gummy. Although slump is not the main factor affecting pumping, a minimum slump of 2.5 inches (63 mm) is required by ACI (1996). As stated by Neville (1987) there may be a slump loss of 25 mm per 1000 ft 300) of pipe line during the pumping depending on the cement type, the atmospheric and material temperature and the length of time the concrete remains in the pipeline.

In a very hot environment it is advisable to cover the pipeline and keep it well wetted. The high heat can lead to a quick setting, thus a precaution should be taken to eliminate delays and ensure that the concrete stays in the pipeline for the shortest time possible. Orchard (1973) proposed that when concreting in low temperatures no special precaution should be taken. It is not necessary to insulate the pipeline as the temperature drop is comparatively small, about 1 0.5 to 1°C drop per 30 m of exposed pipe at −18°C.

The pumping always begins with the lubrication of the pipeline by mortar or cement slurry. The lubrication is followed by the pumping of concrete. Normal working pressures developed by concrete pumps are between 700 and 1750 KPa but much higher pressures can be developed in the event of pipe blockage. The capacity of the pump depends on the workability of the concrete and finally, the pumps and the pipeline should be completely cleaned (Murdock (1991), Neville (1987), and Orchard (1973)).

Many repair and strengthening projects have tight formwork space, thus constraining concrete placement. These projects usually have tighter spacings between the reinforcement and the existing concrete surface, and between reinforcement and formwork. SCC's flowability lends itself well to concrete beams, slabs, and columns for "form and pump" repairs that are commonly found in structural restoration and strengthening projects. The design of formwork can be more challenging for pumped concrete. In the case of pumped self-consolidating concrete, a stronger formwork design is needed as the head pressure created by the truly liquid material is greater than those seen in conventional concrete (Miller 2009).

2 RESEARCH OBJECTIVE

The aim of this study was to evaluate the influence of pumping on the fresh properties of selected self-consolidating concretes. A pumping distance was used to determine the change in the unconfined workability, flow rate, dynamic segregation resistance, passing ability, rheological properties, volumetric air content, and air void characteristics.

3 EXPERIMENTAL PROGRAM

3.1 Raw materials

The fine aggregate met the requirements of ASTM C 33. All matrices were prepared with a constant water-to-cementitious materials ratio of 0.4, a uniform cement factor of 391 kg/m^3, and a constant amount of fly ash representing 20% of the cement weight. The mixing and testing were performed at a ready-mixed plant. The concretes were completely truck-mixed in accordance with a modified ASTM C 94 testing method.

3.2 Testing program

The unconfined workability, the flow rate, the dynamic stability and the passing ability of the selected self-consolidating concretes were measured by the slump flow, T_{50}, and VSI tests; and the J-ring test, in accordance with the ASTM C 1611 and C 1621, respectively.

A compact rheometer for fresh concrete, as shown in Figure 1, was used for the determination of the relative yield stress and the plastic viscosity of the selected matrices.

The ASTM C 173 "Standard Test Method for Air Content of Freshly Mixed Concrete by Volumetric Method" was used to measure the air content of the fresh matrix. A newer form of air void evaluation, referred as an Air Void Analyzer (AVA) was used to determine the voids characteristics of the trial fresh self-consolidated concrete. The test apparatus determines the volume and size distributions of entrained air voids, and calculates the spacing factor and specific surface. The testing procedure was as follows: (1) a plexiglass cylinder (riser column) was filled with a viscous liquid (glycerin-based) at the base and topped off with water, (2) a mortar sample of 20 cm^3 was extracted with a wire cage (to sieve out any aggregate larger than 6 mm, and (3) the mortar sample was injected with a syringe into the bottom of the riser column. From this point, the test was monitored by the computer software. A stirring rod, running in the mortar for 30 seconds, allowed the release of entrained air, which then floated at the top of the column, where there were caught by an inverted Petri dish connected to a balance to measure the change in suspended mass. According to Stokes Law, the rate of rise in the bubbles is a function

Figure 1.   Two-point BT2 concrete rheometer.

of their size, and the larger bubbles rise faster than the small ones.

4 DISCUSSION OF RESULTS

Tables 1 and 2 present the pre- and post-pumping test results of the trial fresh self-consolidated concrete at 60 m pumping distance. The slump flow, T_{50} time, VSI and J-ring tests were performed to determine the influence of pumping on the workability of fresh self-consolidating concretes. In general, the pumping affected the fresh characteristics of SCC by decreasing the unconfined workability, flow rate, and passing ability; and by increasing the dynamic segregation resistance.

Average decreases of 45 and 50 mm in unconfined workability of the trial self-consolidating concretes made with 635 and 711 mm slump flows, respectively, were recorded after pumping. These losses were greater than the adopted 25 mm tolerance, indicating that a remediation of the slump loss due to pumping is necessary.

The influence of pumping on dynamic stability is documented in the Tables 1 and 2. Pumping affected the stability of the selected SCCs by improving the visual stability index (VSI), from 1 (stable matrix) to 0 (highly stable matrix) for the mixtures made with 711 mm slump flow. The 635 mm slump flow SCCs type remained highly stable after pumping.

Table 1. Pre- and post-pumping fresh properties of 635 mm slump flow SCC (L = 60 m).

	Pre-Pumping	Post-Pumping
HRWR (ml/kg)	2.145	2.145
VMA (ml/kg)	0.39	0.39
AEA (ml/kg)	0.203	0.203
Temp. (°C)	11.7	15.5
Slump flow (mm)	641	597
T_{50} (sec.)	2.75	1.01
VSI	0	0
J-ring value (mm)	32	35
Yield stress (N-mm)	168.78	224.35
Plastic viscosity (N-mm sec/m)	1.37	0.60
Volumetric air content (%)	10.50	10.00
Air content (%)	11.15 (8.4)[a]	10.35 (8.2)[a]
Specific surface (mm⁻¹)	32.32	27.95
Spacing factor (mm)	0.1168	0.1448

[a]The number in parenthesis represents the entrained air, while the other number represents the sum of the entrapped and entrained airs.

Table 2. Pre- and post-pumping fresh properties of 711 mm slump flow SCC (L = 60 m).

	Pre-Pumping	Post-Pumping
HRWR (ml/kg)	2.53	2.53
VMA (ml/kg)	0.65	0.65
AEA (ml/kg)	0.1625	0.1625
Temp. (°C)	18.7	17.22
Slump flow (mm)	714.5	666.8
T_{50} (sec.)	2.22	1.03
VSI	1	0
J-ring value (mm)	28.7	31.8
Yield stress (N-mm)	118.12	169.23
Plastic viscosity (N-mm sec/m)	1.47	0.39
Volumetric air content (%)	5.25	5.25
Air content (%)	7.4(5.7)[a]	7.4(5.4)[a]
Specific surface (mm⁻¹)	37.24	27.6
Spacing factor (mm)	0.1346	0.1803

[a]The number in parenthesis represents the entrained air, while the other number represents the sum of the entrapped and entrained airs.

The trial self-consolidating concretes were designed to produce high to moderate passing ability. After pumping, the measured J-ring values of the selected trial matrices remained within the allowable limit of 25 to 50 mm.

The influence of pumping on the rheological performance of the selected matrices was investigated by comparing the pre- and post-pumping relative yield stress and relative plastic viscosity as shown in the Tables 1 and 2. For both slum flow matrices, the yield stress increased and plastic viscosity decreased after pumping.

In order to provide adequate freezing and thawing protection, the selected self-consolidating concretes were designed to generate: (1) air content of $6 \pm 1\%$, (2) specific surface of air voids lower than 25 mm⁻¹, and (3) spacing factor of air voids smaller than 0.200 mm. On the other hand, while the air content of the matrices made with 711 mm slump flow were within the $6 \pm 1\%$ limit, higher air contents than excepted were generated in the 635 mm slump flow matrices due to the discrepancy in the loading of the dried material at the ready mixed-plant. Irrespective of the slump flow, the air content obtained from the two test methods remained unaffected by the pumping action. However, the air voids characteristics were affected by the pumping without exceeding the recommended limits. The pumping generated larger sizes of air bubbles (or lower specific area) accompanied with increases in the spacing factors.

5 CONCLUSIONS

The influence of pumping on fresh properties of the selected self-consolidating concretes was investigated and can be summarized as given below:

- Average decreases of 45 and 50 mm in unconfined workability of the trials self-consolidating concretes made with 635 and 711 mm slump flows, respectively, were recorded after pumping.
- The matrices flow rates, as evaluated by the T_{50} time, were increased from low to high due to the pumping action.
- The impact of pumping on the rheological properties of self-consolidating concrete was manifested by a moderate increase in relative yield stress and a significant decrease in relative plastic viscosity.
- After pumping, the measured J-ring values of the selected trial matrices remained within the allowable limit of 25 to 50 mm.
- Irrespective of the slump flow, the air content obtained from the volumetric air content test method remained unaffected by the pumping action.
- The pumping affected the air void characteristics by increasing the size of the air bubbles (decreasing the specific area) accompanied with increases in the spacing factors.

ACKNOWLEDGMENTS

The authors would like to acknowledge the financial support of the Nevada Department of Transportation Grant number P 077-06-803. Thanks are also extended to a number of admixture manufactures and concrete suppliers who contributed materials used in the investigation. Their named are withheld to avoid any concern of commercialization or private concern.

REFERENCES

American Concrete Institute 1996. Placing Concrete by Pumping Methods, *Reported by ACI Committee ACI* 304.2R, 304.2R-1 to 304.2R-25.
American Society for Testing and Materials 2004. Standard Specification for Concrete Aggregates (ASTM C 33). *Annual Book of ASTM Standards* Vol. 4.02: 10–16.
American Society for Testing and Materials 2004. Standard Specification for Ready-Mixed Concrete (ASTM C 94). *Annual Book of ASTM Standards* Vol. 4.02: 47–56.
American Society for Testing and Materials 2005. Standard Test Method for Slump Flow of Self-Consolidating Concrete (ASTM C 1611). *Annual Book of ASTM Standards* Vol. 4.02: 36–41.
American Society for Testing and Materials 2005. Standard Test Method for Passing Ability of Self-Consolidating Concrete by J-Ring (ASTM C 1621). *Annual Book of ASTM Standards.* Vol. 4.02: 42–45.
Barfield, M.E. 2008. Air Void Characteristics of Air-Entrained Self-Consolidating Concrete. *Thesis for the degree of Master of Science.* University of Nevada Las Vegas USA 199pp.
Diawara, H. 2008. Parametric study of self-consolidating concrete. *Doctoral dissertation under the supervision of N. Ghafoori.* University of Nevada Las Vegas, USA 370p.
Dodson, Vance H. 1990. *Concrete Admixtures.* New York: Van Nostrand Reinhold.
Miller, M. and Frye, M. 2009. SCC Proves Successful in Repair and Strengthening Projects, *Concrete Construction website.*
Murdock, L.J., Brook, K.M., and Dewar, J.D. 1991. *Concrete Material and Practice (Sixth Ed.)* London: Edward Arnold Publishers 470pp.
Neville, A.M., and Brooks, J.J. 1978. *Concrete Technology.* Longman Scientific and Technical Publisher.
Orchard, D., F. 1973. *Concrete Technology (Third Ed.)* Vol.2, New York—Toronto: John Wiley & Sons.

Concrete Solutions – Grantham, Mechtcherine & Schneck (eds)
© *2012 Taylor & Francis Group, London, ISBN 978-0-415-61622-5*

A comparative study of anti-corrosion products for the protection of reinforcement in monuments

A. Gralińska-Grubecka & J.W. Łukaszewicz

Department of the Conservation of Architectonic Elements and Details, Nicolaus Copernicus University,
Institute for the Study, Restoration and Conservation of Cultural Heritage, Toruń, Poland

ABSTRACT: The conservation of cultural heritage, especially concrete monuments is a demanding and unsolved task. This work focuses on the problem associated with corrosion of steel in concrete historical structures. The main aim was to search for the appropriate restoration materials in a group of commercial composites for their future use in the conservation of works of art. Laboratory tests compared the effectiveness of the corrosion protection of proprietary products for repairing reinforced concrete. The products were examined in three stages of corrosion with tests in climatic chambers (condensation test, sulphur dioxide test and salt mist spray test). Laboratory examination included adhesion tests, evaluation of water absorption, assessment of workability and ease of application. Two preparations were selected from the group, which ensured very high corrosion protection of reinforcement. These products can be especially recommended for the repairs of historical monuments made of reinforced concrete and artificial stone.

1 INTRODUCTION

The problem of repairing historic reinforced concrete monuments is currently very common and urgent. Many concrete monuments which were erected in the 1930s–1960s are now threatened by deterioration (Figs. 1, 2). Most of them are in drastically poor condition and demand proper conservation (Domasłowski et al. 2000; Gralińska 2008).

They have to be saved through sensitive repair and effective protection. The essential value of conservation is to preserve monuments in their

Figure 2. Portrait of Daniel Janasz in Szreniawa Museum—an example of corroded reinforcement.

authenticity, to save the original material. Conservation has its own set of principles, established in The Venice Charter and requires the use of high quality products.

A large number of proprietary products are available for the repair of reinforced concrete structures, including the protection of reinforcement.

Figure 1. Portrait of Daniel Janasz in Szreniawa Museum—a section with visible corrosion.

They all are recommended to be very effective, but in fact they were not previously examined for use in the preservation of monuments. The choice of the appropriate product for bar protection in industrial concrete without historical value is not as significant as with listed monuments. In the first case, on the anti-corrosive coating, which covers the reinforcement, later a second coat of new very high quality concrete is applied. This new concrete lagging provides excellent protection for reinforcement. Unfortunately historic concrete has often a very low strength, high water absorption, high open porosity and very thin lagging (Gralińska 2008, Gralińska et al. 2010). In accordance with the principles of conservation, during the repair of monuments cavities should be filled with suitable material with compatible parameters. It is not permitted to use commercial concrete with a high strength, designed for construction engineering repair. This prime difference from the usual repair of reinforced concrete means that special attention should be paid to the selection of a proper material for reinforcement protection. Results of this examination will help, especially restorers of works of art in choosing the most appropriate product, which can be used within the historical monumental conservation trade.

2 EXPERIMENTAL

2.1 Tested materials

The most suitable product, which will ensure the optimum corrosion protection for steel bars in concrete monuments was selected from eleven commercial products for reinforcement protection. The chosen products are produced by noted companies, specialising in the production of repair materials for the building industry and for monument conservation. All products are widely used in the construction industry. The precise composition of materials is patented. The products can include additional ingredients such as: corrosion inhibitors, colloidal silica, amorphous silica, silica sand, silica flour and calcium carbonate. The products were divided into four groups, taking into consideration the number of components, function and chemical nature. The main products tested are given below, with a description.

2.1.1 Ia group of products
One-component cement Portland mortar modified with redispersible polymer powders and additional ingredients, which are both anti-corrosive bar coating and bonding agents before application of repair mortars:
    Product no. 1—Kerabuild Ferri
    Product no. 2—Zentrifix KMH
    Product no. 3—Asocret-KS/HB

Product no. 4—Monotop-610
Product no. 5—Viscacid PCC Grund

2.1.2 Ib group of products
One-component cement mortar modified with redispersible polymer powders and additional ingredients, which are only corrosion protection for bars:
    Product no. 7—Maxrite Passive
    Product no. 8—Cerinol MK

2.1.3 II group of products
Two-component cement mortar (first component—cement Portland mortar with additional ingredients, second component—polymer dispersion in water), which are both corrosion protection for bars and bonding slurry for the repair of concrete:
    Product no. 6—Mapefer

2.1.4 III group of products
Two or three component products based on an epoxy resin which both give corrosion protection for bars and a bonding coat for concrete lagging:
    Product no. 9—Funcosil Epoxi-Rostschutz (first component—epoxy resin solution in solvents with anti-corrosive pigments and fillings, second component—hardener solution in solvents). The manufacturer recommends to sprinkle the second layer of this product with dry quartz sand in order to improve adhesion to concrete.
    Product no. 10—SikaTop-Armatec 110 EpoCem (first component—epoxy resin dispersion in water, second component—epoxy resin hardener dispersion in water, third component—cement mortar and additional ingredients)

2.1.5 IV group of products
One-component polymer dispersion in water with inhibitors, which is only for corrosion protection for the bars:
    Product no. 11—Maxrest Passive.

2.2 Samples preparation

Anti-corrosion products were applied in accordance with the manufacturer's recommendations of mixing proportions of the individual component and the required time interval between the first and second layer application. The products were applied on two groups of rods, made of construction steel S 235 JRG Ø 8 mm, cut into sections of 15 cm with a hole at one end for hanging up in the aging chambers and for the attachment of a number. The first group consisted of rods covered with a thin, even layer of rust. The second group consisted of thoroughly cleaned rods—according to manufacturer's demands to an St 3 degree, which means that the surface was close to the metallic lustre, with no signs of rust, coatings and other contamination (EN ISO 112944-4:2001). In total, each product was applied on 13 bars. The usage of the corroded rods was dictated by practical experience. The conservation of works of art strives to retain the maximum amount of original material and therefore a precise cleaning of the rods in all areas can sometimes be difficult.

2.3 Evaluation of workability, colour and ease of application

Workability and ease of application on steel rods were evaluated during mixing of the ingredients. All products showed very good workability. Ease of application was dependent on the viscosity and running quality of the product and was varied from very good to difficult. Table 1 contains the assessment of the ease of application on a scale from 1—the best to 4—the least convenient application, as well information about the products' colour. Materials had different colours, some of them very intensive, for example with no's. 1, 6, 8 and 9. Very intensive colour may be sometimes a disadvantage, particularly during conservation of a concrete sculpture with a very thin lagging.

2.4 Corrosion test—methods of examination and results

The samples were subjected to corrosion tests in accordance with EN 15183:2006—Products and systems for the protection and repair of concrete structure. The test consisted of three stages of examination in climatic chambers:

- First stage—ten cycles of condensation;
- Second stage—ten cycles (24 h each) of sulphur dioxide activity with general moisture condensation in accordance with EN ISO 6988:2000;
- Third stage—five days of storage in a neutral salt mist in accordance with EN 60068-2-11:2002.

Table 1   Assessment of the ease of application.

Product number	Ease of application	Colour
1	1—very good	Intensive green
2	1—very good	Grey
3	3—worse	Grey
4	2—good	Grey
5	4—difficult	Grey
6	1—very good	Blue
7	4—difficult	Grey
8	1—very good	Rusty brown
9	1—very good	Claret
10	1—very good	Grey
11	1—very good	Black

Samples were hung up in a climatic chamber (VC 4033 Vötsch Industrietechnik) in a vertical position with control rods in order to validate the test conditions. One cycle of condensation consisted of 8 hours at a temperature of 40°C and 16 hours at a temperature of 21°C in a vented chamber (relative humidity < 75%). At the end of the first stage the coated surfaces were subjected to observation with a naked eye and under an optical microscope. All preparations passed the first stage of examination with positive results, except two samples—cleaned to St 3 rods, which were covered with product no. 1. The surface of these two samples showed a few spots of corrosion.

During the second stage, samples were inspected and photographed after two consecutive days. After two days the first clear symptom of corrosion was observed on samples covered with product no. 11, especially on the cleaned bars. Spots of corrosion on the samples covered with product no. 1 became more extensive. Between four and six days, existing corrosion had increased. After eight days all cleaned bars with product no. 3 had small stains of rust. After ten days the previously observed corrosion changes had deepened and samples covered with products no.: 8, 10, 2, 6, 5 began to corrode.

The sequence of the numbers corresponds to the intensity of corrosion (from the most to the least corroded). There were no corrosion changes on products no.: 4, 7 and 9.

During the third stage samples were inspected after the third and fifth day. Observations of the coating's surface enabled the tested products to be put in order—with regard to their anti-corrosion properties. The size of the corroded surfaces and the numbers were noted.

Preparations nos. 4 and 9 provided the best protection against corrosion. None of the samples covered with these products observed changes. Preparation no. 7 was also very effective, but only in the case of cleaned rods.

After the observation of the coating's surface, materials were removed mechanically from the group of cleaned rods (to the St 3), in order to assess the scope of under film corrosion. Ranking of all products according to their effectiveness of corrosion protection after three stages of corrosion tests is given in Table 2.

Additionally a separate group of samples were tested directly in the salt fog chamber, and also in the condensation chamber and later again in the salt fog chamber. The results of this test differed slightly from the results obtained after three stages of examination, however, it confirmed the excellent properties of corrosion protection of products no. 4 and 9 and the total lack of corrosion protection by preparation no. 11.

Table 2. The order of products according to their effectiveness of corrosion protection (from the best—1, to the worst protection—7).

	Evaluation of corrosion changes on coatings surface (product number)	Evaluation of corrosion changes on rods surface— under film corrosion (product number)
1	4, 9, 7 (in the case of cleaned rods)	4, 9
2	5	2, 6, 7
3	3, 6	3, 5
4	2, 10, 7 (in the case of corroded rods)	10
5	8	8
6	1	1
7	11	11

2.5 Adhesion test—method of examination and results

The adequate adhesion of a product to the reinforcing steel is a guarantee of durability of the repair. Examinations were performed according to EN ISO 4624:2003 (Paints and varnishes—Pull-off test for adhesion) in order to compare the coating's adhesion of the tested products to smooth steel plates. The products were applied in the form of two-layered coatings on steel rigid plates. The measuring steel punches with a diameter of 20 mm were glued to coatings with the help of two-component solvent free epoxy resins. We then measured the minimum tensile stress necessary to detach or to rupture the coating. Data presented in Table 3 are not the absolute values, but only comparative test results.

The highest adhesion to steel had coatings made from product no. 11, i.e. 2.30 MPa, similarly high adhesions were found with products no. 3 and 6, about 1.50 MPa. Other products were characterised by lower adhesion to steel in the range from the highest 1.32 MPa for product no. 8 to the lowest 0.94 MPa for products no. 2 and 10.

2.6 Water absorption and changes in coatings appearance—method of examination and results

Water and water vapour penetrating into the coating, in contact with the surface of metal can initiate corrosion. The *excessive sorption* of water vapour and water by protective coatings may be their disadvantage.

Water vapour sorption was examined by measuring the weight gain (after one, two and five days in conditions of high humidity—92%) of the glass plates covered with the products. Water absorption was analysed by dipping the glass plates covered

Table 3. Comparative adhesion test results.

Product number	Tensile stress	
	MPa	Kind of detachment: a/b— adhesive detachment between the ground and the first layer of coating, b/c—adhesive detachment between the first and second layer of coating
1	1.14	10% a/b; 90%—cohesive detachment in coating
2	0.94	85% a/b; 15%—cohesive detachment in coating
3	1.52	90% a/b; 10%—cohesive detachment in coating
4	0.94	100% a/b
5	1.06	75% a/b; 25%—cohesive detachment in coating
6	1.41	30% a/b; 70% b/c
7	0.98	90% a/b; 10% b/c
8	1.32	95% a/b; 5% b/c
9	1.25	100% a/b
10	1.00	70% b/c; 30% b—cohesive detachment in the first layerof coating
11	2.30	100% a/b

Table 4. Comparison of water vapour sorption for products coatings after 1, 2 and 5 days.

Product number	Water vapour sorption %		
	After 1 day	After 2 days	After 5 days
1	1.66	2.57	3.76
2	0.56	0.79	1.31
3	0.73	1.27	2.29
4	1.10	1.70	2.74
5	0.25	0.50	0.90
6	1.20	1.87	2.59
7	0.51	0.93	1.81
8	0.69	1.05	1.70
9	0.52	0.96	1.16
10	1.39	2.42	4.02
11	5.80	7.25	24.64

with two layers of tested products in distilled water for one, two, four and seven days. Changes in mass and the coating's appearance were studied.

Table 4 and Figure 3 illustrate water vapour sorption. Coatings made from products with no's 5 and 9 were marked by the lowest water vapour sorption, in contrary to products with no's 1, 10 and 11, which had the highest sorption, especially product no. 11. Table 5 and Figure 4 show water absorption for tested coatings. Coating from epoxy resin (product

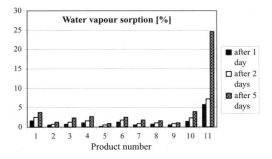

Figure 3. Comparison of water vapour sorption for products coatings.

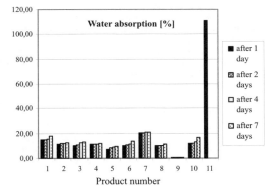

Figure 4. Comparison of water absorption values for products coatings.

Table 5. Comparison of water absorption values for products coatings after 1, 2, 4 and 7 days.

Product number	Water absorption %			
	After 1 day	After 2 days	After 4 days	After 7 days
1	15.2	15.2	15.7	18.1
2	11.4	11.8	12.2	12.4
3	10.2	10.9	12.4	13.3
4	11.3	11.3	11.7	12.0
5	7.3	8.2	9.3	9.6
6	10.5	10.7	11.6	13.7
7	20.4	20.6	20.8	20.9
8	10.1	10.2	10.4	11.3
9	0.6	0.6	0.8	0.9
10	11.8	11.8	13.0	16.8
11	110.8	–	–	–

no. 9), as suspected at the beginning, absorbed an *insignificant amount of water*. The weight gain of this coating after 24 h in comparison to its initial mass (dry coating) was only 0.56%. Low water absorp-

tions were observed for coatings from preparations no. 5, i.e. 7.32%, higher with the no's. 3, 6, 8—about 10%, even higher with no's. 2, 4 and 10—about 11%. High water absorption characterised coatings made from product no. 1, i.e. 15.17% and even higher no. 7, i.e. 20.38%. There weren't any changes in coating appearance made from product no. 9. The colour of the rest of the coatings except product no. 11 slightly darkened. Coatings made from product no. 11 were thoroughly non-resistant to water—the coating came unstuck from the undercoat, swelled and widened, in some places the colour changed from transparent-brown to milky-white. The water absorption of this coating was even 110.78%.

3 RESULTS

Laboratory tests showed that among a group of eleven anti-corrosion commercial products for protection of the reinforcement, the best results of tests in climatic chambers were found to be three products, no's. 4, 7 and 9.

Preparations no. 4 and 9 provided the best protection against corrosion. After corrosion tests none of the samples coated with these products—even on uncleaned rods, covered with a layer of rust, no corrosive effects were observed. Preparation no. 7 was also very effective, but only in the case of cleaned rods, according to manufacturer recommendations.

Product no. 4—Monotop-610 is one-component cement Portland mortar modified with redispersible polymer powders with the addition of amorphous silica and corrosion inhibitor—sodium nitrite, whereas the preparation no. 9—Funcosil Epoxi-Rostschutz is a two-component material, based on epoxy resin with the addition of anti-corrosion pigment—trizinc bis (orthophosphate).

The coating made of Funcosil Epoxi-Rostschutz has no pores, does not absorb any water and has a high adhesion to steel. In addition, this preparation characterises an easy workability and allows for uniform application on rods. Similarly Monotop-610 allows easy and uniform application on the bars, but it has a lower adhesion to steel.

Another advantage worth mentioning is that both products constitute anti-corrosion protection for steel bars and also a bonding layer under repair concrete. In the case of Funcosil Epoxi-Rostschutz the manufacturer recommends to sprinkle the second layer of product with dry quartz sand in order to improve adhesion to concrete.

Because of the high demands of art restorers in relation to the effectiveness of performance of used repair materials, this research showed two very effective preparations for the corrosion protection of reinforcement, which can be used with confidence in the repair of monuments.

ACKNOWLEDGEMENTS

Authors would like to thank Mrs Alina Tomasze-wska-Szewczyk and Mr Krzysztof Lisek for their help during examination.

This study was funded by the Nicolaus Copernicus University in Torun at the grant from UMK 313-Z. The examination in climatic chambers was performed at the Institute of Construction Technology in Warsaw, Department of Durability and Protection of Buildings, with the cooperation of Mrs Joanna Kokowska and Mr Włodzimierz Gromek.

REFERENCES

Domasłowski, W., Kęsy-Lewandowska, M., Krause, J., Łukaszewicz, J.W. 2000. *Study on the conservation of masonry objects (concrete, brick) in the Auschwitz-Birkenau Concentration Camp,* Torun: *Nicolaus Copernicus University.*

Gralińska A. 2008, Assessment of the condition of the reinforced concrete monuments: Nicolaus Copernicus Monument in Torun (1974) and Brotherhood in Arms in Szczecin (1967), *Corrosion Protection* 5s/A/(2008): 71–78.

Gralińska, A. 2008, Causes of destructions of Nicolaus Copernicus monument and Wielkopolska's Insurgents monument made of artificial stone. In J.W. Łukaszewicz (ed.) *11th International Congress on Deterioration and Conservation of Stone, Proc. Torun 15–20 September 2008*, Vol. I, 113–120.

Gralińska A., Łukaszewicz J.W., Topolska W. 2010, Historical Busts Made of Cement Morta—Methods of Examination and Causes of Corrosion. In J. Valek (ed.), *2nd Historic Mortars Conference & RILEM TC 203-RHM Repair mortars for historic masonry; Proc. Prague, 22–24 September 2010.*

EN ISO 12944-4:2001—Paints and varnishes. Corrosion protection of steel structures by protective paint systems. Types of surface and surface preparation, ISO 8501-1:2007—Preparation of steel substrates before application of paints and related products—Visual assessment of surface.

EN 15183:2006—Products and systems for the protection and repair of concrete structure-Test methods-Corrosion protection test.

EN ISO 6988:2000—Metallic and other non organic coatings—sulphur dioxide test with general condensation of moisture (0.2 l SO₂).

EN 60068-2-11:2002—Environmental testing—Part 2: Tests. Test Ka: Salt mist.

EN ISO 4624:2003—Paints and varnishes. Pull-off test for adhesion.

Concrete Solutions – Grantham, Mechtcherine & Schneck (eds)
© 2012 Taylor & Francis Group, London, ISBN 978-0-415-61622-5

Comparison of concrete expansion and stiffness due to alkali-silica reactivity

M.S. Islam & N. Ghafoori
University of Nevada Las Vegas, Las Vegas, USA

ABSTRACT: The main objective of this study was to compare expansion and loss of concrete stiffness due to the adverse effect of Alkali-Silica Reactivity (ASR). Concrete cylinders made with four different aggregates were cured in water at 20°C, and in 1N NaOH at 80°C. The Loss In Stiffness (LIS) between water- and alkali-cured cylinders was determined at 28 and 180 days, and was correlated with the expansion of the mortar bars containing the companion aggregate source at the ages of 14, 28 and 56 days. The study revealed that the 28-day LIS of concrete cylinders showed no distinct correlation with the expansion of the mortar bars at the above mentioned ages. However, the 6-month LIS of the concrete cylinder showed a good correlation with the 14-, 28- and 56-day ASR-induced expansion. ASR classifications of the trial aggregates showed a perfect agreement based on the failure criteria of the mortar bars and alkali-cured prisms and those obtained from the loss in stiffness of the concrete cylinder.

1 INTRODUCTION

Alkali-Silica Reaction (ASR) is a common cause of concrete cracking which can result in significant damage to concrete structures. The deterioration caused by ASR is fairly slow, but progressive. Generally, when the concrete reaches the age of 5 to 10 years, cracking due to the ASR becomes visible. ASR distress can also be seen in structures that are more than 100 years old and some structures that are only a few years old.

Alkali-Silica Reactivity (ASR) is a chemical reaction between the reactive forms of silica in aggregates and potassium and sodium alkalis, which mostly come from Portland cement. The reaction forms an alkali-silica gel, which swells by extracting water from the surrounding cement paste, thereby inducing pressure, expansion and cracking of the aggregate and surrounding paste. The potential reactivity of aggregates depends on many factors, such as aggregate mineralogy, degree of crystallinity, and solubility of the silica in high-pH concrete pore solution (Folliard et al. 2005).

There are various standard methods to evaluate the alkali-silica reactivity of an aggregate. Due to deficiencies in older ASR evaluation tests of ASTM C 227 and ASTM C 289, the use of ASTM C 1260 (Mortar-Bar Method) and ASTM C 1293 (Concrete Prism Test) become more popular because the tests can evaluate not only the levels of ASR but also the extent of reactivity. In most cases, the accelerated mortar bar test (ASTM C 1260) is a reasonable indicator of alkali-silica reactivity.

A variety of criteria have been suggested to describe potentially harmful reactions, with a maximum permissible expansion of 0.1% after 14 days testing being the most usual quoted. It is also recommended to use the extended expansion limits of 0.28% at 28 days and 0.47% at 56 days, proposed by Islam (2010).

ASTM C 1293 requires a long time to evaluate ASR of an aggregate. Therefore, modifications of the ASTM C 1293 test are being used to show the same results in a shorter span of time. Modifications of ASTM C 1293 can be made by (i) changing the solution type and/or solution strength, (ii) altering curing environment, and (iii) changing the duration of the test. Prisms cured in the 1N NaOH at 80°C showed the most rapid testing procedure due to the initial concrete alkali content (Touma et al. 2001). However, the modification is unreliable for determining the potential alkali-reactivity of aggregates at the immersion ages of 14 days (Islam 2010, Bérubé & Frenette 1994).

The structural behavior of concrete is affected by alkali-silica reactivity. The durability, serviceability and the safety of the installation in the long run can be impaired by ASR (Bach et al. 1993). ASR-induced expansion and cracks lead to loss of concrete mechanical properties, such as strength and stiffness, which tends to deform the structures and disturb the internal force (Leger et al. 1996). Losses in elastic modulus are observed between 20% and 50% for the expansion of 0.10 to 0.30% (Rotter 1996).

A number of former investigations concluded that the ultimate compressive strength does not affect ASR at the immersion age of 28 days (Nixon & Bollinghaus 1985, Swamy & Al-Asali 1989, Monette et al. 2000). At the early stages of immersion, however, the strain increases due to the micro-cracking which develops as soon as alkali-silica reactions take place. Owing to that, concrete cylinders made with reactive aggregates experience a loss in stiffness in as little as 28 days of immersion.

The stiffness of water-cured cylinders at low temperatures increases with the immersion age. At the extended immersion age, the stiffness of concrete cylinders decreases with increasing the storage temperature. The relationship of the normalized elastic modulus (Ecr/Ec) in compression with the temperature (T) ranging from 20 to 120°C can be expressed in Equation 1 (Chang et al. 2006).

$$E_{cr}/E_c = -0.00165*T + 1.033 \qquad (1)$$
For 20°C < T < 120°C

The effect of compressive strength of a particular concrete on ASR, therefore, is a function of time (Ahmed et al. 2003, Swamy 1992, Jones & Clark 1997, Clay 1989). Excluding the level of reactivity and the onwards time, the losses in compressive strength depends on some other parameters, such as mix design, type of aggregate, and storage conditions etc.

Alkali-silica reaction in concrete reduces the young's modulus of concrete significantly (IStructE 1992, Jones & Clark 1997, Monette et al. 2000, Tarek et al. 2003, Giaccio et al. 2008). The reduction is mainly due to micro-cracking, rather than the expansion as the losses in engineering properties do not occur at the same rate or in proportion to the expansion (Swamy & Al-Asali 1989). Rivard and Ballivy (2005) emphasized that surface cracking did not seem to have a significant effect on the modulus of elasticity. Recently, Giaccio et al. (2008) revealed that the period of stable crack propagation was less affected than the period of unstable crack growth which was widely extended, showing that the capability of controlling crack propagation decreased leading to premature failure. However, it could significantly reduce the bond and bearing strength of reinforced concrete that leads to increasing the deflections in the overall structure (Kapitan 2006).

A general agreement among the previous research studies has demonstrated that a substantial loss in concrete stiffness is experienced due to the alkali-silica reactivity. However, the studies often contradicted each other regarding the immersion age at which the loss in stiffness due to alkali-silica reactivity occurs.

2 RESEARCH SIGNIFICANCE

This study evaluates the Loss In Concrete stiffness (LIS) due to alkali-silica reactivity at the immersion ages of 28 and 180 days. The study presents statistical analyses to establish the failure criteria of LIS due to alkali-silica reactivity. Additionally, the levels of ASR of the trial aggregates are evaluated based on the proposed loss in stiffness of concrete cylinders, and the expansion limits of mortar bars at 14, 28 and 56 days, and those of alkali-cured prisms at the ages of 4, 8 and 13 weeks.

3 EXPERIMENTAL PROGRAM

The aggregates utilized in this study were acquired from various locations in the state of Nevada. The identification and the mineralogy of the aggregates are shown in Table 1. Based on the chemical compositions, the aggregates were classified as dolomite-limestone (NV-1), dolomite (NV-2), dacite (NV-3) and andesite (NV-4). ASTM Type V Portland cement with alkali content of 0.42% Na_2O_{eq} meeting the requirements of ASTM C 1260 was used in preparing the mortar bars and concrete cylinders. Table 2 illustrates the chemical compositions of Portland cement.

3.1 Mortar bars

Four mortar bars were prepared with each trial aggregate, and using the requirements of ASTM C 1260, which included certain crushed aggregate gradation, a water-to-cement ratio (by weight) of 0.47, and the graded aggregates to cement ratio (by weight) of 2.15.

The mixing procedures were performed according to ASTM C 305. After 24 hours of

Table 1. Mineralogy of the investigated aggregates.

Agg. ID	SiO_2	Al_2O_3	Fe_2O_3	CaO	MgO	Na_2O	LOI
NV-1	13.5	0.4	0.29	32.6	13.09	0.12	39.4
NV-2	1.83	0.38	0.28	30.6	20.18	0.14	45.4
NV-3	63.09	11.5	3.48	6.9	1.97	4.50	6.43
NV-4	59.33	17.15	5.83	5.3	2.54	5.52	1.83

$^*Na_2O_{eq} = Na_2O + 0.658 * K_2O$.

Table 2. Chemical compositions of Portland cement.

SiO_2	Al_2O_3	Fe_2O_3	CaO	MgO	Na_2O^*	SO_3	LOI
21	3.6	3.4	63.1	4.7	0.42	2.6	1.3

$^*Na_2O_{eq} = Na_2O + 0.658 * K_2O$.

moist curing, the specimens were demolded, and initial readings were taken before immersing in tap water at 80°C for 24 hours for which the zero readings were recorded immediately. Afterward, the test mortar bars were placed in an air-tight container of 1N sodium hydroxide solution at the temperature of 80°C. The expansion readings of the mortar bars were taken at the immersion ages of 3, 6, 10 and 14 days, and weekly thereafter up to 98 days.

3.2 *Concrete prisms*

Concrete prisms from each trial aggregate were prepared with a specific aggregate gradation, water-to-cement ratio of 0.45, and cement content of 420 kg/m^3 (708 lbs/yd^3), according to the requirements of ASTM C 1293. The absorption and moisture content of the graded aggregates were also included in the determination of the design water of each mixture. For each aggregate source, three concrete prisms were cast from a constant volume of 0.35 ft^3 (0.01 m^3) concrete. After 24 hours of moist curing, the specimens were placed in water at 80°C for 24 hours after which zero readings were taken immediately. The prisms were then fully submerged in a 1N NaOH solution in an air-tight plastic container held in an oven maintaining the temperature of 80°C. The expansion readings were taken at once per week until the immersion age had reached to 13 weeks.

3.2 *Concrete cylinders*

Twelve 102 mm by 204 mm (4 in. by 8 in.) cylinders containing each selected aggregate were cast from 0.031 m^3 (1.1 ft^3) of concrete. The constituents of each cylinder were: (i) water-to-cement ratio of 0.45, (ii) cement content of 420 kg/m^3 (708 lbs/yd^3), (iii) coarse aggregate to unit volume of concrete

of 0.6. After demolding, six cylinders were stored at a temperature of 20°C with a Relative Humidity (RH) of 100%, and the remainders were immersed in the 1N NaOH solution at an elevated temperature of 80°C. Three water-cured and three alkali-cured cylindrical specimens were subjected to uni-axial compression tests as per requirements of the ASTM C 39 and ASTM C 469 at the immersion ages of 28 and 180 days.

4 RESULTS AND DISCUSSIONS

4.1 *Alkali-silica reactivity based on ASTM C 1260*

The expansion of the mortar bars containing each trial aggregate as related to the immersion age is illustrated in Figure 1. As can be seen, the ASR expansion increases with an increase in the test duration. However, the progression in expansion varies depending on aggregate type.

The levels of alkali-silica reactivity of the trial aggregates were evaluated based on the 14-day expansion criteria of 0.10%, proposed by

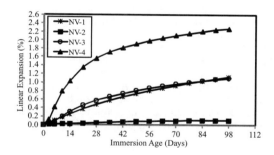

Figure 1. The expansion of the trial aggregates.

Table 3. Percent Loss In Stiffness (PLIS).

| Agg. ID | Water-cured cylinders at 20°C | | | Alkali-cured cylinders at 80°C | | | | |
	4-week stiffness (GPa)	26-week stiffness (GPa)	PLIS of water-cured cylinders between 4 and 26 weeks	4-week stiffness (GPa)	26-week stiffness (GPa)	PLIS of alkali-cured cylinders between 4 and 26 weeks	PLIS of alkali-cured cylinders at 4 weeks	PLIS of alkali-cured cylinders at 26 weeks
NV-1^R	27.4	29.2	−6.53	25.5	20.6	19.19	7.04	29.48
NV-2^I	44.4	48.5	−9.32	40.9	44.2	−8.09	−7.92	−8.95
NV-3^R	36.9	40.1	−8.60	29.9	25.4	14.78	19.07	36.49
NV-4^R	26.5	30.6	−15.63	13.4	13.2	1.54	49.22	56.76

Negative (−) sign indicates a gain in strength.
R = reactive based on the failure limits of mortar bars and alkali-cured prisms.
I = innocuous based on the failure limits of mortar bars and alkali-cured prisms.

ASTM C 1260. Additionally, the expansion limits of 0.28% at 28 days and 0.47% at 56 days, proposed by Islam (2010), were also utilized to classify the reactivity of the investigated aggregates. In this study, aggregates producing ASR expansions of less than 0.10% at 14 days, 0.28% at 28 days and 0.47% at 56 days were considered as innocuous, and those exceeding the criteria were classified as reactive or potentially reactive aggregates. The 14-, 28- and 56-day expansion limits resulted in the three aggregates (NV-1, NV-3 and NV-4) as reactive, and the remaining one (NV-2 aggregate) as innocuous.

4.2 Alkali-silica reactivity of modified ASTM C 1293

The ASR-induced expansions of alkali-cured prisms increased with an increase in test duration, and the progression in expansion varied primarily depending on the mineralogy of the investigated aggregate groups. For instance, the prisms made with the NV-2 aggregate group expanded very slowly, and those prepared with the NV-1, NV-3 and NV-4 aggregate groups expanded progressively with an increase in the immersion age. The study showed that the high alkali solution (1N NaOH) elevated alkali content of the prisms, which ultimately resulted in high expansions for the reactive aggregates during the 3-month testing period.

The 4-week failure criterion of alkali-cured prisms of 0.040%, suggested by Fournier, Bilodeau, and Malhotra (1994), resulted in the NV-1 aggregate group being classified as innocuous, and the remaining three aggregates, reactive. The 8- and 13-week extended failure limits of 0.105 and 0.165%, respectively, suggested by Islam (2010), produced identical results to those generated at the early immersion age of 4 weeks.

4.3 The loss in stiffness of concrete cylinders

Table 4 illustrates the 28-day and 6-month loss in stiffness of alkali-cured cylinders and the loss in stiffness of alkali-cured cylinders between the ages of 28 and 180 days. In addition, the ASR classifications of the trial aggregates based on the extended expansion limits of ASTM C 1260 and modified ASTM C 1293 are documented in Table 4. Based on the findings of Table 4, the following observations are made:

a. Overall, the stiffness of water-cured cylinders at 20°C increased with an increase in immersion age due to the increased hydration and lack of favourable environment for ASR reactions.
b. At the early immersion age (28 days), increasing the curing temperature from 20°C to 80°C resulted in a loss in stiffness due to the combined effects of increased hydration and alkali-silica reactivity. Since the loss in stiffness due to the temperature effect was nearly identical for all aggregates, the loss in stiffness between the alkali-and water-cured cylinders mainly depended on the aggregate reactivity. As such, the cylinders made with reactive aggregates experienced more loss in stiffness than those prepared with innocuous aggregates.
c. Extending the immersion age from 28 to 180 days, the loss in stiffness in the alkali-cured specimens increased due to the dual effects of extensive ASR-induced expansion and elevated temperature. Since the loss in stiffness due to increased temperature remained the same for all aggregates, the net loss in stiffness varied

Table 4. The loss in stiffness (LIS) of concrete cylinders as related to the expansion of mortar bars at various immersion ages.

Agg. ID	Immersion Age (Days)	Expansion (%)	Analytical LIS (%)	Experimental LIS (%)
NV-1	14	0.247	30.7	
	28	0.475	31.2	29.5
	56	0.799	32.1	
NV-2	14	0.030	8.8	
	28	0.056	8.8	8.9
	56	0.093	8.8	
NV-3	14	0.307	35.4	
	28	0.569	34.9	36.5
	56	0.867	33.9	
NV-4	14	1.023	56.8	
	28	1.549	56.9	56.8
	56	1.975	56.9	

depending on aggregate reactivity. The loss in stiffness between the alkali- and water-cured cylinders at 180 days exceeded that obtained at 28 days.

d. For the alkali-cured cylinders at 80°C, the loss in stiffness between the immersion ages of 28 days and 180 days also increased due to the ASR-induced expansion and continued deteriorate in MOE with increases in immersion age.

The results of the study clearly revealed that the alkali-silica reactivity affected the stiffness in the concrete. The stress-strain curves of the water- and alkali-cured cylinders made with the NV-3 reactive aggregate at the immersion ages of 28 and 180 days are shown in Figure 2. As can be seen, at the early age of immersion (28 days), the compressive strength of the cylinders cured in the 1N NaOH at 80°C was higher than that cured in water at 20°C because more hydration took place in the cylinders of alkali-cured specimens. However, in the case of the immersion age of 6 months, the ultimate compressive strength of alkali-cured cylinder was less than that of water-cured cylinders. With an increase in the test duration from 28 to 180 days, the compressive strength of the water-cured cylinders increased, and that of alkali-cured specimens decreased.

The characteristics of the cylinders prepared with the NV-1 and NV-4 aggregates exhibited a similar behavior to that of the cylinders made with the NV-3 aggregate group. In the case of the NV-2 innocuous aggregate group, the strength increased with an increase in test duration for the alkali- and water-cured specimens. Additionally, at the same test duration, the strength increased with increasing the immersion temperature.

It was shown that the ultimate strain of the alkali-cured cylinder prepared with reactive aggregates increased with an increase in the test duration due to the micro-cracks developed on the surface of the specimens. As can be seen, the stiffness of the alkali-cured cylinders made with the NV-2 aggregate increased and that prepared with the

remaining three aggregate groups decreased for the water-cured cylinders. The modulus of elasticity of water-cured specimens increased with the immersion age. At the extended immersion age, the MOE of concrete cylinders decreased with increasing storage temperature.

Extending the immersion age to 6 months, and substituting the value of T for 80°C in Equation 1, the expected normalized stiffness [$E_{c(6\,m\text{-Na})}/E_{c(6\,m\text{-w})}$] is 0.901. In other words, the stiffness of the concrete cylinder at 80°C is approximately 0.901 times of the stiffness at 20°C at the immersion age of 6 months. Once the cylinders are immersed for a period of 6 months, the MOE at the elevated temperature is less than that cured at the room temperature.

4.4 ASR-induced cracks on the test cylinders

The ASR-related cracks on the surface of the test cylinders were also examined as shown in Figure 5. At the early age of testing, tiny cracks were developed at the outer zone of the specimens made with reactive aggregate due to the tension exerted by the alkali-silica reactions. As the immersion age increased, tremendous alkali-silica reactions took place in the specimens of reactive aggregates resulting in expansion and surface cracking. As can be depicted, the 6-month alkali-cured cylinders made with the NV-3 aggregate group experienced severe map cracks (Fig. 3(b)), which was a common symptom of ASR. Conversely, no visible cracks were observed on the surface of the test specimens made with the NV-1 innocuous aggregate group (Fig. 3(a)).

(a) Prisms made with NV-2 innocuous aggregate

(b) Prisms made with NV-3 reactive aggregate

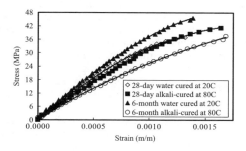

Figure 2. Stress-strain curve for the NV-3 reactive aggregate.

Figure 3. ASR cracks on the alkali-cured concrete cylinders.

4.5 Failure mechanisms of concrete cylinders

The differences in the crack pattern of the sound and damaged concretes were reflected in the mode of failures. The failure mode of the undamaged concrete cylinders containing innocuous aggregate was cone shaped (Fig. (4a)), and the specimen was broken suddenly with a boisterous sound. On the other hand, the effect of ASR-induced cracks on the stress field within a damaged cylindrical specimen made with reactive aggregates became a progressive fracture (Fig. 4(b)). Damaged concrete cylinders failed in an irregular fashion, predominantly by the ASR cracks, with a tranquil sound. The cylinders of reactive aggregates having a 14-day expansion of 1.10% and 28-day LIS of 56.8% failed into columnar shaped with several chunks of concrete through the direction of the loading, as shown in Figure 4(b).

4.6 Relationship between LIS of concrete cylinders and the expansion of mortar bars, and determination of failure criteria of LIS

The loss in the modulus of elasticity of concrete cylinders at 28 days was correlated against the expansion of mortar bars made with the companion aggregate source at the immersion ages of 14, 28 and 56 days. No distinct correlation was extracted from the loss in MOE and the expansion of the mortar bars, because the reduction is mainly due to micro-cracking, rather than the expansion as the losses in engineering properties do not occur at the same rate or in proportion to the expansion (Swamy and Al-Asali 1989). At the early age of immersion, the micro-cracking was progressive and varied from aggregate to aggregate.

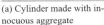

(a) Cylinder made with in-nocuous aggregate

(b) Cylinder made with reactive aggregate

Figure 4. Failure modes of concrete cylinders.

ASR-induced cracks of the cylinders progressed with an increase in the immersion age. At the extended immersion age of 6 months, the cracks due to alkali-silica reactivity entered a stabilized phase. Due to that, the loss in stiffness of the 6-month concrete cylinders and the expansion of the mortar bars at 14, 28 and 56 days showed a good correlation, as represented in Equation (2). The statistical data for Equation (2), such as the regression parameters a, b and c, prob(t) of each regression parameter, co-efficient of multiple determination (R^2), and Prob(F), are documented in Table 6. The R^2 value of each regression curve showed a good fit between the 6-month LIS and the expansion of mortar bars at 14, 28, 56 and 98 days.

$$Y = a + b\,X + c\,\exp(-X) \qquad (2)$$

where:
Y is the LIS of concrete cylinders at 6 months
X is the expansions of mortar bars at 14, 28 and 56 days.

The loss in stiffness of concrete cylinders made with each trial aggregate at the immersion age of 6 months was also evaluated by substituting the expansion of mortar bars at the ages of 14, 28 and 56 days in Equation 2. The results are documented in Table 4. As can be observed, the 14-, 28- and 56-day expansion of each trial aggregate resulted in an identical LIS of concrete cylinders prepared with companion aggregate source. Additionally, there is a good agreement existed between the experimental and analytical LIS of concrete cylinders made with four trial aggregates at the age of 6 months.

The failure criteria based on the loss in stiffness of concrete cylinders due to the alkali-silica reactivity was also established by substituting the 14-, 28- and 56-day suggested expansion limits of mortar bars of 0.10, 0.28 and 0.48%, respectively, in Equation (2). The analysis resulted the failure limits of LIS of concrete cylinders of 16.78, 22.56 and 22.8% based on the suggested expansion criteria of the mortar bars at the ages of 14, 28 and 56 days, respectively. As the inherent reactivity of an aggregate depends on several factors, it is recommended that an aggregate is considered as innocuous if the 6-month LIE of the cylinders made with the companion aggregates is less than 17%, and potentially reactive if that is more than 25%, and slowly reactive if otherwise.

4.7 Levels of alkali-silica reactivity of the trial aggregates

Table 5 documents the levels of alkali-silica reactivity of the trial aggregates based on the failure criteria of the 6-month LIS of concrete cylinders, and the expansion limits of ASTM C 1260 at 14, 28 and 56 days, and those of modified ASTM C

Table 5. The levels of alkali-silica reactivity based on the expansion limits of ASTM C 1260 and modified ASTM C 1293 and the loss in concrete stiffness at 6 months.

	ASTM C 1260			Modified ASTM C 1293			
	14-day[a]	28-day[b]	56-day[b]	4-week[c]	8-week[d]	13-week[d]	LIS at 6 months[e]
Agg. ID	0.10%	0.28%	0.47%	0.04%	0.105%	0.165%	(17%)
NV-1	R	R	R	R	R	R	R
NV-2	I	I	I	I	I	I	I
NV-3	R	R	R	R	R	R	R
NV-4	R	R	R	R	R	R	R

I = Innocuous (not reactive); R = Reactive; [a]Based on ASTM C 1260; [b]Proposed by Islam (2010); [c]Fournier, Bilodeau, and Malhotra (1994); [d]Islam (2010); [e]Loss in stiffness of 17%.

Table 6. The statistical data for equation 2.

Statistical parameters		14-day	28-day	56-day
Regression	a	210.894	80.600	35.535
parameters	b	−78.250	−4.944	12.961
	c	−205.876	−75.69	−30.62
Prob(t) of	a	0.083	0.135	0.306
parameters	b	0.139	0.686	0.383
	c	0.090	0.159	0.392
Prob(F)		0.049	0.067	0.108
R^2		0.998	0.996	0.988
Standard error (%)		1.66	2.31	3.60

1293 at the immersion ages of 4, 8 and 13 weeks. As can be seen, a strong correlation existed on the ASR classifications of the trial aggregate groups among the LIS and the expansion limits of mortar bars and alkali-cured prisms.

5 CONCLUSIONS

Based on the results of this study, the following conclusions can be made.

1. The alkali-silica reactivity of the trial aggregates showed a perfect correlation based on the aggregate mineralogy and the extended failure criteria of ASTM C 1260 at 28 and 56 days, and those of modified ASTM C 1293 at the immersion ages of 8 and 13 weeks.
2. The 28-day stiffness of concrete cylinder was affected due to the adverse effect of alkali-silica reactivity. However, the loss of stiffness (LIS) did not occur in the same proportion to the expansions of the mortar bars at the immersion ages of 14, 28 and 56 days.
3. The LIS of concrete cylinders increased mainly with an increase in micro-cracking due to

alkali-silica reactivity, which is a function of test duration.
4. The loss in stiffness of concrete cylinders prepared with each trial aggregate became stable at the immersion age of 6 months, and showed a good indicator of alkali-silica reactivity. The failure criteria of the 6-month LIS due to alkali-silica reactivity were also evaluated based on the expansion limits of mortar bars.
5. The proposed analytical model was capable of determining the loss in stiffness of concrete cylinders from the expansion results of the mortar bars containing companion aggregate. The levels of ASR of the selected aggregates based on the proposed failure criteria of the loss in stiffness of concrete cylinders reflected the identical conclusion to those obtained from the expansion limits of mortar bars at the immersion ages of 14, 28 and 56 days.
6. The ASTM C 1260 coupled with the results of the loss in stiffness of concrete cylinders and those of modified ASTM C 1293 can be used as a reliable indicator to predict the potential for deleterious alkali-silica reactivity.

ACKNOWLEDGEMENTS

The authors would like to acknowledge Nevada Department of Transportation (NDOT) for providing materials and financial support throughout the study. Thanks are also extended to the aggregate and cement producers for providing raw materials for this investigation.

REFERENCES

Ahmed, T., Burley, E., Rigden, S. and Abu-Tair, A. 2003. The effect of alkali reactivity on the mechanical properties of concrete, Construction and Building Materials 17: 123–144.

Bérubé, M.-A. and Frenette, J. 1994. Testing concrete for AAR in NaOH and NaCl solutions at 38°C and 80°C. *Cement and Concrete Composites* 16(3): 189–198.

Bach, F., Thorsen, T.S. and Nielsen, M.P. 1993. Load-carrying capacity of structural members subjected to alkali-silica reactions, *Construction and Building Materials* 7(2): 109–115.

Chang, Y.F., Chen, Y.H. Sheu, M.S. and Yao, G.C. 2006. Residual stress-strain relationship for concrete after exposure to high temperatures, Cement and Concrete Research 36(10): 1999–2005.

Folliard, K.J., Ideker, J., Thomas, M.D.A. and Fournier, B. 2005. Assessing aggregate reactivity using the accelerated concrete prism test. *International Center for Aggregate Research*, Texas, USA.

Fournier, B., Bilodeau, A. and Malhotra, V.M. 1994. Effectiveness of High-Volume Fly Concrete in Controlling Expansion Due to Alkali-Silica Reaction, pp. 721–756.

Giaccio, G., Zerbino, R., Ponce, J.M. and Batic, O.R. 2008. Mechanical behavior of concretes damaged by alkali-silica reaction, *Cement and Concrete Research* 38: 993–1004.

Islam, M.S. 2010. Performance of Nevada's aggregates in the alkali-silica reactivity of Portland cement concrete. *Doctoral Dissertation*, University of Nevada, Las Vegas, USA, Paper 243, http:// digitalcommons. library.unlv.edu/thesis-dissertations/243.

Istruct, E. 1992. Structural Effects of Alkali-Silica Reaction, Technical Guidance on the Appraisal of Existing Structures, *The Institution of Structural Engineers*, London, England.

Jones, A.E.K. and Clark, L.A. 1997. The effects of ASR on the properties of concrete and the implications for assessment. *Engineering Structures* 20(9): 785–791.

Kapitan, J.,G. 2006. Structural assessment of bridge piers with damage similar to alkali-silica reaction and/or delayed ettringite formation. *Master Thesis*, University of Texas at Austin, USA.

Leger, P., Cote, P. and Tinawi, R. 1996. Finite element analysis of concrete swelling due to alkali-aggregate reactions in dams. *Computers and structures* 60(4): 601–611.

Monette, L., Gardner, J. and Grattan-Gellew, P. 2000. Structural effects of the alkali-silica reaction on non-loaded and loaded reinforced concrete beam. *The 11th International Conference on Alkali-aggregate Reaction*, Quebec, Canada, pp. 999–1008.

Nixon, P.J. and Bollinghaus, R. 1985. The effect of alkali aggregate reaction on the tensile and compressive strength of concrete, *Durability of Building Materials* 2: 243–248.

Rivard, P. and Ballivy, G. 2005. Assessment of the expansion related to alkali-silica reaction by the Damage Rating Index method. *Construction and Building Materials* 19: 83–90.

Swamy, R.N. and Al-Asali, M.M. 1988. Engineering properties of concrete affected by alkali-silica reaction. *ACI Materials Journal* 85: 367–37.

Swamy, R.N., Editor. 1992. *The alkali-silica reaction in concrete,* Blackie and Son Ltd., Glasgow, London.

Tarek, M.U., Hamada, H. and Yamaji, T. 2003. Alkali-silica reaction-induced strains over concrete surface and steel bars in concrete. *ACI Materials Journal* 100(2): 133–144.

Touma, W.E., Fowler, D.W. and Carrasquillo, R.L. 2001. Alkali-silica reaction in Portland cement concrete: testing methods and mitigation alternatives. *International Center for Aggregates Research*, Texas, USA, Research Report ICAR 301–1f.

Concrete Solutions – Grantham, Mechtcherine & Schneck (eds)
© 2012 Taylor & Francis Group, London, ISBN 978-0-415-61622-5

Evaluation of restrained shrinkage of repair materials under the local environment of Riyadh

M.I. Khan, T.H. Almusallam, S.H. Alsayed, Y.A. Al-Salloum & A.A. Almosa
Department of Civil Engineering, College of Engineering, King Saud University, Saudi Arabia

ABSTRACT: Shrinkage of repair material is the major factor inducing cracking in concrete repairs. Induced cracks in repair materials are due to restrained shrinkage. The ring test is commonly used to assess the potential for restrained shrinkage induced cracking due to its simplicity and versatility. The restrained ring test is becoming widely used as a standard test method to assess the potential for early-age cracking in concrete. In this investigation, a ring test set up was developed to measure the restrained shrinkage of various repair materials available in the local market. Keeping in view the importance of the local environment, two environment conditions were used; Lab Environment (Temperature $23 \pm 2°C$) and the open environment of Riyadh. These environmental conditions were used taking into account the local environmental conditions. The samples were outside for almost one year and encountered all weather conditions of Riyadh. It has been observed that some materials although manufactured by highly reputed companies didn't comply fully in restrained shrinkage tests.

1 INTRODUCTION

In Saudi Arabia, the majority of concrete structures constructed more than three decades ago suffer because of lack of quality control and severe weather conditions. Concrete structures are prone to deterioration due to the very hot and harsh environmental conditions. Saudi Arabia covers a large area and is characterized by considerable differences in climate from one region to another, from the hot humid coastal areas to dry inland, and also by the extreme difference in temperature between winter and summer. Due to the hostile environment, the deterioration of concrete structures often takes place before their service life. Therefore, the structures deteriorate and need urgent repair.

The term concrete repair refers to any replacing, restoring, or renewing of concrete or concrete surfaces after initial placement. The need for repairs can vary from minor imperfections to major damage resulting from structural failure. The chosen method of repair can only prove to be successful if the new material interacts well with the parent concrete and forms a durable barrier against ingress of carbon dioxide and chlorides. The properties and durability of repair systems are governed by the properties of the three phases namely, repair, existing substrate, and interface (transition zone) between them [Vaysburd et al., 2001]. Properly designed, implemented, and functioning man-made systems, with a minimum number of undesirable side effects, require the application of a well-integrated systems approach as reported by Emmons & Vaysburd

(1995). Smoak (2002) reported that in evaluating the causes of failures, it is essential to consistently use a systematic approach to concrete repair. Problems may arise since a dimensionally unstable repair material is placed against a dimensionally stable substrate concrete, as any significant drying shrinkage and creep will no longer exist in the substrate concrete due to its long term exposure to the environment and the service loading. Internal stresses will be generated due to shrinkage and creep in the repair material which need to be evaluated before a durable repair can be specified

Shrinkage of repair material is the major factor inducing cracking in concrete repairs. It has been reported that the repair mortars are restrained against shrinkage by the substrate concrete and steel reinforcement within the repair patch [Yuan, and Marosszeky, 1991]. Induced cracks in repair materials are due to restrained shrinkage. The amount of shrinkage depends on many factors including the cement content, aggregate properties, the mixture composition, temperature and the relative humidity of the environment, the age of the concrete and the size of the structure. The ring test is commonly used to assess the potential for restrained shrinkage induced cracking due to its simplicity and versatility. The restrained ring test is becoming widely used as a standard test method to assess the potential for early-age cracking in concrete mixtures. In the ring test the concrete is cast around a hollow steel cylinder. As the concrete dries, shrinkage is prevented by the steel ring, thus resulting in the development of tensile stresses in the concrete. The ring specimen geometry is frequently preferred because of the difficulties associated with providing adequate end restraint in other methods.

Test methods used to examine the effect of restrained shrinkage in a repair material generally rely on cracking to occur in the mortar within a given time period [Dector and Lambe, 1993]. The most widely used test method for restrained shrinkage is to cast a repair material in the Coutinho Ring [Coutinho, 1995] (steel ring) and monitor the performance of the repair material over 28 days. The Coutinho Ring serves as a restraint for the shrinking mortar, therefore, tension is induced into the sample as the repair material tries to shrink. The repair material is assumed to have passed the restrained shrinkage test if no cracks are evident at 28 days. This test was proposed to be included in the British Department of Transport standard, BD/94 [DoT, 1994]. The German BAM Trough Test [Maultzch, 1987] also evaluates the performance of a mortar under restrained shrinkage conditions.

In this investigation, the ring test set up was developed to measure the restrained shrinkage of various repair materials available in the local market. Keeping in view the importance of the local environment, two environmental conditions were used; lab Environment (Temperature 23 ± 2°C) and the open Environment of Riyadh. These environmental conditions were used taking into account the local environmental conditions. The samples were outside for almost one year and encountered all weather conditions of Riyadh. It has been observed that some materials although manufactured by highly reputed companies utterly failed in restrained shrinkage test irrespective of temperature variations.

2 EXPERIMENTAL PROGRAM

2.1 Material selection

Nine candidate materials, three from each of micro-concrete repair materials, cementitious repair mortars and cementitious polymer modified mortars, were selected. The selection of the repair material was based on the best selling materials manufactured by the top three companies Fosroc, Sika and MBT available in the Kingdom of Saudi Arabia. The designation, properties and application of these Micro-Concrete Repair Materials (MCRM), Cementitious Repair Mortars (CRM) and Cementitious Polymer Modified Mortars (CPMM) are shown in Tables 1, 2 and 3, respectively.

Mixture proportions and mixing for all selected materials were employed as per the recommendations suggested by the manufacturer. Curing procedures for each repair material were also

Table 1. Details of micro-concrete repair materials.

Material	Properties	Application
MCRM-1	Free-flowing, shrinkage compensated	High strength structural elements
MCRM -2	Free-flowing, shrinkage compensated	High strength structural elements
MCRM -3	Free-flowing, shrinkage compensated	High strength structural elements

Table 2. Details of cementitious repair mortars.

Material	Properties	Application
CRM-1	Shrinkage controlled	Hand applied vertical & overhead
CRM-2	Shrinkage controlled	Spraying vertical & overhead
CRM-3	Multi purpose for hot climates	Hand applied vertical & horizontal

Table 3. Details of cementitious polymer modified mortars.

Material	Properties	Application
CPMM-1	Multi purpose for hot climates	Dry/Wet spray vertical, overhead & horizontal
CPMM-2	For hot climates	Wet spray vertical & overhead
CPMM-3	Multi purpose	Hand applied

followed exactly in accordance to the manufacturers' recommendations where practicable.

2.2 Testing procedure

2.2.1 Restrained shrinkage

The restrained shrinkage is commonly measured using the ring test [Shah and Balaguru, 1992], however, in this investigation a modified ring test [Momayez, et al., 2005] was used which takes into account the real situation encountered in the interface between substrate and the repair material. The dimensions of the restrained shrinkage specimen are shown in Figure 1.

A specially prepared mould, diameter 305 mm and height 140 mm, was used for the substrate concrete whereas a diameter of 375 mm and height 140 mm were used for the repair material. The substrate concrete was cast in the mould (diameter 305 mm and height 140 mm) and demoulded the following day. After curing for 28 days, the surface of the interface of the substrate was prepared using sand blasting for a proper bond with the repair material. The substrate specimen was placed in steel cylindrical moulds having diameter 375 mm and height 140 mm as shown in Figure 2. Before pouring the mixed repair material the sand blasted surfaces of the specimens were thoroughly washed to clean the mould and the excess water was dried out. Repair material was then cast in the steel mould containing the concrete specimens by means of a scoop and was tamped by using the tamping rod as shown in Figure 3.

These specimens were demoulded after 24 hrs and spray cured and covered by plastic for the targeted days. One from the two replicates in each set of inside and outside cast was cured for 7 days and the other continued to be spray cured till 28 days. All these specimens were watched closely for the appearance of the shrinkage cracks. Once discovered, the specimens were subjected to crack width measuring by means of a microscope having a least count of 0.02 mm as show in Figure 4.

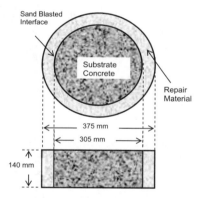

Figure 1. Specimen dimensions used for restrained shrinkage (ring test).

Figure 2. Substrate specimen in the mould for ready for casting repair material.

Figure 3. Casting of repair material for restrained shrinkage.

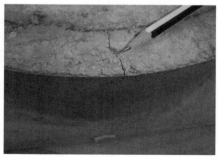

Figure 4. Specimen showing restrained shrinkage crack.

3 RESULTS AND DISCUSSION

3.1 *Comparison of compressive strength*

Restrained shrinkage was monitored for all types of repair materials in this investigation. For this test two environmental conditions were employed, Lab Environment (Temperature 23 ± 2°C) and Outside (Open Environment of Riyadh).

These environmental conditions were used taking the local environmental conditions into consideration. Samples were also kept outside the laboratory in the open environment conditions of the Riyadh Region. These samples were outside for almost one year and encountered all weather conditions of Riyadh.

3.1.1 Micro concrete repair material

Micro Concrete repair materials, MCRM-1 and MCRM-2 and MCRM-3 were investigated for restrained shrinkage behavior. Restrained shrinkage of these materials was monitored for various curing conditions up to a period of one year. Restrained shrinkage measurements are presented in Figures 5, 6 and 7 for MCRM-1, MCRM-2 and MCRM-3, respectively.

The restrained shrinkage of MCRM-1 cured in the lab environment and cured outside, increased continuously up to about 400 days as can be seen from the steep curves as shown in Figure 5. After about 400 days, the shrinkage remained almost constant throughout, as can be seen from the

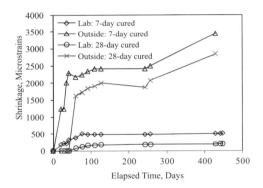

Figure 5.   Restrained shrinkage of MCRM-1.

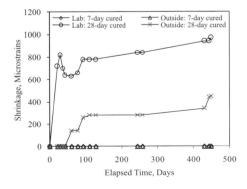

Figure 6.   Restrained shrinkage of MCRM-2.

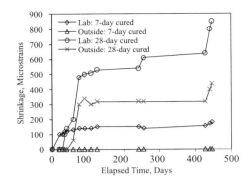

Figure 7.   Restrained shrinkage of MCRM-3.

flat curves of this figure. At around 100 days the restrained shrinkage of MCRM-1 in the laboratory environment was about 200 microns for 7-day cure and 500 microns for 28 day cure and for the outside environment specimens was about 3000 microns.

MCRM-3 showed shrinkage at an initial stage, all specimens were in their respective environments to monitor shrinkage (Figure 7). After about 50 days the pattern of shrinkage of MCRM-3 cured in the Lab environment and cured outside was similar to that of MCRM-1. However, the maximum shrinkage was restricted to about 700 microns at about 200 days.

3.1.2 Cementitious repair mortar

Cementitious Repair Mortars, CRM-1, CRM-2, CRM-3 and CRM-4 were investigated. CRM-2 and CRM-3 are hand applied whereas CRM-1 and CRM-4 are spray applied materials.

Hand applied: Restrained shrinkage of CRM-2 and CRM-3 is presented in Figures 8 and 9, respectively. Both CRM-2 and CRM-3 showed high shrinkage at the initial stage, for outside specimens.

Restrained shrinkage of CRM-2 cured in the Lab environment and cured outside increased continuously up until about 100 days except the 28 days specimen cured in the lab which did not show any cracks as can be seen from the steep curves shown in Figure 8. At 100 days, the shrinkage of CRM-2 was about 700 microns for the specimen cured in the lab and for 7 days outside cure the shrinkage of the specimen was about 1200 microns while for outside 28 days cure it was about 2200 microns. The shrinkage remained almost constant up to 200 days as can be seen from the flat curves of Figure 8.

The pattern of restrained shrinkage of CRM-3 cured in the lab environment and cured outside was similar to that of CRM-2. However, the maximum shrinkage was restricted to about 1400 microns at

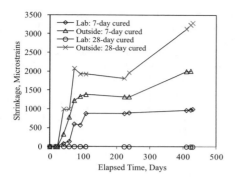

Figure 8. Restrained shrinkage of CRM-2 (Hand applied).

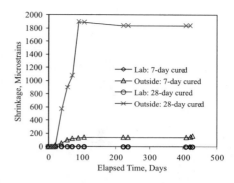

Figure 10. Restrained shrinkage of CRM-1(Spray applied).

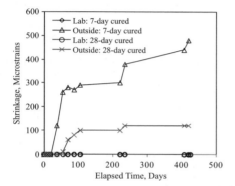

Figure 9. Restrained shrinkage of CRM-3 (Hand applied).

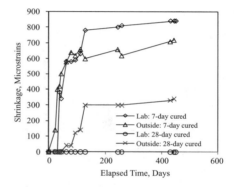

Figure 11. Restrained shrinkage of CRM-4 (Spray applied).

about 200 days as shown in Figure 9. Similarly, for the outside cured CRM-3, shrinkage was also the same pattern as CRM-2.

Spray applied: The restrained shrinkage of CRM-1 and CRM-4 is presented in Figures 10 and 11, respectively. All specimens were in their respective environments to monitor shrinkage. There was a sharp increase in shrinkage for up to 100 days and then a steady increase was maintained.

Restrained shrinkage of CRM-1 cured in the Lab environment did not show any cracks and, when cured outside for 7 days and 28 days, shrinkage increased continuously up until about 100 days and reached 200 microns and 1800 microns for the outside and lab environments, respectively (Fig. 10).

The restrained shrinkage of CRM-4 cured in the Lab environment and cured outside increased sharply up until about 100 days then there was a steady increase up to about 150 days during which the shrinkage value reached for the 7 days Lab environment, 800 microns (Fig. 11).

3.1.3 Cementitious polymer modified mortar

The restrained shrinkage of CPMM-1 is presented in Figure 12. It can be seen that all curing regimes showed high shrinkage at an initial stage. There was a sharp increase in shrinkage up to about 50 days and then a steady increase was maintained.

The restrained shrinkage for lab cured CPMM-1 specimen was about 4000 microns at 70 days then there was a steady increase until it reached 5000 microns at about 250 days and after that the shrinkage remained constant. Outside cured specimens had a sharp increase until 70 days and then a steady increase up to 7000 microns at 250 days, whereas the shrinkage of CPMM-2 and CPMM-3 was marginally low (Fig. 13).

Figure 13 shows the shrinkage of all materials investigated for both lab and outside environments. It can be seen that MCRM-1, CRM-2 and CPMM-1 showed 3000, 2000 and 7000 microstrains, respectively. Figure 14 shows the cracks developed in the outside environment.

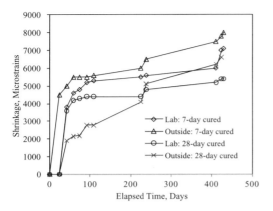

Figure 12. Restrained shrinkage of CPMM-1.

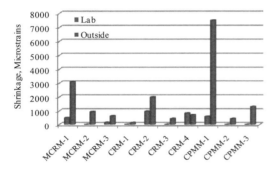

Figure 13. Restrained shrinkage after exposure of 400 days (initial curing 7 days).

Figure 14. Restrained shrinkage cracks.

4 CONCLUSIONS

Almost all the materials cured in the lab environment and outside showed higher drying shrinkage as compared to the humid cured specimens.

CPMM-1, CRM-1, CRM-2 cured in the lab and outside environments showed drying shrinkage was high at about 2000 microns whereas the shrinkage in humid cured material specimens was limited to about 700–800 microns.

CRM-3, CRM-4 and MCRM-1 cured in the lab environment and outside showed drying shrinkage as high as about 1400 microns.

The outside environment (hot weather of Riyadh) influenced almost all materials but a drastic influence was witnessed in MCRM-1, CRM-2 and CPMM-1.

REFERENCES

Coutinho, A. 1995. The influence of the type of cement on its cracking tendency. *RILEM Bulletin*, 5, 26–40.
Dector, M.H. & Lambe, R.W. 1993. New materials for concrete repair—Development and testing. *The Indian Concrete Journal*, 475–480.
Department of Transport. 1994. *Specification for the repair of concrete highway structures*. Draft standard BD/94, UK.
Emmons, P.H. & Vaysburd, A.M. 1995. The total system concept—Necessary for improving the performance of repaired structures. *Concrete International* 17(3): 31–36.
Johnston, C.D. & Sidwell, E.H. 1968. Testing concrete in tension and compression. *Magazine of Concrete Research* 20(65): 221–228.
Maultzch, M. 1987. Properties of PCC for repair of concrete structures. In *Proceedings of 5th International Congress on Polymers in Concrete*, Brighton, UK, 22–24, 301–304.
Momayez, A.M.R. Ehsani, Rajaie, A. & Ramezanianpour A. 2005. Cylindrical specimen for measuring shrinkage in repaired concrete members. *Construction and Building Materials* 19, 107–116.
Poston, R.W., Kesner, K., McDonald, J.E., A.M. Vaysburd, & Emmons, P.H. 2001. Concret repair material performance—laborratory study. *ACI Material Journal* 98(2): 137–145.
RILEM. 1963. Direst tensile tests of concrete. *RILEM Bulletin* 20, 84–90.
Shah, S.P. & Balaguru N. 1992. Plastic and Shrinkage. In *Fiber reinforced cement composites*. New York: Mc-Graw Hill.
Smoak, W.G. 2002. Guide to concrete repair. *USBR report*, Denver Federal Center Denver, Colorado, USA.
Vaysburd, A.M., Sabnis, G.M., Emmons, P.H. & McDonald, J.E. 2001. Interfacial bond and surface preparation in concrete repair. *The Indian Concrete Journal* 27–33.
Yuan, Y.S. & Marosszeky, M. 1991. Major factors affecting the performance of structural repair. In *Proceedings of the ACI International Conference on Evaluation and Rehabilitation of Concrete Structures and Innovations in Design*, Hong Kong, ACI-SP128, Vol. 2, 819–837.

Concrete Solutions – Grantham, Mechtcherine & Schneck (eds)
© 2012 Taylor & Francis Group, London, ISBN 978-0-415-61622-5

Experimental research of the intensity of corrosion processes influence by tensile stress for reinforcing steel covered with polymer sulphur composites

M. Książek

Timber and Monumental Heritage Structures, Division of Building Materials, Institute of Building Engineering, Wrocław University of Technology, Wrocław, Poland

ABSTRACT: This paper presents the results of the experimental research and analyses indicating the usefulness of polymer sulphur composites to the protection against corrosion of reinforcement. In paper presents the personal investigations and the methodology. After the analysis of the initial results the optimum compositions have been chosen for the experimental research.

This paper presents investigation results of corrosion rate for steel reinforcement bars that have been covered with polymer coating and have been exposed to tensile stresses in a solution simulating the pore-liquid of concrete. An experimental investigation of the tendencies that occur during the corrosion process of reinforcing steel covered with polymer and exposed to tensile stress has been attempted. One aim of the investigation was to determine the effect of tensile stress on corrosion rate for St3S-b steel covered with a polymer sulphur coating and exposed to an aqueous environment that was to simulate the pore-liquid of concrete contaminated with chloride ions. The samples underwent loading in a axial state of stress including varied values of tensile stress, and at the same time the corrosion rate was determined potentiostatically. The potentiostatic investigation was carried out in order to determine the parameters describing the corrosion rate of the samples tested. The corrosion rate for the steel decreased by orders of magnitude when covered with protective coating even though became unsealed at load exceeding kN. A small decrease of corrosion rate was found for the steel that had not been covered with polymer coating when placed in model pore-liquid of concrete and exposed to tensile stress increase.

1 INTRODUCTION

Corrosion is a major problem from the social, economic, technical and scientific points of view. Despite extensive research and numerous papers on this subject, the problem has not been completely solved yet. It is estimated that in highly developed countries losses due to corrosion annually amount to about a thousand dollars per capita. In Poland they are estimated at 6–10% of the GDP (Hoła & Książek, 2009; Książek, 2011).

Corrosion contributes to the shortening of the service life of building structures, i.e. to a reduction in their capability to perform the required functions over a given period of time.

Corrosion also affects practically all building materials, not only steel, concrete or reinforced concrete (of course, no building material, structural element or building is everlasting). Generally speaking, the fight against corrosion comes down to providing a given material or element with protection whereby its failure free service life is significantly extended (Hoła & Książek, 2009;

Klakočar-Ciepacz & Książek, 2003; Książek, 2011).

Corrosion of the reinforcing steel and concrete may result from the action of the ambient gaseous or water environments. It may also be due to the improper choice of components (including additions and admixtures) from which the concrete was made (Klakočar-Ciepacz & Książek, 2003; Książek, 1999; Książek, 2001).

The degradation of reinforced concrete may be caused by corrosion of the reinforcing steel or the concrete or by the simultaneous corrosion of the reinforcing steel and the concrete (Zybura, 1994; Zybura, 2003; Zybura, 2007). The considerable porosity of concrete and cracks in or damage to the concrete cover contribute to the diffusion, absorption and adsorption of gases and to the diffusion of the substances dissolved in the pore liquid deep into the concrete. All kinds of aggressive substances from the surrounding environment diffuse into the inside of concrete and directly or indirectly cause the corrosion of the reinforcing steel, which usually ends in the loss of adhesion of the concrete to the steel, manifesting itself in the fracturing, loosening and spalling of the concrete cover (Brandt, 1994; Czarnecki & Emmons, 2002; Hoła, 2002; Wieczorek, 2001; Wieczorek, 2002).

Surface protection of the reinforcing steel, in the form of a hermetic protective coating, considerably reduces or prevents the access of the surrounding gas or water environment to the reinforcing steel (Brandt, 1994; Cairns & Ramli, 1995; Czarnecki & Garbacz, 1995; Hadje-Ghafari & et al., 1994). Various materials, e.g. polymer epoxy resins (Hoła & Książek, 2009; Klakočar-Ciepacz & Książek, 2003; Książek, 2011), inhibiting agents (inhibitors) (Jaśniok M. & Jaśniok, T. & Zybura, 2003; Jaśniok, T. & Zybura, 2004; Jaśniok, M. & Zybura, 2007; Zybura, 1994; Zybura, 2003; Zybura, 2007), noble metal admixtures (Hoła & Książek, 2009; Klakočar-Ciepacz & Książek, 2003; Książek, 2011), or cathodic protection (Jaśniok M. & Jaśniok, T. & Zybura, 2003; Jaśniok, T. & Zybura, 2004; Jaśniok, M. & Zybura, 2007; Zybura, 1994; Zybura, 2003; Zybura, 2007) are used for this purpose.

It seems that such protection can be provided by coating rebars with a polymer sulphur composite composed of a sulphur binder (S_8), fillers and proper additives. Even though sulphur binders show: resistance to many aggressive water solutions, low absorbability, surface hydrophobicity and quite high (tangent and normal) adhesion to the surface of many materials (including metallic surfaces), they have not been used for this purpose before (Hoła & Książek, 2009; Klakočar-Ciepacz & Książek, 2003; Książek, 2011).

In order to demonstrate the suitability of sulphur polymer composites for the surface protection of concrete steel experimental research was carried out in the Institute of Building Engineering at Wrocław University of Technology. The research included: the experimental determination of sulphur polymer composite composition and manufacturing conditions, tests of the composite's selected physical, chemical and mechanical properties. The research included: tests of its tangent and normal adhesion to plain and ribbed reinforcing bars and to standard cement mortar and concrete, the determination of the mass decrement resulting from storage in aqueous solutions of acids, hydroxides and salts and in water and the polarization investigation of rebars subjected to tension in a solution modelling the pore liquid in carbonated concrete contaminated with chlorine ions (Hoła & Książek, 2009; Klakočar-Ciepacz & Książek, 2003; Książek, 2011).

2 DESCRIPTION OF INVESTIGATIONS

Sulphur polymer composites were investigated in two stages. In the first stage, compositions were fixed and thirty test sulphur polymer composites were prepared and pretested. When fixing the compositions, the binder (S_8) content was changed in the range of 55–65%. Mineral powder, silica dust from a drying plant, high-silica sand and plain sand and cement were used as the filler. Carbon black and anthracene oil were used as additives. The pretesting included preparing composites and determining their basic physical and mechanical properties, such as: bulk density, absorbability by wt., bending strength and splitting tensile strength. The experimental results are reported in detail in (Hoła & Książek, 2009; Klakočar-Ciepacz & Książek, 2003; Książek, 2011).

The results of the preliminary tests were analyzed and the sulphur polymer composite having the best properties among the tested composites was selected for further studies. The composition of the composite is given in Table 1 and its experimentally determined properties are shown in papers (Hoła & Książek, 2009; Klakočar-Ciepacz & Książek, 2003; Książek, 2011).

The adhesion of a 0.2–4.0 mm thick sulphur polymer composite layer to plain St3S reinforcing steel samples and ribbed 34GS steel samples, 10 mm in diameter and 160 mm long, was tested.

The tangent adhesion of a 1.5 mm thick sulphur polymer composite layer to rebars under tension and bending and to rebars being pushed out of this composite was tested on plain steel St3S samples and ribbed steel 34GS samples, 10 mm and 20 mm in diameter and 160 mm long.

Also the adjacent adhesion of concrete to reinforcing bars coated with a 1.5 mm thick layer of the sulphur polymer composite was tested on plain reinforcing steel St3S and ribbed steel 34GS samples, 10 mm and 20 mm in diameter and 160 mm long.

The decrease in the mass of rebars coated with the composite and stored in aqueous solutions of acids and salts and in water for 1 year was determined using plain St3S steel samples, 10 mm and 20 mm in diameter and 160 mm long.

Polarization investigations of tensioned rebars coated with the sulphur polymer composite were carried out on plain St3S reinforcing steel samples immersed in a solution modelling the porous liquid

Table 1. Composition of selected sulphur polymer composite.

Content in [%] of total composite mass		
Binder Sulphur S_8 [%]	Filler Mineral quartz dust [%]	Additive Carbon black [%]
63	33	4

258

1a)

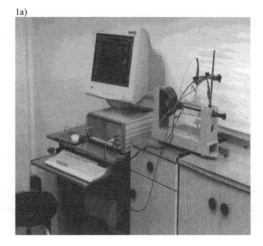

1b)

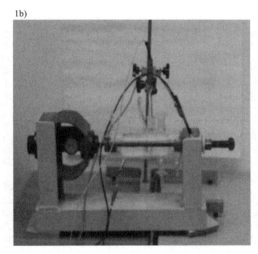

Figure 1. Device for polarization testing of tensioned rebars: 1a) and 1b) view of rig.

2a) 50x

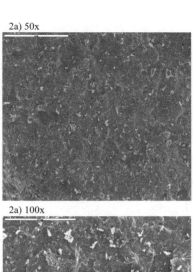

2a) 100x

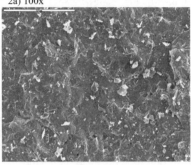

2b) 100x

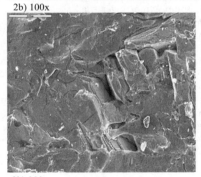

2b) 200x

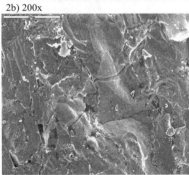

Figure 2. SEM images of bending strength test fracture surfaces of: a) polymer sulphur composite, b) polymerized sulphur.

in carbonated concrete contaminated with chloride ions. The samples were 10 mm in diameter and 290 mm long. A general view of the polarization test device is shown in Figure 1a, b (Hoła & Książek, 2009; Klakočar-Ciepacz & Książek, 2003; Książek, 2011).

In order to select a polymer sulphur composite for further studies, the bending strength test fracture surfaces of the composites were examined under 50×, 100× and 200× magnification, using a Jeol JSM-800LV scanning electron microscope. The aim was to check for microfractures, cracks and other defects which had arisen during the making of the specimens. The results of the examinations are shown in Figure 2. The results for the polymer sulphur composite under a magnification of 50× and 100× and for polymerized sulphur under a magnification of 100× and 200× are shown in respectively Figure 2a and b.

The images show that the polymer sulphur composite has a very homogenous structure with uniformly distributed filler grains, without any microcracks, air voids or other defects. Whereas the fracture of the polymerized sulphur shows structural defects, in the form of microcracks and air voids, which arose in the course of solidification.

The polymer sulphur composite was prepared by melting components at a temperature of 150°C and then by cooling to ambient temperature. The hot fluid was used for covering the surface of a surgical steel nail and for fixation on this surface porous alumina grains.

3 TEST RESULTS AND THEIR ANALYSIS

3.1 Adhesion of sulphur polymer composite layer to rebars under tension and bending

Figure 3 shows at what average values of stress σ_{pm} tensioning plain and ribbed rebars 10 mm in diameter a 0.2–4.0 mm thick layer of the tested sulphur polymer composite became unstuck from the surface of the rebars. According to this figure, regardless of the polymer layer thickness, this stress was higher for the ribbed reinforcing bars. In this case, the maximum stress σ_{pm} (amounting to 560 MPa) occurred when the thickness of the polymer layer was in the range 1.3–1.6 mm. Whereas in the case of the plain rebars stress σ_{pm} was less dependent on the polymer composite layer, although at a thickness of 0.5–0.6 mm this stress was higher, amounting to 320 MPa.

Figure 4 shows at what average bending stress σ_{dm} in plain and ribbed rebars 10 mm in diameter

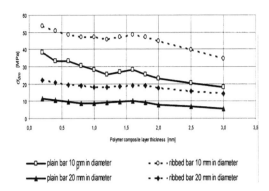

Figure 4. Average values of stress bending rebars 10 mm and 20 mm in diameter, at which sulphur polymer composite layer of different thickness gets unstuck.

a 0.2–3.0 mm thick layer of the tested sulphur polymer composite separated from the surface of the rebars. Also here this stress was higher in the ribbed rebars. According to Figure 4, the stress σ_{dm} was the highest when the polymer composite layer was 0.2 mm thick. Also as the thickness of the layer increased, the bending moment at which the layer became unstuck generally decreased. But at the layer thickness of about 1.4–1.6 mm the downward trend of stress σ_{dm} clearly slowed down, reaching a distinct local minimum. For example, in the ribbed rebars coated with the composite this stress amounted to 48.4 MPa.

The tests have shown that the separation of a 0.2–4.0 mm thick layer of the sulphur polymer composite from the surface of tensioned and bent ribbed rebars always occured at higher values of stress than in the case of plain rebars of the same diameters. The optimum thickness of the layer for ribbed reinforcing bars was 1.5 mm. In the case of bent plain and ribbed reinforcing bars, the optimum thickness of the layer was 0.2 mm, though it seemed that it can be as well 1.5 mm.

3.2 Adjacent adhesion of sulphur polymer composite layer to reinforcing bars

The averages values of tangent adhesion τ_{wm} of a 1.5 mm thick sulphur polymer composite layer to plain and ribbed rebars 10 mm and 20 mm in diameter are shown respectively in Figure. 5.

According to the test results, the adjacent adhesion of a 1.5 mm thick sulphur polymer composite layer to the ribbed rebars was twice that of the plain rebars of the same diameter. It was also higher than in the case of the smaller diameter rebars, regardless of whether they were plain or ribbed.

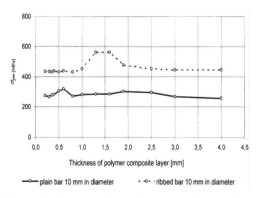

Figure 3. Average values of stress tensioning rebars 10 mm in diameter, at which sulphur polymer composite layer of different thickness gets unstuck.

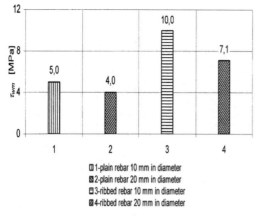

Figure 5. Average values of adjacent adhesion of 1.5 mm thick sulphur polymer composite to plain and ribbed rebars 10 mm in diameter and 20 mm in diameter.

3.3 Tangent adhesion of sulphur polymer composite to rebars in pushed-out test

The average values of adjacent adhesion τ_{wm} of the sulphur polymer composite to plain and ribbed rebars 10 mm in diameter in the push-out test and the same results for rebars 20 mm in diameter are shown respectively in Figure 6.

According to the test results, the average values of adjacent adhesion of the composite to the ribbed rebars were much higher than those for the plain rebars. They were also higher for the smaller diameter (10 mm) rebars as compared to the 20 mm diameter rebars, regardless of whether they were plain or ribbed.

3.4 Tangent adhesion of concrete to rebars coated with sulphur polymer composite

The test results for adjacent adhesion τ_{wm} of ordinary concrete to plain rebars 10 mm in diameter, coated with a 1.5 mm thick layer and to plain rebars 20 mm in diameter are shown respectively in Figure 7. The results denoted by the digits 1, 2 and 3 are for ordinary concrete made using respectively: rounded aggregate, crushed basalt aggregate and crushed granite aggregate. The average values of this adjacent adhesion to rebars 10 mm in diameter and 20 mm in diameter, coated with a 1.5 mm thick layer of the sulphur polymer composite are shown in Figure 8.

For comparison purposes, Figures 7 and 8 show the adjacent adhesion (τ_{wm}) of ordinary concrete, made using respectively rounded aggregate, crushed basalt aggregate and crushed granite aggregate, to uncoated rebars.

It follows from the results shown in Figures 6 and 7 that in comparison with the

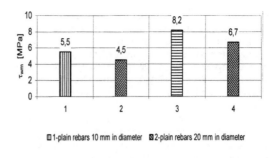

Figure 6. Average values of tangent adhesion of sulphur polymer composite to plain and ribbed rebars 10 mm in diameter and 20 mm in diameter, being pushed out of composite.

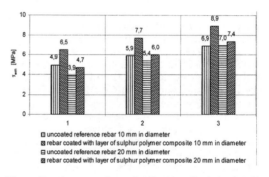

Figure 7. Average values of adjacent adhesion of ordinary concrete to plain rebars 10 mm in diameter and 20 mm in diameter, coated with 1.5 mm thick layer of sulphur polymer composite, 1—concrete made using rounded aggregate, 2—concrete made using crushed basalt aggregate and 3—concrete made using crushed granite aggregate.

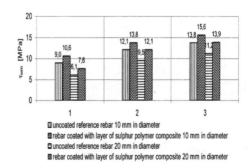

Figure 8. Average values of adjacent adhesion of ordinary concrete to ribbed rebars 10 mm in diameter and 20 mm in diameter, coated with 1.5 mm thick layer of sulphur composite, 1—concrete made using rounded aggregate, 2—concrete made using crushed basalt aggregate, 3—concrete made using crushed granite aggregate.

uncoated reference rebars, higher values of adjacent adhesion to both plain and ribbed rebars 10 mm and 20 mm in diameter were obtained when the rebars were coated with a layer of the sulphur polymer composite. Then the adhesion values were in the range 4.7–15.6 MPa depending on the kind of aggregate used, the rebar diameter and the grade of the rebar steel.

Therefore it can be concluded that a 1.5 mm thick layer of sulphur polymer composite applied to plain and ribbed rebars of different diameters does not reduce their adjacent adhesion to concrete.

3.5 Mass loss of plain rebars in aqueous solutions of acids, hydroxides and salts and in water

Figure 9 shows the average mass loss (in%) for plain rebars 10 mm in diameter, coated with a 0.6 mm and 1.5 mm thick layer of sulphur polymer composite, immersed in acid aqueous solutions for 1 year. According to the figure, the average mass loss for plain rebars coated with the composite and stored in 5% solutions of sulphuric acid (H_2SO_4) and hydrochloric acid (HCl) and in a 10% solution of ethanoic acid (CH_3COOH) was small— below 0.9%. Whereas in a 5% solution of nitric acid (HNO_3) the average mass loss for the rebars was larger, amounting to respectively 3.5 and 3.9%, depending on the protective layer thickness. One should note that the loss in the mass of the rebars coated with the tested composite depended only to a small degree on the thickness of the coating.

Figure 10 shows the mass loss for rebars 10 mm in diameter, stored in aqueous solutions of hydroxides and in water. According to the figure, the average mass loss for the rebars, coated with a 0.6 mm and 1.5 mm thick layer of the sulphur polymer composite, stored in a saturated solution of calcium hydroxide ($Ca(OH)_2$) and in water, was negligible, being in the range 0.1–0.4%. Whereas in both a 5% solution of sodium hydroxide (NaOH)

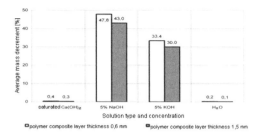

Figure 10. Average mass loss [%] for plain rebars 10 mm in diameter, coated with layer of sulphur polymer composite, stored in aqueous solutions of hydroxides and in water for 1 year.

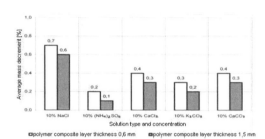

Figure 11. Average mass loss for plain rebars 10 mm in diameter, coated with layer of sulphur polymer composite, stored in aqueous solutions of salts for 1 year.

and a 5% solution of potassium hydroxide (KOH) this loss was very large, amounting to respectively 47.8% and 30.0%.

The average mass loss for rebars 10 mm in diameter, coated with the composite and stored in aqueous solutions of salts are shown in Figure 11. According to the figure, the average mass loss for the rebars stored in: a 10% solution of sodium chloride (NaCl), a 10% solution of ammonium sulphate (($NH_4)_2SO_4$), a 10% solution of calcium chloride ($CaCl_2$), a 10% solution of potassium carbonate (K_2CO_3) and a 10% solution of calcium carbonate ($CaCO_3$) is slight, being in a range of 0.1–0.7%.

The investigations have shown that after storage in aqueous solutions of acids, hydroxides and salts and in water the loss in the mass of plain reinforcing bars coated with a layer of the sulphur polymer composite depended mainly on the type of environment and to a lesser degree on the thickness of the coating. For example, for the 1.5 mm thick sulphur polymer composite layer the largest loss in the mass of the rebars was recorded in a 5% solution of HNO_3—3.9% and in 5% solutions of hydroxides KOH and NaOH—30% and 43%, respectively. The smallest loss in the mass of the rebars, i.e. 0.1%, was recorded in water.

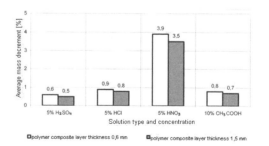

Figure 9. Average mass loss (in%) for plain rebars 10 mm in diameter, coated with layer of sulphur polymer composite, stored in aqueous solutions of acids for 1 year.

Similar results as for the 10 mm diameter rebars were obtained for the 20 mm diameter rebars (Hoła & Książek, 2009; Klakočar-Ciepacz & Książek, 2003; Książek, 2011).

3.6 Polarization investigations of tensioned rebars coated with sulphur polymer composite

Investigation results have been obtained as standard computer diagrams with stationary potentials E_0 and corrosion currents I_0 indicated.

An overview of all corrosion current densities i_0, stationary potentials E_0, at loads P, tensile stresses σ_0 and corrosion rates H_t is presented in (Hoła & Książek, 2009; Klakočar-Ciepacz & Książek, 2003; Książek, 2011). Corrosion rate H_t has been calculated basing on current densities i_0 measured prior and with using a formula:

$$H_t = 1.123 \cdot k \cdot i_0 \qquad (1)$$

where: k = 1.042 g/Ah means the electrochemical equivalent for iron.

Figure 12 shows corrosion rate H_t versus time (in a time interval of 3–168 hours) at a constant rebar tensile stress σ_a of 194.5 MPa. The rebars were plain rebars 10 mm in diameter, coated with a 0.5 mm and 1.5 mm thick layer of the sulphur polymer composite, immersed in a solution modelling the pore liquid in carbonated concrete contaminated with chloride ions.

According to the figure, after a tensile stress (σ_a) of 194.5 MPa was reached, the corrosion rate (H_t) changed during a time interval of 3–168 hours as follows: it increased initially and after 90 hours from the beginning of the test it started decreasing, amounting to about 0.0010 mm/year after 168 hours. It was lower in the case of the rebars coated with a 1.5 mm thick layer of the sulphur polymer composite. At this layer thickness, the corrosion rate was only very slightly dependent

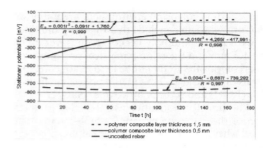

Figure 13. Stationary potential versus time and constant tensile stress $\sigma_a = 194.5$ MPa for plain rebars 10 mm in diameter, coated with sulphur polymer composite and for uncoated rebars.

on time and on the increasing tensile stress in the rebars. Within the test time interval it remained at an almost constant level of 0.000186–0.000242 mm/year. As the figure shows, the corrosion rate for the uncoated rebars was higher by three orders of magnitude. The corrosion rate over time is described by the equations given in Figure 12.

The very low, nearly constant corrosion rate in the case of the rebars coated with a 1.5 mm thick layer of the sulphur polymer composite is beneficial. Therefore such a layer can be considered as contributing to the protection of the reinforcing steel against corrosion in the solution modelling the porous liquid in carbonated concrete contaminated with chloride ions.

Figure 13 shows the dependence between stationary potential E_o, time and tensile strength for the tested rebars coated with a 0.5 mm and 1.5 mm thick layer of the sulphur polymer composite. For comparison purposes, the stationary potential E_o in similar uncoated rebars is shown. The dependencies are described by the included equations.

According to the test results, once a tensile strength σ_a of 194.5 MPa was reached in the rebars, a slight increase in stationary potential over time was observed. In the case of a 1.5 mm layer, potential E_o remained constant (close to 0 mV) during the whole test period. It also remained constant for the uncoated reference rebars, but at a level much different from 0 mV.

4 CONCLUSIONS

It can be concluded from the test results that the tested sulphur polymer composite can provide surface corrosion protection to the reinforcing steel in concrete. Sulphur composites have not been applied for this purpose before.

The tests have shown that a proper thickness of the sulphur polymer composite and the type of

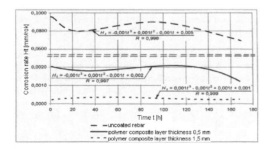

Figure 12. Corrosion rate versus time at constant tensile stress $\sigma_a = 194.5$ MPa for plain rebars 10 mm in diameter, coated with sulphur polymer composite and for uncoated rebars.

surrounding corrosion environment are important factors. One can conclude that the optimum thickness of the sulphur polymer composite layer should be 1.5 mm and the reinforcing steel protected with this composite should not be used in aqueous solutions of nitric acid (HNO_3) and potassium hydroxide (KOH) and sodium hydroxide (NaOH).

The aim of investigation was to evaluate tendencies of the corrosion process for St3S-b reinforcing steel when covered with polymer sulphuric coating and exposed to tensile stress. Steel samples were loaded in a way that their yield points were much exceeded; at the same time these samples were exposed to an action of the solution similar to that of pore-liquid of concrete and additionally contaminated with chloride ions (pH = 9.14). The composition was as follows: 0.015 M $NaHCO_3$ + 0.005 M Na_2CO_3 + 0.001 M NaCl. The corrosion rate for the steel decreased by 2 ÷ 3 orders of magnitude when covered with protective coating, even though it became unsealed at a load exceeding 88.5 MPa.

The author is aware that although the range of the tests carried out so far is quite wide, still further tests are needed to ultimately determine the suitability of the sulphur polymer composite for the surface protection of the reinforcing steel in concrete against corrosion. Also a simple and practical technology of applying this material to the surface of reinforcing steel needs to be developed.

REFERENCES

Brandt, A.M. 1994. Problem of durability of high performance concrete. *RILEM-3C-Workshop "Durability of HPC"*. Vienna.

Cairns, J., & Ramli B.A. 1995. Influence of Rib Geometry on Strength of Epoxy-Coated Reinforcement. *ACI Structural Journal*. No. I-II.

Czarnecki, L. & Garbacz, A. 1995. Evaluation of polymer coating-crack-bridging ability. *International Colloquium "Industrial Floors"'95*. Esslingen.

Czarnecki, L. & Garbacz, A. & Łukowski, P. & Clifton, J. 1999. Polymer Composites for Repairing of Portland Cement Concrete. Compatibility Project, NIST Report. *United States Department of Commerce, National Institute of Standards and Technology*. Gaithersburg MD.

Czarnecki, L. & Emmons, P.H. 2002. Naprawa i ochrona konstrukcji betonowych. *Wyd. Polski Cement*. Kraków.

Gillot, Z.E. & et al. 1982. *"Sulphur 82"*: 1–45. London.

Hadje-Ghafari, H. & et al. 1994. Bond of Epoxy-Coated Reinforcement: Cover, Casting Position, Slump, and Consolidation. *ACI Structural Journal*. No. I-II.

Hoła, J. 2002. Experimentally determined effects of technological and service factors on stress-induced destruction of concrete under compression. *Engineering Transactions*, Vol. 50: 251–265. Wrocław.

Hoła, J. & Książek, M. 2009. Research on usability of sulphur polymer composite for corrosion protection of reinforcing steel in concrete. *Archives of Civil and Mechanical Engineering*. Vol. 9, No. 1: 47–59.

Jankowski, L. & Pędziwiatr, J. & Styś, D. 1998. Some research problems due to the bond phenomenon between steel and concrete. *18th Symposium on Experimental Mechanics of Solids*. Jachranka.

Jaśniok, M. & Jaśniok, T. & Zybura A. 2003. Assessment the corrosion risk of reinforcing concrete using the DC and AC methods. Gliwice.

Jaśniok, T. & Zybura, A. 2004. Modelling of Polarization Range of Steel Bars in Corrosion Test of Reinforced Concrete. *14th Conference "KONTRA 2004" Durability of Buildings and Protection Against Corrosion*. Zakopane.

Jaśniok, M. & Zybura, A. 2007. Zabezpieczenie i regeneracja zagrożonych korozją konstrukcji z betonu. O przeciwkorozyjnym działaniu otuliny betonowej na zbrojenie, *"Przegląd Budowlany"* No. 1/2007: 20–25.

Klakočar-Ciepacz, M. & Książek, M. 2003. Investigation of the intensity of corrosion processes influence by tensile stress for reinforcing steel covered with sulphuric coating. *Chemicals in sustainable agriculture*. Jesenik: 761–765.

Książek, M. 1999. The sulphur binders - Their potential possibilities of using in buildings. Issue 75. *CONFERENCE No. 26*: 71–78.

Książek, M. 2001. The mechanical destruction of sulphur composites. Issue 80. *CONFERENCE No 76*: 105–112.

Książek, M. 2004. Usefulness of polymer sulphur composites to the protection against corrosion of reinforcement and concrete. *Doctoral dissertation. Series PRE report. No. 3/2004*. Wrocław.

Książek, M. 2006. Polarisation for Reinforcing Steel Covered with Polymeric Sulphuric Coating under the Tensile Stress. *15th Conference "KONTRA 2006" Durability of Buildings and Protection Against Corrosion*, Zakopane.

Książek, M. 2008. Examination on the influence of tensile stress on corrosion rate of reinforcing steel covered with polymeric sulphuric coating. *Kompozyty, No. 4*: 349–353.

Książek, M. 2009. Polarization investigations of tensioned rebars coated with sulphur polymer composite. *Kompozyty, No. 3*: 234–237.

Książek, M. 2010. The experimental research on adhesion and mass loss for reinforcing steel covered with polymeric sulphuric composites. *Kompozyty, No. 4*: 374–379.

Książek, M. 2011. The experimental and innovative research on usability of sulphur polymer composite for corrosion protection of reinforcing steel and concrete. *Composites. Part B: Engineering*. Vol. 42, iss. 5: 1084–1096.

Nicles, G. 1968. *Inorganic Sulphur Chemistry*. Amsterdam-London-New York.

Ściślewski, Z. 1999. *Ochrona konstrukcji żelbetowych*. Arkady. Warszawa.

Thelford, T. 1995. Coating Protection For Reinforcement. Comite Euro-International Du Beton. *State of the Art Report*: 51.

Treece, R.A. & Jirsa, J.O. 1989. Bond Strength of Epoxy-Coated Reinforcing Bars. *ACI Materials Journal*, No. III-IV.

Tuller W.N. 1954. The Nature of Sulphur, Data Book, New York.

Wieczorek, G. 2001. Pore solution properties in concrete with chlorides, *Kurdowski Symposium "Science of cement and concrete"*, Kraków.

Wieczorek, G. 2002. Korozja zbrojenia inicjowana przez chlorki lub karbonatyzację otuliny. *Dolnośląskie Wydawnictwo Edukacyjne*, Wrocław.

Zybura, A. 1994. Modelling of the Reinforcement Corrosion of the Scratching Concrete Cover. *Corrosion of Cement Paste*, Kraków.

Zybura, A. 2003. Zabezpieczenie konstrukcji żelbetowych metodami elektrochemicznymi. *Wydawnictwo Politechniki Śląskiej*, Gliwice.

Zybura, A. 2007. Electrochemical corrosion protection of concrete structure reinforcements. *"Ochrona przed Korozją" No. 1/2007.*

Concrete Solutions – Grantham, Mechtcherine & Schneck (eds)
© 2012 Taylor & Francis Group, London, ISBN 978-0-415-61622-5

Corrosion analysis of reinforced geopolymer concretes

K. Kupwade-Patil, E.N. Allouche, S. Vaidya & E.I. Diaz-Loya
Louisiana Tech University, Ruston, Louisiana, USA

ABSTRACT: A corrosion study was performed on specimens prepared as per ASTM G109. The specimens were designed to simulate corrosion behavior of steel reinforcement bars in a bridge deck when subjected to elevated chloride levels. The specimens incorporated three rebars, representing the top and bottom reinforcement meshes. Chloride was diffused into the concrete matrix, leading to the formation of an oxygen concentration cell and consequently chloride induced corrosion. Durability of Geopolymer Concrete (GPC) specimens prepared using one Class 'C' and two Class 'F' fly ash stockpiles was compared with that of identical specimens prepared using Ordinary Portland Cement (OPC). Specimens were subjected to accelerated corrosion using impressed current and conventional saltwater exposure. Corrosion behavior was evaluated using corrosion potentials, polarization resistance and electrochemical impedance spectroscopy. GPC specimens made from three fly ash sources exhibited lower corrosion rates, chloride ion penetrability and diffusion coefficients when compared with their OPC counterparts. At the end of the testing period OPC specimens exhibited corrosion product formation along with significant leaching. In contrast, the GPC specimens displayed no signs of leaching or corrosion product formation. Overall, the GPC specimens exhibited higher resistance to chloride induced corrosion compared with the OPC specimens, suggesting that GPC concrete might serve as substitute for OPC in reinforced concrete structures located in marine environments or subjected prolong exposure to brackish water.

1 INTRODUCTION

Concrete being a porous material is susceptible to the migration of deleterious species such as chlorides as shown in Figure 1 (Broomfield 2007). Various external sources, including sea salt spray, direct sea water wetting, deicing salts and contaminated aggregates, can be sources of chloride contamination in reinforced concrete structures. Chlorides diffuse into the capillary pores of the concrete and come into contact with the steel rebar. The protective oxide layer adsorbs chloride ions leading to the formation of ferrous chloride $FeCl_2$ as shown in Equation 1 (Ahmad 2006). The ferrous chloride reacts with moisture to form ferrous hydroxide [$Fe(OH)_2$] rust, a white greenish precipitate.

$$Fe^{2+} + 2Cl^- \rightarrow FeCl_2 \tag{1}$$

$$FeCl_2 + 2OH^- \rightarrow Fe(OH)_2 + 2Cl^- \tag{2}$$

1.1 Corrosion in bridge deck

Reinforcement corrosion in civil infrastructure is a multi-billion dollar per year problem (Bentur, 1997). A significant amount of damage due to reinforcement corrosion is noted in bridge decks.

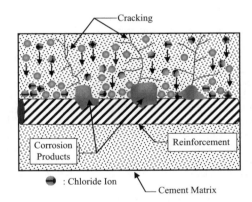

Figure 1. Mechanism of chloride induced corrosion in reinforced concrete.

This type of corrosion is driven by chlorides from deicing salts and pH reduction due to carbonation. Cracking in concrete bridge decks facilitates the ingress of chlorides and other harmful agents, thus accelerating deterioration in the reinforcing steel.

1.2 Geopolymer concrete

Geopolymers are a family of inorganic binders and are similar to zeolitic materials with amorphous microstructure (Davidovits 2008, Provis and van Deventer 2009). The polymerization process involves a rapid reaction under alkaline conditions of silica-aluminum minerals. These result in a 3D polymeric chain and a structure of Si-O-Al-O bonds. The alkaline liquids frequently used are sodium hydroxide (NaOH) or Potassium Hydroxide (KOH) in combination with sodium silicate. The solid phase could consist of Si content rich byproducts such as coal derived fly ash, slag or rice husk (Diaz et al. 2010, Chindaprasit et al. 2011). In addition, Al rich materials such as kaolin, bentonite and burned clays can also serve as precursors for the geopolymerization process.

GPC production can take place using both, low and high calcium based fly ash stockpiles. Factors such as particle size distribution, degree of vitrification, location of glass diffraction maximum and the presence of impurities (Ca, LOI) can affect the mechanical properties of the resulting GPC such as compressive strength and elastic modulus (Diaz et al. 2011).

1.3 Durability of geopolymer concrete

Previous studies showed that the expansion and shrinkage are generally well controlled in the case of geopolymer concretes. Furthermore, the homogenous nature of the geopolymer matrix contributes to high compressive strength and resistance to chemical attack and shrinkage (Provis and van Deventer 2009).

The potential for ASR in geopolymer concrete is considered minimal, even when high alkali content is used (Provis and van Deventer, 2009). Alkali Silica Reaction (ASR) is initiated during the dissolution and condensation polymerization process, while the material is still in a gel like form. ASR test results indicated that OPC showed a higher expansion by a factor of six (6) when compared to GPC specimens (Kupwade-Patil and Allouche, 2011). In addition, OPC specimens showed signs of severe leaching, minor cracking and a possible indication of delayed ettringite formation. XRD analysis of GPC specimens revealed an amorphous layer which was formed via reaction between the geopolymeric gel and calcium on the surface of the aggregates, resulting in a strong bond at the aggregate/matrix interface.

Limited research has been conducted to date regarding corrosion resistance of steel reinforcement embedded in GPC matrices. Previous durability related studies suggested that fly ash based geopolymers are able to passivate the steel reinforcement, and the stability of the passive layer depends on the concentration of the activator solution (Provis and van Deventer 2009). This paper reports intermediate results of a comprehensive

investigation into the susceptibility of steel reinforcement embedded in geopolymer concrete matrices to chloride induced corrosion.

2 EXPERIMENTAL PROCEDURE

2.1 Specimen configuration and preparation

An experimental investigation was undertaken to evaluate the effect of chloride induced corrosion on reinforced GPC specimens manufactured from Class F and C fly ash stockpiles. Class F fly ashes were obtained from Dolet Hills' Power Generation Station (PGS), located near Mansfield, Louisiana and a PGS located at Avon Lake, Ohio, and were designated 'Dolet Hills' and 'Ohio', respectively. Class C fly ash was obtained from the Monticello PGS located at Mount Pleasant, TX, and was designated 'Monticello'. ASTM G109 specimens were cast using the fly ash based GPC and Portland cement Type I. The steel rebars were 0.4 in. (10 mm) in diameter and 15 in. (381 mm) in length, as shown in Figure 2. The specimens were 280 mm (11 in.) in length, 115 mm (4.5 in.) in width and 150 mm (6 in.) in height. Plexiglas dams of 75 mm (3 in.) wide by 150 mm (6 in.) long, and 75 mm (3 in) height were secured using silicone caulk on the top of the cementitious specimens.

The GPC specimens were prepared using an activator solution (a 1:1 blend of sodium silicate and 14 M sodium hydroxide), which was mixed with the designated fly ash, fine aggregates and coarse aggregates. Three specimens each were prepared using fly ash stockpiles from Dolet Hill, Monticello and Ohio, as shown in Figure 3. The OPC specimens were prepared using Type I cement following ASTM C 192 (ASTM 2010).

The specimens were subjected to wet-dry cycle saltwater exposure, with the solution being placed in the Plexiglas dams during the wet cycles. The

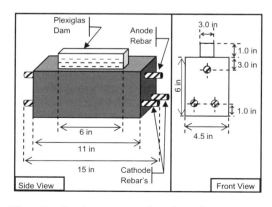

Figure 2. Specimen setup and configuration.

| Dolet Hill Fly Ash | Ohio Fly Ash |
| Monticello Fly Ash | OPC |

Figure 3. GPC specimens made from Dolet Hill, Ohio and Monticello fly ash.

wet-dry cycle saltwater consisted of 14 days of 7.5% NaCl solution exposure (wet cycle), followed by air exposure for an additional 14 days (dry cycle). A high concentration NaCl solution was used to simulate severe conditions and accelerate corrosion. A loose fitting plastic cover was used to minimize atmospheric evaporation. A relative humidity of 50 ± 5% was maintained during the experiment.

2.2 Electrochemical measurements

Half cell potential measurements were performed as per ASTM C 876 (ASTM 2010). A copper-copper sulfate (Cu/CuSO$_4$) half cell reference electrode (manufactured by Tinkor and Rasor Inc., San Gabriel, CA) was used to measure the corrosion potential. The corrosion potential was measured relative to the reference electrode using a multimeter (Gardner Bender, Milwaukee, WI). The corrosion potentials were recorded to the nearest 0.01 V.

Electrochemical polarization scans were taken using a Solarton potentiostat (model no 1287) manufactured by Roxboro Group Company (UK). The scans were taken in the range of −25 mV to +25 mV at a scanning rate of 0.2 mV/sec. A plot of current versus potential was generated. The slope of the potential versus current density at the origin of the plot is defined as the polarization resistance (R$_p$). This can be related to the Stern-Geary relationship to find the corrosion current density (I$_{corr}$) (Jones 1995). The IR drop was corrected using (R$_p$ = R − R$_\Omega$) where R is the total resistance measured by the polarization resistance scan and R$_\Omega$ is the concrete resistance.

The polarization resistance (R$_p$) is the ratio of the change in measured potential (ΔE) to the change in applied current per unit area (Δi), expressed as:

$$Rp = \frac{\Delta E}{\Delta i} \quad (3)$$

The corrosion current density (I$_{corr}$) is calculated using the value of R$_p$ and the proportionality constant, B:

$$I_{corr} = \frac{B}{Rp} \quad (4)$$

The resulting value of I$_{corr}$ was used to calculate the Corrosion Rate (CR) which was derived from the Faraday's law ASTM G102 (ASTM 2010):

$$CR = \frac{K_1 \times I_{corr} \times EW}{\rho} \quad (5)$$

where CR is corrosion rate (mpy = mils per year), K$_1$ is Faraday's constant, EW is the Equivalent Weight, and ρ is density (8.02 g/cm^3).

Titanium was used as a counter electrode, while Cu/CuSO$_4$ was used as a reference electrode. The reinforcement was connected to the working electrode on the impedance analyzer. Measurements were taken using the sweep frequency mode of a Solartron SI 1260 impedance/gain-phase analyzer, (Slough, Berkshire, UK). Measurements were taken as per ASTM G3-89. Real impedance versus imaginary impedance (Nyquist plots), frequency versus impedance magnitude (Bode plots) and frequency versus phase angle were plotted using Z-view software. Equivalent circuit analysis using Z-view software (manufactured by Scribner Associates, Inc) was used for calculating the diffusion coefficients.

Traditionally, ASTM C 1556 is used to estimate the chloride diffusion coefficients of cementitious mixtures ASTM C 1556 (ASTM 2010). In this work Electrochemical Impedance Spectroscopy (EIS) was used to evaluate the diffusion coefficients experimentally using a Nyquist Plot, a graph expressed in polar coordinates using gain and phase frequency response (Kupwade-Patil et al. 2010). The equivalent circuit used for estimating the diffusion coefficients, commonly referred to as Randle's equivalent circuit model, is given Figure 4.

Randle's equivalent circuit consists of an active electrolyte resistance (R$_s$) in series with a parallel

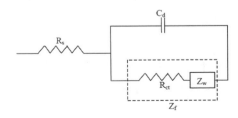

Figure 4. Randles circuit used for measuring diffusion coefficients.

combination of double layer capacitance C_d and impedance Z_f. From the Nyquist plot the real and imaginary parts of the impedance can be related using:

$$Z'' = Z' - R_s - R_{ct} + 2\sigma^2 C_d \qquad (6)$$

$$\sigma = \frac{RT}{n^2 F^2 A \sqrt{2}} \left(\frac{1}{D_o^{1/2} C_R} + \frac{1}{D_R^{1/2} C_R} \right) \qquad (7)$$

where Z' is the real component of the impedance, Z'' is the imaginary component of the impedance, R_s is the electrolyte resistance, R_{ct} is the resistance of charge transfer, C_d is the capacitance of electrode/electrolyte interface, σ is the coefficient of Warburg impedance, R is the gas constant, T is the absolute temperature, F is Faraday's constant, A is the area of electrode interface, D_o is the diffusion coefficient in the oxidized state, D_R is the diffusion coefficient in the reduced state and C_o and C_R are the concentration at reduced and oxidized states.

EIS was also used to study the effect of corrosion at the rebar/concrete interface. An accepted model for analyzing the rebar/concrete interface is shown in Figure 5 (Gu et al. 1997). It consists of three arcs, named the concrete matrix, the interfacial film adjoining the concrete matrix and the polarization resistance arc. The circuit consists of three parallel combinations of resistors and frequency dependent capacitors, known as the Constant Phase Element (CPE) (Orazem and Tribollet 2008).

Gu et al. distributed the total impedance (Z_t) into a summation of Concrete matrix impedance (Z_c), Interfacial film impedance (Z_i) and Polarization Impedance (Z_p), as shown in Figure 6. The Z_c was related to (R_c and C_c), Z_i to (R_i and C_i) and Z_p to (R_p and C_p) respectively.

$$Z_t = Z_c + Z_i + Z_p \qquad (8)$$

The polarization resistance (R_p) can be related to the corrosion process by using Equation [4]. Rp is inversely related to the corrosion current density (I_{corr}), hence a decrease in R_p causes Icorr and the corrosion rate (CR) to increase.

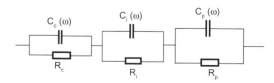

Figure 5. Equivalent circuit model for three parallel combinations of resistor and capacitor.

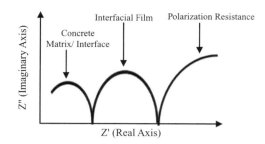

Figure 6. Interpretation of Nquist plot to corrosion characteristics at the rebar/concrete interface (Gu et al. 1997).

Macrocell corrosion measurement was done by calculating the voltage drop across a 100 Ω resistor (R) (ASTM 2010). This voltage (V) drop was used to calculate the corrosion current (I) by using Ohm's law given by,

$$I = \frac{V}{R} \qquad (9)$$

The macrocell current density is given by:

$$I_{mac} = \frac{I_o - I_i}{A} \qquad (10)$$

where I_{mac} is the macrocell current density in $\mu A/cm^2$, I_o and I_i are the output and input flow of electrons in the reinforcement in μA, and A is the surface area of the steel element in cm^2. A positive value for I_{mac} indicates the anodic state while a negative value means that it is cathodic.

Charge passed through the reinforced concrete specimen can be used to predict the chloride ion permeability ASTM C 1202 (ASTM 2010). The total current (I_j) is measured from the voltage (V_j) developed between the anodic and cathodic reinforcement that are separated by a 100 Ω resistor,

$$I_j = \frac{V_j}{100} \qquad (11)$$

The Charge Density (CD) in coulombs is given by (ASTM G109),

$$CD_j = CD_{j-1} + \left[\left(t_j - t_{j-1} \right) \times \left(\frac{i_j - i_{j-1}}{2} \right) \right] \qquad (12)$$

where CD = Charge density, t_j = time in seconds at which the measurement of macrocell current occurred, i_j = macrocell current (amps) at time t_j.

3 RESULTS AND DISCUSSION

3.1 *Corrosion potential and rates*

The corrosion potential of the top and bottom reinforcement bars is shown in Figures 7 and 8, respectively. An increase in corrosion potential until −202 mV was observed for the top reinforcement in all specimens after 7 days of severe saltwater exposure (Refer to Fig. 7). An increase in corrosion potential to −348 mV was observed on the specimens prepared with Monticello fly ash, while the rest of the specimens were −220 mV after 13 days of saltwater exposure. A sudden rise in corrosion potential was observed on the OPC specimens from −291 mV to −360 mV at the end of the 19th day of exposure.

Following 33 days of saltwater exposure the corrosion potential of the OPC specimen increased from −412 mV to −529 mV, while the GPC specimens were in the range of −323 mv (GPC–Ohio) to −392 mV (GPC-Monticello). The corrosion

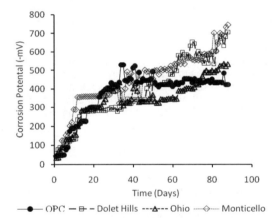

Figure 7. Corrosion potential of the top reinforcement.

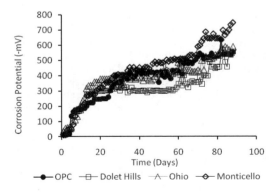

Figure 8. Corrosion potential of bottom reinforcement.

potential increased for all the specimens following 88 days of post saltwater exposure.

At day 88, corrosion potential values of −734 mV, −684 mV, −523 mV and −423 mV were observed for GPC (Monticello), GPC (Dolet Hills), GPC (Ohio) and OPC specimens, respectively. Corrosion potentials of −456 mV, −567 mV, −578 mV and −747 mV were measured at the bottom reinforcement for specimens prepared from Dolet Hills, Ohio, OPC and Monticello fly ash, respectively. Table 1 provides a guideline for interpreting corrosion potential values. A potential value of −734 mV is an indication of cathodic behavior, and could possibly be generated by lack of oxygen, resulting in controlled corrosion.

The Monticello specimens exhibit relatively high corrosion activity values during the test period. One possible explanation is that Monticello fly ash is a Class C Fly ash, and thus relatively rich in calcium. During saltwater exposure the NaCl may have reacted with the excess calcium that may not have been a part of the geopolymerization process, forming calcium chloride ($CaCl_2$). The formation of calcium chloride could have initiated corrosion of the reinforcement by lowering the pH value (Taylor 1997, Rixom and Mailvaganam 2002).

The OPC specimen showed a 90% increase in corrosion activity after 19th day (to −360 mV) followed by a steady increase to −412 mV following 32 days of saltwater exposure. The sudden increase in corrosion potential to −529 mV on day 33 possibly indicates breakdown of the passive layer of the reinforcement and initiation of corrosion. The specimens made from Ohio and Dolet Hill fly ash were still in the passive state after 33 days of saltwater exposure.

ASTM C 876 states that corrosion potential is not an indication of corrosion current and does not provide an overall justification to the chemistry of the working electrode (reinforcement). Corrosion rates using Linear Polarization Resistance (LPR) were measured to detect the possible indication of corrosion currents.

The corrosion rates for the top and bottom reinforcement rebars are shown in Figures 9 and 10,

Table 1. Interpretation of corrosion potential (ASTM C 876).

Half—cell potential reading vs Cu/CuSO$_4$	Probability of corrosion (%)
Less negative than −200 mV	<90%
Between −200 mV and −350 mV	Increased likelihood
More than −350 mV	>90%

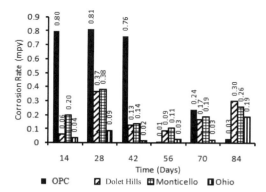

Figure 9.   Corrosion rates of the top reinforcement.

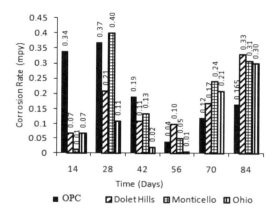

Figure 10.   Corrosion rates of the bottom reinforcement.

Table 2.   Interpretation of corrosion rates (Broomfield 2007).

Corrosion rate (mpy)	Damage (Years)
<0.10	No corrosion damage
0.10 < CR < 0.5	10–15
0.5 < CR < 5.0	2–10
>5.0	<2

* mpy: mils per year.

0.09 μA/cm^2 (0.04 mpy), 0.21 μA/cm^2 (0.09 mpy) and 0.04 μA/cm^2 (0.02 mpy) were recorded for the Ohio specimens after 14, 28 and 42 days, respectively. The Monticello GPC specimens exhibited corrosion rates in the range of 0.34–0.92 μA/cm^2 (0.14–0.38 mpy) in the first 42 days of saltwater exposure. Corrosion rates of the bottom reinforcements after 14 days were 0.02 μA/cm^2 (0.01 mpy) for GPC Monticello and 0.17 μA/cm^2 (0.07 mpy) for the Dolet Hills and Ohio GPC specimens (Refer to Fig. 10). The top reinforcement of GPC specimens were in the range of 0.02 μA/cm^2 (minimum value) to 0.90 μA/cm^2 (maximum value) indicating a range from no damage to corrosion expected in 10–15 years. The GPC specimens did not allow high corrosion currents, possibly via limiting penetration of chloride ions via the capillary pores. The GPC matrix helped to maintain the passivity of the reinforcement, thus delaying the onset of corrosion in the reinforcement.

3.2   Chloride ion penetrability

The charge passed via the cementitious matrix was calculated using Equation 12. The passage of charge enables the estimation of chloride ion penetrability. OPC specimens yielded values of 87, 1014, 2721, 4267, 5806 and 7585 coulombs after 14, 28, 42, 56, 70 and 84 days of saltwater exposure, respectively as shown in Figure 11. At the end of day 56 values equal to 446 (Dolet Hill), 2175 (Ohio) and 1072 (Monticello) coulombs were observed for the GPC specimens. Following 84 days of saltwater exposure charge values of 763, 5009 and 1617 coulombs were observed for the Dolet Hills, Ohio and Monticello GPC specimens respectively.

Moderate chloride ion penetrability was observed among the OPC specimens after 42 days and high chloride ion penetrability after 56 days of saltwater exposure (Refer to Table 3). This suggests that the chloride ion ingress was rapid and initiated high corrosion rates. This condition could have led to a breakdown of the passive layer on the reinforcement and formation of corrosion products, which at later stages could initiate cracking in the

respectively. The OPC specimens exhibited corrosion rates of 1.95 μA/cm^2 (0.80 mpy), 1.97 μA/cm^2 (0.81 mpy) and 1.85 μA/cm^2 (0.76 mpy) for the top reinforcement after 14, 28 and 42 days of wet-dry cycle saltwater exposure as shown in Figure 9. Corrosion rates of 0.83μA/cm^2 (0.34 mpy), 0.90 μA/cm^2 (0.37 mpy) and 0.46 μA/cm^2 (0.19 mpy) at the bottom reinforcement were detected after 14, 28 and 42 days. Due to the porous nature of OPC, chloride ions penetrated into the capillary pore and were in the vicinity of the top rebar.

The top rebar was rich in chlorides while the bottom rebar had more oxygen available forming an oxygen-concentration cell, which caused the initiation of corrosion currents. High corrosion rates for the OPC specimens indicate breakdown of the passive layer, suggesting damage within 2–10 years, as shown in Table 2.

Corrosion rates for the Dollet Hills GPC specimens were 0.14 μA/cm^2 (0.06 mpy), 0.90 μA/cm^2 (0.37 mpy) and 0.31 μA/cm^2 (0.13 mpy), while

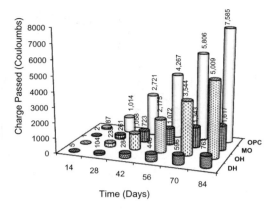

Figure 11. Macrocell current results on GPC and OPC specimens.

Table 3. Interpretation of chloride ion penetrability (ASTM C1202).

Charge passed (Coulombs)	Chloride ion penetrability
>4000	High
2000 to 4000	Moderate
1000 to 2000	Low
>100	Negligible

matrix. Following 56 days of saltwater exposure the GPC specimens exhibited low chloride ion penetrability, suggesting limited presence of chloride ions at the rebar/matrix interface. This could be attributed to the overall low permeability of the GPC matrix, as well as a possible interaction at the rebar/matrix interface that provides an additional protection from the onset of corrosion.

3.3 Electrochemical impedance spectroscopy

Nyquist plots for GPC and OPC specimens at 14, 42 and 88 days are shown in Figures 12–14 respectively. EIS was used to evaluate the effect of corrosion at the rebar/concrete interface. At the end of the 14th day, the OPC specimens had the shortest length as compared to the GPC specimens, as shown in Figure 12. The shortest length indicates lower values of polarization resistance (R_p) and higher corrosion current density (Icorr). The polarization resistance of GPC values at 42 and 88 days was higher than the OPC values, suggesting higher resistance to the charge transfer across the metal/electrolyte interface, and thus lower corrosion rates (Refer to Figs. 13 and 14).

The phase angle versus frequency plots are shown in Figures 15–17. Following 14 days of

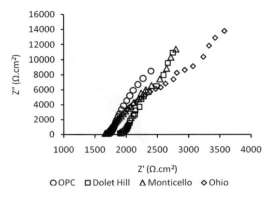

Figure 12. Nyquist plot for rebar for GPC and OPC specimens after 14 days.

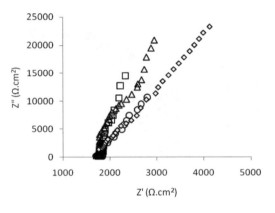

Figure 13. Nyquist plot for rebar for GPC and OPC specimens after 42 days.

saltwater exposure, phase angle values of 120°, 87°, 76° and 67° were recorded for the Ohio, Dolet Hills, Monticello and OPC specimens, respectively. Following 42 and 88 days of saltwater exposure the OPC specimens exhibited phase angle values of 10° and 8°, respectively. The decrease in phase angle of the OPC specimens is attributed to the initiation of pitting and possible domination of the formation of uniform corrosion products on the reinforcement (Mancio et al. 2008, Zhang et al. 2001).

Bode plots were prepared for the OPC and GPC specimens following 14, 42 and 88 days of saltwater exposure, and are shown as Figures 18–20, respectively. Following 14 days of exposure, the bode plots for the OPC specimens exhibited flatter curves compared to their GPC counterparts, suggesting the initiation of corrosion currents and the breakdown of the passive film of the steel bar reinforcement in the OPC specimens (see Fig. 14).

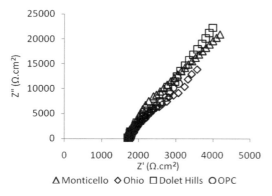

Figure 14. Nyquist Plot for rebar for GPC and OPC after 88 days.

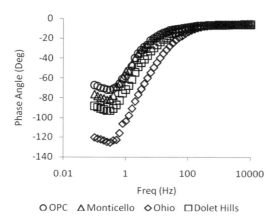

Figure 15. Phase angle versus frequency plot after 14 days.

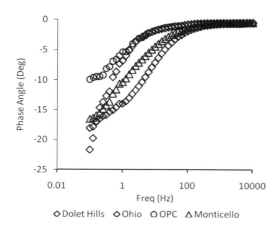

Figure 16. Phase angle versus frequency plot after 42 days.

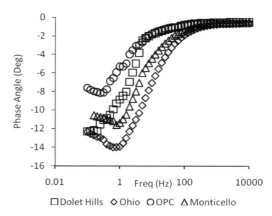

Figure 17. Phase angle versus frequency plot after 88 days.

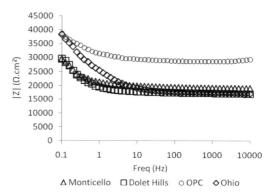

Figure 18. Bode plot after 14 days of saltwater exposure.

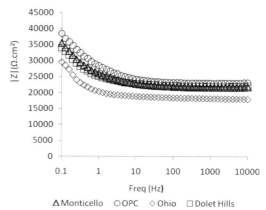

Figure 19. Bode Plots after 42 days of saltwater exposure.

274

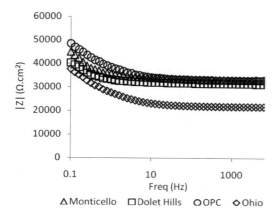

Figure 20. Bode plot after 88 days of saltwater exposure.

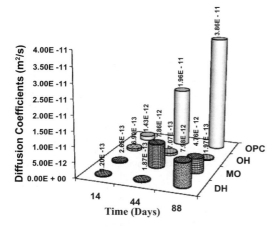

Figure 21. Diffusion Coefficients obtained at 14, 44 and 88 days using EIS.

The GPC specimens exhibited steeper slopes, which is indicative of more resistance to charge transfer between the anodic (top) and cathodic (bottom) rebars (i.e., no signs of corrosion currents). The Bode plots constructed after 42 and 88 days of exposure reveal flattened curves for the GPC and OPC specimens, indicating the initiation of corrosion (Zhang et al. 2001, Kupwade-Patil 2010).

The Bode plot after 88 days (Fig. 20) indicates that the Ohio specimens exhibited the greatest resistance to chlorides, displaying a higher slope as compared to the other specimens.

Diffusion coefficients were obtained via EIS, and are shown in Figure 21. OPC specimens yielded diffusion coefficients of 1.43×10^{-12}, 1.96×10^{-11} and 3.86×10^{-11} m²/s after 14, 44 and 88 days of saltwater exposure, respectively. Bentur and others

suggested a benchmark for diffusion coefficient of 1.63×10^{-12} m²/s for corrosion initiation for unprotected reinforced concrete made with 0.5 w/c ratio (Bentur et al. 1997). At the end of the 42nd day the OPC specimens exhibited values greater than this bench mark, indicating signs of corrosion.

An average GPC diffusion coefficient of 3.0×10^{-12} m²/s was obtained for the GPC specimens following 44 days of saltwater exposure. This diffusion coefficient value is ~7 times lower than the value measured for the OPC specimens (1.96×10^{-11} m²/s). Following 88 days of saltwater exposure the GPC specimens exhibited an average diffusion coefficient (4.31×10^{-12} m²/s) that is nearly an order of magnitude lower compared to the OPC specimens (3.86×10^{-11} m²/s). These observations provide strong indication that the GPC specimens exhibit higher resistance to chloride ion diffusion, inhibiting ingress and preventing the breakdown of the passive layer of the reinforcement. Hypothetical mechanism for this superior performance includes chemical bonding between the aluminum and the chloride ions or lower permeability of the GPC matrix.

3.4 Visual inspection

Images of the OPC specimens after 88 days are shown in Figures 22 and 23 (magnified image of the reinforcement). Corrosion products can be seen on the bottom rebars along with the leaching of sodium chloride salts. The severe saltwater exposure caused the chlorides to break down the passive layer and initiate corrosion product formation. The corrosion products could have also weakened the bond between the reinforcement and cement matrix.

In contrast, visual inspection of the GPC specimens after 88 days of severe saltwater exposure

Figure 22. OPC samples exhibiting corrosion products after 88 days of saltwater exposure.

Figure 23. Magnified image of OPC specimens exhibiting leaching and corrosion products.

Figure 24. GPC specimens exhibiting no signs of corrosion products at the rebar/concrete interface after 88 days of saltwater exposure.

revealed no signs of corrosion products on the reinforcements (See Fig. 24). Visual inspection and the corrosion data suggest that the GPC specimens are highly resistant to severe chloride exposure.

4 CONCLUSIONS

The GPC specimens did not allow high corrosion currents, possibly due to inhibition of chloride ion penetration via the capillary pores. The GPC specimens exhibited lower average diffusion coefficients by a factor of ~9 as compared with their OPC counterparts. The low chloride ion penetrability in the GPC specimens implies a lower chloride ion concentration at the rebar/concrete interface.

The EIS data indicates that the OPC specimens suggested the presence of pitting and/or uniform corrosion. In contrast, no pitting or uniform corrosion were implied by the EIS data collected for the GPC specimens. Extensive corrosion products formation along with leaching of sodium chloride salts were observed for all OPC specimens. The GPC matrix maintained the passivity of the reinforcement over the 88 days observation period, significantly delaying the on-set of reinforcement corrosion.

Overall, GPC specimens exhibited higher resistance to chloride induced corrosion compared with the OPC specimens, suggesting that GPC concrete might serve as substitute for OPC in reinforced concrete structures located in marine environments or subjected to prolonged exposure to brackish water.

REFERENCES

ASTM G 3-89. 2010. Standard practice for conventions applicable to electrochemical measurements in corrosion testing, West Conshohocken, ASTM International.
ASTM G 102. 2010. Standard practice for calculation of corrosion rates and related information from electrochemical measurements, West Conshohocken, ASTM International.
ASTM G 109. 2010. Standard test method for determining the effects of chemical admixtures on the corrosion of embedded steel reinforcement in concrete exposed to chloride environments, West Conshohocken, ASTM International.
ASTM C 192. 2010. Standard practice for making and curing concrete test specimens in the laboratory, West Conshohocken, ASTM International.
ASTM C 876, Standard test method for half-cell potentials of uncoated reinforcing steel in concrete, West Conshohocken, ASTM International.
ASTM C 1202, 2010. Standard test method for electrical indication of concrete's ability to resist chloride ion penetration, West Conshohocken, ASTM International.
ASTM C 1156. 2010. Standard test method for determining the apparent chloride diffusion coefficient of cementitious mixtures by bulk diffusion, West Conshohocken, ASTM International.
Ahmad, Z. 2006. Principle of Corrosion Engineering and Corrosion Control, Netherlands, Butterworth-Heinemann.
Bentur, A. Diamond, S. and Berke, S. 1997. Steel Corrosion in Concrete, London, E & FN Spon.
Broomfield, J. 2007. Corrosion of Steel in Concrete, London, Taylor and Francis.
Chindaprasirt, P. Chareerat, T. Hatanaka, S. and Cao, T. 2011. High-strength geopolymer using fine high-calcium fly ash, *ASCE Journal of Materials in Civil Engineering*, Vol.23 (3) 264–270.
Davidovits, J. 2008. Geopolymer Chemistry and Applications, France, Institut Geopolymere.

Diaz, E.I, Allouche, E. and Eklund, S. 2010. Factors affecting the suitability of fly ash as a source material for geopolymers, *Fuel*, Vol. 89 (5) 992–996.

Diaz, E.I, Allouche, E. and Vaidya, S. 2011. Mechanical properties of fly-ash-based geopolymer concrete, *ACI Materials Journal*, Vol. 108 (3) 300–306.

Gu, P. Elliot, S. Hristova, R, Beaudoin, J. Brousseau, R. and Baldock, B. (1997). A study of corrosion inhibitor performance in chloride contaminated concrete by electrochemical impedance spectroscopy, *ACI Materials Journal*, Vol. 94 (46) 385–395.

Jones, D. 1995. Principle and Prevention of Corrosion. New Jersey, Prentice Hall.

Kupwade-Patil, 2010, Mitigation of chloride and sulfate based corrosion in reinforced concrete via electrokinetic nanoparticle treatment, Ph.D. thesis, Louisiana Tech University, Ruston.

Kupwade-Patil, K and Allouche, E. Effect of Alkali Silica Reaction (ASR) in Geopolymer Concrete, World Coal Ash Conference, 9–12 May, 2011, Denver.

Kupwade-Patil, K. John, T.J. Mathew, B. Cardenas, H. and Hegab, H. Diffusion analysis of chloride in concrete following electrokinetic nanoparticle treatment, Proc. of ASME. International Conference on Nanochannels, Microchannel and Minichannels, 2–4 August, 2010, Montreal, Canada.

Mancio, M. Carlos, C. Zang, J. John, T.H. Monteiro, P. and Ali, A. (2008). Evaluation of concrete resistance of steel dowels used for concrete pavements, *ASCE Journal of Materials in Civil Engineering*, Vol. 20 (10) 650–658.

Orazem. M. and Tibollet. B. 2008. Electrochemical Impedance Spectroscopy, New Jersey, Wiley.

Provis, J.L. and van Deventer, J.S. 2009. Geopolymers: Structure, processing, properties and industrial applications, Boca Raton, CRC Press.

Rixom, R. and Mailvaganam, N. 2002. Chemical Admixture for Concrete, New York, Taylor and Francis.

Taylor, H.F.W. 1997. Cement Chemistry, London, Thomas Telford.

Zhang, Z. Monteiro, P and Morrison, H.F. (2001). Noninvasive surface measurements of corrosion impedance of reinforcing bar in concrete-Part. 1: Experimental results, *ACI Materials Journal*, Vol 89 (2) 116–125.

Concrete Solutions – Grantham, Mechtcherine & Schneck (eds)
© 2012 Taylor & Francis Group, London, ISBN 978-0-415-61622-5

The role of ascorbic acid on the adsorption to passive iron surface

H. Tian
Institute of Oceanology Chinese Academy of Sciences key laboratory of corrosion science in Shandong, Qingdao China
Graduate University of Chinese Academy of Science, Beijing China

W. Li & B. Hou
Institute of Oceanology Chinese Academy of Sciences, key laboratory of corrosion science in Shandong, Qingdao China

D. Wang
Max-Planck Institute for Polymer Research, Mainz, Germany

ABSTRACT: From cyclic voltammetry and in situ Raman spectroscopy measurements experiments have shown that, the adsorption mechanism of ascorbic acid onto iron surface was attributed to its ability to form a surface complex which tends to stabilize interstitial Fe^{II} in the Fe^{III} state and result in progressive development of an insoluble film. The analytical investigation through the use of rotating electrochemical quartz crystal microbalance (rEQCM) showed that the adsorption isotherms of ascorbic acid on iron in the active and passive state followed Langmuir-Freundlich behaviour from which the adsorption constant, standard free energy of adsorption and heterogeneity could be calculated. It is proposed that inhibitor molecules attach to film surface by means of chemical adsorption, where the interstitial cations were fixed in the octahedral sites for a stable nano-crystalline.

1 INTRODUCTION

Steel embedded in concrete is normally in a passive state against corrosion due to a thin iron oxide layer that forms on the steel surface and remains stable in the highly alkaline environment of the concrete. For the initiation of corrosion, this protective film can be destroyed (i.e., de-passivated) and this can be mainly done by the presence of chlorides or by carbonation of the cover concrete (Söylev et al., 2008). The use of corrosion inhibiting admixtures has grown over the last 25 years because they provide a level of protection and longevity that would be too expensive to achieve otherwise (Chen et al., 2010).

An ideal inhibitor would be a compound preventing corrosion without unfavourable effects on the properties of concrete and also without environmental hazards. Generally, the inhibitors used in concrete are inorganic compounds such as phosphates, chromates and nitrites (Ann et al., 2006 & Sanchez et al., 2011) or organic compounds based on amines or organic acids (Al-Mehthel et al., 2009), although some of them have toxic effects and pollute the environment. Application of small bio-molecules (Vitamin or antibacterial drugs often considered as possible substitutes) as

environmental-friendly, low cost, readily available corrosion inhibitors would be favourable. Ascorbic acid and mimosa tannin have been investigated also for comparative purposes as some previous work has shown that these compounds used in cases of pitting corrosion can act by competitive surface adsorption prior to the ingress of chlorides (Ferreira et al., 2004 & Akrout et al., 2004). Ascorbic acid has already been proved as a good steel corrosion inhibitor in saturated $Ca(OH)_2$ solution (Valek et al., 2008).

It is believed that the presence of an organic molecule in the corrosive media inhibits corrosion of metals by adsorbing at the metal-solution interface to suppress the incorporation of aggressive ions (Soylev et al., 2007). The well known adsorption mechanism valid for the studies in the oil and gas industry does not mean that it may be so successfully employed in reinforced concrete. In the former case, the molecules act directly on bare steel in acidic and neutral media. However, due the high alkalinity in concrete, there is already a protective oxide layer on the steel surface and the adsorption has to be on this passive layer rather than bare steel only (Ormellese et al., 2009 & Diamanti et al., 2008). Nowadays, very little information is available on the adsorption modes of this organic molecular-passive iron surface system.

The aim of this work is to make an investigation on the adsorption mechanism of ascorbic acid on passive iron surfaces by means of cyclic voltammetry, in situ Raman spectroscopy and rotating electrochemical quartz crystal microbalance (rEQCM) tests. Yet there have been a number of questions that the adsorption mode may also be dependent on the chemical composition of the aggressive ions and cement paste, but understanding how they function is an ongoing process that relies on experience to identify the most important issue (molecular and passive layer first) and on theory to untangle and describe the individual effects.

2 EXPERIMENTAL

2.1 Cyclic voltammetry and in situ Raman measurements

A self-designed Teflon cell was used for the cyclic voltammetry and in situ Raman investigations as shown in Fig. 1. A 5mm thick disc was cut from a 1cm diameter iron rod (offered by *Goodfellow Cambridge Ltd.*) and encased in epoxy with only the polished surface exposed. The disc was connected to the Parstat-2273 (*Princeton*) as the working electrode. The reference electrode was a saturated calomel electrode (SCE) with Luggin capillary. The counter electrode was a Pt ring disc. 1M NaOH solutions were prepared because the redox processes in the passive layer are well differentiated and it is not far from the alkalinity found in cement pastes from standard Portland cement (the upper limit corresponding to highly alkaline cements). Furthermore, unlike other alkaline media, NaOH was considered inert which allowed treating adsorption of ascorbic acid as a single component system (Marinković et al., 1996 & Ahlverg et al., 1990).

Raman measurements were performed using a Jobin Yvon T64000 Raman spectrometer equipped with notch filter to separate the emitting light and the Rayleigh component. The excitation light was the green Ar laser beam (514.5 nm). Excitation laser power on the samples was filtered to 0.65 mW to avoid thermal effects for the sensitive iron oxides. The water immersion microscope attachment was a 50 × long working objective. The detector was an air-cooled CCD having holographic gratings with 600 grooves/mm.

2.2 Adsorption measurements with the rEQCM

This study is based on methods (Kern et al., 2000) and patents obtained by P. Kern and D. Landolt. The mechanical parts of the experimental devices

Figure 1. Self-designed device for in-situ Raman investigations.

were prepared and fabricated by D. Wang from *Max-Planck Society* in Germany and L. Wang from *Lanxess Energizing Chemistry* in Germany and *CH Electrochemical Instruments* in China.

A Zahner potentiostat (*IM6 Germany*) was used, and a platinum wire served as a counter electrode. Two reference electrodes were employed: a Hg/HgO 1M KOH and a saturated electrode (SCE). All potentials in this paper are referred to the SCE because this electrode is the most employed for measurements on concrete rebar in the laboratory. The rEQCM electrode and its characterization are described elsewhere in detail (Kern et al., 2000). The 10 MHz AT cut quartz crystals with a sensitivity factor of 0.217 Hz·cm^2·ng^{-1} (Vatankhah et al., 2003) were contained in exchangeable holders mounted on a rotating shaft. The 400 nm thick Fe electrodes were prepared by electro-deposition on a 190nm thick sputter deposited Au film with an adhesion layer of 30 nm Cr.

For adsorption studies in the active potential region (Kern et al., 2001), the electrodes were immersed in 0.1 M NaClO$_4$ and a cathodic polarization at −1.5V was applied; a plateau in the EQCM signal after an initial mass loss indicated the complete removal of the oxide. All solutions were adjusted to 25°C and to pH 8.6 with NaOH which is the isoelectric point of the Fe$_2$O$_3$ passive film. Ascorbic acid has a pK value of 4.17, hence, it exists as anions in neutral solutions. Perchlorate used as the supporting electrolyte showed no specific adsorption on iron and NaOH was considered inert which allowed us to treat adsorption of Ascorbic acid as a single component system.

For adsorption in the passive potential region, the electrodes were immersed in 1M NaOH solution. The oxide was formed by sweeping the potential from -1.25 to $0.25\,V$ at $5\ mVs^{-1}$ and holding the potential at $0.25\,V$ until the current density had dropped to a few $\mu A\ cm^{-2}$ and the frequency became stable.

The electrodes were polarized at $-1.25\,V$ for adsorption in the active region and at $+0.25\,V$ for the passive region and maintained at those potentials throughout the sequential inhibitor additions. After applying a constant potential, the inhibitor concentration was increased in steps by adding $20\,ml$ of solution containing 1×10^{-4}, 10^{-3} (2 times), 5×10^{-3} (2 times), 1×10^{-2} (5 times) and $2 \times 10^{-2}\,M$ (5 times) ascorbic acid to an initial volume of $50\,ml$ solution.

The frequency change Δf is given with respect to the absolute resonant frequency of the quartz crystal and contains two contributions (Kern et al., 2001):

$$\Delta f = \Delta f_{m,ads} + \Delta f_{\eta,b(c)} \qquad (1)$$

where $\Delta f_{m,ads}$ is the frequency shift due to the adsorbing species at the electrode and $\Delta f_{\eta,b(c)}$ is the concentration dependent frequency shift resulting from viscosity and density changes in the electrolyte layer sensed by the EQCM. However, effects of $\Delta f_{\eta,b(c)}$ on the EQCM become important only at concentrations above $10^{-2}\,M$, therefore, in the following, Δf always refers to the frequency values $\Delta f_{m,ads}$.

3 RESULTS AND DICUSSION

3.1 Cyclic voltammetry and in situ Raman spectroscopy investigations

In order to investigate the adsorption mechanism of ascorbic acid onto the iron surface, cyclic voltammetry in 1M NaOH blank solution and with addition of various ascorbate concentrations were performed. The different peaks observed in the voltammogram of Fig. 2 are assigned as follows (Joiret et al., 2002). The peak I is attributed to the reduction of adsorbed hydrogen on the iron surface formed during the cathodic polarization. The anodic peaks II and III and the cathodic peaks X and XI are assigned to the redox processes between Fe^0 and Fe^{II}:

$$Fe + 3H_2O \Leftrightarrow FeO + 2H_3O^+ + 2e^- \qquad (2)$$

It is possible that Fe^0 is derived from the disproportionation reaction of FeO in the passive layer formed by the process associated to peak II, according to Eq. (3)

$$4FeO \rightarrow Fe^0 + Fe_3O_4 \qquad (3)$$

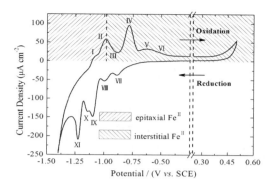

Figure 2. The cyclic voltammogram of iron electrode in 1M NaOH blank solution purged with N_2, scan rate $0.5\,mV\cdot s^{-1}$ (1st cycle).

The presence of magnetite at highly cathodic potential corresponding to peak III was verified experimentally by in situ Raman spectra (Fig. 3 (A)). The transformation of Fe^{II} may take place and the oxidation of Fe^{III} thus formed gives rise to peak III.

Peaks IV and IX are due to the formation of magnetite:

$$3Fe(OH)_2 + 2OH^- \Leftrightarrow Fe_3O_4 + 4H_2O + 2e^- \qquad (4)$$

Peaks V and VI in anodic sweep and VII and VIII in cathodic sweep are attributed to the formation of two different Fe^{III} species obtained from magnetite oxidation:

$$2Fe_3O_4 + 2OH^- \Leftrightarrow 3\gamma Fe_2O_3 + H_2O + 2e^- \qquad (5)$$

$$Fe_3O_4 + OH^- + H_2O \Leftrightarrow 3\alpha FeOOH + e^- \qquad (6)$$

The formation of goethite needs less energy than maghemite because of the topotactic nature of the reaction thus may correspond to peaks V and VIII. The electric charge, Q (Fig. 4), involved for each peak has been evaluated by considering a Gaussian function for convolution, in order to verify its compatibility with the reactions proposed above. Fig. 4 shows that the charges associated to peaks III–VI are close to that determined for the corresponding cathodic peaks VII–X. This observation corroborates therefore the association of different peaks made above.

It is postulated that there are two Fe^{II} species having different energy state, one possibility is that anodic polarization from relatively negative values of around $-1.1\,V$ to more positive potentials, corresponding to the range of peak II, causes the formation of epitaxial Fe^{II} near the oxide surface. Another possible source is the interstitial Fe^{II},

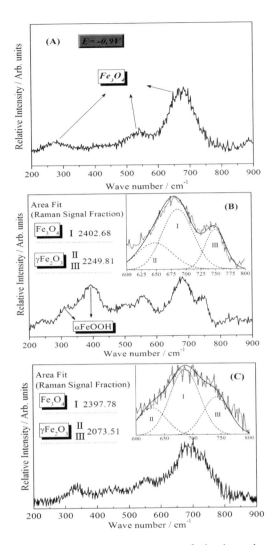

Figure 3. Insitu Raman spectra of the iron electrode in 1 M NaOH blank solution at different anodic polarization potentials (A): E = −0.9 V; (B): E = −0.5 V; (C): E = 0.5 V.

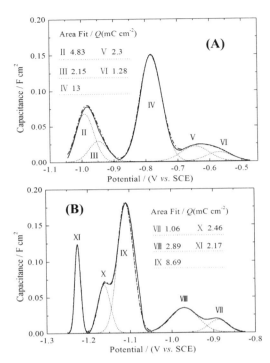

Figure 4. Gaussian convolution and charge involved for each peak of the voltammogram given in Fig. 2 (A): the anodic branch; (B): the cathodic branch.

dispersed in the oxide interstices, that continues forming in the whole forward scan interval of potential from −1.4 to 0.5 V.

If Fe^{III} involved in peak III is entirely formed by the reaction depicted by Eq. (3), the charge of peak III should be one fourth of that of peak II. Fig. 4 (A) indicates that this ratio is practically one half. Likewise, according to Eq. (4) the charge associated to peak IV should be one third of the sum of peak II and III, whereas the observed value is much bigger. Both remarks probably corroborate

the formation of interstitial Fe^{II} when the potential scans positively.

According to Eqs. (5) and (6), the sum of charge involved in peaks V and VI is one third of that needed to completely transform magnetite formed at peak IV into ferric oxide. Fig. 4 (A) indicates that only one fifth of charge is found to form the latter species. That is to say, for the potential above peak IV, there is a high amount of accumulation of magnetite at the electrode surface. This consideration is supported by the results of Raman spectra (Figs. 3 (B) and (C)) that indicate the presence of magnetite in the potential sweep towards more anodic domain corresponding to a typical passive state.

When a real passivity scale is analyzed using Raman spectroscopy, it is seldom that one of the spectra obtained on pure iron oxide is recorded but often a mixture of different oxides presented above. In order to correlate the Raman intensity with a mass fraction of each oxide, a decomposition method was therefore used to approximately quantify the amounts of the different compounds. As revealed by Fig. 3 (B), the strongest peak at 675 cm⁻¹ proves the existence of magnetite, whereas, maghemite is characterised by intensive bands at

650 and 750 cm⁻¹. The formation of goethite is also evidenced by several narrow bands appeared in the range of 300–500 cm⁻¹, which is consistent with Eqs. (5) and (6) proposed above. However, at potentials more anodic (Fig. 3 (C)), this species disappears probably it dissolves. As already reported previously for the magnetite-maghemite binary mixture, the "shadowing effect" underlines that magnetite cannot be detected by Raman spectra unless it is present almost alone as pure compound (Dubois et al., 2008). Figs. 7 (B) and (C) show that the contribution of magnetite to Raman signals remains a significant fraction of about 50%. It can therefore be concluded that the passive layer experimentally detected is composed of a highly dominant magnetite and some other minor oxide compounds.

It is generally accepted that surface energy considerations can stabilize spinel Fe_3O_4 over thermodynamically stable γ-Fe_2O_3, which may help to explain why the magnetite is preferentially accumulated on the electrode surface rather than transformed into a hydrated Fe^{III} oxide. Thus, it could be deduced that only a small part of magnetite is used in the formation of Fe^{III} species, whose contribution to Raman signals is relatively weak (Figs. 3 (B) and (C)) for a tiny weight fraction of less than 10% [38]. The maghemite in this potential range is therefore likely related to the electrical reorganisation of the film with interstitial Fe^{III}. The emission rate of this ion species that will result from partial oxidation of interstitial Fe^{II}, as postulated above, is not potential dependent. Coincidentally, Fe^{2+} and Fe^{3+} have been found leaving the ring-disk electrode at whole potential cycle, which indicates that a fraction of interstitial Fe^{II} and Fe^{III} injected into the solution, and another trapped inside the film contribute to the process observed by anodic peaks.

The hypothesis upon which the present work is based is in good agreement with the point defect model. The truncated version of PDM (Macdonald et al., 2006) as applied to iron in alkaline media is shown schematically in Fig. 5. The passive oxide film has been described as a bilayer consisting of an inner barrier layer based on magnetite-type structure, that grows directly on the iron surface (Reaction C), and an outer layer of γ-Fe_2O_3 precipitated via the hydrolysis of interstitial iron cations ejected from the barrier layer (Reaction B) or by hydrolytic restructuring of the barrier layer itself. The film behaves as a highly doped n-type semiconductor due to a preponderance of iron interstitials and oxygen vacancies as electronic donors.

The above assumptions are confirmed by the analysis of cyclic voltammetry curves recorded in solutions containing ascorbic acid. As observed in Fig. 6, the addition of 10^{-3} M ascorbic acid

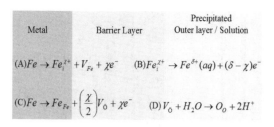

$$(A)\, Fe \rightarrow Fe_i^{\chi+} + V_{Fe} + \chi e^-$$ $$(B)\, Fe_i^{\chi+} \rightarrow Fe^{\delta+}(aq) + (\delta - \chi)e^-$$

$$(C)\, Fe \rightarrow Fe_{Fe} + \left(\frac{\chi}{2}\right) V_{\ddot{O}} + \chi e^-$$ $$(D)\, V_{\ddot{O}} + H_2O \rightarrow O_O + 2H^+$$

Figure 5. Schematic of physicochemical processes that occur with a passive film according to the truncated point defect model; Fe = iron atom; $Fe_i^{\chi+}$ = interstitial iron; $Fe^{\delta+}(aq)$ = iron cation in out layer / solution; Fe_{Fe} = iron ion in cation lattice; $V_{\ddot{O}}$ = oxygen vacancy; O_O = oxygen ion in anion lattice.

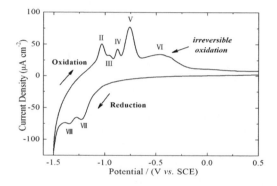

Figure 6. Cyclic voltammogram of iron electrode in 1M NaOH solution with addition of 10^{-3} M ascorbic acid, scan rate 0.5 mV·s⁻¹ (2nd cycle).

significantly alters the redox behaviour of the passive film on iron. Under a positive polarization, four peaks are well resolved, corresponding to the successive oxidation of iron to higher valence states ($Fe^0 \rightarrow FeO \rightarrow Fe_3O_4$). Subsequently, in the backward scan, the overlapping reduction peaks appear, suggesting thus a counterpart conversion of Fe_3O_4 to Fe^0. It is interesting to note that a current increase is observed for potentials more anodic than −0.5 V. This irreversible oxidation process may concern the adsorbed ascorbic acid molecules because it has been observed neither in Fig. 2 nor in previous research works involving iron in NaOH solutions. This argument is supported by Raman spectra (Fig. 7) obtained at the potential of peak VI up to −0.3 V, the intense bands at around 675 cm⁻¹ are connected with the formation of magnetite. The strong absorption at 625 cm⁻¹ has been attributed to the C-C stretching of five-membered lactone ring system with various vibrational bands in the region 800–900 cm⁻¹ arising from C-O in-plane deformation (coupled with the neighbouring

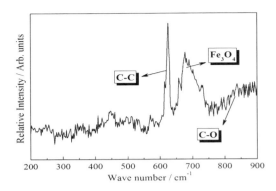

Figure 7. In situ Raman spectra of the iron electrode in 1 M NaOH solution with addition of 10^{-3} M ascorbic acid at the anodic polarization potential of -0.3 V.

vibrations along the conjugated bonds), which shows the presence of an ascorbic acid molecule-inner barrier layer adsorbed system. The disappearance of the outer layer can be interpreted in terms of reduced interstitial Fe^{II} emission. In other words, inhibitor molecules may act as depolariser of the cathodic reaction in iron corrosion.

Ascorbic acid chelating properties could account for both, the irreversible oxidation process and the disappearance of out layer mentioned in the PDM. Chang and Matijević have proposed two mechanisms of iron oxide behaviour in the presence of a chelating agent (Chang et al., 1983): (1) solution coordination mechanism and (2) surface complexation mechanism. The first involves reaction of chelating agent with interstitial Fe^{II}, released from the barrier layer, via ligands thereby promoting autoxidation of Fe^{II} to Fe^{III}. The second assumes surface complexation of iron oxide with chelating species. In this case, after the formation of a surface complex, the relative bond strength of Fe-ion with lattice oxygen and with the chelating molecule will be of outmost importance. If the lattice bond with Fe-ion is sufficiently weakened, the entire complex will be released into the solution. However, if the bond is stable enough, the complex will stay adsorbed at film surface, where the conformation of chelating agent in its adsorbed form will play an essential role. It was shown that this process is pH dependent and, in a higher pH environment, iron intersitials can be bonded to the terminal oxygen anions, giving iron-oxygen double bonds, at which the anion charge is delocalized and strong Lewis acidity can appear enabling formation of outer sphere complexes. Hence, interstitial Fe^{II} release could be significantly reduced by formation of Fe^{III}-complex that results in progressive development of a surface insoluble film. Stabilization of iron in Fe^{III} state can be explained by formation of highly stable surface complexes with the inhibitor ligands. Stability constants of the investigated compounds with Fe^{III} are listed elsewhere (Das et al., 2003).

Fig. 8 shows that the charge involved in oxidation peaks II–V are four times that determined for reduction peaks. This discrepancy indicates that the inner barrier layer is apparently stabilized by the adsorbed inhibitors such that upon cathodic polarization the reduction reaction is suppressed.

It has been reported in the literature (Valek et al., 2008) that the increase in the concentration of a chelating agent may change its activity towards iron dissolution from inhibitive to stimulative. Solubility of a complex is to a large extent determined by iron/ligand ratio, where for higher ratios sparingly soluble mono or polynuclear complexes could be formed. It may be concluded that the increase in ligand concentration and the resulting decrease of the iron/ligand ratio in the near electrode layer create favourable conditions for soluble complexes formation, while at low concentration, insoluble ones are formed. As seen from Fig. 9, the difference in the behaviour of iron in 10^{-3} M and 10^{-2} M solutions is particularly obvious at potentials more positive than -0.5 V where for 10^{-2} M solution a new anodic current peak appears. Absence of the corresponding reduction peak may indicate the lack of accumulation of reaction products due to the dissolution of iron caused by formation of a soluble Fe^{II}-complex, resulting in passive film deterioration. High spin Fe^{II} species, probably attributable to the Fe^{II}-ascorbate complex were identified, by Mössbauer spectroscopy, at the mild steel surface after exposure to ascorbate solution of concentrations higher than 0.005 M (Nigam et al., 1990). Hence, the possible explanation for lower inhibitor efficiency at higher concentrations is the occurrence of reductive dissolution through the soluble Fe^{II}-ascorbate complex formation as opposed to the sparingly soluble Fe^{III}-complex formation at lower ascorbic acid concentrations.

3.2 Adsorption analysis with the rEQCM

Adsorption experiments with the stepwise addition of Ascorbic acid were performed at different potentials and resulted in the frequency responses given in Fig. 10. The inhibitor when added to the base electrolyte led to an increase in resonance frequency, which according to Sauerbrey's equation corresponds to a mass loss of the electrode. This behaviour is in qualitative agreement with the solvent substitution model proposed by taking into account the fact that the EQCM senses not only the mass of the electrode, but also that of the electrolyte layer immediately adjacent to the surface (Gan et al., 2000). The organic molecules adsorbing at the iron surface, occupying a large steric volume, replace several layers of much smaller, but well-oriented water molecules. This leads to a decrease in the density of the electrolyte layer immediately adjacent to the electrode surface, and hence of the effective mass sensed by the crystal. All Δf curves display a maximum.

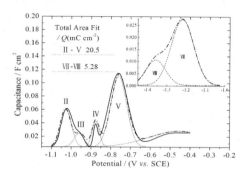

Figure 8. Gaussian convolution and total charge involved for the peaks of the voltammogram given in Fig. 6.

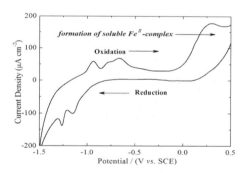

Figure 9. Cyclic voltammogram of iron electrode in 1M NaOH solution with addition of 10^{-2} M ascorbic acid, scan rate 2 mV·s⁻¹ (3rd cycle).

It is assumed that this concentration corresponds to formation of an ascorbic acid monolayer at the electrode. Apparently, more water is replaced during adsorption on iron than on iron oxide. The maximum is reached at a lower concentration on iron, which indicated an earlier monolayer formation. Consistent with these observations, an XPS study showed that the inhibitor adsorbs better on iron in the active than in the passive state (Olsson et al., 2000). Linear sweep experiments also showed it to be more effective in suppressing the anodic dissolution in the active region (Kern et al., 2002). This can be due to a different packing density of the inhibitor or to the nano-scale roughness and chemical effects of the oxidized surface. On the other hand, the adsorption of inhibitor anion is rendered more easily since the iron surface is more positively charged with respect to the potential of zero charge. Therefore, the subsequent derivation of adsorption isotherms is needed to further elucidate the considerations.

The surface coverage (θ) as a function of ascorbic acid concentration was obtained from EQCM data by the following equation:

$$\theta = \frac{\Delta f}{\Delta f_{max}} \qquad (7)$$

The double logarithmic plots of $\frac{\theta}{1-\theta}$ versus C were fitted to the Langmuir-Freundlich isotherm model (Eq. (8)) and yielded straight lines with regression coefficients almost equal to 1 (Fig. 11).

$$\theta = \frac{(KC)^h}{1+(KC)^h} \qquad (8)$$

where K is the adsorption constant, C the concentration and h ($0 \le h \le 1$) the heterogeneity parameter. The LF model describes multisided

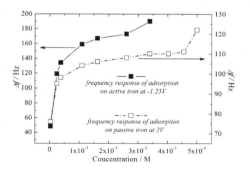

Figure 10. Frequency shift of the ascorbic acid adsorption on active and passive iron as a function of inhibitor concentration.

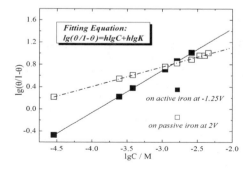

Figure 11. Curve fitting to the Langmuir-Freundlich isotherm for ascorbic acid adsorption on active and passive iron.

Table 1. Fitting results from the Langmuir-Freundlich isotherm applied to rEQCM adsorption data.

System	h	K	ΔG^0_{ads} (KJ/mol)
On active iron at −1.25 V	0.75	8400	−32.35
On passive iron at 2 V	0.35	148871	−39.62

* The heterogeneity parameter h, the adsorption constant K and the standard free energy of adsorption ΔG^o_{ad} formed on iron surface

adsorption on heterogeneous surfaces neglecting interactions between adsorbed molecules.

Adsorption constant K is related to the standard free energy of adsorption ΔG^o_{ads} by Eq. (9).

$$K = \frac{1}{55.5} \exp\left(\frac{-\Delta G^o_{ads}}{RT}\right) \quad (9)$$

All the obtained thermodynamic parameters were given in Table 1. The energy distribution of adsorption sites on active iron is clearly narrower than on the oxide surface, indicating a more homogeneous behaviour. K and ΔG^o_{ads} are significantly higher for passive films than for active iron. Generally, for values of ΔG^o_{ads} up to −20 KJ · mol^{-1}, the type of adsorption is regarded as physisorption, the process is due to electrostatic interactions between molecules and charged metal, while the values around −40 KJ · mol^{-1} or smaller are associated with chemisorption as a result of sharing or transferring of electrons to form coordinate type bonds. Ascorbic acid adsorbed on iron in the active state form bonds with adsorption energy comparable to complex interactions which may involve both chemisorption and physisorption. However, the value of ΔG^o_{ads} for adsorption on iron in the passive state indicated that the mechanism was a typical chemisorption.

4 CONCLUSION

- Ascorbic acid significantly altered the redox behaviour of the passive oxide film. The interstitial iron cations emission could be reduced by formation of a Fe^{III}-complex Stabilization of iron in the Fe^{III} state can be explained by formation of highly stable surface complexes with the ascorbic acid ligands.
- The adsorption model of ascorbic acid on iron in the active and passive state obeyed the Langmuir-Freundlich isotherm. The adsorption process was spontaneous. The value of the standard free energies of adsorption indicated that ascorbic acid adsorbed on iron in the passive state was a typical chemisorption mechanism.

REFERENCES

Ahlberg, E. & Friel, M., J. Electrochem. Soc. 137 (1990) 1196.
Akrout, H., Bousselmi, L. & Dalard, F., J. Mater. Sci. 39 (2004) 7341.
Al-Mehthel, M. & Dulaijan, S. Construc. Build. Mater. 23 (2009) 1768–1774.
Ann, K.J., Jung, H.S. & Kim, H.S. Cem. Concr. Res. 36 (2006) 530–538.
Chen, W., Du, R. & Ye, C. Electrochim. Acta 55 (2010) 5677–5682.
Chang, H.C. & Matijević, E. J. Colloid Interface Sci. 92 (1983) 479.
Das, C.M. & Sudersanan, M. J. Appl. Electrochem. 33 (2003) 333.
Diamanti, M.V., Ormellese, M. & Pedeferri, M. Cem. Concr. Res. 38 (2008) 1349–1353.
Dubois, F., Mendibide, C. & Pagnier, T., Corros. Sci. 50 (2008) 3401–3409.
Ferreira, E.S., Giacomelli, C. & Spinelli, A. Mat. Chem. Phys. 83 (2004) 129.
Gan, F., Dai, Z. & Wang, D., Corros. Sci. 42 (2000) 1379–1388.
Joiret, S., Keddam, M. & Takenouti, H., Cem. Concr. Compos. 24 (2002) 7–15.
Kern, P. & Landolt, D., Corros. Sci. 44 (2002) 1809–1824.
Kern, P. & Landolt, D. Electrochim. Acta 47 (2001) 589–598.
Kern, P. & Landolt, D. J. Electroanal. Chem. 500 (2001) 170–177.
Kern, P. & Landolt, D. J. Electrochem. Soc. 147 (2000) 318–325.
Macdonald, D.D. & Sun, A. Electrochim. Acta. 51 (2006) 1767–1779.
Marinković, N.S., Calvente, J.J. & Kováčová, Z., J. Electrochem. Soc. 143 (1996) L171.
Nigam, A.N., Tripathi, R.P. & Jangid, M.L. Corros. Sci. 30 (1990) 201.
Olsson, C., Agarwal, P. & Landolt, D. Corros. Sci. 42 (2000) 1197.
Ormellese, M., Taffaini, G. & Ganazzoli, F. Corros. 3 (2009) 22–26.
Söylev, T.A. & Richardson, M.G. Constr. Build. Mater. 22 (2008) 609–622.
Soylev, T. & McNally, C. Cem. Concr. Res. 37 (2007) 972–977.
Sanchez, M. & Alonso, M. Constr. Build. Mater. 25 (2011) 873–878.
Valek, L., Martinez, S. & Brnardić, I. Corros. Sci. 50 (2008) 2705–2709.
Vatankhah, G., Lessard, J. & Jerkiewicz, G. Electrochim. Acta 48 (2003) 1619.

Concrete Solutions – Grantham, Mechtcherine & Schneck (eds)
© 2012 Taylor & Francis Group, London, ISBN 978-0-415-61622-5

Geopolymer concrete: A concrete of the next decade

D.B. Raijiwala & H.S. Patil

Department of Applied Mechanics, S V National Institute of Technology, India

ABSTRACT: This paper presents the progress of the research on making geopolymer concrete using the thermal power plant fly ash, (Ukai) Gujarat, India. The project aims at making and studying the different properties of Geopolymer concrete using this fly ash and the other ingredients locally available in Gujarat. Potassium hydroxide and sodium hydroxide solution were used as alkali activators in different mix proportions. The actual compressive strength of the concrete depends on various parameters such as the ratio of the activator solution to fly ash, molarity of the alkaline solution, ratio of the activator chemicals, curing temperature etc. In recent years concrete usage around the world has been second only to water. Ordinary Portland Cement (OPC) is conventionally used as the primary binder to produce concrete. The amount of the carbon dioxide released during the manufacture of OPC due to the calcinations of limestone and the combustion of fossil fuel is in the order of one ton for every ton of OPC produced. In addition, the extent of energy required to produce OPC is only next to steel and aluminum. Attempts to reduce the use of Portland cement in concrete are receiving much attention due to these environment-related issues. Fly ash-based Geopolymer concrete is a 'new' material that does not need the presence of Portland cement as a binder. The role of Portland cement is replaced by low calcium fly ash. Geopolymer is an inorganic alumino-hydroxide polymer synthesized from predominantly silicon (Si) and aluminum (Al) materials of geological origin or byproduct materials such as fly ash. The term Geopolymer was introduced to represent the mineral polymers resulting from geochemistry. The process involves a chemical reaction under highly alkaline conditions on Si-Al minerals, yielding polymeric Si-O-Al-O bonds in amorphous form.

1 GEOPOLYMER CONCRETE

The production of one ton of cement emits approximately one ton of carbon dioxide to the atmosphere which leads to global warming conditions. A need of the present status is, should we build additional cement manufacturing plants or find alternative binder systems to make concrete. On the other scenario huge quantities of fly ash are generated around the globe from thermal power plants and generally used as a filler material in low level areas. Alternative binder systems with fly ash to produce concrete eliminating cement is called "Geopolymer Concrete".

Geopolymer is a type of amorphous alumino-hydroxide product that exhibits the ideal properties of rock-forming elements, i.e., hardness, chemical stability and longevity. Geopolymer binders are used together with aggregates to produce geopolymer concretes which are ideal for building and repairing infrastructure and for precast units, because they have very high early strength, their setting times can be controlled and they remain intact for a very long time without any need for repair. The properties of geopolymer include high early strength, low shrinkage, freeze-thaw resistance, sulphate resistance and corrosion resistance. These high-alkali binders do not generate any alkali-aggregate reaction. The geopolymer binder is a low-CO_2 cementious material. It does not rely on the Calcinations of limestone that generates CO_2. This technology can save up to 80% of CO_2 emissions caused by the cement and aggregate industries.

2 EXPERIMENTAL PROGRAM

In this work, low-calcium (ASTM Class F) fly ash-based geopolymer was used as the binder, instead of Portland or other hydraulic cement paste, to produce concrete. The fly ash-based geopolymer paste binds the loose coarse aggregates, fine aggregates and other un-reacted materials together to form the geopolymer concrete, with the presence of admixtures. The manufacture of the geopolymer concrete was carried out using the usual concrete technology methods as in the case of OPC concrete in the Applied Mechanics laboratory of S.V. National Institute of Technology, Surat. The silicon and the aluminium in the low-calcium fly ash react with an alkaline liquid that is a combination of sodium hydroxide and potassium hydroxide solutions to form the geopolymer paste that binds the aggregates and other un-reacted materials.

2.1 Materials

Geopolymer concrete can be manufactured by using the low-calcium (ASTM Class F) fly ash obtained from coal-burning power stations. Most of the fly ash available globally is low-calcium fly ash formed as a by-product of burning anthracite or bituminous coal.

Commercial grade potassium hydroxide in pellet form (97% –100% purity) and sodium hydroxide solution (Na_2O = 18.2%, SiO_2 = 36.7%, Water = 45.1%) were used as the alkali activators. The potassium hydroxide pallets were dissolved in the required amount of water according to the desired molarity. Locally available aggregate and fine river sands were used as aggregates for the concrete. Note that the mass of water is the major component in both the alkaline solutions. For improving the workability of the concrete superplasticiser was used.

2.2 Mixture proportions

The different mixture proportions used to make the trial geopolymer concrete specimens in this study are given in Table 1.

2.3 Mixing and curing

Mixing of all the materials was done manually in the laboratory at room temperature. The fly-ash and aggregates were first mixed homogeneously and then the alkaline solutions which were made one day before and superplasticiser were added to the mixture of fly ash and aggregates. The Potassium hydroxide and the sodium hydroxide solutions were first mixed with each other and stirred to obtain a homogeneous mixture of the solutions before adding them to the solids. The mixing of the total mass was continued until the binding paste covered all the aggregates and mixture become homogeneous and uniform in color.

A pan type concrete mixer that offers mechanical shearing action can be used for obtaining a uniform mixture with less effort. Use cube (150 × 150 × 150 mm) specimens. The fresh

Table 1. Mixing proportion.

Ingredients	Unit	Mixture 1	Mixture 2	Mixture 3	Mixture 4	Mixture 5	M25 Mix
Fly ash	kg/m³	425	425	425	425	425	425 (cement)
Fine aggregates	kg/m³	505	505	505	505	505	563
CA 10 Dn	kg/m³	442	442	442	442	442	493
CA 20 Dn	kg/m³	663	663	663	663	663	740
Alkaline solution / FA	–	0.35	0.35	0.35	0.35	0.35	–
Potassium Silicate /KOH	–	2.5	2.5	2.5	2.5	2.5	–
Molarity of potassium hydroxide solution	–	8M	10M	12M	14M	16M	–

Table 2. Quantity estimation and planning of experiment.

Description	Compressive strength test	Split tensile test	Flexural test	Pullout test	Durability test
Specimen size (mm)	Cube (150 × 150 × 150)	Cylinder (150 Dia. & 300 Height)	Beam (100 × 100 × 500)	Cube (150 × 150 × 150)	Cube (150 × 150 × 150)
No. of specimen	3	3	3	3	3
Days of testing	1, 7, 14, 28	1, 7, 14, 28	1, 7, 14, 28	1, 7, 14, 28	1, 7, 14, 28. 56
Total no. of specimen	12	12	12	12	15
Volume of each specimen (Cum)	0.003375	0.0053	0.005	0.003375	0.003375
Volume for all specimen	0.0405	0.0636	0.0600	0.0405	0.0506

Total volume of concrete in Cum = 0.25.

geopolymer concrete was used to cast cubes of size 150 × 150 × 150 mm to determine its compressive strength. The specimens were prepared according to the method followed by Hardjito et al. (2009). Each cube specimen was cast in three layers by compacting manually as well as by using a vibrating table. Each layer received 25 strokes of compaction by a standard compaction rod for concrete, followed by further compaction on the vibrating table. The specimens were wrapped by plastic sheet to prevent loss of moisture and placed in an oven. Since the process of geopolymerisation needs curing at high temperature, the specimens were cured at 80°C temperature for 24 hours in the oven. They were temperature cured for 24 hours then left to open air (room temperature 25°C) in the laboratory until testing.

3 OBSERVATION AND TEST RESULTS

3.1 General

In the present work, the effects of various salient parameters on the compressive strength of low-calcium fly ash-based geopolymer concrete are discussed by considering the ratio of alkaline solution to fly ash by mass 0.35 constant throughout. The parameters considered are as follows:

1. Concentration of Potassium hydroxide (KOH) solution, in Molar.
2. Ratio of sodium hydroxide solution-to-Potassium hydroxide solution, by mass.
3. Curing temperature (Results are widely variable and do not fall in the scope of this paper).
4. Effect of wet-mixing Time.
5. Influence of handling time on compressive strength.
6. Effect of super plasticizer on compressive strength.

Table 3. Compressive strength & time.

| Days | Compressive strength (Mpa) | | | | | |
	M25	8M	10M	12M	14M	16M
1	4.92	16.42	20.18	23.1	24.12	25.02
7	25.36	28.33	30.14	33.16	34.28	35.10
14	28.42	34.22	35.24	39.12	40.18	41.18
28	30.33	37.36	40.29	42.44	43.00	44.14

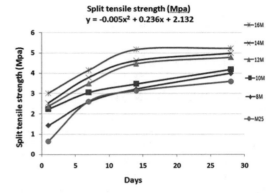

Figure 2. Development of tensile strength v/s days.

Table 4. Split tensile strength & time.

| Days | Split test (Mpa) | | | | | |
	M25	8M	10M	12M	14M	16M
1	0.66	1.44	2.24	2.38	2.54	3.02
7	2.62	2.6	3.06	3.5	3.8	4.16
14	3.14	3.22	3.48	4.48	4.64	5.18
28	3.6	4.0	4.2	4.8	5.0	5.24

Table 5. Flexural strength & time.

| Days | Flexural test (Mpa) | | | | | |
	M25	8M	10M	12M	14M	16M
1	1.1	2.28	3.44	3.5	3.55	3.72
7	3.12	3.52	3.98	4.3	4.34	4.68
14	3.98	4.21	5.5	5.76	5.82	6.04
28	4.54	5.2	6.0	6.6	6.66	7.18

7. Effect of super plasticizer on slump of concrete.
8. Effect of water-to-geopolymer solids ratio by mass on compressive strength (Ratio was kept constant throughout the experimental study).
9. Stress-strain relation of geopolymer concrete in compression.

All the cube moulds were tested for compressive strength using the compression testing machine in

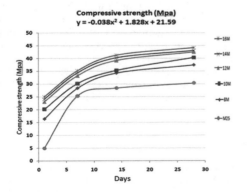

Figure 1. Development of comp. strength v/s days.

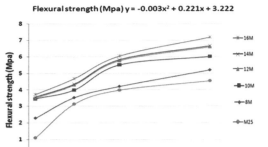

Figure 3. Development of flexural strength v/s days.

Table 6. Pull out strength & time.

	Pull out test (Mpa)					
Days	M25	8M	10M	12M	14M	16M
1	2.08	3.08	6.76	7.14	7.78	8.12
7	5.62	6.62	8.32	8.74	8.96	9.20
14	7.8	8.88	9.88	10.78	10.98	11.44
28	8.9	9.96	10.56	11.34	12.46	13.02

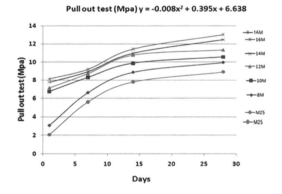

Figure 4. Development of pill out strength v/s days.

Table 7. Loss in weight & time.

	Pull out test (Mpa)					
Days	M25	8M	10M	12M	14M	16M
1	0.84	0.34	0.20	0.09	0.04	0.04
7	1.68	1.02	0.47	0.33	0.22	0.20
14	3.21	2.07	0.82	0.59	0.39	0.29
28	4.84	3.00	1.01	0.78	0.53	0.51
56	5.66	3.44	1.44	0.88	0.62	0.60

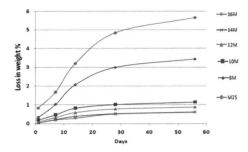

Figure 5. Loss of weight v/s days.

the Applied Mechanics laboratory of S.V. National Institute of Technology, Surat. Compressive strength of concrete cubes were tested at the age of 1, 3, 7, and 28 days. Fig. 1 shows the testing of cubes cured at 80°C temperature. After testing, there was equal cracking of all four exposed faces with little or no damage to the faces (top and bottom) in contact with the platens. Cracking was in vertical zigzag pattern.

4 CONCLUSIONS

- Compressive strength of GPC increases over controlled concrete by approx 1.5 times at 28 days.
- Splitting tensile strength of GPC increases over controlled concrete by approx 1.45 times at 28 days.
- Flexural strength of GPC increases over controlled concrete by 1.6 times at 28 days.
- In pull out test, GPC increases over controlled concrete by approx 1.5 times at 28 days.
- In the durability test, there was decrease in weight loss by 10 times (At 56 days% loss in weight reduced from 5.66% to 0.60%).
- It was observed that at 12 molarity of KOH, the gain in strength remained very moderate and the reason was at temperature of 80°C for 24 hours the poly condensation process had already completed and particle interface was also achieved.
- Further good structural properties can be achieved with increase in polymerization temperature along with prolonged curing period in oven.

REFERENCES

Alonso, S. & Palomo, A. 2010. Alkaline Activation of Metakaolin and Calcium hydroxide Mixtures: Influence of Temperature, Activator Concentration and Solids Ratio. Material Letters, 47(1–2): pp. 55–62.

Balaguru, P., Kurtz, S. & Rudolph, J. 1997. Geopolymer for Repair and Rehabilitation of Reinforced Concrete Beam, Geopolymer Institute.

Buonicore, A.J. & Davis, W.T. 2000. New York: Van Nostrand Reinhold.

Cheng, T.W. & Chiu, J.P. 2008. Fire-resistant Geopolymer Produced by Granulated Blast Furnace Slag. Minerals Engineering, 16(3): pp. 205–210.

Davidovits, J. 2009. Properties of Geopolymer Cements. in First International Conference on Alkaline Cements and Concretes. 2005. Kiev, Ukraine, SRIBM, Kiev State Technical University.

Edward, S.W. 2009. Drying Shrinkage of Heat-Cured Fly Ash-Based Geopolymer Concrete, Modern Applied Science, Vol. 3, No. 12.

František, Š., Doležal, J., Svoboda, P., Kopecký, L., Pawlasová, S. Lucuk, M., Dvořáček, K., Beksa, M. Myšková, L.R. & Šulc, R. 2007. Concrete based on fly ash geopolymers International journal of material science- Vol. 3.

Greer, W.L., Johnson, M.D., Morton, E.L., Raught, E.C., Steuch, H.E. & Trusty, Jr. C.B. 2008. Portland Cement, in Air Pollution Engineering.

Hardjito, D., et al. 2008. The Development of Fly Ash-Based Geopolymer Concrete. ACI Materials Journal, 101(6).

Hardjito, D. & Rangan, B.V. 2009. Development and Properties of Low Calcium fly ash—based Geopolymer Concrete, Research Report GC 1, Faculty of Engineering, Curtin University of Technology, Perth, Australia.

Hardjito, D. & Rangan, B.V. 2009. Development and Properties of Low Calcium fly ash—based Geopolymer Concrete, Research Report GC 2, Faculty of Engineering, Curtin University of Technology, Perth, Australia.

Malhotra, V.M. 2000. Making Concrete "Greener" With Fly Ash. ACI Concrete International. 21(5): pp. 61–66.

Malhotra, V.M. 2005. Introduction: Sustainable Development and Concrete Technology. ACI Concrete International. 24(7): p. 22.

Mehta, P.K. 2003. Reducing the Environmental Impact of Concrete. A Concrete International, 23(10): pp. 61–66.

Rangan, V.B. 2008. Studies on Fly Ash-Based Geopolymer Concrete, Malaysian Construction Research Journal, Vol. 3, No. 2.

Thokchom, S., Ghosh, P. & Ghosh, S. 2009. Acid Resistance of Fly ash based Geopolymer mortars, International Journal of Recent Trends in Engineering, Vol. 1, No. 6.

Thokchom, S., Ghosh, P. & Ghosh, S. 2009. Effect of Na2O Content on Durability of Geopolymer Mortars in Sulphuric Acid, International Journal of Chemical and Biomolecular Engineering 2:1.

Thokchom, S., Ghosh, P. & Ghosh, S. 2009. Resistance of Fly Ash based Geopolmer Mortars in Sulfuric Acid, ARPN Journal of Engineering and Applied Sciences, Vol. 4.

Thokchom, S., Ghosh, P. & Ghosh, S. 2010. Performance of Fly ash Based Geopolymer Mortars in Sulphate Solution, Journal of Engineering Science and Technology Review 3 (1) 36–40.

Concrete Solutions – Grantham, Mechtcherine & Schneck (eds)
© 2012 Taylor & Francis Group, London, ISBN 978-0-415-61622-5

Numerical investigation on the effect of concrete-FRP bond on the flexural behavior of RC beams

S. Sajedi, F. Ghassemzadeh, M. Shekarchi, F. Faraji & M. Soleimani
School of Civil Engineering, University of Tehran, Tehran, Iran

ABSTRACT: In the last decade, Fiber Reinforced Polymer (FRP) plates have been successfully used for rehabilitation of reinforced concrete members. Although various experimental investigations have been conducted for assessment of the structural behavior of these members, for considerable cost saving, finite element analysis can be used to provide a valuable supplement to the laboratory investigations, especially in parametric studies. This paper presents the results of a nonlinear three-dimensional finite element analysis in evaluation of the flexural behavior of RC beams strengthened with externally bonded CFRP plates. The effect of interface modeling on the accuracy of results is investigated in this study. Results show that for achieving rational results, the bond between the concrete and FRP plate should be considered in the modeling.

1 INTRODUCTION

Many different procedures have been used to repair and rehabilitate concrete structures. One of the more common methods is the use of Fiber Reinforced Polymers (FRPs) as external reinforcement for enhancing the performance of the structure. Recent studies have shown that FRP-retrofitting can be very useful to improve the behavior of RC structures under both short-term and long-term service loadings (Ferretti, & Savoia 2003). However, for flexural strengthened RC beams, peeling of the FRP plate can lead to the premature failure of the concrete member before reaching the enhanced capacity (Ritchie et al. 1991). Two common types of debonding failure can occur at the interface: end peeling and shear-tension failure. End peeling can initiate at any flexural crack and propagates from there to the end of the FRP reinforcement, and shear-tension failure initiates at the ends of the FRP plate, resulting in the propagation of a horizontal crack, and causes separation of the concrete cover (Arduini & Nanni 1997). Thus, for the safe and economic design of externally bonded FRP systems, the effect of bond between FRP and concrete should be considered.

Various parameters can affect the bond strength of an FRP-concrete interface such as: the concrete strength, the bond length, the FRP plate axial stiffness, the FRP-to-concrete width ratio, the adhesive stiffness, the adhesive strength, the surface preparation of the concrete, the concrete surface tensile strength and the aggregate content (Lorenzis et al. 2001; Lu et al. 2005; Pan & Leung 2006). Due to the nonhomogeneous, nonlinear and anisotropic behavior of concrete materials, and the complicated process of damage at the interface, in many cases, the currently available design and simplified analysis tools cannot predict the accurate performance of retrofitted RC beams. To overcome these problems, nonlinear finite element analysis can be used. Supaviriyakitc et al. (2004) conducted non-linear finite element analysis on reinforced concrete beams strengthened with externally bonded FRP plates. As the epoxy is usually much stronger than concrete, they assumed perfect compatibility between the FRP and concrete. The model was verified against the experimental data of load-deflection, load carrying capacity and failure mode of the strengthened beams. They concluded that FE analysis can capture the cracking process for the shear-flexural peeling and end peeling failures. Coronado and Lopez (2010) performed analytical modeling of debonding between FRP and concrete using the crack band approach. They showed that more accurate results can be achieved by modeling of the interface between concrete and FRP. They concluded that their proposed method has the capability to predict the load-deflection response, strain distributions and failure modes of retrofitted beams.

In this paper, the flexural behavior of the RC beams strengthened with externally bonded CFRP plates is investigated. The nonlinear finite element program, ANSYS, is used to simulate the studied beams in two categories: a) by assuming perfect bonding between concrete and CFRP without any sliding or debonding, and b) by assuming the tensile and shear contacts between concrete and CFRP.

2 NUMERICAL SIMULATION

2.1 Finite element model

Reinforced concrete beams A5, A7 and C6 from the experimental study of Rahimi and Hutchinson (2001) strengthened with CFRP sheets was simulated in ANSYS and used to calibrate the designed model. The materials properties of these beams are presented in Table 1. It should be noted that in the models, the contribution of the adhesive layer is neglected.

As seen in Table 1, the compressive strength of concretes used in the beams varied from 54 MPa to 69 MPa. In this study, the value of 58.6 MPa was used as a compressive strength of all beams. Detailed descriptions of the testing procedures and geometry of specimens are given in reference (Rahimi & Hutchinson 2001). Figure 1 shows the model of a quarter part of the strengthened reinforced concrete beams with CFRP plate in ANSYS.

2.2 Concrete modeling

An eight-node solid element (solid65) was used to model the concrete materials. The element is capable of plastic deformation, cracking in three orthogonal directions and crushing. When a crack occurs in an analysis, the stress available at that node drops to zero, which often causes convergence problems. Stress relaxation allows for a more gradual reduction helping in obtaining a converged solution. In this study, the crushing

capability of the concrete element was turned off and the tensile stress relaxation after cracking was activated in order to avoid the convergence problems. The nonlinear elastic option is considered to define the material behavior of concrete for the numerical study, by using multilinear elastic option (MELAS). It allows greater flexibility in changing important parameters like the compressive and tensile strengths of concrete. The compressive uniaxial stress–strain relationship for the concrete model was obtained using the following equations to compute the multilinear elastic stress–strain curve (MacGregor 1992).

$$f = E_c \varepsilon / \left(1 + (\varepsilon / \varepsilon_0)^2\right) \tag{1}$$

$$\varepsilon_0 = 2 f_c' / E_c \tag{2}$$

The multilinear elastic material uses the Von-Mises failure criterion along with the Willam and Warnke (1975) model to define the failure of the concrete. Figure 2 shows the compressive uniaxial stress–strain relationship that was used in this study.

It should be pointed out that as shown in Figure 2, the first point is assumed as $0.3 f_c'$ for calculating the linear part. The Poisson ratio of concrete is assumed to be 0.2 for both repair concretes and substrate. Shear transfer coefficient, β_t, represents the conditions of the crack face. The value of β_t ranges from 0.0 to 1.0, with 0.0 representing a smooth crack (complete loss of shear transfer) and 1.0 representing a rough crack (no loss of shear

Table 1. Mechanical properties of materials.

Mechanical properties	Concrete	CFRP	Reinforcement	Adhesive layer
Comp. strength (MPa)	54–69	–	–	70
Tensile strength (MPa)	3	1532	–	25
Mod. of elasticity (GPa)	25	127	210	7
Yield stress (MPa)	–	–	575	–
Poisson's ratio	0.2	0.3	0.3	0.3

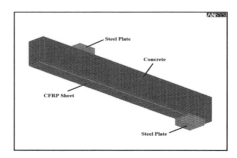

Figure 1. Modeling of quarter part of reinforced concrete beams.

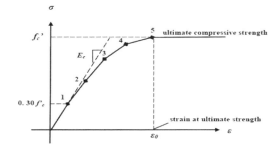

Figure 2. Simplified compressive uniaxial stress–strain curve for concrete.

transfer). But based on the recommendations (Bangash 1989; Hemmaty 1998) the values between 0.05 and 0.25 should be considered as a value of β_t. In this study, the coefficient for open cracks (β_t) was set to 0.3 and the coefficient for closed cracks was assumed to be 0.9. Also, the value of the stiffness multiplier for the cracked tensile condition was taken as 0.6 in this study. In the material model, the density for the concrete was not added.

2.3 Reinforcing steel model

Fanning (2001) modeled the response of the reinforcement using the discrete and smeared model for reinforced concrete beams and concluded that the best strategy for reinforcement modeling is the discrete model. In the discrete model, the concrete and the reinforcement mesh share the same nodes and the concrete occupies the same regions occupied by the reinforcement. A 3D spar element (link8) was used to model the steel reinforcement in the discrete model. This element is capable of plastic deformation. Perfect bonding between the concrete and steel reinforcement was considered in this study. The bond between steel reinforcement and concrete was assumed as perfect. The stress–strain relationship for steel was modeled with a bilinear representation, identical in tension and compression, as shown in Figure 3. The tangent modulus for the plastic part was taken as $Esp = 0.01E_s$, where E_s is the initial modulus (El-Tawil et al. 2001).

2.4 Steel plate model

An eight-node solid element, Solid45, was used for modeling the steel plates at the support of the beam and loading location in order to avoid the stress concentration problems. This element is modeled as a linear isotropic element. A modulus of elasticity equal to 2.1×10^6 kg/cm² and Poisson's ratio of 0.3 were used for the plates.

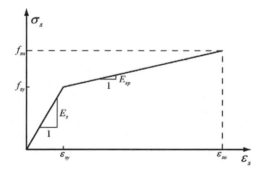

Figure 3. Idealization of steel stress–strain behaviour.

2.5 CFRP plate model

The FRP composites are orthotropic materials; that is, their properties are not the same in all directions. Thus, the Solid 46 layered element could be used to model FRP composites. However in this study, based on the experimental data, linear elastic properties of CFRP in various directions have not been reported and so, Solid45 was used for modeling CFRP plates.

2.6 Contact behavior

Two types of local failures exist at the interface between the concrete and FRP: shear and tensile failures. When the shear stress at the interface exceeds the maximum allowable shear stress, shear failure happens. Tensile failure occurs when the tensile stress at the interface between the two layers exceeds the maximum allowable tensile strength and leads to debonding. In order to model the bond and separation of the concrete and FRP, contact pairs with debonding capabilities were implemented. Contact pairs consist of two elements: a target element (TARGE170) and a contact element (CONTA174). These elements define the boundary between the surfaces of the concrete and FRP, and have the ability to model delamination of the two surfaces. In order to allow for separation between the concrete and the FRP, a Cohesive Zone Material Model (CZM) was used. The bond between the concrete and FRP was defined by using the real constant for the contact pairs, and the CZM material model inputs. The CZM model has bilinear behaviour by using one of two set options; traction and separation distances, or traction and critical fracture energies. In this analysis, the traction and separation distances option was used which has 6 input options; maximum normal contact stress (σ_{max}), contact gap at the completion of debonding (u_c^n), maximum equivalent tangential contact stress (τ_{max}), tangential slip at the completion of debonding (u_c^t), artificial damping coefficient (η), and an option indicator for tangential slip under compressive normal contact stress (β). The artificial damping is included to compensate for convergence problems that are caused by modeling debonding. For proper assessment of contact behaviour between FRP plate and concrete, the contact parameters should be determined from bond strength tests such as direct tension test and direct shear test. In this study, the bond between concrete and FRP is assumed constant in the length of interface. Table 2 shows the assumed parameters in the interface modeling of investigated beams.

Because the thickness of the CFRP layer in the Beam A7 is less than others, then the maximum values of tensile and shear stresses for Beam A7

Table 2. Contact parameters used in ANSYS.

Beam	σ_{max} (MPa)	τ_{max} (MPa)	u_c^n (mm)	u_c^t (mm)
A5	2.5	2.5	0.15	0.15
A7	1.5	1.5	0.15	0.15
C6	2.5	2.5	0.15	0.15

were assumed less than Beams A5 and C6. It should be noted that ANSYS suggests the value be between 0.01 and 0.1 for the artificial damping coefficient. In this analysis the value was taken as the minimum suggested value of 0.01 for all the models.

3 RESULTS AND DISCUSSION

Figure 4 presents the comparison between experimental data and the finite element simulation for A5, A7 and B6 beams. From the results, it can be concluded that, by considering the effect of bond between concrete and CFRP plate in the modeling, the accuracy of results will improve. This is due to the influence of debonding of the CFRP plate before it fails on the flexural behaviour of the strengthened beams. Debonding can reduce the structural role of the CFRP plate, reduce stiffness of the structure, change the direction of crack paths and consequently increase the damage of concrete member. For reaching more accurate results, it seems that the bond between the CFRP and concrete should be obtained from the experiment in the length of interface. Also the stress–strain behaviour of concrete and steel, and properties of CFRP plate in all directions are important factors.

The ultimate load capacity and corresponding mid-span deflections for the studied beams are presented in Table 3. As can be seen, there is a good agreement between the experimental results and numerical simulation when the effect of the interface between concrete and CFRP is considered in the modeling.

Crack distribution for Beam C6 with considering the interface between concrete and CFRP under about 100 KN is shown in Figure 5. In ANSYS software, cracking is available in three orthogonal directions at each integration point which is indicated by a red (first crack), green (second crack), or blue (third crack) circle. The cracking represented from the finite element model is not a finite crack, but an area where cracking occurs. Cracking in multiple directions indicates considerable cracking, and is regarded as a location where visible cracking can occur.

Figure 6 shows the debonding and sliding tendency of CFRP plate from concrete in beam C6 under ultimate loading. It can be seen from the

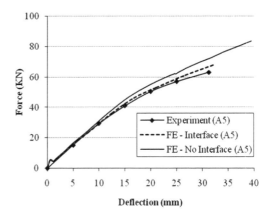
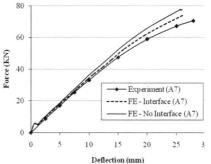
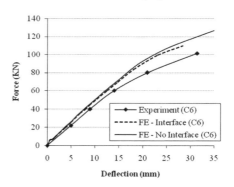

Figure 4. Predicted and experimental load-deflection results for investigated beams.

figure that the nodes of CFRP and concrete are not on the top of each other and also there is a gap between the ends of the CFRP plate and concrete which shows that sliding and debonding occurred, which is in agreement with the experimental results. Debonding depends on various parameters. The difference between the elastic modulus of the plate and the concrete, the thickness of CFRP plate, and the bond strength between concrete member and CFRP which depends on the properties of the adhesive layer and environmental conditions are

Table 3. Failure loads and corresponding displacements.

Beam	P_{num} (KN)	u_{num} (mm)	P_{exp} (KN)	u_{exp} (mm)
A5				
No-Interface	83.66	39.4	63.2	31.3
Interface	68.1	32.3		
A7				
No-Interface	77.7	26	70.6	27.9
Interface	74.6	26.3		
C6				
No-Interface	147.9	48	101.4	31.4
Interface	109.7	28.3		

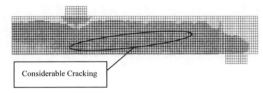

Considerable Cracking

Figure 5. Crack distributions in Beam C6 under 100 KN.

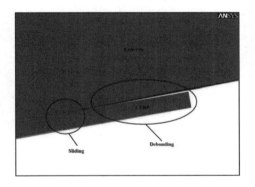

Figure 6. Debonding and sliding tendency of Beam C6 under 109.7 KN.

important factors in concentration of stresses at the interface layer and debonding/sliding of CFRP plate.

The results of experimental data showed the concrete shear failure followed by cover separation and plate detachment for beams A5 and A7, and cover failure followed by plate debonding for beam C6 which presents a good agreement between the failure modes in experimental tests and numerical results.

CONCLUSIONS

Nonlinear finite element analysis of the flexural behaviour of strengthened RC beams with externally bonded CFRP sheets was investigated in this study. Results show that modeling of the bond between FRP plate and concrete members is necessary in order to make a rational prediction of the flexural behaviour of beams. Numerical models considering the effect of the interface showed good agreement with the experimental results in both load-deflection response and failure mode of members. Although for accurate assessment of the debonding process, experimental tests could be done to determine the bond properties between FRP and concrete; however, it seems that there is potential for substituting the experimental programs by numerical methods in order to conduct the sensitivity analysis on the various thicknesses of FRP plates and bond strength to determine the debonding tendency of FRP plates.

REFERENCES

Arduini, M. & Nanni, A. 1997. Parametric study of beams with externally bonded FRP reinforcement. *ACI Structural Journal* 94(5): 493–501.

Bangash, M.Y.H. 1989. Concrete and concrete structures: numerical modelling and applications. *Elsevier Science Publishers Ltd.*, London, England.

Coronado, C.A. & Lopez, M.M. 2010. Numerical modeling of concrete-FRP debonding using a crack band approach. *Journal of Composites for Construction, ASCE* 14(1): 11–20.

El-Tawil, S., Ogunc, C., Okeil A. & Shahawy, M. 2001. Static and fatigue analysis of RC beams strengthened with CFRP laminates. *Journal of Composites for Construction ASCE* 5(4): 258–267.

Fanning, P. 2001. Nonlinear models of reinforced and post-tensioned concrete beams. *Electronic Journal of Structural Engineering*. University College Dublin, Earlsfort Terrace, Dublin 2, Ireland.

Ferretti, D. & Savoia, M. 2003. Cracking evolution in R/C tensile members strengthened by FRP-plates. *Engineering Fracture Mechanics* 70: 1069–1083.

Hemmaty, Y. 1998. Modelling of the shear force transferred between cracks in reinforced and fiber reinforced concrete structures. *Proceedings of the ANSYS Conference*. Vol. 1, Pittsburgh, Pennsylvania.

Lorenzis, L.D., Miller, B. & Nanni A. 2001. Bond of fiber-reinforced polymer laminates to concrete. *ACI Materials Journal* 98(3): 256–264.

Lu, X.Z., Teng, J.G., Ye, L.P. & Jiang, J.J. 2005. Bond–slip models for FRP sheets/plates bonded to concrete. *Engineering Structures* 920–937.

MacGregor, J.G. 1992. Reinforced concrete mechanics and design. *Prentice-Hall, Inc., Englewood Cliffs,* N.J.

Pan, J. & Leung, C.K.Y. 2006. Effect of concrete composition on FRP/concrete bond capacity. *Measuring, Monitoring and Modeling Concrete Properties* 743–748.

Rahimi, H. & Hutchinson, A. 2001. Concrete beams strengthened with externally bonded FRP plates. *Journal of Composites for Construction, ASCE* 5(1): 44–56.

Ritchie, P.A., Thomas, D.A., Lu, L.W. & Connelly, G.M. 1991. External reinforcement of concrete beams using fiber reinforced plastics. *ACI Structural Journal* 88(4): 490–500.

Supaviriyakit, T., Pornpongsaroj, P. & Pimanmas, A. 2004. Finite element analysis of FRP-strengthened RC beams. *Songklanakarin Journal of Science Technology* 26(4): 497–507.

Willam, K.J. & Warnke, E.P. 1975. Constitutive model for triaxial behavior of concrete. *Seminar on Concrete Structures Subjected to Triaxial Stresses, International Association of Bridge and Structural Engineering Conference.* Bergamo, Italy, 174 p.

Concrete Solutions – Grantham, Mechtcherine & Schneck (eds)
© 2012 Taylor & Francis Group, London, ISBN 978-0-415-61622-5

Evaluation of the hydration of concrete mixtures by ultrasonic testing

A.A. Shah
King Saud University, Kingdom of Saudi Arabia

Y. Ribakov
Ariel University Center of Samaria, Ariel, Israel

ABSTRACT: Proper evaluation of the hydration process of concrete mixtures is essential and useful to assess the quality of concrete mixtures and cement mortars used for the repair of structures. Currently the penetration resistance test is widely used to evaluate the strength development of fresh mortar and concrete. Ultrasonic through transmission and wave reflection methods are reliable alternative techniques for evaluating the strength development in concrete mixtures. Experiments demonstrate the accuracy of the above mentioned methods. The ultrasonic waveforms were continuously examined during the tests and compared with the strength development obtained from the standard penetration resistance test. The test results are analyzed and it is shown that the ultrasonic wave velocity and reflection coefficient have a strong linear relationship with the strength development. Additionally, a rapid increase in the wave velocity and frequency amplitude may be utilized as a tool to indicate a beginning of the strength in the fresh mixtures. The results show that using the ultrasonic testing techniques is a promising way to evaluate the strength development in early age concretes and mortars.

1 INTRODUCTION

The evaluation of mechanical properties of concrete using nondestructive techniques is known as one of the most challenging tasks in civil engineering (Boutin & Arnaud, 1995). Several techniques that meet this demand are currently in use (Malhotra & Carino, 2004). Some of them are based on propagation of ultrasonic waves and others are focused on measuring the thermal history or certain mechanical quantities, such as penetration depth or pullout force of concrete. Further techniques deal with microwaves, electrical impedances and acoustic emissions (Malhotra & Carino, 2004). This paper will concentrate on ultrasonic techniques.

For on-site workability, the concrete must remain in the plastic state for a sufficient period of time. Therefore, it is important to monitor its setting time. Assessment of a cement-based materials' hydration state is of great importance regarding economical and safety aspects. With this knowledge, the efficiency of repairing concrete elements and structures can be raised, or the time for form removal can be optimized. With respect to quality control, the setting time can be verified (Boumiz et al., 1996).

As soon as cement and water are mixed, the paste will start to stiffen immediately as a result of the hydration reaction. To regulate the stiffening

process, it is common to add calcium sulfate to the cement (Ozturk et al., 1999).

The setting and hardening process of cement mortar are very important to understand as proper setting and hardening characteristics of cement mortar may help in the effective repair of structural elements.

The concrete mix hardening process can be principally divided into five parts. As known, immediately after mixing, the cement grains are dissolved in water (Grübl et al., 2001). At this stage, the first reaction occurs. After that the second stage begins and the concrete mixture is plastic for a period of several hours. The third stage is called the acceleration period: during this stage, the temperature increases and the material consolidates. At the end of this stage, the hydration and the temperature are maximal, plasticity disappears and hardening begins. At stage 4, deceleration of the temperature curve occurs. Stage 5 is characterized by leveling off the temperature curve (Grübl et al., 2001; Stark & Wicht 1998; Stark et al., 2001).

The initial setting time (set) is another factor that is important for the hydration reaction process. It is defined as the time at which the concrete mixture is no longer workable. It is known that an increase in the mixture stiffness and temperature during the setting period corresponds to the hydration reaction between water and tricalcium silicate (C_3S) (Stark et al., 2001).

The hydration reaction process continues until the plasticity disappears. In other words, if the final set occurs, then the mixture has started to harden. Concrete in this stage has some stiffness and can carry a certain load (Stark et al., 2001). After the final set, hardening continues and the rate of hydration and temperature decrease during this stage; however, the mixture strength still develops continuously (Stark et al., 2001).

Akkaya et al. (2003) have demonstrated that accurate evaluation of the initial and final setting times is required for optimizing the formwork removal time as well as for concrete quality assessment. It is especially important in repaired concrete elements because it improves the durability and strength of the repaired material.

A standard testing procedure for determining the initial and final setting times of fresh concrete is described in ASTM C403 (ASTM, 2005). The initial and final sets are defined as the times when the resistances of the mortar to penetration by standard needles are equal to 3.5 and 27.6 MPa, respectively. As reported by Ozturk et al., (2006), the penetration resistance test enables the evaluation of strength development, but it does not allow measurement of the physical properties of the concrete mixture.

Several studies have been carried out to investigate the effectiveness of using ultrasonic testing techniques to evaluate setting times and the quality of the concrete mixture (Ye et al., 2005; Ozturk et al., 2006). The formation of microstructure in early age cement paste and concrete was examined with an ultrasonic experimental set-up (Ye et al., 2005). Research parameters included the influence of curing temperature (isothermal curing at 20, 30 and 40°C), water/cement ratio (0.40, 0.45 and 0.55) and amount of aggregate. In parallel with the experiments, the cement hydration model HYMOSTRUC was utilized to simulate the formation of the microstructure. The cement paste was considered as a four-phase system consisting of water, unhydrated cement, hydration products and that part of the hydration product that causes the contact between the hydrating cement grains (the so called "bridge volume") (Ye et al., 2005). A correlation has been found between the growth of bridge volume calculated with the model and changes in the pulse velocity. It is believed that ultrasonic pulse velocity (UPV) measurements can represent a valuable tool to investigate the development of the microstructure at early age.

A test setup using the ultrasonic wave reflection technique was used to monitor the hydration process of early-age cement-based materials throughout their setting and hardening (Ozturk et al., 2006). The stiffening behavior of cement pastes was monitored. Specimens were produced and kept under constant curing conditions. Immediately after placing the cement paste, the data collection started and continued throughout the setting process. The obtained ultrasonic data was correlated to mechanical and chemical properties of the specimens. The results illustrated that the applied experimental wave reflection technique is suitable to monitor the stiffening of cement pastes accurately.

However, a reliable evaluation procedure has not been established due to less sensitivity to monitor the setting behavior of cement pastes, lack of information about the physical properties of the mixture like strength, elasticity, cracking etc. Hence the technique used in (Ye et al., 2003; Ozturk et al., 2006) does not allow monitoring the critical processes inside the cement paste and concrete.

The use of ultrasound is promising. The ultrasonic technique is often used to establish the uniformity of concrete and to estimate its in-situ strength (Ye et al., 2003). The advantages of the use of this technique include its accuracy, easy test procedure and nondestructive characteristics (Ozturk et al., 2006). Additionally, in the author's opinion, it has also a great potential for a quantitative description of the development of microstructure in early-age concrete. On the other hand the penetration resistance or pin penetration test has been found to give results with a low accuracy (Ozturk et al., 1999; Rapoport et al., 2000; Akkaya et al., 2003).

The current study is aimed to investigate the potential benefits of using ultrasonic testing techniques as a tool to evaluate the hydration reaction process in early age mortars. The ultrasonic wave measurements performed by Chotickai et al., (2006) on the mortars with various water-cement ratios (w/c) were used. The acquired data were compared with the strength development evaluated using the standard penetration resistance test. Comparison of penetration resistance test with the ultrasound methods will be shown.

2 NDE TECHNIQUES

Useful NDE techniques for monitoring the setting and hardening process of concrete were presented (Ozturk et al., 1999; Rapoport et al., 2000). These techniques are based on measuring the ultrasonic wave reflection factor (WRF) between the hardening concrete and a steel mold. The methods can be used to assess the in situ properties of concrete in repaired structures and elements at very early ages so that corrective measures can be taken.

To measure the waveforms using the through transmission technique, two transducers are placed in line on opposite sides of the specimen

(Boumiz et al., 1996; Popovics 1990; Grosse & Reinhardt 1996; Grosse 2002). The elastic stress waves are generated by an electro-acoustical transducer and propagate through the specimen. The pulses received by the second transducer are converted into electrical energy, and the transit time is determined (Grosse & Reinhardt 1996; Grosse 2002). The ultrasonic pulse velocity (Cp) that is further calculated strongly correlates with the material properties (strength, stiffness, durability etc.) Hence, Cp can be used to access mechanical properties and quality of concrete.

According to the wave propagation theory, the ultrasonic pulse velocity can be obtained as (ASTM C 597):

$$Cp = \sqrt{\frac{E(1-v)}{\rho(1+v)(1-2v)}} \qquad (1)$$

where E is the modulus of elasticity, ρ is the density, and v is the Poisson's ratio of the material.

The wave reflection technique (Ozturk et al., 2006; Ozturk et al., 1999; Rapoport et al., 2000; Akkaya et al., 2003) is based on a measurement of the wave amplitude reflected at an interface of two media. When the direction of the ultrasonic wave propagation is normal to the interface, some ultrasonic energy is transmitted through the boundary and some is reflected.

The wave reflection coefficient is defined as the amplitude ratio between the incident and reflected waves and is written as follows;

$$R = \frac{A_{reflected}}{A_i} = \frac{Z_2 - Z_1}{Z_2 + Z_1} \qquad (2)$$

where R is the wave reflection coefficient, $A_{reflected}$ and A_i are the amplitudes of the reflected and incident waves, respectively, Z_1 is the acoustic impedance of the region in which the wave is approaching the interface, and Z_2 is the acoustic impedance of the region beyond the interface. It is obvious from the expression that the negative sign of the reflection coefficient is obtained when ultrasonic wave propagates from a high impedance material to one of lower impedance. This negative sign indicates the change in phase for the reflected wave.

The setting and hardening processes of concrete can be considered as the most critical time period during the life of concrete or shotcrete that is used as a repair material. The proposed method uses the wave reflection coefficient of high-frequency shear waves to reliably monitor not only the progress of hydration process of cementitious materials at early ages but to monitor the concrete material properties such as compressive strength and elastic modulus as well. With excellent setting and hardening behavior achieved by the mortar used in repair materials, the concrete strength and durability can effectively be enhanced.

3 EXPERIMENTS AND RESULTS

Cement mortars with of w/c 0.4, 0.5, and 0.6 were used for ultrasonic wave measurements and standard penetration resistance tests that were carried out previously by (Chotickai et al., 2006). The freshly mixed mortar was placed into a standard cylindrical mould for the penetration resistance test and an acrylic mould for ultrasonic testing. The test ASTM C 403 (2005) was first performed at three and a half hours after the initial contact was made between cement and mixing water. The readings were obtained with a 30-minute interval until at least one penetration resistance of greater than or equal to 27.6 MPa was obtained (Chotickai et al., 2006).

The obtained test results are shown in Figures 1 and 2. As follows from these figures, the wave reflection measurements yield more accurate results than the through transmission ones. It was reported (Chotickai et al., 2006) that high ultrasonic wave attenuation was observed in the through transmission tests for several hours after the initial contact of cement and water, while the mortars still had considerable plasticity (Fig. 1).

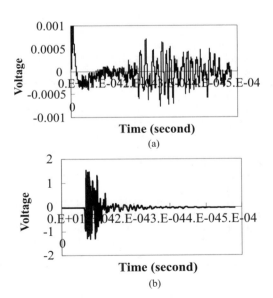

Figure 1. Waveforms obtained from through transmission measurement on 0.5-w/c mortar (a) 1 hour after mixing, and (b) 12 hours after mixing (Chotickai et al., 2006).

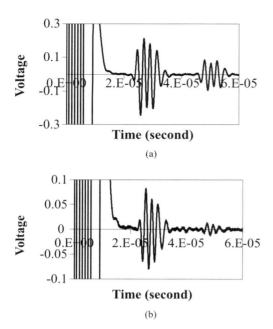

(a)

(b)

Figure 2. Waveforms obtained from wave reflection measurement on 0.5-w/c mortar (a) 1 hour after mixing, and (b) 12 hours after mixing (Chotickai et al., 2006).

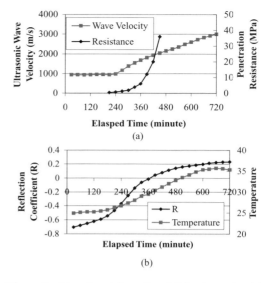

(a)

(b)

Figure 3. Experimental results of 0.5-w/c mortar (a) relationship between wave velocity and penetration resistance with elapsed time, and (b) relationship between reflection coefficient and temperature with elapsed time (Chotickai et al., 2006).

Cementitious materials contain few or no cracks as long as they are in a plastic state. Internal micro-cracking appears as soon as the concrete or cement mortar gains hardness. Propagation of ultrasonic waves faces different degrees of attenuation upon interaction with these cracks. Naturally due to the absence of early age cracks i.e., when the material's plasticity is still present, attenuation of ultrasonic signals should be as small as possible. Hence, compared to the through transmission measurement method, the wave reflection method yielded waveforms data with the least attenuation level for the mortars in plastic state. It, therefore, helps to record more accurately the arrival time and reliably estimate the compressive strength and elastic moduli that are very essential to be used in repair materials.

As the mortars hardened, a high signal-to-noise ratio of the ultrasonic waveforms was obtained and the arrival time could be more accurately estimated. It means that the wave reflection measurement method is more reliable in assessing the concrete properties than the through transmission method.

The results presented in Fig. 3 reveal that during the initial period of hydration, the ultrasonic wave velocity is relatively low and slowly increasing. An abrupt increase in the ultrasonic wave velocity occurs at several hours after mixing when certain strength is developed in the mortar (Fig. 3(a)). Similarly Fig. 3(b) illustrates that though there is a gradual initial increase at low temperatures, a slightly quicker increase in reflection coefficient after a sufficient period of mixing with increase in mixture temperatures was observed. These results show that the through transmission measurement does not provide sufficient sensitivity to the change in mechanical properties of the fresh mortars during the initial period of hydration; however, it may be used to evaluate an onset of the strength development in the specimen.

To investigate the possibility of using the ultrasonic wave velocity in strength assessment of fresh mortars, the relationship between ultrasonic wave velocity and the penetration resistance was examined (Chotickai et al., 2006). It was revealed that the penetration resistance and the change in wave velocity tend to have a linear relationship after a certain amount of strength developed in the specimens. This offers great possibilities for the application of the wave reflection method to use as a tool to non-destructively determine the in-place strength of retrofitted concrete structures.

The relationship between the strength development in fresh mortars and the acoustic impedance was investigated by (Chotickai et al., 2006). It was reported that a strong linear relationship between the penetration resistance and the change in the acoustic impedance. This relationship is important because it demonstrates the sensitivity of the physical change in mortar with the change in acoustic impedance. It, therefore, helps us in determining the strength of the cement paste with the change in acoustic impedance that later on has to be used in the repaired or retrofitted materials.

The results obtained by (Chotickai et al., 2006) have shown that the ultrasonic wave characteristics may be used as a tool to evaluate physical changes developed in fresh mortars. Similarly, this method is equally helpful in measuring the strength development in repaired materials used for retrofitting the existing concrete structures.

To provide useful information on the relationship between the strength development and the frequency amplitude (harmonic amplitude, that is amplitude measurements in a frequency domain), variations of the two parameters with elapsed time were examined. The results have demonstrated that an increase in the amplitude of the low frequency range may be used to evaluate the strength development in fresh mortars. For all w/c cement pastes or concretes, the frequency amplitudes are relatively constant with slight strength development. However, the frequency amplitude starts to increase considerably after the gain in strength by the mix is increased. Hence low frequency but high level amplitudes as generated by the proposed method can be very useful in accurately evaluating the strength development in repaired materials used for retrofitting RC elements.

4 APPLICATIONS IN SHOTCRETE

Shotcrete is employed in particular for repair works, for immediate temporary support of tunnel walls following excavations in unstable ground, for stabilisation of bridges and for concreting in difficult locations, such as abutments, undersides of beams and interiors of chimneys (Lea, F.W. 1998; Jolin, M. & Lacombe, P. 2000). The possible use of wave reflection ultrasound measurements for monitoring setting and hardening of mortar for shotcrete can be very useful.

De Belie et al. (2005) investigated the sensitivity of different accelerating admixtures to monitoring setting and hardening of mortars for shotcrete. Accelerator type (alkaline aluminate or alkali-free) and dosage, and accelerator-cement compatibility were evaluated.

The results for ultrasound velocity and energy indicated that the ultrasound measurements are sensitive to the effect of cement type, accelerator type and dosage on the binding and hardening behavior of the mortar, which are very essential for effectively using the mortar in repair materials. A stepwise increase of the accelerator dosage

resulted in increasing values for the pulse velocity at early ages. While non-accelerated mortar showed a dormant period of about 30 min before the pulse velocity started to increase sharply, no such threshold could be noticed in the accelerated mortar (see Figures 4 and 5).

Similarly it was observed that the alkaline accelerator had a larger accelerating effect on the microstructure development than the alkali—free accelerator, especially at ages below 90 minutes. The effect of the alkali-free accelerator was at very early age more pronounced on mortar containing CEM I in comparison with CEM II, while the alkaline accelerator had a larger influence on mortar containing CEM II. The increase of ultrasound energy could also be related to the setting phenomenon and the maximum energy was reached when the end of workability was approached.

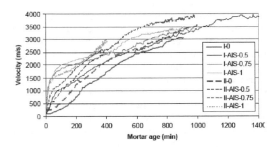

Figure 4. Ultrasound velocity (hand picked onset time) vs. age for mortars containing the alkalifree accelerator AlS (top) or the alkali aluminate based accelerator AlA (bottom). Mortars were prepared us ing the cement types I 42.5 R (I) or CEM II/A-LL 42.5 R (II) and an accelerator dosage of 0, 0.5, 0.75 or 1 time the maximum allowable dosage of 50 ml per kg cement (De Belie et al., 2005).

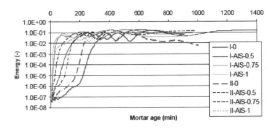

Figure 5. Ultrasound energy (normalized) vs. age for mortars containing the alkali—free accelerator AlS (top) or the alkali aluminate based accelerator AlA (bottom). Mortars were prepared using the cement types I 42.5 R (I) or CEM II/A-LL 42.5 R (II) and an accelerator dosage of 0, 0.5, 0.75 or 1 time the maximum allowable dosage of 50 ml per kg cement (De Belie et al., 2005).

5 CONTROL OF HIGH STRENGTH CONCRETE LAYER (HSC)

This method is also suitable for preservation and restoration of high strength concrete layers used in repaired elements. The technique can be very useful to manage the rate of concrete deterioration on concrete streets, highways and airports. Without changing concrete grade, this non-overlay method can be used to repair isolated areas of distress. Using a high strength concrete layer the possible application of the proposed technique includes concrete's strength improvement, full- and partial-depth repair, dowel bar retrofit, cross stitching longitudinal cracks or joints, diamond grinding and joint and crack resealing.

The wave reflection technique can be used to address specific problems or bring concrete back to its original quality. When repairing a concrete element, design data, construction data, loading data, environmental data, previous repairing activities and concrete surface condition must all be taken into account. Concrete elements repaired with an HSC layer using Ultrasonic Wave Reflection assessment can effectively last for 15 years (Ozturk et al., 2006).

Based on the potential of the proposed method, it could equally be used well in controlling fiber distribution in fibered high strength concrete elements. Excellent distribution of fibers can be very helpful in protecting the concrete structure from deterioration for a long period of time. Experimental studies on this subject have seldom been conducted. It is, therefore, recommended to perform extra experiments on checking the validity of the proposed technique in investigating the control of fibers in fibered reinforced high strength concrete elements.

6 CONCLUSIONS

Two different ultrasonic testing techniques for evaluating the strength development in mortars were compared. The wave reflection method yields more accurate results, compared to the through transmission one. Additionally, the second method is not sensitive enough to the changes in the fresh concrete mixtures' mechanical properties during the initial hydration stage. It can be used for evaluating the beginning of strength development that is useful for calibrating the ultrasonic wave velocity and the change in degree of attenuation in a low frequency range.

Available experimental data shows a strong relationship between the ultrasonic wave characteristics and the penetration resistance. Acoustic impedance was also found sensitive to the strength development in fresh concrete mixtures. Hence the sensitivity of the physical development of mortar changes, as the acoustic impedance varies.

The wave reflection ultrasound measurements can be used for evaluation of mortar strength in repair materials such as shotcrete. The ultrasound measurements were found to be sensitive to such material properties as strength, stiffness and durability, which are very essential for the effective use of shotcrete for repairing RC structures and elements.

The results that were obtained in the frame of this study form a basis for using the ultrasonic testing techniques to evaluate the strength development in early age mortars. Additionally, it also helps in evaluating the characteristics of the mortar, so that it can be effectively used in retrofitting.

REFERENCES

Akkaya, Y., Voigt, T., Subramaniam, K.V. & Shah, S.P. 2003. Nondestructive measurement of concrete strength by an ultrasonic wave reflection method. *Materials and Structures*, 36(8): 507–514.

ASTM Standard C 597. 2002. Standard test method for pulse velocity through concrete. *American Society of Testing and Materials*, 2002.

ASTM Standard C 403. 2005. Standard test method for time of setting of concrete mixtures by penetration resistance. *American Society of Testing and Materials*.

Boumiz, A., Vernet C. & Tenoudji, F.C. 1996. Mechanical properties of cement pastes and mortars at early ages. Journal of Advanced Cement-Based Materials, 3: 94–106.

Boutin, C. & Arnaud, L. 1995. Mechanical characterization of heterogeneous materials during setting. European Journal of Mechanics, A/Solids, 14(4): 633–656.

Chotickai, P., Hirose, S. & Kimoto, K. 2006. Evaluation of strength development in early age mortars using ultrasonic testing. *Symposium on Infrastructure Development and the Environment SEAMEO-INNOTECH*, 7–8 December 2006, University of the Philippines, Diliman, Quezon City, PHILIPPINES.

De Belie, N., Grosse, C.U., Kurz, J. & Reinhardt, H.W. 2005. Ultrasound monitoring of the influence of different accelerating admixtures and cement types for shotcrete on setting and hardening behaviour. Cement and Concrete Research, 35(11): 2087–2094.

Grosse, C.U. & Reinhardt, H.W. 1996. Setting and hardening of concrete continuously monitored by elastic waves. *International RILEM Conference*: 415–25.

Grosse, C.U. 2002. About the Improvement of US measurement techniques for the quality control of fresh concrete. *Otto Graph Jorunal*, 13.

Grübl, P., Weigler, H. & Karl, S. 2001. Beton—art, herstellung und eigenschaft. *Ernst & Sohn*, Verlag für Architekten und technische Wissenschaften GmbH, Berlin, (in German).

Jolin, M. & Lacombe, P. 2000. Le béton projeté: nouveaux développements et applications. Canadian Journal of Civil Engineering, 27: 383–388 (in French).

Lea, F.W. 1998. Lea's chemistry of cement and concrete, P.C. Hewlett (ed.), London, UK.

Malhotra, V.M. & Carino, N.J. 2004. Handbook on Non-destructive Testing of Concrete, (Eds.), CRC Press, Ann Arbor.

Ozturk, T., Rapoport, J., Popovics, J.S. & Shah, S.P. 1999. Monitoring the setting and hardening of cement based materials with ultrasound. *Concrete Science and Engineering*, 1: 83–91.

Ozturk, T., Kroggel, O., Grubl, P. & Popovics, J.S. 2006. Improved ultrasonic wave reflection technique to monitor the setting of cement-based materials. *NDT & E International*, 39(4): 258–263.

Popovics, S., Rose, J.L. & Popovics, J.S. 1990. The behaviour of ultrasonic pulses in concrete. *Cement and Concrete Research*, 20(2): 259–270.

Rapoport, J., Popovics, J.S., Subramaniam, K.V. & Shah, S.P. 2000. The use of ultrasound to monitor the stiffening process of Portland cement concrete with admixtures. ACI Materials Journal, 97(6): 675–683.

Stark, J. & Wicht, B. 1998. Anorganisch Bindemittel—Zement—Kalk—Spezielle Bindmittel (vol. 109). *Schriften der bauhaus-universität weimar*, (in German).

Stark, J., Möser, B. & Eckart, A. Zementhydratation—neue Ansätze. *ZKG International; 01/2001 und 02/2001* (in German).

Ye, G., Van Breugel, K. & Fraaij, A.L.A. 2003. Experimental study and numerical simulation on the formation of microstructure in cementitious materials at early stage. *Cement and Concrete Research*, 33(2): 233–239.

Concrete Solutions – Grantham, Mechtcherine & Schneck (eds)
© 2012 Taylor & Francis Group, London, ISBN 978-0-415-61622-5

Self crack healing of strain hardening cementitious composite incorporating expansive agent and crystalline additive

K. Sisomphon, O. Copuroglu & E.A.B. Koenders
Faculty of Civil Engineering and Geosciences, Delft University of Technology, Delft, The Netherlands

ABSTRACT: This research studies the self-healing potential of strain hardening cementitious composites (SHCC) incorporating crystalline additive (CA) and calcium sulfo-aluminate based expansive additive (CSA). A four point bending set-up was used to pre-crack the SHCC specimens at the age of 28 days. Thereafter, the specimens were submerged in water for 28 days to create a self-healing process. The experimental results indicated that the SHCC specimens with CSA and CA showed a superior surface crack closing ability. The precipitation of calcium carbonation can be observed on the surface crack of the specimens. Eventually, the healed specimens were bent until failure to evaluate the possibility of mechanical recovery. The specimens submerged in water showed a significant improvement of mechanical recovery compared to those air-cured specimens which were used as references. After the self-healing process, the deflection capacity can recover about 60–150% compared to the original specimens. The mechanical recovery was in the order of M1 (Control) < M3 (CA) < M2 (CSA) < M4 (CA + CSA).

1 INTRODUCTION

The self-healing phenomenon in cement-based materials has been observed for decades. The mechanisms are currently based on the precipitation of calcium carbonate and further hydration of unreacted particles. These particles can be ordinary Portland cement as well as other types of cementitious materials, which had not been fully hydrated in the initial stage of hydration, particular in low w/c mixes. There are various practical experiences and experimental studies (Wagner (1974), Ripphausen (1989), Edvardsen (1999)) that have demonstrated that the healing of a crack in cementitious materials leads to a reduction of water permeability over time. From the mechanical point of view, however, such a mechanism is not highly promising in healing typical cracks in concrete because of the limited remaining potential. Generally, the volume of hydration product of conventional cementitious materials is not sufficient to bond and fill large cracks.

It was recently found that the control of crack width is essential in obtaining consistent and robust self-healing behavior (Li (2003), Qian et al. (2009)). Engineered Cementitious Composite (ECC), a new type of ductile, fiber reinforced, cement-based material, can achieve self-controlled tight crack widths with the aid of micromechanics theory that does not depend on steel reinforcement and structural dimensions (Li (2003)). Compared with the conventional cement matrix, this tight crack formation has a superior self-healing phenomenon in ECC. Li and Yang (2007) reported that a maximum crack width of 50 μm is necessary to achieve full recovery of mechanical and transport properties in ECC material. This low limitation would be due to a low expansion ratio of the hydration products of Portland cement. Recently, various alternative cementitious materials have been used in the research of self-healing concrete. Hosada et al. (2007), Kishi et al. (2007) and Sisomphon and Copuroglu (2010) investigated the self-healing potential of concrete when calcium sulfoaluminate based expansive agent (CSA) was used as a cement replacement material. Jaroenratanapirom and Sahamitmongkol (2010) evaluated the self-healing performance of mortars with different additives namely, fly ash (FA), silica fume (SF) and crystalline admixture (CA). Qian et al. (2010) reported the self healing ability of ECC incorporating limestone powder, blast furnace slag and nanoclay.

In an effort to improve the self-healing potential of fiber reinforced strain hardening cementitious composite (SHCC), the SHCC mixtures incorporating the combined use of CSA and CA was evaluated. The effect of additives on surface crack closing ability and mechanical recovery of pre-cracked specimens was investigated.

2 EXPERIMENTAL INVESTIGATION

Ordinary Portland cement CEM I 42,5 N, crystalline admixture and expansive additive were used. Crystalline admixture (CA) is a synthetic cementitious material which contains Portland cement, very fine treated silica and other active chemicals. Some chemical components react with $Ca(OH)_2$ to form crystalline products which disconnect pores and fill cracks in the concrete. The crystalline products can only occur when sufficient moisture is present. The main application of the crystalline admixture is to improve the water tightness and to stop leakage of concrete structures. It is also classified as one of the hydrophilic waterproofing materials (Yodmalai et al., (2010)).

Apart from CA, a mixture of synthesized calcium-aluminate crystal, anhydrite and free lime—a ternary blend expansive additive (CSA), which is a commercial product normally for shrinkage compensation, was used. The expansion can be described by a simplified chemical equation:

$$C_4 A_3 \underline{S} + 8C\underline{S} + 6C + 96H \rightarrow 3(C_3 A \cdot 3C\underline{S} \cdot 32H),$$

where $C_4 A_3 \underline{S}$ = hauyne; $C\underline{S}$ = anhydrite; C = f-CaO; H = water; $C_3 A \cdot 3C\underline{S} \cdot 32H$ = ettringite. The recommended dosages of CA and CSA are 1.5% and 10% by mass of total cementitious materials, respectively. Polyvinyl alcohol (PVA) fibers with a length of 8 mm and diameter of 40 μm were used in the content at 2% by total volume (~1.3% by mass) as suggested by Qian et al. (2009).

All mixtures were designed based on a water-to-cementitious ratio of 0.25. The mix designs are given in Table 1. Superplasticizer (SP), Glenium ACE30, was used to achieve a workable condition of the mixtures. To prepare specimens, all powders were pre-mixed in a Hobart mixer for 2 min low speed. Water and superplasticizer were then added, and the mixture was mixed at low speed for another 2 min, followed by 2 min high speed. Eventually, PVA fibers were slowly added at low speed mixing, and then the mixture was mixed at high speed for another 2 min. The fresh mixture was cast into a mould with the dimension of 240 mm × 60 mm × 10 mm. The filled containers were vibrated on a vibrating table. After 24 h, the specimens were demoulded and subsequently damp cured at a controlled temperature of 25 ± 2°C and 95 ± 5% RH for 3 days. Eventually, all specimens were exposed to laboratory air for another 25-day period.

Each specimen was cut into four pieces with dimensions of 120 mm × 30 mm × 10 mm. Then, these specimens were used in a four-point flexural test. The support span of the four-point flexural test setup was 110 mm and the loading span was 30 mm as showed in Fig. 1.

The experiment was performed under deflection control at a constant rate of 0.01 mm/s. The deflection was measured with two LVDTs attached on each side of specimens, and the result was obtained based on the average values of two LVDTs. Three specimens from each mix were bent until failure to evaluate the flexural strength together with deflection capacity. It would be remarked that deflection capacity was defined as the deflection at which the bending flexural stress reached maximum.

To investigate self-healing potential, specimens were bent to 1.2 mm of deflection. Thereafter, these pre-cracked specimens were cured in water for 28 days. It has to be noted that the specimens were continuous submerged in fresh tap water at 20°C in which the water was replaced once every 12 h. Specimens with different mix proportions were cured in separated water containers. In the meantime, some pre-cracked specimens were

(a) Photograph

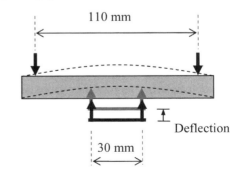

(b) Schematic illustration

Figure 1. Set-up for four point flexural test.

Table 1. Mix design of SHCC mixtures by weight.

Mix	OPC	CSA	CA	Water	SP	Fiber
M1	100	–	–	25	0.3	1.3
M2	90	10	–	25	0.3	1.3
M3	98.5	–	1.5	25	0.3	1.3
M4	88.5	10	1.5	25	0.3	1.3

exposed to laboratory air. This air-cured conditioning was used as a reference. After 28 days healing process, all specimens were reloaded until final failure.

3 RESULTS AND DISCUSSION

The basic mechanical behaviour of SHCC is demonstrated in Figs. 2–4. The typical flexural stress—deflection curves of SHCC specimens is

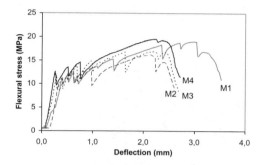

Figure 2. Typical flexural stress—deflection curves of SHCC.

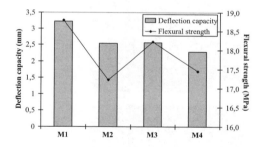

Figure 3. Deflection capacity and flexural strength.

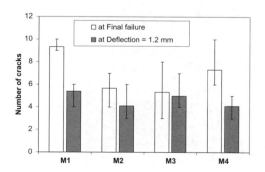

Figure 4. Number of cracks formed: white bars (*at final failure*), gray bars (*at* 1.2 mm *deflection*).

shown in Fig. 2. All mixtures show high tensile strain capacity which is a typical behavior of SHCC. As the supplementary additives were used, however, it is clearly seen that the deflection capacities were reduced. The average values of flexural strength and deflection capacity are given in Fig. 3. The average values were obtained from three measurements. The numbers of cracks are shown in Fig. 4.

As supplementary materials were added, the deflection capacities and flexural tensile strength were decreased. The numbers of cracks formed were reduced as well. As reported by Qian et al. (2009), the deflection capacity can be linearly correlated to tensile strain capacity. Therefore, the deflection capacity can be used in practice for quality control of SHCC type materias due to the simplicity of the four point bending test, as long as the material has been pre-qualified as a truly strain hardening material. It was also reported that SHCC has a tensile strain capacity of at least 2–4%, which is about 200–400 times that of normal concrete (Qian et al., (2009)).

Although CSA and CA additions showed some negative effects on the mechanical properties of the original SHCC, the benefit of supplementary materials can be obviously seen after the healing period. The self-healing potential was observed on pre-cracked specimens which were initially bent to a deflection of 1.2 mm. After the self-healing process, the specimens were reloaded until failure. The numbers of newly formed cracks after reloading are demonstrated in Fig. 5. In all cases, new cracks formed more under water-curing compared to air-curing. For the air-cured regime, there was no significant difference in the numbers of new cracks formed among all specimens: the numbers of new cracks formed were about 3–5. For the water-cured regime, however, it is obviously seen that more new cracks were formed, particularly for the M4 specimen.

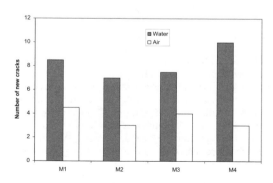

Figure 5. Effect of conditioning of the number of new cracks formed: gray bars (*in water*), white bars (*in air*).

As seen in Fig. 6, the deflection capacity from different mixtures and healing conditions reveals the recovery of deflection capacity, particularly for M2 and M4. The deflection capacities of healed M2 and M4 were even higher than those of the original specimens. In the case of M4 with water curing, the deflection capacity had recovered about 150% compared to the original specimens. The recovery of deflection capacity was in the order of M1 (Control) < M3 (CA) < M2 (CSA) < M4 (CA + CSA). For the air-cured regime, the recovery of deflection capacity was minimal for all mixtures.

Apart from mechanical recovery, surface crack closing is a major self-healing mechanism, particularly in view of durability. To investigate surface crack closing potential, the surface cracks on pre-cracked SHCC specimens were evaluated by stereomicroscope. Figs. 7 and 8 show the photomicrographs of surface cracks of M1 and M4 specimens before and after the healing process (water-cured regime), respectively. The largest crack from each specimen was used for comparison.

The ability of self crack closing was found on both specimens. The appearance of crack closing seen on the surface would be mostly due to the precipitation of calcium carbonate which deposited on the surface of specimens. In previous work (Sisomphon and Copuroglu (2010)), the microstructure of cracks were also observed on petrographic thin-section through a polarized microscope, and it was also clearly revealed the significant formation of calcium carbonate on surface crack of mortar (Fig. 9a).

It was hypothesized that the hydration products had been leached and re-crystallized in water that had flowed into the crack (Ahn and Kishi (2010)). In this study, the SHCC with CSA and CA (M4) showed a more superior self-healing ability. Even though M4 had a larger initial crack width, the surface crack was almost completely sealed within 7 days. Under a higher magnification, the significant formation of calcium carbonate can be observed on the surface crack of M4. The addition of CSA would play a role in the precipitation of calcium carbonate. It is possible that the carbonate products could not be calcium carbonate alone. This could be involved with the reaction of ettringite with carbon dioxide which yield a carbonate analog of ettringite. As another possible hypothesis, the net-like formation of ettringite inside the crack would serve as a support, and allow more precipitation of calcium carbonate (Fig. 9b). It is also possible that the mixtures with CA and CSA create more dissolved Ca^{2+}. This has to be investigated in future studies.

In Sisomphon and Copuroglu (2010), a similar finding was also observed on pre-cracked mortars which had larger initial crack widths (100–400 μm).

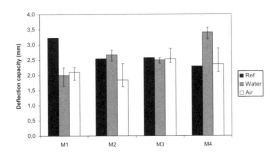

Figure 6. Deflection capacity of healed specimens under different conditioning schemes: black bars (references), gray bars (*in water*), white bars (*in air*).

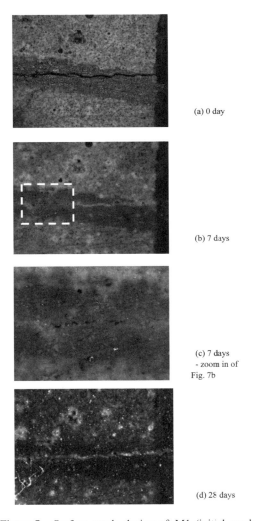

(a) 0 day

(b) 7 days

(c) 7 days
- zoom in of
Fig. 7b

(d) 28 days

Figure 7. Surface crack closing of M1 (initial crack width ~45 μm).

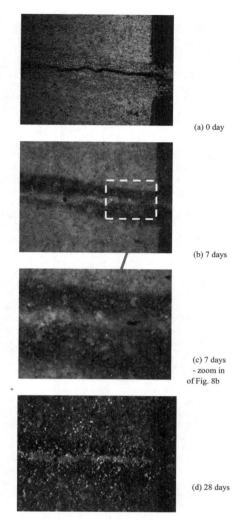

(a) 0 day

(b) 7 days

(c) 7 days
- zoom in
of Fig. 8b

(d) 28 days

Figure 8. Surface crack closing of M4 (initial crack width ~65 μm).

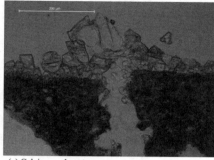

(a) Calcium carbonate

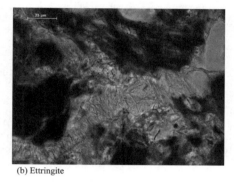

(b) Ettringite

Figure 9. Healing products formation in the mortars with CSA addition (Sisomphon and Copuroglu (2010)).

Moreover, the expansion of the bulk matrix due to ettringite formation would play a role on the contraction of crack width. As reported in another study (Sisomphon and Copuroglu (2011)), confinement is necessary for the self healing phenomenon of mixtures with expansive additives. The confinement would improve self crack closing ability, and minimize microcracks in the interfacial transition zone between matrix and aggregate. The PVA fibers might have a benefit in regard to the free-expansion control restraint in SHCC specimens.

It is obviously seen that the precipitation of calcium carbonate plays an important role in the self-healing of cement-based materials, particularly for surface crack sealing. The carbonate ions in the matrix itself are usually rather low. Hence, the concentration of carbonate ions in the exposed water is a major factor in the self healing mechanism. It is also clearly seen that the significant formation of calcium carbonate was found on surface cracks of the mortar, while the formation inside the crack was rather minimal. In view of the type of cementitious materials used, different cementitious materials would contribute different amounts of dissolved Ca^{2+} ions to form calcium carbonate. In order to optimize self-healing ability, these phenomena would be clarified in future studies. It has to be remarked that the formation of healing products (i.e., C-S-H, ettringite or calcium carbonate) on crack walls might not be a sole crack closing phenomenon. The expansion of the bulk matrix behind the crack walls could play a more important role on the contraction of crack width.

4 CONCLUSIONS

This paper presents the experimental results of an investigation into the self-healing potential of strain hardening cementitious composites (SHCC) incorporating crystalline additive (CA) and calcium sulfo-aluminate based expansive additive (CSA). The results from this study indicate the following conclusions:

- There is a high potential for using CA and CSA as self healing materials in SHCC.
- From the basic mechanical point of view, as supplementary materials were added, the deflection capacities and flexural tensile strength of SHCC were decreased. The numbers of cracks formed were reduced as well.
- After healing, however, the deflection capacity of SHCC with additives recovered about 60–150% compared to the original specimens. The mechanical recovery was in the order of M1 (Control) < M3 (CA) < M2 (CSA) < M4 (CA + CSA). It is obviously seen that more new cracks were formed, particularly for M4 specimen.
- In view of transport properties, the combined use of CSA and CA is beneficial with respect to the surface crack closing phenomenon. On surface cracks, it seems that calcium carbonate is a major healing product. The significant formation of calcium carbonation can be observed on the surface crack of SHCC with CA and CSA.

ACKNOWLEDGEMENT

The authors would like to thank Agentschap, Ministry of Economic Affairs NL for the financial support granted for the projects SHM08729 and SHM08707, as well as materials and technical supports from Denka Chemical GmbH. Authors also thank Xypex Corporation for their material support.

REFERENCES

Ahn, T.H. and Kishi, T. (2010). "Design of Self-Healing Concrete Based on Various Mineral Admixtures" Proceedings of the JCI Annual Convention 2010, Saitama, Japan, pp. 1583–1588.

Edvardsen, C. (1999). "Water Permeability and Autogenous Healing of Cracks in Concrete", *ACI Materials Journal*, 96(4): 448–454.

Hosada, A. et al. (2007). "Self Healing of Crack and Water Permeability of Expansive Concrete", *First International Conference on Self Healing Materials*, Noordwijk, The Netherlands. (in CD).

Jaroenratanapirom, D. and Sahamitmongkol, R. (2010). "Effects of Different Mineral Additives and Cracking Ages on Self-healing Performance of Mortar", *Proceedings of the 6th Annual Concrete Conference*, Petchaburi, Thailand: 551–556.

Kishi, T. et al. (2007). "Self-Healing Behavior by Cementitious Recrystallization of Cracked Concrete", *First International Conference on Self Healing Materials*, Noordwijk, The Netherlands. (in CD).

Li, V.C. (2003). "On Engineered Cementitious Composites (ECC)—a Review of the Material and Its Application", *Journal of Advanced Concrete Technology*, 1(3): 215–230.

Li, V.C. and Yang, E.H. (2007). "Self Healing in Concrete Materials", *Self healing materials: An alternative approach to 20 centuries of materials science*, 161–193.

Qian, S. et al. (2009). "Self-Healing Behavior of Strain Hardening Cementitious Composites Incorporating Local Waste Materials", *Cement and Concrete Composites* 31(9): 613–621.

Qian, S. et al. (2010). "Influence of Curing Condition and Precracking Time on the Self-healing Behavior of Engineered Cementitious Composites", *Cement and Concrete Composites* 32(9): 613–621.

Ripphausen, B. (1989). "Investigation of the Water Permeability and Repair of Reinforced Concrete Structures with Through Cracks", PhD thesis, RWTH Aachen, Aachen, Germany. (in German).

Sisomphon, K. and Copuroglu, O. (2010). "Some Characteristics of a Self Healing Mortar Incorporating Calcium Sulfo-aluminate Based Agent", *Proceedings of the 2nd International Conference on Durability of Concrete Structures*, Sapporo, Japan: 157–164.

Sisomphon, K. and Copuroglu, O. (2011). "Self Healing Mortars by Using Different Cementitious Materials", *The International Conference on Advances in Construction Materials through Science and Engineering*, Hong Kong, Chaina SAR. (to be published).

Wagner, E.F. (1974). "Autogenous Healing of Cracks in Cement-Mortar Linings for Gray-iron and Ductile-iron Water Pipe", *Journal of the American Water Works Association*, 66(6): 358–360.

Yodmalai, D. et al. (2010). "Water Sorptivity, Water Permeability, Autogenous Shrinkage, and Compressive Strength of Concrete with Crystalline Materials", 15th National Convention on Civil Engineering, Ubonrachatani, Thailand. (in CD).

Concrete Solutions – Grantham, Mechtcherine & Schneck (eds)
© 2012 Taylor & Francis Group, London, ISBN 978-0-415-61622-5

Properties of fine cement concretes with carbonaceous nanoparticles

S.N. Tolmachev & O.A. Belichenko
Kharkov national automobile und highway University, Kharkov, Ukraine

ABSTRACT: Problems of the impact of carbonaceous nanoparticles on the properties of fine cement concretes are considered. The introductions of carbonaceous nanoparticles into fine cement concretes with water is shown to improve engineering properties of concrete mixes and the physical and mechanical indices of concretes. Such effect makes it possible to change the structure of vibropacked and compacted cement stone and fine cement concretes as supported by electronic research data. It has been determined that the efficiency of carbonaceous nanoparticles depends on the engineering features of fine concretes (compaction and vibropacking).

1 INTRODUCTION

In recent years scientists of different countries have been actively pursuing investigations over the area of production and application of ultradispersive materials (Gusev, A.I. 2005). It has been known that the reduction of structure element sizes (grains, particles, crystallites) lower than a threshold value can result in a perceptible change of the whole composite properties whose composition consists of such particles. In large measure, this is especially true in regard to the concrete studies. Within the limits of developing a scientific line of investigation called nanotechnologies attempts are taken to control structure formation processes for creating materials with predetermined properties.

1.1 General ideas about processes of the structure formation in cement composites

The structure formation kinetics in the early stage predetermines the further processes of a structure and the physical and mechanical properties of cement composites (Kruglitsky, N.N. 1976). The structure formations of a cement system is represented as the interaction processes of the cement binder with water or solutions of chemical admixtures. On the basis of A.A. Baykov and P.A. Rebinder's works (Baykov, A.A. 1948 and Rebinder, P.A. 1966) it has been determined that the structure formation process of cement composites is carried out in three periods: preliminary—solution of cement minerals in water; a colloidal period—the formation of a coagulation structure (the change-over to an adhesive state); crystallization—the formation of a coagulated and crystallized structure. At the stage of cement mineral solution in water, a saturated solution of the cement minerals is formed and an oversaturated solution is formed for the less soluble formations. In the oversaturated newly formed solution, during the period of crystallization nuclei of new phases are formed. The interaction between them is carried out with formation of an intermediate coagulated and crystallized structure. The limiting stage of such structure formation is the initial nucleation-nucleating centre. At the next stage the crystal growth is prevailing, the water film is getting thin, crystals converge and then they are spliced. The formation of crystallization contacts takes place resulting in the formation of the crystallized structure of hardening cement paste.

The change-over process velocity of the coagulated and crystallized structure to the crystallization structure can be controlled by various means. At the expense of this process control we can control forming physical and mechanical properties of cement composites (Shchukin, E.D. 1985). Different methods are used for this purpose, for example, for activation of structure formation processes: the advent of admixtures, grinding hydrated cement to the particle size of initial cement milling, water processing in the magnetic field, physical and chemical and physical-mechanical actions (Shchukin, E.D. 1985 and Kruglitsky, N.N. 1975).

Improving activation methods of structure formation processes in cement systems can result in the emergence of new more improved composites on the basis of cement binders. The application of nanoparticles is one of the urgent developing methods of effects on the processes of structure formation of cement composites.

1.2 Purposes and problems of studies

In the Kharkov national automobile und highway University at the manufacturing engineering department of the technology of road building materials the studies have been conducted as to application of nanoparticles in concrete studies in particular, for heavy fine cement concretes.

The search which we have pursued showed that at present there is no well-marked undestanding in the interpretation of the mechanism of the effect of nanoparticles on the cement system. This doesn't allow us to control, structure formation processes for creating composites with predetermined properties. The basic purpose of the studies which we are carrying out is to reveal the mechanism of structure formation on a submicro- and microlevel in fine cement through activation of processes in mixing concrete ingredients with water by means of modified nanoparticles.

1.3 Hypotheses for studies

The analysis of conducted investigation makes it possible to propose the scientific hypotheses: the limiting stage of the crystal formation process is a primary contact in the nucleating centre. Particle additions of colloidal size into the medium of the oversaturated mineral solution in water will facilitate intensive crystal formation, that is, nanoparticles are capable of acting as crystallization centres supporting higher cement hydration and creating the strong structure of hardening cement paste and solutions

2 MATERIALS AND METHODS OF STUDIES

The following materials have been used in studies: cement PTS I-500 H with activity at an age of 28 days 49.3 MPa, quartz sand with modulus of grain size $M_{gs} = 1.8 \dots 2.4$. For mixing concrete ingredients with water distilled water has been used. Carbonaceous nanoparticles (CNP) in the form of the water suspension (hydrosol) with a concentration of 0.9 g/l were introduced into cement systems. The suspension was obtained in dispersing carbonaceous particles in an ultra-sonics mill (Zelensky, O.I. 2009). Samples of the cement paste and fine concretes were hardened in normal conditions at a temperature +20°C and relative humidity 95%. These samples were also cured in the steam-curing chamber by conditions: 3 + 4 + 10 + 2. Where 3—curing time of compositions (in hours), 4—heating time of the steam-curing chamber (in hours), 10—curing time of compositions in the steam—coring chamber at a constant temperature (in hours), 2—cooling time of compositions. Pressing was carried out at a pressure of 40 MPa.

3 THE ANALYSIS OF OBTAINED RESULTS

3.1 Physical and chemical investigations of a water system with carbonaceous nanoparticles (CNP's)

In heavy cement concretes some structure levels can be singled out: macro-, meso-, micro- and a sub-microstructure. It is evident that the character of a forming a more dispersive structure will determine the structure quality of the following more coarse level. Then, the correct sampling of a condition and application time of activated effect at the submic-rolevel can improve properties of all levels of the cement composite structure. The O.P. Mchedlov-Petrosyan (Mchedlov-Petrosyan, O.P. 1962) correspondence principle is based on this which points to the fact that it is necessary to apply activation at the required time for the defined level of the structure. At a later time this principle is embodied in the I.M. Grushko (Grushko, I.M. 1965) scientific school of thought for all levels of the structure.

Studies of the submicrostructure—mixing cement composites with water, containing different CNP concentrations were carried out with the help of the contact conductivity apparatus method. The conductivity apparatus method is a set of electro-chemical methods of analysis based on the measurement of electrical resistance and the calculation of electrical conductivity of solutions depending on concentration. Advantages of the conductivity apparatus method consist of high sensitivity and precision and simplicity and automation of measuring methods. The studies were carried out by means of MCP BR 2821 Hand-held LCR Meter. Solutions of different CNP concentrations were put in turn into the cell of the conductivity apparatus and after that measurements of electric resistance of solutions at a room temperature of +20°C were conducted.

Studies allowed us to determine (Fig. 1) the availability of two changes in thef electric

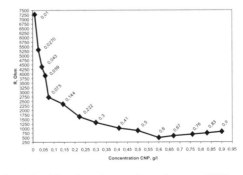

Figure 1. Electric resistance dependence on CNP concentration in the hydrosol.

resistance variation curve corresponding to CNP concentrations of 0.075 g/l or 0.6 g/l.

Based on the obtained values of electric resistance (R, Ohm) for the hydrosol the electric conductivity of λ solutions by the formula $\lambda = 1/R$ was calculated. The conductivity χ of the studied solutions was determined by the formula $\chi = B/R$ where $B = 4.15\ 10^{-2}\ (cm^{-1})$—the constant of the conductivity apparatus cell, R—electric resistance (Ohm).

On the basis of the calculated data the conductivity dependence of the solutions on concentration (Fig. 2) has been plotted. Evidently, the availability of two extreme is observed in the field of concentration 0.075 g/l and 0.6 g/l and this testifies about the availability of two fields of critical concentration of micelle formation (CCM) in the hydrosol.

In the concentration field of 0.075 g/l (Figs. 1, 2) less marked change is observed and this testifies about the wider field of formation concentration of spherical micelle structures (CCM₁). On the plot (Fig. 1) very much more pronounced extremum for concentration of 0.6 g/l is so apparent and this testifies about the availability of the narrower concentration field-critical concentration of micelle formation (CCM) of the highest order (CCM₂).

To understand the CNP form electron microscopic studies of the hydrosol for a concentration field of 0.075 g/l were performed (Fig. 3).

In the CCM field in the particles concentration of 0.075 g/l the hydrosol is primarily chaotically located particles of a spherical form as in Brownian motion. Accumulations (aggregates) of particles are also present which are probably formed owing to the action of Van der Vaals forces.

In the opinion Z.Ya. Berestneva (Berestneva, Z.Ya. 1950) the spherical form of colloidal particles in sols is clarified that in dispersion the amorphous phase is formed and hereafter the crystallization process is developed as a secondary one.

Then, it is conceivable that such primary crystals can act as centres of crystallization. Their introduction into composites containing cement will result in quick formation around them of dense crystallization aggregations not only at a level of the submicrostructure but also at more coarse and dispersive levels.

Investigation to determination of the pH of the hydrosol and its density with different CNP concentrations showed that significant changes in the given characteristics are not observed. Data as to the definition of surface tension showed that for the hydrosol with CNP the surface tension decreases in comparison with the surface tension of the distilled water. This makes it possible as a first approximation to correlate the CNP action effect with the action effect of surface-active substances (SAS).

The hydrosol viscosity with different CNP concentration was determined with the help of a glass viscosimeter with a capillary diameter of 0.54 mm. The relative viscosity was calculated as the relation-ship of water outflow time in the viscosimeter to the hydrosol outflow time of different CNP concentration. On the basis of the obtained results the dependence of the relative hydrosol viscosity on CNP concentration has been plotted (Fig. 4).

Minima of the relative viscosity on the concentration curve of the CNP content in the general

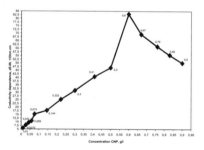

Figure 2. Conductivity dependence of solutions on CNP concentration in the hydrosol.

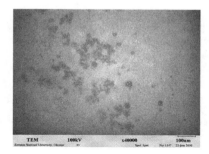

Figure 3. Electronic and microscopic CNP image in concentration 0.075 g/l.

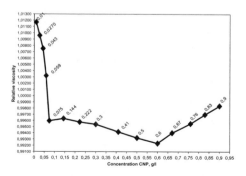

Figure 4. Dependence of the relative hydrosol viscosity on CNP concentration.

tendency for its enhancement are evident. Minima are observed at CNP concentration of 0.075 g/l and 0.6 g/l. Similar of results of independent studies allows up to make a conclusion about reliability of the obtained data during experiments about the availability of two CCM fields in the hydrosol with CNP.

3.2 *Investigation of the CNP effect on cement slurry mobility*

We have developed measuring methods of cement slurry cone spread. During the performance of the searching experiment it was found that maxima of strength are observed in the field of the CNP content of 0.0045% and 0.0225% from cement mass. This corresponds to concentration of nanoparticles in hydrosols 0.013 g/l and 0.075 g/l. Thus, measurements of a cone spread value of the cement slurry were conducted in the CNP content in the range between 0.0045% … 0.27% of the cement mass. In particular, Fig. 5 shows dependences of cement slurry mobility from the water-cement ratio at two CNP consumptions. It was visually determined that in introduction of hydrosols into the cement slurry composition on the basis of CNP on the surface of the cement slurry metallic luster emerges and mobility variation of compositions is observed.

It is evident that with increasing the water-cement ratio from 0.24 to 0.26 a sharp enhancement of mobility for all compositions is observed. The further enhancement of the water-cement ratio for control compositions results in insignificant variation of cone spread. Thus, for the control composition increasing the water-cement ratio from 0.24 to 0.3 increases the cone spread by 1.28 times.

With CNP introduction into the cement slurry at a W/C = 0.24. The cone spread decreases for both CNP values in comparison with the control compositions. The tendency for cone spread stabilization provides evidence about what is happening in the processes of system structurization. It should be pointed out that for the CNP content of 0.0045% by cement mass increasing the water-cement ratio from 0.24 to 0.3 increases the mobility of compositions by 1.6 times in comparison with control compositions. The introduction of cone spread of 0.0225% CNP by cement mass results in the decreasing in comparison with control compositions.

3.3 *Investigation of CNP effect, on strength of vibro-compacted cement stone of natural hardening and after heat and humid treatment*

Studies have been carried out on CNP effect estimation on hardening cement paste strength after natural hardening at a constant W/C = 0.26. which corresponds to the normal density of the cement used. On the basis of the obtained data the graph of vibro-compacted cement strength dependence on the CNP content (Fig. 6) has been plotted.

Studies showed that by 7 days of natural hardening a maximum of strength in the CCM field in CNP consumption of 0.6 g/l (which corresponds 0.18% of CNP from cement mass) is observed. The strength of the vibro-compacted hardening cement paste at this content of nanoparticles increases by 15% in comparison with the control composition. After 28 day of natural hardening, maxima correlate two CCM fields (CNP consumption is 0.075 g/l and 0.6 g/l which corresponds to 0.0225% and 0.18% of CNP from cement strength). The hardening cement paste strength at these concentration increases by 1.5 times in comparison with the control composition. It is evident that the CNP action effect in low concentrations (0.075 g/l) manifests itself in later terms of hardening (28 days).

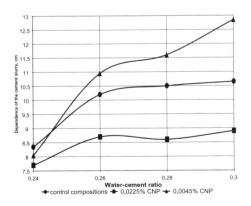

Figure 5. Mobility dependence of the cement slurry on the water-cement ratio.

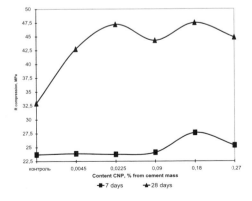

Figure 6. Vibro-compacting cement stone strength dependence of natural hardening on the CNP content.

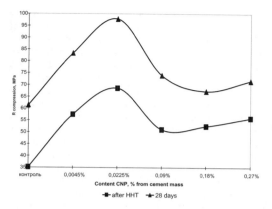

Figure 7. Dependence of vibro-compacting cement stone strength after heat and humid treatment on CNP content.

Data which we obtained previously testifies that the optimal temperature of the heat and humidity treatment (HHT) is 60°C (Belichenko, O.A. 2009). Studies were performed to show the effect of CNP on vibro-compacted hardening cement paste strength in HHT conditions (Fig. 7). Studies showed that with increasing the CNP content to 0.075 g/l (that corresponds to 0.0225% from cement mass) the vibro-compacted hardening cement paste strength increases immediately after HHT by 1.9 times in comparison with the control composition. By 28 days after HHT for the same CNP consumption the strength increases by 1.6 times in comparison with the control content.

After the enhancement of the CNP content up to 0.3 g/l (which corresponds to 0.09% by cement mass) results in decreasing strength. The further enhancement of CNP consumption results in only a very small increase in strength of composition with CNP in comparison with control compositions.

The effectiveness of technology of vibro-compacted cement paste hardening shows that heat and humid treatment is about twice as effective as natural hardening.

3.4 Kinetics of strength increase of vibro-compacting fine cement concretes of natural hardening and after HHT in time on bending and compression

The investigation of physical and mechanical properties of fine cement concretes of natural hardening with composition of C:S = 1: 2 showed (Fig. 8) that the strength in bending composition with CNP consumption of 0.0045% and 0.0225% from cement mass by 3 days of hardening increases in 1.3 and 1.2 times, respectively, in comparison with control composition.

By 7 days of natural hardening, strengths of all compositions practically did not change in comparison with control compositions. After 28 days of hardening the strength of control compositions stabilized and the strength of composition with CNP continues to increase steadily without a tendency to decrease. For CNP consumption at 0.0045% by cement mass in bending the strength is higher by 1.27 times and in composition of 0.0225% by mass of cement the strength is higher by 1.44 times compared to control compositions.

The strength in compression of compositions with CNP consumption of 0.0225% by cement mass after 3 days of natural hardening (Fig. 9) is 10% higher than in control compositions. For compositions with CNP consumption of 0.0045% by cement mass after 3 days of natural hardening the strength is lower than in control compositions.

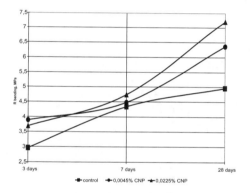

Figure 8. Strength dependence of vibro-compacted fine cement concretes of natural hardening with time in bending.

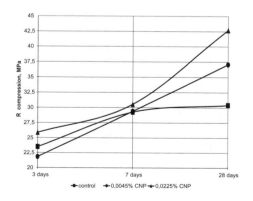

Figure 9. Strength dependence of vibro-compacted fine cement concretes of natural hardening with time in compression.

By 7 days of natural hardening the strength of all composition were practically the same. At 28 days of hardening strength stabilization for control compositions is observed. For compositions with CNP the strength in compression increases steadily and it has no tendency to decreasing. For compositions with the CNP of 0.0045% by cement mass the strength in compression by 1.25 times and for the CNP content of 0.0225% by cement mass—by 1.44 times in compression with control compositions.

Studies of physical and mechanical properties of fine cement concretes of C:S = 1:3 composition (Figs. 10, 11) showed that both after HHT (humidity and heat treatment) and at 7 days after the strength of compositions with CNP and the control composition were practically the same.

At 28 days compositions with CNP consumption of 0.0225% by cement mass in bending increases by 27% in comparison with the control composition.

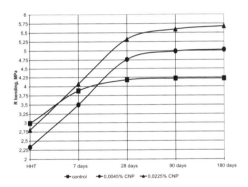

Figure 10. Kinetics of vibro-compacted fine cement concrete strength increase after HHT with time in bending.

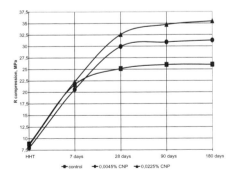

Figure 11. Kinetics of vibro-compacted fine cement concrete strength increase after HHT with time in compression.

For CNP consumption of 0.0045% by cement mass the strength increased by 14% in comparison with the control composition. In further hardening at an age of 90 days, strength stabilization was observed in bending of the control composition but the strength of composition with CNP consumption of 0.0225% by cement mass increased steadily and exceeded the strength of the control composition by 1.33 times. For the composition with CNP consumption of 0.0045% by cement mass, a similar tendency was observed, the strength by 90 days increased by 1.2 times in comparison with the control composition. It was evident that by 180 days of hardening the strength of compositions in bending with CNP consumption of 0.0045% and 0.0225% by cement mass had stabilized, but were considerably higher than in control composition (by 1.8 and 1.4 times respectively).

The strength of the vibro-compacted fine cement concrete in compression (Fig. 11) after HHT at 7 days for the control compositions and the CNP compositions were approximately the same. By 28 days of hardening the strength of the composition with CNP content of 0.0225% by cement mass was 1.3 times higher and for compositions with CNP consumption of 0.0045% by cement mass 1.2 times higher, in comparison with the control composition. In further hardening, stabilization of strength was observed in compression of control compositions. By 90 days of hardening, the strength of compositions with a CNP consumption of 0.0225% by cement mass in compression increased further and exceeded the strength of the control composition by 1.34 times. The strength of the composition with a CNP content of 0.0045% by cement mass by 90 days had stabilized and didn't change further but in so doing it exceeded the strength of the control composition by 1.2 times. Further hardening resulted in an inconsiderable smooth increase and stabilization of strength of the compositions with CNP. By 180 days of hardening, the strength of compositions with a CNP consumption of 0.0225% by cement mass was higher than in control compositions by 1.38 times.

It should be noted that the kinetics of strength increase of compositions with CNP is higher than in control compositions and it did not have a tendency to decrease. For control compositions by 28 days and later days of hardening stabilization of strength was observed.

Studies of physical and mechanical properties of fine cement concretes of natural hardening with the composition of C:S = 1:1.5 showed (Fig. 12) that the strength of compositions with the CNP consumption of 0.0045% and 0.0225% by cement mass in bending after 3 and 7 days of hardening did not change, practically in comparison with control compositions.

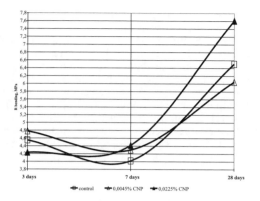

Figure 12. Strength dependence of vibro-compacted fine cement concretes of natural hardening with tame in bending.

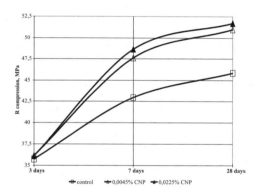

Figure 13. Strength dependence of vibro-compacted fine cement concretes of natural hardening with tame in compression.

At 7 days of hardening, a strength decrease of all compositions in comparison with 3 days was observed. By 28 days of hardening the strength of composition with a CNP consumption of 0.0225% by cement mass had increased by 1.26 times in comparison with the control compositions. And for CNP consumption of 0.045% by cement mass the strength was enhanced only slightly by 8% in comparison with control compositions. Studies of the strength in compression showed (Fig. 13) that by 3 days of natural hardening the strength of all compositions was the same. By 7 days, a strength increase of the compositions with CNP consumptions of 0.0045% and 0.0225% by cement mass to 12% and 14% respectively was observed in comparison with control compositions.

By 28 days of natural hardening a strength increase of compositions with CNP consumption of 0.0045% and 0.0225% by cement mass to 10% and 12% respectively were observed in comparison with the control composition.

3.5 Effectiveness of CNP application in the technology of vibro-compacted fine cement concretes

For revealing the CNP application effectiveness in the technology of vibro-compacted fine cement concretes of compositions with a deferent ratio of a binder and aggregate with optimal CNP content of 0.0225% by cement mass, which were hardened in natural conditions, were manufactured.

It is evident (Figs. 14, 15) that with increasing proportions of aggregate effectiveness of the nanoparticles decreased but in so doing the strength of

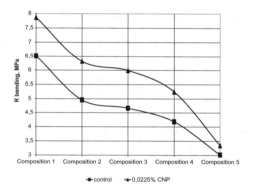

Figure 14. Strength dependence in bending of vibro-compacted fine cement concretes from the ratio of binder-aggregate: composition 1-C:S = 1:1.5; composition 2-C:S = 1:2; composition 3-C:S = 1:2.5; composition 4-C:S = 1:3; composition 5-C:S = 1:4.

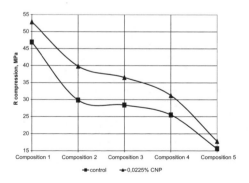

Figure 15. Strength dependence in compression of vibro-compacted fine cement concretes from the ratio of binder-aggregate: composition 1-C:S = 1:1.5; composition 2-C:S = 1:2; composition 3-C:S = 1:2.5; composition 4-C:S = 1:3; composition 5-C:S = 1:4.

compositions with CNP was significantly higher than in control compositions. For vibro-compacted fine concretes with the content of C:S = 1:1.5 in bending the strength was higher by 1.2 times than in control compositions (Fig. 14). For concretes of the composition of C:S = 1:2. The strength was higher by 1.24 times, for the composition C:S = 1:2.5—by 1.34 times, for compositions of C:S = 1:3—by 1.29 times and for the compositions of C:S = 1:4 the strength was higher by only 10%.

A similar tendency of strength change was observed in compression (Fig. 15). For vibro-compacted fine cement concretes of composition C:S = 1:1.5. the strength in compression was only higher by 13% compared to control compositions. For concretes of the compositions of C:S = 1:2—C:S = 1:2.5. The strength was higher by 1.33 times. For compositions of C:S = 1:3—the strength was higher by 1.23 times, and for the compositions of C:S = 1:4 the strength was only higher by 14%.

Thus, in going from hardened cement paste to aggregate cement systems—fine concretes—the CNP application effectiveness reduced.

Previously pursued investigations of the strength of crushed stone concretes (fraction 5 ... 10 mm and 10 ... 20 mm) showed (Tolmachev, S.N. 2010), that CNP application effectiveness reduced abruptly. Displacement of the optimal CNP content to reduction of nanoparticle concentrations was observed.

3.6 Investigation of CNP effect on the strength of pressed cement paste of natural hardening

Studies of the pressed hardened cement paste strength with a humidity of 10% showed (Fig. 16) that at 3 days of natural hardening, maxima in a region of CNP content of 0.0045% and 0.0225% by cement mass are evident.

The strength in these CNP consumptions increased by 1.4 times and 1.37 times, respectively, in comparison with the control composition. By 28 days of hardening a peak is observed for the CNP content of 0.0225% by cement mass and the strength increased by 1.3 times in comparison with the control composition. Further increase of the CNP content resulted in a reduction of the pressed hardening cement paste strength to a level of the control composition.

3.7 Studies of CNP effect on the strength of pressed fine cement concrete with natural hardening and after HHT

Studies to reveal the optimum humidity for compositions and the optimum CNP content of pressed fine cement concretes of the content of C:S = 1:1.5 of natural hardening and after HHT were carried out.

It is evident (Fig. 17) that the optimum humidity of compositions in which considerable enhancement of the strength of pressed fine concretes after HHT is 8.5%. For the given humidity with enhancement of the CNP content up to 0.0135% and 0.0225% from cement mass the strength is augmented by 1.47 and 1.53 times, respectively, in comparison with the control composition.

A similar regularity is observed for naturally hardened pressed fine concretes (Fig. 18).

With CNP introduction at a rate of 0.0045% by cement mass, a strength reduction is observed in comparison with the control composition. A further increase of the CNP content results in a sharp increase of the strength of CNP containing compositions. At optimum humidity of 8.5%

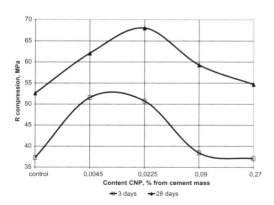

Figure 16. Strength dependence on the CNP content of pressed hardened cement paste after natural hardening.

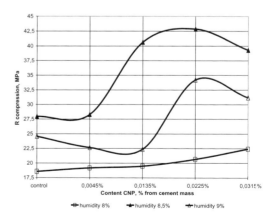

Figure 17. Strength dependence of the pressed fine cement concrete after HHT from the CNP content.

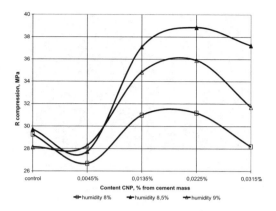

Figure 18. Strength dependence of the pressed fine cement concrete of natural hardening on the CNP content.

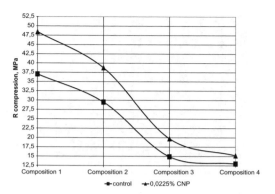

Figure 19. Strength dependence of pressed fine cement concretes from the ration of binder-aggregate: composition 1-C:S = 1:1; composition 2-C:S = 1:1.5; composition 3-C:S = 1:2; composition 4-C:S = 1:3.

compositions and the CNP content up to 0.0225% by cement mass the strength is enhanced by 1.32 times in comparison with the control composition. Further increase of the CNP content results in strength reduction of all compositions.

Thus, optimum humidity of pressed fine cement concretes, on which essential enhancements of the strength is observed is 8.5% with a CNP addition of 0.0225% by cement mass.

Comparing naturally hardened vibro-compacted and pressed fine cement concretes with the composition of C:S = 1:1.5 (Figs. 13 and 18) it is significant that the strength of pressed concretes is higher than vibro-compacted ones for the optimal CNP consumption of 0.0225% by cement mass (for pressed concretes the strength is higher by 1.32 times and for vibro-compacting ones is only increased by 1.12 times in comparison with control compositions).

So, from the viewpoint of the manufacturing technology of fine cement concretes, pressing is more effective than vibro-compacting.

3.8 CNP application effectiveness in the technology of pressed fine cement concretes

For revealing CNP application effectiveness in the technology of pressed fine cement concretes compositions with different ratios of binder and aggregate with the optimal CNP content of 0.0225% by cement mass hardened in natural conditions were made (Fig. 19).

For pressed fine cement concretes a similar tendency of CNP application effectiveness reduction with increase of aggregate proportions is observed but in so doing the strength of concretes with CNP is also higher than in control compositions. Pressed fine concretes with the optimal CNP content of 0.0225% by cement mass with the composition of C:S = 1:1. C:S = 1:1.5. C:S = 1:2 showed strength in crease of 1.3. 1.32 and 1.32 times, respectively, higher than in the control composition. For the concrete composition of C:S = 1:3 the strength is only higher be 17% in comparison with the control composition.

Thus, in pressed fine cement concretes a similar regularity of CNP application effectiveness reduction as for vibro-compacted ones was observed.

3.9 Electronic and microscopic investigations of the vibro-compacted hardened cement paste and the fine cement concrete

For revealing the CNP effect on the processes of structure formation of the vibro-compacted hardening cement paste and the fine cement concrete electronic and microscopic investigation using the JSM-840 scanning electron microscope were carried out.

Electron and microscopic investigation of the hardened cement paste at an age of 28 days for water cement (W/C) ratio showed that under a magnification of x3000 essential distinctions in the structure of the cement stone without CNP and with CNP at a rate of 0.0225% by cement mass (Figs. 20, 21) were detectable.

For control compositions without CNP (Fig. 20) structural defects in the form of pores were characteristic, the large-sized crystalline structure and chaotic location of crystalline splices were evident.

For compositions with CNP at a rate of 0.0225% by cement mass (Fig. 21) the absence of defects was characteristic, the fine crystalline structure, which was added to dense massive and continuous blocks is evidence that such a structure accounts

Figure 20. Electron and microscopic image of the vibro-compacted hardened cement paste of the control composition without CNP.

Figure 22. Electron and microscopic image of the vibro-compacted fine cement concrete of the control composition without CNP.

Figure 21. Electron and microscopic image of the vibro-compacted hardened cement paste with the CNP consumption of 0.0225% by cement mass.

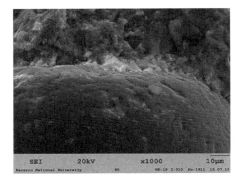

Figure 23. Electron and microscopic image of the vibro-compacted fine cement concrete with CNP of 0.0225% by cement mass.

for the large strength of hardening cement paste with CNP.

Electron and microscopic photographs (Figs. 22, 23) of fine cement concretes at an age of 28 days of hardening illustrate distinctions in the structure of the contact zone and the pore concrete structure with CNP. The contact zone "hardened cement paste-aggregate" in concrete without CNP has a pronounced boundary of division (Fig. 22) which illustrate the bad inter- action between the cement stone and the binder. Adjacent to it a pore is located and this illustrates the presence of defects in the contact zone. It is possible to see too that destruction of all struc- ture took place by the contact zones and the availability of smooth cavities shows that. There is also a great number of different defects of the structures and pores.

For compositions with CNP (Fig. 23) the more dense finely porous (open-worked) structure of the solution part with uniform and homogeneous

distribution of pores is evident. The contact zone of concrete with CNP is presented by fine crystalline dense new formations, the contact zone boundary between binder and hardened cement paste is blurred it testifies about its high strength.

3.10 *Electron and microscopic investigation of pressed hardened cement paste and fine cement concrete*

Investigation of CNP effect on the structure for- mation process of the pressed hardened cement paste and fine cement concrete by means of the JSM-6329 scanning electron microscope were carried out.

It is evident for the control composition (Fig. 24) that the loose large-sized structure with chaotic location of crystalline splices is characteristic. Pores of a different diameter are present. For com- positions with the CNP consumption of 0.0225% by cement mass (Fig. 25), the crystalline structure

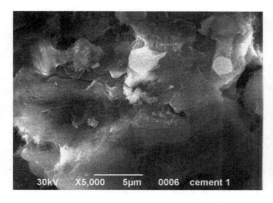

Figure 24. Electron and microscopic image of the pressed hardened cement paste of the control composition without CNP.

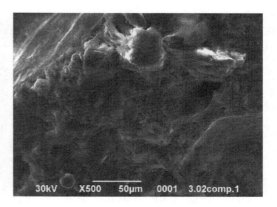

Figure 26. Electron and microscopic image of the pressed fine cement concrete of the control composition without CNP.

Figure 25. Electron and microscopic image of the pressed hardened cement paste with the CNP consumption of 0.0225% by cement mass.

Figure 27. Electron and microscopic image of the pressed fine cement concrete with CNP of 0.0225% by cement mass.

with more dense new formation and uniformly distributed smaller pores is characteristic.

It should be noted that for the pressed hardened cement paste similar regularities of hardening and structure formation as for vibro-compaction one are observed.

The similar regularity is observed for natural hardening pressed fine cement concretes (Figs. 26, 27). For the control composition of the pressed fine cement concrete (Fig. 26), the loose pore structure is characteristic. For composition with CNP (Fig. 27) the more dense fine structure is evident.

Thus, the cited data of microscopic investigation shows the great degree of crystallization of the concrete structure with CNP. This is characteristic as for the contact zone "hardened cement paste-aggregate" and for the pore space and this is responsible for a great concrete strength with such particles.

4 CONCLUSIONS

1. It was determined that the hydrosol containing different CNP concentrations has regions of the critical concentration of micelle formation at CNP concentrations of 0.075 g/l and 0.6 g/l.
2. It was illustrated that the CNP particles in the region of CCM 0.075 g/l hat a spherical form. From here on, the process of their crystallization is progressing as the secondary one.
3. It was shown that for the CNP content at a rate of 0.0045% and 0.0225% by cement mass a variation of cement slurry mobility is observed and this indicates the weak plasticizing properties of the hydrosol with CNP.
4. It was found that with enhancement of aggregate proportions in the composition of vibro-compacted, pressed fine cement concretes a reduction of the CNP effectiveness is observed.

5. It was demonstrated that at the optimum CNP content of 0.0225% by cement mass, the strength of naturally hardened, vibro-compacted fine cement concretes with the composition of C:S = 1:1.5 increases by 12%.

6. It was determined that for naturally hardened, pressed fine cement concretes the strength increases by 1.3–1.4 times and by 1.5 times after HHT.

7. It was demonstrated that the structure of vibro-compacted hardened cement paste and fine cement concretes with the optimum CNP consumption of 0.0225% by cement mass differs from the structure of hardened paste and concrete without CNP by smaller-sized crystalline and dense new formations, uniform distribution of pores of smaller radius.

8. It was established that for the pressed hardened cement paste and fine cement concretes with the optimum CNP consumption of 0.0225% by cement mass the small-sized crystalline structure is characteristic and in the concrete structure without CNP there are pores of a different diameter and a chaotic location of crystalline new formation is observed.

9. It was shown that from the viewpoint of manufacturing technology of fine cement concretes with CNP, pressing is more effective than vibro-compacting.

REFERENCES

Baykov, A.A. 1948. Meeting of works. Volume 5. Works in the field of knitting substances and fire-resistant materials: 272. Moskow: Publishing house of the Academy of sciences.

Belichenko, E.A. & Tolmachev, S.N. 2009. Variationregularites of cement composition properties, containing the carbonaceous nanoparticles. In Moskow, L. Ya. Karpov NIFKHI, *All-Russian conference "Physical and chemical aspects, their properties and application"; Volume of abstracts of papers, octiber-november 2009: 10–19.* Russcha: Moskow.

Berestneva, Z.Ya., Koretskaya, G.A. & Kargin, V.A. 1950. Electronic and microscopic investigation of TiO$_2$—sols and mechanism of formation of colloidal particles. *Colloidal journal*: 5(12): 336–341.

Grushko, I.M., Glushenko, N.F. & Il'in, A.G. 1965. Structure and durability of road cement concrete: 136. Kharkov: Visha shkola: Publishing house at Kharkover university.

Gusev, A.I. 2005. Nanomaterials, nanostructures, nanotechnologies: 416. Moskow: Fizmatlit.

Kruglitsky, N.N. 1976. Physical and chemical mechanics of dispersive structures in magnetic fields: 193. Kyiv: Naykova dumka.

Kruglitsky, N.N., Grankovskiy, I.G. & others. 1975. Formation of dispersive structures of binding materials in the presence of small additions of clay minerals. *Physical and chemical mechanics and lyophilization of dispersive structures* 7: 152–157.

Mchedlov-Petrosyan, O.P. 1962. Physical and chemical bases of technology of concrete: 350. Kyiv: Naykova dumka.

Rebinder, P.A. 1966. The Physical and chemical mechanics of dispersive structures. The collection of articles: 400. Moskow: Nayka.

Shchukin, E.D. & others. 1985. Physical and chemical mechanics of natural dispersive system: 264. Moskow: MGU publishing house.

Tolmachev, S.N., Belichenko, E.A. & Kholodniy, A.G. 2010. Technological, mechanical and structural characteristics of cement system with carbonaceous colloidal particles. *Building materials* 9: 96–100.

Zelensky O.I., Bogatyrenko, S.I. & Shmalko, V.M. 2009. Kinds of carbonaceous of nanoparticles separated from carbons and products of its heat processing. In Kharkiv; V.N. Karasin KHNU, *Physical and chemical fundamentals of formation and modification of micro and nanostructures (FMMN'2009); Collected scientific papers of International scientific conference, 21–23 October 2009 Vol. 1: 66–69.* Ukraine: Kharkov.

Concrete Solutions – Grantham, Mechtcherine & Schneck (eds)
© 2012 Taylor & Francis Group, London, ISBN 978-0-415-61622-5

The search for alternative reinforcement materials for concrete

H.G. Wheat & S. Dale
Mechanical Engineering Department, University of Texas at Austin, Austin, TX, USA

ABSTRACT: The desire to extend the service life of structures made with reinforced concrete has led to increased efforts to find alternative reinforcement materials to ordinary carbon steel. These alternatives may be in the form of coated steel or inherently more corrosion resistant alloys such as solid stainless or stainless-clad steel.

This paper describes an investigation in which concrete specimens containing alternative reinforcement materials were intermittently exposed to chloride-containing environments. The specimens were made in accordance with a modified version of ASTM G 109 and exposed for more than eight years. One group was exposed in the laboratory, and the other at a beach site at NASA Kennedy Space Center in Florida. They were examined based on current generated between top and bottom reinforcement as well as Electrochemical Impedance Spectroscopy (EIS). The results of this investigation will be discussed in terms of their significance on the anticipated long-term behavior of alternative reinforcement materials.

1 INTRODUCTION

Alternative reinforcement materials for concrete are expected to lead to lower penetration rates of aggressive species like chlorides and/or higher chloride thresholds. One problem in the evaluation of these materials is that it may be difficult to distinguish between their behavior and performance, particularly based on short-term tests. This has led investigators to create accelerated testing procedures and examine these materials in simulated solutions or slurries and to use reinforcement configurations that maximize corrosion (Wheat et al. 2003, Hartt et al. 2007, Trejo & Halman 2009). However, even in these cases, corrosion mechanisms unique to behavior in concrete may be overlooked.

Epoxy Coated Reinforcement (ECR) has been used as an alternative to black or carbon steel since the late 1970s. This occurred after a very extensive search of reinforcement materials that included more than 20 alternatives (Clifton et al. 1975). After ECR was in widespread use and especially after several premature failures in Florida (Weyers 1985, Weyers & Cady 1987, Sagues & Powers 1990), several factors became an issue. One of these was the level of damage associated with ECR and the effect this damage on the long-term behavior of ECR.

Because of this situation, another research program was developed to revisit ECR and to examine other cost-effective organic, inorganic, ceramic, metallic, and non-metallic coatings for use as reinforcement in concrete (McDonald et al. 1998). The research program included many different bar types in simulated solutions and at least twelve bar types in concrete. The bar types in concrete included bars with three bendable and three non-bendable epoxies; as well as bars made using 304 and 316 stainless steel, copper-clad steel, galvanized steel, spray metallic reinforcement, and of course black steel as a control. At about the same time, another investigation was initiated at the University of Texas at Austin (Deshpande 2000, Seddelmeyer 2000, Jung 2002, Wheat et al. 2003, Wheat et al. 2006). This research program also included many alternative materials tested in simulated solutions as well as concrete; all to be compared with black steel. The bar types in this investigation were two epoxy coated bars made with bendable epoxy coatings, an epoxy coated bar made with a non-bendable or rigid epoxy coating, galvanized steel (galvanized before or after bending), nylon coated steel, PolyVinyl Chloride (PVC) coated steel, stainless steel clad steel and solid stainless steel. The concrete specimens were cast in 1999 and they have been tested as a function of salt water or salt laden air exposure since that time. This paper is a follow up to results that were reported in 2007 (Wheat & Liu, 2007).

2 EXPERIMENTAL PROCEDURE

Alternative reinforcement materials were cast in concrete (concrete macrocells) or immersed in simulated pore solutions to which various amounts of NaCl were added. This paper will focus on the concrete specimens.

The concrete specimens were made in accordance with a modified version of ASTM G 109 (ASTM 1999). This included a bent top bar such that there was induced stress at the bend. For the tests involving the concrete macrocells, candidate materials were cast in concrete having nominal dimensions of 254 mm in length, 229 mm in depth, and 203 mm in height, as shown in Figure 1. The reinforcing bars were cleaned with a wire brush, degreased in methanol, but otherwise used in the as-received condition. The bars had few defects and no additional damage was created. The mix design for the concrete based on kg per cubic meter included: cement, 251; water, 98; coarse aggregate, 1080; fine aggregate, 795; and fly ash, 59. Therefore, the concrete had a water:cement ratio of 0.39 and a water:cementitious material ratio of approximately 0.32. This resulted in extremely good quality concrete with a strength of 7170 psi (49.4 MPa). While the strength is quite high, it is not atypical of the quality of concrete that would be used with alternative reinforcement materials, especially with the more corrosion resistant materials.

The total number of concrete macrocells cast was 176. Forty of the concrete macrocells contained the alternative reinforcement material in both the top and bottom mat. Eighty concrete macrocells contained the alternative reinforcement in the top mat and black steel in the bottom mat. Forty other concrete macrocells were cast with only a bent alternative reinforcement material at the top and four were cast with only straight black bars at the bottom. In this way, different alternative reinforcement materials could be paired together; for example galvanized and epoxy, galvanized and PVC, etc. Twelve of the 176 concrete macrocell specimens were controls, containing black steel. All of the specimens have been described in detail elsewhere (Deshpande 2000, Wheat et al. 2003).

Once the concrete macrocells were cast and cured for 28 days, twelve macrocells (ones containing alternative reinforcement material in the top and black bars in the bottom) were set aside

for later testing. These will be known as Set C. In September of 1999, salt water ponding was initiated for 142 of the concrete macrocells. These will be known as Set A. In September of 2000, salt water ponding was initiated for 22 of the concrete macrocells that contained only top bars. These will be known as Set B. The ponding cycle was such that the concrete macrocells were exposed to salt water ponding for two weeks, after which the solution was removed and the macrocells were dry for two weeks. Macrocell currents were measured every two weeks for the first few years. In September of 2004, fourteen of the concrete macrocell specimens were selected for special testing. Seven were taken to the beach facility at NASA Kennedy Space Center in Florida. They will be known as Set A-NASA. The other seven continued to be tested under laboratory conditions. They will be known as Set A-Lab. These macrocells contained bars coated with nylon, PVC, rigid epoxy, bendable epoxy, as well as galvanized steel, solid stainless steel, and black steel.

Because the quality of the concrete was quite good, it was recognized that the time to corrosion would probably be rather long. For example, average values of macrocell currents for all of the concrete macrocellsl, even ones containing the black steel bars were approximately 10 microamps after two years. Therefore, tests were also carried out in simulated pore solution to which NaCl was added over a period of time. The simulated pore solution was 0.3 N KOH plus 0.05 N NaOH (Wheat et al. 2003). Others have conducted tests in simulated pore solution as well as saturated calcium hydroxide, in hopes of establishing correlations and being able to project the performance in actual concrete (Hartt & Powers 2003, Hartt et al. 2007). However, there is not always good correlation between the performance of the reinforcement in solution and in concrete. This is why the opportunity to expose the concrete macrocells at the beach facility at NASA Kennedy Space Center was viewed positively and as a possible way of conducting accelerated testing. That site is known to have a particularly corrosive environment. The concrete macrocells in Set A-Lab continued to be exposed to salt water ponding every two weeks, while the concrete macrocells in Set A-NASA were exposed to the environmental conditions at the beach site at NASA.

It should also be noted that beginning at 164 weeks, selected specimens were examined periodically using Electrochemical Impedance Spectroscopy (EIS). This is an electrochemical technique that is used frequently to study coated metals and it has been used to study coated metals in concrete (Wheat & Liu, 2007). The test setup for EIS testing in concrete is shown in Figure 2.

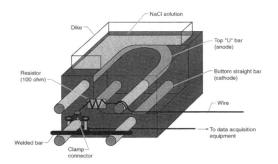

Figure 1.   Typical concrete macrocell specimen.

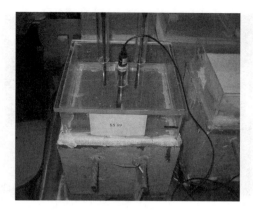

Figure 2. Test setup for EIS testing.

Figure 3. Photograph of the concrete macrocells in Set A-NASA after they were returned to Austin.

Bars in concrete often show capacitive behavior when the coated bars have little or no damage. They will also generally show relatively high impedance. Once the coating is damaged and/or there is penetration into the coating, the capacitive behavior is lost, resistive and/or mixed behavior is observed and the impedance decreases. The behavior is shown in the form of Nyquist or Bode plots or in some cases the impedance at a given frequency is noted. Since it is usually the case that the effects on coatings are most noticeable at low frequencies, the impedance at a frequency of 0.1 Hz is sometimes used as a parameter in concrete. This was used in this investigation. The equipment for EIS testing consisted of a Model 353 Potentiostat and a Lock-in Amplifier made by EG&G Princeton Applied Research. The initial and final frequencies were 100,000 Hz and 0.01 Hz, respectively; the AC amplitude was 10 mV; the DC potential was 0 V; and the reference electrode was Saturated Calomel Electrode (SCE).

3 RESULTS AND DISCUSSION

When the seven concrete macrocells were returned to Austin, TX after four years of exposure at the beach facility at NASA Kennedy Space Center in Florida, there was a noticeable difference in the appearance of those seven specimens compared to the specimens that had been tested for the additional four years in the lab. It should be noted that the total exposure time was eight years; Set A-Lab (four years lab + four years lab) and Set A-NASA (four years lab + four years NASA).

The front of four of the concrete macrocells from NASA can be seen in Figure 3. Figures 4 to 8 show details of the testing arrangement. It should be noted that the dikes were broken during the

Table 1. Comparison of average values of log Z (Ω) at 0.1 Hz for rebars in concrete (Wheat & Liu, 2007).

Time (weeks)	164	175	186	198
Black	3.98	4.07	4.11	4.07
Nylon	6.81	6.90	6.83	6.50
PVC	6.82	6.85	6.85	6.63
Rigid E	4.59	4.65	4.66	4.66
Bendable E	6.49	6.53	6.57	6.36

return shipping; that is why they are missing. The coatings on the protruding bars were either fully or partially delaminated and the protruding black steel also showed deterioration. The protruding bars made of galvanized steel and solid stainless steel showed little or no deterioration.

As mentioned in the procedure, EIS testing was initiated at 164 weeks. These results have been described before, but they are included here in Table 1 so that comparisons can be made (Wheat & Liu, 2007). Note that for the period from 164 weeks to 198 weeks, there was very little change in the average impedance (Z) values at 0.1 Hz. This was attributed to the extremely good quality of the concrete.

The results are quite surprising, especially because of the appearance of the protruding bars. It would seem that, in the case of the PVC and nonbendable or rigid epoxy coated bars, the impedance actually increased. This would suggest that the performance of these bars actually improved at the beach site and this is definitely counter-intuitive. One explanation is the possibility that the increase in the corrosion damage of the protruding bars may have actually resulted in cathodic protection of the bars inside the concrete since the bars were in two environments. Another possible explanation involves the variability of the performance between similar

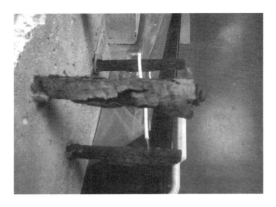

Figure 4. Photograph of epoxy coated bar from Set A-NASA. Concrete macrocell is on its side to reveal severe delamination of the epoxy coating.

Figure 7. Photograph of stainless steel bars in Set A-NASA. No deterioration is evident on the stainless steel bars.

Figure 5. Photograph of concrete macrocell containing nylon coated bar in Set A-NASA. Severe delamination is evident.

Figure 8. Test setup for EIS testing of Set A-NASA concrete macrocells.

Table 2. Comparison of values of log Z (Ω) at 0.1 Hz for Rebars in Concrete.

Time (416 weeks)	Set A-Lab	Set A-NASA
Black	3.91	3.74
Nylon	6.93	6.54
PVC	5.77	7.44
Rigid E	4.73	6.23
Bendable E	7.09	5.83

Figure 6. Photograph of galvanized bars in Set A-NASA. Concrete macrocell is on its side, very little deterioration is evident on the galvanized bars.

types of bars in different concrete macrocells. When values of impedance were examined at 198 weeks and 416 weeks for specimens tested in the lab, the comparisons were more reasonable. The impedance values at 416 weeks were similar to those at 198 weeks, although some variability is evident.

It is noteworthy to compare the results of another investigation in which EIS testing was conducted. In this case the impedance at 0.1 Hz was measured in concrete macrocells that had been exposed to salt water conditions for 96 weeks (McDonald et al. 1998). In that case, for concrete macrocells containing uncracked concrete and straight epoxy coated bars (bendable coating with 0.004% damage area) coupled to black steel, the log of the impedance at 0.1 Hz at the beginning at end of the 96-week exposure period was 7.9 and 5.9, respectively. When the coated bars had 0.5% damage, the log of the impedance values was 4.4 and 3.1, respectively.

Therefore, to have the values increase as a function of exposure is certainly not expected and may well be attributed to cathodic protection. In hindsight, it probably would have been better to eliminate the protruding portions or to protect those portions from the environment.

It should be noted that other tests aimed at reducing the time to corrosion have also resulted in certain anomalies with respect to the behavior of concrete under test conditions other than ASTM G 109, especially when very corrosion resistant materials are used (Trejo & Halman 2009).

It should also be pointed out that more recent tests are indicating much improved performance of epoxy coated reinforcement in concrete (Lee et al. 1995, Lee et al. 2011).

4 CONCLUSIONS

The search for alternative reinforcement materials for concrete is ongoing.

Generally, when alternative materials are tested according to ASTM G 109 or a modified version of ASTM G 109, results are similar to those obtained in actual concrete. However, these tests can be extremely long, especially when the quality of the concrete is good and undamaged corrosion resistant materials are used.

Efforts to accelerate the testing by exposing concrete macrocells in an extremely corrosive beach site did not show accelerated corrosion of the alternative materials in reinforced concrete, presumably because protruding steel used for attachment for electrochemical testing provided cathodic protection of the steel inside the concrete.

If extremely corrosive environments are used in the future, the protruding portions should be eliminated or protected from the environment.

Laboratory tests continued to show small decreases in impedance over time as a function of time and salt water exposure when electrochemical impedance spectroscopy was used.

ACKNOWLEDGMENTS

The background information for this paper was part of Texas Department of Transportation Project 4904 (Feasibility of Hot Dipped (Zinc) Galvanizing and Other Coatings for the Protection of Reinforcing Steel). The authors are grateful to the co-investigators, Drs. David W. Fowler and James O. Jirsa and for the support of the Texas Department of Transportation and the efforts of Robert Sarcinella and Lloyd Wolf.

The authors are also grateful to the NASA Sabbatical Program and to Dr. Luz Marina Calle and the Corrosion Group at NASA Kennedy Space Center.

REFERENCES

ASTM, G. 109-99a, American Society for Testing and Materials (1999), Standard Test Method for Determining the Effects of Chemical Admixtures on the Corrosion of Embedded Steel Reinforcement In Concrete Exposed to Chloride Environments, ASTM, West Conshohocken, PA, 1999.

Clifton, J.R, Beeghly, H.F. & Mathey, R.G. 1975, "Nonmetallic Coatings for Concrete Reinforcing Bars," Report No. NBS BSS-65, Federal Highway Adminstration, Washington, D.C., August 1975, 44 p.

Deshpande, P.G. 2000, "Corrosion Performance of Polymer Coated, Metal Clad and Other Rebars as Reinforcements in Concrete," M.S. Thesis, University of Texas at Austin, May 2000.

Hartt, W.H. & Powers, R.G. 2000, "Corrosion Resistant Alloysfor Useas ReinforcementinConcrete,"Bi-Annual Progress Report (April 1–September 30, 2003); October 30, 2003.

Hartt, W.H., Powers, R.G., Lsogorski, D.K., Lemus, V. & Virmani, Y.P. 2007, "Corrosion Resistant Alloys for Reinforced Concrete," Report No. FHWA-HRT-07-039, Federal Highway Administration, Washington, DC, July 2007.

Jung, C. 2002, "Investigation of Corrosion Performance of Coated, Metal Clad, and Other Types of Rebar," M.S. Thesis, University of Texas at Austin, May 2002.

Kahhaleh, K.Z., Jirsa, J.O, Carrasquillo, R.L. & Wheat, H.G. 1994, "Macrocell Corrosion of Fabricated Epoxy-CoatedSteel in Concrete, R.N. Swamy, ed., Sheffield Academic Press, Sheffield, England, pp 1244–1253(1994).

Lee, S.K., McIntyre, J.F. & Hartt, W.F. 1995, "Performance of Epoxy Coated Reinforcing Steel in Highway Bridges, Final Report 370, National Cooperative Highway Research Program (Project No. 10-37), Transportation Board, NationalAcademy Press, Washington, D.C., 1995.

Lee, S.K. 2001, Informal presentation at Corrosion 2011, Houston, March 2011.

McDonald, D.B., Pfeifer, D.W. & Sherman, M.R. "Corrosion Evaluation of Epoxy-Coated, Metallic Clad, and Solid Metallic Reinforcing Bars in Concrete,

Report No. FHWA-RD-98-153, Federal Highway Administration, Washington, D.C., December 1998.

Sagues, A.A, & Powers, R.G. 1990 "Effect of Concrete Environment on the Corrosion Performance of Epoxy-Coated Reinforcing Steel," Paper 311, *Corrosion 90, National Association of Corrosion Engineers*, April 1990.

Seddelmeyer, J.D. 2000, "Feasibility of Various Coatings for the Protection of Reinforcing Steel-Corrosion and Bond Testing," M.S. Thesis, University of Texas at Austin, May 2000.

Trejo, D. & Halmen, C. 2009, Corrosion Performance Tests for Reinforcing Steel in Concrete: Test Procedures, Report No. FHWA/TX-09-0-4825-PI.

Weyers, R.E. 1985 *Evaluation of Epoxy Coated Reinforcing Steel In Eight Year Old Bridge Decks*, p. 24, Lafayette College, Easton, PA(1985).

Weyers, R.E. & Cady, P.D. 1987 "Deterioration of Concrete Bridge Decks from Corrosion of Reinforcing Steel", *Concrete International*, 9,1(1987), pp 15–20.

Wheat, H.G., Fowler, D.W. & Jirsa, J.O. 2003, "Challenges in Evaluating Different Reinforcement Materials," *Corrosion 2003*, Paper No. 03297, NACE International, Houston, TX, 2003.

Wheat, H.G. 2006 "Laboratory and Field Observations of Corrosion of Alternative Reinforcement Materials," *Corrosion '06*, Paper 355, NACE, Houston, 2006.

Wheat, H.G. & Liu, G., 2007, "Monitoring the Corrosion Behavior of Coated Reinforcement for Concrete," ECS Transaction, 2007.

Concrete Solutions – Grantham, Mechtcherine & Schneck (eds)
© 2012 Taylor & Francis Group, London, ISBN 978-0-415-61622-5

Determination of the crack self-healing capacity of bacterial concrete

V. Wiktor & H.M. Jonkers
Delft University of Technology, Delft, The Netherlands

ABSTRACT: Cracking, either as a network of finer cracks or as larger cracks, allow oxygen, water, oxygen, chloride and other aggressive agents to penetrate the concrete matrix to reach the reinforcement. Under certain circumstances, small cracks in concrete can heal. However, the maximum crack width which can undergo autogenous healing is between 0.1 and 0.3 mm, depending on exposure conditions. The aim of this paper is to investigate the crack healing of non- and bacteria-based healing agent-treated concrete specimens along the crack depth thanks to thin section observations, and then to compare them with the results obtained from the surface crack-healing quantification. The results showed that the bacteria-based self-healing agent can be successfully applied to promote and enhance the self-healing capacity of concrete as it results in the formation of a dense mineral layer along the crack wall. Additionally, several locations along the cracks are blocked by mineral formation in bacteria-based concrete while only few are noticed in controls.

1 INTRODUCTION

Crack formation is a commonly observed phenomenon in concrete structures. Although micro crack formation hardly affects structural properties of constructions, increased permeability due to micro crack networking may substantially reduce the durability of concrete structures due to risk of ingress of aggressive substances (e.g. chloride) particularly in moist environments (Schlangen & Joseph, 2009). This can lead to the premature corrosion of steel reinforcement that results in high costs for preventive maintenance and repair. Under certain circumstances, small cracks in concrete can heal. This phenomenon is known as 'autogenous healing' of concrete. Precipitation of calcium carbonate has been reported to be the most significant factor influencing this autogenous healing. However, the maximum crack width which can undergo autogenous healing is, in several studies, estimated to be between 0.1 and 0.3 mm, depending on exposure conditions (Hearn, 1998; Edvarsen, 1999; Aldea et al. 2000; Schlangen & Joseph, 2009).

In order to improve the often observed autogenous crack-healing potential of concrete, specific agents can be incorporated in the concrete matrix. In the present study a novel two-component bio-chemical self-healing agent embedded in porous expanded clay particles was added to the concrete mixture. In this manner, the expanded clay particles not only represent an internal reservoir but also constitute both a structural element of concrete as well as a protective matrix for the self-healing agent. Upon crack formation the two-component

bio-chemical agent consisting of bacterial spores and calcium lactate are released from the particle by crack ingress water. Subsequent bacterially mediated calcium carbonate formation results in physical closure of micro cracks, that delays further ingress of water and decreases the inward diffusion rate of chloride and oxygen. Moreover, as the metabolically active bacteria consume oxygen, the agent may act as an oxygen diffusion barrier protecting the embedded passivated steel reinforcement against corrosion.

To compare the self-healing capacity of bacteria-based and control concrete specimens, the specimens were immersed in tap water after multiple crack formation. In a first stage, weekly observations with stereomicroscope enabled the monitoring of the crack healing in time from a crack surface point of view. Results quantitatively showed that (Wiktor & Jonkers, 2011a,b), from a crack surface point of view, crack widths up to 0.46 mm were healed in bacteria-based concrete whereas the crack healing in the control concrete was limited to crack widths up to 0.18 mm. That the observed doubling of crack-healing potential was indeed due to metabolic activity of bacteria was supported by oxygen profile measurements which revealed O_2 consumption by bacteria-based but not by control specimens.

The aim of the present paper is to investigate the crack healing along the crack depth thanks to thin section observations on bacteria-based and control concrete, and then to compare them with the results obtained from the surface crack-healing quantification (Wiktor & Jonkers, 2011a,b).

2 MATERIAL AND METHODS

2.1 Preparation of the two-component self-healing agent

Light Weight Aggregates (LWA) (expanded clay particles Liapor R 1–4 mm, Liapor GmbH Germany) were impregnated twice under vacuum with a calcium lactate- (80 g/liter), yeast extract- (1 g/liter) solution, followed by a final impregnation step with a bacterial spore suspension. After each impregnation treatment, expanded clay particles were dried in an oven for 5 days at 37°C. The impregnated expanded clay particles obtained contained 6% (by weight) calcium lactate and $1.7 * 10^5$ bacterial spores g^{-1} particles.

2.2 Preparation of mortar test specimens

Reinforced mortar test specimens were prepared with ordinary Portland cement (CEMI 42.5 N, ENCI, The Netherlands), fine aggregate (sand) and LWA either impregnated with bacterial spores and calcium lactate (bacteria-based specimens) or non-impregnated (control specimens).

Reinforced prismatic specimens with dimensions of $4 \times 4 \times 16$ cm were cast. In each specimen, one zinc plated steel bar (4 mm diameter, 26 cm long) was placed in the middle horizontal axis of the mould with both ends of the bar extending for 5 cm. After 24h curing, specimens were carefully unmoulded, tightly sealed in plastic foil to avoid evaporation of water, and kept at room temperature for further curing.

After 56 days curing, the specimen-embedded steel reinforcement bar was stretched by computer controlled application of tensile force resulting in the formation of multiple cracks, 12 to 14, in the mortar specimen. The widths of the induced cracks varied from 0.05 to 1 mm.

2.3 Self-healing incubation conditions

Two cracked mortar specimens (1 control and 1 bacteria-based) featuring a high number of individual cracks with varying crack widths were immersed horizontally in tap water (3.5 cm water column covering the specimens) in a plastic bucket which was kept open to the atmosphere during the whole incubation period to allow free diffusion of oxygen and carbon dioxide over the water-air interface. After 100 days, the specimens were removed from water and dried in oven at 35°C prior to thin section preparation.

2.4 Preparation of thin sections

After drying, all samples were fully impregnated with low viscosity epoxy mixed with 1% by weight of hudson yellow pigment prior to thin sectioning. Thin sections were then prepared from each sample, using a Pelcon automatic thin section machine. A Leica DM RXP petrographic microscope and a Leica DFC 420 camera were used to acquire images.

3 RESULTS

The first observations of the thin sections show that for both, control and bacteria-based specimens, cracks which appeared to be closed at the surface were essentially open for the remainder of their length (Fig. 1). Some authors also reported that crystalline carbonate may line crack margins, but a crack wider than 20–50 μm is rarely completely filled (St John and al., 1998; Yang et al., 2009).

This may be explained by the fact that once the entrance of the crack is blocked by calcium carbonate formation, no further ingress of water, CO_2 and O_2 is made possible either to react with the cement paste (carbonation) or to maintain the bacteria active (calcium-lactate conversion). This also means that the ingress of other, aggressive agents such as chloride will be delayed.

Meanwhile, a closer examination of the thin sections points out that the crack-healing potential was higher in bacteria-based than in control concrete. Hence, although the cracks were not completely filled along their length, a significant layer of calcium carbonate was formed along the crack walls of bacteria-based specimen. Its thickness varied from 0.05 to 0.2 mm which resulted in a significant decrease of the actual crack width (Figs. 2a, b) and led to the bridging of cracks as large as 0.35 mm (Fig. 2b). In the control specimen, we observed a much thinner layer, with varying thickness which did not exceed 0.06 mm (Figs 2e, f).

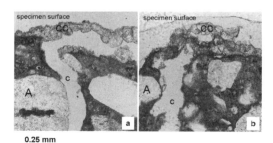

0.25 mm

Figure 1. Thin section observations of the crack-healing along the crack length from the specimen surface, (A) Aggregate, (CC) Calcium Carbonate, (c) Crack—(a) Control specimen, (b) bacteria-based specimen.

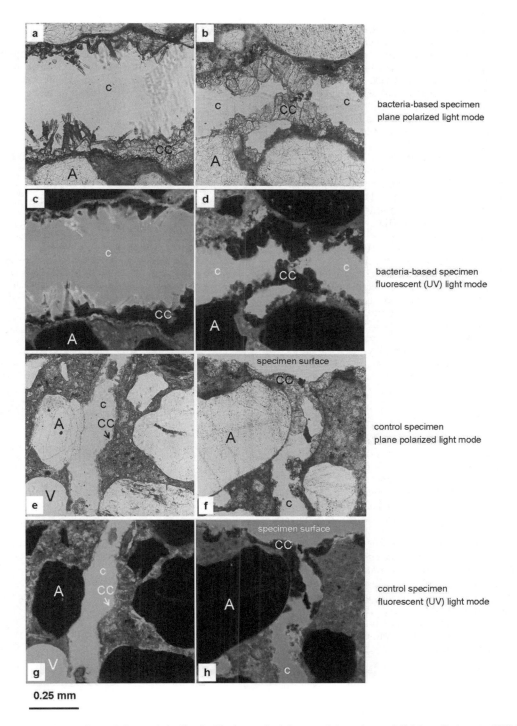

bacteria-based specimen
plane polarized light mode

bacteria-based specimen
fluorescent (UV) light mode

control specimen
plane polarized light mode

control specimen
fluorescent (UV) light mode

0.25 mm

Figure 2. Observations of the crack-healing inside the crack. A large and dense layer of Calcium Carbonate (CC) is formed along the crack wall of bacteria-based specimen (a–d). Whereas a very thin and less dense layer (CC) is noticed for the control specimen (e–i). Pictures c, d, g, h are the observations made in fluorescent light mode of the images a, b, e, f respectively. (A) Aggregate, (CC) Calcium Carbonate, (V) air void, (c) Crack.

In the control specimen, the formation of calcium carbonate was essentially the result of the carbonation of the cement paste; hence the closer to the specimen surface, the thicker the layer was; whereas in the bacteria-based specimen, the addition of the two component self-healing agent significantly enhanced mineral precipitation. This resulted in the formation of a significant mineral layer either close to the surface area or deeper in the specimen.

Moreover, when observed in fluorescent light mode, the newly formed mineral layer appeared darker than the surrounding cement paste in the bacteria-based specimen only, indicating that it may also be denser. Additionally, we noticed that several locations along the cracks of bacteria-based concrete were blocked by mineral formation, presumably calcium carbonate, while only a few are observed in the control.

Therefore, the addition of the bacteria-based self-healing agent to the concrete mixture resulted in a better crack healing compared to the control not only from a surface point of view (Wiktor & Jonkers, 2011a), but also along the crack length (Fig. 2). Moreover, the dense mineral layer produced on the crack wall may act as a protective layer and may constitute a barrier against the diffusion of aggressive agents through the crack walls.

4 CONCLUSIONS

The results presented in this study pointed out how important it is to correlate the quantification of the crack-healing made from a surface point of view to observations of thin sections. Even though cracks appeared to be completely healed from the surface, they remained partially/or totally open from the inside, for both control and bacteria-based concrete.

Meanwhile, the results also showed that the bacteria-based self-healing agent can be successfully applied to promote and enhance the self-healing capacity of concrete as it results in the formation of a dense mineral layer along the crack wall. Additionally, several locations along the cracks were blocked by mineral formation in bacteria-based concrete while only a few were noticed in controls.

ACKNOWLEDGMENT

Theure authors acknowledge the financial support from IOP Self Healing Materials Grant, Project SHM08704, "Bio-chemical self-healing agent to prevent reinforcement corrosion in concrete".

REFERENCES

Aldea, C.M., Song, W.J., Popovics, J.S. & Shah, S.P. 2000. Extent of healing of cracked normal strength concrete. *Journal of Materials in Civil Engineering* 12:92–96.

Edvardsen, C. 1999. Water permeability and autogenous healing of cracks in concrete. *ACI Materials Journal* 96:448–454.

Hearn, N. 1998. Self-sealing, autogenous healing and continued hydration: What is the difference? *Materials & Structures* 31:563–567.

Schlangen, E. & Joseph, C. 2009. Self-healing processes in concrete, in S.K. Gosh (eds), *Self-healing materials: Fundamentals, design strategies, and applications*, 141–182, WILEY-VCH verlag GmbH & Co. KGaA, Weinheim.

St John, D.A., Poole, A.B. & Sims, I. 1998. Concrete Petrography: A handbook of investigative techniques, Arnold and John Wiley & Sons Inc.

Wiktor, V. & Jonkers, H.M. 2011a. Quantification of crack-healing in novel bacteria-based self-healing concrete. Cement & Concrete Composites doi:10.1016/j.cemconcomp.2011.03.012.

Wiktor, V. & Jonkers, H.M. 2011b. Un nouveau béton auto-cicatrisant grâce à l'ajout de bactéries, *Matériaux et Techniques*, accepted.

Yang, Y., Lepech, M.D., Yang, E.H. & Li, V.C. 2009. Autogenous healing of engineering cementitious composite under wet-dry cycles, *Cement & Concrete Research* 39:382–390.

Concrete Solutions – Grantham, Mechtcherine & Schneck (eds)
© 2012 Taylor & Francis Group, London, ISBN 978-0-415-61622-5

Degradation mechanism and repair technology of a concrete structure of a railway ballastless track

Z. Yi, H. Li, Y. Xie & Y. Tan
China Academy of Railway Sciences, Beijing, China

ABSTRACT: Repairing cracks in ballastless tracks plays an important role in ensuring the durability of concrete and the safe operation of a railway. Combining the service characteristics of ballastless track, based on the analysis of concrete crack cases appearing in ballastless track projects, both abroad and domestic, the causes for concrete cracks are put forward. Together with the characteristics of high-speed railways, technical requirements for the repair of ballastless track structural concrete are presented. In the end, according to the different crack grades of concrete ballastless track, repairing processes for the concrete cracks have been put forward.

1 INTRODUCTION

Ballastless track is a structural style of track whose roadbed with particulate ballast is replaced by cement-based materials (concrete or cement-asphalt mortar). Ballastless track has been adopted widely for its advantages of mature technologies, smooth track, high degree of standardization, good workability and small amount of maintenance. Although ballastless track is an advanced track structure with the characteristic of reducing the maintenance, many engineering practices indicated that concrete structure of ballastless track can easily crack (Ozaka, Y. & Suzuki, M. 1986). Moreover, the cracks can be extended due to the dual function of long-term fatigue loads and natural factors after operation. Cracks in concrete slabs will be the channels for the corrosion medium entering into the internal part of the slabs. Under the existence of Cl⁻ or CO_2, and a suitable environment, the reinforcement in the slab will be subjected to accelerated corrosion. This will reduce the durability of concrete structures and affect vehicle running safety. So it is very important to adopt appropriate technical measures to repair the cracked concrete structure of ballastless track for improving the durability of ballastless track and ensuring the safety of train operation. The paper analyses the characteristics and cause of cracks in ballastless track. The technical requirements and repair processes of concrete crack of ballastless track have also been put forward.

2 CRACK CHARACTERISTICS OF BALLASTLESS TRACKS

2.1 Cracks in the roadbed slab of double-block ballastless structures

In order to avoid crack inactivation of concrete structures due to tensile stress action, Slab ballastless track is designed according to the "no stretching resistance" principle, that is maintaining the structure in low or zero tensile stress as the base principle of design. There are many cracks in roadbed slab concrete, due to the interface between the old (sleeper) and new concrete (roadbed slab concrete), see Figure 1. Cracks happen 2–3 days after the initial setting time and the width of the cracks develop with the time. There are two kinds cracks in roadbed slabs, one type of crack appears in the four corner of sleeper, such splayed cracks universally occur at the interface between the corner of the sleeper and the roadbed slab concrete. The cracks between the corresponding twin block sleepers become into one crack crossing over the whole roadbed slab. And the other crack is in the cross direction or oblique direction cracks; some of them lie in the position of the expansion joint. Along the cast direction of the concrete, cross cracks appear at intervals. In addition, sometimes the hydraulic base layer cracked along the precracking, will cause the upper roadbed slab to form reflective cracks.

Figure 1.   Crack in roadbed slab.

2.2   Cracks in base concrete

The base of ballastless track is a C32/40 reinforced concrete structure. As a kind of bulk mass, the base concrete must be cast continuously. Figure 2 shows some cracks in the base concrete. The main characteristics of cracks in base concrete are as follows.

1. Crack of base concrete is vertical with the roadbed. Along the track direction the cracks appear in periodic intervals, and the interval gap covers from 5 m to 15 m. Moreover, the depth of crack reaches the whole thickness of base.
2. Some cracks appear in the position of the expansion joint and the crack extends down the expansion joint.
3. The base concrete of slab ballastless track is easily cracked at the site of the convex plate. Cracks also can be found in the middle of the track slab, seen Figure 2(b).
4. The width of the crack reaches the total width of track, once the crack appears.
5. A few cracks appear about 10 cm from the road-bed slab. The widest of the cracks can reach 0.5 mm.

2.3   Crack in track slab

Track slabs are a kind of precast concrete structure. The principle of the design of track slabs is a "no crack" design, but some cracks can be found in the track slab due to load action, environmental factors (such as temperature) and creep of concrete. Figure 3 shows cracks in a track slab. Longitudinal cracks which are induced by non-homogeneous stress are easy to appear in the range of the fastener. There are many cracks in the inner side of the frame track slab, and some cracks run through the total depth of the track slab.

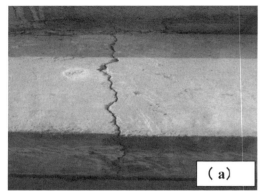

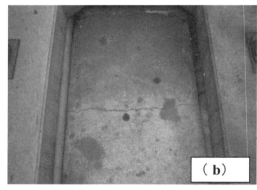

Figure 2.   Crack in the base concrete.

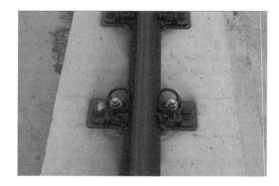

Figure 3.   Crack in track slab.

Some cracks generate form lifting, some generate from the steam curing system of the track slab, and some from the structure of the track slab. It is reported that most track slab cracks are induced by alkali aggregate reaction and salt attack and some track slabs have been changed in Japan. The main characteristics of cracks in track slab are as following.

1. The crack width is small. Most cracks are less than 0.2 mm.
2. Cracks extend and widen slowly.
3. Stress cracks and deformation cracks coexist.

3 CRACK CAUSE ANALYSIS OF RAILWAY BALLASTLESS TRACK

The condition of concrete crack is that the tension stress generated by deforming under restraint is bigger than its tensile strength and then cracking happens. Therefore, the conditions influencing concrete crack includes the deformation size, the degree of restraint, and the real-time tensile strength. Cracking reasons can be divided into two categories: First is a structural crack, induced by the external load, including the main stress of the conventional structural calculation and other structural secondary stresses. Second are material cracks, caused by non-stress deformation, mainly induced by the temperature stress and concrete shrinkage.

3.1 Cracks caused by the change of temperature

Temperature cracking is a kind of crack caused by the temperature changing in the concrete structure or non-uniform temperature distribution. The surface cracks of the temperature crack usually appear during the time of construction. However, deep and penetrating cracks often happens two to three months or even more after concrete casting, for example, the cracks in the base structure and hydraulic base layer, which approximately parallel the structural member or the short edge of the structural member, and appear sectional along the track. At the same time the width of the cracks change with the seasons, and the cracks are wide in the winter and narrow in the summer. Temperature difference can be divided into three types: temperature difference between inside and outside concrete caused by the hydration heat of cement, temperature change of the whole structure and the temperature gradient from the surface to the bottom surface of structure.

3.1.1 Temperature difference caused by the hydration heat

In the initial concrete casting stage, cement hydration processes produce a large amount of hydration heat, and most of the heat is produced in 3 days. Because concrete is a poor conductor of heat, the hydration heat accumulates in the concrete, often causing the temperature of internal concrete to rise significantly, while the concrete surface temperature is the outdoor temperature, which forms the temperature

difference between inside and outside concrete. When the tensile stress in the initial concrete setting stage caused by this temperature difference exceeds its tensile strength, it will result in concrete cracks. This temperature difference can reach 15 centidegreeor more. The design temperature difference of Germany RHEDA track is 25 centidegree. Therefore, strain differences between inside and outside the concrete can be up to 0.25‰. In the long term, considering the creep of concrete, this strain remained nearly 1/2 of the initial strain.

3.1.2 The temperature change of the whole structure

The overall concrete structure will uniformly change under the temperature changes by season and due to the sunlight change cycle. This can cause compression or expansion of concrete. When these compressions or expansions have no vertical restraints or the restraint is very small, the resulting temperature force can be neglected. But due to the concrete structure of ballastless track it is subject to many constraints in the longitudinal direction. The longer the concrete structure; the greater the thermal stress caused. It may result in concrete occur through cracks. In a cycle of sunlight, the temperature change of the whole ballastless concrete structure can reach 25~30 centidegree in the hot summer months. Over a whole year, the cyclical temperature changes due to the seasons can cause temperature differences between highest and lowest temperature of up to 50~70 centidegree.

3.1.3 Temperature gradient

For concrete structures in the sun, their upper surface temperatures are high and the lower surface temperature is low. The thermal conductivity of concrete is very low. There is therefore a temperature gradient along the height direction of track slab. The track temperature gradient can lead to warpage and surface transverse cracks. In one measurement, the local maximum temperature was 38 centidegree, the temperature difference between top and bottom surface of the 19 cm thick track slab reached 15 centidegree. Variation is approximately an exponential function curve.

3.1.4 Cracks caused by the deformation of the rail

When constructing the double-block ballastless structure, the first precise position is the rail, the double-block sleepers and which are fastened tightly to the rails, and then the concrete infill is cast. When the track is in the sun and the outside temperature is relatively high, the temperature of rail increases sharply and the rail will extend. But the concrete is still in the state of setting and the concrete strength approaches zero. It cannot resist the deformation stress, and then the concrete cracks.

3.2 Crack caused by concrete shrinkage

There are many types of concrete shrinkage, amongst which the main causes of concrete cracking are drying shrinkage and plastic shrinkage.

3.2.1 Drying shrinkage

Cracks caused by drying shrinkage are caused by the drying shrinkage deformation of concrete, which often happens after some time from finishing and curing the concrete or after finishing concrete casting. This time can be from one week up to much longer times. The evaporation of water in the concrete paste will produce drying shrinkage which is a non-reversible process. In the common condition, the drying shrinkage deformation of most aggregate is very small, which may be neglected. The drying shrinkage deformation of hardened cement paste is large, and is often several hundreds of microstrain, even a thousand microstrain. When the concrete dry shrinkage deformation strength is bigger than stretching resistance of the concrete cracking will happen in the concrete.

3.2.2 Plastic shrinkage

Plastic shrinkage cracks form due to rapid early water loss and can be due to many factors, which include atmosphere, temperature of concrete, relative moisture, the surface wind velocity and the concrete mix design. Plastic crack can be easily influenced by temperature, wind velocity and moisture. Under conditions of high wind velocity, high temperature and low moisture in the environment, this kind of crack can form easily. After the concrete's initial setting, the concrete begins to form structure and loses flowing power, but its force is very slow. In this period, more water lost will create a large plastic shrinkage. Cracks will happen in the concrete which has no ability to resist shrinkage stresses. Plastic cracks are a kind of distribution shape in random and multilateral. The cracks in the surface can be fairly wide, the length of which can vary from several inches to several feet (ca. 10 cm to 1 m or more). Plastic cracks in the surface of road bed slabs, in the base concrete surface and the hydraulic base layer surface may happen. The influence of plastic cracking is not severe for a building not subjected to movement, but it is different for the ballastless track structure. The passing trains will make plastic crack open and close repeatedly, and lead the width of the crack to develop continuously.

3.3 Structure design

3.3.1 New and old concrete binding interface

For the double-block ballastless track, the sleepers are precast. The sleeper surface is the combination of old and new concrete. The surface is smooth, making it less effective at bonding with the roadbed concrete. Concrete shrinkage in different directions easily occurs at the corner of the sleepers. After the concrete hardens, it will cause stress concentrations at the corner. The concrete crack development can be increased due to drying shrinkage, and as time goes on extended and widened.

3.3.2 Construction joints

Many factors influence the crack width and spacing. The designer's calculations are often a relatively large deviation from the actual situation. From the current design of the concrete base, whether it is plain concrete or reinforced concrete, shrinkage cracking can occur, sometimes right through the concrete base. The key reason is the distance between construction joint, designed too far apart.

4 TECHNICAL REQUIREMENTS FOR THE REPAIR OF THE CONCRETE STRUCTURE OF BALLASTLESS TRACK

The characteristics of ballastless track, such as exposed service condition, periodical fatigue load, short time demand of maintenance window, and high transportation speeds, cause the particularity and complexity of the repair of concrete structure of ballastless track, which are different from repairing any other concrete structure (Xie Y, et al. 2009).

4.1 The repair process should be simple and rapid

The time of maintenance window of ballastless track is short. No halt of the transportation is another difficulty of the repairing work. The most obvious difference between railway and road is that the repair work for railways can only be carried out in one track. In the related specification (Temporary provisions of design for railway from Beijing to Shanghai), it is required that the total maintenance window time should be not more than 4 hours. With removal of the time spent on the way to and from the maintenance place, the effective time for the ballastless track repair work repair work is sometimes only 2–3 hours. Therefore, the repair process must be simple and rapid, to ensure the repair work can be finished in the short maintenance window time.

4.2 Repair materials should be high performance

To ensure the repair work can be completed in a short time, and do not affect the train traffic safety, the repair process requires that the repair materials should have high early strength and rapid consolidation. All the concrete structures will be exposed in the open air. Much water will exist in the cracks, so that the repairing materials should be consolidated in a humid condition. Ballastless track always endures wind and rain, sun exposure, ice and snow accumulation, etc. It requires repair materials with a high durability.

Ballastless track concrete slab is different from the other concrete structures. It comprises strip structures exposed to the elements. The track slab is not only subject to the fatigue loading of the train, but also subject to the impact of cyclical changes of atmospheric temperature. Therefore, the crack repair materials for track slabs should have good physical properties, chemical properties, mechanical properties and durability. Taking into account the main factors of structure, materials and construction aspects of ballastless track slab, in order to achieve high durability and long-term repair purposes, for an ideal repair material for ballastless track slabs, the following properties should be taken into account:

- Good compatibility with old concrete,
- workability,
- curing time,
- adhesive performance,
- shrinkage,
- deformation properties,
- thermal expansion coefficient,
- durability,
- economy (Popovics s. et al. 1992).

4.3 Repairing tools should be small in size and light in weight

The characteristics with high transportation speed and the short time demand of the maintenance window for ballastless tracks mean that the repairing process should be simple and rapid. To ensure the repair work can be finished rapidly, the repairing tools should be small in size and light in weight. The cracks of concrete slab of ballastless track are small and numerous. Small tools are easily operated. Light tools will help to arrive at the repair site quickly and improve the efficiency of repair operations.

5 REPAIRING PROCESS FOR CONCRETE CRACK OF BALLASTLESS TRACK

Based on the technical requirements for repairing concrete cracks of ballastless track, according to the different grade of concrete crack, the following repair processes are put forward.

5.1 Repair technology for small cracks in concrete

Small cracks in the concrete structure of ballastless track are defined as cracks with width less than

0.2 mm. For this type of crack, the surface sealing method is proposed to be used. The repairing process is as follows.

1. Clean the crack area, use the steel brush bristles on both sides of the cracks, and remove dust with a vacuum cleaner.
2. Weigh and prepare the appropriate amount of surface sealing repairing materials.
3. To improve the bond strength of surface sealing and concrete matrix, brush a layer of primer material along the crack surface.
4. After the primer material is surface dry, brush the surface with sealing material. Brushing more than 3 times and the thickness of the coating should be over 300 μm. Cement-based polymer emulsion is a suitable sealing material. The polymer can ensure the good bonding of the coating and the base. Cement can ensure the durability of the coating.

5.2 Repair technology for wide cracks in concrete

Wide cracks in the concrete structure of ballastless track are defined as cracks with width over 0.2 mm. For this type of crack, the gravity filling method is proposed to be used. The repairing process is as follows.

1. Using vacuum cleaners and brushes remove debris within the cracks.
2. Using electric blower remove moisture in the crack.
3. Pour low viscosity resin material into the crack groove. Penetrate the internal cracks with low viscosity resin material. Epoxy or polyurethane resin can be used as repairing materials.
4. When the repair material is cured, polish and smooth the surface.
5. If necessary, brush the surface with sealing material. Cement-based polymer emulsion can be used as the sealing material.

This repairing process is very simple. It is very appropriate for the rapid repair work in the short "maintenance window". The key factor for the repair is the selection of repair materials. It requires the repair material has low viscosity and low surface tension, so as to ensure the crack perfusion. In addition, the repairing should cure fast and have good toughness.

6 CONCLUSIONS

1. The causes for the concrete cracks in ballastless track involve the concrete material, the construction technology, environmental conditions and structure measure, such as the

structure interface and construction joints. Due to the complex causes, it is necessary to give an overall consideration to material, design and construction.

2. The characteristics of ballastless track structure decide the particularity and complexity of the repair of the concrete structure of ballastless track. Repair techniques for cracks should meet the requirements of being simple and rapid, should use high performance materials and be possible with small and light tools.

3. According to the crack size, concrete track slab crack repairs use different repair techniques. Surface sealing is a proper method to repair the cracks with width less than 0.2 mm. For the width over 0.2 mm, the gravity filling process is a good method for repair.

REFERENCES

Ozaka, Y.; Suzuki, M. 1986. Shear failure of reinforced concrete beams and effect of repair by epoxy resin injection. Publication SP - American Concrete Institute. 637–670.

Popovics. s., Rajendram. N., Penko. m. 1992. Rapid hardening cements for repair of concrete. *ACI Journal and Aggregates*. 37 (1): 3–7.

Xie Y, Li H, Feng Z. 2009. Concrete Crack of Ballastless Track Structure and its Repair. *International Journal of Railway*. (2): 310–316.

Non destructive testing and diagnosis of problems

Concrete Solutions – Grantham, Mechtcherine & Schneck (eds)
© 2012 Taylor & Francis Group, London, ISBN 978-0-415-61622-5

Computerized assessment of the moisture and thermal originated deterioration of concrete facades

F. Al-Neshawy, J. Piironen & J. Puttonen
Department of Civil and Structural Engineering, School of Engineering, Aalto University, Finland

ABSTRACT: Temperature and moisture are two of the main factors in physical, chemical and biological deterioration of building facades. Deterioration processes are typically caused by thermal and moisture movements in the building materials. The continuous monitoring of temperature and relative humidity provides information about the long-term performance and deterioration of building facades. Documenting the performance of the building facades through monitoring can enhance the understanding of the long term deterioration of building facade materials and changes in the structural behaviour of facades due to aging.

The aim of this study is to develop a computerized monitoring and deterioration prediction system for concrete facades. The study consists of laboratory work and field measurements. The laboratory work focuses on designing a monitoring network system and testing of the moisture and thermal originated deterioration of concrete. The field measurement is carried out by monitoring the temperature and relative humidity of three repaired concrete facades for more than five years.

The result of the research will improve the building construction industry by providing methodologies and systems for monitoring and predicting the performance of building facades. The scientific relevance of this research will be the improved correspondence between laboratory studies and observations of deterioration in practice.

1 INTRODUCTION

Most concrete structures are required to remain in service for at least 50 years. Usually deterioration is so slow that no early intervention is required. However, for some combinations of structure and environment, design or workmanship is inadequate and premature deterioration is an issue. Deterioration of concrete structures may arise internally due to the properties of materials or externally due to the surrounding environment. The deterioration of house building represents a huge cost in terms of unscheduled maintenance and repair as well as a potential public safety concern. This deterioration is expected to become increasingly important with time. According to the Department of Statistics Finland, the value of house building renovation was about 4.3 billion Euros in 2009, which was 35 per cent of the total value of house building construction.

Two of the most important factors in building deterioration subjected to outdoor conditions are moisture and temperature. Moisture is a major factor in the physical deterioration processes that are typically caused by restrained moisture movements and freezing or it can be connected to chemical or biological attacks. In addition, moisture will increase the heat flow through a structure and thus increase the consumption of heating energy (Huovinen et al., 1998).

Karagiozis (2002) has focused on controlling the accumulation of moisture in building envelopes. The focus on improving the thermal performance of building envelope has affected other aspects of building enclosure performance, most notably moisture performance. Building envelope tightness and insulation levels have increased over time, as have the number of problems due to moisture accumulation. Moisture accumulation seriously restricts not only the life span of building envelopes, but also impacts indoor air quality and thermal performance.

According to Norris et al. (2008), the current destructive testing systems and methods for the internal moisture evaluation are expensive and time consuming. In addition, these techniques require intensive labour and special equipment to gain access to remote locations. Handheld moisture meters are usually used in spot checks to assess changes in the moisture content of the building components or to determine surface wetting patterns in order to determine sources and extent of wetness. Data acquisition systems are usually used for long-term monitoring: a data acquisition system consists of temperature and humidity sensors and data loggers for collecting data for further processing and archiving (Lindblom-Patkus 2007).

An objective of this research was to test the new possibilities offered by Information and Communication Technology (ICT) to be used in the building repairing and maintenance. The purpose of the research was to develop a methodology to assess the effect of the ambient environment on the components of concrete building facades (Al-Neshawy 2007). This paper focuses on the development of a relative humidity and temperature monitoring network system for repaired concrete building facades. The paper also illustrates outputs from this innovative monitoring system.

2 MOISTURE ORIGINATED DETERIORATION OF CONCRETE STRUCTURES

Moisture originated damage can be divided into three types of deterioration processes: biological, chemical, and physical, as shown in Table 1.

This paper is focusing only on the prediction of the moisture originated deterioration of concrete facades, such as the corrosion of carbonated concrete reinforcement, and the frost damage of concrete.

Papadakis (2005) introduced a simplified carbonation depth formula for concrete with time, in terms of relative humidity (RH) and of the water cement ratio (w/c) of concrete. The carbonation depth for concrete with water cement ratio w/c ≤ 0.6 is calculated using Equation 1.

$$X_C \approx 1650 \left(\frac{W}{c} - 0.38 \right) \left(1 - \frac{RH}{100} \right) \left(y_{CO_2} t \right)^{0.5} \quad (1)$$

The carbonation depth for concrete with water cement ratio w/c > 0.6 is calculated using Equation 2.

Table 1. Moisture originated deterioration of concrete structures.

	Deterioration causes	Defect
Physical	Freezing and thawing	Cracking, scaling
	Moisture changes	Shrinkage cracking, delamination
	Temperature changes and gradients	Curving of elements and plates
Chemical	Carbonation	Reinforcement corrosion
	Alkali-aggregate reaction	Delamination, cracking
	Salt crystallization	Cracking, spalling
Biological	Biological growth	Mould problems

$$X_C \approx 1650 \left(\frac{(w/c) - 0.25}{[1 + 2.6(w/c)]^{0.5}} - 0.38 \right) \left(1 - \frac{RH}{100} \right) \left(y_{CO_2} t \right)^{0.5} \quad (2)$$

where w/c = the water cement ratio of concrete; RH = the relative humidity [%]; y_{co2} = the ambient CO_2 content by volume 0.015 [mol m^{-3}]; and t = the time in years.

The time to cracking the cover is equal to the period required for the carbonation front to reach the bar (period to initiation of corrosion) plus the time necessary for the layer of rust to build up around the bar to the thickness required to cause longitudinal splitting of the cover due to circumferential tension in concrete (corrosion propagation period).

According to Morinaga (1988 cited in Papadakis et al., 1992), for usual environmental temperature (20°C) and 55% < RH < 95%, the carbonation related corrosion propagation period (in years) can be approached by Equation 3.

$$t_{pr,carb} = \frac{6 \cdot (1 + 0.2 \cdot d_c)^{0.85}}{65 \cdot (RH/100) - 35} \quad (3)$$

where RH = the relative humidity and d_c = the concrete cover [mm].

The freezing thawing index (FT) is defined as the number of freezing or thawing oscillations when temperatures oscillate around 0°C for those structures that are almost at the moisture saturation level (Mukhopadhyaya et al., 2005). The higher the number of cycles indicates the greater potential for frost damage. The freezing thawing index is defined in Equation 4.

$$FT_{(i)} = \sum_{h=2}^{k} X_{FT(i,h)}$$
$$X_{FT(i,h)} \begin{cases} = 1, \text{ if } T_{(i,h)} * T_{(i,h-1)} < 0 \text{ and } RH_{(i,h)} \geq RH_{cr} \\ = 0, \text{ if } T_{(i,h)} * T_{(i,h-1)} \geq 0 \text{ and } RH_{(i,h)} < RH_{cr} \end{cases} \quad (4)$$

where i = index for the considered part of the structure; h = the time of measurement; $T_{(i,h)}$ = the measured temperature at a particular time step [°C]; $RH_{(i,h)}$ = the measured relative humidity at a particular time step [%]; RH_{cr} = the user-defined critical threshold value of relative humidity level above which moisture damage is more likely to occur [%]; and k = the total hours in a particular year, i.e., either 8760 or 8784 hours.

3 RHT-MNS MONITORING NETWORK SYSTEM

One goal was to develop a relative humidity and thermal monitoring method to understand the

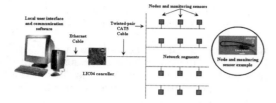

Figure 1. Schematic diagram of the (RHT-MNS) relative humidity and thermal monitoring network system.

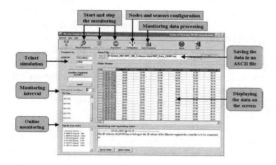

Figure 2. The graphical user interface of the relative humidity and temperature output module.

Figure 3. The graphical user interface of the data processing module.

moisture and thermal performance of repaired building facades, the proposed RHT-MNS network and RHT-MNS monitoring software were developed to gather and analyze large amounts of thermal and moisture data.

The RHT-MNS network was built on a Linet Light Network, Linet Oy Ltd. 9. The RHT-MNS network consists of a controller (LIC04), shown in Fig. 3, and nodes to which the relative humidity and the temperature sensors are connected. The controller provides configuration services and enables communication with the data acquisition system. The network system may contain up to 200 nodes connected to a twisted-pair CAT5 cable with a maximum total length of 1000 meters. A schematic diagram of the RHT-MNS monitoring network system is illustrated in Figure 1.

The relative humidity and temperature sensors were chosen to provide the required functionality for correct system operation. For the RHT-MNS monitoring network system, three different types of sensors were selected to be connected to the nodes: PT100 sensors for temperature measurements and HMP44 and SHT15 sensors for relative humidity measurements. The choice of HMP44 and PT100 sensors was based on stability, accuracy and the long experience in using these sensors. SHT15 was selected based on its low price and compatibility with the network nodes. The calibration of the relative humidity sensors were confirmed by the manufacturers.

The RHT-MNS software communicates between the host computer and the RHT-MNS network controller, and it collects and processes the monitored data. The software was developed using Microsoft Visual Basic 6.0. The RHT-MNS monitoring software runs on Microsoft Windows platforms. The RHT-MNS software consists of four basic modules: a system configuration module, a Telnet simulation module, a relative humidity and temperature output module and a data processing module. The interface of the RHT-MNS software is shown in Figure 2.

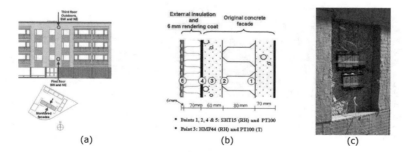

(a)   (b)   (c)

Figure 4. The repaired facade of the monitored building and the location of the installed temperature and relative humidity sensors.

The data processing module processes the monitored temperature and relative humidity data. The data processing module was developed using Visual Basic for Applications under Microsoft Excel.

For testing the developed RHT-MNS monitoring network system, field research was carried out to monitor the relative humidity and temperature of a repaired concrete facade. The building, shown in Figure 4, is a four-storey apartment building built with concrete sandwich elements. The concrete facade was repaired by adding 70 mm external mineral wool insulation and rendering system (Sto AG, Sto Therm Vario, Finexter Oy) which consists of a 6 mm of rendering coat and a glass fibre mesh.

The monitoring system was installed in the facades facing northeast and southwest, as illustrated in Figure 4. The nodes and sensors were installed on the first and on the third floor of the building, as shown in Figure 4(a). The sensors were installed through the cross-sections of the facades as shown in Figure 4(b). The thermal and moisture condition was monitored at a regular interval of 15 minutes.

4 RESULTS OF THE MONITORING OF THE MOISTURE AND TEMPERATURE

As shown in Figure 5, the daily average relative humidity of the outer concrete panel dropped from 83% to 44% within the first year. During the year 2006 and 2010, the average relative humidity was 55%. The temperature of the original outer concrete panel remained above 0°C for the majority of the time. Using the average relative humidity of 55%, the carbonation related corrosion propagation period is estimated to be 36.6 years. These results indicate that the progress of reinforcement corrosion and frost deterioration of the original concrete facade has strongly decelerated.

The carbonation depth is proportional to (time)^1/2 with the time independent carbonation coefficient. For concrete facades, the carbonation coefficient varies from 1.5 to 3.5 depending on the location of the facade, shown in Figure 6. As shown in Fig. 6, the average relative humidity during the year 2005–2010 is 80%. The carbonation depth for concrete with water cement ratio w/c = 0.45 and the average relative humidity, which is calculated using

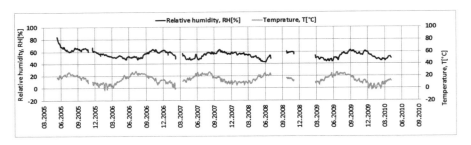

Figure 5. The daily average temperature and relative humidity of the original outer concrete panel of the repaired facade in the north-east direction—Point 4 in Figure 4(b). The discontinuity in the two curves reflect missing data during four periods of time.

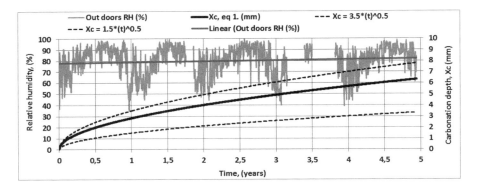

Figure 6. Effect of the north-east outdoors relative humidity on carbonation depth.

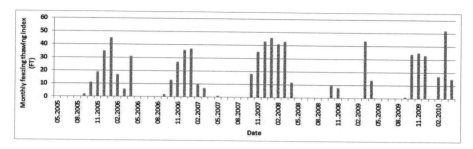

Figure 7. The values of the freezing thawing index for the rendering coat of the repaired facade in the north-east direction—Point 5 in Figure 4(b). There was a data loss during 11.2008–03.2009 which affected the calculation of freezing index during those time.

Equation 1. The estimated carbonation depth after 5 years is about 6 mm.

The results of the freezing thawing index with critical moisture of 75% for the rendering coat of the repaired facade are shown in Fig. 7. The higher the number of cycles indicates the greater the potential for frost damage.

5 CONCLUSIONS

The need for a new method for monitoring of temperature and moisture in repaired building facades was recognized. Specifically, the new method should to be non-destructive, yet able to measure the thermal and moisture conditions at exact and predefined locations inside the structure. The approach chosen to fill the defined need was the RHT-MNS monitoring network system that uses sensors and nodes that are embedded inside the building structures at the time of rehabilitation, and a controller connected to a host computer for reading the signals from the sensors.

These results indicate that the progress of reinforcement corrosion and frost deterioration of the original concrete facade has strongly decelerated. The freezing thawing index (FT) is defined as the number of cycles when the temperature oscillates between the freezing and thawing point for the facade components that are almost at the moisture saturation level. Increased freezing thawing index values indicate an increased severity of the frost action and a higher damage potential.

REFERENCES

Al-Neshawy, F. 2007. A network system for monitoring the thermal and moisture performance of repaired concrete facades. Thesis for the degree of Licentiate of Science in Technology. Department of structural engineering and building technology. Helsinki University of Technology. Espoo. Finland.

Huovinen, S., Bergman, J. & Hakkarainen, H. 1998. Deterioration defects and repair methods of facades, Laboratory of structural engineering and building physics, Helsinki University of Technology. Espoo, Finland. Report 78.

Karagiozis, A.N. 2002. Building Enclosure Hygrothermal Performance Study Phase I. ORNL/TM-2002/89, Oak Ridge National Laboratory, Oak Ridge, TN.

Lindblom-Patkus, B. 2007. Monitoring temperature and relative humidity. Northeast document conservation centre. Online at: http://www.nedcc.org/resources/leaflets/2The_Environment/02TemperatureAndHumidity.php [Accessed 25.04.2011].

Linet Oy Ltd. 2007. Commercial home network technology. Online at: http://www.linet.fi/html/network.html [Accessed 25.04.2011].

Mukhopadhyaya, P., Kumaran, K., Nofal, M., Tariku, F. & van Reenen, D. 2005. Assessment of building retrofit options using hygrothermal analysis tool. The proceedings of the *7th symposium on building physics in the Nordic countries*, Reykjavik, Iceland, 13–15 June, 2005, 1139–1146.

Norris, A., Saafi, M. & Romine, P. 2008. Temperature and moisture monitoring in concrete structures using embedded nanotechnology/microelectromechanical systems (MEMS) sensors. *Construction and building materials* (22): 111–120.

Papadakis, V.G. 2005. Estimation of concrete service life: the theoretical background. [online] Patras, Greece: Building Technology & Durability, Patras Science Park S.A. Available from: http://www.ppap.info/eucon.gr/images/stories/docs/tb/tb.pdf [accessed 25.04.2011].

Papadakis, V.G., Fardis, M.N. & Vayenas, C.G. 1992. Effect of composition, environmental factors and cement-lime mortar coating on concrete carbonation. *Materials and Structures* 25(5): 293–304.

Concrete Solutions – Grantham, Mechtcherine & Schneck (eds)
© *2012 Taylor & Francis Group, London, ISBN 978-0-415-61622-5*

Non-destructive electrical resistivity measurement technique: Evaluation of concrete strengths

Nabil H. El-Ashkar

Arab Academy for Science, Technology and Maritime Transport, Alexandria, Egypt

ABSTRACT: The process of controlling concrete quality has proven to be a vital and essential procedure in concrete construction to ensure the quality of the constructed facility. The quality control procedures generally depend on the results of compressive strength testing for standard concrete specimens manufactured during the concrete construction process. The results of these specimens do not represent the whole sources of variations in the actual concrete strength because these samples are taken or extracted in the middle of the concrete construction process just before casting, compaction and curing which does not represent the actual condition in the real structure as stated by the ACI 214R-02 committee report. This fact calls for the need of a performance based quality control system that depends on the actual concrete strengths in the concrete structure under real construction conditions. Concrete electrical resistivity measurements are one of the promising techniques that can be used to evaluate concrete strength. This technique can be considered as a simple and low cost technique for evaluating the actual concrete quality during the construction process and also for actual inspection of the concrete structure.

This research aims to understand the relation between the concrete Surface Electrical Resistivity Measurements (SERM) and the different concrete strengths (such as compressive strength, tensile strength and flexural strength). Moreover, it is targeted to study and appraise the concrete SERM as a Non Destructive Test (NDT) for evaluation of the concrete strength and comparing it with other NDTs. These objectives are achieved through designing and conducting an extensive experimental program. The parameters involved in this research are water-to-cement ratio, age and the presence of silica fume as a replacement of cement content. Eight concrete mixes were designed and cast and more than 135 specimens were tested in compression, splitting tension and flexure. SERM were collected for theses samples at different ages using Wenner technique just before strength testing, and Schmidt rebound hammer was also used for comparison purposes.

The results of this study illustrated the sensitivity of the SERM to both age and water-to-cement ratio, while the effect of silica fume was less pronounced. It was shown that the higher the water-to-cement ratio for all the mixes, the lower the SERM, while age had the opposite effect. Moreover, relations between SERM and different concrete strengths were observed. In this research, linear statistical regression models were developed to represent the relation between the SERM and the different concrete strengths. Also the effect of the shape of the specimens on SERM was investigated.

1 INTRODUCTION

For several decades, concrete has been the dominant construction material for most construction projects. The reason for the popularity of concrete can be mainly summarized in its superior technical properties, economy, availability of its raw materials and manufacturing simplicity compared to other more complicated competitive construction materials. Concrete is also characterized by the variability in properties of its ingredients which has a major influence on its properties in general. Therefore, the selection of concrete-making materials and the uniformity of such raw materials have a great impact on concrete quality. Moreover, the manufacturing and construction processes and the maintenance of the concrete structures play an important role in the concrete quality affecting structure integrity and the life cycle of concrete structures.

It is often necessary to test concrete structures after the concrete has hardened to determine whether the structure is suitable for its intended purposes. The quality of concrete is mainly judged by its compressive strength directly affecting the load-bearing capacity and durability of concrete structures, but the compressive strength test is destructive and causes damage to the concrete therefore concrete testing is a challenging problem. Many engineers, who are concerned when they want to measure the quality and strength of a building because strength testing is destructive, are turning to non-destructive testing techniques.

Generally, during construction, the concrete quality control process is performed based on concrete samples taken from the concrete batches just before casting. The concrete strength and its variation in results extracted from these concrete samples can be an indicator for two general sources of variations. The first source is the changes and variations due to the raw material variations and also variations in the concrete manufacturing process which ACI 214R-02 committee report (ACI, 2002) calls "Batch-to-Batch Variation". The other source of variation reported by the same committee is "Within Test Variation" resulted from sampling, manufacturing, curing and testing of the concrete samples. The true strength of the concrete structure and its variations depends, in addition to the two pre-mentioned sources, on a third source of variation that can be called the "Construction Practice Variation" which takes place after extracting the concrete sample from the concrete batch. This shows that this method of quality control does not truly represent the concrete quality and another method representing performance-based quality control is needed to evaluate the concrete quality (GjΦrv 2003, Sengul & GjΦrv 2008, Ferreira & Jalali 2006, 2010).

The objective of this research is to evaluate the use of surface electrical resistivity measurements (SERM) as a non-destructive performance based quality control tool that can be used in concrete construction. This can serve as a quality control tool to assess the concrete strength at different ages, with different water to cement ratios and different ingredients. For this purpose, several parameters were studied: including the water to cement ratio, the concrete age and the presence of silica fume. For comparative reasons, other non-destructive measurements were taken for the concrete using a Schmidt rebound hammer tester in correspondence with the surface electrical resistivity measurements (SERM).

2 NON-DESTRUCTIVE TESTING

Concrete structures should often be tested after the concrete has hardened to determine whether the structure is suitable for its intended and designed purposes. These tests should preferably be done without any damage to the concrete and with no effect on the integrity of the concrete structure. The tests available for concrete inspection range from the completely non-destructive, where there is no damage to the concrete, through those where the concrete surface is slightly damaged, to partially destructive tests, such as core tests and pullout and pull off tests, where the surface has to be repaired after the test. Generally, non-destructive testing can be applied to both old and new structures. For new structures, the principal applications are likely to be for quality control or the resolution of doubts about the quality of materials or construction. The testing of existing structures is usually related to an assessment of structural integrity or adequacy. In either case, if destructive testing alone is used, for instance, by removing cores for compression testing, the cost of coring and testing may only allow a relatively small number of tests to be carried out on a large structure which may be misleading. Non-destructive testing can be used in those situations as a preliminary to subsequent coring (Malhotra & Carino 2004).

2.1 Schmidt rebound hammer

This widely known and used non-destructive technique depends essentially on concrete surface hardness by impacting the concrete surface with a given energy of impact and measuring the rebound. Schmidt rebound hammer generally consists of a spring controlled hammer that slides on a plunger. The hammer is pressed against the concrete and against the force of the spring until the end of its retraction. At this point the hammer is released to impact the concrete surface and then retracts with a pointer on a guided scale that represents the rebound number (Mehta & Monteiro 2006). The detailed procedure is fully described in ASTM C805 (ASTM, 2008) and a schematic diagram showing the rebound hammer is presented in Figure 1.

The rebound hammer is famous for getting quick and inexpensive results for checking the uniformity of hardened concrete using a simple technique (Malhotra & Carino 2004). The results of this method are known to be affected by different parameters such as the surface smoothness, the surface moisture content, the aggregate type, the degree of carbonation, the direction of the hammer during the test and the age and size of the specimen.

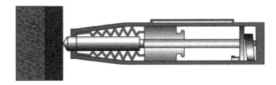

Figure 1. Schematic diagram for the Schmidt rebound hammer (ACI 228.1 R-03).

2.2 Surface Electrical Resistivity Measurements (SERM)

Variations in concrete electrical properties due to the effect of different concrete exterior or interior factors have been studied (Kazberuk & Jezierski 2005, Su et al., 2002) as the basis for understanding durability and in different non-destructive techniques. The properties include electrical resistance, dielectric constant, and polarization resistance. The conduction of electricity by moist concrete could be expected to be essentially electrolytic which depends on the evaporable water content of concrete that varies with water-to-cement ratio, the degree of hydration, and the degree of saturation. This water contains ions, primarily Na^+, K^+, Ca^{2+}, SO_4^{2-}, and OH^-, whose concentrations vary with time which also greatly affect the concrete conductivity or resistivity (Malhotra & Carino 2004).

The resistivity of concrete is an important parameter in the corrosion of reinforced concrete structures as high-resistivity concrete has little possibility of developing reinforcement corrosion (Andrade et al., 2009, Morris et al., 2004, Millard et al., 1989). Concrete resistivity measurements have also been explored lately in damage detection for concrete structures (Lataste et al., 2003).

SERM can be collected using several different techniques, however the most famous arrangement is the four point probe called the "Wenner Technique" which is shown in Figure 2. The Wenner Method uses a four-point probe in contact with the measured material where a low frequency alternating electrical current is passed between the two outer electrodes whilst the voltage drop between the inner electrodes is measured as shown in Figure 2.

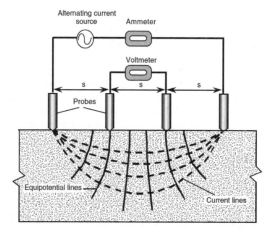

Figure 2. Four-probe resistivity test (Malhotra & Carino 2004).

The equation for calculating the Surface Electrical Resistivity (ER) from the Electrical Resistance (R) is shown as follow:

$$ER = 2\pi s \times R \qquad (1)$$

where

s distance between probes (as shown in Figure 2)
R = electric resistance = $\Delta V/I$
ΔV voltage drop between the inner electrodes
I electrical current.

3 EXPERIMENTAL DETAILS

This research aims to study the surface electrical resistivity measurements (SERM) conducted on concrete surfaces using the Wenner testing method. The relationships between these measurements and different measured strengths (compression, splitting tensile and flexural) at different ages are investigated in this research also. Another widely used non-destructive concrete testing technique, Schmidt Rebound Hammer, is used in this study for comparison purposes.

To achieve the pre-mentioned objectives, a comprehensive experimental program was planned and conducted and the results will be outlined in this study. Among the main parameters involved in this research is the water-to-cement ratio which ranged from 0.25 to 0.55 to cover a wide range of the used concrete while the slump was kept in the range of 10 to 20 cm by using superplasticizer. The other parameter used in this study is the presence of silica fume as a replacement of cement content of 0 and 10 percent. A total of 8 mixes were designed and cast in this study. For mix design purposes, the following assumptions were made: the cement content (or the binder content [cement + Silica fume] for mixes containing silica fume) was kept constant at 450 kg/m³, air content = 2%, the ratio of coarse aggregate to fine aggregate was kept = 2 and the used water to cement ratios were 0.25, 0.35, 0.45 and 0.55. Based on these assumptions, the absolute volume method is used to assess the mix proportions and the quantities for each component. The details for all of the 8 mixes are shown in Table 1. In this study, the coarse aggregate used was crushed pink limestone with a nominal maximum aggregate size of 20 mm while clean sand was used and both aggregates satisfied the requirements of the Egyptian specifications. The cement used was Portland cement CEM I which satisfies Egyptian specifications.

For each mix, the slump was measured immediately after pouring the concrete and a total

Table 1. Concrete mix design.

Mix No.	Cement (Kg/m³)	Silica fume (Kg/m³)	Water (Kg/m³)	W/C	Coarse agg. (Kg/m³)	Fine agg. (Kg/m³)
1	450	0	247.5	0.55	1073.4	536.7
2	405	45	247.5	0.55	1073.4	536.7
3	450	0	202.5	0.45	1155.4	577.7
4	405	45	202.5	0.45	1155.4	577.7
5	450	0	157.5	0.35	1237.3	618.7
6	405	45	157.5	0.35	1237.3	618.7
7	450	0	112.5	0.25	1319.3	659.6
8	405	45	112.5	0.25	1319.3	659.6

Figure 4. The used Schmidt rebound hammer tester.

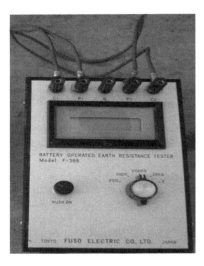

Figure 3. The earth resistance tester used.

of 17 specimens (9 cubes 100 * 100 * 100 mm, 4 cylinders [D * L] 75 * 150 mm and 4 beams 75 * 75 * 250 mm) were cast then tested after hardening. All the specimens were cured in a lime bath until the testing age. The concrete cubes were tested in compression at ages 3, 7 and 28 days (3 cubes at each age) while the cylinders and beams were tested in splitting tension and flexure respectively at ages of 7 and 28 days (2 specimens of each shape at each age).

All the concrete specimens were tested (while completely saturated with water) just after removing them from water using two non-destructive techniques (Schmidt rebound hammer and Surface electrical resistivity measurements SERM) just before destructive testing was conducted. The instrument used for collecting the SERM was a battery operated digital earth resistance tester model F–366 which is shown in Figure 3. This apparatus was adapted to directly measure resistance in Ohm. Four different ranges or scales (20, 200, 2000 and

20,000 Ohm) of electrical resistance measurements were available to assure high accuracy when measuring low and high electrical resistance. The accuracy of this tester was ±1% of the maximum value in the range being used. It was calibrated by the Atomic Energy Authority in Alexandria before use and it was found that the error did not exceed ±0.2%. An equal distance between the four brass probes of 25 mm was set for all the measurements on all of the specimens.

For electrical resistance measurements, the measuring process was performed differently for each specimen. The measurements were conducted on the four surfaces parallel to the direction of casting for each specimen, and then these readings were averaged. After that each concrete cube specimen was tested in compression and the average of the three specimens for each age was determined. For the cylinder specimens, each cylinder was measured four times using the Wenner technique on two perpendicular planes along its side and parallel to its main axis. A total of 8 readings for each age were gathered then averaged, after that the cylinders were tested in splitting tension. For the beam specimens, the specimens were measured along the two surfaces parallel to the casting direction. Four readings were gathered for each age and averaged then the two beam specimens were tested in flexure using a simple beam with a three-point loading technique and a span of 225 mm.

The concrete specimens were tested also using a Schmidt Rebound Hammer—shown in Figure 4—along the same surfaces used for measuring the electrical resistivity. For each specimen, 12 measurements were collected and the readings were averaged for each age and each type of specimen. For comparison purposes, all the specimens were kept completely saturated during all the destructive and non-destructive testing process.

4 RESULTS AND DISCUSSIONS

In order to investigate the electrical resistivity measurements as a performance-based quality control non-destructive tool for the assessment and evaluation of concrete strengths such as compressive strength, splitting tensile strength and flexural strength for different concrete mixes with different parameters an objective was set to study the effect of age and water-to-cement ratio on the different strengths and to compare this effect with the effect on the electrical resistivity measurements and other NDT. Then, the relationship between the different strengths and the surface electrical resistance measurements (SERM) were investigated to model this relationship. Also, the effect of the specimen shape and type of loading on electrical resistivity was investigated.

4.1 Effect of water-to-cement ratio

The water-to-cement ratio is one of the main parameters that affect the properties of concrete and especially the different concrete strengths due to its effect on porosity and voids of the concrete microstructure. This means that it is important for any method for non-destructive testing to be sensitive to this factor to truly represent the concrete strength. The effect of water-to-cement ratio on cube compressive strength for different ages and for mixes containing only Portland cement and mixes containing 10 percent replacement of silica fume is presented in Figure 5-a. This figure shows the usual conclusions as to the harmful and adverse effect of increasing water to cement ratio on the concrete compressive strength, the increase in the compressive strength with age and a slight increase in the compressive strength due to the presence of silica fume. These effects are also similarly demonstrated for other concrete strengths such as the concrete splitting tensile strength and the flexural strength as shown in Figures 5-b and 5-c, respectively.

Figure 6 shows the results of the resistivity measurements performed on the saturated concrete cubes just before conducting the compressive strength test. This figure presents the effect of water-to-cement ratio on electrical resistivity at different ages and with silica fume replacement of 0 and 10% by weight. From this figure, it can be seen that increasing the water to cement ratio resulted in a reduction in the electrical resistivity of the concrete measured using the four point Wenner test method. As the concrete is a porous material and as the electric current is mainly transferred inside the concrete through the movement of the ions dissolved in the pores liquid, therefore the SERM is largely affected by the pore structure, porosity and the pore size distribution. Consequently, the reduction in SERM accompanied with the increase in water to cement ratio can be attributed to the increase in the porosity of the concrete leading to increase in the concrete conductivity.

It was also observed from Figure 6 that for the mixes containing silica fume, the presence of the silica fume caused a slight increase in the concrete SERM compared with those concrete mixes

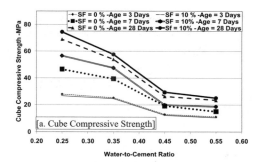

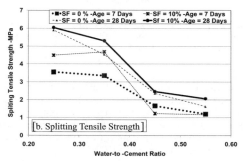

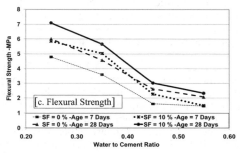

Figure 5. Effect of w/c ratio on concrete strengths (a. Cube strength—b. Splitting tensile strength—c. Flexural strength) at different ages. Silica fume replacement 0 &10% by mass.

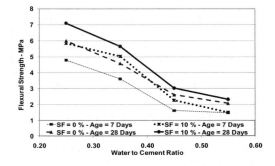

Figure 6. Effect of water-to-cement ratio on electrical resistivity at different ages with silica fume replacement of 0 and 10% by mass.

353

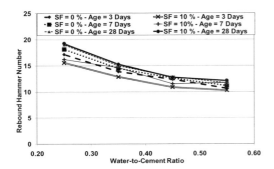

Figure 7. Effect of water-to-cement ratio on Schmidt hammer rebound number at different ages with silica fume replacement of 0 and 10% by mass.

with no silica fume. This can also be attributed to the pozzolanic effect of the silica fume represented in reducing the concrete porosity by plugging the pores and the enhancement of the pore size distribution leading to a reduction in the concrete conductivity and increase in SERM.

Schmidt hammer as a popular technique for concrete non-destructive testing is used in this study to compare its results with the SERM technique. The results for the rebound number taken for the concrete cubes just before testing in compression test are presented in Figure 7. This figure demonstrates the effect of the water to cement ratio on the rebound number where the increase in the water to cement ratio resulted in a reduction in the rebound number as stated in many references (Mehta & Monteiro 2006, Malhotra & Carino 2004). However, the significant increase in the water to cement ratio (from 0.25 to 0.55) did not show a considerable change in the Schmidt hammer rebound number as shown in Figure 7. Also the presence of silica fume did not show any noticeable or consistent change for the Schmidt rebound number results at any water to cement ratio. Based on the previous data, it can be seen that the SERM results were more significantly affected with two important parameters affecting the concrete strengths than the Schmidt hammer rebound number results. So, it can be concluded that the SERM technique is more sensitive to the parameters affecting the concrete strengths.

4.2 Effect of age on surface electrical resistivity measurements of concrete

The concrete age is one of the main factors affecting concrete strength due to the hydration of the Portland cement resulting in a hydrated cement that has a larger volume which leads to plugging of the concrete pores and reducing the concrete

voids. But this fact can also affect the SERM results where by plugging the concrete pores and reducing the concrete internal voids, the ability of the pore solution to carry or conduct the electrical current is significantly reduced. This effect is presented in Figure 8 which shows the effect of age on the SERM results for concrete cubes made with different water to cement ratio. From Figure 8, it can be concluded that the increase in concrete age resulted in an increase in the SERM for all the mixes with different water to cement ratios and for mixes with 10% silica fume replacement.

It can also be seen that the rate of the increase in the SERM is reduced with time as the increase in the SERM from 3 to 7 days age is higher than the increase in the SERM from 7 to 28 days as shown in Figure 8. This shows how much the SERM depends on the hydration rate which starts fast at concrete early age and then slows down with age. On the other hand, the results of the effect of age on the Schmidt rebound hammer, which are presented in Figure 9, show a slight change in the rebound number due to the change in the concrete age is taking place. Consequently, it can be seen that SERM can be an effective method to capture the behavior of the concrete strengths with time.

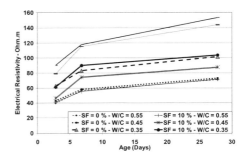

Figure 8. Effect of sge on electrical resistance for cubes made with different water-to-cement ratio.

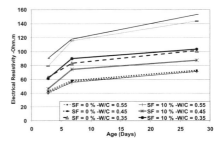

Figure 9. Effect of age on Schmidt hammer rebound number for cubes made with different water-to-cement ratio.

354

4.3 Relation between the strengths and Surface Electrical Resistivity Measurements (SERM)

Although it was shown before that the SERM results are more sensitive to the main parameters affecting the concrete strengths such as water to cement ratio, age and presence of silica fume, the main challenge is still the relationship between the concrete strength and the SERM. The results of concrete cube compressive strength against SERM results are presented in Figure 10 for mixes with different water to cement ratios at different ages. From this figure it can be noticed that a linear relation between cube compressive strength and SERM can be established by linear regression analysis. This relationship is as follows:

$$f_c = 0.59 * ER - 14.69 \qquad (2)$$

where

f_c is the cube compressive strength and
ER   is the measured surface electrical resistivity for the same cube specimen.

As the coefficient of determination for this model $R^2 = 0.91$, this means that the proposed model will show an accurate prediction for the compressive strength based on the SERM results for these specimens.

On the other hand, Schmidt rebound number results were collected for the same concrete cubes after collecting the SERM results then the compression test was performed immediately. The results of the cube compressive strength against the rebound number are presented in Figure 11 for different concrete mixes at different ages. From this figure it can be seen that a correlation between these two variables can exist and a linear regression model is proposed as shown in the figure. However, the

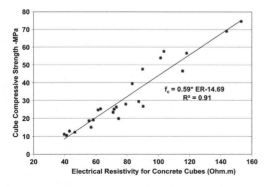

Figure 10. Relationship between cube compressive strength and electrical resistivity for cubes at different ages and water-to-cement ratios.

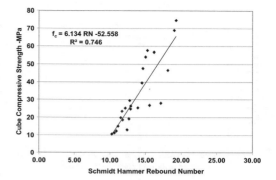

Figure 11. Relationship between cube compressive strength and Schmidt hammer rebound number for cubes at different ages and water-to-cement ratios.

coefficient of determination R^2 calculated for this model = 0.746 which is much lower than the one for the SERM data with the cube compressive strength. This means that the SERM results are more accurate in predicting the cube compressive strength than Schmidt rebound number. Moreover, it can be noticed that the value of coefficient of the parameter ER in the SERM model (which is 0.59) is much lower than the coefficient of the parameter RN (Rebound number) in the rebound number model (which is 6.134). This shows that the SERM model is much less sensitive to the prediction errors of the cube compressive strength than the rebound number because a change or error of the SERM by a unit will only cause a change or error in the cube compressive strength by 0.59 MPa, while the change or error of the rebound number by a unit will result in a change or error of the cube compressive strength by 6.134 MPa. This means that in case of a small error of 1 unit—for example—the error in predicting the cube compressive strength will be much lower in case of using the SERM technique than the Schmidt hammer technique.

Other models are proposed for the relation between the cylindrical splitting tensile strength vs. SERM and the flexural strength vs. SERM as shown in Figures 12 and 13. From these figures it can be noticed that a good correlation between the concrete splitting tensile and flexural strengths and SERM exists.

The following linear regression models are proposed for the prediction of these concrete strengths:

For the prediction of concrete splitting tensile strength

$$f_{cy} = 0.054 * ER - 3.01 \qquad (3)$$

The coefficient of determination for this model $R^2 = 0.92$

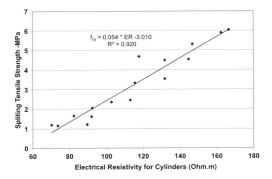

Figure 12. Relationship between splitting tensile strength and electrical resistance for cylinders at different ages and water-to-cement ratios.

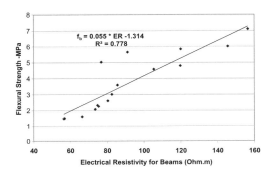

Figure 13. Relationship between flexural strength (using simple beam third-point loading) and electrical resistance for beams at different ages and water-to-cement ratios.

where

f_{cy} is the cylindrical splitting tensile strength and

ER   is the measured surface electrical resistivity for the same cylinder specimen

For the prediction of concrete flexural strength

$$f_b = 0.055 * ER - 1.314 \qquad (4)$$

The coefficient of determination for this model $R^2 = 0.778$

where

f_b is the flexural strength and
ER   is the measured surface electrical resistivity for the same beam specimen.

4.4 *Effect of specimen shape on SERM*

To evaluate the effect of the concrete specimen shape on the SERM, two plots for the SERM results for the different specimen shapes used

(Cubes, Cylinders and Beams) were constructed as shown in Figures 14 and 15. In Figure 14 the relations between SERM for concrete cubes as a vertical axis and SERM for the concrete cylinder and beam shaped specimens as a horizontal axis are plotted. Moreover, a linear regression model was proposed based on the available data to evaluate the effect of the specimen shape on SERM. From this figure it can be seen that the ratio between the SERM for the specimens with cubical and beam shapes is almost 1 which means that these results are almost equal with a coefficient of determination of 0.9834. On the other hand, the ratio between SERM for the specimens with cubical and cylindrical shaped is 0.7817 which is very close to the same ratio between SERM for beam and cylindrical shaped specimens (0.791) as shown in Figure 15. This means that the change of the shape from a cube to beam shape did not show significant effect on SERM while the change of the

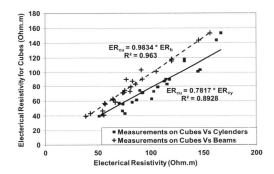

Figure 14. Relationship between electrical resistance measurements for cubes and electrical resistance measurements for cylinders and beams at different ages and water-to-cement ratios.

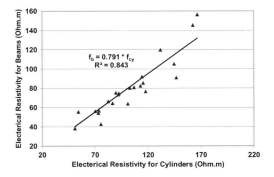

Figure 15. Relationship between electrical resistance measurements for beams and electrical resistance measurements for cylinders at different ages and water-to-cement ratios.

shape from cube or beam to cylinder showed an increase in SERM of around 25%.

5 SUMMARY AND CONCLUSIONS

During the last decades the construction industry has become more and more complicated and as good control over all the aspects of the construction projects is becoming more difficult than ever, the need for a concrete performance based quality control tool is growing. Moreover, the quality control process using the results of the compression test for specimens collected at the construction site does not reflect the real conditions of the concrete structure itself. In this research a comprehensive experimental program was conducted aiming to evaluate the use of SERM as a Non destructive technique to evaluate the different concrete strengths. Based on the results of this study the following conclusions can be claimed:

- The Surface Electrical Resistivity Measurements (SERM) technique used for concrete specimens is sensitive to the change in different parameters, studied in this research, such as water to cement ratio and concrete age, which influence the concrete strengths.
- The SERM results seem to be more sensitive to the above mentioned parameters than the Schmidt rebound number technique as shown in this study.
- A linear relation between the cube compressive strength and SERM results can exist. Moreover, a linear regression model that relate the cube compressive strength and SERM results is proposed in this study and is proven to be more sensitive than the one for Schmidt rebound number technique which was suggested in this study also.
- Similar linear regression models were proposed in this study to relate the SERM results with the splitting tensile strength and the flexural strength.
- The change in the specimen shape from cube to beam showed very little effect on the SERM results, however the SERM results for the cube and beam shaped specimens showed a lower value (around 80%) than the cylindrical shaped specimens.

REFERENCES

ACI 214R-02. 2002. Evaluation of strength test results of concrete ACI Manual of Concrete Practice, American Concrete Institute. Farmington Hills, Michigan USA.

ACI 228.1 R-03 2003. In-Place Methods to Estimate Concrete Strength ACI Manual of Concrete Practice, American Concrete Institute. Farmington Hills, Michigan USA.

ASTM C805 2008. Standard Test Method for Rebound Number of Hardened Concrete. American Society for Testing and Materials. 100 Barr Harbor Dr. West Conshohocken, PA. USA.

Andrade C., D'andréa R., Castillo A. & Castellote M. 2009. The Use of Electrical Resistivity as NDT method for the Specification of the durability of reinforced concrete. DTCE'09, Non-Destructive Testing in Civil Engineering. Nantes. France.

Ferreira M. & Jalali S. 2006. Quality control based on electrical resistivity measurements ESCS-2006: European Symposium on Service Life and Serviceability of Concrete Structures Helsinki, Finland: 325–332.

Ferreira M. & Jalali S. 2010. NDT measurements for the prediction of 28-day compressive strength. NDT & E International 43 (2): 55–61.

Gjφrv O. 2003. Durability of Concrete Structures and Performance-Based Quality Control. ICPCM—A New Era of Building, Cairo, EGYPT.

Kazberuk M. & Jezierski W. 2005. Evaluation of concrete resistance to chloride ions penetration by means of electrical resistivity monitoring. journal of civil engineering and management 4 (2): 109–114.

Lataste J., Sirieix C., Breysse D. & Frappa M. 2003. Electrical resistivity measurement applied to cracking assessment on reinforced concrete structures in civil engineering. NDT&E International 36: 383–394.

Malhotra V.M. & Carino N.J. (2nd Ed) 2004. Handbook on nondestructive testing of concrete. New York: CRC Press LLC.

Mehta P.K. & Monteiro P.J.M. (3rd Ed) 2006. Concrete: Microstructure, Properties, and Materials. New York McGraw-Hill Companies, Inc.

Millard S., Harrison J. & Edwards A. 1989. Measurement of the electrical resistivity of reinforced concrete structures for the assessment of corrosion risk. British Journal of NDT 31 (11): 617–621.

Morris W., Vico A. & Vázquez M. 2004. Chloride induced corrosion of reinforcing steel evaluated by concrete resistivity measurements. Electrochimica Acta 49: 4447–4453.

Sengul O. & Gjφrv O. 2008. Electrical resistivity measurements for quality control during concrete construction. ACI Material journal 105 (6): 541–547.

Su J., Yang C., Wu W. & Huang R. 2002. Effect of moisture content on concrete resistivity measurement. Journal of the Chinese Institute of Engineers 25 (1): 117–122.

Concrete Solutions – Grantham, Mechtcherine & Schneck (eds)
© *2012 Taylor & Francis Group, London, ISBN 978-0-415-61622-5*

Applicability of an electromagnetic wave method for estimation of chloride content of coastal structures

J. Nojima
JP Design Co., Ltd., Tokyo, Japan

T. Mizobuchi
Hosei University, Tokyo, Japan

ABSTRACT: It is very difficult to detect chloride-induced corrosion early, because it is not possible to confirm the degradation of concrete until cracks induced by corrosion expansion of reinforcing bars appear on the concrete surface. Thus, development of truly nondestructive tests to estimate the chloride content in concrete could make it possible to study the changes in chloride concentration over time, without having to physically approach the structure, or cause any damage to it. Such methods would greatly improve our ability to foresee the possibility of reinforcement corrosion at early stages, and enable us to take the required corrective action at an appropriate time. In this paper we evaluate the applicability of a non destructive method by which it is possible to estimate the chloride content included in the cover concrete in existing structures using an electromagnetic wave method. The results of surveys of three marine structures in different environmental conditions are reported.

1 INTRODUCTION

Chloride-induced corrosion has been recognized to be caused by internal factors in which chloride ions are entrapped in concrete by using materials with chlorides and by external factors in which chloride ions gradually permeate and diffuse from the concrete surface such as in marine structures or from deicing salts used to melt away snow on highways, etc. It is very difficult to detect chloride-induced corrosion early because it is not possible to confirm the degradation of concrete until cracks induced by corrosion expansion of reinforcing bars appear on the concrete surface.

Thus, in order to detect chloride-induced corrosion at an early stage, it is necessary that the chloride content in the neighborhood of the reinforcing bar is investigated by carrying out chemical analysis using cores drawn from the RC structure and cut off at fixed intervals in the depth direction or by using gradient drilled dust samples collected from different depths. In addition, it is important to estimate chloride content in which corrosion of reinforcing bars. Drilling cores can be structurally unacceptable, may damage the reinforcement and the repair could be aesthetically unappealing, and of course only very limited sampling can actually be carried out. In addition, driling cores to estimate the chloride content in concrete makes it impossible to study the changes in chloride content over time (at exactly the same place). Thus, development of truly

nondestructive tests to estimate the chloride content in concrete could make it possible to study the changes in chloride concentration over time, without having to physically approach the structure, or cause any damage. Such methods would greatly improve our ability to foresee the possibility of reinforcement corrosion at early stages, and enable us to take required corrective action at an appropriate time.

In this study, it has been shown from laboratory tests under limited conditions that chloride content within concrete could be estimated by using electromagnetic waves as one of the non-destructive tests. Experiments to estimate the chloride content in concrete using electromagnetic waves have been carried out which could be used on existing concrete structures, with convenient measuring instrument using a fixed frequency.

In this paper, in order to evaluate the applicability of such a non destructive method to estimate the chloride content included in cover concrete in existing structures, the results of surveys of three marine structures in different environmental conditions are presented.

2 OUTLINE OF INVESTIGATION

2.1 *Procedure on estimation of chloride content using electromagnetic wave*

The dielectric constant of dry concrete varies in between 4 to 10, and that of wet concrete in the range of 10 to 20. Thus, the dielectric constant of concrete varies depending on the moisture content of concrete. As mentioned above, the dielectric constant is the same for both fresh water and seawater.

As shown in Figure 1, when the distance to the reflecting surface, i.e. reinforcing bar, is known, it can be shown that changes in the properties of the electromagnetic waves such as the dielectric constant are caused by differences in the properties of the intervening medium (which in this case is concrete) such as the moisture content. Furthermore, it can also be confirmed that changes of dielectric constant in the electromagnetic waves aren't caused by differences in the chloride content in concrete (Fig. 3).

As mentioned above, the conductivity is likely to vary considerably with the amount of chloride ions in the concrete. That is to say, when an electrolyte like sodium chloride exists in the concrete, it seems to change the electrical properties such as conductivity in comparison with concrete without the chloride ions. Therefore, it was detected that changes in the reflected waveform of the electromagnetic waves were caused by differences in chloride ion concentrations in the concrete.

2.2 Example of experiment using aqueous solution

As an example of estimation of chloride content using electromagnetic waves, a laboratory experiment using aqueous solution is shown in the following. Experiments were carried out to explore the effect of varying chloride ion concentration in an aqueous medium on the reflected waveforms of electromagnetic waves. The chloride ion concentration in water was changed from 0% to 10%. As shown in Figure 2, measurements of electromagnetic waves were carried out using the aqueous solution of different chloride concentrations filled to a depth of

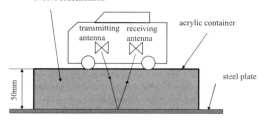

Figure 2. Experiment using the aqueous solution.

50 mm in plastic containers. These containers were placed on a steel plate to facilitate reflection of the electromagnetic waves. The reflected waves were studied to understand the effect of the intervening chloride concentration.

Figure 3 shows results of dielectric constant at the each content of chloride ions. As shown in past studies, the dielectric constant was hardly affected by the difference in chloride content.

Figure 4 shows an example of the output of the reflected waveforms for each chloride content. Though the wheels of antenna rested directly on the upper surface of the container filled with sodium chloride aqueous solution, an air space between the antenna and the upper surface of the container, and that between the upper surface of the container and upper surface of aqueous solution, could not be avoided. Thus, the set up resulted in three reflected waveforms—one off the surface of the container, the other off the aqueous surface solution, and a third one from the surface of the bottom steel plate. Obviously, only the last mentioned waveform is of interest and analyzed further.

Figure 5 shows results of the amplitude of third wavelength at each chloride ions concentration. As shown in Figure 4 the amplitude decreased depending upon increasing in chloride ions concentration. When the chloride ion concentration exceeded 2%, the values of the amplitude almost did not change. On the other hand, the values of the amplitude changed greatly when the chloride concentration is 1% or less. It has been found that that reinforcement corrosion in concrete structures is caused when content of chloride ions exceeded 0.3 kg/m^3~2.4 kg/m^3 (0.03%~0.24% of chloride ions concentration) in the neighborhood of the bars. Thus, as the values of the amplitude by the electromagnetic waves changed greatly in the low range of chloride ions concentration, it was possible to estimate the chloride ions concentration in the concrete from the values of the amplitude in the electromagnetic waves.

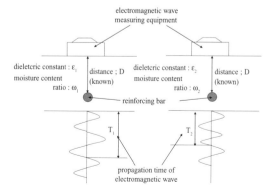

Figure 1. Concept of electromagnetic wave measurement.

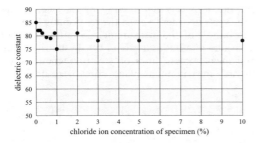

Figure 3. Relationship between chloride ions concentration and dielectric constant in the aqueous solution.

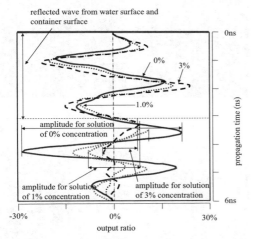

Figure 4. Example of output waveforms in aqueous solution.

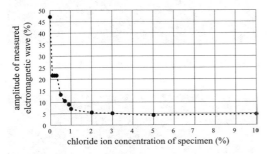

Figure 5. Relationship between chloride ion concentration and amplitude in the aqueous solution.

Table 1. Specifications of electromagnetic wave measuring equipment.

Item	Specifications
Rader frequencies	1.0 GHz
Measurement method	Impulse method
Transmission voltage	17Vp-p (at load 50Ω)
Horizontal resolution	80 mm

measured waveform of
reinforced concrete specimen

········· measured waveform of
plain concrete specimen

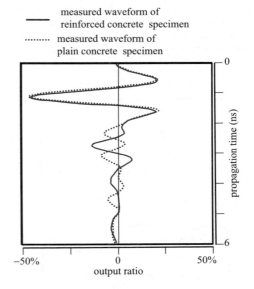

Figure 6. Effect of reinforcing bar in measured waveform.

3 MEASUREMENT METHOD

For measurement of electromagnetic waves, an antenna of about 1.0 GHz with specifications as given in Table 1 was installed. As shown in Figure 6, the scale of the monitor was fixed at the level of the gain of the machine when the measurement was started, and the amplitude of the reflected electromagnetic wave estimated using that scale (Full scale = 100%). Figure 7 shows an example of a waveform with subtraction.

Moreover, since the reflected wave from the reinforcement and the reflected wave from concrete are likely to interfere with the reflected wave in concrete with reinforcing bars, the reflected waveform only of the concrete was subtracted from the measured waveform of the concrete with reinforcing bars. Thus, as shown in Figure 6, the effect of only the presence of the reinforcement in the member of reinforced concrete could be independently studied.

4 FIELD SURVEY

For the purpose of investigating the applicability of the method of estimating content of chloride ions using electromagnetic waves in reinforced concrete structures, investigations in three coastal structures have been carried out using electromagnetic waves so far. The investigated places were the deck of a coastal structure at which ships are moored, a loading bridge for coal and the walls for inspection in an intake pump. Figures 8 to 10 show each investigated place and Figure 11 shows the measurement of the content of chloride ions using electromagnetic waves.

Firstly, an exploration of reinforcement bars was carried out to confirm the position of reinforcing bars by moving the electromagnetic antenna on each member. In the position where existence of the reinforcing bars was confirmed, the content of

chloride ions was measured using the electromagnetic wave in order to cross the reinforcing bars. As an example of the measurement, Figure 12 shows positions of reinforcing bars on the marine deck and measurement lines of electromagnetic wave. In each measurement place, cores were drilled at

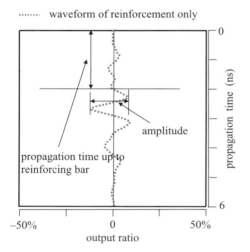

Figure 7.   Example of waveform with subtraction.

Figure 9.   Loading bridge of coal.

Figure 10.   Walls for inspection in intake pump.

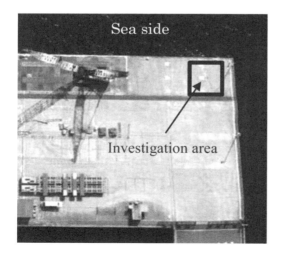

Figure 8.   Sea deck.

Figure 11.   Measurement using electromagnetic wave.

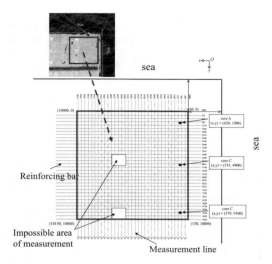

Figure 12. Example of investigation area.

Figure 13. Situation of drilled cores.

3 to 4 places in order to evaluate the accuracy of estimation of the content of chloride ions using the electromagnetic wave. For example, Figure 12 shows the location points of cores on the marine deck and Figure 13 shows the situation of the drilled cores.

5 INVESTIGATION RESULTS AND DISCUSSIONS

Using the results of the three field surveys, a multiple regression analysis was carried out for calculation of the content of chloride ions estimated formula by electromagnetic wave. As shown in Table 2, the environmental conditions and condition of mix proportions of the concrete are different for each investigation, and have been used to determine the predictor variables in multiple regression

analyses to estimate the content of chloride ions, the amplitude value, the dielectric constant, water cement ratio and service life at the region of measurement are selected and the estimates of the content of chloride ions are compared with the content of chloride ions obtained by chemical analysis. The result of comparing the content of chloride ions obtained by chemical analysis with the content of chloride ions, C_c as the criterion variable estimated by the multiple regression analysis taking the dielectric constant ε and the amplitude value α, water cement ratio W/C and service life of the structure as the predictor variables using equation 1 below is shown in Figure 14.

$$C_c = -0.393\alpha - 5.30 \times 10^{-2}\varepsilon + 0.142W/C$$
$$+ 8.91 \times 10^{-2}t - 2.28 \qquad (1)$$

As shown in Figure 14, the multiple regression coefficients were 0.89 and the estimates were reasonably accurate.

In this study, water-cement ratio was added to the explanatory variable in the multiple regressive equation, as it is clear that the diffusion of the content of chloride ions was largely affected in past researches by the capillary voids in the concrete. In addition, the service life was added in the multiple-regressive explanatory variable in order to consider the effect of aging degradation which originates from cracks caused by drying shrinkage in the concrete, etc. By adding these explanatory variables in the multiple-regression, it seems that it is possible that the content of chloride ions using electromagnetic wave obtain high estimation can be estimated approximately. Therefore, when estimating the content of chloride ions, the dielectric constant, amplitude vales of reflected electromagnetic waves, water cement ratio and service life of the structure should be considered. The example of distribution of the content of chloride ions in the each measurement place estimated using the above equation is shown in Figures 15 to 17. Though the content of chloride ions obtained by the cores becomes an evaluation in the point, as shown in Figures 15 to 17, it is possible that the estimation of the content of chloride ions using the electromagnetic wave shows as a plane. Figures 15–17 show the content of chloride ions calculated on the basis of measurement results as contour lines that show the distribution diagram synthesized with the field photograph. By superimposing distribution of the content of chloride ions and field photograph, it is possible to confirm how actually the content of chloride ions in the measurement place is distributed. In addition, Figures 15–17 show results of estimation of the content of chloride ions calculated by multiple regression analysis in

Table 2. Environmental conditions and condition of mix proportion of concrete.

Investigation place	Location	Water cement ratio	Type of cement	Service life
Loading bridge of coal	Okinawa prefecture	0.55	Flyash cement type B	23 years
Sea deck	Kanagawa prefecture	0.45	Blast furnace slag cement type B	10 years
Walls for inspection in intake pump	Okayama prefecture	0.55	Blast furnace slag cement type B	40 years

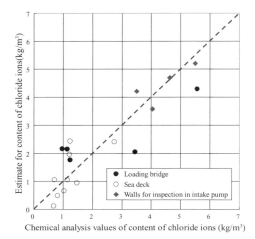

Figure 14.   Estimate of content of chloride ions.

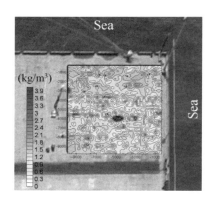

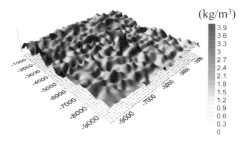

Figure 15.   Distribution of the content of chloride ions.

(Sea deck)

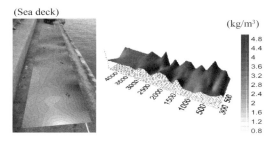

Figure 16.   Distribution of the content of chloride ions (Loading bridge for coal).

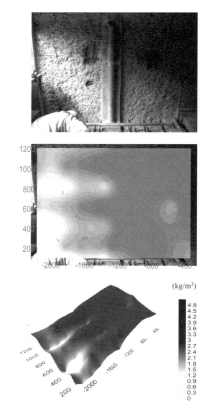

Figure 17.   Distribution of the content of chloride ions (walls for inspection in intake pump).

a 3-dimensional map. In these figures, the height direction is the content of chloride ions.

6 ESTIMATION METHOD ON DISTRIBUTION CURVE OF CHLORIDE CONTENT USING ELCTROMAGNETIC WAVE

Since the value estimated using the electromagnetic wave method is the average of chloride content from the concrete surface to the reinforcing bar, it is not possible to evaluate the distribution of chloride content. Therefore, chloride content can be overestimated, when chloride content has not reached the reinforcing bar. Then, it seems to be possible that the chloride content in the reinforced concrete is estimated to a good accuracy by utilizing the estimation method on distribution of chloride content in reinforced concrete shown in the following.

First of all, in an object position, chloride content is measured or estimated by some methods, for example chipping investigation or impedance measurement. Next, the average chloride content from concrete surface to reinforcing bar is estimated using the electromagnetic wave method. Figure 18 shows the relationship between results from each measurement mentioned above.

Generally, it is possible to obtain a permeation depth of chloride content using the Fick's law of diffusion. It is possible to obtain chloride content in an arbitrary position and in an arbitrary time by solving the differential equation showed in Equation 2.

$$\frac{\partial C}{\partial t} = D_c \frac{\partial^2 C}{\partial x^2} \qquad (2)$$

$$C(x,t) = C_0\left(1 - erf\left(\frac{x}{2\sqrt{Dc \cdot t}}\right)\right) \qquad (3)$$

where, C shows chloride content in an arbitrary position (x) and in an arbitrary time (t) (kg/m^3), D_c shows the value of diffusion coefficient of chloride ions into concrete (cm^2/year), C_0 shows chloride content at concrete surface (kg/m^3). erf (s) is the error function defined by Equation 4 as follows;

$$erf(s) = \frac{2}{\sqrt{\pi}}\int_0^s e^{-\eta^2}\,d\eta \qquad (4)$$

Results from past studies give the value of diffusion coefficient of chloride ions into concrete in Equation 5 in the following equation.

$$log\,D_c = a\left(\frac{W}{C}\right)^2 + b\left(\frac{W}{C}\right) + c \qquad (5)$$

where, a, b and c are coefficients determined by the type of cement and W/C is water cement ratio.

It is possible to calculate total chloride content permeated from the concrete surface by using chloride content in concrete surface estimated using some methods and the value of diffusion coefficient into concrete gotten from Equation 6.

$$C(t)_{total} = \int C(x,t)\,dx \qquad (6)$$

Where, $C(t)_{total}$ is total chloride content permeated from the concrete surface in an arbitrary time.

As shown Figure 19, by determining the permeation depth so that the total chloride content obtained in Equation 6 may be equivilant

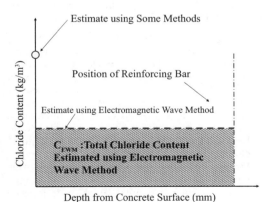

Figure 18. Estimation of chloride content in cover concrete.

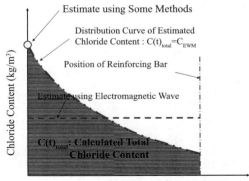

Figure 19. Estimate of distribution curve of chloride content.

365

to the average chloride content obtained by the electromagnetic wave method, it is possible to estimate the distribution of the chloride content from concrete surface.

At present, as shown Figure 20, in order to verify the distribution of chloride content estimated from both measurement results, chemical analysis to investigate chloride content within concrete is carried out with cores drilled from the specimens.

Figures 21–23 show results of comparing the estimated values with measurement values by chemical analysis. In shown Figures 21–23, the measurement values and the estimate values in each investigation place were almost equivalent to the results of chemical analysis.

From the above results, it is shown that it is possible that the method proposed in this study using these nondestructive testing methods almost estimates the distribution of the content of chloride ions.

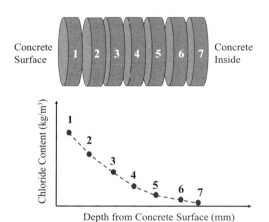

Figure 20. Verification of distribution of chloride content.

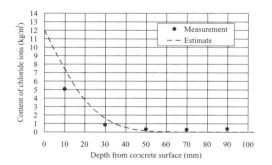

Figure 21. Example of comparison of distribution of content of chloride ions (Sea deck).

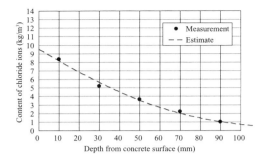

Figure 22. Example of comparison of distribution of content of chloride ions (Loading bridge for coal).

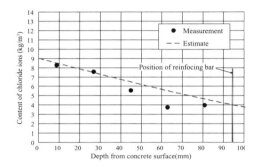

Figure 23. Example of comparison of distribution of content of chloride ions (Walls for inspection in intake pump).

7 CONCLUSIONS

The present research examined the applicable method which is possible to estimate the chloride content included in cover concrete using an electromagnetic wave method which is non-destructive. The knowledge gained from this study can be outlined as follows.

- Though the environmental conditions and the mix proportions of the concrete were different from each investigation area, the content of chloride ions can be estimated with fairly good accuracy from the measurement of electromagnetic waves. The dielectric constant, amplitude vales of reflected electromagnetic waves, water-cement ratio and service life should be considered when estimating the content of chloride ions.
- Using the estimate of average content of chloride ions to the reinforcing bar by electromagnetic wave and surface content of chloride ions by estimate using some methods, it is shown that it is possible to estimate the distribution of content of chloride ions in the cover concrete.

366

As many problems have been held on application to reinforced concrete structures, further work needs to be carried out on the influences of environmental conditions, shape of the structure, moisture condition in concrete, etc.

REFERENCES

Arthur v.H. 1954. Dielectric Materials and Applications, Artech House Publishers.

Daisuke H. & Toshiaki M. 2005. Experimental Study on Applicability of Measuring Method of Chloride Content using Electromagnetic Wave in Reinforced Concrete Structures, The Third US-Japan Symposium on Advancing Applications and Capabilities in NDE.

Japan Society of Civil Engineering 2003. Enactment of Test Method for Diffusion Coefficient of Chloride Ion in Concrete and Trend of Test Method of normalization desired, Concrete Engineering Series 55. (in Japanese).

Junnichi A. & Toshiaki M. 2003. Study on Measurement of Chloride Content using Electromagnetic Wave in Reinforced Concrete Structures", Non-Destructive Testing in Civil Engineering.

Kazumasa M. et al. 1999. Relationship between water content and relative dielectric constant in concrete, Japan Society of Non-Destructive Inspection, Proceedings of the 1999 Spring Symposia, 91–94. (in Japanese).

Taketomo K. et al. 2004. Experimental Study on Evaluation of Content of Chloride Ions in Reinforced Concrete Using Electromagnetic Waves, Annual Proceedings of Concrete Engineering, Vol. 25, No. 1, Japan Concrete Institute, 1673–1678. (in Japanese).

Toshiaki M. et al. 2002. Considerations on the measurement of chlorides in reinforced concrete by electromagnetic waves, Annual Proceedings of Concrete Engineering, Vol. 24, No. 1, Japan Concrete Institute, 1509–1514. (in Japanese).

Toshiaki M. & Junnichi A. 2003. Experimental Study on Measurement of Chloride Content using Electromagnetic Wave in Reinforced Concrete Structures, Structural Faults and Repair-2003, 241–248.

Toshiaki M. & Kumiko S. 2005. Experimental Study on Applicability of Measuring Method of Chloride Content using Electromagnetic Wave in Reinforced Concrete Structures, The 11th International Conference on Fracture.

Toshiaki M. et al. 2008. Applicability of Estimation of Chloride Content in Cover concrete using Electromagnetic Wave and Impedance Method, on Site Assessment of Concrete, Masonry and Timber.

Toahiaki M. et al. 2008. Applicability of Estimation of Chloride Content in Cover concrete using Electromagnetic Wave, Structural Faults and Repair-2008.

Concrete Solutions – Grantham, Mechtcherine & Schneck (eds)
© 2012 Taylor & Francis Group, London, ISBN 978-0-415-61622-5

A fundamental study on quantitative assessment of steel corrosion by a new NDT method with induction heating

K. Kobayashi, R. Nakamura & K. Rokugo
Gifu University, Gifu, Japan

S. Nakazawa
Gifu Institute of Engineering, Motosu, Japan

ABSTRACT: This study aimed at developing a new non-destructive test method using Induction Heating (IH) and infrared thermography for quantitative assessment of rebar corrosion. Rebars under cover concrete were heated with an IH device, and the effects of rebar diameter and corrosion amount on the temperature distribution on the cover concrete surface were investigated using an infrared thermography camera. A larger corrosion amount suppressed heat diffusion from the rebars to the cover concrete and reduced the increase in surface temperature of the cover concrete.

1 INTRODUCTION

Among many deterioration factors of RC structures, rebar corrosi on is known to accelerate deterioration at a high rate and to have a critical impact on mechanical performance of the structure. A new non-destructive test method that enables a rapid and quantitative assessment of RC structures deteriorated by rebar corrosion is highly desirable.

Electrochemical techniques such as half-cell potential methods and polarization resistance methods have been commonly used for investigation of rebar corrosion. These techniques also unfortunately have numerous limitations. For example, the half-cell potential method can only indicate the possibility of an on-going corrosion, but fails to provide a quantitative measure of the amount of corrosion or the residual rebar diameter. Polarization resistance methods can measure the corrosion rate theoretically, but for obtaining the amount of corrosion with this method, frequent measurements must be made right after the construction. Moreover, precise values of the coefficients used in the calculation of the corrosion rate from the polarization resistance data do not exist. Other NDT methods studied for their applicability in the determination of the amount of steel corrosion include the radar method and the impact echo method, while their reliability remains low.

Around 1980, Hillemeier and his team developed a novel NDT method by combining Induction Heating (IH) with infrared thermography (Hillemeier, 1982 & 1984). Although the purpose of their initial works was to detect reinforcement under cover concrete, several studies have been carried out

recently in order to examine this method's applicability to measure the extent of corrosion in RC elements. Oshita et al. have developed a new NDT method of measuring the corrosion amount using IH and an infrared thermography camera (Oshita et al. 2009). In this method, IH is used as shown in Figure 1 (Kobayashi & Banthia, 2011) so as to heat rebars only under the cover concrete. Using the low thermal conductivity of corrosion products that is less than that of sound steel by two orders of magnitude, and less than that of concrete by one order, this inhibits diffusion of heat generated by IH in corroded rebars to the cover concrete. A measurement of the temperature distribution on the concrete surface with an infrared camera can therefore determine rebar corrosion as shown in Figure 2 (Kobayashi & Banthia, 2011).

To make this method practically applicable, the effects of rebar diameter, corrosion amount, cracks on cover concrete, cover depth, and ambient conditions on the temperature distributions

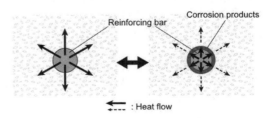

Figure 1. Effect of low heat conductivity of steel corrosion products on thermal diffusion (Kobayashi & Banthia, 2011).

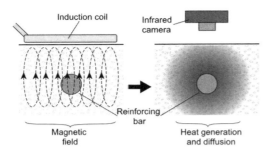

Figure 2. Induction heating and infrared thermography used for detection of corrosion in reinforcing steel in concrete (Kobayashi & Banthia, 2011).

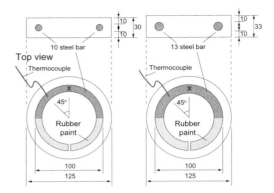

Figure 3. Dimensions of specimens.

Table 1. Experimental parameters.

Bar diameter (mm)	Corrosion loss (%)
10	0, 2, 5, and 10
13	0, 2, 5, and 10

of the concrete surface must be clarified. In this study, as the first step for developing a new NDT technique using IH, the thermal behaviour of rebars and of cover concrete were investigated to determine the effects of rebar diameter and corrosion amount on the temperature distribution of the concrete surface.

2 EXPERIMENTAL PROCEDURE

2.1 Test specimens

Specimens used in this study were cylindrical with a diameter of 125 mm (Fig. 3). Round steel bars of φ10 and φ13 were embedded at a cover depth of 10 mm in a circular form with an outer diameter of 125 mm. The specimen with the φ10 bar had a height of 30 mm, while the specimen with the φ13 bar had a height of 33 mm. The steel bars were deformed into the circular shape to match the shape of the coil of the IH device in an attempt to heat the bars as uniformly as possible. To prevent the specimens from splitting due to expansion of the steel bars as corrosion progresses, a half of the bar was coated with rubber paint for corrosion protection. Therefore, the target part of the experiment was the semicircular upper half of the bar in plan view of Figure 3.

Concrete with a water/cement ratio of 0.55 was used. Target corrosion ratios of steel bars were set to 0, 2, 5 or 10% as shown in Table 1 respectively so that there were a total of eight types of specimens. Steel corrosion was accelerated using an electrolytic corrosion method. The duration of corrosion acceleration was determined using the following experimental formula (Tamori et al. 1988):

$$W = 0.766 \times i \times t \qquad (1)$$

where W = Corrosion amount (g); i = Corrosion current (A); t = Corrosion acceleration time (hour).

2.2 Experimental procedure

A domestic use Induction Heating (IH) cooker with a disk-shaped induction coil and a rated output of 4.6 kW was used as the induction heater. The specimens were placed on the cooker and heated with a maximum power output. The steel bars had to be heated sufficiently to raise the temperature on the concrete surface by thermal diffusion, but not more than necessary because excessive heating would cause the heat to propagate to the entire specimen, making it difficult to detect the steel bar or its corrosion based on the temperature distribution on the concrete surface. An appropriate heating time was determined in consideration of these through preliminary tests and set to be five minutes for the φ10 specimens and four minutes for the φ13 specimens, respectively.

For thermography, a NEC/Avio Thermo shot F30S camera with a thermal sensitivity of 0.1 °C and a spectrum range of 8–13 µm was used. The temperature of the steel bar inside the specimen was measured every five seconds from the start of the induction heating using a thermocouple soldered to the bar. After the heating, thermographs of the concrete surface were taken every 30 seconds with an emissivity of ε = 0.92 using an infrared camera to record the temperature distributions. The distance between the camera and the specimen was set to be 50 cm.

The tests were carried out in a laboratory at 20 °C with due care taken to minimize impacts of ambient conditions on the results.

Table 2. Relationship between the targeted corrosion loss and the actual corrosion loss.

φ10		φ13	
Target corrosion loss	Achieved corrosion loss	Target corrosion loss	Achieved corrosion loss
0%	0%	0%	0%
2%	2.93%	2%	2.39%
5%	7.34%	5%	5.70%
10%	14.8%	10%	13.58%

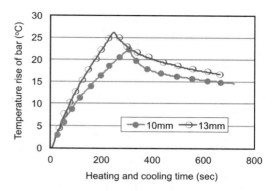

Figure 4. Effect of diameter on temperature rise of steel bar.

(a) φ10

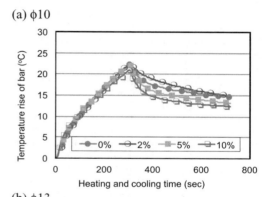

(b) φ13

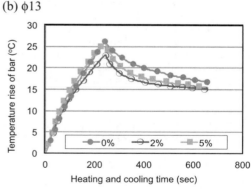

Figure 5. Effect of corrosion ratio on temperature rise of steel bar.

After all the tests had finished, the corrosion amount was quantified by taking the rebars out of the specimen and immersing them in a 10% di-ammonium hydrogen citrate solution at 60 °C for 24 hours to remove the rust. The loss of mass of the rebar was then determined to obtain the amount of corrosion. These were then compared with theoretical (and targeted) values of corrosion loss. Table 2 shows the relationship between the targeted corrosion loss and the actual corrosion loss. While the acieved corrosion loss was larger than the target corrosion loss, a reasonable correlation existed between them, regardless of the bar diameter. Therefore, henceforth, the specimens will be referred to by their respective targeted corrosion losses.

3 TEMPERATURE CHANGE OF STEEL BAR

3.1 Effects of bar diameter

Figure 4 shows temperature changes of non-corroded steel bars of different diameters in the specimens. At the time point of 240 seconds, the temperature of the φ13 steel bar was higher than that of the φ10 steel bar by 6.8 °C. The more rapid temperature rise in the thicker steel bar can be attributed to the nature of the induction heating that heats up the metal surface quickly, since the φ13 steel bar has a larger projected area against the heating device. This result suggests that a larger steel diameter would make the assessment easier.

3.2 Effects of corrosion amount

Figure 5 shows temperature changes of steel bars with various corrosion ratios. Due to a discon-nection by rupture of the thermocouple during the electrolytic corrosion process in the φ13 speci-men with a corrosion rate of 10%, the graph of Figure 5b does not include its data.

While the past studies (Oshita et al. 2009; Kobayashi & Banthia, 2011) have shown that steel bars with a higher corrosion ratio exhibit a higher temperature due to the low thermal conductivity of corrosion products, there was no substantial difference in the maximum temperature of the φ10 specimens with different corrosion ratios.

In this study, one half of the circular bar was coated with rubber paint for corrosion protection in order to avoid splitting of specimen due to an expansive pressure caused by steel corrosion. However, as will be discussed in conjunction with the temperature distributions on the concrete surface in the next section, the temperature of the concrete surface above this painted part of steel bar was higher, implying that heat diffused easily through the rubber paint from the steel bar into the cover concrete. Therefore, it is suspected that heat inhibited from diffusing by the corroded layer on the unpainted steel bar surface then diffused through the adjacent rubber-painted part into the concrete, as a result of which there was no particular impact observed of the corrosion amount on the temperature of the corroded steel bar. There remains some scope for improvement in the shape and structure of the specimens employed in this study. On the other hand, since the steel bar temperature was generally constant irrespective of the degree of corrosion, it was considered possible to estimate the impact of corrosion on the diffusion of heat to the concrete surface under the same boundary conditions, and thus we went on carrying out the experiment with these specimens.

The impact of corrosion amount on the temperature of steel bars was hardly observed in the $\phi13$ specimens (see Fig. 5b), except for the specimen with a 2% corrosion loss that showed a slightly smaller temperature rise than the others. Possible causes for this would be uneven corrosion distribution on the steel bar along its length, and uneven thermal diffusivity of cover concrete due to the presence of coarse aggregates in concrete with a small cover depth. To eliminate such factors, plural specimens having the same conditions should be prepared to investigate variations among the specimens. Also, the temperature distribution along the steel bar should be investigated using plural thermocouples attached to the bar.

4 TEMPERATURE DISTRIBUTION ON COVER CONCRETE

4.1 Thermography after the heating

Figures 6 and 7 show thermographs taken 30 seconds after the induction heating. In both of the $\phi10$ and $\phi13$ specimens, the temperature was higher along the steel bars with little variation in specimens with smaller corrosion amounts. On the contrary, in the specimens with larger corrosion amounts, the temperature of the concrete was lower above the uncoated part of steel bar. This confirms the nature of corrosion products that inhibits thermal diffusion.

Figure 8 shows the outer appearance of the $\phi13$-5% specimen (see Fig. 7c). Cracks with a

(a) $\phi10mm$-0%

(b) $\phi10mm$-2%

(c) $\phi10mm$-5%

(d) $\phi10mm$-10%

Figure 6. Thermographs taken 30 sec after the heating ($\phi10$ mm).

maximum width of about 0.6 mm were formed along a boundary between low-temperature and high temperature regions. The sudden temperature drop was therefore considered to be due to heat

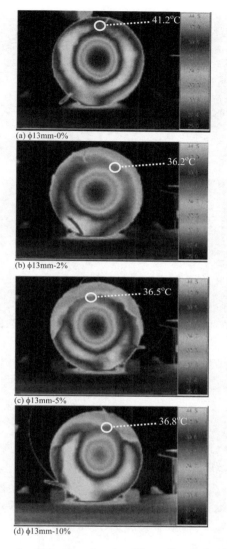

(a) φ13mm-0%

(b) φ13mm-2%

(c) φ13mm-5%

(d) φ13mm-10%

Figure 7. Thermographs taken 30 sec after the heating (φ13 mm).

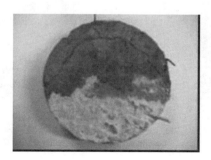

Figure 8. Specimen φ13 mm-10%.

diffusing from the steel bar toward the concrete surface being accumulated in air inside cracks, resulting in a lower temperature on the concrete surface as has been reported (Negishi et al. 2010).

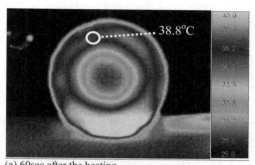

(a) 60sec after the heating

(b) 120sec after the heating

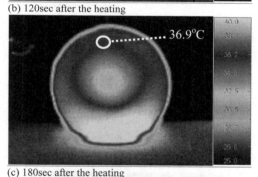

(c) 180sec after the heating

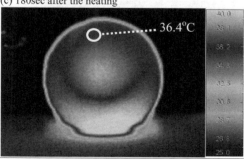

(d) 240sec after the heating

Figure 9. (continued).

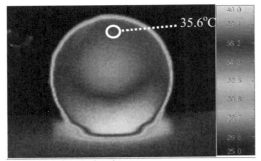

(e) 300sec after the heating

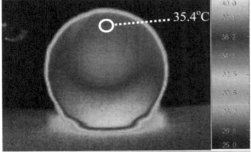

(f) 360sec after the heating

Figure 9. Temperature distributions on the concrete surface of the specimen φ10-0% between 60 to 360 sec after the heating.

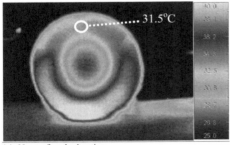

(a) 60sec after the heating

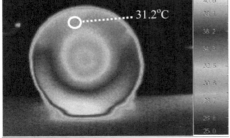

(b) 120sec after the heating

Figure 10. (continued).

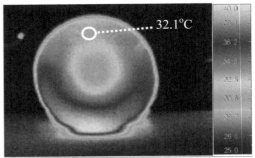

(c) 180sec after the heating

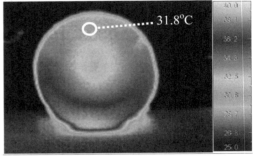

(d) 240sec after the heating

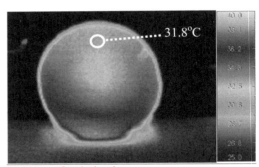

(e) 300sec after the heating

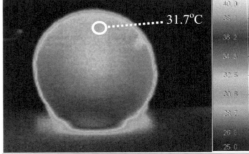

(f) 360sec after the heating

Figure 10. Temperature distributions on the concrete surface of the specimen φ10-10% between 60 to 360 sec after the heating.

Figures 9 and 10 show the transitions of temperature distribution on concrete surface of the specimens φ10-0% and φ10-10%. As can be seen in Figure 9, the temperature of the upper half, where the steel bar was not painted, of the specimen φ10-0% was highest just after the heating, being indicated by a very bright color, and then fell gradually as time passed. On the contrary, the temperature change of the upper half of the specimen φ10-10% can hardly be observed in Figure 10. This suggests that the heat that has generated on the steel bar was released gradually into the cover concrete because corrosion products block the diffusion of heat from the bar to the cover concrete.

4.2 The effects of corrosion amount and steel bar diameter on the temperature of the concrete surface

Figure 11 shows the temperature hysteresis on the concrete surface after the heating. The graph shows temperatures at point x in Figure 3 estimated from the thermographs taken by the infrared camera.

The temperature was low in specimens with large corrosion amounts and high in specimens with small corrosion amounts. Besides, while the surface temperature of specimens without corrosion (0%) began to decrease immediately after the heating was stopped, the temperature kept increasing for about a minute even after the heating was stopped in specimens with corroded steel bars. This can be attributed to the small thermal conductivity of corrosion products surrounding the steel bars and inhibiting heat from diffusing into the cover concrete.

Table 3 shows the difference in surface temperature measured 30 sec and 420 sec after the heating. The temperature dropped largely in non-corroded steel bars of both diameters, while the temperature increased in the specimens with a 5% or 10% corrosion amount. However, there was no significant difference in the degree of temperature rise between the 5% corrosion specimen and the 10% corrosion specimen. With the specimens used here, because of the small cover depth, corrosion products formed on the steel surface can easily diffuse into the electrolyte. Thus, in specimens with larger corrosion amounts (5% and 10%), the amount of corrosion products remaining at the interface between the steel and cover concrete is considered to peak out at a certain level even though corrosion progresses further. In this case, thus, the actual corrosion loss would be larger than estimated by measurements using IH.

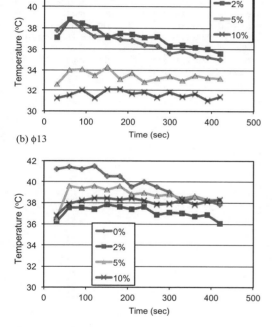

Figure 11. Concrete surface temperature measured at point x in Figure 3.

Table 3. Difference in surface temperature measured 30 sec and 420 sec after the heating.

Steel bar	Corrosion ratio (%)	Temperature at 30 sec (°C)	Temperature at 420 sec (°C)	Temperature difference (°C)
φ10 mm	0	37.8	35.0	−2.8
	2	37.1	35.6	−1.5
	5	32.6	33.2	+0.6
	10	31.2	31.4	+0.2
φ13 mm	0	41.2	37.8	−3.4
	2	36.2	36.1	−0.1
	5	36.5	36.3	+1.8
	10	36.8	38.3	+1.5

5 CONCLUSIONS

This study aimed at developing a new non-destructive test method using Induction Heating (IH) and infrared thermography. Rebars under cover concrete were heated by IH, and the effects of rebar diameter and corrosion amount on the temperature distributions on the cover concrete surface were investigated using an infrared thermography camera. The following conclusions were drawn:

- With IH heating, the larger the steel bar diameter, the larger the temperature rise.
- The larger the corrosion amount, the smaller the temperature rise on the concrete surface immediately after the heating.
- With a cover depth of 10 mm, the temperature on the concrete surface continues to rise even after the heating if the corrosion amount is about 5% or more.
- With a cover depth of 10 mm, the temperature distribution on the concrete surface does not change further after the amount of corrosion exceeds 5%.
- Corrosion cracks as large as 0.6 mm wide inhibit thermal diffusion.

ACKNOWLEDGMENT

This work was supported by Grant-in-Aid for Scientific Research (C) 22560460.

REFERENCES

Hillemeier B. 1982. Method of determining the location, orientation and pattern of reinforcing members in reinforced concrete, United States Patent 4309610.

Hillemeier B. 1984. Location of reinforcement by induction-thermography. In: Proceedings of SPIE, Thermosense VII, vol 520, pp 197–206.

Kobayashi K. & Banthia N. 2011. Corrosion detection in reinforced concrete using induction heating and infrared thermography. Journal of Civil Structural Health Monitoring, Springer.

Negishi S. & Oshita H. 2010. Influence of crack on concrete temperature in reinforced concrete corrosion diagnosis. Proc JCI 32(1): 1745–1750 (in Japanese).

Oshita H. Horie H. Nagasaka S. Taniguchi O. Yoshikawa S. 2009. Nondestructive evaluation of corrosion in reinforced concrete by thermal behavior on concrete surface due to electro-magnetic heating. Journal of JSCE E65(1): 76–92 (in Japanese).

Tamori K. Maruyama K. Odagawa M. Hashimoto C. 1988. Cracking behavior of reinforced concrete members due to corrosion of reinforcement. Proc JCI 10(2): 505–510 (in Japanese).

Concrete Solutions – Grantham, Mechtcherine & Schneck (eds)
© 2012 Taylor & Francis Group, London, ISBN 978-0-415-61622-5

Comparative study of techniques to evaluate the corrosion activity of rebars embedded in concrete

E. Marie-Victoire
Laboratoire de Recherche des Monuments Historiques Champs-sur-Marne, France

A. Proust
Mistras group SA, Sucy-en-Brie, France

V. L'Hostis
Commissariat à l'Energie Atomique, Saclay, France

F. Vallot
Laboratoire Régional de l'Est Parisien, Vaux-le-Pénil, France

ABSTRACT: Generalized corrosion induced by a carbonation of the concrete is the most deleterious decay mechanism encountered in the field of historical monuments made of concrete in France. As a consequence, there is a need for reliable diagnosis tools to monitor on site this corrosion process on existing structures. The most used techniques are based on electrochemical measurements which lead to a snapshot of the corrosion activity. They are climatic condition dependent and more worryingly they are affected by any disturbance of the electrochemical equilibrium, which could be caused by the use of restoration treatment such as migrating corrosion inhibitors, for example. Therefore the purpose of this study was to look for alternative corrosion diagnosis techniques adapted to carbonated concrete. For several years, acoustic emission monitoring, which has proven its efficiency in the field of metal corrosion localization when a direct contact with metal is possible, has been under development to detect corrosion of rebars embedded in concrete, but most of the studies concern concrete affected by chloride pollution. To evaluate the potential application of acoustic emission monitoring to carbonated concrete, a first feasibility study was performed on naturally carbonated reinforced concrete samples. In a second step, classical linear polarization measurements were compared to acoustic emission surveys, on artificially carbonated concrete slabs submitted to natural aging to activate the corrosion process. Measurements were then performed under controlled climatic conditions favorable to corrosion (20 °C, 90% RH), and the slabs were finally opened to validate the conclusions. The results first indicated that the concrete cover attenuates a lot the acoustic emission signals linked to the corrosion process induced by concrete carbonation, which are anyway at a much reduced level compared to chloride induced corrosion. But when the measurements were possible, passivity could be distinguished from corrosion activity, either through LPR measurement or acoustic emission monitoring.

1 INTRODUCTION

Carbonation induced corrosion of the rebars is the main decay mechanism of historical buildings made of reinforced concrete. Due to a decrease of pH linked to a reaction between cement portandite and atmospheric carbon dioxide, in carbonated concrete, the passive layer of oxides covering carbon steel rebars in sound concrete is destroyed and a uniform corrosion can develop if enough water and oxygen are available. As the volume of the oxides formed can vary from two to six times higher than that of steel, stress develops in the

concrete matrix. When the concrete tensile strength is exceeded, cracking is generated in the cement matrix, and generally leads to spalling. This very expansive type of corrosion can induce important loss of concrete, which is of major concern in the field of cultural heritage. Consequently, to be able to evaluate the corrosion state of rebars embedded in concrete is essential, either for diagnosis purposes, or to evaluate conservation treatments. Potential mapping combined with resistivity and LPR measurements are commonly used for such purposes, but they are clearly climatic condition dependant and they are disturbed by conservation treatments such as migrating corrosion inhibitors or realkalisation, which generate a perturbation of the electrochemical equilibrium of the concrete, evidencing the need for alternative techniques.

On another hand, acoustic emission monitoring is among the most used for metal corrosion diagnosis in industrial sites (pipelines, tanks…). Actually, there are quite a lot of phenomena such as local micro-displacements, cracks nucleation or propagation…, which generate a rapid release of energy, inducing transient elastic waves that can be monitored thanks to acoustic emission sensors (Idrissi 2008). In the case of metal corrosion, the most emissive and the most energetic (Fregonese 2001) mechanism producing such elastic waves has been evidenced as hydrogen bubbling. More recently, less emissive phenomena such as friction of hydrogen at the steel surface and in the pits (Idrissi 2008, Fregonese 2001), or as rupture of an oxide film (Fregonese 2001) have also been detected with AE monitoring.

Applied to concrete, the technique was perfected for prestressing (Ramadan 2008) or post-tensioned strands (Proverbio 2009) corrosion cracking, and loaded concrete cracking monitoring (Yoon 2000).

Concerning rebar corrosion monitoring, several studies have evidenced the ability of AE to detect corrosion (Assouli 2005, Idrissi 2003, Ing 2005, Lyons 2005, Ohtsu 2006), and even earlier than traditional electrochemical corrosion (Li 1998). But in most cases it is not precisely corrosion which was detected but more micro-cracks induced by the corrosion reaction. Thus the growth of oxides at the steel-concrete matrix interface induces strain, and when locally the tensile strength is exceeded, failure occurs. The strain energy is then partly spent to produce micro-cracks and partly emitted as acoustic emissions (Ing 2005).

Some authors differentiated two steps: shear cracking linked to the onset of corrosion and tensile cracking linked to the cracking propagation (Ohtsu 2006). Other authors also identified the passive layer bursting (Idrissi 2003) or the friction of corrosion products at the inner sides of pores or against the walls of the cracks as acoustic emission producing phenomena (Assouli 2005, Idrissi 2003), with specific signal signatures.

But most of the experiment were performed on solutions or concrete heavily chloride polluted. The purpose of this study was to determine if acoustic emission detection could be applied to carbonated reinforced concrete. Therefore a comparative study of electrochemical techniques and acoustic emission monitoring was performed at first on naturally carbonated concrete samples and, in a second step, on reinforced concrete slabs, artificially carbonated, under controlled and corrosive temperature and relative humidity.

2 TESTING PROTOCOL

A first feasibility study was performed on naturally carbonated concrete, in order to evaluate if carbonation induced corrosion could be detected through AE monitoring. Then, several series of both electrochemical measurements and acoustic emission surveys were comparatively performed on a set of reinforced concrete slabs. Finally the slabs were opened for a checking autopsy.

2.1 Naturally carbonated concrete samples

Samples were collected on claustras of Raincy Notre-Dame church (Fig. 1a), built between 1921 and 1923 in the Parisian suburb. Due to complete carbonation of the 8 cm-thick reinforced concrete claustras (Fig. 1b) decorating the façades, most of them were removed and identically rebuilt.

The concrete was composed of a mix of ordinary Portland cement ($350 kg/m^3$), and siliceous-calcareous aggregates (maximum diameter = 10 mm), very heterogeneous and yet exhibiting a 47 MPa compressive strength, with a 16% open porosity.

From these concrete claustras, seven 120 mm-long samples were sawn. On each sample, for the electrochemical measurements, a wire was welded on one extremity of the rebar (6 mm in diameter), and then both extremities of each sample were epoxy coated to avoid edge effects.

2.2 Artificially carbonated concrete slabs

Reinforced concrete slabs (dimensions $300 \times 300 \times 50$ mm) were cast according to the EN1604 (1996) standard using an ordinary Portland cement (CEMI 42.5), Palvadeau aggregates (maximum diameter = 16 mm), with a water to cement ratio of 0.7, leading to a 15% open porosity and a 24 Mpa compressive strength.

a)   b)

Figure 1. a) Raincy Notre-Dame church; b) original reinforced concrete claustras decorating the façades.

The slabs were reinforced with 3 rebars numbered 1 to 3 (diameter = 6 mm, length = 400 mm), isolated on 75 mm on both extremities with an epoxy resin (Fig. 2). The slabs were removed from their wood formwork 48 h after casting and were submitted to a 28 days cure in water.

Then, except for the sound concrete reference (Table 1), all the slabs were artificially carbonated (1 month pre-conditioning at 45 °C and 60% RH and then aging 3 months in a climatic chamber at 20 °C, 60% RH and 50% CO_2).

2.3 *Electrochemical measurements*

Concerning the electrochemical tests, rest potential (using a CANIN© corrosimeter, equipped with a $Cu/CuSO_4$ reference electrode), resistivity (using a Gecor6©) and linear polarization measurements were performed according to the RILEM recommendations (Elsener 2003, Polder 2000, Andrade 2004), but only the LPR data will be presented in this paper. However, it is to be noticed that whatever the series of experiment performed, the testing conditions lead to:

• a concrete resistivity in the range of 30–220 kΩ.cm (the higher 220 kΩ.cm being reached only very locally, in the slab corners, due to edge effects),

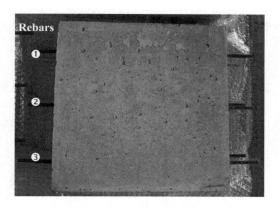

Figure 2. Concrete slabs reinforced with 3 rebars numbered 1 to 3, isolated on both extremities with an epoxy resin.

Table 1. Slab references.

Slab reference	Condition
H160604_T	Sound
G090604	Carbonated
F090604	Carbonated
H090604	Carbonated
E110604	Carbonated

• and potential values in the range of –330 and –540 for the carbonated concrete and –10 and –260 for the sound reference.

For the LPR measurements, a Gecor6©, producing a modulated confinement was chosen (Fig. 3). This device is based on a 3 electrode system with (Fig. 4) the rebar as the working electrode, a stainless steel disc as the Counter Electrode (CE), from which a galvanostatic pulse is injected (internal current), and a $Cu/CuSO_4$ electrode as reference.

To confine the current, the Gecor6© is equipped with an external guard ring producing a counter current (external current), adjusted to equilibrate internal and external currents thanks to two $Cu/CuSO_4$ reference electrodes (S1 and S2).

From the LPR measurements a corrosion current (I_{corr}) can be extrapolated according to

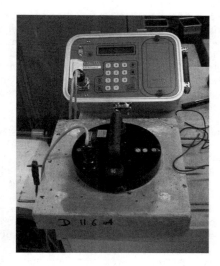

Figure 3. LPR measurements were performed using a Gecor6©.

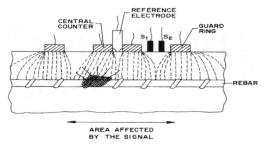

Figure 4. Modulated confinement set up of the Gecor6© (Andrade 2004).

equation 1, where R_p is the polarization resistance and B a constant (chosen value: B = 26 mV).

$$I_{corr} = B/R_p \qquad (1)$$

On each slab, after a preliminary moistening of the concrete surface, LPR measurements were performed on the center of each 3 rebars, using a wet sponge to ensure electrical conductivity. For each testing point, the results presented correspond to an average value based on 3 valid measurements (Martinez 2008).

2.4 Acoustic emissions

For the first series of feasibility tests, a MISTRAS 8 channel acquisition system, with an integrated preamplifier (40 dB gain), which was associated to 8 R15 resonant sensors (150 kHz central frequency). On seven of the samples, one sensor was placed on the unwired extremity of the rebar, while on the 8th one a second sensor was positioned on the concrete surface (Fig. 5), in order to evaluate the attenuation due to the concrete cover. To optimize the contact, a silicon grease was used as coupling agent and a rubber band was wrapped around the samples to maintain a constant pressure on the sensors.

For the second and third series of tests, a high acquisition speed SAMOS 64 channel system, with an integrated preamplifier (60 dB gain) was preferred. In order to try to localize the events to be recorded, on each slab 4 resonant sensors (3 R15 and a new R3I sensor specifically designed to monitor corrosion of concrete reinforcement, with a 30 kHz central frequency) were placed on each corner (Fig. 6). A polyurethane mastic (Foamseal© 30–45) was used as coupling material and a rubber band was again placed around the slabs.

Several parameters were monitored upon which the most significant were:

- the AE activity (A: which corresponds to the cumulated amount of hits) versus time,
- the AE intensity (I: which corresponds to the cumulated relative energy of hits: a historic way

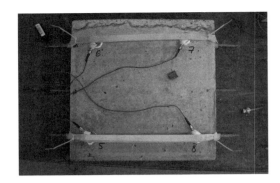

Figure 6. On each slab, 4 sensors were fixed to the concrete surface using a coupling mastic and a rubber band.

of measuring energy, roughly proportional to absolute energy) versus time,
- and the maximum absolute value of the signal during the measurement (ABS Ener).

2.5 Testing conditions

For the feasibility study, carried out in 1999, the naturally aged samples were immersed in water 1 day before 3 days of continuous measurement.

To assess more constant measuring conditions, the second and third series of tests were performed under controlled conditions. In that aim, the slabs were stored one day before and during the 3 days of testing in a climatic aging room, with fixed 20 °C temperature and 90% relative humidity (Fig. 7), to enhance the corrosion activity. LPR measurements were performed at the end of those 3 days of AE monitoring.

The second and third comparative tests were carried out respectively in November 2007 and March 2009, the slabs being submitted to natural aging outdoors in between.

Finally, after two more years of natural aging outdoors, a final series of LPR measurements was performed in March 2011, outdoors (9 °C, 58% RH) prior to the checking autopsy.

2.6 Autopsies

Two carbonated samples and the concrete sound reference were opened to validate the results of the tests performed on the concrete slabs. For the carbonated concrete slabs, rebars showing the highest corrosion activity were selected.

Carbonation depths were then verified, by spraying phenolphthalein on the freshly opened concrete. As phenolphthalein is a pH indicator, which turns pink for pH values higher than 8–10, it constitutes a good carbonation gauge. Effectively,

Figure 5. For the first feasibility tests, on one of the samples, in order to evaluate the attenuation due to the concrete cover, one sensor was placed on the rebar and another on the concrete.

Figure 7. Acoustic emission measurement setup, placed in a climatic aging room during the tests.

carbonation induces a pH decrease from initial values of around 14 in sound concrete towards values lower than 9 in carbonated concrete.

3 RESULTS

3.1 First feasibility tests

The feasibility tests, performed in 1999 on naturally carbonated concrete, showed that corrosion could be detected when a direct contact with the rebars was possible, with a signal signature distinct from cracking (high amount of low intensity hits for corrosion vs lower amount of very energetic hits for cracking), but also that the detection was more difficult at this frequency (150 kHz) through the concrete cover due to a significant attenuation of the signal (amount of hits detected up to 6 times lower, Fig. 8 and up to 10 times less energetic, Fig. 9).

Furthermore, if the preliminary one-day wetting procedure had properly enhanced the corrosion activity, as during the 3 days of measurements the samples were stored in standard laboratory conditions (20 °C, 60 % RH), they were gradually drying, which was quite disturbing.

Therefore, the second and third sets of tests, were carried out with more sensitive equipment and settings and with environmental conditions stable during the 3 days of measurements.

3.2 Second set of tests (2007)

3.2.1 LPR measurements
According to the RILEM recommendations, corrosion currents derived from the LPR measurements indicated (Fig. 10 and Table 2):

– a negligible to moderate corrosion activity for the carbonated slabs, with a majority of low activity;

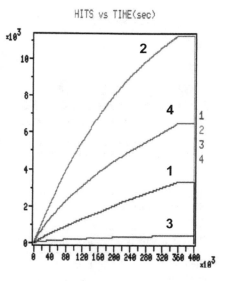

Figure 8. Acoustic emission activity (cumulated amount of hits) measured per channel (1 to 4) during the feasibility tests, versus time.

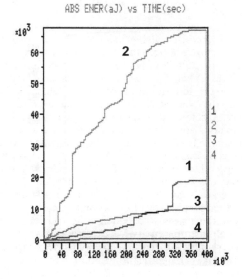

Figure 9. Acoustic emission absolute energy measured per channel (1 to 4) during the feasibility tests, versus time.

– and an expected negligible corrosion activity for the sound concrete reference.

It is to be noticed that for 3 of the 4 carbonated slabs the corrosion activity was lower for the center rebars, indicating an edge effect, that could be either due to an insufficient carbonation

381

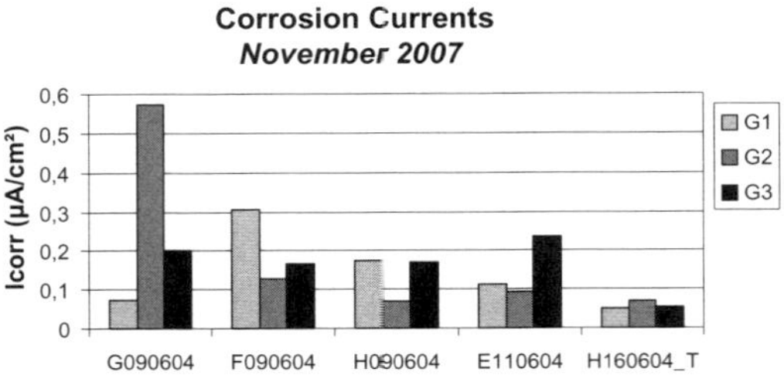

Corrosion Currents
November 2007

Figure 10. Corrosion currents calculated from the LPR results obtained during the November 2007 tests.

Table 2. Corrosion currents thresholds recommended by the RILEM (Andrade 2004).

Corrosion activity	Icorr ($\mu A/ cm^2$)
High	Icorr > 1
Moderate	0.5 < Icorr < 1
Low	0.1 < Icorr < 0.5
Negligible	Icorr < 0.1

of the concrete in the center of the slabs or to a moistening gradient.

3.2.2 Acoustic emission monitoring

It is first to be noticed that the hits intensity was on the whole quite low, and quite disturbed by interferences linked to the climatic room machinery. Due to this low amplitude of the hits whatever the slabs, the pointed localization of the events, initially expected, was impossible. As a consequence, as an important concrete attenuation was observed during the feasibility tests, and as the sensors were placed on the 4 corners of each slab, the emissions recorded have been attributed to the rebars closest to the sensors (rebars 1 and 3), the emissions due to the central rebar being probably more attenuated and therefore below the detection threshold.

On that basis, the concrete sound reference with almost no activity, was clearly distinct from the carbonated concrete (Table 3). Concerning the latest (Fig. 11), significant variations were observed from one slab to another (E110604 being clearly more emissive than G090606), but also on a given slab from a rebar to another (on E110604, rebar 1 being much less emissive than rebar 3).

As the phenomena likely to produce ultrasonic elastic waves in the samples are limited, and as a clear difference was observed between the sound reference and the carbonated samples, one can reasonably conclude that the emissions recorded in the carbonated slabs could be linked to corrosion activity.

Table 3. Cumulated acoustic emission activity (A) and intensity (I) recorded per slab during the November 2007 tests.

Slab	Average AE activity (Hits amount)	Average AE intensity (aJ)
H160604_T	199	1200
G090604	460	1840
F090604	1045	5300
H090604	634	4940
E110604	2683	10890

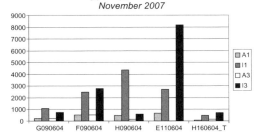

Cumulative acoustic emission Activity (A) and Intensity(I, aJ) per rebar and slab
November 2007

Figure 11. Cumulative acoustic emission activity (A) and intensity (I, expressed in aJ) recorded per rebar (on rebars 1 and 3) and per slab during the November 2007 tests.

3.2.3 Comparison

Both LPR measurements and acoustic emission monitoring revealed a generally low corrosion activity. With both techniques, the sound concrete reference could be clearly distinguished from the carbonated slabs, and some variations in the corrosion activity were detected between the carbonated slabs. As LPR measurements are instantaneous, to try to compare the results of both techniques per slab and per rebar, the acoustic emission activity and intensity were normalized per hour.

Nevertheless, no clear correlation was observed between instantaneous corrosion currents and either acoustic emission activity (Fig. 12) or intensity (Fig. 13) whatever the carbonated slab.

3.3 Third set of tests (2009)

As the corrosion activity was globally quite low in November 2007, in order to enhance it, the slabs were submitted to 1.5 years natural aging outdoors. Then a third set of measurements was performed with conditions similar to that of 2007.

3.3.1 LPR measurements

Instantaneous corrosion rates calculated from the LPR measurements (Fig. 14) indicated, according

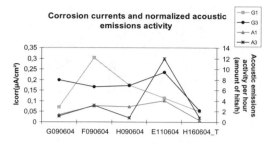

Figure 12. Normalized acoustic emission activity (A) and corrosion currents recorded per rebar and per slab. November 2007 tests.

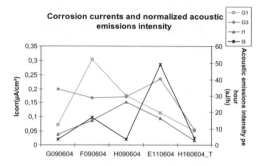

Figure 13. Normalized acoustic emission intensity (I) and corrosion currents recorded per rebar and per slab. November 2007 tests.

to the RILEM recommendation (Table 2) mostly low corrosion for the carbonated slabs and a negligible corrosion for the sound concrete reference.

The edge effect observed in 2007 was confirmed in 2009, with higher corrosion rates on rebars 1 and 3 than on the centered rebar 2 for the same 3 of the 4 carbonated slabs.

Finally, the corrosion activity clearly increased between 2007 and 2009 for the 3 rebars of slabs H090604 and E110604; when for 2 of the 3 rebars, it decreased for slabs G090604 and F090604 (Fig. 15).

So globally the corrosion activity was lightly enhanced by the natural aging, but quite heterogeneously.

3.3.2 *Acoustic emission monitoring*

The 3 days of AE monitoring performed in March 2009 did not lead to any exploitable data. Effectively, the climatic room engines lead to a quite high interference background that could have hidden the eventual AE signals that could come from the corrosion activity of the slabs. However, even when the climatic room was stopped almost no hits were recorded.

3.4 *Fourth set of tests (2011)*

3.4.1 *LPR measurements*

Finally, prior to the checking autopsy, a last series of LPR measurements was realized outdoors in march 2011, after two more years of natural aging.

Except for the sound concrete reference, for all the slabs (Fig. 16), the corrosion activity was in the range of low to moderate, according to the RILEM recommendation (Table 2). Concerning the edge effect observed in the 2 first sets of measurements, it was not visible anymore in 2011. Yet a significant increase of the corrosion activity of rebar 2 was noted for 3 of the 4 carbonated slabs, towards values comparable to that of rebar 1 (Fig. 17).

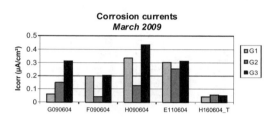

Figure 14. Corrosion currents calculated based on the LPR results obtained in March 2009.

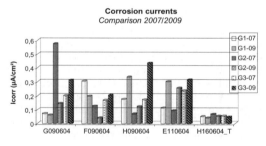

Figure 15. Comparison of the corrosion currents obtained respectively in November 2007 (07) and March 2009 (09).

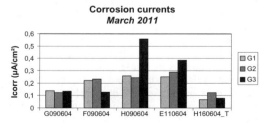

Figure 16. Corrosion currents calculated based on the LPR results obtained during the November 2011 tests.

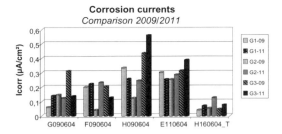

Corrosion currents
Comparison 2009/2011

Figure 17. Evolution of the corrosion currents calculated based on the LPR results obtained from November 2007 to March 2011.

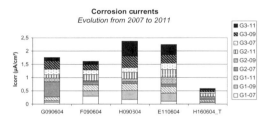

Corrosion currents
Evolution from 2007 to 2011

Figure 18. Evolution of the corrosion currents calculated based on the LPR results obtained from November 2007 to March 2011.

3.5 *Final autopsy (2011)*

3.5.1 *Slabs to be autopsied selection*
On the basis of both the LPR measurements (Fig. 18) and the acoustic emission survey (Fig. 11), during the whole period of the study, the slabs where the corrosion seemed to be the more active were H090604 and E110604. Therefore both slabs were opened around their rebars 1 and 3 (which were *a priori* the 2 rebars the most concerned by the AE monitoring). The sound concrete reference was also opened around its rebar 3.

3.5.2 *Phenolphthalein tests*
Phenolphthalein tests confirmed the absence of carbonation of the sound concrete reference (Fig. 19) and revealed a total carbonation of the concrete around rebar 1 for both slabs H090604 and E110604. But around rebar 3 of slab E110604 (Fig. 20), at least on half of the rebar's length the cement matrix was not fully carbonated. Around rebar 3 of slab H090604 (Fig. 21), 2 pink spots were observed indicating that the carbonation was not complete. In both cases, the non-carbonated areas were located on the extremities of the rebars, the central part of any rebar of the carbonated slabs (where the LPR measurements were performed) being always carbonated.

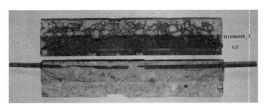

Figure 19. Phenolphthalein test performed on rebar 3 of slab H160604_T, confirming the absence of carbonation of the sound concrete reference.

Figure 20. Phenolphthalein test performed on rebar 3 of slab E110604, indicating that on half of the rebar's length, the concrete was only partly carbonated.

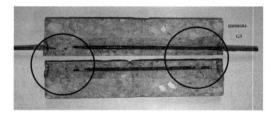

Figure 21. Phenolphthalein test performed on rebar 3 of slab H060604, revealing 2 spots of non-fully-carbonated concrete.

3.5.3 *Visible corrosion*
Visual observation of rebar 3 of the sound concrete reference indicated an absence of active corrosion: the passive layer seeming completely preserved.

Concerning the carbonated slabs, in concordance with the phenolphthalein tests, a generalized corrosion was observed on the whole length of rebar 1 for slabs H090604 and E110604, when locally on the extremities of the rebars, in the non-carbonated areas, rebar 3 did not show active corrosion on slab H090604 (Fig. 21), which was even more evident on slab E110604 (Fig. 20).

Yet, whatever the rebar, for any of the carbonated slabs, the central part was systematically corroded.

Chemical removal of corrosion has been scheduled for the rebars of the carbonated slabs, in order to evaluate more precisely the weight of metal lost.

4 DISCUSSION

When cumulating the results of the 3 sets of tests performed on slabs, according to the LPR measurements, the slabs that have evidenced the highest corrosion activity are E110604 and H090406. It is interesting to note that those 2 slabs were also showing the higher activity and intensity during the first set of November 2007 tests. This could indicate that AE monitoring was able to detect corrosion earlier than LPR measurements, which is in concordance with Li's results (Li 1998).

Concerning the AE monitoring either on the naturally carbonated and on the artificially carbonated concretes, both the amount of hits and their intensity were quite low compared to that observed on chloride polluted concrete (Li 1998), which could mean that the corrosion induced by carbonation might be less emissive. On another hand, for most of the experiments performed on chloride polluted concrete, the AE sensors were placed directly on the rebars, and the first feasibility clearly showed that the concrete cover attenuates noticeably the AE signals. Some authors also showed that corrosion is more easily detected in high strength concrete (Ing 2005), more energy being released during micro-fracture for concrete of higher mechanical performances. However, the concrete used to cast the slabs of this study was a rather low quality concrete (24 Mpa Compressive strength).

Moreover, if during the March 2009 tests, the parasite noises generated by the aging room were quite disturbing, even when stopping the machinery, the slabs did not appear emissive. Two hypothesis could be suggested:

- first, some authors have evidenced that higher energy is released either at the beginning of the corrosion reaction (Li 1998), and at the beginning of micro-cracking (Ing 2005),
- secondly, Wheat (2009) and Yoon (2000) have observed that the higher the corrosion currents the lower the AE signals.

Thus the LPR measurements clearly showed an increase of the corrosion activity between 2007 and 2009. This could mean that if AE monitoring could be an interesting technique for early detection of corrosion, it could not detect correctly heavy corrosion, which is nevertheless in contradiction with some recent studies performed on chloride polluted concrete (Proust 2010).

5 CONCLUSIONS

The purpose of this study was to explore the possible use of AE as a corrosion monitoring tool for carbonation induced corrosion in concrete.

The results indicated that AE surveys can detect corrosion in carbonated concrete. But the signals were rather low in activity and intensity, which made the monitoring quite tricky, all the more that a noticeable attenuation was observed when the tests were performed through the concrete cover.

On another hand, a good agreement was found between the LPR measurements and the state of corrosion of the rebars on the basis of visual observations.

Comparing LPR and AE monitoring, the results were not correlated, but there was a lack of data to be compared, as the second set of AE monitoring dead not lead to exploitable measurements. Nevertheless a global analysis of all the results obtained during the 3 sets of measurements performed on slabs showed that AE monitoring could be able to detect corrosion earlier than classical electrochemical techniques.

Finally, metal weight loss is scheduled to allow more precise conclusions for this study, but further experiments are clearly needed to confirm those promising results (sensor position versus LPR measurement location, static aging room using salts to reduce parasite noises...), but may also be to improve the sensitivity of the AE equipment and for instance explore a new frequency range.

ACKNOWLEDGEMENTS

The investigations and results reported in this paper were supported by the French Ministry of Culture and Communication.

REFERENCES

Andrade C., Alonso C., Gulikers J., Polder R., Cigna R., Vennesland O., et al. Test methods for on-site corrosion rate measurement of steel reinforcement in concrete by means of the polarization resistance method: RILEM TC 154-EMC Recommendations. *Materials and Structures* 37 (2004): 623–643.
Assouli B., Simescu F., Debicki G. & Idrissi H. Detection and identification of concrete cracking during corrosion of reinforced concrete by acoustic emission coupled to the electrochemical techniques. *NDT&E International* 38 (2005): 682–689.
Elsener B., Andrade C., Gulikers J., Polder R. & Raupach M. Half-cell potential measurements— Potential mapping on reinforced concrete structures: RILEM TC 154-EMC Recommendations. *Materials and Structures* 36 (2003): 461–471.

EN1604: 1996 Thermal insulating products for building applications. Determination of dimensional stability under specified temperature and humidity conditions.

Fregonese M., Idrissi H., Mazille H., Renaud L., Cetre Y., Initialtion and propagation steps in pitting corrosion of austenitic stainless steels: monitoring by acoustic emission. *Corrosion Science* 43 (2001): 627–641.

Idrissi H., Limam A. Study and characterization by acoustic emission and electrochemical measurements of concrete deterioration caused by reinforcement steel corrosion. *NDT&E International* 36 (2003): 563–569.

Idrissi H., Ramadan S., Maghnouj J., Boulif R. Modern concept of acoustic emission, coupled with electrochemical measurements for monitoring the elastomer-coated carbon steel damage in phosphoric acid medium. *NDT&E International* 63 (2008): 382–388.

Ing M., Austin S. & Lyons R. Cover zone properties influencing acoustic emission due to corrosion. *Cement and Concrete Research* 35 (2005): 284–295.

Li Z., Li F., Zdunek A., Landis E., Shah S.P. Application of acoustic emission technique to detection of reinforcing steel corrosion in concrete. *ACI materials Journal* 95 (1998): 68–76.

Lyons R., Ing M. & Austin S. Influence of diurnal and seasonal temperature variations on the detection of corrosion in reinforced concrete by acoustic emission. *Corrosion Science* 47 (2005): 413–433.

Martinez I., Andrade C., Rebolledo N., Bouteiller V., Marie-Victoire E., Olivier G. Corrosion characterization of reinforced concrete slabs with different devices. *Corrosion Science* 64 (2008): 107–123.

Ohtsu M. & Tomoda Y. Quantitative NDE of corrosion in reinforced concrete by acoustic emission. In Concrete Solution 2006: *Proceedings of the 2nd international conference, St Malo France, 27–29 June 2006*. Watford: BRE Press.

Polder R., Andrade C., Elsener B., Vennesland O., Gulikers J., Weidert R. et al. Test methods for on site measurement of resistivity of concrete: RILEM TC 154-EMC Recommendations. *Materials and Structures* 33 (2000): 303–611.

Poverbio E. Evaluation of deterioration in reinforced concrete structures by AE technique. In Eurocorr' 2009: *Proceedings of the European corrosion Congress, Nice, France, 6–10 September 2009*. Dechema: Frankfurt.

Proust A., Lenain J.C., Watson R.R., Idrissi H. Détection de corrosion des armatures de béton armé par la technique d'émission acoustique. In THEMA-COR'2007: *Proceedings of the XVth thematic school: Anticorrosion & durabilité dans le bâtiment, le génie Civil et les ouvrages industriels, Hauteville-sur-mer, France, 33th of september-5th of october 2007*. Presses polytechniques et universitaires romandes: Lausanne, cop 2010.

Ramadan S., Gaillet L., Tessier C., Idrissi H. Detection of stress corrosion cracking of high-strength steel used in prestressed concrete structures by acoustic emission technique. *Applied Surface Science* 254 (2008): 2255–2261.

Wheat, H.G. Long-term investigation of alternative reinforcement materials for concrete. In Concrete Solution 2009: *Proceedings of the 3rd international conference, Padova, Italy, 29 June-2 July 2009*. London: Taylor and Francis group.

Yoon D.J., Weiss W.J., & Surendra P. Shah S.P. Assessing damage in corroded reinforced concrete using acoustic emission. *Journal of Engineering Mechanics* (2000): 273–283.

386

Concrete Solutions – Grantham, Mechtcherine & Schneck (eds)
© *2012 Taylor & Francis Group, London, ISBN 978-0-415-61622-5*

Evaluation of mechanical parameters in repair concrete with impact-echo test method

S.R. Moghadam, M.H. Eftekhar, M. Shekarchi, S. Javidmehr & A. Dousti
Construction Materials Institute, University of Tehran Iran

M. Valipour
Construction Materials Institute, Department of Civil Engineering, University of Tehran, Iran

ABSTRACT: In the field of repair of concrete structures, the need often arises to place new concrete next to old existing concrete. Examples of these applications include the repair of structures where the deteriorated concrete must be replaced with new concrete. One of the most important things in repair concrete is similarity between old existing concrete and the new replacement concrete, therefore numerous tests should be done in order to achieve suitable and compatible repair, which are normally time and cost consuming.

Nowadays utilization of Impact-Echo (IE) method for nondestructive testing of concrete structures is common. This method is based on propagation of low-frequency stress waves through concrete which are reflected by internal flaws and external surfaces. Its use has resulted in savings times and money in repair and retrofit on many large structures. The IE test method as a nondestructive method can help to facilitate experimental program, considering this method is less expensive and it is less time consuming comparison to the destructive methods.

In this paper, several mixture designs have been used for recommended repair concrete. Mechanical parameters (compressive strength and modulus of elasticity) have been assessed by conventional methods. The main object of this study is attaining to empirical correlation to use the results of IE method for evaluation of compressive strength and modulus of elasticity. Consequently, the results illustrated that the correlation have been proven to be useful to these two mechanical parameters.

1 INTRODUCTION

Use of Non-destructive test methods for concrete structures is becoming inevitable nowadays. One of the special cases in which implementation of these test methods can supply the engineers with valuable data is repair and rehabilitation of structures. Non-destructive test methods can be used prior to a repair project to evaluate the immensity of the repair and the condition of the structure. One of these test methods which is based on propagation of stress waves in concrete is the Impact-Echo method.

Investigators established the impact-echo method wherein the transient time domain waveforms obtained from the impact of a steel sphere on a concrete slab containing artificial flaws are recorded and analyzed in a frequency domain. Frequency analysis of recorded surface displacement waveforms was used to determine the location of honeycombing, the depth of surface-opening cracks and ungrouted ducts (Carino et al., 1986). All the current findings in impact-echo have been summarized in a book called "Impact-Echo

Nondestructive Testing of Concrete and Masonry" which is a summary of the results of analytical, laboratory and field studies dealing with different applications of Impact-Echo method (Sansalone & Streeet 1997). Some investigators presented a new inspection of Impact-echo that it is the first non-destructive technology to be part of a regulating standard for quality control in civil engineering in Germany (Grosse et al., 2006).

An example of the use of IE method as a test preceding repair works is the repair project of a shell roof in Seattle Kingdom, in which the impact-echo Test Method was used along with infrared thermography, mechanical sounding, coring and visual investigations to identify near-surface voiding and through-thickness honeycombs (Aggelis & Shiotani 2006). IE can be implemented as a seismic method to evaluate crack depth in concrete dams (Hassani et al., 1997). One of the other applications of the IE test is to assess bonding condition between the facing stones, mortar, and inner rubble core in stone masonry structures as discussed in a repair project in Canada (Sadri 2003).

There is often a need to evaluate the in-situ parameters of repair concrete as in repair works, compatibility and in some cases, similarity of the substrate concrete and the suggested repair should get into account. In other words, not only the durability of repair material but also the compatibility of the repair with the base concrete is the key to a durable repair design (Morgan 1995). When used as an alternative to conventional test methods to evaluate some characteristics of repair concrete, these test methods can decrease the evaluation costs in a large extent. They can be even implanted in a project site to assure that the repair devises the as-built characteristics of each mixture (Carino 2001). To guarantee the correlation between the data gained by non-destructive test methods and the results of conventional concrete test methods, there is a rising need to analyze the data achieved by these test methods to prove them as reliable ones or suggest a correlation between the conventional and NDT methods results. There have been some efforts in analysis of IE method results. Aggelis et al. have used P-wave velocity as a means to investigate the repair characterists in large concrete blocks (Aggelis et al., 2010). Cheng et al. have suggested a formula to predict the thickness-amplitude in the Impact Echo testing for given thickness, impact–receiver distance, and P-wave speed by numerical simulation, potentially able for quantitative evaluation of the bond between concrete and the substrate layer (Cheng et al., 2007). Colla et al. have also assessed the influence of source frequency on Impact Echo data quality for testing concrete structures. Results showed the expected frequencies of interest should possibly be located closer to the wave center frequency than adjacent to the maximum frequency (it being understood that the maximum input frequency should be higher than the frequencies to be measured). It would so be ensured that sufficiently large amplitude frequency components are excited in the frequency range of interest and the successful identification of the relevant frequency peaks would be facilitated. This would positively affect the quality of the data and ease data interpretation in the case of complex structures (Colla et al., 2003).

In this paper, several mix designs have been used for the recommended repair concrete. Mechanical parameters (compressive strength and modulus of elasticity) have been assessed by conventional methods. The main objective of this study is to attain an empirical correlation to use the results of IE method for evaluation of compressive strength and modulus of elasticity. Consequently, the results illustrated that the correlation have been proven to be useful to these two mechanical parameters.

2 PRINCIPLES OF IMPACT-ECHO METHOD

Impact-echo is based on the use of transient stress waves generated by a short-duration, elastic impact of a small steel sphere on a concrete surface. In this regard, the impact generates low-frequency stress waves. These waves propagate into the structure and are reflected by flaws. Surface displacements caused by the reflection of these waves are recorded by a displacement transducer located adjacent to the impact. The resulting displacements versus time signals are transformed into the frequency domain and plots of amplitude versus frequency are obtained. Multiple reflections of stress waves between the impact surface and flaws result in producing the patterns of wave reflection and transient resonances, which can be identified in the spectrum and used to evaluate the integrity of the structure or determination of the location of flaws (Sansalone & Streeet 1997).

In this study, a software program namely PIES was used for calculation of stress wave velocity (P-wave velocity). This software controls and monitors the testing and displays the results in numerical and graphical forms.

In classical rigid-body dynamics, if a transient force is suddenly applied to an elastic body in the form of transient stress, the corresponding displacements are propagated outwards as elastic waves. The three main types of elastic waves are P-waves (compressive waves), S-waves (Shear Waves), and R-waves (Rayleigh waves). The velocity of P-waves may be determined by (Sharma 1986).

$$C_P = \sqrt{\frac{E(1-\upsilon)}{\rho(1+\upsilon)(1-2\upsilon)}} \qquad (1)$$

where E denotes Young's modulus, υ represents Poisson's ratio and ρ is density of the material.

The test system i.e., PIES used in the study is composed of three components including impactors, a receiving transducer and a portable computer. In this research the steel balls have a diameter of 12.7 mm. These steel balls produce frequencies up to 97 kHz corresponding to 41 mm wavelength (assuming a wave speed of 4000 m/s). Moreover, an approximate relationship has been reported between the diameter of the sphere and a so-called maximum frequency in the PIES manual. It has been demonstrated that these values help to choose the appropriate sphere size according to the particular measurement aims. Therefore, the waves with this frequency can be diffracted by distributed micro cracks.

In the test, the impactor is applied at 6 points of the side surface of the specimens. The values (stress wave velocity) of these points were the same. The distance between the impactor and receiving transducer is the length of specimens i.e., 150 mm. For the range of applied impact duration, the frequencies in the stress pulse generated by impact are sufficiently low, scattering at interfaces between aggregate particles and cement binder in concrete. In general, the solid concrete responds homogenously to the propagating waves. Moreover, the Sample Rate and the Number of Samples are respectively 500 kHz and 1024.

3 MATERIALS AND CONVENTIONAL TESTS

In this study 4 mixture designs have been selected randomly from several mixture designs that have been recommended for repaired concrete. One cube (150 × 150 × 150 mm) for each of the 4 mixtures has been used to calculate the compressive strength and stress wave velocity based on the IE method. One cylinder (150 × 300 mm) for each of the 4 mixtures has been used to calculate the modulus of elasticity. The specimens were stored at 23°C in the laboratory and the condition of curing was based on ASTM C 192.

Slag cement was used in all mixtures (with 30% of granulated blast furnace slag). Two mix designs were with cement content of 400 kg/m³ while the two other mix designs contained 380 kg/m³ of cement. The used aggregate was well-rounded limestone with a maximum size of 19 mm and its grading was within the ASTM C 33 limits. A polycarboxylic-based superplasticizer with solid content of 36% and specific gravity of 1.07 was employed in all the mixtures. Some of the mixtures had 5% of silica fume. Some mixtures had 0.85 kg/m³ of polypropylene fibers. The mixtures had water/cement ratios of 0.4 and 0.45. One of the mixtures contained 0.06% of an air-entraining agent. The mixture proportions are listed in detail in Table 1.

Compressive strength has been calculated at 28 ages and modulus of elasticity has been calculated based on ASTM C 469. In this test the speed of loading was 240 kPa/s. based on ASTM C 469 and loading continued until the stress level on the specimen became 40% of the compressive strength.

4 RESULTS AND DISCUSSIONS

Figure 1 shows compressive strength vs. stress wave velocity. In this figure, compressive strength has been gained by conventional methods. It can be deduced that correlation between these two parameters is suitable. Though the values of compressive strength for 4 mixture designs that have been chosen randomly between several mixture designs that are recommended for rehabilitation of damaged structure are nearly the same, their values of stress wave velocity are different and can be distinguished. Therefore the use of the IE method can be useful to estimate the compressive strength. The correlation factor between these two parameters is 0.93, which means that the estimation of compressive strength obtained by a relationship between stress wave velocity and compressive strength can be reliable.

This study suggests that some randomly selected specimens from several mix designs can provide the investigators with a relationship by which the compressive strength can be represented. Like the method used in the current study, compressive strength of these selected specimens should be obtained by conventional test method and then the stress wave velocity in these mixtures should be calculated by the IE method. Compressive strength values can be estimated by drawing the best line between these data, as depicted in Figure 1. By a rise in number of mixtures that have been selected for measurement of compressive strength by conventional methods, the accuracy of this estimation increases and the estimation will be more reliable. It can be used as a strategy to save a considerable amount of budget.

Table 1. Mixture designs of specimens.

No	W/C	SF (%)	Cement (kg/m³)	Fibers (kg/m³)	AEA (%)
1	0.4	–	400	0.85	–
2	0.45	–	400	0.85	–
3	0.4	5	380	0.85	–
4	0.4	5	380	–	0.06

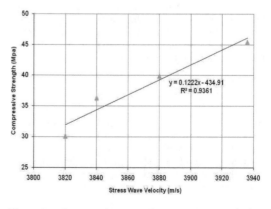

Figure 1. Compressive strength vs. stress wave velocity.

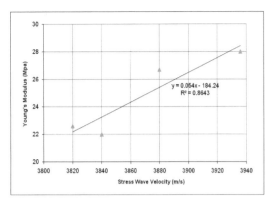

Figure 2.   Modulus of elasticity vs. stress wave velocity.

Figure 2 shows modulus of elasticity vs. stress wave velocity. In this figure modulus of elasticity has been obtained by a conventional test method. It can be deduced that correlation between these two parameters is less than the correlation observed in evaluation of compressive strength, which means that the use of IE method for calculating the modulus of elasticity is less suitable in comparison with the use of IE method for attaining the compressive strength. Although the correlation factor between the modulus of elasticity and the stress wave velocity is less than the previous parameters, the value of correlation is not low ($R^2 = 0.86$). Therefore estimation of the modulus of elasticity by IE method is recommended when the approximate value of modulus of elasticity is needed.

This study suggests that companies make the concrete or rehabilitated concrete can use the recommended strategy for estimation of compressive strength and modulus of elasticity. These companies can obtain stress wave velocity by the IE method and compressive strength and modulus of elasticity by conventional methods in some mixture designs then, they can calculate the parameters of other specimens by using the strategy that has been introduced in this study. The companies can update the formula that is achieved by drawing the best line monthly or fortnightly or weekly, therefore the accuracy will rise.

5   CONCLUSIONS

It was shown that the sensitivity of stress wave velocity to compressive strength is more than the sensitivity of stress wave velocity to modulus of elasticity. Therefore estimation of the compressive strength by IE method is more reliable than the estimation of the modulus of elasticity by this method.

The investigators can estimate the most important parameters (Compressive strength and modulus of elasticity) of repair concrete by calculating these parameters by means of conventional tests (in some of mix design specimens) and attaining the stress wave velocity by IE method.

REFERENCES

Aggelis, D.G., Hadjiyiangou, S., Chai, H.K., Momoki, S. & Shiotani, T. 2010. Longitudinal waves for evaluation of large concrete blocks after repair, *Elsevier Science Publisher, NDT&E International*.

Aggelis, D.G. & Shiotani, T. 2006. Repair evaluation of concrete cracks using surface and through-transmission wave measurement, *Elsevier Science Publisher, Cement and Concrete Composites 29 (2007) 700–711*.

Carino, N.J. 2001. The Impact Echo method, an overview, *US National Institute of Standards and Technology*.

Carino, J.N., Sansalone, M. & Hsu, N.N. Flaw detection in concrete by frequency spectrum analysis of impact-echo waveforms, *vol. 12, Int. adv. Nondestr. Test, Gordon & Breach Science, 1986, pp. 117–146*.

Cheng, Chia-Ch, Lin, Yiching, Hsiao, Chia-Men, Chang, Hsiang-Chieh, 2003. Evaluation of simulated transfer functions of concrete plate derived by impact-echo method, *Elsevier Science Publisher, NDT&E International 40 (2007) 239–249*.

Colla, C. & Lausch, R. 2003. Influence of source frequency on impact-echo data quality for testing concrete structures, *Elsevier Science Publisher, NDT&E International 36 (2003) 203–213*.

Grosse, C.U., Beutel, R., Reinhard, H.W. & Kruger, M. 2006. Impact-Echo techniques for non-destructive inspection of concrete structures, *Congress in Concrete Repair, rehabilitation and retrofitting, 461–465, Alexander*.

Hassani, F.P., Guevermont, P., Momayez, M., Sadri, A. & Saleh, K. 1997. *Application of Non- destructive Evaluation Techniques on Concrete Dams, Elsevier Science Publisher, Int. J. Rock Mech. & Min. Sci. 34:3–4, paper No. 125*.

Morgn, D.R. 1996. Compatibility of concrete repair materials systems, *Elsevier Science Publisher, Construction and Building Materials, Vol. 10, No. 1, pp. 57–67*.

Sadri, Afshin, 1995. Application of impact-echo technique in diagnoses and repair of stone masonry structures, *Elsevier Sience publisher, NDT&E International 36 (2003) 195–202*.

Sansalone, M. & Streett, W.B. Impact-echo: Nondestructive testing of concrete and masonry, *Bullbrier Press, Jersy shore, PA (1997)*.

Sharma P.V. Geophysical method in geology, *Elsevier Science Publisher, (1986) p. 442*.

Concrete Solutions – Grantham, Mechtcherine & Schneck (eds)
© 2012 Taylor & Francis Group, London, ISBN 978-0-415-61622-5

Wireless localization of areas with a high corrosion risk on reinforced concrete structures

K. Reichling & M. Raupach

Institute of Building Materials Research, Aachen University, Germany

ABSTRACT: Different non destructive diagnostic tools are available to assess the condition of a reinforced concrete structure. Potential mapping is an approved method to locate areas with a high risk of chloride induced corrosion. Hereby the reinforcement serves as working electrode in order to measure the potentials vs. an external reference electrode connected electrolytically to the concrete surface. For special cases where this procedure is not applicable a novel approach has been developed at the Institute of Building Materials Research of Aachen University, ibac, to locate critical areas by using a set of external electrodes. The results are converted and displayed as a vector, comparable with a compass, so that the critical areas can be located directly during the measurement.

1 INTRODUCTION

The diagnosis of the condition of a structure is a fundamental part of the maintenance of buildings. In aggressive environments reinforced concrete structures may suffer from reinforcement corrosion. Chloride induced corrosion is typically observed at structures in maritime environments or for transport facilities (e.g., bridges, car parks). Depending on the exposition, this type of corrosion occurs typically in local spots. The localisation of these critical areas allows a targeted and economic repair of the structure.

In most cases potential mapping is a suitable method to find the critical spots. With this well known procedure, a reinforcement connection and a continuous electrical connection of the rebars is required to gain assessable results. In some cases one or both of these requirements are not given. For example:

- if the structure consists of segments without reinforcement continuity (e.g., precast and/or prestressed ceiling segments) or
- if the local destruction of the concrete cover is not allowed (e.g., nuclear power plants, after local repairs or when measurements are done frequently).

In order to localize critical areas for these special cases, a non-destructive measuring method is developed and presented in this paper.

2 MEASURING POTENTIAL GRADIENTS WITHOUT REINFORCEMENT CONNECTION

Between the depassivated and passive areas of the reinforcement, a potential field is formed in the surrounding electrolyte of the concrete. The potentials reaching the concrete surface may be measured vs. a reference electrode (see Fig. 1). For this purpose the reinforcement serves as working electrode and an external electrode as reference. Both must be connected electrically to a high resistance voltmeter and electrolytically by the concrete.

Alternatively to this conventional setup, a second external electrode can also be used as working electrode (Isecke 1990, Marquardt & Cziesielski 1987, Menzel & Preusker 1989).

The applicability of this method was investigated in the following laboratory test. A reinforced

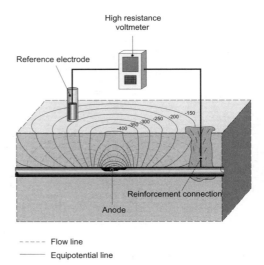

High resistance voltmeter

Reference electrode

-150
-200
-250
-300
-350
-400

Reinforcement connection

Anode

- - - - - Flow line

———— Equipotential line

Figure 1. Setup for conventional potential mapping.

concrete beam (10 × 15 × 70 cm) was cast with two electrically disconnected reinforcement bars. The concrete consisted of an OPC (CEM I) with a w/c = 0.45 and a chloride content of 2.5 wt.-%/ cement to ensure depassivation of the steel. The concrete cover depth was 3.5 cm. After curing for a period of approximately two months potential measurements were carried out with different electrode combinations. In any of the 3 test setups one external RE (Cu/CuSO₄) was moved in steps of 5 cm at the top of the beam. Three different electrode combinations were investigated as described below (see Fig. 2):

1. Within the first test setup the potentials were measured by using the left reinforcement bar as working electrode and an external Cu/CuSO₄ electrode as reference electrode. As mentioned above the reference electrode was moved stepwise over the top of the beam from the left to the right end.
2. Then the test was repeated, but the right reinforcement bar served as working electrode.
3. Within the third test setup a second external reference electrode served as working electrode and stayed in the first measurement point (x = 2.5 cm) while the other reference electrode was moved.

Temporal potential changes were minimized by pre-wetting the concrete surface 30 min. before the measurement was carried out.

In order to compare the results, the potential differences E(x) of the tests 1 and 2 were calculated by subtracting the potential value at x = 2.5 cm (Ex = 2.5 cm) from the other values ($E_{x, measured}$) of the corresponding test (see Equation 1).

$$E(x) = E_{x, measured} - E_{x=2.5\,cm} \tag{1}$$

The results are shown in Figure 3. Two conclusions can be drawn:

a. The values measured with the left reinforcement bar serving as working electrode are similar compared to the values measured with the right reinforcement bar.
b. The potential differences measured with a second external electrode serving as working electrode correspond to the values measured with a reinforcement connection.

This leads to the conclusion that the potential differences can be measured by using only external

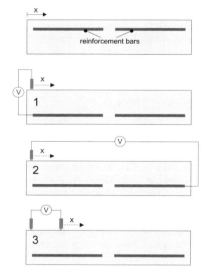

Figure 2. Schematic illustration of the different test setups.

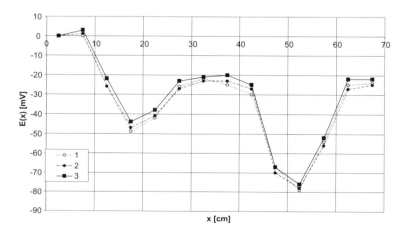

Figure 3. Results of the test series shown in Figure 2.

electrodes. Even if single reinforcement bars are electrically (not electrolytically) disconnected, the potential differences can be measured, assuming that the electrolytic resistance between the electrodes does not affect the readings significantly.

3 WIRELESS LOCALISATION OF CRITICAL AREAS

As mentioned above the potential difference between two points may be measured at the concrete surface by 2 external electrodes. In this case the potential gradient can be determined by dividing the potential difference by the distance of the electrode positions. The result can be displayed as a vector which shows from one electrode to the other (see Fig. 4). However, the direction of the vector depends on the position of the electrodes. By using a third electrode it is possible to determine a vector direction which correlates with the according potential distribution.

Therefore the measurement setup (so-called Delta-Sensor) consists of three electrodes positioned in the shape of an equal-sided triangle. In each of the 3 corners a copper/copper sulphate electrode is situated. By means of a high resistance voltmeter the readings are taken by measuring two potential differences between the three electrodes.

In a second step a vector space in a three dimensional Cartesian coordinate system is described mathematically (see Fig. 5). Hereby the x and y axes are parallel to the concrete surface. The potential values are plotted in z direction. The potential value in one of the three points is specified to zero. The mathematical connection of the three points results in a vector space with an inclination corresponding to the potential gradient at the investigation area.

The direction and the degree (gradient) of the inclination are essential to localise critical areas. To gather the gradient from the reading, the unit vector normal to the vector space is determined. In a next step the projection of the unit vector parallel

to the concrete surface (x-y space) is determined. As result a vector length and a vector angle are calculated for each reading (see Fig. 6). The direction of this projected vector always points to the lowest potential values. The length of the vector correlates with the potential gradient. The higher the potential gradient is, the steeper the vector space is and the longer the projected vector gets.

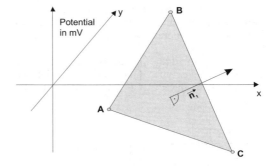

Figure 5. Illustration of the vector space in the three dimensional Cartesian coordinate system.

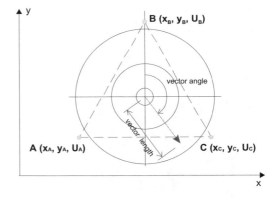

Figure 6. Illustration of the projection of the unit vector.

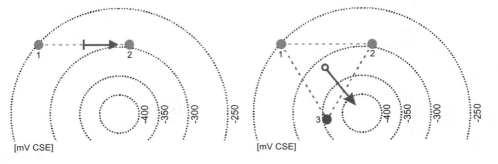

Figure 4. Determination of the potential gradient for 2 and 3 external electrodes.

4 APPLICATION OF THE NOVEL METHOD

In order to verify the novel method, test measurements were carried out on two slab specimens.

The configuration of both slabs are shown in Figures 7 and 8. The main differences between both specimens were the shape and the dimensions of the active areas. Slab A shows a centric anode and slab B a linear anode which are electrically connected with all cathodes of each slab. Chlorides were only added in the concrete in the active areas (anodes). The concretes were produced with a w/c of 0.5.

As shown in Figure 8, slab B consisted of two different cement types. One half of the slab was produced with an OPC (CEM I) and the other half with a BFS (CEM III) so that different resistivities and potential gradients could be estimated.

The concrete surface of slab A was pre-wetted 30 minutes before the first reading was taken. First of all a conventional potential mapping with one external electrode and the reference electrode serving as working electrode was carried out. After that, 3-electrode readings were taken with an electrode distance of 10 cm and 20 cm for slab A and 20 cm for slab B.

In Figure 9 the results are shown for slab A. The triangle in the right bottom area of the specimen displays the distance between the electrodes.

Based on the theoretical assumptions mentioned above the directions of the vectors must be perpendicular to the equipotential lines, which is given in most cases.

Increasing potential gradients must result in decreasing distances between the equipotential lines. For a 3 electrode setup the vector lengths must increase with increasing gradients, which could also be shown in both readings in Figure 9. The values of the gradients correlating with the vector lengths are indicated on the right bottom side in Figure 9.

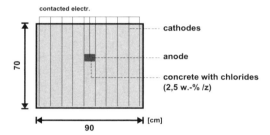

Figure 7. Configuration of slab A.

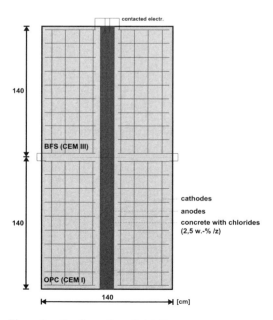

Figure 8. Configuration of slab B.

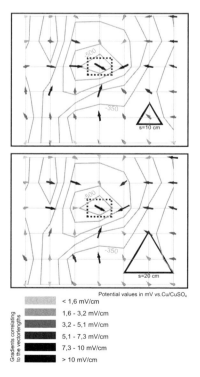

Figure 9. Potential map and vectors for an electrode distance of 10 cm (top) and 20 cm (bottom) measured on slab A.

Comparing the readings with different electrode distances leads to the conclusion that the results are very similar. But the readings seem to be sensitive to a discontinuous, unsymmetrical shape of the potential distribution. In this case adequate electrode sizes must be chosen to reduce this effect.

Slab B was measured twice by using a 3 electrode setup and an electrode distance of 20 cm. The first measurement was carried out before and the second one after wetting. The results of the measurements on slab B are shown in Figures 10 and 11.

It can be seen that in the area of the cathodes, the potential gradients are less steep in the OPC concrete than in the concrete made with BFS.

This may be explained by the higher resistivity of a BFS cement. Nevertheless in the area of active steel bars, the gradients seem to be equal because the concrete in this area is the same.

Due to wetting, the potential gradients decrease. This effect is due to the higher porosity: more distinctive in the concrete area made with OPC cement. Again the direction and length of the vectors based on the 3 electrode measurement correlate well with the potential map. In the case of pre-wetting, the area of relatively steep gradients is wider which can also be seen in the vector plot.

It can be concluded that the different potential gradients of the dry and the pre-wetted concrete could be determined satisfactorily.

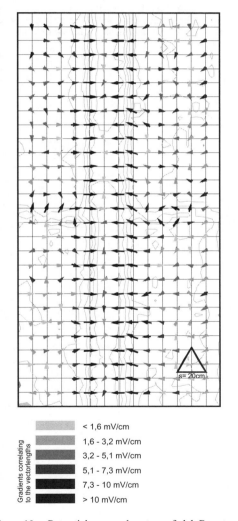

Gradients correlating to the vectorlengths

	< 1,6 mV/cm
	1,6 - 3,2 mV/cm
	3,2 - 5,1 mV/cm
	5,1 - 7,3 mV/cm
	7,3 - 10 mV/cm
	> 10 mV/cm

Figure 10.   Potential map and vectors of slab B, not pre-wetted.

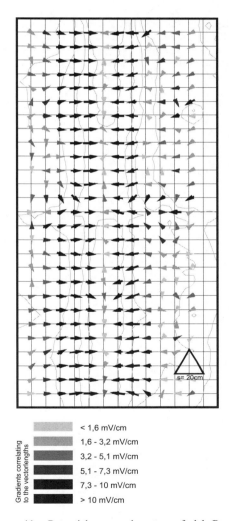

Gradients correlating to the vectorlengths

	< 1,6 mV/cm
	1,6 - 3,2 mV/cm
	3,2 - 5,1 mV/cm
	5,1 - 7,3 mV/cm
	7,3 - 10 mV/cm
	> 10 mV/cm

Figure 11.   Potential map and vectors of slab B, pre-wetted.

5 CONCLUSION

From the results described above the following conclusions can be drawn:

1. Potential differences can be measured at the concrete surface by using at least 2 external electrodes without a reinforcement connection.
2. The continuity of the reinforcement is not obligatory as long as the resistivity between the electrodes (e.g., the steel rebars and the reference electrodes or two external electrodes) does not affect the readings significantly. However, continuity will be important for a successful repair by cathodic protection.
3. By adding a third external electrode the direction of a vector showing to the area with the most negative potential values corresponding to the potential gradient, can be determined.
4. The measurements on several slab specimens verified the applicability of the method regarding the direction of the resulting vectors and the potential gradients.
5. Due to the fact that pre-wetting results in a widening of the potential funnels, the localisation of critical areas could be improved.

REFERENCES

Isecke, B. 1990. Potentialmessung zur Ermittlung von Bewehrungskorrosion. Darmstadt: Freunde des Instituts für Massivbau e.V.,—In: Darmstädter Massivbau-Seminar 4,

Marquardt, H. & Cziesielski, E. 1987. Anwendung der elektrochemischen Potentialdifferenzmessung zum zerstörungsfreien Auffinden korrodierender Bewehrung im Hochbau. Berlin: Institut für Baukonstruktionen und Festigkeit Fachgebiet allgemeiner Ingenieur-bau der Technischen Universität Berlin.

Menzel, K. & Preusker, H. 1989. Potentialmessung: Eine Methode zur zerstörungsfreien Feststellung von Korrosion an der Bewehrung. In: Bauingenieur 64, Nr. 4, S. 181–186.

Concrete Solutions – Grantham, Mechtcherine & Schneck (eds)
© 2012 Taylor & Francis Group, London, ISBN 978-0-415-61622-5

Automated multi-sensor systems in civil engineering for condition assessment of concrete structures

M. Stoppel, A. Taffe & H. Wiggenhauser
Federal Institute for Materials Research and Testing (BAM), Berlin, Germany

J.H. Kurz & C. Boller
Fraunhofer Institute for Nondestructive Testing (IZFP), Saarbrücken, Germany

ABSTRACT: Infrastructure is subject to continuous ageing. This has given life cycle management of infrastructure an important role. Therefore an increasing demand for reliable inspection and monitoring tools is noticeable. A combination of different non-destructive test methods is often necessary to receive reliable results for material characterization, flaw detection and the determination of component specific geometry parameters. Regarding concrete structures, thickness measurements are combined with flaw detection and additional information about reinforcement and tendon ducts is required. Therefore, a multi-sensor measurement approach is necessary with a high degree of automation. Otherwise a time consuming succession of manual measurements has to be performed which would prevent practical applications. A modular control and data acquisition approach is described and the application of two different automated measurement devices is shown. The BetoScan system consists of a self-navigating mobile robot. The system is especially designed for the investigation of reinforced concrete slabs or bridge decks exposed to de-icing salts. The data acquisition of the OSSCAR system, a multi-sensor scanner, is similar to the robot approach. These different applications are based on a similar kernel allowing the modular use of different contact and non-contact sensors. The described general concept of multi-sensor data acquisition and data analysis presented here is not limited to the field of civil engineering applications.

1 INTRODUCTION

Infrastructure is subject to continuous ageing. This has given life cycle management of infrastructure an important role. Therefore an increasing demand for reliable inspection and monitoring tools is noticeable. The prediction of the service life of a new structure at the design stage or the diagnosis and the evaluation of the residual service life of existing structures is a key aspect of concrete structure management. Life-cycle analysis and risk evaluation methods can be beneficially used to assess existing structures: actions on structures, inspection-oriented design and construction, characteristics of components and structures, life-cycle costs, risk analysis and the environmental performance of a structure over its lifespan are important factors which have to be considered when the remaining service life of an infrastructure building is in question. If the possibility of efficient inspections during construction, operation and maintenance has already been considered during the design phase, one pre-requisite for reliable assessment is given (Haardt, 2010).

Assessment of the safety of engineering works must be conducted by examining all aspects of their behaviour and all possibilities for failure which can be manifested. Analyzing potential critical situations of structures in Europe is performed by identifying so-called limit states (Diamantidis, 2001). A limit state is defined as a condition beyond which a structure is no longer able to satisfy the provisions for which it was designed. However, one has to distinguish between ultimate and serviceability limit states. Primarily, the reactive maintenance approach has been implemented in Europe to manage the road infrastructure network with respect to deterioration. This approach may be valid for well-managed structures without defects and exposed to unchanging loads. This approach is unsatisfactory for structures containing structural deficits and subjected to increasing loads, modifications or widening measures for which they are not designed. Therefore, a paradigm change from reactive to proactive infrastructure management is required and non-destructive inspection methods play a key role here.

A reliable prognosis of the condition and behavior of a structure is an important basis for effective service life management. In order to determine the most economical point in time for repair measures in the life-time of a structure, a knowledge about the deterioration process at exposed regions as well as a detailed knowledge about the current condition of the whole structure is essential (NRC, 2009). Different concepts were developed depending on the type of infrastructure and the construction material. However, in general, information about cracks and flaws and corrosion, as well as the states of material degradation have to be retrieved. A combination of different non-destructive test methods is often necessary to receive reliable results for material characterization, flaw detection and the determination of component specific geometry parameters.

In general, critical damage cannot be eliminated especially when the boundary conditions of the original design criteria change or when the lifetime is increased.

Two automated multi-sensor systems for different applications of non-destructive testing in civil engineering were developed. They are based on the same data acquisition kernel and a flexible data analysis concept and are described in the following (Kurz et al., 2009; Dobmann et al., 2010). Both approaches are designed for delivering input data for proactive condition assessment of civil infrastructure.

2 AUTOMATED MULTI-SENSOR NON-DESTRUCTIVE TESTING IN CIVIL ENGINEERING

2.1 Data-acquisition, -control and -evaluation of automated multi-sensor systems

Pro-active condition assessment is still a future task for infrastructure management; however, automated non-destructive testing methods are a major contribution to this concept. Data acquisition with multi-sensor systems has become an important approach for different research and application areas, where mainly non-invasive and non-destructive investigations are required. A simple and well known example in the field of medical sciences is that in medical diagnoses visual inspection is often combined with radiographic (x-rays) and ultrasonic investigations. However, this is a manual approach related to the expert system 'medical doctor' and performed stepwise. In case of technical applications, an automated multi-sensor approach is used where several sensors perform the measurements simultaneously. Figure 1 shows the principle parts of a multi-sensor approach which can be subdivided into three components: the combined sensors, the data acquisition, including reliable data-control and data analysis, and the data-evaluation.

The scheme of tasks where multi-sensor approaches are required is always similar. Generally

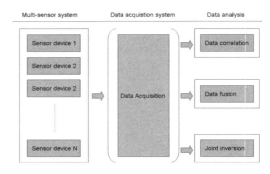

Figure 1. Principle of multi-sensor data acquisition and analysis.

multiple-parameter dependent or even ambiguous problems have to be solved which is usually not possible by using only one measurement method delivering one parameter. Therefore, different methods have to be applied and the combination of the results leads to a unique assessment. A technically combined approach reduces the inspection risk since the reliability of the inspection task increases and therefore the costs are reduced.

The data analysis of multi-sensor measurement systems offers several possibilities depending on the type and quality of collected data. The most simple but often very effective approach is a direct comparison of these results. An expert system e.g., in the form of an inspector's brain is required to correlate the different analysis results and performs the assessment. The next 'higher level' of data analysis is data fusion. Data fusion is generally defined as the use of techniques that combine data from multiple sources and gather that information in order to draw conclusions, which will be more efficient and potentially more accurate as if received just from a single source (Gros, 2001). Joint inversion or multi-objective optimization means the simultaneous minimization (or maximization) of several objective (target) functions, for instance by use of generic or evolutionary algorithms. Further details about these concepts can be found in (Kurz et al., 2009).

Without going into details, the use of a multi-sensor approach requires a high flexibility of the data acquisition system. It has to be guaranteed that any combination of the implemented sensors can be chosen. Furthermore, it should be possible that supplementary sensors can easily be implemented in the modular data acquisition system. In most cases this depends on an open protocol of the digital interface used (RS232, USB, Ethernet, etc.) provided by the manufacturer of the measurement device. Because today no national or international standards exist to define the documentation format for data exchange in automated NDT, especially this task is not easy to solve. This requires opening of the interfaces of the individual hardware of different industrial manufacturers which *a priori* do not support the same procedure. Under the consideration of the described concepts and these technical boundary conditions two automated multi-sensor systems for different applications of non-destructive testing in civil engineering were developed. They are based on the same data acquisition kernel and a flexible data analysis concept and are described in the following. Both approaches are designed for delivering input data for proactive condition assessment of civil infrastructure.

2.2 *BetoScan—An automobile multi-sensor robot system for non-destructive diagnoses of reinforced concrete structures*

A large number of parking structures and bridge decks are suffering from severe corrosion problems world-wide. This is mainly due to the ingress of de-icing salts, but also in connection with marine environments, and combined with insufficient concrete quality the steel reinforcement starts to corrode causing cracking, spalling and losses in cross section, finally leading to a reduced loading capacity of the whole structure. This situation has been the basis for a project: to develop a robotic system called BetoScan which is able to drive over large floors and measure the relevant parameters of the concrete surface simultaneously. The collected data is stored for each investigated point of the structure allowing complex evaluations of the data regarding the assessment of the condition, prognosis of the future state, design of measures for protection and repair as well as quality control.

The BetoScan-system consists of a mobile robot platform, which is able to navigate quasi-autonomously over horizontal areas. It is equipped with different sensors for non-destructive measurements (see Figure 2). At first an orientation cruise is required where the robot is able to detect walls, piles and other barriers with its horizontal 270° laser scanner. Based on these detections the user has to generate a digital map of the location. Within this map an inspection area has to be defined and an optimized inspection roadmap where the robot will scan the area in form of a meander will be generated automatically. The ultrasonic sensors on the front side allow the robot to detect even movable obstacles to avoid collisions.

The sensors are able to collect the data at a driving speed up to 0.1 m/s, although the robot could speed up to 1 m/s. So the system is able to investigate surfaces of some hundred square meters with one set of batteries. The accumulator pack at the top of the platform (Figure 2, black boxes) provides enough energy for a minimum of 8 hours.

Figure 2. The BetoScan robotic system with ndt sensors.

Figure 3. NDT methods of the BetoScan-system.

All measured raw data is stored in an XML format along with the individual local positioning information of the platform (Kurz et al., 2009). A computer in the platform stores all relevant data, which are then downloaded via WLAN to a notebook of the operator and are organized in a database. The analysis software can be used to handle the data in the database in order to generate the maps on site.

To investigate reinforced concrete structures, different commercially available sensors have been chosen to be integrated in the robotic system (see Figure 3). The integrated measuring instruments can still be used as standard handhelds, so that the manual collection of additional data is possible.

Especially for concrete structures exposed to de-icing salts, the first step of a condition survey should in many cases be a potential mapping of the whole concrete surface. Within the project, Proceq's instrument "Canin +" is used in combination with a copper/copper sulfate reference wheel electrode. In order to generate concrete cover depth maps of the whole surface, Proceq's "Profometer 5+" based on the eddy current method and Mala's GPR ProEX system based on the radar method are attached to the system. The knowledge of the concrete cover depths can be very helpful for the assessment of the condition of structures in order to design an adequate repair measure or to control the application quality after replacement of the concrete cover by a repair mortar.

With the ultrasonic system "A1220 Monolith" from Acsys the structure thickness can be determined in a point grid over the whole surface. One advantage of this specific instrument is the possibility to connect the ultrasonic sensor heads on concrete without any coupling gel, which simplifies the automation of the measurement. As mentioned above, the ultrasonic sensor needs a direct connection to the concrete surface. Therefore the robot platform has to stop moving while doing the measurement. A pneumatic system in the frame of the attachment module presses the sensor onto the floor while the whole measuring procedure is carried out. To investigate the relative moisture distribution of the areas near to the concrete surface, the microwave sensors "Moist PP" and "Moist RP" from HF-Sensor are used. These sensors do not need a direct connection to the concrete surface.

2.3 OSSCAR multi-sensor manipulator for bridge inspection

Based on a similar data acquisition kernel to the one of the BetoScan system, a multi-sensor manipulator called OSSCAR was developed mainly for bridge inspections. The aim here too is to improve the data density and the data quality through sensor combinations. The sensors used here are: Profometer (eddy current testing for concrete cover and rebar position), Acsys A1220 (ultrasound for geometrical information about the components especially about tendon ducts and flaws therein) and Mala ProEx (radar) for geometrical information of the component and evaluation of the reinforcement position. Two different sensor carriers can be used. One combining eddy current testing and radar and two ultrasound probes with a pneumatic contact control are mounted one on the other, but can only be used separately.

The frame provides a testing area of 50×100 cm² with focus on a quick installation and easy change of the measuring position (Figure 4). Testing tasks to be carried out with the scanner are:

Figure 4. Photo of the scanner together all devices that can be used for automation (Radar: Mala Pro-Ex, Eddy current: Proceq Profometer 5+, Ultrasound: ACSYS A1220).

- Imaging of the geometry
- Location, depth, diameter of multi-layer reinforcement
- Location and depth of multi-layer tendon ducts
- Quality assurance for complete grouting of tendon ducts
- Location of grouting defects in existing constructions.

Due to the small dimensions it fits in narrow corners and can be used even for columns. It is easy to transport and even small manholes can be used for access (less than 1×1 m²) to a bridge because the frame with its three beams is mounted directly on the structure to be measured. For non-destructive testing special vacuum feet have been developed.

The OSSCAR approach is the combination of Radar, ultrasonic-echo and eddy-current using commercially available devices. Radar is the method for the detection of metallic reflectors but it shows limited penetration depth especially in young concrete or if the concrete is structured close mehed with reinforcement. In this case ultrasonic methods reach greater depths for thickness measurement but show limited resolution of single rebars. Eddy current allows detailed information of the upper reinforcement layer such as the precise concrete cover or the bar diameter. An engineering office that owns this equipment has the flexibility to use each device as a single hand-held device or as a scanner driven automated method with the option of method combination.

3 MEASUREMENTS

Though both presented systems are designed under the same basic platform they have their own focus regarding the resolution of measurement data per area.

3.1 Large areas and major grids (BetoScan)

The BetoScan system is able to scan hundreds of square meters per day in tracks in form of a meander. The actual output is dependent on the selected grid and on the maximum allowed speed (which is directly related to the highest possible data rate output of the measurement devices in connection with the demanded grid in the heading direction). As a result the BetoScan movement has to be optimized to reach an optimum area capacity (Stoppel 2011).

In the heading direction, a measurement grid of 1 cm for every contactless NDT-sensor is possible. The space between tracks depends on the demanded resolution. Usually a spacing between 0.20 m and 1.0 m will be selected. For non-contactless sensors (e.g., ultrasound) a grid of 0.5 m in both directions is selected as a balance between resolution and area capacity.

Figure 5 shows a surface plot of the measured concrete cover data. The analysis software allows zooming into every zone (zoomedsquare). The resolution is not so good as to resolve every rebar, because the selected grid is too large (in this case 0.02 m by 0.25 m). However, the purpose here was to detect areas with low concrete cover.

Figure 6 shows the ultrasound point-contact sensor while being pressed to the surface. The plot shows the calculated thickness for each of the 500 measurement points in a grid of 0.5 m by 0.5 m. One area has an average thickness of about 0.35 m (lighter colour), in the second area a beam underneath increases the thickness to 0.8 m (darker colour in upper portion).

Figure 7 shows the robot while performing potential mapping at a BAM specimen with a chloride induced corroding rebar. The surface plot shows a potential cone with voltages lower than −300 mV where corrosion activity can be estimated.

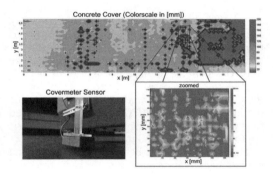

Figure 5. Measurement results with eddy current cover meter (5 × 20 m² area).

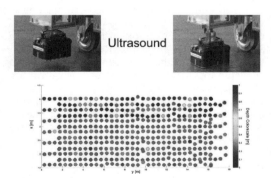

Figure 6. Measurement results for component thickness with ultrasound (3 × 18 m² area).

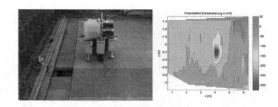

Figure 7. Robot with wheel electrode and measurement results for potential mapping.

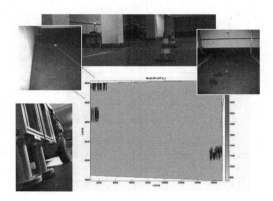

Figure 8. Robot with microwave moisture sensors and detected areas.

Figure 8 demonstrates the detection of wet areas. During the inspection, in which the ultrasound measurements took place, two microwave moisture sensors with two different penetration ranges were mounted on the robot. The surface plot indicates three areas with a high moisture content.

The examples above only show an excerpt of the capabilities of the BetoScan system. All measurements can take place at the same time and with a persistent accuracy. All measurement data are initially digitally linked to their corresponding position. These are the main advantages to reduce the effort for time consuming measurements and to receive multiple data for congruent areas.

3.2 Small areas and minor grids (OSSCAR)

In contrast to BetoScan the main focus of the OSSCAR project was to develop a scanning system for smaller regions of interest to be scanned with a dense grid to make reconstruction calculations possible.

Figure 9 shows the scanner underneath a bridge deck to inspect a horizontal beam.

Figure 10 shows the measurement results. The top plot indicates the surface near reinforcement, measured by the eddy current cover meter.

Figure 9. OSSCAR scanner underneath bridge deck scanning horizontal areas (Taffe et al., 2011).

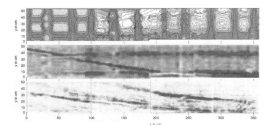

Figure 10. Measurement results for eddy current, radar and ultrasound on the same investigation area (0,5 m by 4 m) (Taffe et al., 2011).

The middle plot indicates the tendon ducts in the layer behind the reinforcement (0,10 to 0,15 m depth). This plot was reconstructed out of the radar data.

The lower plot indicates tendon ducts in a deeper layer at a depth of 0,20 to 0,30 m. This plot was reconstructed out of ultrasound data.

Because all the data was sampled with the three devices on the same congruent area, a comprehensive illustration of the inner structure is generated. Each method plays out its advantage in a different depth range.

4 CONCLUSIONS

Pro-active condition assessment is still a future task for infrastructure management, however, automated non-destructive testing methods are a major contribution to this concept. Data acquisition with multi-sensor systems has become an important approach for different research and application areas, where mainly non-invasive and non-destructive investigations are required. In case of technical applications an automated

multi-sensor approach is used where several sensors perform the measurements simultaneously.

The scheme of tasks where multi-sensor approaches are required is always similar. Generally multiple-parameter dependent or even ambiguous problems have to be solved, which is usually not possible by using only one measurement method delivering one parameter. Therefore, different methods have to be applied and the combination of the results leads to a unique assessment. A technically combined approach reduces the inspection risk since the reliability of the inspection task increases and therefore the costs are reduced.

The data analysis of multi-sensor measurement systems offers several possibilities depending on the type and quality of collected data. The most simple but often very effective approach is a direct comparison of these results. An expert system e.g., in form of an inspector's brain is required to correlate the different analysis results and performs the assessment. The next 'higher level' of data analysis is data fusion. Data fusion is generally defined as the use of techniques that combine data from multiple sources and gather that information in order to achieve inferences, which will be more efficient and potentially more accurate than if they were achieved by means of a single source (Wikipedia). Joint inversion or multi-objective optimization as further 'higher level' means the simultaneous minimization (or maximization) of several objective (target) functions, for instance by use of generic or evolutionary algorithms. Further details about these concepts and how the data acquisition of the BetoScan and OSSCAR system was designed to fulfill the requirements for theses analysis approaches can be found in Kurz et al. (2009).

The capability of the BetoScan system is that all measurements can take place at the same time and with a persistent accuracy. It is guaranteed that any combination of the implemented sensors can be chosen. Supplementary sensors can easily be implemented in the modular data acquisition system. The multi sensor approach asks for opening of the interfaces of the individual hardware of different industrial manufacturers which do not *a priori* support the same procedure. Regarding the OSSCAR system a higher grid density is required to allow the application of reconstruction algorithms. Using ultrasound, radar, and eddy current for concrete cover determination, detailed information about the inner structure in different depth layers is gained. Since all data was sampled with the three devices on the same congruent area, a comprehensive illustration of the inner structure is generated. Each method plays out its advantage in a different depth range. Both approaches presented here are designed for delivering input data for proactive condition assessment of civil infrastructure.

The multiple-sensor applications discussed here for construction engineering are designed for the investigation of reinforced concrete and tendon ducts. The advantage is that large surfaces can be investigated in short times and the measurements are of reproducible quality. This guarantees the data quality for recurrent inspections. However, the general concept of multi-sensor data acquisition and data analysis presented here is not limited to the field of civil engineering applications. Multi-sensor applications offer better inspection possibilities for complex material and constructions. Especially in case of subordinated assessments, reliable data sets including geometrical and material state information can be guaranteed. The data analysis of multi-sensor measurements still offers a variety of research capabilities and the simplification of sensor changes (hardware and software adaptations) are under current investigation.

Intelligent combination of different methods along with advanced data processing makes best use of today's capabilities of NDT-CE methods.

ACKNOWLEDGEMENTS

Developments to OSSCAR and BetoScan are financially supported by the Federal German Ministry of Economics and Technology; furthermore, the contributions of all partners in these collaborative research projects are gratefully acknowledged.

REFERENCES

Diamantidis, D. 2001. Probabilistic Assessment of Existing Structures. RILEM Publications S.A.R.L.

Dobmann, G., Kurz, J.H., Taffe, A. & Streicher, D. 2010. Development of Automated Non-Destructive Evaluation (NDE) Systems for Reinforced Concrete Structures and Other Applications. In: Maierhofer, C., Reinhardt, H.-W., Dobmann, G., eds.: Non-destructive Evaluation of Reinforced Concrete Structures: Volume 1: Deterioration Processes and Standard Test Methods. Cambridge, Woodhead, 30–62.

Gros, X.E. Applications of NDT data fusion, Kluwer Academic Publishers, p. 277. 2001.

Haardt, P., 2010. Personal Communication. Bundesanstalt für Straßenwesen (BASt), Germany.

Kurz, J.H., Rieder, H., Stoppel, M. & Taffe, A. 2009. Control and Data Acquisition of Automated Multi-Sensor Systems in Civil Engineering. Proceedings of Non-Destructive Testing in Civil Engineering 2009, NDT-CE, Paris, Laboratoire Central des Ponts et Chaussées (LCPC): 433–439.

NRC (National Research Council), 2009. Sustainable Critical Infrastructure Systems. A Framework for Meeting 21st Century Imperatives. Report of a Workshop, the National Academies Press, Washington, D.C.

Stoppel, M. 2011. Differenzpotentialfeldmessung in der automatisierten Prüfung von Stahlbetonbauteilen. PhD thesis, Saarland University, Germany.

Taffe, A., Kind, T., Kurz, J.-H. & Stoppel, M.: Bauwerkscanner zur automatisierten und kombinierten Anwendung zerstörungsfreier Prüfverfahren im Bauwesen, Beton- und Stahlbetonbau 106 (2011) 4, Ernst & Sohn, S.267–276. http://www.wikipedia.org → sdata fusion

Concrete Solutions – Grantham, Mechtcherine & Schneck (eds)
© 2012 Taylor & Francis Group, London, ISBN 978-0-415-61622-5

A study on non-destructive measurement using Prompt Gamma-ray Analysis of chloride profile in concrete

I. Ujike, S. Okazaki & M. Yamate
Graduate School of Science and Engineering, Ehime University, Matsuyama, Japan

H. Matsue
Japan Atomic Energy Agency, Quantum Beam Science Directorate, Tokai, Japan

ABSTRACT: This study develops a method for measuring the distribution of chloride concentration in concrete by Prompt Gamma-ray Analysis (PGA). PGA is a multi-elemental analysis technique based on nondestructive neutron technology. When the chloride concentration near the surface is known and its distribution profile is assumed by an error function, the distribution of the chloride concentration can be comparatively evaluated with good accuracy using PGA as already reported. However, under conditions such as rainfall or carbonation, the peak of chloride concentration is located at a certain depth inside the concrete and not near the concrete surface. To detect chloride concentrations at various depths below the surface, the present study proposes varying the incident angle of the neutron irradiation beam on the surface of the object. This method proves to be successful in measuring the arbitrary distribution of chloride concentrations in concrete.

1 INTRODUCTION

Japan has seen significant growth in the last fifty years in the construction industry. It has been reported that within the next several decades, 50% of residential buildings will be fifty years old or more (MLIT 2009). Considering such a forecast, efficient maintenance within the budget limits are needed, and the infrastructure management is shifting from corrective preservation to preventive preservation. Preventive maintenance is advantageous because detailed inspections are performed before the manifestation of deterioration, and appropriate measures are taken for maintaining the structure.

The corrosion of steel reinforcements by chlorides is of utmost concern in the degradation phenomena of concrete structures. Advanced chloride-induced deterioration is visually detected by the presence of corrosion cracks. To implement a preventive maintenance strategy, chloride ions have to be monitored in the concrete structures before cracks appear.

Steel reinforcement bars in concrete structures are protected from corrosion by passivating films, which form around the surface of steel reinforcement under alkaline conditions in concrete. However, when the threshold chloride ion concentration is exceeded, film depassivation occurs and active corrosion takes places through the fractured film. Therefore, for predicting the progress of chloride-induced

deterioration before the onset of reinforcement corrosion, it is essential to monitor the chloride ion concentration in concrete around steel reinforcement. The following outlines the currently used method for measuring the chloride ion content in concrete: Concrete cores are drilled from the structures and then divided into different sections corresponding to different depth profiles. Each section is powdered and the chloride ion content is determined from potentiometric titration measurements. This method is disadvantageous because it is time consuming and expensive; core drilling damages the building structure, and multiple core samples for repeated measurements cannot be taken at the same position in the structure.

The present study is a fundamental investigation necessary for the development of a non-destructive method to measure the distribution of chloride ion concentration in cover concrete via prompt gamma-ray analysis (PGA). PGA is a multi-elemental, non-destructive analysis technique. A nondestructive method for measuring the distribution of chloride ion concentrations in surface layers of concrete using PGA has been reported (Ujike et al., 2010). Using this method, the estimation of chloride concentration distribution in concrete is accurately determined when the chloride concentration gradually decreases from the surface. However, the estimation is poor when the chloride concentration is arbitrary and does not follow a decreasing trend. This study proposes a method of varying the angle of neutron irradiation on the surface for measuring the arbitrary distribution of chloride ion concentrations.

2 EXPERIMENTAL METHODS

2.1 *Prompt Gamma-ray analysis*

Prompt gamma-rays are characteristic high energy gamma-rays emitted from a subject, when thermal neutrons are captured by the nucleus of the elements contained in the subject (Yonezawa 2003). In PGA, the prompt gamma-rays are detected by a radiographic detector. Because thermal neutrons with high transmission are irradiated, no pretreatment (such as powdering) of the sample material is required. The energy of the emitted prompt gamma-rays is dependent on the intrinsic energy of the processes occurring in the nucleus; therefore, many elements in the subject can be analyzed simultaneously according to the measurement of count by energy. Figure 1 is an example of prompt gamma-ray spectrum of concrete with chloride. The elements are analyzed quantitatively from position and height of the energy peaks. For example, the peak at 1163 keV in Figure 1 is due to chloride ions. The sensitivity to chloride ions is high using PGA; therefore, low concentrations, in the range of hundreds ppm, can be measured.

2.2 *Equipment*

In this study, the research reactor JRR-3 at Japan's Atomic Energy Agency (JAEA) was installed with PGA equipment. The neutron beam (flux 108 neutrons/cm²/s, width 5 mm) from the reactor is applied to the samples. Prompt gamma rays emitted from the sample are detected by a high-purity germanium detector, which is aligned perpendicular to the incident direction of the neutron beam.

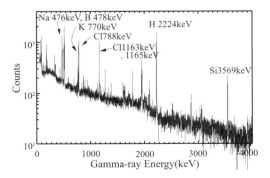

Figure 1. Example of gamma-ray spectrum of concrete with chloride.

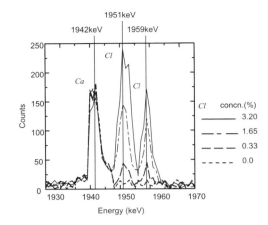

Figure 2. Gamma-ray spectrum near the object energy.

To quantitatively analyze the chloride ion concentration, the internal standard method was used in this study. Calcium was selected as the internal standard element, because it is present in cement in large amounts. The ratio of the counts for prompt gamma-rays for chloride to that of calcium was used as the index; hereinafter, it is referred to as the counting ratio. For this study, 1951 and 1942 keV are the energies of the prompt gamma-rays from chloride and calcium, respectively. The reactivity of these elements at these energies is relatively high, and because their prompt gamma-ray energies are close to each other, any fluctuations in prompt gamma-ray counts will affect both energies to the same extent. Figure 2 shows an example of the prompt gamma-ray spectrum near the energy of interest for this study. The counts for chloride at 1951 and 1959 keV increase with increasing chloride concentration in the concrete samples. However, the count for calcium at 1942 keV is almost constant. The fluctuations in the calcium gamma-ray count mainly depend on the amount of cement in the sample. For samples containing a large amount of aggregate, the peak counts for calcium and chloride decrease because of the decrease in the cement content in the sample. However, because we use the counting ratio, which remains constant in our analysis, PGA is advantageous in that no adjustment is necessary to account for varying aggregate contents in the samples.

2.3 *Mortar boards*

In this study, two types of mortar boards were used. Mortar boards with dimensions of $40 \times 40 \times 50$ mm and made from Ordinary Portland cement and silica sand are used for examining the influence of the concrete mix with different water-cement ratio and different sand-cement ratio on the prompt gamma-ray counts. The water-cement ratios were 40%, 50% and 60%. The sand-cement ratio was changed from 0% to 200%. The chloride concentration in the mortar boards was adjusted to 3 wt% of chloride to cement. This value is the amount of mixed-in chloride.

Another type of mortar board with dimensions of 70 × 30 × 5 mm and made from Ordinary Portland cement and silica sand was used for evaluating the arbitrary concentration distribution of chloride. The water-cement and sand-cement ratios were 40% and 100%, respectively. The chloride concentration in the mortar boards was varied from 0% to 3% in increments of 0.5%, and ten mortar boards were combined in a set. Figure 3 shows example of one set with ten mortar boards. An arbitrary concentration distribution was established by combining the boards with various chloride concentrations, because it is difficult to produce by penetration a concrete specimen with the arbitrary distribution of chloride ions in a short time. However, the chloride does not mix with all of five mortar boards from the sixth mortar board. For the PGA done in this study, the detectable range was adjusted to be the thickness of five mortar boards. The contributing gamma rays emitted from chloride ions contained in mortar boards beyond the fifth are defined as noise, because it has been reported that the chloride concentration calculated from the counting ratio varies at this depth and no reliable values are obtained (Ujike et al., 2010). Mortar boards without chloride ions are used in the sixth to tenth mortar boards for maintaining consistent experimental conditions. The following three cases were considered for the chloride concentration in the mortar boards:

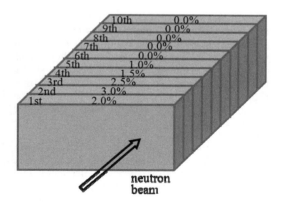

Figure 3. Example of combined mortar boards in a set.

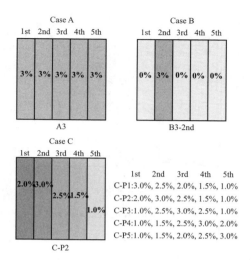

	1st	2nd	3rd	4th	5th
C-P1:	3.0%,	2.5%,	2.0%,	1.5%,	1.0%
C-P2:	2.0%,	3.0%,	2.5%,	1.5%,	1.0%
C-P3:	1.0%,	2.5%,	3.0%,	2.5%,	1.0%
C-P4:	1.0%,	1.5%,	2.5%,	3.0%,	2.0%
C-P5:	1.0%,	1.5%,	2.0%,	2.5%,	3.0%

Figure 4. Combined chloride concentrations in the first to fifth mortar boards for Cases A–C.

Case A: All five mortar boards have the same chloride concentration.

Case B: Only one mortar board contains chloride; the other four contain no chloride.

Case C: The chloride concentration in each mortar board is mutually different.

Figure 4 shows examples of the combination of five mortar boards used in cases A, B and C, respectively. For case A, a numeral affixed to the letter A represents the chloride concentration in the mortar boards. For case B, the first number indicates the chloride concentration in a given mortar board while the second number indicates the position of the given mortar board. For case C, the sequential chloride concentration in all five mortar boards are given and the number attached to P indicates the position of the mortar board with the maximum chloride concentration.

3 RESULTS AND DISCUSSION

3.1 Calibration curve for evaluating chloride concentrations

As shown in Figure 2, the gamma-ray counts for chloride increases and that for calcium is almost constant when the concentration of chloride ions in the mortar board increases, indicating that the counting ratio is proportional to the chloride concentration.

Figure 5 shows the counting ratio versus chloride concentrations for cases A and B. The proportionality constant (given by the slop of the lines in Figure 5) for case A is larger than those obtained

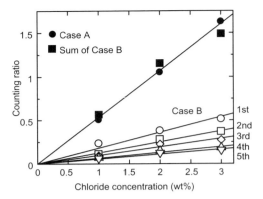

Figure 5. Relationship between chloride concentration and counting ratio.

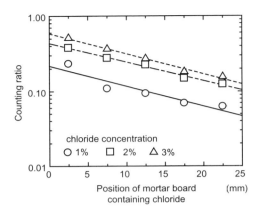

Figure 6. Effect of position of mortar board containing chloride on counting ratio.

for all case B combinations. Furthermore, in case B combinations, it is seen that the constant of proportionality decreases when the chloride mortar board is moved from the irradiated surface (first position) of the specimen to the opposite side (fifth position). This decrease is attributed to the fact that the number of neutrons reaching the fifth mortar board is less than the number impinging on the first mortar board because of absorption and scattering within the material. Thus, when evaluating the chloride concentration, it is necessary to consider the distance from the irradiated surface. And, black squares in Figure 5 are sum of the counting ratio of case B at each chloride concentration. As shown in Figure 5, the counting ratios of case A are in good agreement with the sum of the counting ratios for case B at each chloride concentration. That is, the principle of superposition consists between case A and case B. Thus, for evaluating the chloride concentration in concrete using PGA, we must consider a calibration curve that accounts for the mortar board position of the chloride.

As the number of transmitted neutrons decreases exponentially because of scattering and absorption in the material, the generation of prompt gamma-rays also decreases exponentially. The semi-log plot of Figure 6 shows the relationship between the counting ratio and the position of the mortar board that contains chloride. The straight lines in Figure 5 are regression lines expressed with the following equation obtained by a least squares method.

$$R = aC \cdot e^{-bd} \qquad (1)$$

where, R is the counting ratio, C is the chloride concentration, d is the distance from the irradiation surface (i.e., distance from the irradiation

surface to the center of the mortar board with chloride), a and b are regression coefficients, and aC is the counting ratio at position $p = 0$. Coefficient b gives the slope of the lines in Figure 6. Because the counting ratio is proportional to the chloride concentration, and if position p is constant, the straight lines in Figure 6 should be parallel. Although some data points are not on the lines, the regression lines in Figure 6 can be considered parallel for our purposes. The coefficients a and b depend on factors such as the neutron source, detector, and measuring time; therefore, these values have to be kept constant in a set of measurements. The calibration curves in Figure 6 are not dependent on the thickness of the mortar boards. If the calibration curve is obtained using a 2 mm mortar board, the evaluation of the chloride concentration at 2 mm intervals is performed as previously reported (Yamada, 2009).

3.2 *Effect of mix proportions on counting ratios*

The effect of varying the concrete mix on the counting ratios is examined. Figure 7 shows the effect of water-cement ratio on the counting ratio of chloride in mortar. The counting ratio hardly changes with varying water-cement ratios. Figure 8 shows the effect of sand-cement ratio on the counting ratio. In contrast, varying the sand–cement ratios (Figure 8) affects the counting ratio to a greater extent; however, the variation coefficient on the counting ratio is small at only 4.8%.

Because there are no significant differences in the counting ratios on varying the water–cement and sand–cement ratios, the effect of the concrete mix on the calibration curves is not significant. Therefore, samples with arbitrary water–cement and sand–cement proportions can be used for the calibration curves, and there is no problem in the

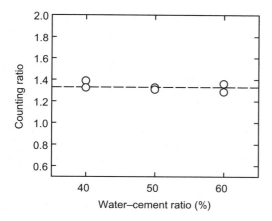

Figure 7. Effect of water-cement ratios on the counting ratio.

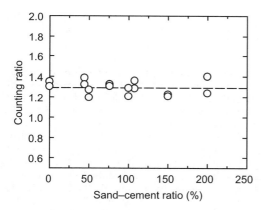

Figure 8. Effect of sand-cement rations on the counting ratio.

application of the calibration curve for materials in which the concrete-mix proportions are unknown. However, when the limestone is used for the aggregate, this method of utilizing the calcium as the internal standard element cannot be used. For that case, the counts of chloride may be used directly in consideration of concrete mix.

3.3 Measurement of the distribution of chloride concentrations in samples

3.3.1 Varying the irradiation angle

For the PGA in this study, the detectable range was adjusted to be the thickness of five mortar boards as mentioned above. We propose to evaluate the arbitrary chloride distribution by measuring gradual changes in the detectable range of prompt gamma-ray emission. As shown in Figure 9, the irradiation angle θ of the neutron irradiation beam

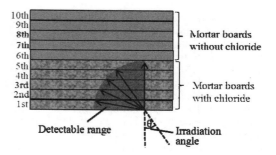

Figure 9. Irradiation angle changing method.

Table 1. Relationship between irradiation angle and detectable mortar boards.

Irradiation Angle	Distance from surface (mm)				
	2.5	7.5	12.5	17.5	22.5
80°	1st	1st	1st	1st	1st
65°	1st	1st	2nd	2nd	2nd
50°	1st	1st	2nd	3rd	3rd
35°	1st	2nd	2nd	3rd	4th
0°	1st	2nd	3rd	4th	5th

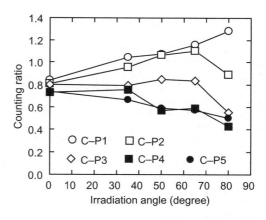

Figure 10. Change of counting ratio with the increase of the irradiation angle of neutron beam.

on the sample surface is gradually varied at 80°, 65°, 50°, 35°, 0°.

Table 1 shows the relationship between the irradiation angle and the detectable penetrable range, given by the depth in mm corresponding to the first to fifth mortar boards. The incident irradiation angle was set so that increments of one mortar board are incorporated into the detectable range with decreasing incident irradiation angle.

Figure 10 shows the change of the counting ratio with varying incident neutron irradiation angles.

The measured mortar boards were specifically combined because the position of mortar board with maximum chloride concentration is different. When the irradiation angle is 80°, the counting ratios of C-P3, C-P4 and C-P5 are almost the same values because only the first mortar board is in the detectable range, and the counting ratios of C-P2 and C-P1 are approximately twice and thrice this value, respectively. The relationship between them corresponds to the chloride ion concentration of the first mortar board. For C-P1, when the irradiation angle is reduced from 80°, the counting ratio decreases gradually with decreasing irradiation angle because the mortar boards with low chloride ion concentrations fall within the detectable range. Conversely, for C-P5, the counting ratio increases gradually with decreasing irradiation angle because the mortar board with high chloride ion concentration is detected. For C-P2, C-P3 and C-P4, when the irradiation angle is reduced from 80°, the counting ratio increases with decreasing irradiation angle until the mortar board with the maximum concentration of chloride is detected. This fact indicates that the position of the mortar board containing the maximum chloride ion concentration can be located by changing the irradiation angle.

3.3.2 Evaluation of the distribution of chloride concentrations in mortar boards

As illustrated in the previous section, on decreasing the incident irradiation angle, chloride concentrations at an increased depth below the surface can be detected. The evaluation of the chloride concentration of mortar boards is as follows.

At an irradiation angle of 80°, only the first mortar board is within the detectable range and the chloride concentration in the first mortar board is obtained from the measured counting ratio using the following equation:

$$C_1 = \frac{R_{80}}{\sum_{i=1}^{5} a \cdot e^{-bd_i}}$$

$$= \frac{R_{80}}{a(e^{-2.5b} + e^{-7.5b} + e^{-12.5b} + e^{-17.5b} + e^{-22.5b})} \quad (2)$$

where C_1 is the chloride concentration in the first mortar board, R_{80} is the measured counting ratio at irradiation angle 80°, $d_i = 5i-2.5$ (distance from surface to center of each mortar board), and a and b are the coefficients of the calibration curve.

At an irradiation angle of 65°, the chloride concentrations in the first and second mortar boards are detected. The chloride concentration in the first mortar board (C_1) is a known from the measurement at an irradiation angle of 80°. The chloride concentration in the second mortar board (C_2) is calculated using the following equation:

$$C_2 = \frac{R_{65} - aC_1(e^{-2.5b} + e^{-7.5b})}{a(e^{-12.5b} + e^{-17.5b} + e^{-22.5b})} \quad (3)$$

where R_{65} is the measured counting ratio at an irradiation angle 65°.

Similarly, at irradiation angles 50°, 35° and 0°, the chloride concentration in the mortar boards are obtained using following equations (4), (5) and (6), respectively.

$$C_3 = \frac{R_{50} - aC_1(e^{-2.5b} + e^{-7.5b}) - aC_2e^{-12.5b}}{a(e^{-17.5b} + e^{-22.5b})} \quad (4)$$

$$C_4 = \frac{R_{35} - aC_1e^{-2.5b} - aC_2(e^{-7.5b} + e^{-12.5b}) - aC_3e^{-17.5b}}{ae^{-22.5b}} \quad (5)$$

$$C_5 = \frac{R_0 - a(C_1e^{-2.5b} + C_2e^{-7.5b} + C_3e^{-12.5b} + C_4e^{-17.5b})}{ae^{-22.5b}} \quad (6)$$

where C_3, C_4 and C_5 are the chloride concentrations in third, fourth and fifth mortar boards respectively, R_{50}, R_{35} and R_0 are the measured counting ratios at irradiation angles 50°, 35° and 0°, respectively.

Figures 11–15 show the chloride concentration distribution obtained from varying the irradiation angle. As shown in Figures 11, 12 and 14, this method accurately determines the position of the mortar board containing the highest chloride concentration in C-P1, C-P2 and C-P4. The evaluated chloride concentrations for C-P1 and C-P2 agree qualitatively with the known concentrations. For C-P3 and C-P5 shown in Figures 13 and 15, respectively, although the peak position of the chloride concentration does not correspond to the correct mortar board, the distribution shape of the

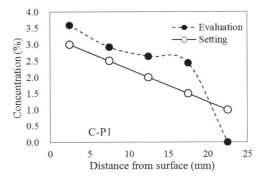

Figure 11. Evaluation of chloride concentration distribution in C-P1 by varying the detectable range.

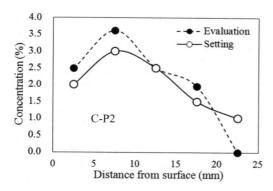

Figure 12. Evaluation of chloride concentration distribution in C-P2 by varying the detectable range (C-P2).

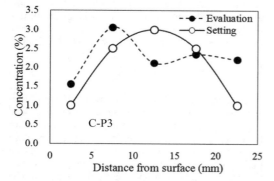

Figure 13. Evaluation of chloride concentration distribution in C-P3 by varying the detectable range.

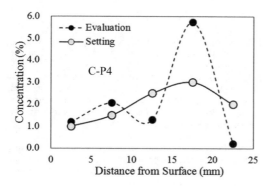

Figure 14. Evaluation of chloride concentration distribution in C-P4 by varying the detectable range.

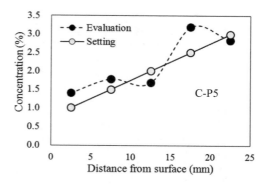

Figure 15. Evaluation of chloride concentration distribution in C-P5 by varying the detectable range.

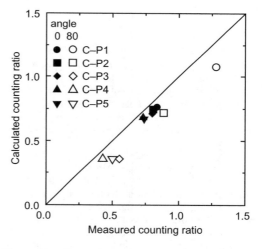

Figure 16. Comparison of measured counting ratios and calculated counting ratios at 0° (filled symbols) and 80° (open symbols).

chloride concentration roughly follows the correct trend.

The evaluated values on the first and second mortar boards are overestimated. Overestimating the chloride concentration on the first and/or second mortar boards can contribute to underestimating the concentration on other mortar boards. The counting ratio calculated by the overestimated chloride concentration is subtracted from the measured counting ratio, as indicated in equations (4)–(6).

This overestimation mentioned above is caused by the noise generated outside the detectable range. Figure 16 shows the comparison of the measured counting ratio and the calculated counting ratio at the irradiation angles of 0° and 80°, respectively. The calculated counting ratio is the sum of the values calculated by substituting a set value for the chloride concentration of each mortar board into the calibration curve. The measured values are greater than the calculated values and the difference between measured and calculated values is more

411

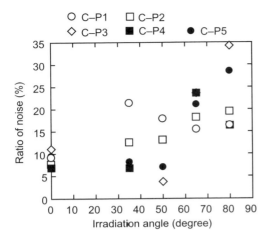

Figure 17. Effect of irradiation angle on noise.

remarkable in the case of irradiation angle 80°. As shown in Figure 9, there are mortar boards that contain chloride ions, which are undetected at the 80° irradiation angle measurement. The chloride ions outside the detectable range contribute to the noise and the noise is enlarged. The chloride concentration in the first mortar board is evaluated using equation (2). Because the measured counting ratio R_{80} contains noise, the chloride concentration in the first mortar board is overestimated.

Figure 17 shows the effect of the irradiation angle on the ratio of noise to the measured counting ratio. In this study, the difference between the measured counting ratio and the calculated counting ratio is defined as noise. The ratio of noise tends to increase with an increase in the irradiation angle roughly. Therefore, to improve the accuracy in evaluating the chloride concentration using the changing irradiation angle method, it is necessary to subtract the noise from the measured counting ratio appropriately.

4 CONCLUSIONS

This study investigates the nondestructive measurement of the distribution of chloride concentrations by prompt gamma-ray analysis in combined mortar boards with different chloride ion concentrations. The following conclusions were drawn within the scope of the study.

1. The counting ratio of chloride to calcium is proportional to the chloride concentration and decreases exponentially with increasing depth from the surface.

2. The water-cement ratio and sand-cement ratio do not significantly influence the counting ratio; therefore, the calibration curve can be applied to different concrete mixes.
3. The position of the peak of chloride ion concentration can be determined by varying the irradiation angle.
4. Measuring arbitrary chloride ion distributions is possible by changing the neutron beam irradiation angle, although the resulting chloride ion concentration measured this way is overestimated in the vicinity of the surface.

Because the present study is a basic research to utilize the PGA for the non-destructive measurement of concrete structures, the neutron beam from the research reactor is used as neutron source. As a research in the future, it is necessary to examine the applicability of the proposal method in this study by using the portable neutron source like californium used in a previous study (Saleh 2000).

ACKNOWLEDGEMENTS

The authors would like to thank the Japan Society for the Promotion of Science for the financial support given by the Grant-in-Aid for Science Research, as a part of the present study. PGA in this study was carried out as the part of the shared facility use system of the Independent Administrative Institution Japan Atomic Energy Agency. The authors also thank JAEA for installing the PGA system.

REFERENCES

Ministry of Land, Infrastructure, Transport and Tourism, 2009. *White Paper on Land, Infrastructure, Transport and Tourism in Japan 2009.*

Saleh, H.H and Livingston, R.A. 2000. Experimental evaluation of a portable neutron-based gamma-spectroscopy system for chloride measurements in reinforced concrete. *Journal of Radioanalytical and Nuclear Chemistry.* Vol. 244, No. 2: 397–371.

Ujike, I., Okazaki, S. Yamada, Y. and Matsue, H. 2010. A fundamental study on non-destructive measurement of chloride concentration in concrete by Prompt Gamma-ray Analysis, *proceedings of Sixth International Conference on Concrete under Severe Condition, Environment and Loading*: CD-ROM.

Yamada, Y., Ujike, I., Okazaki, S. and Matsue, H. 2009. Study on non-destructive measurement of chloride distribution in concrete by PGA. *Proceedings of the Japan Concrete Institute*, Vol. 31, No. 1: 1981–1986. (in Japanese).

Yonezawa, C. 2002. Prompt γ-ray analysis with reactor neutrons. *Japan Analyst,* Vol. 51, No. 2: 61–96. (in Japanese).

Concrete Solutions – Grantham, Mechtcherine & Schneck (eds)
© 2012 Taylor & Francis Group, London, ISBN 978-0-415-61622-5

NDT based evaluation of rubber modified self-compacting concrete

M. Usman, M. Rahman & A. Al-Ghalib
School of Architecture, Design and the Built Environment, The Nottingham Trent University, Nottingham, UK

ABSTRACT: A non-destructive testing (NDT) evaluation was undertaken on rubber modified self-compacting concrete (RMSCC) mixtures to estimate fundamental mechanical and dynamic properties such as strength, natural frequencies, dynamic modulus of elasticity and Poisson's ratio. These are important parameters in order to obtain better information on the material properties for subsequent repair strategy and potential strength prediction. The consistency of the mixture production was assessed by V-funnel and L-box tests. The dynamic properties of all manufactured specimens were then determined non-destructively at 7 and 28 days using a portable ultrasonic non-destructive digital indicating tester (PUNDIT) and an impact echo (IE). The results showed that, compared to the conventional self-compacting concrete (SCC), the slump, together with the passing and filling ability of RMSCC mixtures was lower despite a higher dosage of superplasticiser in the fresh mixtures. In addition, as expected, the RMSCC mixtures exhibited lower strength, lower natural frequencies, lower dynamic modulus of elasticity (E_d) and marginally higher Poisson's ratio. The results indicate that both IE and PUNDIT have the potential to estimate properties of RMSCC, although PUNDIT has shown greater accuracy on the predicted properties.

1 INTRODUCTION

Self-compacting concrete (SCC) is a special type of concrete material where noisy and expensive vibration is avoided by adding superplasticiser into the fresh mixtures to achieve a similar level of compaction. This relatively new technology is gaining increased popularity in construction industry as it provides an environmentally friendly way of concrete production without compromising the quality of concrete.

Rubber Modified Self Compacting Concrete (RMSCC) is the product of SCC with partial replacement of aggregate with rubber particles. In the UK, more than 100,000 used tyres are removed from vehicles on a daily basis. The introduction of the European Union (EU) Landfill Directive has introduced a ban on whole tyres being sent to landfill sites (EA, 2010). Re-using this waste material in the civil engineering industry can help prevent the environmental pollution as well as the design of more economical structures which strategically incorporate waste into the designs.

Since most countries in the world avoid/forbid the stockpiling of scrap tyres, this presents the engineers with a readily available, cheap to use material with the possibility of major, positive impacts on the environment across the world (Najim and Hall 2010).

The addition of rubber can increase the vibration absorption of a concrete slab structure paving

the way for research into the use of RMSCC for damped flooring, for mounting machinery (Najim and Hall, 2010), as well as light rail vibration reduction in cities. The addition of rubber aggregate also increases the deformability of the RMSCC mix before failure with the capacity to hold post-failure loads due to the addition of rubber aggregate (RA) (Bignozzi and Sandrolini, 2006).

RMSCC has been recommended for use in the production of road kerbs, roads, non-bearing concrete walls (El-Gammal et al., 2010).

It can also be used for architectural applications such as nailing concrete, false facades, stone backing as well as interior construction due to its light unit weight. Although RMSCC is lower in strength, it can still be used for the construction of sidewalks, driveways and selected road construction applications like crash barriers around bridges due to its high toughness qualities (Eldin and Senouci, 1993, Reda et al., 2008). RMSCC can also be used for vibration dampening in foundation pads for machinery and railway stations. It provides resistance to impact or explosion such as railway buffers, bunkers and jersey barriers or as a trench fill material and pipe bedding (Nehdi and Khan, 2001).

The application of RMSCC has also been seen as a positive step towards sustainable development as it can recycle high amounts of waste whilst providing a cheaper alternative to traditional materials (Topçu and Bilir, 2009). The use of RMSCC has also been recommended for roadway central reservations that offer combined protection and traffic noise reduction, improved thermal and acoustic insulation for small machinery housing structures as well as improved thermal insulation for flooring in buildings (Najim and Hall, 2010, Bignozzi and Sandrolini, 2006). The energy absorption qualities of rubberized concrete have also been confirmed by (Khaloo et al., 2008).

The addition of rubber aggregate in the concrete mixtures exhibits a loss in strength and stiffness as the amount of rubber aggregate is increased and therefore, it is rarely used in mass civil engineering application. However, the common misconception that has held the application of this innovation back has been the traditional idea that the most important property of concrete is its compressive strength. This view needs to change to a "design by function" approach which will allow concrete incorporating rubber to be the preferred material over the applications stated above in projects across the world (Nehdi and Khan, 2001).

The idea of NDT, or in-situ testing, can be dated as far back as 1948. It has been developed to get around the problem of damage caused by conventional tests like core sampling. Although, some minor local damage does occur, it is not significant enough to impact the performance of the structure. This allows NDT to have a significant advantage over destructive testing (DT) as the same area can be monitored for changes over a period of time. This increases safety and allows for a faster as well as an economical construction process. In addition, when suitably calibrated, NDT can also assess the strength of the concrete. This is because NDT is usually comparative in its nature (Neville, 1995).

Over the past decades, different types of NDT evaluation techniques have emerged and some of them have gained acceptance as a structural condition assessment tool. Impact Echo (IE) and Ultrasound methods are among the most successful techniques that can be used to determine the mechanical properties of a concrete structure. These two methods were adopted as part of this study. The IE method is based on the idea of impact, or mechanically generated stress waves. Since its development, the IE method has been used successfully for measuring the thickness and detecting flaws in plate-like structures, such as bridge decks, slabs, and walls and for detecting flaws in bar-like structures, such as circular, square, and rectangular columns, and for detecting flaws in I-girders (Sack and Olson, 1995). Details of this method can be found elsewhere (Sansolane & William, 1997). Ultrasonic testing was reported to be first used in the USA in the mid 1940's. The basic

concept is to measure the amount of time it takes for ultrasonic pulses to travel through a concrete member. By also knowing the distance between the sender and the receiver, the pulse velocity can be calculated. (Bungey, 2006, El- Reedy, 2009). The wave velocity within concrete depends on the elastic properties of the concrete as well as its mass. If this mass and the velocity of the propagation are known, it is possible to assess the elastic properties of concrete (Bungey, 2006).

In this paper, the results from NDT investigations on RMSCC to evaluate dynamic properties such as natural frequencies, dynamic modulus of elasticity and Poisson's ratio are presented. The results were compared with the control SCC mixtures manufactured under the same conditions.

2 EXPERIMENTAL PROGRAM

2.1 Mixture production

The rubberised mixtures (RMSCC1 and RMSCC2) mixtures were produced with a fixed, 28% fines replacement with rubber particles of 1–4 mm size and with two quantities of super-plasticiser (SP). The mixture type, gradation of each mixture and quantity of the additives were taken from earlier research conducted by (Bignozzi and Sandrolini, 2006). The mixture composition is given in Table 1.

The workability and passing ability of each mixture type were investigated by a slump, v-funnel and L-box test according to recommendations given in the European Guidelines for Self-Compacting Concrete (EFNARC, 2005).

2.2 Workability and passing ability

The slump test revealed, as shown in Figure 1, that an increase in SP quantity increased the flow of both SCC and RMSCC. However, the results also showed that the increased SP dosage of RMSCC 2 had a limited effect whereas SCC CS2 saw a major increase in slump flow in relation to RMSCC1

Table 1. Mix design.

Material	SCC CS1	RM SCC 1	SCC CS2	RM SCC 2
Gravel (kg)	9.86	9.86	9.86	9.86
Sand (kg)	18.9	13.64	18.9	13.64
Rubber Aggregate (kg)	0.00	1.89	0.00	1.89
CEM II/A-LL (kg)	5.92	5.92	5.92	5.92
Water (kg)	3.12	3.12	3.12	3.12
SP(kg)	0.37	0.37	0.55	0.55

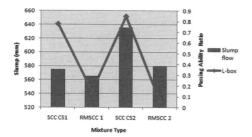

Figure 1. Variations in slump flow and L-box passing ability.

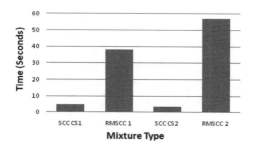

Figure 2. Variation in V-funnel times.

Figure 3. Cube samples.

and SCC CS1 respectively. During the testing, it appeared as if the RA within the RMSCC mixture behaved like a binder preventing free flow.

The passing ability ratio from the 3 bar L-box test, as shown in Figure 1, indicated that RMSCC has a much lower passing ability ratio when compared to SCC. It also shows that for SCC, an increase in SP did not have much impact in greatly enhancing the passing ability.

However, the increase in SP seems to have had a negative effect on the passing ability of RMSCC. This difference was also clearly observed, visually, whilst conducting the testing. The RA within the RMSCC mix under both cases was the limiting factor which affected the passing ability. As the mix travelled through the L-box, the RA seemed to create a blocking effect at the top of the opening which gradually increased until the stoppage of flow. Another key aspect that was observed during the L-box test was the fact that the RMSCC testing took noticeably longer than their respective SCC control samples.

The v-funnel test results, to investigate the viscosity and filling ability of the fresh mixtures, are shown in Figure 2. The results indicate that RMSCC has a high viscosity and low filling ability compared to SCC. The increase in SP further compromised these characteristics which was an unexpected outcome. An increase in SP caused the

concrete within the V-funnel to consolidate quickly allowing the thixotropic phase to be accelerated for RMSCC. Therefore, once the gate was opened, the flow increase was gradual and was further affected by the friction caused by RA rubbing against the funnel walls. The addition of RA also increased the critical energy point for the thixotropic effect to return to its original state.

For each mixture type six specimens were produced. Each specimen went through NDT testing before undergoing compressive testing.

A picture of the specimens is shown in Figure 3. Testing was conducted at 7 day and 28 day intervals using PUNDIT and IE. At first, the IE test method was used to measure the resonant frequencies of each specimen. This was then followed by the measurement of Ultrasound Pulse Velocity (UPV) of each cube using PUNDIT. Once the NDT tests were completed, each cube was weighed prior to compressive strength testing.

3 DYNAMIC MECHANICAL PROPERTIES

3.1 Strength

The compressive strength of the various samples is shown in Table 2. SCC CS2 and RMSCC 2 samples were marginally weaker compared to SCC CS1 and RMSCC 1 at the 7 day interval. At the 28 day testing interval it was found that the samples with a higher SP dosage had 'made up' the short fall in strength. The increased SP dosage also helped to increase the total strength of the RMSCC 2 test samples when compared with RMSCC 1.

However, at the 28 day test interval the SCC CS2 sample was found marginally weaker when compared with SCC CS1. This is possibly because the increased dosage of SP seems to have a retarding effect on SCC.

Table 2. Compressive strength.

Mixture	7 days		28 days	
	Mean weight (kg)	Mean strength (MPa)	Mean weight (kg)	Mean strength (MPa)
SCC CS 1	2.2	15.2	2.3	22.6
RMSCC 1	2.1	9.7	2.1	13.4
SCC CS 2	2.2	13.8	2.3	21.4
RMSCC 2	2.1	9.0	2.1	15.0

Table 3. NDT testing results.

	7 Days			28 Days		
	IE		PUNDIT	IE		PUNDIT
Mixture type	f_1 kHz	f_2 kHz	UPV km/s	f_1 kHz	f_2 kHz	UPV km/s
SCC CS 1	15.8	22.1	3.6	16.4	22.9	3.7
RMSCC 1	14.7	20.6	3.4	15.0	21.0	3.4
SCC CS 2	14.7	20.5	3.4	16.5	23.1	3.8
RMSCC 2	14.2	19.8	3.3	15.5	21.7	3.5

3.2 Frequency and pulse velocity

Prior to the compressive strength test, the first two natural frequencies (f_1 and f_2) natural frequencies and the pulse velocity of each specimen were determined using IE and PUNDIT. The results are shown in Table 3. In terms of resonant frequency, it is clear that there was a slight difference caused by age for both f_1 and f_2. The addition of rubber resulted in the reduction of the frequencies, of around 1 kHz, for both RMSCC samples when compared to their respective control samples. This is likely to have been caused by the dampening effect of the RA.

In terms of UPV, it is clear that the UPV increases overtime for all samples. This is an expected result as the strength of the concrete increases over time. However, the increase in UPV from the 7 to 28 day interval for SCC CS2 and RMSCC 2 was greater when compared with the increase for SCC CS1 and RMSCC 1. This was probably influenced by the increased strength observed between 7 days and 28 days.

3.3 Dynamic modulus of elasticity (E_d)

The measured frequency and UPV were utilised to calculate the dynamic modulus of elasticity. Five different methods were chosen from published literatures and they are shown in Table 4.

Table 4. Dynamic modulus of elasticity formulae.

Ref		Formula
1	(Zheng, 2008)	$$E_d = \frac{\rho V^-(1+\mu)(1-2\mu)}{1-\mu} \quad (1)$$ E_d = Dynamic Elastic Modulus (GPa) ρ = Density (kg/m^2) μ = Dynamic Poisson's Ratio V = UPV (m/s)
2	(Topçu and Bilir, 2009)	$$E = \left|\frac{(u-p)}{\_}\right| \times 10^{-2} \quad (2)$$ E = Dynamic modulus of elasticity (GPa) u = UPV (km/s) ρ = Density (kg/m^2) g = acceleration due to gravity (9.81 m/s^2)
3	(Kumar et al., 2005)	$$E_d = D \times M \times (f_1)^2 \quad (3)$$ Where f_1 is fundamental longitudinal frequency, Hz; and M, mass of specimen, kg D for Prism (N-s^2) $D = 4{,}000 \times (L \div bt)$ L = length (m), b, t = cross sectional dimension (m)
4	(Kumar et al., 2005)	$$E_d = 0.49 f_{ck} + 0.86\, D \quad (4)$$ for $20\text{MPa} \leq f_{ck} \leq 45\text{MPa}$ and $1\, day \leq$ t ≤ 28 days Where, f_{ck} = characteristic compressive strength of concrete specimen, MPa; and D is dynamic modulus constant For prism $D = [t + 3{,}4784]$ t = age of concrete in days
5(i)	(Popovics et al., 2008) (adopted in ACI)	$$E = 1.25\, E_d - 19 \quad (5)$$ E = Static elastic modulus (GPa) E_d = Dynamic elastic modulus (GPa)
5(ii)	(Kumar et al., 2005)	$$E_s = 5000\sqrt{f_{ck}} \quad (6)$$ f_{ck} = characteristic compressive strength of concrete specimen, MPa E_s = Static elastic modulus
5(iii)	(Reynolds et al., 1988)	$$f_{ck} = f_{cm} - \lambda_n \times s_n \quad (7)$$ f_{cm} = Mean Value $\lambda_n = 1.64$ s_n = Standard Deviation of test values f_{ck} = Characteristic compressive strength

The calculated dynamic moduli at 7 and 28 days are presented in Figures 4 and 5 respectively.

The results indicate that the relationship used by Zheng (2008), in Equation 1, offers results that are close to the results provided by the relationship offered by the ACI through Equations 5, 6 and 7. This is especially the case for SCC CS2 where the value was almost exactly the same as the one predicted with other values being within 10% to 15% of the actual values. This also shows that the Poisson's ratio from IE testing has presented a decent data set. The equation also predicts the low early strength of SCC CS2 and RMSCC samples at the 7 day testing interval.

Using equation 4, it is possible to calculate the dynamic modulus according to the relationship purposed by Kumar et al. (2005). The E_d values obtained by work conducted in this project do not match the relationship proposed by Kumar at the 28 day interval. Using the ACI method as the benchmark for actual values of E_d, it is clear that using PUNDIT and the Poisson's ratio from IE and Equation 1 offers the best estimate for E_d.

3.4 Poisson's ratio

Using the first two resonance frequencies f_1 and f_2 from IE testing was used in equation 3 (Kumar, 2005) to calculate the dynamic Poisson's ratio.

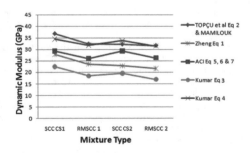

Figure 4. Dynamic modulus at 7 days.

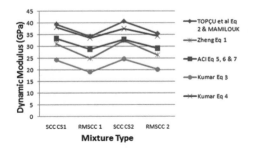

Figure 5. Dynamic modulus at 28 days.

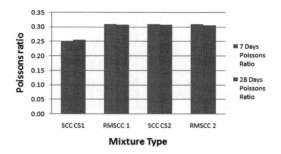

Figure 6. Changes in poisson's ratio over time using IE.

$$v = A_1(f_2 \div f_1)^2 + B_1(f_2 \div f_1)^2 + C_1 \qquad (8)$$

where

$$A_1 = -8.645\left[\frac{L}{D}\right]^2 + 24.442\left[\frac{L}{D}\right] - 12.478$$

$$B_1 = 34.559\left[\frac{L}{D}\right]^2 - 101.72\left[\frac{L}{D}\right] + 56.172$$

$$C_1 = -34.861\left[\frac{L}{D}\right]^2 + 105.98\left[\frac{L}{D}\right] - 62.731$$

The results are shown in Figure 6. It can be seen that with the exception of SCCCS1, there was a slight decrease in Poisson's ratio over time across all samples.

This is an expected outcome as the concrete gets stronger over time. The testing has also shown that the Poisson's ratio for SCC CS1 was less than the value of RMSCC1. However the difference was significantly reduced with increasing plasticiser into the mixtures. It is appeared that addition of rubber did not have significant influence on flexibility if there were higher doses of plasticiser used into the system.

4 CONCLUSIONS

The findings from this investigation were;

- Increasing SP quantity improved the flow rate of both SCC and RMSCC. However, RMSCC had a lower flow rate compared to SCC. This is likely to be the effect of low density and smaller rubber particles resisting the flow. In addition to that, compared to SCC, RMSCC had a high viscosity and low filling ability.
- As expected, the compressive strength of RMSCC mixtures was found to be 30–40% less at 28 days than conventional SCC.

417

- In terms of dynamic properties, both Impact Echo and Ultrasound techniques gave reliable results. In addition, NDT based measurement of pulse velocity and frequency used in Zheng's (2008) equation offered the best estimation of dynamic modulus of elasticity. Compared to the control SCC, both RMSCC mixtures tended to give 10–15% lower dynamic modulus.
- NDT based estimations of Poisson's ratio were variable among all mixtures. However, RMSCC tended to exhibit a marginally higher Poisson's ratio.

REFERENCES

Bignozzi, M.C. & Sandrolini, F. 2006. Tyre rubber waste recycling in self-compacting concrete. *Cement and Concrete Research, 36* (4), 735–739.

Bungey, J.H. (ed.). 2006. *The Testing of Concrete in Structures.* Taylor & Francis.

EFNARC. 2005. *The European Guidlines for Self-Compacting Concrete—Specification, Production and Use.* Retrieved 12 29, 2010, from European Concrete: http://www.europeanconcrete.eu/publications/guidelines

Eldin, N.N. & Senouci, A.B. 1993. Rubber-tire practices as concrete aggregate. *Journal of Civil Engineering Materials 5* (4), 478–496.

El-Reedy M.A. (ed.) 2009. *Advanced Materials and Techniques for Reinforced Concrete Structures.* Cairo, Egypt: CRC Press.

El-Gammal, A., Abdel-Gawad, A.K., El-Sherbini, Y. & Shalaby, A. 2010. Compressive strength of concrete utilizing waste tire rubber. *Journal of Emerging Trends in Engineering and Applied Sciences 1* (1), 96–99.

IAEA. 2002. *Guidebook on non-destructive testing of concrete structures.* International Atomic Energy Agency, Vienna.

Khaloo, A.R., Dehestani, M. & Rahmatabadi, P. 2008. Mechanical properties of concrete containing a high volume of tire–rubber particles. *Waste Management 28,* 2472–2482.

Kumar, M., Kanwar, V. & Kumar, S. 2005. Non-destructive Evaluation of Dynamic Properties of Concrete. *IE (I) Journal 86,* 53–57.

Mamlouk, M.S. & Zaniewski, J.P. 2009. *Materials for Civil and Construction Engineering.* In M.J. Horton (ed.), London: Pearson Education LTD.

Najim, K.B. & Hall, M.R. 2010. A review of the fresh/hardened properties and applications for plain- (PRC) and self-compacting rubberised concrete (SCRC). *Construction and Building Materials 24* (11), 2043–2051.

Neville, A.M. (ed.) 1995. *Properties of Concrete.* Harlow: Pearson Education Ltd.

Nehdi, M. & Khan, A. 2001. Cementitious composites containing recycled tire rubber: An overview of engineering properties and potential applications. *Cement, Concrete and Aggregates, CCAGDP 23* (1), 3–10.

Popovics, J.S., Zemajtis, J. & Shkolnik, I. 2008. ACI-CRC *Final Report—A Study of Static and Dynamic Modulus of Elasticity of Concrete.* American Concrete Instite, Urbana.

Reda Taha, M.M., El-Dieb, A.S., Abd El-Wahab, M.A. & Abdel-Hameed, M.E. 2008. Mechanical, fracture, and microstructural investigations of rubber concrete. *Journal of Materials in Civil Engineering 20,* 640–649.

Reynolds, C.E., Steedman, J.C. & Threlfall, A.J. 1988. *Reinforced concrete designer's handbook.* Taylor & Francis.

Sack, D.A. & Olson, L.D. 1995. Advanced NDT methods for evaluating concrete bridges and other structures. *NDT&E International 28* (6), 349–357.

Sansalone, M.J. & William, B.S. 1997. Impact-echo: Non-destructive evaluation of concrete and masonry, Bullbrier Press, ISBM 0961261064.

The Environment Agency. 2010. *Tyres.* Retrieved 1230, 2010, from Enviroment Agency: http://www.environment-agency.gov.uk/business/topics/waste/114455.aspx

Topçu, I.B. & Bilir, T. 2009. Experimental investigation of some fresh and hardened properties of rubberized self-compacting concrete. *Materials and Design 30,* 3056–3065.

Turatsinze, A. & Garros, M. 2008. On the modulus of elasticity and strain capacity of Self-Compacting Concrete incorporating rubber aggregates. *Resources, Conservation and Recycling 52,* 1209–1215.

Uygunoglu, T. & Topçu, I.B. 2010. The role of scrap rubber particles on the drying shrinkage and mechanical properties of self-consolidating mortars. *Construction and Building Materials 24* (7), 1141–1150.

Zheng, L.E. 2008. Experimental investigation on dynamic properties of rubberized concrete. *Construction and building materials 22,* 939–947.

Concrete Solutions – Grantham, Mechtcherine & Schneck (eds)
© 2012 Taylor & Francis Group, London, ISBN 978-0-415-61622-5

Evaluation of bridge decks using Ground Probing Radar (GPR)

V. Utsi
Utsi Electronics Ltd., Sarek, Newton Road, Harston, Cambridge, UK

A. Birtwisle
Atlas Geophysical Ltd., Garden House, Heol Giedd, Ystradgynlais, UK

ABSTRACT: GPR is often used as an instrument to detect delamination in bridge decks. As the top layers can be thin, 10 to 50 mm, a high resolution GPR has to be used to give accurate depths. This paper shows by simulations and practical results that a 4 GHz GPR will give the required resolution. If detection of reinforcement bars is also wanted, the GPR needs to be close to the surface.

1 INTRODUCTION

Modern bridges in the UK are usually constructed with reinforced concrete with a layer of asphalt on top as the wearing layer. GPR can be used to detect some of the problems that are due to faulty design and wear and tear. A common problem is delamination of the asphalt. When vertical cracks develop from the surface down, rain can then cause water to fill the delamination void. Any frost will cause the water to expand, spreading the delamination and causing the asphalt to lift off.

As water gets into the concrete, the rebars will corrode and cause cracking of the surrounding concrete, weakening the whole bridge structure.

This paper shows the importance of using the right frequency and position of the GPR to be able to detect the delamination, its content and the rebars.

Modelling is first used to demonstrate the expected result for different GPR configurations, real data is then shown to illustrate the practical performance.

2 MODELLING

For a single interface the reflection coefficient, A, depends on the dielectric constants, Er, of the materials on either side of the interface. With asphalt/air (A1) or asphalt/water (A2), the reflection coefficient is approximately of the same amplitude but of opposite polarity.

$A = (\sqrt{Er1} - \sqrt{Er2})/(\sqrt{Er1} + \sqrt{Er2})$.
$A1 = (3 - 1)/(3 + 1) = 0.5$
$A2 = (3 - 9)/(3 + 9) = -0.5$

The wavelength in air for a 1 GHz frequency is 300 mm. A 1 mm gap is therefore much smaller

than the wavelength, giving a response that is a differentiation of the transmitted waveshape. In water, the wavelength is 33 mm (9 times shorter). The gap is still a lot smaller than a wavelenth, but the waveform is differentiated over a longer time, giving a larger amplitude return (6 times larger).

GprMax 2D (Giannopoulos 2005) is used for modelling. The model simulates the delamination of a wearing course layer of asphalt with two rebars 150 mm below the surface, 6 mm diameter each.

The delamination is in two areas, both at a depth of 40 mm. The first is a 1 mm airfilled gap and the second a waterfilled 1 mm gap.

The simulations are done with rickershaped pulses at three frequencies, 3 GHz, 1.5 GHz and 900 MHz. The first set of data is with the antennas groundcoupled and the second with the antennas 100 mm above the surface.

The simulation grid is 1 mm * 1 mm with an area of 1 m * 0.6 m. There are some simulation area corner reflections visible in the airlaunched antenna models.

The data is plotted using ReflexW software which is also used for processing the real bridgedeck data. The timesweep is 4.4 nS.

In Figure 1, note the multiple strong triple transit reflections of the water filled gap.

Figure 3 shows the delamination layer revealed by a ground-coupled 900 MHz antenna (see also Figure 4).

Figure 4 shows that when the antennas are lifted off the ground, the delamination layers are weaker but more separated from the surface reflection.

In Figures 4, 5 and 6, the hyperbolic reflections from the rebars are shallower making the detection of closely spaced rebars more difficult.

The conclusion from the simulations is that a GPR with a frequency higher than 3 GHz is required

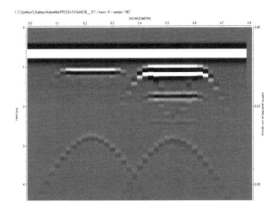

Figure 1.   3 GHz antenna, ground coupled.

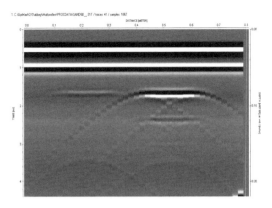

Figure 4.   3 GHz antenna, 10 cm off ground.

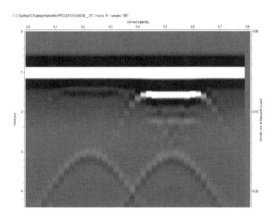

Figure 2.   1.5 GHz antenna, ground coupled.

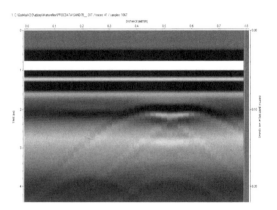

Figure 5.   1.5 GHz antenna, 10 cm off ground.

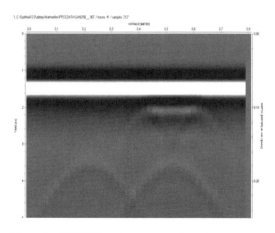

Figure 3.   900 MHz antenna, ground coupled.

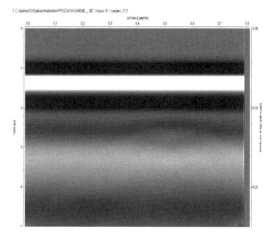

Figure 6.   900 MHz antenna, 10 cm off ground.

to give good resolution for the classification and detection of thin delamination.

As long as the bandwidth of the antenna is large enough, the change in polarity of the return signal from an air filled and waterfilled gap is clear, see Figures 2 and 4.

3 REAL BRIDGE DECK MEASUREMENTS

Many of the bridges crossing the UK motorway network belong to the UK Highways Agency. Where these bridges carry local (non-trunk) roads, the surfacing belongs to the local authority. Establishing the thickness of the surfacing materials, the condition of the bond between

Figure 7. Bridge deck.

Figure 8. Side view of bridge.

surfacing and bridge deck and the condidtion of the structure beneath is an important part of managing the maintainance strategy of the structure. To be able to achieve this via non-destructive methods saves time and money. GPR data acquisition is fast, can be conducted without the need for traffic management and can provide a cost effective solution to the bridge engineer's requirements.

The following data examples were acquired on behalf of the UK Highways Agency's contractors, from concrete bridge structures across the M5 motorway in Devon (UK) and the M6 motorway in Cumbria.

Data were acquired by mounting the GPR antenna on a survey vehicle and driving at slow speed (<10 kph) across each bridge deck. The data were sampled at 10 mm intervals controlled by a hub-mounted shaft encoder. GPS data were not recorded during this survey although could have been if required.

GPR profiles were positioned along the middle, nearside and offside wheel-tracks of each lane of the carriageway crossing the structure.

Data analysis was undertaking using Reflex W software produced by Dr Karl Sandmeir. Results were plotted in CAD and Microsoft Excel for use by the bridge engineers.

The equipment used was Utsi Electronics' Groundvue 3 with 1.5 GHz and 4 GHz antennas.

The deck of the bridge is shown in Figure 7 with the sideview with the pillar supports in Figure 8.

At 1.5 GHz, Figure 9, the asphalt to concrete interface is clearly visible at about 70 mm with large amplitude rebar returns. There is no hint of a wearing layer interface in this section.

At 4 GHz, Figures 10 to 12, the wearing layer is clearly detectable at depth varying from 10 to 40 mm. Some areas have large amplitudes, a sign of delamination. In Figure 10, the extra reinforcement at the pillars is seen at the centre of the plot. Figure 11 is the data from the beginning of the bridge, showing the multilayering of the asphalt and the rebar geometry.

One method of location of rebars is to migrate the hyperbolic responses from the targets. This is done assuming a velocity in the asphaltic wearing

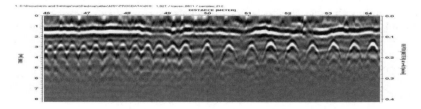

Figure 9. 1.5 GHz antenna, ground coupled.

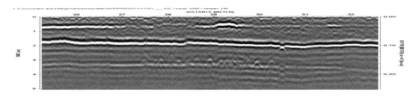

Figure 10. 4 GHz antenna, ground coupled.

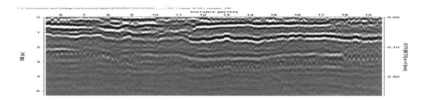

Figure 11. 4 GHz antenna, ground coupled.

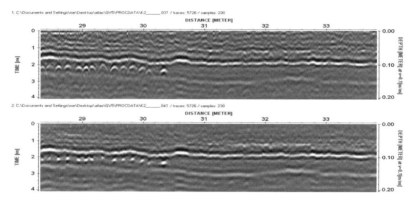

Figure 12. 4 GHz antenna, without/with migration.

course. A search for the best fit velocity, and therefore accurate depth calibration can be done by changing the velocity until the best 'focus' of the rebars is achieved. This is shown in the lower part of Figure 10.

However, when it comes to detecting the presence of rebars, the human eye is much better at detecting the faint hyperbolic shape than the migrated weak point. The rebars at the bottom of Figure 10 are an example of this. As the depth resolution is very high, the trace sampling distance has to be low, typically less than 10 mm, when rebars are to be measured to avoid distance aliasing.

4 CONCLUSION

As long as the frequency of a GPR antenna is higher than 3 GHz, It is possible to measure the layering in asphalt with a resolution better than

10 mm. This means it is a fast way to detect and map delamination of the wearing course and asphalt/concrete bond. The much larger return from a waterfilled delamination means this can be differentiated from an air filled gap.

The delamination of fibre reinforced polymers structures with its thin layers was the first application of the 4 GHz GPR antenna.

Other applications of high frequency antenna with this performance is the detection of concrete repair problems like corrosion due to salt ingress. This causes moisture retention and microcracking which changes both the speed and attenuation of the radiowave in the affected area.

REFERENCES

Sandmeier, K. Reflex-Win V6.0 www.sandmeier-geo.de (accessed 27 July 2011).

Concrete Solutions – Grantham, Mechtcherine & Schneck (eds)
© *2012 Taylor & Francis Group, London, ISBN 978-0-415-61622-5*

Structural life management system of box culverts for power transmission lines

S.K. Woo, Y.C. Song & J.H. Jo
Korea Electric Power Research Institute, Daejeon, Korea

J.H. Park
nexGeo, Seoul, Korea

Y. Lee
Daejeon University, Daejeon, Korea

ABSTRACT: The construction of underground structures such as box culverts for electric power transmission is increasing more and more, and the life extension of these structures is very important. The development of structural life management systems that address structural integrity evaluation is needed and widely discussed. Therefore, the Structural Life Management System (SLMS-BC) for box culverts has been developed. SLMS-BC consists of three parts, aging investigation system using a 3D optic scanner, Database system and structural integrity evaluation system. SLMS-BC makes significant progress in maintenance technology for box culverts and has a number of advantages compared with conventional methods by visual inspection.

1 INTRODUCTION

Box culverts for electrical power transmission began to be constructed in the mid-1970s in Korea and are increasing in numbers recently due to power demand growth and underground installation of transmission lines. The amount of related maintenance work also continues to increase because of the increasing usage life of the constructed box culverts. The existing structural integrity investigation and evaluation methods for these box culverts, affected by the subjective judgment of the investigator, are not quantitative and have the disadvantage of consuming excessive time and effort. Therefore, for an objective and efficient integrity evaluation of box culverts, there is a need to develop a more systematic and rational maintenance system that quantitatively reflects the structural performance. As such, this study seeks to contribute to establishing a scientific maintenance system by developing a box culvert maintenance DB system using a 3D optical scanner and a high-definition camera and integrating this system with a box culvert structural integrity evaluation system.

2 STRUCTURAL LIFE MANAGEMENT SYSTEM FOR BOX CULVERT

2.1 System outline

The system developed in this study is composed of three parts: an aging investigation system using a 3D optical scanner; a maintenance DB system managing the degradation data and repair history data of box culverts; and a structural integrity evaluation system that executes integrity evaluation utilizing the box culvert data collected from the diagnostic and maintenance DB system (Fig. 1).

With the large quantity of box culvert degradation data gained through the diagnostic system linked to the maintenance DB system, the maintenance work efficiency is doubled, and with the box culvert data obtained from these systems used as the input data for the structural integrity evaluation system, objectivity is secured in terms of structural integrity evaluation.

2.2 Aging investigation system of box culvert

When the development of the aging investigation system is considered in terms of main units, it can be divided into the following modules: obtaining 3D image data, lining up and matching the obtained 3D images, measurements based on actual 3D coordinates, and input/output system related to data management and storage. The development of the 3D image data obtaining system can be divided into scanning system development using a laser slit beam and optical 3D scanning system development. The optical scanner of this system is a 3D scanner based on the space encoding method that uses a pattern beam.

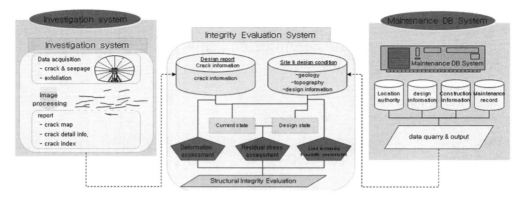

Figure 1. Outline of structural integrity evaluation system.

Its scan range is 400×300 mm, degree of precision less than 0.1 mm, and scan cycle time less than 1 second (Fig. 2).

2.3 Structural integrity evaluation system

The structural integrity evaluation system was designed to select the evaluation target items based on the DB and laser scanning data, calculate the evaluation value and weight for each evaluation item, and deduce the integrity evaluation results by using a technique for incorporating the calculations. The system was built so that the variables needed for the evaluation are linked to the maintenance DB system and automatically entered as input, thus excluding repetition of additional data input during the evaluation. Simplification of the system was achieved by incorporating the crack patterns in a menu from which a selection can be made from 8 patterns.

In addition, since it is difficult to have evaluation done by an expert on a regular inspection basis and not every evaluation item can be inspected because of the characteristics of box culvert structures, there will necessarily be instances where a non-expert has do the evaluation or where some of the evaluation items cannot inspected. To resolve this problem, in this system the inspection results of each inspection item were quantified based on the fuzzy concept, and the evaluation technique of the evaluation system used the fuzzy integral which has excellent applicability for subjective decision making problems and makes it possible to do an appropriate evaluation even when some evaluation items are omitted.

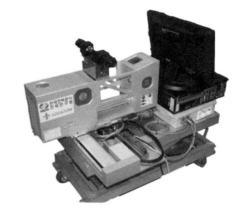

(a) 3D Scanning System

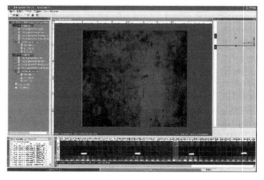

(b) Image processing S/W

Figure 2. Aging investigation system of box culvert.

2.4 DB system for maintenance

In consideration of this system's future compatibility and scalability, a standardization of the box culvert DB information was implemented. Accordingly this was reflected in the system's design based on reference to the Transmission and Substation Geographic Information System (TGIS) operated within KEPCO. Incorporation of the DB item table for the box culvert facilities used in the TGIS in the box culvert structural integrity evaluation system enabled the system to prevent repeated input of the same items and confusion by users. Furthermore, through the data analysis of similar systems such as the Structural Integrated Degradation DB System (SIMS), which is a nuclear power plant structural maintenance system, and the Water Tunnel Maintenance System (DB of Japan's Central Research Institute of Electric Power Industry), the degradation and repair/reinforcement history management technique was referenced and reflected in the system's design.

By displaying the box culvert information on a single screen, the maintenance DB system allows immediate access to information for each item; and by organizing the maintenance lists in a tree structure form, it increases the use intuitiveness. For various degradation states and repair histories resulting from aging, a history of maintenance based on yearly changes was made possible by codifying the investigation and repair periods of the degradation object; and by showing the degradation object and maintenance DB on a planar diagram in linkage with the box culvert image data. The system allows the user to verify together each degradation object information and the repaired degradation object information.

3 APPLICATION ANALYSIS FOR BOX CULVERT

Fig. 3 shows the test system in use. The results from using the optical scanner showed that fine data verification for the weathered area is possible, but the verification of the measurement results for the water leakage area was difficult. Therefore, the function that makes possible identification by visual inspection based on the change in the laser brightness value and on the scanner's projector image

Figure 3. On-site application test for box culvert.

response value was supplemented. In addition, since there is no change in the 3D shape information for simple water leakage without surface and height gaps, it was difficult to verify water leakage when the shape measurement was done by using the 3D scanner. Hence the method of using a 2D black and white image was applied in the inspection system for water leakage verification.

4 CONCLUSIONS

The research results of this study are as follows.

1. The structural life management system developed through this study is a system not for just evaluating box culverts. This system integrates the database conversion of data obtained from the operation of the on-site investigation system, the image processing and the integrity evaluation algorithm to work together seamlessly.
2. By replacing the part of the existing investigation process that depended on visual observation with a diagnostic system of a structural integrity evaluation system, data objectivity was secured. The related work efficiency was increased by going a step beyond the existing method of managing maintenance history as a ledger and managing it through a maintenance DB system.
3. In addition, to improve the work efficiency of the maintenance work manager, DB information standardization was achieved based on the DB items of the existing maintenance system. In developing the interface part between each system modules, priority was placed on consideration of user convenience.
4. It is deemed that the structural life management system developed in this study can contribute to improving the efficiency of the structural integrity evaluation work process for box culvert.

REFERENCES

Choo, J.H., Kim, H.T., 2008, The Enhanced Assessment of the Integrity on Underground Structure by using the Primary Inspection in Precise Safety Diagnosis. *Proc. of Korea Society of Civil Engineer(KSCE)*, 4171–4174.

Haibara, T., Nakatsui, K., Ito, M. and Nakatsubo, Y., 1997. "Evaluation of load carrying capacity of aged RC sewers", *Proceedings of the 52th Annual Conference of JSCE* 6, 576–577.

Honda, G.H., 1999. Experimental study of deformation capacity of box culvert by horizontal load. *Proceedings of Japan Concrete Institute.* 21(3):1261–1266.

Osako, K., Koiwa, S., Kitahashi, N., Akimoto, E. and Nakatsui, K., 1998. A rehabilitation technology by SPR method and evaluation of load carrying capacity. *Proceedings of JCI Symposium on Repair and rehabilitation of concrete structures.* 120–123.

Shi, Z., Nakano, M., Ishibashi, A. and Yoshida, T., 1998. Assessment of load carrying capacity of tunnel lining with inner reinforcement by the elastic softening model, *Proceedings of JCI Symposium on Repair and rehabilitation of concrete structures.* 83–86.

Shi, Z. and Nakano, M., 1998. Numerical approach based on the energy criterion in fracture analysis of concrete structures, *Proceedings FRAMCOS-3*, AEDIFICA-TIO Publishers, D-79104 Freiburg, Germany.

Yokoyama, H., Osako, K., Koiwa, S., Kitahashi, N. and Akimoto, E., 1997. A new technique for sewer rehabilitation applicable to noncircular cross sections: Development and Application.

Zihai Shi, et al. 2001. Numerical Analysis of Mutiple Cracks In Concrete Using The Discrete Approach, *Journal of Structural Engineering*, ASCE, 1085–1091.

Zihai Shi., 2004. Numerical Analysis of Mixed-Mode Fracture in Concrete Using Extended Fictitious Crack Model, *Journal of Structural Engineering*, ASCE, 1738–1747.

Concrete Solutions – Grantham, Mechtcherine & Schneck (eds)
© 2012 Taylor & Francis Group, London, ISBN 978-0-415-61622-5

Modular Corrosion Measurement System (CMS) for electrochemical NDT

K. Ahlborn, F. Berthold & W. Vonau
Kurt-Schwabe-Institut für Mess—und Sensortechnik e.V. Meinsberg, Germany

H. Grünzig & U. Schneck
Concrete Improvement Technologies GmbH, Germany

H. Jahn & J. Köhler
Sensortechnik Meinsberg GmbH, Germany

ABSTRACT: Combination, comparison and application of electrochemical methods to evaluate the state of corrosion of reinforcing steel, taking the condition of concrete into account, in principle have been demonstrated in the past. In this contribution, a modular Corrosion Measurement System (CMS) for the determination of electrochemical parameters of the concrete as well as of the steel reinforcement is introduced. The system possesses a specialised measurement and control device, an electrochemical measuring cell with a multi electrode assembly to be used for surface measurements and for measurements to characterise the concrete steel and application software to analyse and interpret the experimental data with the objective of an estimation of corrosion conditions of reinforced concrete.

1 INTRODUCTION

Status checks of reinforced concrete structures are doubtless very important concerning the safety of buildings and the initiation of value-preserving and safety-relevant measures (Elsener et al., 1996). In this connection it is desirable to provide a cost-effective and appropriate on-site method including the required measuring equipment for its application. To achieve this aim, a number of electrochemical investigations have been carried out both separately and in combination, first on representative test pieces in the laboratory and later on real objects. Thereby different ambient conditions were considered, e.g., depending on the season.

As a result of the research, a measuring cell and a measuring device that is optimally equipped for its use were aimed for the special case of the space-resolved determination of the corrosion state of reinforced concrete. A further objective was also to allow users of the measuring system, who are not highly skilled in that field, an interpretation of the acquired data material. Therefore by the end of this project, software was to be developed for the data processing and the visualisation of the state of corrosion of the evaluated ferro-concrete.

2 ELECTROCHEMICAL MEASURING CELL

The combination measuring cell (CMC) (Fig. 1) that can be positioned on the surface to be evaluated is designed both for a time-resolved use at user-selected points and for space-resolved laminar investigations. It forms a composite-arrangement of metal and reference electrodes.

Figure 1. Combination measuring cell (CMC) used for corrosion investigations of reinforced concrete.

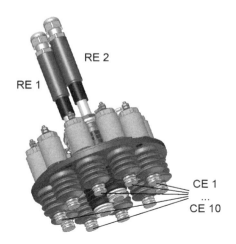

Figure 2. Combination measuring cell (engineering drawing).
-case remove.
CE 1 ... CE10: Current conducting electrodes for the polarisation of reinforcing steel and to characterise the concrete surface.
RE1, RE2: Reference electrodes.

For polarisation of the steel reinforcement in the concrete, ten metal electrodes consisting of stainless steel are arranged around two reference electrodes, all contained in a cylindrical steel case. Additionally, a temperature sensor is integrated. Because of the resilient mounting of the metal electrodes, unevenness of the concrete surface to be examined can be compensated. An optimal contact between electrodes and concrete is ensured by the use of a wettable fleece that is stretched over the front face of the metal electrodes. Depending on the measurement method used, the electrodes can be interconnected.

Figure 2 shows the combined measuring cell.

For comparative measurements, robust long-term stable reference electrodes are necessary. For the monitoring of steel structures with electrochemical methods up to now reference electrodes of the 1. kind (e.g., Cu/CuSO$_4$ (Arup 1990) und MnO$_2$/Mn$_2$O$_3$ (Arup et al., 1997)) and systems based on C, Ti (Castro et al., 1996, Duffo et al., 2010) Pb and Zn as well as reference electrodes of the 2. kind (Ag/AgCl, Cl$^-$) are used. The classification of reference electrode systems is described in detail e.g., by Schwabe 1986.

For the application within the CMS, position independent reference electrodes with special internal electrolyte for different climatic conditions were developed. In this connection the conventional Cu/CuSO$_4$-half cell was modified in that way that a gelformer was added to the CuSO$_4$-solution that surrounds the copper electrode and thereby, the solution was immobilised.

Figure 3. Ag/AgCl solid state reference electrode.

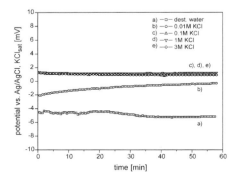

Figure 4. Potential-time behaviour of a polymer based Ag/AgCl solid state reference electrode in different measurement solutions.

A polymer based electrode with an epoxy or polyester resin, filled with KCl as ionic conductor and containing an Ag/AgCl reference element, represents a novel solid state reference system which can be used independent of position. Compared to an Ag/AgCl, KCl$_{sat}$. electrode the solid state reference electrode shows potential differences <5 mV when switching between different measurement solutions. Figure 3 shows a Ag/AgCl reference half cell, used in the equipment. Figure 4 shows the Potential-Time behaviour of a typical Ag/AgCl reference cell in different test solutions.

3 METHODICAL STUDIES WITH THE CMC

With CMS one has a good tool for the measurement for condition analysis of reinforced concrete elements. By combination of several measurement methods with a specialised potentiostatic system and the application of these methods in parallel using the novel combination measuring cell, on the one hand it is possible to optimise the methods by variation of parameters and on the other hand to interpret different measuring values per measuring position in a comparative manner. In Table 1 the measuring process at one place is exemplary shown.

Table 1. Typical test procedure of the CMS.

Measurement	Application	Remark	Analysis
1	Impedance of the concrete surface	4-electrode-principle	$Z_S = f(f)$
2	EIS (electrochemical impedance spectroscopy); impedance between surface and reinforcement	Potentiostatic	$Z_C = f(f)$, R_D
3	Potential of the reinforcement	Measurement duration for the otential adjustable: e.g., t = 60 s	$U_0 = f(t)$
4	GPM galvanostatic pulse method	Duration of the polarisation and current amplitude adjustable: e.g., t = 60 s, I_K = 500 µA	$U_K = f(t)$, R_P, R_D
5	Potential of the reinforcement	Measurement duration for the potential adjustable: e.g., t = 60 s	$U_0 = f(t)$
6 (optional)	LPR (linear polarisation resistance) potentiostaic polarisation with IR-compensation	$U_P \approx \pm 50$ mV, v = 0.1 mV s^{-1}	$I_P = f(U_P)$, R_P, R_D

Designations:

Z_S: calculated impedance of the concrete surface

Z_C: calculated impedance of the concrete between combination measuring cell and reinforcement contact + Ohmic resistance of the reinforcement

U_0: measured potential of the reinforcement in the current-free state

I_K: effective constant current during a galvanostatic polarisation

U_K: measured polarisation potential at current I_K

U_C: Ohmic voltage drop at current I_K: $U_C = U_{K|t=0}$

U_R: galvanostatic polarisation potential of the reinforcement: $U_R = U_K - U_C$

U_P: potentiostatic polarisation potential (corrected by the Ohmic voltage drop U_D)

U_D: Ohmic voltage drop during a potentiostatic polarisation

I_P: measured potentiostatic polarisation current

v: rate of change of the potentiostatic polarisation voltage U_S

R_P: polarisation resistance of the reinforcement

R_D: resistance between surface and reinforcement (Ohmic resistance)

C_P: capacity of the phase boundary layer at the reinforcing steel

IR-compensation (Ohmic drop compensation): During the potentiostatic polarisation an Ohmic IR-drop (in the main: resistance between surface and reinforcement) between reference electrode (as part of the CMC) and the working electrode (reinforcement) can disturb the effective polarisation of the reinforcement. The measuring- and control device of the CMS can compensate this Ohmic voltage drop according to the current interrupt method (Oelßner et al., 2006). This very complex and sophisticated method is used in polarisation resistance measurements on reinforced concrete (Nygaard 2008) for about thirty years.

Parameters such as measurement period, polarisation current, polarisation voltage and frequency range can be varied quickly for an optimal condition analysis. It is possible to detect time-dependent different conditions of reinforcing steel at several places or at one point by estimation of a number of measured parameters, e.g.:

– potential of the reinforcement
– potential-time behaviour of the reinforcement during as well as after galvanostatic measurement
– current-potential behaviour during potentiostatic measurement

For the optimisation of the specialised measurement and control device as well as of the procedures for the complex analysis and interpretation of the measurement data, several investigations were carried out using a potentiostat/galvanostat Gamry Reference 600 (www.gamry.com). This device is especially suited for basic investigations (also concerning IR-compensation) because of its extensive configuration options. The following measurements and analyses (made with the system Gamry Refernce 600 and the CMC) are related to one point of the concrete construction.

In Fig. 5 measured and calculated parameters from point P 6 of a reinforced concrete pavement in external conditions are shown. The contact with the reinforcement was made at a distance of about 0.5 m from the measuring point of the CMC. The determination of the polarisation resistance R_P can be carried out by analysis of the adjustment behaviour of the galvanostatic polarisation potential $U_R = U_K - U_C$ (Fig. 5.1 A) or by analysis of the slope of the potentiostatic current-potential curve in the range around about ±50 mV of the corrosion potential (Fig. 5.2 A). It is remarkable that (concerning the determination of the polarisation resistance R_P) comparable results to the galvanostatic pulse method could be achieved by using an IR-compensation in the process of the potentiostatic polarisation.

As can be seen in Fig. 5.1 B the Ohmic voltage drop U_C is about four times greater than the effective polarisation potential U_R of the reinforcement. These results match very well with the values from potentiostatic polarisation measurements (Fig. 5.2) to determine the polarisation resistance and the concrete resistance.

The final value of the galvanostatic polarisation voltage mostly cannot be received during real polarisation periods. For this reason the determination of polarisation resistances can be obtained by regression analysis of the measured data with the simple and, for a lot of applications, appropriate, model according to Fig. 5.1 C. Accurate results deliver the use of a lossy capacity (Birbilis et al., 2004) that is also known from impedance measurements (Göhr 1981). For the equivalent circuit according to Fig. 5.1 C the transfer function [run of the voltage vs. $R_P//C_P$ with parameter a as measurand of the non-ideal capacitive behaviour $(0 < a \leq 1)$] is given as Equation (1).

$$U(t) = I \cdot R_P \left(1 - e^{-\left(\frac{t}{R_P \cdot C_P}\right)^a} \right) \tag{1}$$

In Table 2 results of several resistance calculations are summarised. From this it is noticeable that the complementary methods can provide good pre-conditions for correct quality assessments.

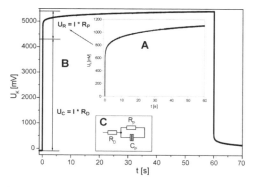

Figure 5. Results of field measurements with the CMC from point 6 at the concrete pavement.

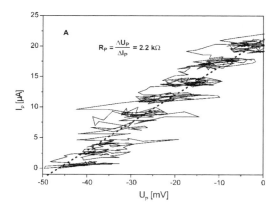

Figure 5.1. Galvanostatic polarisation.
$I_K = 500\ \mu A$, $t = 60\ s$.
A. Analysis of the galvanostatic polarisation potential U_R.
B. Calculated polarisation potential $U_K = f (I_K)$.
C. Model of the concrete-steel arrangement.

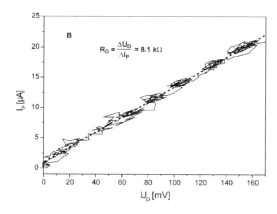

Figure 5.2. Potentiostatic polarisation with IR-compensation $\Delta U_P = 50\ mV$, $v = 0.1\ mV\ s^{-1}$.
A. Determination of the polarisation resistance R_p
B. Determination of the resistance between surface and reinforcement R_D (Ohmic resistance).

Table 2. Compilation of results of calculated parameters from point 6 of a reinforced concrete pavement outside.

Method	Polarisation resistance R_p	Resistance between surface and reinforcement (Ohmic resistance) R_D
GPM	2.9 kΩ	8.8 kΩ
LPR	2.2 kΩ	8.1 kΩ
EIS	–	10 k … 8 kΩ (f = 100 mHz … 100 Hz)

430

4 SPECIALISED MEASUREMENT AND CONTROL DEVICE

Another task was the realisation of a complex, modular measurement and control system which enables a recording of the relevant parameters for further processing and analysis by an external computer system. A recent structure with pre-located impedance converters, to minimise the influence of electromagnetic disturbance, a module for measuring surface resistance and concrete resistance and a potentiostat/ galvanostat module to perform complex measurements of different electrochemical methods are the core of the system. The control unit, consisting of an embedded PC, is responsible for the correct connection of the modules to the cell, depending on the selected measurement principle and also for the communication to the modules via a CAN bus. Simultaneously, the embedded PC unit records, analyses, reduces and stores the data for access by the external evaluation system. Communication is done via an Ethernet interface with a special protocol, placed on the TCP / IP protocol. The system also operates independently without additional power supply, therefore a battery pack and a charging system were implemented. Figure 6 shows diagrammatically the structure of the modular acquisition system.

The first research was successfully performed in the laboratory with dummy cells. Different configurations and the reproducibility with data

acquisition rates of 1000samples/s were tested. Initial investigations in free-field confirmed the results of the laboratory tests.

5 PROCEDURES FOR THE COMPLEX ANALYSIS AND INTERPRETATION OF THE MEASUREMENT DATA

The CMS was created to provide not only a huge set of corrosion relevant measurement data, but to characterise the corrosion status of the reinforcement as a result of internal, automated cross-checking of the received data. It was the aim to enable also operators who are not specialised in corrosion science, to run a corrosion survey with sound results and safe interpretation. This includes also cases where no definite interpretation can be given—caused either by unsafe measurement conditions or by uncertain internal assessment results. It is in-tended to close the usual gap between data measurement and their logical and mathematical interpretation within one system.

A whole sequence of different measurements will be run on every sampling point. The scope of measurements covers the quality of reinforcement connection, the rest potential, surface resistivity, resistance between surface and reinforcement and a galvanostatic pulse. Depending on the quality of raw data (Fig. 7), the duration of the automated sequence lasts between 20 and 60 s, and within acceptable time, extended data can be obtained and assessed from large concrete surfaces. If signals e.g., of rest potentials are unstable, the measurement duration will be extended by the control software, and the resistivity value between reference electrode and reinforcement will be taken as one start parameter for calculating the IR drop for the galvanostatic pulse measurement evaluation.

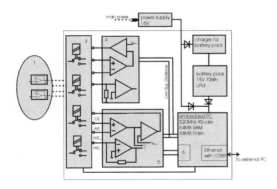

Figure 6. Main structure of the modular acquisition system.
1. CMC with 2 reference electrodes and counter electrodes for different measurement application.
2. Two impedance converter for reference electrodes.
3. Relay matrix to connect the different modules and measurement electrodes to the cell.
4. Module for measurement of the resistance of the surface of the concrete.
5. Potentiostat/galvanostat module with high speed data acquisition and second CPU for EIS measurement.
6. Second interface channel for high speed data transfer to the embedded PC.

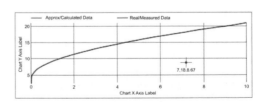

RESULT: A: 2.0000, B: 0.5000, C:0.1000, D: 0.1000
Calculated constants after approximation:
Help: result == 2 ->> good approx. quality
Help: result != 2 ->> bad approx. quality
Result: 2
A: 2.3400, B: 0.5023, C: 0.1005, D: 0.2000
Errors:
Rootmean square deviation Error: 0.0000004226
Maximal Error: 0.0000009531
Average Error: 0.0000003437
Related average Error: 0.0000000225

Figure 7. Quality control of the raw data.

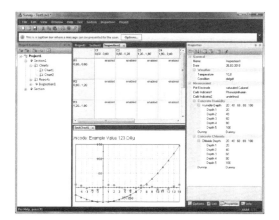

Figure 8. Data comparison of neighbouring measurements.

As a result of the internal data processing, not only the measurement results themselves are provided and displayed, but also information about the status of corrosion activity—for a complete grid of survey. A logical data comparison helps to find the appropriate result or states uncertainties, if contradictions arise (Fig. 8). More detailed information to evaluate even the speed of corrosion can be received from polarisation measurements, which are also included in the system.

In a next step, all these data—sampled on a single measurement location, can be interlinked with the neighbouring values for a more complex evaluation, which follows always logical thoughts. If all different data fit into a common scheme of interpretation (such as negative rest potentials and low resistivity and large galvanostatic potential shift indicating no corrosion, but wet concrete), an automated corrosion assessment will be provided. For special situations, a manual operation is possible, too.

6 CONCLUSIONS

A new corrosion measurement system, consisting of a combination measuring cell and a network-compatible modular measurement and control system is introduced to evaluate the surface of concrete and the corrosion status of reinforcement.

Complex analysis of raw measurement data by internal processing with data comparison enables their logical and mathematical interpretation within one system.

ACKNOWLEDGEMENT

Financial support of extensive parts of this joint research work by the European Union and the Free State of Saxony (SAB project number: 13059/2200) is gratefully acknowledged.

REFERENCES

Arup, H. 1990. Embeddable Reference Electrodes for Use in Concrete, *Nordic Concrete Research*. Publication 9: 6–13.
Arup, H., Klinghoffer, O. & Mietz, J. 1997. Manganese Dioxide Reference Electrodes for Use in Concrete, *EFC-Publications* 25: 40ff.
Birbilis, N., Nairn, K.M. & Forsyth, M. 2004. On the electrochemical response and interfacial properties of steel–$Ca(OH)_2$ and the steel–concrete system measured using galvanostatic pulses. *Electrochimica Acta* 49: 4331–4339.
Castro, P., Sagües, A.A. et al., 1996. Characterization of Activated Titanium Solid Reference Electrodes for Corrosion Testing of Steel in Concrete. *Corrosion* 52(8): 609–617.
Duffo, G.S., Farina, S.B. & Giordano, C.M. 2009. Characterization of solid embeddable reference electrodes for corrosion, *Electrochimica Acta* 54: 1010–1020.
Elsener, B., Flückiger, D., Wojtas, H. & Böhni, H. 1996. Methoden zur Erfassung der Korrosion von Stahl in Beton. *Forschungsbericht Eidgenössische Technische Hochschule Zürich.*
Göhr, H. 1981. Über Beiträge einzelner Elektrodenprozesse zur Impedanz; *Ber. Bunsenges. Phys. Chem.* 85: 274–280.
Nygaard, P.V. 2008. *Non-destructive electrochemical monitoring of reinforcement corrosion*. PhD Thesis, Department of Civil Engineering Technical University of Denmark.
Oelßner, W., Berthold, F. & Guth, U. 2006. The ir drop—well known but often underestimated in electrochemical polarization measurements and corrosion testing. *Materials and Corrosion* 57(6): 455–466.
Schwabe, K. 1986. *Physikalische Chemie. Band 2. Elektrochemie*. Berlin: Akademie-Verlag.
www.gamry.com: Reference 600 Potentiostat/Galvanostat/ZRA.

Patch repair

Concrete Solutions – Grantham, Mechtcherine & Schneck (eds)
© 2012 Taylor & Francis Group, London, ISBN 978-0-415-61622-5

Application of polymer concrete in repair of concrete structures: A literature review

Reza Allahvirdizadeh, R. Rashetnia, Ali Dousti & M. Shekarchi
*Construction Materials Institute, Department of civil Engineering, Faculty of Engineering,
University of Tehran, Tehran, Iran*

ABSTRACT: Use of concrete as a structural material has increased in recent years. It has been found that some concrete structures, even when constructed with high performance concrete, start to deteriorate long before reaching their designed service life. In these cases, cracks occur after the structure has been completed for a few years, which results in the shortening of service life and lowering in durability. Finally as is obvious, durability modification in concrete must be considered in construction or in repair of damaged structures. The durability of a concrete repair is dependent on many factors. In fact, failure of a concrete repair material is more likely to occur due to incompatibility between the repair material and concrete or high shrinkage levels. Moreover, other factors can lead to cracking and debonding, which allows chloride, carbon dioxide or detereoriative agents to penetrate. Based on some research that is presented in this paper, it is proved that polymer concrete has high acid, salt and freeze-thaw resistance in comparison with conventional concrete, high chemical stability under corrosive environments for a long period of time, high compressive strength, low conductivity, high resistance to permeation of water and shows its maximum strength, maximum shrinkage etc. at a young age. A combination of these characteristics makes polymer concrete an attractive choice in repair.

1 INTRODUCTION

Modern concrete is a very durable construction material and, if properly proportioned and placed will give very long service under normal conditions. Many reclamation concrete structures, however, were constructed using early concrete technology, and they have already provided well over 50 years of service under harsh conditions. Such concrete must be inspected regularly to ensure that it is receiving the maintenance necessary to retain serviceability. Managers and foremen of operation and maintenance crews must understand that, with respect to concrete, there is no such thing as economical deferred maintenance. Failure to promptly provide the proper necessary maintenance will simply result in very expensive repairs or replacement of otherwise useful structures (Glenn Smoak, 2002).

So it is obvious that the state of the structure must be under review regularly. One of the most important factors is durability. Durability of concrete is defined as: "its ability to resist weathering action, chemical attack, abrasion or any other process of deterioration. Durable concrete will retain its original form, quality and serviceability when exposed to the environment." (ACI 201.2 R92, 2006). The durability of a concrete repair is an important issue and depends on many factors. Those most often considered are compressive strength and low permeability (Decter & Keleey, 1997).

After all, concrete will need repair, locally if maintained well and generally if users do not attend to that. Repair and rehabilitation of deteriorated concrete is an art as well as science. The repair engineer must have the imagination to select and adapt any of several repair techniques to fix the existing defect (Soudki, 2001). Concrete repair requires a range of materials with different physical and chemical properties and application techniques. Compatibility with the original construction material (called the substrate), structural considerations and ease of use in a wide variety of situations are all crucial. Despite these accepted principles, many architects and engineers design rehabilitation projects without sufficient knowledge of the materials they specify. They often do not appreciate the meaning and importance of compatibility between repair materials and the substrate. It is unclear whether most standard tests are representative of field conditions, yet they are often used to determine durability criteria for field use. The development of performance standards has not kept pace with the development of materials, primarily because of a lack of supporting

Table 1. Concrete repair methods and materials (Soudki, 2001).

Defects	Repair methods	Materials
Live cracks	Caulking Pressure injection with flexible filler Jacketing Strengthening	Elastomeric sealer Flexiable epoxy filler Steel, wire or rod Steel plate, etc.
Domant cracks	Caulking Pressure injection with rigid filler Coating	Cement grout or mortar Rigid epoxy filler
	Overlying	Bituminous coating, Tar Asphalt overlay with membrane
	Grinding and Overlay	Latex modified concrete
	Dry-pack	Dry-pack
	Shotcrete	Fast-setting mortar
	Patching	Epoxy or Polymer concrete
	Jacketing	Steel rod
	Strengthening	Post Tensioning, etc.
Voids Hollows and Honeycombs	Dry pack	Dry pack
	Patching	Portland cement grout
	Resurfacing	Epoxy or Polymer concrete
	Shotcrete	Fast-setting mortar
	Preplaced aggregate	Coarse aggregate and grout
	Replacing	As needed
Scaling damage	Overlaying	Portland cement concrete, Latex modified concrete
	Grinding	Asphalt cement, polymer concrete
	Shotcrete	Fast setting mortar
	Coating	Bituminous
	Replacement	As needed
Spalling damage	Patching	Concrete, Epoxy, polymer
	Shotcrete	Cement mortar
	Overlay	Latex modified concrete
	Coating	Bituminous
	Replacement	As needed

scientific and field data. Thus, it is no surprise that there is a high failure rate with new technologies and materials. A more direct means is required for linking the properties of repair materials with quality and performance of what is actually produced in the field. The challenge for the future involves gaining a better understanding of the mechanisms involved in concrete deterioration as they relate to the environmental conditions in which structures perform; of the effects of material modifications, and of the controlling parameters of new composites (Mailvaganam, Zhang, 2006).

Developing a proper strategy to address concrete problems requires an understanding of the cause of the problem. Understanding the cause allows for a repair that addresses both cause and effect (Soudki, 2001). The first and often most important step of repairing damaged or deteriorated concrete is to correctly determine the cause of the damage. If the cause of the original damage to concrete is not determined and eliminated, or if an incorrect determination is made, whatever damaged the original concrete will likely also damage the repaired concrete. Money and effort spent for such repairs is, thus, totally wasted. Additionally, larger and even more costly replacement repairs will then be required (Glenn Smoak, 2002). Common cause of distress and deterioration of concrete are: Accidental Loadings, Chemical Reactions (Acid Attach, Aggressive-water attach, Alkali-carbonate rock reaction, Alkali-silica reaction, Miscellaneous chemical attach, Sulfate attach), Construction Errors, Corrosion of Embedded Metals, Design Errors (Inadequate structural design, Poor design details), Erosion (Abrasion, Cavitations), Freezing and Thawing, Settlement and Movement, Shrinkage (Plastic, Drying), Temperature Changes (Internally generated, Externally generated, Fire) and Weathering. Concrete repair refers to bringing the structure to its original capacity. It can be classified either cosmetic repairs or rehabilitational type repairs (Soudki, 2001). In Table 1 concrete repair methods and materials are shown for repairs.

As seen in Table 1, polymer concrete is very common in repair methods, which shows its impressive implementation. In this paper we will discuss different types of polymer concretes, their mechanical properties and usage in repair of concrete structures.

2 TYPES OF POLYMER CONCRETE

Polymers in concrete have received considerable attention over the past 35 years (Fowler, 1999). Polymers have been employed as concrete admixtures and based on the mode of their addition, polymer cement concrete is classified as—polymer modified cement concrete or mortars (PMC/PMM), polymer concrete or mortars (PC/PM), polymer impregnated concrete or mortars (PIC/PIM) (Mook Lee et al., 1999). Polymer-impregnated concrete (PIC) was the first concrete polymer composite to receive widespread publicity. PIC has excellent strength and durability properties, but it has few commercial applications. Polymer concrete (PC) became well known in the 1970s and is used for repair, thin overlays for floors and bridges, and for precast components (Fowler, 1999).

PIC first became widely known after Brookhaven National Laboratory and the Bureau of Reclamation in the US performed extensive research on the material in the 1960s, although USSR researchers claimed to have invented Portland cement concrete with a low viscosity monomer, usually methyl methacrylate, which was subsequently polymerized by radiation or thermal catalytic techniques (Fowler, 1999). Or conventionally PICs are prepared by immersing the precast concrete structure in a mixture of monomer and an initiator for a few hours at room temperature and polymerizing the monomer by thermal methods (Mook Lee, Priya Nair, Woo Lee, Hyun Ku, Soon Park, and Young Park, 1999).

PC was used as early as 1958 in the US to produce building cladding. PC consists of aggregate with a polymer binder and contains no Portland cement or water. Polyester-styrene, acrylics and epoxies have been the most widely used monomers/resins, but vinyl ester, furan, and urethane, have also been used. Sulphur is also considered to be a polymer and Sulphur concrete has been used for applications requiring high acid resistance (Fowler, 1999).

Polymer modified concrete (PMC) using latexes has been in use since the 1950s (Fowler, 1999). PMC has been called both polymer Portland cement—concrete (PPCC) and latex-modified concrete (LMC). It is defined as Portland cement and aggregate combined at the time of mixing with organic polymers that are dispersed or redispersed in water. This dispersion is called latex; the organic polymer is a substance composed of thousands of simple molecules combined into large molecules (reported by ACI committee 548, 1994). There are different types of polymer modifier such as acrylic or styrene-butadiene latex (SBR), polyvinyl acetate, and ethylene vinyl acetate. From a construction standpoint PMC has the desirable attribute of being very similar to conventional Portland cement concrete technology. The amount of polymer is usually in the range of 10–20% of the Portland cement binder. There are only a few polymers suitable for adding to concrete; most polymers would produce poor quality PMC (Fowler, 1999).

3 EFFECT OF TEMPERATURE ON POLYMER CONCRETE BEHAVIOR

Building components are subjected during their lifetime to changing temperatures. Depending on the geographical location, the temperature can vary from below zero up to about 80°C in direct sunlight, depending on the color of the surface (Reis and Ferreira, 2006).

Generally the high strength polymer concrete exhibit brittle behavior at room temperature that has limited its usefulness. As structural and repair material, polymer concrete must be able to withstand high stresses under extreme service conditions. Thus knowledge of their fracture properties under various temperature conditions is vitally important in aiding their efficient utilization (Vipulanandan and Dharmarjan, 1988).

The main problem of polymeric materials is related to the viscoelastic properties of the polymer, which result in high sensitivity to temperature. Mechanical properties of polymers, undergoing temperature variations, change considerably, especially within the glass transition temperature range. The glass transition takes place over a wide temperature range, which lies between 20 and 80°C for many resins used in civil engineering. This means that during the service lifetime of the materials the glass transition can occur (Reis and Ferreira, 2006).

Polymer concrete is much more susceptible to high temperature than normal cement concrete because the synthetic viscoelastic resin binder used in producing polymer concrete is more temperature sensitive than the inorganic cement binder in producing normal cement concrete. However, despite this loss in strength, polymer concrete remains at least twice as strong as Portland cement concrete, especially in flexure (Rebeiz, 1995).

An increase in temperature results in loss in strength with an increase in temperature from 25 to 60°C decreasing the compressive strength by about 40% (Rebeiz, 1995).

The fracture parameter ratios of polymer concrete to polymer generally increase or remain almost unchanged with increase in temperature.

As the temperature of the test cycles increases, flexural elasticity decreases and failure becomes more ductile, making values of fracture toughness higher. This increase in the values can be explained by molecular mobility of polymeric chains. This mobility increases with temperature, and is associated with local motions of the less hindered side groups around their equilibrium region, molecular mobility increases profoundly leading to configuration rearrangements of the polymer chain backbones. Loss of the mechanical strength is one consequence of this process. However, when polymers are tempered, there is not enough energy to maintain this mobility and therefore, initial cohesion between polymeric chains is recovered (Reis and Ferreira, 2006).

It seems the continuous cycling to temperatures up to +100°C, more than twice that of the epoxy glass transition temperature leads to some degradation of the epoxy network. This phenomenon, not noticeable for one cycle, becomes evident after a certain number of cycles (Reis and Ferreira, 2006).

As is obvious from the above discussion, engineers must be aware when they select and use polymer concretes, since it is probable that because of temperature change and cycling, the concrete may not show the desired behavior and this will cause defects in the repair.

4 FREEZE-THAW INFLUENCE ON THE POLYMER CONCRETE BEHAVIOR

Freeze-thaw resistance is one of the vital factors in the durability of concrete, and it is now well-established that air entrainment improves freeze-thaw durability. Besides the use of conventional air entraining agents, use of polymers is increasing in the concrete field (Chandra, Aavik and Berntsson, 1982).

Chandra et al. have used film-forming polymer micro particles (CEMOS), hard, not film-forming micro particles (CMT1) and conventional air entrainment in their studies. They concluded that in the specimens with same cement, aggregate content and W/C ratio, concrete with micro particles CEMOS has shown minimum damage by freezing and thawing. The damage noticed is mainly on the border of the aggregate to the cement paste. This indicates that the adhesion between the aggregate and cement paste is weakened by the freeze-thaw cycles and concrete deteriorates. The soft micro particles, when dry, form a continuous film which is hydrophobic in character and works as a semi permeable membrane. There might also be a type of cross-linking between the soft micro particles and some components of the cement matrix. This provides better adhesion between the aggregate and cement paste, and reduces the possibility of the concrete deterioration due to the freeze-thaw test. It is further speculated that these micro particles, due to their air entraining property and hydrophobic character, affect the pore size distribution as well as the distance between the pores in concrete. This further affects the volume surface of water in pores and capillaries in the concrete, which is an important factor in freeze-thaw resistance (Chandra, Aavik and Berntsson, 1982).

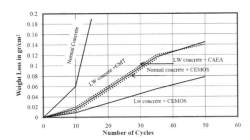

Figure 1. Weight loss of normal concrete, air entrained concrete and concrete with polymers in freeze-thaw cycles (Chandra, Aavik and Berntsson, 1982).

So weight loss of concrete due to freeze-thaw cycles can be a factor of detecting concrete's behavior through these cycles. Figure 1 shows weight loss of different specimens in freeze-thaw cycles (Chandra et al., 1982).

Most of the time, salt solution is used to deice. So it is needed to study polymer concretes subjected to freezing and thawing in the presence of a deicer salt solution.

Bordeleau et al. (1992) made specimens with and without latex modifiers and tested them in freeze-thaw cycles in the presence of a deicer salt solution. They concluded that, the latex-modified concrete specimens absorbed less water during the tests than those made without latex and in general, the latex-modified concretes performed very well during the scaling tests (Bordeleau, Pigeon, Banthia, 1992).

5 EFFECT OF AGGRESSIVE AGENTS ON POLYMER CONCRETE BEHAVIOR

Structures are designated durable if they exhibit the required service properties under the planned service conditions over the project service life with low maintenance costs. Ordinary Portland cement concrete is a ready-to-use, widely available material, but its low durability under some service conditions seems to be the price paid for its universality. The exposure of ordinary cement concrete to acid solutions and alkaline environments brings out a rapid deterioration of the material's external surface. Acid reacts with hydrated and unhydrated compounds and decomposes them and over time; this type of concrete will show signs of wear (Reis, 2010).

Due to the lack of conventional cement concrete structure's durability under certain service conditions, this has drawn the attention to polymer concrete (Reis, 2010).

Different research has been done to understand behavior of polymer concretes in aggressive conditions and have used various parameters such as weight loss, compressive strength, fracture toughness and fracture energy to compare ordinary Portland cement concrete with polymer concrete.

Based on these studies, the degree of deterioration depends on the type of acid and type of polymer that is used in concrete (Chandra and Berntsson, 1983). For example based on works done by Chandra et al. concrete with polymer micro particles is more resistant to hydrochloric acid attack than concrete with a conventional air entraining agent, and concrete with polymer micro particles is less resistant to sulfuric acid than normal concrete without micro particles. Normal concrete with polymer micro particles shows better resistance to lactic acid than normal concrete without micro particles (Chandra and Berntsson, 1983). So it is not true to say that polymer concrete is more durable than conventional concrete, although in most of conditions it is correct. Figures 2 to 4 show weight loss of normal concretes

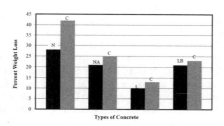

Figure 2. 15% hydrochloric acid solution for 3 months (Chandra and Berntsson, 1983).

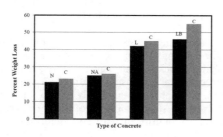

Figure 3. 5% sulfuric acid solution for 6 weeks (Chandra and Berntsson, 1983).

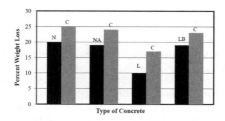

Figure 4. 5% lactic acid solution for 3 months (Chandra and Berntsson, 1983).

and polymer concretes in presence of different acids. (Chandra et al., 1983).

In which:

N-normal concrete
NA-normal concrete with styrene-methylmethacrylate (CEMOS)
L-light weight aggregate concrete with CEMOS
LB-lightweight aggregate concrete with conventional air entraining agent
C-cut sections

Another study (Pacheco-Torgal and Jalali, 2009) compares sulphuric acid resistance of polymer modified, and fly ash cement concretes. Based on the experiments, concrete with polymer impregnation performs better than concrete with polymer addition. The use of a polymer impregnation process enhances the chemical resistance of hardened concrete.

As Figure 5 shows, compressive strength of control fly ash cement concrete (specimen immersed in water) is greater than polymer modified concretes, but the results in sulphuric acid are different.

Sulfur polymer concrete (SPC) specimens showed higher resistance in saline environments. As the test period increases, the compressive strength of polymer concrete showed insignificant decrease during immersion period (O. Mohamed and El Gamal, 2009). Figure 6 shows this.

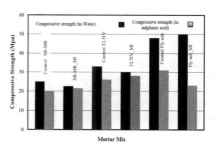

Figure 5. Compressive strength of mortars mixtures made with sulphate resistant cements and fly ash. Control mixtures versus impregnated mixtures (MI) (Pacheco-Torgal and Jalali, 2009).

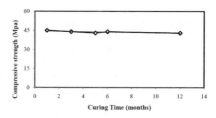

Figure 6. Compressive strength of sulfur polymer concrete cured in 3% saline solution for one year, at 24°C (O. Mohamed and El Gamal, 2009).

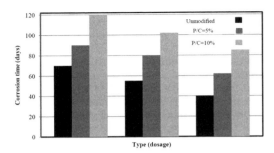

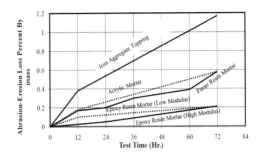

Figure 7. Corrosion time of modified and unmodified concretes (Rossignolo and Agnesini, 2004).

Figure 8. Abrasion resistance of various concrete surface coatings (C. Liu. 1995).

The styrene-butadiene rubber (SBR) modified concrete showed a longer time for corrosion compared to the unmodified concrete, which indicates that SBR—modified concrete offers better protection to steel reinforcement against corrosion. An increase in corrosion time with an increase in cement content was also observed. The crack propagation was very different. A fast longitudinal crack was observed for unmodified concrete, while a slow and curved multidirectional crack was observed for the modified concrete. Figure 7 shows that specimens with a higher polymer concrete ratio are more resistant in a salty environment than specimens with a lower ratio and unmodified concretes. In this figure, the factor of comparison between specimens is time of corrosion.

It could be concluded from this part that generally polymer concretes are more durable than conventional concretes in aggressive conditions, but there are some cases that it is not true, so it is suggested that when these conditions are probable, usage of polymer concrete must be with exact knowledge of the conditions and the polymer concretes behavior in those conditions.

6 WEAR RESISTANCE OF POLYMER CONCRETES

The wear resistance of floor constructions from mortar and concrete with cement binder is very important for their service life, especially in industrial enterprises (SebÖk and Stránĕl, 2004). For example, abrasion damage resulting from the abrasive effects of waterborne gravel, rocks, and other debris circulated over a concrete surface during construction and operation of hydraulic structure has been a major problem. Spillway aprons and stilling basins are particularly susceptible to abrasion. The resistance mentioned may be increased by solutions of synthetic resins hardening after penetration into the structure of mortar or concrete.

Based on work by C. Liu (1981), in general, all coated concretes by polymer epoxies have good resistance to abrasion. The abrasion losses of all coatings were significantly less than the conventional concrete (Figure 8).

Since the damage of concrete surfaces under water flow, caused by abrasive action of waterborne solid particles, is one of the major issues when designing the operation of hydraulic structures (Kryžanowski, Mikoš, Šušteršic, Planinc. 2009) and abrasion of floors in industrial enterprises is a common form of damage to concrete, it is suggested to use polymer concretes in overlays or in repair of damaged concretes.

7 SELECTION OF POLYMER CONCRETE FOR CONCRETE REPAIR

There are many causes of deterioration: physical (cyclic freezing, thawing), chemical (acid attack, sulphate attack, alkali aggregate reaction) and electrochemical (corrosion of steel). Of these, corrosion of steel single-handedly results in almost 90 percent of structural deterioration. Hence, it is essential to identify the cause of deterioration of the structure (Chandra Patnaik and Garg, 2008). Concrete damage can be classified into four main types according to its appearance (Van Gemert, Czarneckit and Bares. 1988):

- Damage to concrete skin or concrete cover the damage can be a continuous corrosion by water, acids or frost action or the concrete skin can be cracked or disintegrated by bad placing or faulty design.
- Corrosion of reinforcement by carbonation, chloride attack, insufficient cover.
- Insufficient quality of concrete cross section, by local loss of material strength or stiffness.
- Excessive deflections of concrete structural members.

After detection, the importance of concrete damage must be evaluated, in order to determine the necessary actions to be taken replacing, repair, strengthening, or protection. In the evaluation the damage is put in one of following categories (Van Gemert, Czarneckit and Bares. 1988):

- Loss of safety against collapse
- Loss of durability
- Damage to exterior appearance
- Effect of damage of small importance

The repair method has gone from simple concrete repair, férocement and polymeric repair to composite repair system. Depending upon serviceability and lifecycle cost, the right material and methodology have to be selected (Chandra Patnaik and Garg, 2008).

Methodology for deteriorated concrete structures depends upon serviceability and application conditions. The most important factors to be considered for durability of repair material are compatibility with existing concrete and method of application. The compatibility of repair material with the existing substrate may be chemical and electrochemical compatibility and dimensional compatibility.

Except for replacement, polymer concrete and polymer cement concrete materials are widely used for repair, strengthening and protection (Van Gemert, Czarneckit and Bares. 1988).

For polymer-based materials, or polymer modified repair materials, performance criteria are much less well established than is the case for traditional materials such as concrete, brick and steel. The engineer therefore lacks the familiar starting point from which to make his materials selection. When selecting any polymeric materials for repair applications, certain key points must be appreciated (Kosendar, Mailvaganam, 2005):

- Their physical properties are uniquely different to traditional construction materials i.e., there is a basic 'mismatch';
- Service conditions usually affect a bonded composite, not an isolated polymer;
- Organic polymers represent an extremely broad class of chemical and physical types. Combined organic/inorganic systems widen the range still further;
- Polymer properties are sensitive to relatively small temperature changes and they are significantly time dependent;
- Ultimate properties can be markedly affected by the ambient conditions during application.
- Polymer behavior is significantly affected in some applications by the behavior of the substrate, particularly how it responds to load.

Based on an adequate model of structural behavior a classification of materials can be set up (Van Gemert, Czarneckit and Bares. 1988).

Monomer systems can be used for effective repair of cracks. A monomer system is a liquid that consists of small organic molecules capable of combining to form a solid plastic. They are very fluid and will soak into dry concrete, filling the cracks, much the same as water does. Monomer systems used for impregnation contain a catalyst or initiator and the basic monomer (REMR technical note CS-MR-3.11, 1991).

If a concrete surface is dried, flooded with the monomer, and polymerized in place, the cracks will be filled and structurally repaired. However, if the cracks contain moisture, the monomer will not soak into the concrete at each crack face end, consequently, the repair will be unsatisfactory (REMR technical note CS-MR-3.11, 1991).

Polymer impregnation has not been used successfully to repair fine cracks. Badly fractured beams have been repaired using polymer impregnation by drying the fracture, temporarily encasing it in a watertight (monomer-proof) band of sheet metal, soaking the fractures with monomer, and polymerizing the monomer. Large voids or broken areas in compression zones can be filled with fine and coarse aggregate before flooding them with the monomer, providing a polymer concrete repair (REMR technical note CS-MR-3.11, 1991).

Concrete structures that are damaged due to cracking and spalling, associated with corrosion of reinforcing bars are often repaired using shallow depth surface patches. Cracking and full or partial delamination of the patch repairs due to shrinkage and continued corrosion is generally unavoidable. The repair typically lasts only for a few years in corrosive environments associated with coastal regions or the use of deicing salts. To provide more durable patch repairs, the use of a fiber-reinforced polymer _FRP_ fabric applied as an overlay on top of a traditional polymer concrete patching material was investigated. The FRP overlay can serve as a secondary reinforcement and act as a barrier against the diffusion of moisture and chloride ions, thereby improving the performance of the patch by reducing cracking and slowing down the corrosion process (Nossoni and Harichandran, 2010).

Corrosion of reinforcing bars in concrete is one of the main causes of structural deterioration. Corrosion reduces the strength, durability, and service life of exposed reinforced concrete structures. As the reinforcement corrodes, its expansion causes cracking and spalling of concrete. Chloride concentration, temperature, relative humidity, cover depth, and concrete quality are the major factors affecting the rate of corrosion. The transformation of metallic iron to rust can result in an increase in volume of up to 600%, depending on the final rust form. The deterioration caused by the corrosion of reinforcing steel in concrete structures has been recognized as one of the greatest maintenance challenges. Corrosion should therefore be treated before it becomes a significant problem (Nossoni and Harichandran, 2010). From these it can be concluded that it is not possible to use polymer concretes in all kinds of repair. At the first step it is necessary to determine the type of damage, its source, and then we can make decision about the method of repair and needed materials. If these steps are skipped, the repair would not be able to properly continue.

8 EXAMPLES OF USING POLYMER CONCRETE IN REPAIR

8.1 Copper mine and refinery

A large copper mine and refinery in the western united states had a dilemma. Their cell houses had experienced severe corrosion and structural degradation of the support columns for the tanks, each holding gallons of electrolyte. The refinery's standard repair procedure was to remove corrosion products from the concrete and steel and then to top them with a polymer-modified Portland-cement mortar. This standard repair method required two to three days per column, and although temporarily effective, did not meet the company's desire for a long-term solution. They decided upon a new approach using a polymer concrete, a bisphenol A based-epoxy. This material was designed for maximum flowability, mechanical properties and chemical resistance. The cost of maintenance for polymer concretes per year of service life is significantly less than that of concrete with applied barrier coating, which may require multiple re-applications over the same number of years of service (Snider and Ramsey, 2009).

There have been thousands of new and old bridges repaired and overlaid with concrete containing Dow styrene butadiene latex. Most have been in the northern climate of United States, where deicing salts are prevalent, although recently there have been projects in Texas, Louisiana, Mississippi, and North Carolina. Some of the more notable projects were: Bascule Bridge on U.S 23, Columbia River Bridge, Marquham Street Bridge, Wiscasset Bridge, Denny Creek Bridge, Clark's Summit Bridge, Sandusky Bay Bridge, O'Hare Departure Ramp, O'Hare Parking Garage, and Solider Field Stadium. At Chicago International Terminal, the elevated road was repaired with latex modified concrete in 1978 (Kuhlmann, 1985).

Polymer concrete with recycled wastes (such as PET and LDPE), were applied in the spillway of Mourão Hydroelectric Power Plant dam, located in the city of Campo Mourão, in the State of Paraná, southern Brazil. The polymeric wasted added to the concrete has given to the material an increase of resistance to underwater erosion-abrasion testing, and this is exactly engineers need in spillways of hydraulic structures (Carlos Alves Galvão, Franke Portella, Joukoski and Mendes. 2010).

8.2 Coastal pump house in Bombay

A pump house is intended to pump water from a storage pond into the sea. A major damage to the structure occurred in the main columns forming the portals of the pump house structure. Beams and columns at the water intake side of the pump were also badly corroded. Reinforcement in columns and beams showed heavy corrosion. It showed heavy scaling too. The portion of column between high and low tide was most damaged. The alternate wetting and drying in sea water, attack of chlorides, attack of effluents which were accumulating in the pond along with general marine environment were the main contributing factors responsible for corrosion. A decision was taken to rehabilitate the damaged portion of the structure with polymer modified mortar in preference to conventional jacketing of elements with concrete (Kamat and Bhedasgaonkar, 1990).

8.3 Lime stone crusher foundation for a cement plant

A leading cement manufacturing plant in Karnataka, India had problems of severe vibrations in its lime stone crusher foundation. The foundation has four main columns supporting the deck on which the crusher is located. One column developed cracks at the column top/deck junction. This also happened to be the location of the construction joint. The crack width increased gradually when the machine continued to be operated even after crack development. This resulted in severe vibrations of the crusher. Very low viscosity monomer injection was selected for impregnation of the core of column by injecting it into the crack under pressure until no more low viscosity monomer could go in. The vibration of the foundation was reduced from over 300 microns to within the acceptable limit. The entire work was done in three days and the crusher was brought back into operation immediately, resulting in minimum shutdown (Kamat and Bhedasgaonkar, 1990).

Overhead water tank at Powai, Bombay: an overhead water tank supplying drinking water to a big campus in Bombay had deteriorated due to ageing and environmental factors. The major problem was corrosion on account of leakage. Critical structural elements had developed severe corrosion. Hence extensive injection grouting using low viscosity monomer, making up of the lost cross section of beams and columns and finally redoing the entire inside of tank with polymer modified mortar were adopted (Kamat and Bhedasgaonkar, 1990).

9 CONCLUSIONS

- Polymer properties are sensitive to relatively small temperature changes and they are significantly time dependent so the application of polymer concrete for the cases with high a range of temperature change is unlikely to be not useful.
- There might also be a type of cross-linking between the soft micro particles of polymers using in concrete and some components of the cement matrix. This provides better adhesion between the aggregate and cement paste, and reduces the possibility of the concrete deformation due to the freeze-thaw test. Polymer concretes are more resistant than conventional concretes either air entrained concretes in freeze-thaw and deicing solutions, so they are one of the best choices in repair of overlays such as bridge overlays.
- The cost of maintenance for polymer concretes per year of service life is significantly less than that of concrete with applied barrier coating, which may require multiple re-applications over the same number of years of service. The service life of polymer concrete repairs is significantly more than repair method with conventional concrete.
- Generally it is not possible to say that polymer concrete is more resistant than conventional concrete in aggressive environments, although in most cases it is true, so when a decision of material in such environments is needed, the type of corrosive agent must be detected and characteristics of desired material must be studied.
- Selection of a proper material for repair is related to the type of damage and cause, so using polymer concrete or any other material for repair must be with enough knowledge about the cause of repair.
- Due to the very low viscosity of some types of monomers which are used in polymer concretes, they can be used in difficult cases with narrow crack widths.

REFERENCES

ACI 201.2 R92. ACI manual of concrete repair, part 3, 2005, American Concrete Institute.

ACI Committee 548. 1994. Abstract of: State-of-the Art Report on polymer-modified concrete. *Materials Journal*. 91.

Bordeleau, D., Pigeon, M. & Banthia, N. 1992. Comparative study of latex- modified concretes and normal concretes subjected to freezing and thawing in the presence of a deicer salt solution, *ACI Materials Journal* 89: 547–553.

Carlos Alves Galvão, J., Franke Portella, K., Joukoski, A. & Mendes, R. 2010. Use of waste polymers in concrete for repair of dam hydraulic surfaces, *Construction and Building Material*. Article in press.

Chandra, S., Aavik, J. & Berntsson, L. 1982. Influence of polymer micropartilcles on freeze-thaw resistance of structural lightweight aggregate concrete, *The international journal of Cement Composites and Lightweight Concrete* 4: 111–115.

Chandra, S. & Berntsson, L. 1983. Technical notes: Influence of polymer on acid resistance of structural lightweight aggregate concrete, *The International Journal of Cement Composites and Lightweight Concrete* 5: 127–131.

Chandra, P. Suresh & Garg, R.P. 2008. Methods of repair, *CW Technology*: 138–144.

Decter, M.H. & Keeley, C. 1997. Duarable concrete repair importance of compatibility and low shrinkage, *Construction and building materials*, 11: 267–273.

Fowler, D.W. 1999. Polymers in concrete: a vision for the 21st century, *Cement & Concrete Composites*: 449–452.

Glenn Smoak, W. 2002. Guide to concrete repair, New York-Hong Kong, United States Department Of The Interior Bureau Of Reclamation.

Kamat M.K. & Bhedasgaonkar, B.V. 1990. Rehabilitation of structurally damaged and corrosion-affected structures using polymer systems, Technical report.

Kosendar & Mailvaganam, 2005. Selection and use of polymer-based materials in the repair of concrete structures, *Journal of Performance of Constructed Facilities*, 19: 229–233.

Kryžanowski, A., Mikoš, M., Šušteršic, J. & Planinc, I. 2009. Abrasion resistance of concrete in hydraulic structures. *ACI Material Journal*, 106: 349–356.

Kuhlmann, L.A. 1985. Latex modified concrete for the repair and rehabilitation of bridges. *The International Journal of Cement Composites and lightweight Concrete*. 7. pp. 241–247.

Liu, C. & Tony. 1981. Abrasion resistance of concrete. *ACI Journal Proceedings* 78: 341–350.

Mailvaganam, N.P. & Zhang, J. 2006. Structural and patch repair in concrete structures, *Cement & Concrete Composites*: 669–670.

Mook Lee, W., Priya Nair, J., Woo Lee, C., Hyun Ku, D., Soon Park, J. & Young Park, H. 1999. Physical and chemical properties of polymer impregnated concrete on the preparation conditions, Technical report.

Mohamed, O. A.M. & El Gamal, M. 2009. Hydromechanical behavior of a newly developed sulfur polymer concrete. *Cement & Concrete Composite*, 31(3): 186–194.

Nossoni, G. & Harichandran, R.S. 2010. Improved repair of concrete structures using polymer concrete patch and FRP overlay, *Journal of materials in civil engineering ASCE*, 22 (314): 314–322.

Pacheco-Torgal, F. & Jalali, S. 2009. Sulphuric acid resistance of plain, polymer modified, and fly ash cement concretes. *Construction and Building Materials.* 23: 3485–3491.

PEMR technical note CS-MR-3.11. 1991. Crack repair method: polymer impregnation. *PEMR.*

Rebeiz, K.S. 1995. Time-temperature properties of polymer concrete using recycled PET. *Cement & Concrete Composites.* 17: 119–124.

Reis, J.M.L. 2010. Fracture assessment of polymer concrete in chemical degradation solutions, *Construction and Building Materials:* 1708–1712.

Reis, J.M.L. & Ferreira, A.J.M. 2006. Freeze- thaw and thermal degradation influence on the fracture properties of carbon and glass fiber reinforced polymer concrete. *Construction and Building MATERIALS,* 20: 888–892.

Rossignolo, J.A. & Agnesini, M.V.C. 2004. Durability of polymer-modified lightweight aggregate concrete. *Cement & Concrete Composites,* 26: 375–380.

SebÖk, T. & Stránĕl, O. 2004. Wear resistance of polymer-impregnated mortars and concrete. *Cement and Concrete Research,* 34: 1853–1858.

Snider, D.E. & Ramsey, H.M. 2009. Polymer concrete for structural restoration and corrosion protection of concrete support columns, *Sauereisen Inc.*

Soudki, K.A. 2001. Concrete problems and repair techniques, *Professional Engineers association,* Beirut, February 2001, Lebanon.

Van Gemert, D., Czarneckit, L. & Bares, R. 1988. Basis for selection of PC and PCC for concrete repair, *The International Journal of Cement Composites and Lightweight Concrete,* 10: 121–123.

Vipulanandan, C. & Dharmarjan, N. 1988. Effect of temperature on the fracture properties of epoxy polymer concrete, *Cement and Concrete Research.* 18: 265–276.

Concrete Solutions – Grantham, Mechtcherine & Schneck (eds)
© 2012 Taylor & Francis Group, London, ISBN 978-0-415-61622-5

Benchmarking laboratory investigated locally available repair materials against their manufacturer's data sheets

M.I. Khan, T.H. Almusallam, S.H. Alsayed, Y.A. Al-Salloum & A.A. Almosa
Department of Civil Engineering, College of Engineering, King Saud University, Saudi Arabia

ABSTRACT: Data sheets provided by manufacturers of repair materials available in Saudi Arabia do not contain all essential data required in the field applications. In addition, the data reported are based on different test standards and, unfortunately, the manufacturers have also the tendency to report favorable performance on the data sheets of their products. The most famous and best selling various cementitious repair materials were selected for this study. Each of these materials was subjected to a series of laboratory tests to determine material properties, which were perceived to be of interest in a repair context and to provide some basic information about their behavior. Compressive strength and flexural strength of each repair material are discussed in detail. The experimentally obtained results of all properties investigated are compared with the results provided by the manufacturer of the repair material in their data sheets. Each material was compared with its equivalent material produced by another manufacturer. Comparison is made on the basis of their composition, properties and application.

1 INTRODUCTION

In the Kingdom of Saudi Arabia, the deterioration of concrete structures is the most important challenge to civil engineers. The majority of the concrete structures suffer because of lack of quality control and severe weather conditions. Therefore, the structures deteriorate and need urgent repair. Furthermore, a great part of the reinforced concrete structures in the relatively moderate environment of the country have already met their intended service life and are in need for some maintenance and repair.

Repair deterioration rates have been aggravated and accelerated by poor construction resulting from shortcomings in design, specifications, supervision, workmanship and quality control. Inadequate workmanship, procedures, or materials results in inferior repairs which ultimately fails. The need for repairs can vary from such minor imperfections to major damages resulting from structural failure. This method of repair can only prove to be successful if the new material interacts well with the parent concrete and forms a durable barrier against ingress of carbon dioxide and chlorides. The properties and durability of repair system are governed by properties of the three phases namely, repair, existing substrate, and interface (transition zone) between them (Vaysburd et al. 2001). Properly designed, implemented, and functioning man-made systems, with a minimum number of undesirable side effects, require the application of a well-integrated systems approach as reported by Emmons & Vaysburd (1995) and Poston et al (2001). Smoak (2002) reported that in evaluating the causes of failures, it is essential to consistently use a systematic approach to concrete repair.

A wide variety of repair materials are available in the local market for the repair of deteriorated concrete structures. These repair materials are available in various compositions manufactured by internationally well-known companies. Data sheets provided by manufacturers of these materials do not contain all essential data required in the field applications. In addition, the data reported are based on different test standards and, unfortunately, the manufacturers have also the tendency to report favorable performance on the data sheets of their products.

In this study, the most famous and best selling varieties of cementitious repair materials were selected. The selection of the repair material was based on the best selling materials available in the Kingdom of Saudi Arabia. Each of these materials was subjected to a series of laboratory tests to determine material properties, which were perceived to be of interest in a repair context and to provide some basic information about their behavior. This evaluation was carried out to target an understanding of material properties and to verify the published properties obtained from the manufacturer's datasheet. Compressive strength and flexural strength of each repair material are discussed in detail. The experimentally obtained results of all properties investigated are compared with the results provided by the manufacturer of the repair material in their data sheets. Each material was compared with its equivalent material produced by another manufacturer. Comparison is made on the basis of their composition, properties and application.

2 EXPERIMENTAL PROGRAM

2.1 *Material selection*

Ten candidate materials, three from micro-concrete repair materials, four from cementitious repair mortars and three from cementitious polymer modified mortars, were selected. The selection of the repair material was based on the best selling materials manufactured by the top three companies Fosroc, Sika and MBT available in the Kingdom of Saudi Arabia. The designation, properties and application of these Micro-Concrete Repair Materials (MCRM), Cementitious Repair Mortars (CRM) and Cementitious Polymer Modified Mortars (CPMM) are shown in Tables 1, 2 and 3, respectively.

Mixture proportions and mixing for all selected materials were employed as per the recommendations suggested by the manufacturer. The curing procedure for each repair material was also followed exactly in accordance to the manufacturers' recommendations where practicable.

2.2 *Testing procedure*

2.2.1 *Compressive strength*

Although compressive strength is not an important material property in many repair applications since they occur in tension zones of structures, compressive strength has become the singular property that is always being reported for a concrete material. In this investigation, concrete specimen (150 mm cubes) were prepared for the measurement of compressive strength; tests were conducted in accordance to BS1881. The measurements for the mortar

Table 1. Details of micro-concrete repair materials.

Material	Properties	Application
MCRM-1	Free-flowing, shrinkage compensated	High strength structural elements
MCRM-2	Free-flowing, shrinkage compensated	High strength structural elements
MCRM-3	Free-flowing, shrinkage compensated	High strength structural elements

Table 2. Details of cementitious repair mortars.

Material	Properties	Application
CRM-1	Shrinkage controlled	Hand applied vertical & overhead
CRM-2	Shrinkage controlled	Spraying vertical & overhead
CRM-3	Multi purpose for hot climates	Hand applied vertical & horizontal
CRM-4	High mechanical strengths	Wet spraying vertical & horizontal

Table 3. Details of cementitious polymer modified mortars.

Material	Properties	Application
CPMM-1	Multi purpose for hot climates	Dry/wet spray vertical, overhead & horizontal
CPMM-2	For hot climates	Wet spray vertical & overhead
CPMM-3	Multi purpose	Hand applied

specimens were conducted on 50 mm cubes in accordance with ASTM C109-93. The measurements were taken at 3, 7, and 28 days using three specimens for each age and average of three is reported as a result.

2.2.2 *Flexural strength*

For the measurement of concrete flexural strength, $100 \times 100 \times 500$ mm prisms were prepared and tests were conducted in accordance to ASTM C78-94. For mortar, $40 \times 40 \times 160$ mm prisms were cast and test was carried out in accordance to ASTM C348-92. The measurements would be taken at 3, 7, and 28 days using three specimens for each age.

3 RESULTS AND DISCUSSION

3.1 *Comparison of compressive strength*

The compressive strength values obtained in the laboratory are compared with the compressive strength values provided by the manufacturer for each of the repair material. Compressive strength comparison of lab obtained results vs data sheet values are presented in Table 4.

3.1.1 *Micro concrete repair material*

Compressive strength comparison of lab results with the data sheet values for MCRM-1 at various ages is presented in Figure 1. Lab results obtained for MCRM-1 at the age of 3 days were higher than the value provided in the data sheet.

Table 4. Comparison of lab investigated compressive strength vs manufacture's compressive strength.

| Name | Source | Compressive strength, MPa | | |
		3 day	7 day	28 day
MCRM-1	Lab	43.0	47.8	55.5
	MDS	30.0	45.0	60.0
MCRM-2	Lab	54.6	58.5	64.8
	MDS	n/a	47.5	67.5
MCRM-3	Lab	35.0	45.9	61.9
	MDS	35.0	45.0	65.0
CRM-1	Lab	38.1	51.0	62.1
	MDS	n/a	n/a	55.0
CRM-2	Lab	22.4	27.8	32.4
	MDS	n/a	35.0	40.0
CRM-3	Lab	25.2	32.4	47.3
	MDS	n/a	n/a	40.0
CRM-4	Lab	20.7	36.7	36.7
	MDS	n/a	n/a	45.0
CRMM-1	Lab	29.4	34.3	39.6
	MDS	n/a	n/a	30.0
CRMM-2	Lab	25.2	32.4	47.3
	MDS	n/a	n/a	45.0
CRMM-3	Lab	17.4	24.1	30.8
	MDS	n/a	n/a	35.0

MDS = manufacturers' data sheet.
n/a = data not available from the manufacturer.

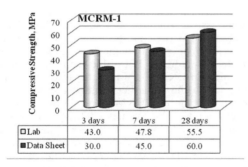

Figure 1. Compressive strength comparison of lab result with data sheet of MCRM-1.

At 7 days, the lab results and the data sheet values were almost similar where as at 28 days the experimental value was lower than the data sheet value. The compressive strength of MCRM-1 obtained from the experimental study and the data sheet provided by the manufacturer was 55.5 MPa and 60 MPa, respectively. The lower result obtained is significant; however, it is not a serious problem.

Compressive strength comparison of lab results with data sheet values of MCRM-2 at various ages is presented in Figure 2. Lab results obtained for

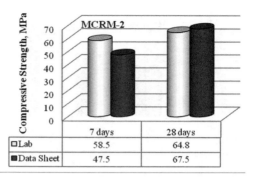

Figure 2. Compressive strength comparison of lab result with data sheet of MCRM-2.

MCRM-2 at the age of 7 days were higher than the value provided in the data sheet. Compressive strengths of MCRM-2 from the experimental study and data sheet were 64.8 MPa and 67.5 MPa, respectively. The lower result obtained is not of much significance.

Compressive strength comparison of lab results with data sheet values for MCRM-3 at various ages is presented in (Figure 3). The lab results obtained for MCRM-3 at the age of 3 and 7 days were similar to that in the data sheet. At 28 days, the lab result was lower than the data sheet value. The compressive strength of MCRM-3 from the experimental study and the data sheet is 61.9 MPa and 65 MPa, respectively. The lower result obtained is not of much significance.

3.1.2 *Cementitious repair mortar*
Compressive strength comparison of lab results compared with with data sheet values of CRM-2 at various ages is presented in Figure 4. Lab results obtained for CRM-2 at the age of 7 days and 28 days are lower than the value provided in the data sheet. At 7 days lab result and data sheet value was 27.8 MPa and 35 MPa, respectively; whilst at 28 days, lab result and data sheet value was 32.4 MPa and 40 MPa, respectively. The lower result obtained for 7 and 28 days is significant, and is a matter of concern.

Hand applied: Compressive strength comparison of lab results with data sheet values of CRM-2 and CRM-3 at 28 days is presented in Figure 5. The lab results obtained for CRM-3 at the age of 28 days were higher than the value provided in the data sheet. At 28 days the lab result and data sheet values for CRM-3 was 47.3 MPa and 40 MPa, respectively. Since the value obtained in the lab is much higher than that of the data sheet, CRM-3 is complying with the data provided by its manufacturer. However, results need to be validated by doing some more tests.

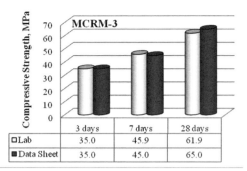

Figure 3. Compressive strength comparison of lab result with data sheet of MCRM-3.

	3 days	7 days	28 days
□ Lab	35.0	45.9	61.9
■ Data Sheet	35.0	45.0	65.0

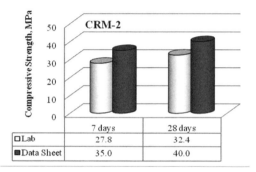

Figure 4. Compressive strength comparison of lab result with data sheet of CRM-2.

	7 days	28 days
□ Lab	27.8	32.4
■ Data Sheet	35.0	40.0

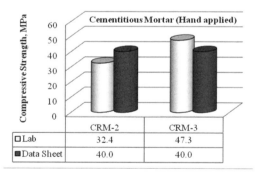

Figure 5. Compressive strength comparison of lab results with data sheet of cementitious repair mortars (Hand applied).

	CRM-2	CRM-3
□ Lab	32.4	47.3
■ Data Sheet	40.0	40.0

Spray applied: Compressive strength comparison of lab results with data sheet values of CRM-1 and CRM-4 at 28 days is presented in Figure 6. The value of compressive strength obtained experimentally for CRM-1 was higher than the value provided in the data sheet. Whilst for CRM-4, the lab result

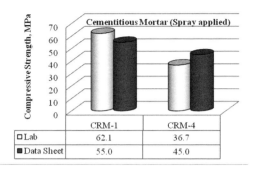

Figure 6. Compressive strength comparison of lab result with data sheet of cementitious repair mortars (Spray applied).

	CRM-1	CRM-4
□ Lab	62.1	36.7
■ Data Sheet	55.0	45.0

was lower than data sheet value. Compressive strength values for CRM-1 obtained from the laboratory tests and the data sheet were 62 MPa and 55 MPa, respectively. Since the value obtained in the lab is much higher than that of data sheet, it can be said that CRM-1 is complying with the data provided by its manufacturer.

The laboratory and the data sheet compressive strength of CRM-4 were 36.7 MPa and 45 MPa, respectively. The lower laboratory result obtained is significant, and is a matter of concern.

3.1.3 Cementitious polymer modified mortar
Compressive strength comparison of the lab result value with data sheet value of cementitious polymer modified mortars at 28 days is shown in Figure 7. The value from lab results obtained for CRMM-1 was higher than the value provided in the data sheet; whilst the lab compressive strengths of CRM-4 and CRMM-3 were lower than data sheet values. CRMM-1 lab result strength and data sheet strengths were 39.6 MPa and 30 MPa, respectively. Since the value obtained in the lab is higher than that of data sheet, it can be said that CRMM-1 is complying with the data provided by its manufacturer. Both CRM-4 and CRMM-3 showed lower lab compressive strength than the data sheet value. The lower compressive strength result obtained for both was significant, and is a matter of concern. However, results need to be validated by doing some more tests.

3.2 Comparison of flexural strength

The flexural strength values obtained in the laboratory were compared with the flexural strength values provided by the manufacturer and its comparison with data sheet values are presented in Table 5.

448

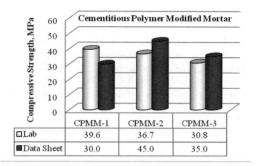

Figure 7. Compressive strength comparison of lab results with data sheets of cementitious polymer modified mortars.

Table 5. Comparison of lab investigated flexural strength vs manufacture's flexural strength.

Name	Source	Flexural strength, MPa		
		3 day	7 day	28 day
MCRM-1	Lab	5.91	6.26	7.51
	MDS	n/a	n/a	n/a
MCRM-2	Lab	5.87	7.43	8.31
	MDS	n/a	n/a	9.00
MCRM-3	Lab	5.71	5.87	6.00
	MDS	n/a	n/a	n/a
CRM-1	Lab	7.84	n/a	9.77
	MDS	n/a	n/a	6.5
CRM-2	Lab	5.32	6.32	8.00
	MDS	n/a	n/a	6.5
CRM-3	Lab	5.80	6.90	10.72
	MDS	n/a	n/a	8.0
CRM-4	Lab	4.93	n/a	7.86
	MDS	n/a	n/a	8.00
CRMM-1	Lab	7.53	7.86	9.09
	MDS	n/a	n/a	6.00
CRMM-2	Lab	5.80	6.90	10.72
	MDS	n/a	n/a	n/a
CRMM-3	Lab	3.48	5.07	6.33
	MDS	n/a	n/a	n/a

MDS = manufacturers' data sheet.
n/a = data not available from the manufacturer.

3.2.1 Micro concrete repair material

The flexural strength comparison of lab results with data sheet values of MCRM-2 at 28 days is presented in Figure 8. The flexural strengths from the experimental study and the data sheet values for MCRM-2 were 8.31 MPa and 9.0 MPa, respectively. MCRM-2 showed a similar trend in its compressive strength as well. MCRM-2 is a material with a certain degree of problems related to its obtained lower tensile

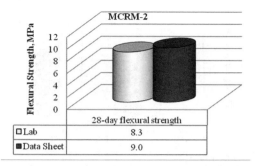

Figure 8. Flexural strength comparison of lab result with data sheet of MCRM-2.

strength compared to the strength given in the data sheet.

3.2.2 Cementitious repair mortar

Hand Applied: Flexural strength comparison of lab results with data sheet values of CRM-2 and CRM-3 at 28 days is presented in Figure 9. Lab results obtained for both CRM-2 and CRM-3 were higher than the values provided in the data sheet. The laboratory result and data sheet values of flexural strength for CRM-2 were 8 MPa and 6.5 MPa, respectively. Whereas the laboratory result and data sheet value of CRM-3 for its flexural strength were 10.7 MPa and 8 MPa, respectively. Since the value obtained in the lab for both CRM-2 and CRM-3 were much higher than that of data sheet, it can be said that both materials comply with the data provided by its manufacturer.

Spray Applied: Flexural strength comparison of laboratory results with data sheet values of CRM-1 and CRM-4 at 28 days is presented in Figure 10. Lab results obtained for both CRM-1 and CRM-4 were higher than the value provided in the data sheet. Flexural strength from the experimental study and the data sheet for CRM-1 were 9.8 MPa and 6.5 MPa, respectively. Whereas the lab result and data sheet values for CRM-4 were 7.9 MPa and 8 MPa, respectively.

Since the flexural strength result obtained in the lab for CRM-1 was higher than that of the data sheet, it can be said that CRM-1 complies with the data provided by its manufacturer. The laboratory result obtained for the flexural strength of CRM-4 was similar to that of the data sheet; therefore, CRM-4 also complies with the data provided by its manufacturer.

3.2.3 Cementitious polymer modified mortar

Flexural strength comparison of experimental values with data sheet values for CRMM-1 and CRM-4 at 28 days is presented in Figure 11. It was

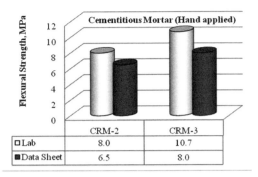

Figure 9. Flexural strength comparison of lab results with data sheets of cementitious repair mortars (Hand applied).

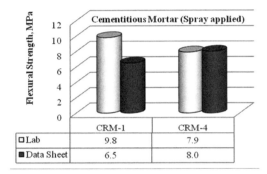

Figure 10. Flexural strength comparison of lab results with data sheets of cementitious repair mortars (Spray applied).

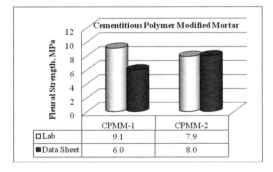

Figure 11. Flexural strength comparison of lab result with data sheet of cementitious polymer modified mortars.

found that the lab result obtained for CRMM-1 was higher than the value provided in the data sheet. Laboratory result and data sheet values for the flexural strength of CRMM-1 were 9.1 MPa

and 6 MPa, respectively. Whereas the lab result and data sheet value for the flexural strength of CRM-4 were 7.9 MPa and 8 MPa, respectively.

Since the experimental result obtained in the lab for CRMM-1 was higher than that of the data sheet, it can be said that CRMM-1 complies with the data provided by its manufacturer. And since the experimental result obtained in the lab for CRM-4 is similar to that of its data sheet, it can be said that CRM-4 also complies with the data provided by its manufacturer.

4 CONCLUSIONS

Compressive strength and flexural strength laboratory results for CPMM-1 and CRM-1 were higher than that of data sheet values, therefore, these materials are complying with the data provided by its manufacturer.

MCRM-1 and CRM-2 showed lower lab compressive strength than the data sheet value. The lower result obtained for both is significant, and is a matter of concern.

Flexural strength lab results obtained for CRM-2 were higher than that of data sheet values, therefore, CRM-2 complies with the data provided by its manufacturer.

Compressive strength and flexural strength lab result for MCRM-2 were slightly lower than that of data sheet values, however, the lower result obtained is not of much significance.

Compressive strength of CRM-3 obtained in the lab was higher than that of data sheet; therefore, complying with the data provided by its manufacturer.

Compressive strength of CRM-4, MCRM-3 and CPMM-3 obtained in the lab was lower than the data sheet value; therefore, these materials are not complying with the data provided by its manufacturer.

REFERENCES

BS 1881: Part 116, 1986. Method for determination of compressive strength of concrete cubes. *British Standard Institution*, London.

Emmons, P.H. & Vaysburd, A.M. 1995. The total system concept—Necessary for improving the performance of repaired structures. *Concrete International* 17(3): 31–36.

Poston, R.W., Kesner, K., McDonald, J.E., Vaysburd, A.M. & Emmons, P.H. 2001. Concrete repair material performance—laboratory study. *ACI Material Journal* 98(2): 137–145.

Smoak, W.G. 2002. Guide to concrete repair. *USBR report*, Denver Federal Center Denver, Colorado, USA.

Vaysburd, A.M., Sabnis, G.M., Emmons, P.H. & McDonald, J.E. 2001. Interfacial bond and surface preparation in concrete repair. *The Indian Concrete Journal* 27–33.

Concrete Solutions – Grantham, Mechtcherine & Schneck (eds)
© 2012 Taylor & Francis Group, London, ISBN 978-0-415-61622-5

Influence of selected aspects of the mixture proportioning on the performance of repair mortars

P. Ramge, H.-C. Kühnen & B. Meng
BAM Federal Institute for Materials Research and Testing, Berlin, Germany

ABSTRACT: Due to the large number of individual constituents, the mixture modification of repair mortar is a complex task. It is almost impossible to change an individual property without influencing other mortar properties. Most properties can be altered by several different measures, which may vary in effectiveness, side effects and cost efficiency. In the presented paper, special attention is paid to the prevention of shrinkage induced constraining cracks, as this is crucial for the durability and service life of a concrete repair task. On the basis of the parameter studies it is shown how it may be beneficial, in certain cases, to accept the worsening of some general properties if by this measure another property, which is essential for the individual application task, can be enhanced significantly. Due to the complexity of the constituents' interactions in repair mortars, even apparently conflicting combinations of admixtures may become necessary.

1 INTRODUCTION

Within the context of a research project funded by the German Federal Ministry of Economics and Technology, the influence of mixture modifications on the properties of repair mortars are being investigated currently at the BAM (Federal Institute of Materials Research and Testing).

The commercially available repair mortars are usually composed of a large number of single constituents. The specified properties of the product are the result of the sophisticated adaption of the single components. However, the systems are often of such complexity that, due to the lack of knowledge about the constituents' interactions, or little changes in raw material qualities, an effective adaptation or optimisation of the mixture is not possible. Bearing in mind the actual changes in the European standardisation process and changes in the raw material prices, it would be well appreciated to have the ability to adjust some properties or to exchange some constituents without totally redoing the mix design from scratch. Besides enhanced knowledge about the mode of action of individual components and their interactions, the aim of the project is the development of a basic recipe that can be adapted on a modular basis for the use in different repair areas such as building construction, bridge construction, hydraulic engineering, drinking water reservoirs and sewers.

For the success of a concrete repair task, not only the durability properties of the repair mortar itself are of importance. Furthermore the repair mortar layer must be able to successfully protect the substrate concrete for the whole remaining service live of the concrete structure. One major hazard for the substrate concrete are cracks in the repair mortar or distortions in the interface layer that enable the quick transport and spreading of water and air to the actual substrate concrete surface. Therefore the properties of the repair mortar have to be adjusted to the subsurface in such a way that cracks can be precluded with the highest possible reliability and that a long lasting bond can be assured. Besides the mortar's tensile strength, the deformation compatibility is therefore the controlling parameter. Stiffness and deformation behaviour of mortar and subsurface must show equal or well adjusted properties, otherwise inner constraining forces, caused by unfavourable reactions to external influences, can lead to local defects up to a total delamination of the repair layer. As shrinkage deformations are time dependent, their progress in the substrate concrete has usually already widely declined when repair measures are carried out. Therefore special attention needs to be given to the constraining forces caused by hindered shrinkage. Whereas for the mortar's stiffness and the temperature deforming behaviour, it should be aimed to match the properties of the substrate concrete as close as possible, for the shrinkage deformations the aim should be their best possible diminishment.

In Ramge et al. (2010c) the problem of shrinkage induced constraining cracks and the interactions between stiffness, tensile strength and shrinkage behaviour of the mortar are dealt with in detail. According to that research, modification measures for the optimisation of mortar properties should always aim to reduce the shrinkage deformations and/or to enhance the tensile strength in relation to the mortar's stiffness.

2 EXPERIMENTAL SETUP

In general, the requirements according to the German repair mortar guideline, RL SIB (2001), issued by the German Committee of Reinforced Concrete, were used as benchmarks for the research project; nevertheless for the parameter studies, the scope of inspection had to be reduced to a necessary minimum in order to examine a great variety of parameter modifications in a reasonable timeframe. The shortened test procedure involved only two sets of three prismatic samples ($4 \times 4 \times 16$ cm^3) per mixture modification. So it was possible to test series with up to 12 mixture variations in one day, thus ensuring identical boundary conditions for the whole test series. The first set of samples was used for the determination of the 7-day strength values (flexural strength and compressive strength) whereas the second set was used to determine the shrinkage deformations until the 91st day. Additionally, the strength values and the carbonation depth were determined on the second set on the 91st day. In some cases the force-deformation-curve was determined during the flexural strength test to gain further information about the stiffness of the mortars. For the investigated mortars, a good correlation between E-modulus and compressive strength could be observed in general. Therefore it is reasonable to consider the tensile strength/compressive strength relation as a qualitative indicator of the tensile strength/stiffness relation for those cases were no specific investigations on the stiffness were carried out.

For the parameter studies the mortar for each set of prisms was mixed individually in a mortar mixer according to DIN EN 196-1. To simulate the mixing process used on site for dry mix products, the premixed dry components were scattered in ⅔ of the water during mixing. After 3 minutes mixing time the remaining ⅓ of the water was subsequently added to the continuing mixing process with a total mixing time of about 5 minutes. Of each mix the spread according to DIN EN1015-3 was determined before filling and vibrating the moulds according to EN 196-1. The moulds were covered with a glass sheet and stored at a relative humidity >95% RH for 24 hours. After demoulding, the prisms were stored in a climate chamber at $(50 \pm 5)\%$ RH and (23 ± 2) °C.

The reference measurement for the shrinkage deformations took place about 20 min after demoulding. The shrinkage specimens were cast with stainless steel pins in their face sides. The length change was measured with a precision of 1μm by means of a measuring device type C according to DIN 52450 involving an inductive displacement gauge.

Flexural strength and compressive strength were determined by means of a hydraulic test press according to DIN EN 196-1.

Carbonation depth was tested by means of the phenolphthalein indicator test on the fresh fracture faces after the flexural strength test.

In general the consistency was held at the same level described as a spread of about 16 cm according to DIN EN 1015-3.

Due to the rather rough storage conditions without any curing after demoulding, the controlling parameter of the hydration process and thus the strength development was the loss of water by evaporation. Therefore there were no major strength gains after the 7th day to be observed.

3 PARAMETER STUDIES

In this paper some results of parameter studies of the mentioned research project are presented. Further results of parameter studies as well as results of the composite specimen tests including sprayed application are published elsewhere (Ramge et al., 2009, Ramge et al., 2010a, b, c).

The starting point of the parameter studies was a commercially used repair mortar, provided by the project partner. This reference mortar is referred to as "mortar 0" in the further text. Due to its composition containing only a minimum range of different constituents, it qualifies ideally for the realisation of parameter studies. Mortar 0 is usually mixed with 13% water content (given as percentage by mass related to the mortar's dry mass).

Even though it is expected that the best possible shrinkage reduction is achieved by means of organic shrinkage reduction agents (SRA) other strategies were investigated as well. The aim was the maximum utilisation of the potentials of the mortar's non organic components. Each series of parameter studies had a reference mixture so that the relevant mixture modifications could be compared against the reference. Nevertheless, the reference mixtures may have differed from series to series as the parameter studies were part of a development of an "optimised mix". In the following parameter studies dealing with the exchange of the cement by other cements, the partial replacement of cement by inert and/or pozzolanic powder components, the use of organic shrinkage reducing agents and the use of polymer dispersion powders are presented.

3.1 Exchange of the cement

For the investigation of the cement's influence on the mortar properties, a test series was carried out in which the cement was replaced by other different cements (all CEM I). In a first step (series I) the existing cement of the reference mortar was replaced directly (by mass) without adjusting anything else in the mixture. The dosage of the superplasticizer (SP) and the water content remained the same. For most of the mortars the obtained consistency was not acceptable anymore, the fresh mortar was far too stiff for a proper application as repair mortar. This may be caused partly by the different granularity of the cements but also significantly by the interaction between the respective cement and the superplasticizer (SP) used. To gain comparable fresh mortar consistencies an additional test series (series II) was carried out in which the desired consistency was obtained by adjusting the SP dosage with the water content remaining unchanged. In both cases the exchange of cement caused higher shrinkage deformations, which was caused by the different chemical mineralogical composition of the cements.

As known from Beltzung & Wittmann (2005) there is a strong relationship between the moisture related deformations (shrinkage and swelling) and the alkali content of a concrete's pore solution. As the superplasticizer used, a melamine sulphonate, itself showed a rather high sodium content, the increased alkali content caused by high superplasticizer dosages must not be ignored. In Figures 1 and 2 the 91-day shrinkage values of the various mortars are plotted versus the alkali content given as Na_2O-equivalent of the respective cements.

In Figure 1 the results are shown without considering the superplasticizer, whereas in Figure 2 the Na_2O-equivalent values are recalculated taking into account the alkali content added by the superplasticizer. As the cements differ not only in their alkali content, the relationship is not as distinct as shown by Beltzung & Wittmann (2005) where experiments with one particular cement clinker were carried out with the variations of the alkali content induced by additional dosage of alkalis. However, for series I, still a general linear dependency is noticeable (coefficient of determination $R^2 = 0.66$). For series II this relationship is disrupted due to the changes in superplasticizer addition. However, if the alkali content of the superplasticizer is regarded as well, the relationship becomes much clearer. The investigations show that the alkali content is a strong parameter of the cement chemistry that influences the shrinkage behaviour, however, only one amongst others.

3.2 Partial replacement of cement by inert or pozzolanic powder components

In this series, dealing with variation in the powder range, part of the cement content of the reference mortar was exchanged by fly ash, limestone filler or a combination of both. A coarse fly ash ($d_{50} = 12.0$ μm) (FA1) and a fine fly ash ($d_{50} = 4.0$ μm) (FA2) as well as a coarse limestone filler ($d_{50} = 11.0$ μm) (LF1) and a fine limestone filler ($d_{50} = 2.6$ μm) (LF2) were used. Between 12.5% and 25% of the cement was replaced by the respective powder. The reference mortar of this series provided a w/c-ratio of 0.37 and an equivalent w/c-ratio of 0.34 respectively (consideration of fly ash with k = 0.4 and consideration of silica fume with k = 1.0). As the replacement of powder constituents changes the characteristic water

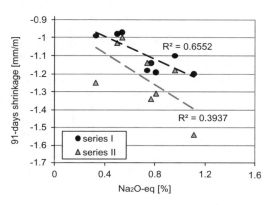

Figure 1. 91-days shrinkage vs. Na_2O-equivalent of the respective cement without consideration of other alkali impacts.

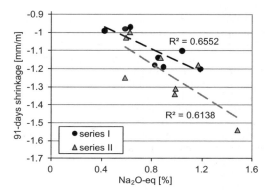

Figure 2. 91-days shrinkage vs. Na_2O-equiv. of the respective cement considering the alkalis induced by the superplasticizer.

demand of the grain compositions, the mixtures had to have different water contents to obtain comparable consistencies. Figure 3 shows some results of the series.

For all modifications of this series, a reduction of the shrinkage deformations in respect to the reference mortar could be obtained. Reductions of up to 0.21% could be achieved as seen in the case of mixture 8. Changes in the powder composition cause changes in the equivalent w/c-ratio and subsequently have an impact on the mortar's strength. In the case of mixture 8, the compressive strength was only 83% of the reference mortar's strength. Mixture 1, however, reached the same strength level as the reference mortar. With 0.11%, the shrinkage reduction of mixture 1 was only half of the amount gained with mixture 8, but still a significant gain compared to the reference mortar. Regarding the strength development, all mixtures behaved similarly. The 7-day strength values reached already 90–95% of the 91-day strength values. Significant differences in the long term strength development caused by different contents of pozzolanic components could not be observed.

The changes in the powder composition also had an impact on the durability of the mortars. The carbonation depth measured after 91 days, for example, differs in this test series from values of 1.8 mm for the reference mixture up to 3.4 mm for mixture 8. Mixture 1 reached a carbonation depth of 2.0 mm.

Concerning the flexural strength to compressive strength ratio, all mortar modifications showed values that implied a better prevention of shrinkage induced cracks than the reference mortar. Especially the mixtures containing fly ash seemed to be beneficial in this respect.

In general the optimisation potential of the partial replacement of cement by inert and/or pozzolanic powder components is caused by two different mechanisms. Firstly the positive influences on strength ratio, durability and shrinkage can be explained by the influence of the powder components on the chemical and mineralogical processes of the hydration and secondly by the reduction of the specific water demand and subsequently the actual water addition, which is often an accompanying effect of the replacement.

For pozzolanic constituents the second effect may even become the dominating one. In the literature it is reported, that in the presence of pozzolanic components, the amount of CSH-phases is increased, which may result in increased shrinkage behaviour. The direct comparison of mixture 1 and 2 as well as mixture 3 and 4 supported these findings as with increasing dosage of fly ash the effect of shrinkage reduction decreased. In general the addition of fly ash in itself seemed to increase

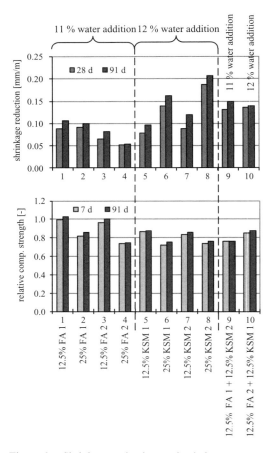

Figure 3. Shrinkage reduction and relative compressive strength values related to the reference for mortars with partial replacement of cement by other powder components.

the shrinkage, but this effect was compensated by the stronger effect of shrinkage reduction through water reduction.

In a second test series on the powder composition, the use of the coarse fly ash (as used in mixture 1 and mixture 2 of the first series) was investigated more precisely. In this series a slightly modified reference mortar was used. The admixture content was varied, and, amongst other changes, a shrinkage reducing agent (SRA) was added. Parallel to the replacement of cement by fly ash, a slight stepwise reduction of the overall powder content and a subsequent increase of the sand content were accomplished. The changes in the mixture proportioning are depicted in Figure 4.

The mortar mixtures were produced with 13% water addition as well as with 12% water addition. Therefore, a range of realised equivalent water cement ratios from 0.34 up to 0.50 were covered.

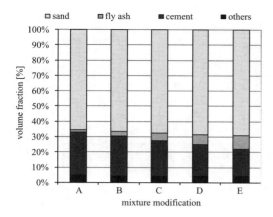

Figure 4. Mixture proportioning of mortars containing coarse fly ash (FA 1).

The mortars' strength values, both flexural strength and compressive strength, decreased linearly with increasing equivalent water cement ratio. The relation between flexural strength and compressive strength increased with increasing water cement ratio, which means with decreasing strength values, which in turn is beneficial for the prevention of shrinkage induced cracks. In this series, the correlation between compressive strength and stiffness was verified by evaluating the force-displacement-plots of the flexural strength tests. Concerning shrinkage and stiffness the composition E showed the best values. However, due to the rather low compressive strength values of 28.6 MPa for 13% water addition and 33.9 MPa for 12% water addition, respectively, and the high carbonation depth values, the mortar does not match the requirements according to the German repair mortar guideline RL SIB. For another application field with lower strength requirements this mortar could be used successfully, for example for the repair of older low strength concrete structures in hydraulic engineering according to the BAW bulletin on shotcrete and sprayed mortar. Due to its better tensile strength/stiffness relation and the lower shrinkage deformations this mortar should be the favoured choice for such applications.

3.3 Use of organic shrinkage reducing agents (SRA) and defoaming agent

The influence of two different organic shrinkage reducing agents (SRA-A and SRA-B) was investigated in a test series. In the dry mortar industry, SRAs are usually batched on a carrier substrate. As the active substances are not solid at room temperature, a dosage into a dry mix would not be possible otherwise. The carrier substrates of the

used SRAs consisted of precipitated silica. As the carrier substrates are not water soluble and provide a large inner surface they may cause interactions with other mortar components, especially at high dosages. They can interact with the powder components and change, for example, the specific water demand of the powder composition or cause a significant reduction of the workability time.

Figure 6 shows the shrinkage deformations for different dosages of each SRA. Due to different active substances both SRAs showed different results. In general the shrinkage reduction increased with increasing SRA dosage, however, the effectiveness decreased with higher dosages.

Figure 7 shows the respective effectiveness of each of the SRAs for dosages between 0% and 2% by mass related to the mortar's dry mass. The depicted values show the reduction of the shrinkage deformations at 91 days compared to the reference mortar without shrinkage reducing agent. It can be noticed that the SRAs not only differed in their general effectiveness but also in the dosage range where the best efficiency was provided.

Besides the desired effect of the shrinkage reduction both SRAs had a strong impact on the fresh mortar properties, which resulted in a strong reduction of the workability time. Figure 8 shows the change of the spread value over time for mortars with different SRA dosages. Mortar 0 was the plain reference mortar without any shrinkage reducing agent. The other mortars all contained the same shrinkage reducing agent (SRA-B). Mortar 2 and mortar 3 contained twice the amount of mortar 1. Mortar 3 additionally contained a small amount of defoaming agent. The rapid decrease of the workability is caused by the carrier substrate (precipitated silica) which in this case functions as an accelerating admixture. Comparative tests, in which the SRA was mixed with the water first, and the carrier substrate filtered out before mixing the mortar, have proven, that the observed workability reduction is not caused by the SRA's active substance, but solely by the carrier substrate. Whereas for a manual application, a shortened workability period may cause problems, it may be acceptable or even favoured for a sprayed application. As long as the mortar can be pumped and sprayed properly, quick stiffening is helpful to minimise the risk of draining off, especially if thick layers are applied.

At certain dosages, the presence of SRA can drastically increase the air entry in the fresh mortar, whereby the strength and the durability of the hardened mortar is influenced in a negative way. In Figure 9 the air content in the fresh mortar is shown versus the SRA dosage with and without carrier substrate. Already very little amounts of SRA increase the air content to the threefold value compared to that without SRA. With increasing SRA

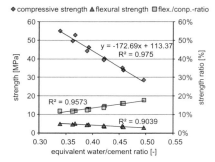

Figure 5. Strength values and flexural strength to compressive strength ratio versus the respective equivalent water/cement-ratio of mortars containing coarse fly ash (FA 1).

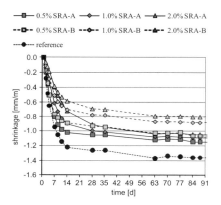

Figure 6. Development of the shrinkage deformations of mortars containing different amounts of shrinkage reducing agents SRA-A and SRA-B.

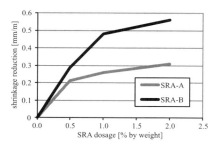

Figure 7. Effectiveness of the shrinkage reducing agents SRA-A and SRA-B in relation to their dosage.

dosage the air content differs only little. Exceeding a certain limit value, increasing SRA dosage causes the air content to go back to the original value again. This limit value differs for both SRAs and is

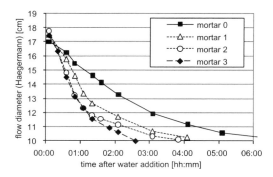

Figure 8. Time dependent development of the spread diameter for mortars containing different SRA dosages.

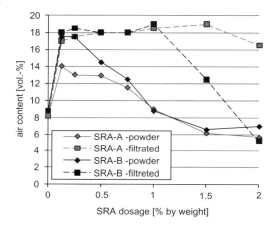

Figure 9. Fresh mortar air content in dependence of the SRA dosage.

also depending on the presence of the carrier substrate. High air contents may be beneficial for the rheological properties and the workability (lower viscosity, unaffected yield stress), but concerning durability and strength they exhibit the same negative influences as higher capillary porosities caused by high w/c-ratios. To prevent these negative effects defoaming agents may be used.

The described effects have a strong impact on the shelf life of dry mortar products. If stored for longer times the SRA may partly volatilise or degenerate in the dry mortar mix, thus changing the concentration of the active substances and subsequently changing the inserted air contend in the fresh mortar. Of some mortar mixtures (mortar 0, mortar 1 and mortar 2) larger charges were produced and stored over a period of up to 1.5 years. The mortar properties were investigated several times during this period. A loss of strength over time of up to 70% during one year for one of the mortars could be observed. However, a clear dependency between the sample's density (changed by different air insertions) and the compressive strength can be seen as shown in Figure 10. Referring to other investigations concerning the influence of the storage of cement on the fresh and hardened concrete properties (Schmidt et al., 2009) it must be expected that the aging of the cement itself can be neglected in this case. In fact it could be verified in comparative tests, in which the stored dry mortar was mixed with and without additional dosage of defoaming agent, that the strength loss is mostly caused by the different air entry in the fresh mortar. Figure 11 shows the results of these tests. In the example of mortar 2, of which two charges existed, mortar 2-a being produced at the same time as mortar 0 and mortar 1 and mortar 2-b being produced half a year later, it can be seen that the air content cannot be predicted solely by knowing the mixture proportioning and the storage time. The effect of higher air contents seems to be controlled by a multitude of individual ambient conditions. To minimize the risk of uncontrollable air contents the dosage of defoaming agent is strongly suggested whenever potentially surface active admixtures are present in the dry mortar mix. The above mentioned example emphasizes that this is also advisable for cases, in which the initial performance tests of the mixture composition do not imply the necessity of a defoaming agent, as the foam building behaviour of the admixtures may change during storage times.

Concerning the ratio of flexural strength to compressive strength, the mixtures with higher air content show more beneficial values in terms of crack prevention.

In general strength and E-modulus are dependent on the mortar's porosity. In most of the cases they can therefore not be influenced independently. However in Ramge et al. 2010c it was shown that the tensile strength value determined in the flexural strength test is strongly influenced by the climate conditions the specimens were exposed to during storage. If the specimens are stored in a low humidity climate like the storage condition B according to RL SIB (i.e. $(50 \pm 5)\%$ RH and (23 ± 2) °C) micro cracks will form on the surface due to the evaporation gradient. These micro cracks influence the flexural strength but do not affect the compressive strength or the E-modulus significantly. Therefore compressive strength values exceeding the minimum normative requirements should be avoided as an increasing compressive strength indicates an increasing stiffness, whereas the obtainable tensile strength is buffered due to the micro cracks on the specimen's surface.

However, if the effect of controlling compressive strength and stiffness by means of the mortar's air

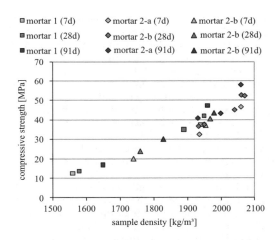

Figure 10. Compressive strength in dependence of the sample density variations caused by increased air entry.

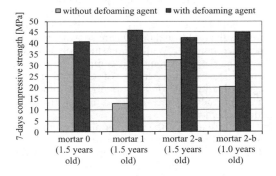

Figure 11. 7-days compressive strength for stored dry mortar products containing SRA-B mixed with and without defoaming agent.

content is to be utilized technically for enhanced crack prevention, a possibility to properly control the air content is needed. Therefore the addition of aluminium powder based air-entraining agents may be useful, as the defoaming agents mainly destroy air bubbles created by surface active substances, but do not hinder the hydrogen releasing reaction of the aluminium powder in the fresh mortar. Even though it sounds contradictory, the dosage of defoaming agents together with (Al-based) air-entraining agents may be reasonable or even necessary.

3.4 Use of polymer dispersion powder

By the use of polymer dispersion powders, the tensile strength can be enhanced. To test these additives in the sense of Polymer-Cement Concrete (PCC) and Sprayed Polymer-Cement Concrete (SPCC), mortar mixtures where made, in which part of the cement was substituted by polymer dispersion powder as well as mixtures, in which the polymer dispersion powder was added to the existing cement amount. The used polymer was a commercial vinyl acetate-ethylene-copolymer powder. Whereas the fresh mortar properties are not influences significantly by the polymer powder, the compressive strength decreases and the flexural strength increases with increasing polymer dosage. For those tests, in which cement was substituted by polymer powder, however, these tendencies are overtaken by the effects caused by a change in the w/c-ratio.

In Figure 12 the strength values of the tests with substituting dosage are shown versus the w/c-ratio. For better visualisation the flexural strength values are inflated ten times in the diagram. Compared to Fig. 5, a stronger decrease of the compressive strength with increasing w/c-ratio and a lesser decrease of the flexural strength can be seen. This is due to the mentioned superposition of the w/c-ratio effects with the effects of the polymer powder. In Figure 13 the test results of the substitutional as well as the additional dosage are shown versus the polymer content. With increasing polymer content, the flexural strength to compressive strength ratio increases, independent of the kind of dosage (substitutional or additional), thus indicating a better ability to prevent or minimize shrinkage induced cracks.

The influence of the polymer dispersion powder on the carbonation of the mortar is insignificant. The increase of the carbonation depth occurring at substituting dosage can be explained by the changed water cement ratio and subsequently the

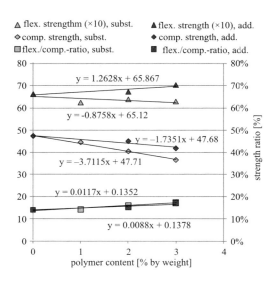

Figure 13. Flexural and compressive strength as well as flexural strength to compressive strength ratio of polymer modified mortars versus the polymer content. Depiction of flexural strength 10-times inflated.

changed porosity of the hardened cement paste. For constant cement contents and unchanged water cement ratios the additional dosage of polymer dispersion powder does not influence the carbonation behaviour. An enhancement of the carbonation resistance that might have been caused by a lesser permeability of the hardened cement paste due to the presence of polymer films in the pore volume could not be observed.

4 CONCLUSIONS AND OUTLOOK

Several possibilities to influence the repair mortar properties by certain mixture modifications have been presented. It became obvious, that it is nearly impossible to control one exclusive property without influencing others. For optimising mixture proportions, always a compromise has to be made, depending on the priorities of the individual properties for the specific application task. For certain applications it might be useful to accept a reduced compressive strength, if this allows better tensile strength to stiffness ratios to prevent the risk of shrinkage induced cracks. The complexity of the interactions even makes apparently inconsistent combinations of admixtures necessary in individual cases. The adjustment of most of the mortar properties can be achieved by different measures with different side effects. Not only the hardened mortar properties but also the fresh mortar properties need to be considered. Due to

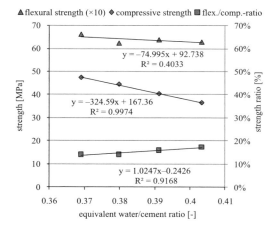

Figure 12. Flexural and compressive strength as well as flexural strength to compressive strength ratio of polymer modified mortars versus the w/c-ratio. Depiction of flexural strength 10-times inflated.

the different processing technology, changes in the fresh mortar properties have different impacts on sprayed application (SPCC) compared to manual application (PCC).

ACKNOWLEDGMENTS

This research project is financed by the 'German Federal Ministry of Economics and Technology' based on a decision of the German Federal Parliament, for which our appreciation and thanks are expressed. Also the 'PAGEL Spezial-Beton GmbH & Co. KG' is to be thanked for their cooperation in this project.

REFERENCES

Beltzung, F. & Wittmann, F.H. 2005. Role of disjoining pressure in cement based materials. *Cement and Concrete Research* 35: 2364–2370.

DIN EN 1015-3 (2006) Methods of test for mortar for masonry—Part 3: Determination of consistence of fresh mortar (by flow table); German version EN 1015-3:1999 + A1:2004 + A2:2006.

DIN EN 196-1 (2005) Methods of testing cement—Part 3: Determination of strength; German version EN 1961:2005.

DIN 52450 (1985) Prüfung anorganischer nichtmetallischer Baustoffe; Bestimmung des Schwindens und Quellens an kleinen Probekörpern, Ausgabedatum: 1985-08.

Federal Waterways Engineering and Research Institute, 2007, BAW Merkblatt Spritzmörtel/Spritzbeton nach ZTV-W LB 219, Abschnitt 5 (BAW-Merkblatt „Spritzmörtel") edition 2007.

German Committee of Reinforced Concrete (DAfStb) 2001. DAfStb-Richtlinie Schutz und Instandsetzung von Betonbauteilen, Ausgabe 2001. Berlin: Beuth Verlag.

Ramge, P., Kühne, H.-C. & Meng, B. 2009. Betoninstandsetzung mit modular zusammengesetzten PCC- und SPCC-Mörteln. In J. Stark (ed) *17th ibausil International Conference on Building Materials, Proc. intern. symp., Weimar, 23–25 September 2009*, vol. 2 pp. 2-0151–2-0156. Weimar: Bauhausuniversität Weimar.

Ramge, P., Kühne, H.-C. & Meng, B. 2010a. MODINSYS modular systems for the protection and repair of concrete structures. In J.B. Aguiar, S. Jalali, A. Cmoes & R.M. Ferrreira (eds), *13th International Congress on Polymers in Concrete, Proc. Intern. Symp., Funchal, Madeira Islands, 11–13 February 2010*, pp. 697–704. Minho: University of Minho.

Ramge, P., Kühne, H.-C. & Meng, B. 2010b. Development of a Modular System for the Protection and Repair of Concrete Structures. *Restoration of Buildings and Monuments*, 16(4/5): 387–400.

Ramge, P., Kühne, H.-C. & Meng, B. 2010c. Parameterstudien zum Einfluss von Rezepturveränderungen auf Schwindverhalten, Rissneigung und Steifigkeit mineralischer Instandsetzungsmörtel. In K. Littmann (ed), *7th International Colloquium Industrial Floors 2010, Technische Akademie Esslingen, Ostfilden/Stuttgart, 14–16 December 2010*, pp. 191–200.

Schmidt, W., Ramge, P. & Kühne, H.-C. 2009. Effect of the storage conditions of cement on the processing and hardening properties of concrete. *Concrete Plant + Precast Technology*, 75(6): 10–17.

Concrete Solutions – Grantham, Mechtcherine & Schneck (eds)
© 2012 Taylor & Francis Group, London, ISBN 978-0-415-61622-5

A rational method for calculation of restrained shrinkage stresses in repaired concrete members

S. Sajedi, A. Razavizadeh, Z. Minaii, F. Ghassemzadeh & M. Shekarchi
School of Civil Engineering, University of Tehran, Tehran, Iran

ABSTRACT: Stresses due to restrained shrinkage have long been recognized as the main causes of cracking and debonding of repaired concrete members especially in hot weather environments. Although several studies have been conducted to investigate this effect, there is no widely accepted method for calculating restrained shrinkage stresses in the repair system. In this paper, a rational numerical method is proposed to determine the tensile stress in repaired concrete members by measuring the free shrinkage values in the laboratory. The effects of repair dimensions, interface surface roughness, and creep relaxation have been considered in the proposed method.

1 INTRODUCTION

In bonded concrete overlays, the evaporation and diffusion process inside the repair concrete result in a non-uniform moisture gradient near the surface (Carlson, 1937) and induce a shrinkage gradient through the repaired layer (Bazant 1989, Weiss 1999 & Moon et al., 2004, 2006). In these cases, restraint from the surrounding structure prohibits the concrete from moving freely and tensile stresses are set up in the repair layer together with shear and peeling stresses at the interface (Rahman et al., 2000). If the tensile stress exceeds the tensile strength of the repair material and/or the stresses at the interface exceed the bond strength, cracking and/or delamination will occur in the patch repair. This phenomenon is more critical in high-strength repair concretes with low water to cement ratios (Shin & Lange 2004) which usually show high shrinkage values in the same conditions.

Several studies have been conducted to investigate shrinkage-cracking behavior of restrained concretes. As many complex and interacting parameters affect shrinkage cracking of restrained concretes, experiments used to yield contradicting results. McDonald et al. (2002) reported that in order to reduce the risk of cracking and delamination in patch repairs, using repair materials with low stiffness would be suitable. On the other hand, Mangat and O'Flaherty (2000) pointed out that the patch repair should have a greater elastic modulus than the substrate to display an efficient interaction with the structure and be more effective in attracting the external loading in the long-term. According to Brown et al. (2007), materials with low free shrinkage strains, low initial modulus of elasticity, high creep potential and high early tensile strength are recommended for overlays. As well as these parameters, dimensions of the repair concrete and roughness of the substrate have an influence on the level of induced stresses in the repair system. As the length of the repair layer increases, both the tensile stress in the repair material and the shear stress at the interface increase (Silfwerbrand 1997) and by increasing the thickness of repair, the tensile stress reduces (Beushausen 2006). A high potential of cracking and debonding in repaired concretes cast on substrates with high roughness and low roughness surfaces are also expected, respectively.

Since, there is a great deal of interest in measuring and evaluating the restrained shrinkage in repaired concrete members by experiment and owing to the complex nature of interacting parameters, numerical analysis techniques are suitable for assessment and control of cracking in repair systems. Yuan and Marosszeky (1994) developed an analytical model to investigate the restrained shrinkage of repaired reinforced concrete members. They concluded that the high shrinkage values can lead to cracking in patch repairs and additional tensile strains in the substrate. However, the expansion of repair material and reduction of tensile stresses due to the creep effect can delay the formation of cracking. Baluch et al. (2008) proposed a simple method for calculating drying shrinkage stresses. They used heat transfer and stress analysis modules in a multi-physics software package in order to calculate drying shrinkage in concrete elements. Although their proposed method can be used for calculating drying shrinkage stresses, the effect of

461

roughness was not considered in their proposed method.

Zhou et al. (2008) developed an analytical model to calculate the stresses and strains in bonded concrete overlays based on the plate theory and the assumption of a linear relationship between shear stress and slip at the interface. This model is able to be used to calculate the induced stresses in the repair material and substrate. However, the amount of interface shear stiffness in their proposed method depends on engineering judgment and can be different for various concretes which can increase the prediction errors. Moreover, the effect of tensile creep on the stress relaxation has not been considered in this model.

Weiss et al. (1998) developed a theoretical model based on fracture mechanics to predict the age of first cracking in restrained concrete slabs considering the effects of restraint condition and creep relief. They compared their model with experimental results and concluded that the age of first cracking in restrained slabs can be predicted by their proposed model. They also commented that using shrinkage reducing admixtures can delay or prevent cracking in restrained specimens.

In this paper, a new method is proposed for calculating the restrained shrinkage gradient and tensile stress at the depth of repaired concrete members by measuring the free shrinkage strains in the laboratory which can be used as a suitable technique for design of compatible repairs for concrete structures.

2 METHODOLOGY

2.1 Shrinkage gradient at the depth of concrete

In order to predict drying shrinkage of concretes as a function of time, ACI (2008) proposed an empirical model by the following equation:

$$\varepsilon_{sh}(t,t_c) = \gamma_{sh} \times 780 \times 10^{-6} \times \left(\frac{t-t_c}{f+t-t_c}\right) \quad (1)$$

$$\gamma_{sh} = \gamma_{sh,tc}\gamma_{sh,RH}\gamma_{sh,vs}\gamma_{sh,s}\gamma_{sh,\Psi}\gamma_{sh,\alpha} \quad (2)$$

where: $\varepsilon_{sh}(t,t_c)$ = shrinkage strain (mm/mm); t = the age of the concrete (days); t_c = the age of the concrete when drying starts at the end of moist curing (days); γ_{sh} represents the cumulative product of the applicable correction factors; f is a constant which depends on the member shape and size of specimen, $t-t_c$ = duration of drying (days), $\gamma_{sh,tc}$ is the initial moist curing coefficient, $\gamma_{sh,RH}$ is the ambient relative humidity coefficient, $\gamma_{sh,vs}$ is dimensional coefficient, $\gamma_{sh,s}$ is the correction factor which reflects the effect of concrete slump, $\gamma_{sh,\Psi}$ is

aggregates content factor, $\gamma_{sh,c}$ is cement content factor, and $\gamma_{sh,\alpha}$ is the air content factor.

Among the above coefficients, the effects of concrete dimensions and ambient relative humidity on shrinkage strain can be calculated by following equations:

$$f = 26.0e^{\left\{1.42\times10^{-2}(V/S)\right\}} \quad (3)$$

$$\gamma_{sh,RH} = \begin{cases} 1.40-1.02RH & for\ 0 \le RH \le 0.8 \\ 3.00-3.00RH & for\ 0.8 \le RH \le 1 \end{cases} \quad (4)$$

$$\gamma_{sh,vs} = 1.2e^{\left\{-0.00472(V/S)\right\}} \quad (5)$$

where: V/S is volume-surface ratio of concrete member and RH is ambient relative humidity.

When free shrinkage of concrete is measured in the laboratory, the estimated shrinkage by equation 1 should be equal to the measured free shrinkage. If there are differences between the results of the model and measured values, the ACI model should be modified. For modification of the ACI equation in order to fit the experimental data to predicted values, Almeida et al. (2006) proposed the method based on the Inverse Analysis (IA) technique. In this method, the constant coefficients apply to modify the shrinkage prediction model(s) while the minimum coefficient of variation (COV) between the experimental results and predicted values is obtained. The modified form of the ACI model after applying IA can be written as:

$$\varepsilon_{sh}(t,t_c) = C_1 \times \gamma_{sh} \times 780 \times 10^{-6} \times \left(\frac{t-t_c}{f+t-t_c}\right)^{C_2} \quad (6)$$

where C_1 and C_2 are modifying coefficients which can be calculated by a trial and error method. A detailed description of this method is given in reference (Almeida et al., 2006).

As mentioned earlier, due to the evaporation process, a non-uniform moisture gradient forms at the depth of concrete. For determining the internal relative humidity (RH) at various depths of concrete specimens with one exposed drying surface, Parrott (1988) suggested the following equation based on the ambient relative humidity:

$$RH = RHA + \frac{(100 - RHA) \times \left[d^X (Y-e)(w-Z)\right]}{d^X (Y-e)(w-Z) + tW} \quad (7)$$

where "RH" is the predicted relative humidity at the depth of concrete (%), "RHA" is the ambient relative humidity (%), "t" is the drying age (days), "d" is the depth from drying surface (mm), "e" is the OPC replaced by pozzolanic materials (%), and "w" is the water/binder ratio. W, X, Y and Z are constants. Although Parrott suggested values to the four parameters such that $W = 8$, $X = 1.35$, $Y = 70$ and $Z = 0.19$, McDonald and Roper (1991) showed that the values of $W = 11.4$, $X = 0.85$, $Y = 128.00$ and $Z = 0.03$ can result in more reliable results.

Introducing expression (7) into Equation (4), for $0 \le RH \le 0.8$ we have:

$$\gamma_{sh,RH} = 1.4 - 0.012$$
$$\times \left(RHA + \frac{(100 - RHA) \times \left[d^X (Y - e)(w - Z) \right]}{d^X (Y - e)(w - Z) + tW} \right)$$

$$(8)$$

Here, introducing Equation (8) into Equation (2) and then into Equation (6), and applying expressions (3) and (5), and assuming $\gamma_1 = \gamma_{sh,tc} \cdot \gamma_{sh,s} \cdot \gamma_{sh,\psi} \cdot \gamma_{sh,c} \cdot \gamma_{sh,\alpha}$ it is found that:

$$\varepsilon_{sh}(t,t_c) = C_1 (1310.4 - 9.5472(RHA$$
$$+ \frac{(100 - RHA) \times \left[d^X (Y - e)(w - Z) \right]}{d^X (Y - e)(w - Z) + tW})) \times e^{\{-0.00472(V/S)\}}$$
$$\times \gamma_1 \times \left(\frac{t - t_c}{26.0 e^{\{1.42 \times 10^{-2} \times (V/S)\}} + t - t_c} \right)^{C_2}$$

$$(9)$$

where $\varepsilon_{sh}(t,t_c)$ is shrinkage strain (micro strain) at the various depths of d for a concrete member from one exposed drying surface. As seen from equation (9), the effects of concrete dimensions and moisture gradient have been considered in the model.

2.2 Restrained shrinkage in repaired concretes

The restrained shrinkage at the top surface of a concrete member is different from free shrinkage value and it depends on the interface texture and restraint conditions. For considering this effect, Abbasnia et al. (2005) proposed the following equation for calculating the restrained shrinkage values at the top surface of concrete based on the free shrinkage values:

$$\varepsilon_r = R\varepsilon_f \qquad (10)$$

where ε_r is the restrained shrinkage at the top surface of concrete; R is the restraint factor that depends on the interface texture and restraint conditions; and ε_f is the free shrinkage of concrete. The average values of restraint factor (R) are given in Table 1.

As seen from Table 1, two types of surface condition at the interface have been investigated: rough and smooth. The restrained shrinkage gradient at the depth of repair concrete can then be determined by introducing Equation (10) into Equation (9):

$$\varepsilon_r(t) = C_1 R(1310.4 - 9.5472(RHA$$
$$+ \frac{(100 - RHA) \times \left[d^X (Y - e)(w - Z) \right]}{d^X (Y - e)(w - Z) + tW}))$$
$$\times e^{\{-0.00472(V/S)\}} \times \gamma_1 \times \left(\frac{t}{26.0 e^{\{1.42 \times 10^{-2} \times (V/S)\}} + t} \right)^{C_2} \qquad (11)$$

The algorithm of the proposed method for calculating restrained shrinkage strains by free shrinkage measurements is presented in Figure 1.

2.3 Interaction between tensile creep and shrinkage

The cracking tendency of concrete members under restrained shrinkage depends not only on the tensile strength but also on the tensile creep characteristics of the concrete (Kovler 1999, Altoubat & Lange 2001 & See et al., 2003). Tensile creep relaxes the induced stresses which may delay or prevent cracking. Tests on the tensile creep behavior of concretes that are available in the literature are limited and conflicting. See et al. (2003) reported that tensile creep of concrete is lower under restrained shrinkage than under a constant stress. So, for proper investigation of the cracking tendency of restrained concrete members subjected to drying, the use of tensile creep properties under constant loads test would lead to unconservative predictions. In this study, for considering the effect of creep relaxation on the induced stresses, the effective modulus of elasticity (E_{eff}) was calculated by the following equation (ACI 209R-92):

$$E_{eff}(t,t_0) = E(t)/(1 + \chi(t,t_0)\phi(t,t_0)) \qquad (12)$$

$$\phi(t,t_0) = 2.35 \times \gamma_c \times (t^{0.6}/(t^{0.6} + 10)) \qquad (13)$$

where $E_{eff}(t,t_0)$ is the effective modulus of elasticity, $E(t)$ is the elastic modulus of repair concrete at age t, $\Phi(t,t_0)$ is the creep coefficient at concrete age t due to the load applied at age t_0, γ_c represents the cumulative product of the applicable correction factors, and χ is an ageing coefficient that can be considered as 0.8 (Ghali & Favre 1994).

Table 1. Average values of restraint factor (R) in different restraint conditions.

Boundary condition	Surface condition	Restraint factor (R)
With eaves	rough	0.83
	smooth	0.69
Without eaves	rough	0.52
	smooth	0.22

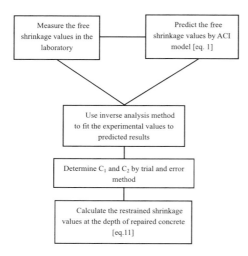

Figure 1. Algorithm of restrained shrinkage calculation at the various depths of repaired concretes.

The tensile stress at the various depths of repair concrete can be calculated by following equation:

$$\sigma_t = E_{eff}(t,t_0) \times \varepsilon_r(t) \tag{14}$$

3 VERIFICATION

The proposed method for calculating restrained shrinkage was verified based on the experimental data presented by Beushausen and Alexander (2007). Specimen A had overlay dimensions of $1600 \times 160 \times 40$ mm without eaves around the perimeter and the texture of the substrate surface was prepared as a smooth texture. Mix proportions of the overlay are presented in Table 2.

Figure 2 shows the overlay free shrinkage strains as a function of time. By prediction of the overlay free shrinkage with the ACI model and applying the IA method in order to modify and fit it into experimental measurements, the values of 0.849 and 0.83 are obtained for coefficients C_1 and C_2, respectively. The modified form of ACI is then:

$$\varepsilon_{sh}(t) = 518 \times \left(\frac{t}{t+32.487}\right)^{0.83} \tag{15}$$

In order to predict the shrinkage strains at the interface, the values of R and d in Equation (11) should be set to 0.22 and 40 mm, respectively. Also, by assuming the values proposed by McDonald and Roper (1991) for W, X, Y and Z in Equation (7), the actual shrinkage strains at the interface can be calculated by following equation:

Table 2. Mix proportions.

Specimen	
Cement (kg/m³)	510
Water (kg/m³)	235
Coarse agg. (kg/m³)	940
Fine agg. (kg/m³)	660
Slump (mm)	80

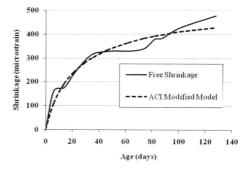

Figure 2. Overlay free shrinkage values for specimen A.

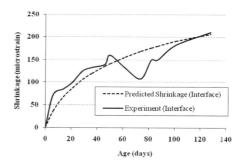

Figure 3. Interface shrinkage values for specimen A.

$$\varepsilon_a(t) = \varepsilon_{free}(t) - \varepsilon_r(t) = 431.889 \times \left(0.737 - \frac{7.685}{0.207t + 21.526}\right)$$
$$\times \left(\frac{t}{t+32.487}\right)^{0.83} \tag{16}$$

Figure 3 shows the comparison between experimental results and predicted values by Equation (16) at the interface:

As seen from Fig. 3, the analytical results of actual shrinkage at the interface are in good agreement with experimental results. Thus, it seems that the proposed method can be used as a simple tool to calculate the restrained shrinkage and tensile stresses at various depths of repair concrete.

4 CONCLUSIONS

A new simple model based on the Inverse Analysis method is developed in this study for calculation of restrained shrinkage strains and tensile stresses at repaired concrete members. The effects of repair dimensions, restraint condition, free shrinkage of overlay and creep relief have been considered in the proposed model. By measuring the free shrinkage strains in the laboratory, it is now possible for engineers to assess the probability of cracking in repaired concrete members and choose the appropriate repair materials with optimum thickness in order to minimize the risk of cracking in repair concretes.

REFERENCES

Abbasnia, R. Godossi, P. & Ahmadi, J. 2005. Prediction of restrained shrinkage based on restraint factors in patching repair mortar. *Cement and Concrete Research*. 35: 1909–1913.

ACI 209.2R-08. Guide for modeling and calculating shrinkage and creep in hardened concrete.

ACI 209R-92. 1997. Prediction of creep, shrinkage and temprature effects in concrete structures. *American Concrete Institue*: Farmington Hills.

Almeida, L.C., Oliveira e Sousa, J.L.A. & Azevedo Figueiras, J. 2006. Application of inverse analysis to shrinkage and creep models. *Measuring, Monitoring and Modeling Concrete Properties*: 151–160.

Altoubat, S. & Lange, D. 2001. Creep, shrinkage, and cracking of restrained concrete at early ages. *ACI Materials Journal*. V. 98, No. 4: 323–331.

Baluch, M.H., Rahman, M.K. & Mahmoud, I.A. 2008 Calculating drying-shrinkage stresses. *Concrete International*: 37–41.

Beushausen, H. 2006. Long-term performance of bonded concrete overlays subjected to differential shrinkage *PhD Dissertation, University of Cape Town*, South Africa.

Beushausen, H. & Alexander, M.G. 2007. Localised strain and stress in bonded concrete overlays subjected to differential shrinkage., *Materials and Structures*. 40:189–199.

Brown, M.D., Smith, C.A., Sellers, J.G., Follirad, K.J. & Breen, J.E. 2007. Use of alternative materials to reduce shrinkage cracking in bridge decks. *ACI Materials Journal*. Vol. 104, No. 6: 629–637.

Bazant, Z.P. 1989. Mathematical modeling of creep and shrinkage of concrete. *John Wiley & Sons*.

Carlson, R.W. 1937. Drying shrinkage of large concrete members. *Journal of the American Concrete Institute*: 327–336.

Ghali, A. & Favre, R. 1994. Concrete structures: stresses and deformations. E&FN SPON.

Kovler, K., Igarashi, S. & Bentur, B. 1999. Tensile creep behavior of high-strength concretes at early ages. *Materials and Structures*. V. 32, No. 219: 383–387.

Mangat, P.S. & O'Flaherty, F.J. 2000. Influence of elastic modulus on stress redistribution and cracking in repair patches. *Cement and Concrete Research*. 30: 125–136.

McDonald, D.B. & Roper, H. 1991. Discussion on the paper factors influencing relative humidity in concrete. *Magazine of Concrete Research*. 43 (157): 305–307.

McDonald, J.E., Vaysburd, A.M., Emmons, P.H., Poston, R.W. & Kenser, K.E. 2002. Selecting durable repair materials: performance criteria-summary. *Concr. Int.* 24: 37–44.

Moon, J.H., Rajabipour, F. & Weiss, W.J. 2004. Incorporating moisture diffusion in the analysis of the restrained ring test. *Proc. 4th Int. Conf. Concrete Under Severe Conditions: Environment & Loading*. Vol. 2 ed. K. Sakai, O.E. Gjorv, and N. Banthia: 1973–1980.

Moon, J.H. & Weiss, W.J. 2006. Estimating residual stress in the restrained ring test under circumferential drying. *Cement & Concrete Composites*. 28: 486–496.

Parrott, L.J. 1988. Moisture profiles in drying concrete. *Advance Cement Research*. 1(3): 164–170.

Rahman, M.K. Baluch, M.H. & Algadhib, A.H. 2000. Simulation of shrinkage distress and creep relief in concrete repair. *Composites Part B: Engineering*: 541–553.

See, H.T., Attiogbe, E.K. & Miltenberger, M.A. 2003. Shrinkage cracking characteristics of concrete using ring specimens. ACI Materials Journal. V. 100, No. 3: 239–245.

Shin, H.C. & Lange, D.A. 2004. Effects of shrinkage and temperature in bonded concrete overlays. *ACI Materials Journal*. V. 101, No. 5: 358–364.

Silfwerbrand, J. 1997. Stresses and strains in composite concrete beams subjected to differential shrinkage, *ACI Structural Journal*. 94: 347–353.

Weiss, W.J. 1999. Prediction of early-age shrinkage cracking in concrete. *PhD Dissertation, Northwestern University*, Evanston, IL.

Weiss, W.J., Yang, W. & Shah, S.P. 1998. Shrinkage cracking of restrained concrete slabs. *Journal of Engineering Mechanics. ASCE*: 765–774.

Yuan, Y.S. & Marosszeky, M. 1994. Restrained shrinkage in repaired reinforced concrete element. *Materials and Structures*. 27, No. 171: 375–382.

Zhou, J., Ye, G., Schlangen, E. & Breugel, K. 2008. Modelling of stresses and strains in bonded concrete overlays subjected to differential volume changes. *Theoretical and Applied Fracture Mechanics*. 49: 199–205.

Concrete Solutions – Grantham, Mechtcherine & Schneck (eds)
© 2012 Taylor & Francis Group, London, ISBN 978-0-415-61622-5

Discussion on crack path of interface between concrete and polymer cement mortar

K. Yamada, A. Satoh, T. Homma & S. Ishiyama
Graduate School of Systems Science and Technology, Akita Prefectural University, Akita, Japan

Y. Shinohara
Structural Engineering Research Center, Tokyo Institute of Technology, Yokohama, Japan

ABSTRACT: The purpose of this paper is a discussion on the mechanisms of the adhesion between concrete and Polymer Cement Mortar (PCM) used for patch repair, searching for the way to achieve better mechanical performance of the interface. The authors investigated the mechanical properties of four types of concrete prism specimens repaired with PCM. After the fracture mechanics test, the surfaces of the specimens were analyzed chemically and physically. The surfaces were finally classified into 7 parts; detached part, fractured parts of concrete or mortar, fractured parts of two types of PCM, interfacial transition zone around coarse aggregate and void. The tensile strength and fracture energy of the classified 7 parts were identified. A new method for the representation of crack paths in a graphic model was developed, which can describe both the fractographic features of the fractured surface and the mechanical properties.

1 INTRODUCTION

Repair work is becoming a mainstream of the construction industry for developed countries after accumulating lots of infrastructure made of concrete. When repairing the concrete structure, the most important point is the strong adhesion of the repair materials to the old concrete.

In that point, there have been many studies that discuss the improvement of the adhesion strength with using improved surface treatment of the old concrete and improvement of the repair materials (Takase et al. 2000; Kurihara et al. 1998). But there have only been a very small number of studies that analyze the fundamental mechanisms of the fracture along the interface between the old concrete and the repair materials. Also few studies evaluate the mechanical properties based on fracture mechanics (Kurihara et al. 1996; Satoh et al. 2009). There should be research work which discusses these fundamental issues for inviting the breakthrough of the technology into repair work and materials.

The fractographic discussion, which deals with the precise investigation of the fractured surface and was mainly employed in the field of metals so far, is the best resort for analyzing the crack paths and the mechanisms of the fracture of concrete. The main theme of this paper is discussing the relation between the fracture mechanics parameters and the fractographic features of the fractured surfaces of the prism specimens which were jointed with different repair materials.

2 EXPERIMENT

2.1 Materials

The four types of repair materials used in this study are listed in Table 1. Also ordinary mortar was used for repair as a reference. The substrate

Table 1. Used repair materials.

Name	Type	Detail of materials
SAG	Primer	Two component type of Epoxy resin primer with no solvent
	Mortar	Polymer cement mortar Premixed type of powdered Acrylic resin adhesive
S22	Adhesive	Two component type of Epoxy resin primer especially for placing joint
KCA	Primer Mortar	Impregnation type of Epoxy resin primer Cation type of polymer cement mortar
KEP	Mortar	Polymer cement mortar from two component type of Epoxy resin emulsion

concrete for the prism specimens which were jointed at the center was ordinary concrete and the mix proportions are listed in Table 2.

2.2 Specimens

All the concrete specimens were jointed after the substrate concrete reached the age of 28 days after casting. Figure 1 depicts the ways of manufacturing the specimens; on the left is the jointed one using SAG, KCA, KEP or mortar, and the on the right with a placing (construction) joint at the centre with the help of S22 resin. The surfaces to be jointed were roughened with a wire brush observing the AIJ standard (JASS5, 2009).

At the top of Table 3, there are four types of mortar specimens for investigating the mechanical properties of mortar and mortar-to-mortar adhesion

Table 2. Mix proportions of concrete and mortar.

Name	W/C %	S/A %	Mass (kg/m³)				Air %
			W	C	S	G	
Concrete	51.4	43.0	177	344	739	1010	4.0
Mortar	51.4	–	305	593	1264	–	4.0

Remarks: W/C (water to cement ratio), S/A (sand to aggregate ratio), G (gravel).

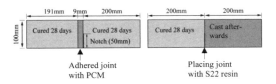

Figure 1. Schematic description of specimens.

properties. At the middle of Table 3, the description PCM (polymer cement mortar) refers to the monolithic specimen made only of the repair material for investigating the mechanical properties of itself.

The substrate concrete or mortar is cured under standard water curing condition at 20°C (W28), while the specimens after the joint were cured under a sealed curing condition at 20°C (S28). The reason for the different curing conditions is that the repair materials should be cured under air not under water.

2.3 Fracture mechanics test

After the curing, a Tension Softening Diagram (TSD) of the specimens was achieved using the results from fracture mechanics tests based on the standards (JCI-SFR3, 2004; RILEM, 1985). The feature of the test is the half depth notch at the center of specimen for a stable fracture progress as Figure 1 shows. Finally the fracture mechanics properties were calculated as listed in Table 4.

2.4 Fractographic analysis

After the fracture mechanics test and following macroscopic observations, the fractured surfaces were measured in terms of height using a 3-D laser scanning machine at the scanning interval of 50 μm both in the X and Y directions. The 3-D data of the surface were processed for calculating the distribution map of height and the local curvature with the help of special software.

The small pieces were cut from fractured surfaces of specimens for EPMA (Electron Probe Micro Analyser) analysis. Among the chemical elements, the distribution of Ca was analyzed to detect CH (Calcium hydroxide) and fine aggregates.

Table 3. Attributes of specimens.

Type	Name	Used material	Curing duration (days)		Attribute
			At repair	After repair	
Mortar	MN	Mortar	W28	–	Monolith
	MNS	Mortar	S28	–	Monolith
	MM	Mortar	W28	W28	Adhered
	MMS	Mortar	W28	S28	Adhered
PCM	SAG	SAG	S28	–	Monolith
Concrete	CN	Concrete	W28	–	Monolith
	CSAGS	SAG	W28	S28	Adhered
	CKCAS	KCA	W28	S28	Adhered
	CKEPS	KEP	W28	S28	Adhered
	CS22S	S22	W28	S28	Placing joint

Remarks: PCM (polymer cement mortar).

Table 4. Mechanical and fracture mechanics parameters.

Type	Name of specimen	Cured age (days)	Fb MPa	Ft MPa	Wcr mm	Gf N/mm
Mortar	MN	W28	6.12	6.07	0.0280	0.0282
	MNS	S28	5.26	5.72	0.0930	0.0366
	MM	W28	4.03	6.24	0.0305	0.0107
	MMS	S28	3.38	5.62	0.0256	0.0079
PCM	SAG	S28	4.93	4.79	0.0259	0.0225
Concrete	CN	W28	4.37	7.07	0.2350	0.1180
	CSAGS	S28	3.23	4.66	0.1590	0.0500
	CKCAS	S28	2.30	4.00	0.2060	0.0790
	CKEPS	S28	1.63	3.31	0.0420	0.0120
	CS22S	S28	4.00	5.81	0.1630	0.0750

Remarks: Fb (flexural strength), Ft (tension softening initial stress or tensile strength), Wcr (critical crack width), Gf (fracture energy).

3 RESULTS

3.1 Mechanical properties

Table 4 shows the resulting mechanical properties. Ft, Wcr and Gf are the fracture mechanics parameters achieved from the TSD, which the authors analyzed using inverse analysis with the help of JCI's program (Uchida et al. 1991).

It is a common opinion that Gf is the most important parameter among many mechanical and fracture mechanics parameters, because it is a direct parameter representing the ductility of the material of the structural element. Figures 2 and 3 show the relationship between Gf and Fb, which shows the enhancement of Gf depends on Fb (the strength of the material).

Gf is the integral of tensile closure stress along the crack width, and the maximum values for them are Ft and Wcr. So, Gf is closely related to both of them. Also it is known that Ft and Fb are closely related (Satoh et al. 2007), then the relationship between Fb and Gf are also very close as Figures 2 and 3 show. The increasing tendency of Gf against Fb looks like a function of second power of Fb. It is the general tendency, because Wcr (which directly affects Gf) is also deeply related to Ft and Fb (Satoh et al. 2009).

It should be noticed that the strength of monolithic PCM is not so strong and not so ductile as the monolith of ordinary mortar. But the repaired concrete prism with PCM is stronger and more ductile than the bulk PCM and the bulk mortar. The strength of repair mortar in Table 3 is higher but the ductility is very low. These facts imply the importance of the coarse aggregate even in the case of jointed specimens, which has a roughened surface of interface.

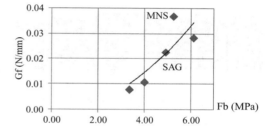

Figure 2. Relation between Gf and Fb for repair materials.

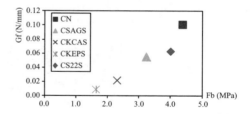

Figure 3. Relation between Gf and Fb for repaired specimens.

3.2 Results from fractographic analysis

3.2.1 Macroscopic observations

The authors made macroscopic observations of the fractured surfaces and classified the surfaces into seven parts from A to G in Table 5. Typical surfaces classified in seven parts are depicted in Figure 4. Part F appears in the fractured surface of concrete, and such specimens have high mechanical performance. On the other hand, specimens which do not have part F have poor mechanical performance. This derives from the depth of the fractured surface; i.e., deep surface accompanies ITZ around aggregates.

469

Table 5. Macroscopic classification of fractured surfaces.

	Name	Crack path	Feature
A	Detached	Straight in the interface	Smooth surface
B	Concrete	Deep in substrate concrete	Emerging the coarse aggregate
C	Mortar	Shallow in substrate concrete	Emerging only cement paste and some fine aggregates
D	Repair-S	Fracture of SAG	Fracture of repair SAG
E	Repair-K	Fracture of KCA	Fracture of repair KCA
F	ITZ	ITZ	Around coarse aggregate
G	Void	Void	Air bubbles

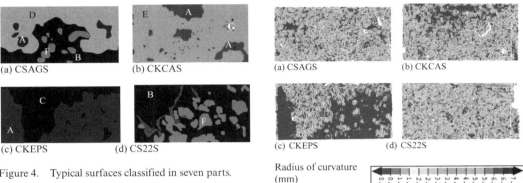

Figure 4. Typical surfaces classified in seven parts.

(a) CSAGS   (b) CKCAS

(c) CKEPS   (d) CS22S

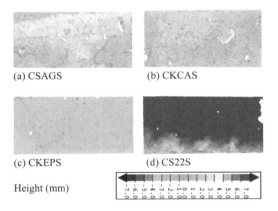

(a) CSAGS   (b) CKCAS

(c) CKEPS   (d) CS22S

Height (mm)

Figure 5. Distribution of the height in fractured surfaces.

3.2.2 Surface roughness
Figure 5 represents the distribution of height in the fractured surfaces, and Figure 6 the distribution of radius of curvature. The base plane for measuring height is the plane of the notch in the specimen. From these figures, it is apparent that CSAGS and CS22S have rougher surfaces than the other specimens.

3.2.3 Results from EPMA analysis
Figure 7 represents a Ca (Calcium) dot map near the fractured surfaces. The lighter the color in

(a) CSAGS   (b) CKCAS

(c) CKEPS   (d) CS22S

Radius of curvature (mm)

Figure 6. Distribution of the radius of curvature in fractured surfaces.

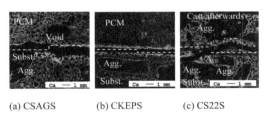

(a) CSAGS   (b) CKEPS   (c) CS22S

Figure 7. Distribution of Ca near interface.
Remarks: Agg. (Aggregate), Subst. (Substrate concrete).

the map is, the higher the concentration of Ca is. The black parts are the void or aggregates mainly consisting of Si (Silicon). The broken lines in Figure 7 represent the original interface of the joint.

Figure 7 indicates that the crack paths of CSAGS and CS22S are meandering and deviating from the interface. One of the reasons for this phenomenon is the ITZ (interfacial transition zone) around coarse aggregate, which is known to be a weak and brittle layer mainly made of CH (Taylor, 1997). In the case of CKEPS, the crack path is straight along the interface where higher concentration of Ca, which is CH, is recognized than the other parts. These facts imply that the crack path near the interface is greatly affected by the uneven distribution of the CH layer.

4 DISCUSSION

4.1 *Mechanical properties and crack paths*

The authors calculated Hmax which is the maximum difference of height measured from the lowest point to the highest point from the results in Figure 5. Figure 8 represents Gf as a function of Hmax, where one can realize the relation between them. The authors also calculated Rr3 from the results in Figure 6, which is a ratio of area where the local radius of curvature is below 3 mm divided by the total ligament area. Figure 9 represents Gf as a function of Rr3, where one can realize the relation between them.

Hmax and Rr3 are the values which represent the quantitative expression of surface roughness and deeply correlated to the Fracture Energy (Gf). As the radius of 3 mm is close to the minimum size of coarse aggregate, Rr3 is the ratio of area which occupies the smallest coarse aggregates, all fine aggregates and rough surface of cement paste. Hmax is related to the projecting and the pulled-out coarse aggregates. Then the aggregate near the interface has an essential effect to determining Gf. In other words, the spatial distribution of the materials near the interface and their order of the strength may be governing Gf.

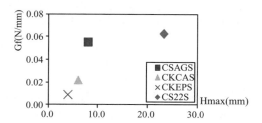

Figure 8. Gf as a function of Hmax.

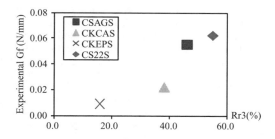

Figure 9. Gf as a function of Rr3.

4.2 *Mechanical properties of the local area*

As the fractured surface consists of seven parts, so the mechanical properties for the entire section should be the summed value of the local contribution from each part. The authors predicted the local Ft and local Gf of the seven parts in the following ways.

The contribution of the tensile stress to Ft of the overall ligament would be proportional to the moment of inertia of each local area multiplied with the strength of each local area. The moment of inertia should be calculated from the neutral axis height at the maximum load under bending. The previous study indicated that the neutral axis height at the maximum load under bending is about 60% from the bottom (Satoh, 2008). Then the following equation is derived for each specimen

$$Ft1 = \sum Ft(x) \times I(x) \qquad (1)$$

where Ft1 is the tensile strength (Ft) of specimen 1, Ft(x) is the tensile stress of each material (x) and I(x) is the moment of inertia of each material (x) around the neutral axis. The summation should be done to the seven parts.

The local Gf can be determined in the same way. But Gf is not proportional to the moment of inertia of seven parts from the neutral axis but proportional to the summed area of each part, which is described in eq.(2).

$$Gf1 = \sum Gf(x) \times A(x) \qquad (2)$$

where Gf1 is the Gf of specimen 1, Gf(x) is the Gf of each material (x) and A(x) is the total area of each material (x). The summation should be done to the seven parts.

There are 15 specimens (5 types and 3 specimens for each) and the unknown local Ft and Gf are seven. Then the local Ft and Gf can be determined based on multivariate statistical analysis. The results are listed in Table 6, where Ft of the detached part and ITZ are predicted to have the same value. The compatibility of these values was checked by composing the overall Ft and Gf from the results in Table 6, which is represented in Figures 10 and 11.

The correlation coefficient $R^2 = 0.74$ for Ft (Fig. 10) whereas $R^2 = 0.83$ for Gf (Fig. 11). It is natural that the range of scatter for strength is larger than the one for Gf.

The authors assumed the local Ft of ITZ is the pulled-out strength measured with an aggregate adhered to cement paste, of which the surface has a saw cut surface or a polished one. But usual surfaces of aggregates are rough and have many dents on them. Then the real pull-out strength may be higher than the value used in this study.

Table 6. Predicted local Ft and Gf.

Item	Detached	Concrete	Mortar	PCM		
				SAG	KCA	ITZ
Ft (MPa)	2.56	7.07	7.5	4.05	3.55	2.56
Gf (N/m)	4	98	78	85	40	23

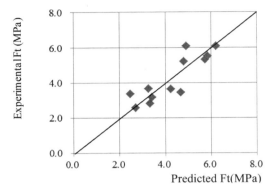

Figure 10. Predicted and experimental Ft.

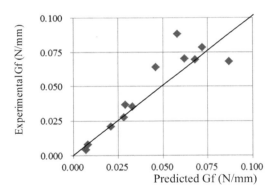

Figure 11. Predicted and experimental Gf.

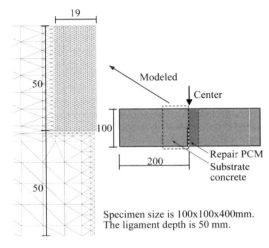

Specimen size is 100x100x400mm.
The ligament depth is 50 mm.

Figure 12. Modelled region of fractographic model.

4.3 Representation of crack paths in a model

4.3.1 Proposition of fractographic model

The observed surfaces of the specimens had unique crack paths. But mechanical properties of the specimens of the same mixture were almost the same regardless of the crack paths, even though they had some scatter. Then the variety of crack path is not the essential fact for the mechanical properties, and the various crack paths should be represented by a model within a range of some scatters.

To discuss the relationship between fractographic features and the mechanical properties, a two-dimensional graphic model is useful. The authors propose a graphic model which depicts

materials near an interface layer on triangular grids for that purpose. The triangular grids are convenient both for the FEM analysis with plate elements and for the ones with lattice elements. The model is named "fractographic model" in this research, of which the modeled region is depicted in Figure 12.

4.3.2 Detail of fractographic model

The materials for the model are seven; an interface layer, mortar as a matrix, aggregates, Interfacial Transition Zone (ITZ) around the aggregates, two types of repair materials (SAG and KCA) and some voids. The mechanical properties of them are listed in Table 6. In the two-dimensional model, it is common that the area fractions of each material are the volume fractions of each material, which the authors obeyed.

To draw a two-dimensional model, the size of the aggregate should be decided. Though the aggregate is a mixture of various sizes of sand and gravel, it is very convenient if the single representative size of the aggregate is decided. The authors regard fine aggregate as matrix (i.e. mortar), and modeled various sizes of coarse aggregates to a single size of aggregates which has a representative size.

There are some representative sizes for coarse aggregate such as dF (a nominal size), dW (a weighed volume average size), dS (an averaged size in terms of surface area), dV (an averaged size in terms of

472

volume) and dL (an arithmetic mean size) (Murata et al. 1996). The calculated sizes are listed in Table 7. The authors chose dF as a representative size among them as it is used widely in mix design and close to the average of all representative sizes. The size dF is calculated with equation (3) in which FM is a fineness modulus. The shape of the aggregates is modeled to a hexagon.

$$dF = 10^{(FM-3.237)/3.322} \qquad (3)$$

The representative size of void is modeled to the maximum size of void, because the location of voids is essential for the crack path. The voids are depicted in the model as triangles of which the area is 2 mm².

4.3.3 Representation of fractographic model

Figure 13 represents some examples of fractographic models for jointed specimens with an interface layer at the centre. The interface may be produced by placing of concrete after the hardening of the formerly placed concrete (i.e., placing joint). From Case (a) to (c), the region of 19×50 mm in the left part adjacent to the centre of a specimen is depicted. These are the cases for the placing joint at the centre. The Case (d) shows the patched repair PCM (right) on the surface of concrete (left) which has a straight layer of placing. The Case (e) shows the monolithic concrete with no joint.

It is important to know that the location of aggregates has a limited variety if one tries to place them evenly in the given area. Though the variety of the location of voids is vast, the density of them in a limited area is much the same if the distance between voids are kept equal. These facts are what make the fractographic model here proposed effective.

Table 7. Representative sizes of aggregates.

Aggregate	F.M. –	dF mm	dW mm	dS mm	dV mm	dL mm
Fine agg.	2.63	0.66	1.63	0.18	0.24	0.15
Coarse agg.	6.68	11.87	12.67	9.02	9.55	8.55

Note: F.M. stands for fineness modulus.

4.4 Application of fractographic model

4.4.1 Prediction method of crack path

It is possible to predict a crack path if one applies some assumptions listed below.

1. The crack path extends along the route which consumes minimum Gf in due succession from the start point to the end at the localizing stage of the crack. When localizing the crack, the consumed energy is strongly governed by Ft (tensile strength). So, minimum Gf is synonymous to minimum Ft.

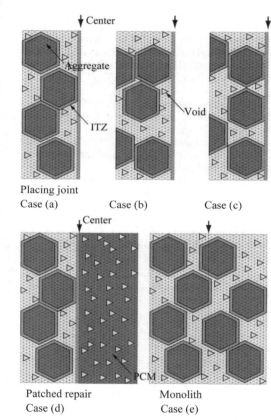

Figure 13. Examples of fractographic model.

Table 8. Area fraction of materials of models in Figure 14.

Crack path	Aggregate %	Mortar %	ITZ %	Interface %	Void %	PCM %	Sum %
(a)–(c)	40.0	36.4	15.6	5.3	2.7		100
(d) Left	40.0	36.4	15.6	5.3	2.7		100
Right					7.8	92.2	100
(e)	40.0	41.7	15.6		2.7		100

Note: Experimental air content is 2.8%.

473

2. The minimum local Ft is estimated in a lump at each time of estimation within a certain length; a size of aggregate or a distance between voids. (Fig. 14)

3. The minimum local Ft is a macroscopic one measured along the path. Ft in Table 6 is based on the projected area, which should be converted into the one based on the real area. Ft in Table 6 should be divided by 1.1, which comes from the division of the real length divided by the projected length. After the path is predicted, Gf is calculated along it.

If these assumptions are applied, the cases which need to be surveyed for the correct path are not vast but only several as the next section explains. The authors predicted crack paths of four different combinations of materials near the interface. That surveyed was the Case (b) in Figure 13.

4.4.2 Path prediction for concrete-PCM interface

Two conditions of the crack path for the Case (b) were surveyed; one is a case which has a layer of weak PCM is patched to the surface of concrete (Fig. 15), and another is a case which has a layer of strong PCM (Fig. 16).

In the region [1] in Figure 15, there are 4 possibilities of extension of crack; A to D. The predicted Ft for each path is; 3.36 MPa for D, 3.79 MPa for A, 3.80 MPa for B and 4.60 MPa for C. Then the path is determined to take D in PCM following the assumptions above mentioned. In the next region

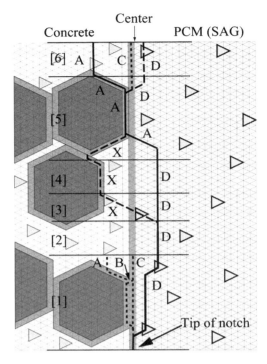

Figure 15. Crack paths for weak PCM.

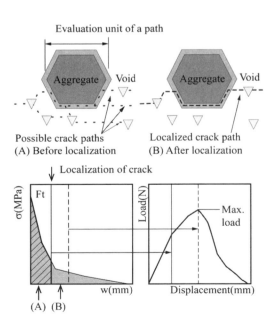

Figure 14. Evaluation method of a crack path.

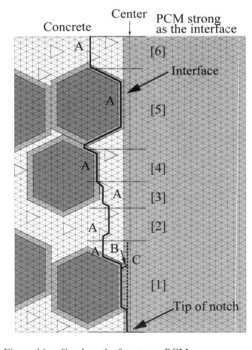

Figure 16. Crack paths for strong PCM.

474

[2], the prediction is easy. In the region [3], Ft of the path [3]D is 3.68 MPa whereas the [3]X is 6.43 MPa, so the path is [3]D. But if the unit of the summation is supposed to be [3] + [4] + [5], Ft for the path [3]D-[5]A represented in solid lines amounts to be 3.77 MPa whereas Ft for [3]X-[5]A represented in broken lines is 3.73. (See Table 9) Then there is a high possibility that the path changes its route to the latter. The same situation occurs in the region [6]; Ft for the path [6]A is 4.35 MPa, but the minimum Ft is 3.68 MPa for the path [6]D. But the correct path is [6]A, because the correct path in the region [5] is [5]A-A-A which can be directly connected to the path [6]A. Ft for the path [5]A-A-A is 3.84 MPa whereas the path [5]A-A-D is 4.16 MPa. The overall averaged Ft, Gf and the area ratios of the fracture surface is listed in Table 10, which are consistent to the experimental values.

The above mentioned case is the composition of concrete, a strong interface that is treated with resin primer and the patched layer of weak PCM. If the PCM layer is stronger than the interface and the concrete as well, the path changes as depicted in Figure 16. The resulted overall mechanical properties are listed in Table 11. Though the path is complex and Ft is high, Gf is very low in this case.

4.4.3 Path prediction for concrete-concrete interface

Figure 17 represents the concrete-concrete interface such as the placing joint or a concrete layer cast afterwards for some purpose (reinforcement or repair). In this case Ft and Gf for the interface is

Table 9. Survey for a path of minimum Ft in Figure 15.

Elements	[3]D	[3]X	[3]D-[5]A	[3]X-[5]X
Interface		2.0	2.0	2.0
ITZ		1.5	24.0	52.0
Mortar		5.0		5.0
PCM	9.0	3.0	30.5	3.0
Void		6.0		6.0
Ft (MPa)	3.68	6.43	3.77	3.73
Gf (N/m)	77.3	85.8	64.1	38.9

Table 10. Consistency of the prediction for PCM layer.

Comparison issues			Predicted	Experimental
Mechanical properties	Ft	MPa	3.36	2.86–3.52
	Gf	N/m	50	46–58
Area ratio	ITZ	%	23	15
	PCM	%	57	41
	Others	%	20	45

Note: The experimental Ft is bending strength.

Table 11. The effect of the weak PCM.

Elements	Ft (MPa)	Gf (N/m)	Weak PCM	Strong PCM
Interface	5.06	85.0	13.0	8.5
ITZ	2.56	23.0	16.5	76.0
Mortar	7.50	78.0	6.5	22.5
PCM	4.05	85.0	65.0	0.0
Void	–	–	9.0	12.0
Broken elements in the path			110.0	119.0
Ft (MPa)			3.41	3.69
Gf (N/m)			59.8	38.4

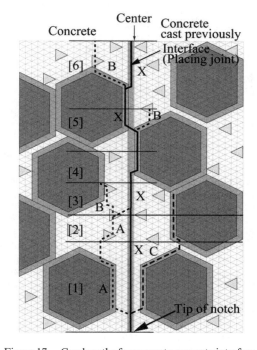

Figure 17. Crack paths for concrete-concrete interface.

low because of the bleeding water which ascends along the surface of the concrete cast beforehand. The mechanical properties of the interface are about the half of the mortar, and then there is a limited chance for the crack to divert from the interface.

The solid lines in Figure 17 represent the predicted path. The mechanical properties and the area ratio of the fracture surface are listed in Table 12, which tells the consistency of the prediction. The path C in Figure 17 has much chance to occur, because Ft is almost the same as the path X.

Figure 17 is the ordinary case for a placing joint in which the interface is roughened but is almost straight. In some cases of placing joints, the

Table 12. Consistency of the prediction for concrete-concrete.

Comparison issues			Predicted	Experimental
Mechanical	Ft	MPa	3.42	3.03–3.60
properties	Gf	N/m	36.5	30–41
Area ratio	ITZ	%	29	20
	Others	%	71	80

Note: The experimental Ft is bending strength.

Table 13. The effect of the deeply roughening.

Elements	Ft (MPa)	Gf (N/m)	Concrete-concrete	Deeply roughened
Interface	4.05	45.0	74.0	48.0
ITZ	2.56	23.0	30.0	56.0
Mortar	7.50	78.0	0.0	2.0
Void	–	–	0.0	0.0
Broken elements in the path			104.0	106.0
Ft (MPa)			3.42	3.21
Gf (N/m)			36.5	32.8

surface to be joined with fresh concrete is deeply roughened for better adhesion. Figure 18 represents such a case of placing joint in which some coarse aggregates project into the concrete to be cast afterwards with a rugged interface.

The solid lines in Figure 18 represent the predicted path. There emerges a side effect in the region [5] where coarse aggregates conglomerate producing a straight layer of ITZ. Although the crack path extends into mortar elements and the number of broken elements are larger, the calculated Ft and Gf for the deeply roughened case is lower than that of the slightly roughened one. It can be noted that the deeply roughened surface for the placing joint does not always produce better performance. This effect derives from the formation of ITZ on the surface of aggregates.

4.4.4 Path prediction for monolithic concrete

The model cannot predict the path for monolithic concrete, if one uses the same procedure and mechanical properties mentioned so far. Figure 19 represents the fractographic model which has the same distribution of aggregates as Figure 18 exclusive of the interface. Among many paths, the path [1]X-[2]X-[3]X-[4]X-[5]X-[6]E (to be called path E) is the predicted path in which the mechanical properties are the same values as mentioned in Table 6. In this case, the path X opts to extend along the ITZ. Then the path becomes very rough, but predicted mechanical properties are 3.19 MPa for Ft and 30.4 N/m for Gf. These values are 1/1.5 (for Ft) and 1/4 (for Gf) of the experimental values.

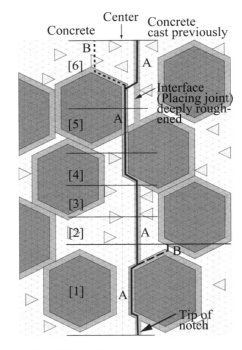

Figure 18. Effect of deeply roughening.

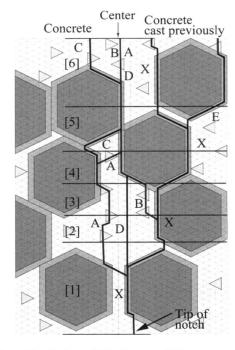

Figure 19. Path prediction for monolithic concrete.

The reason for this derives from the local Ft and Gf used for the prediction listed in Table 6. They do not include the dowel effect of the aggregate. In the case of the shallow ITZ which emerges on the surfaces near the interface for the placing joint or patched repair depicted in Figures 15–18, the local Ft and Gf are reasonable. But in the case of very a rough interface, these mechanical properties should include the effect from dowel action. Another reason for the inconsistency derives from the effect of the three-dimensional distribution of aggregates, which cannot be considered on a two-dimensional model. The area ratio of ITZ of the predicted path in Figure 19 amounts to 89% of the surface, but the experimental value is about 50%.

Then there should be some mechanisms that induce the crack path into the mortar part. For example, path [2]A or path [2]D in Figure 19 should be possible to occur to satisfy the fractographic features and high mechanical properties. The one mechanism is a hidden aggregate behind the mortar part as mentioned above, and another reason is the high Ft of ITZ for the deep path around aggregate.

The authors made simulations in which Ft for ITZ was changed. Table 14 lists the values for the simulation and the results. As the strength of ITZ gets closer to that of mortar, the ratio Ft[1]/Ft gets closer to 1.0. The crack path is path E at the low Ft of ITZ, but when Ft is 4.20 MPa, all the paths have almost the same Ft. When the Ft for ITZ is larger than 4.20, the crack path has been changed to the path [1]X-[2]A-[3]A-[4]A-[5]A-[6]A (to be called path A). The ratio of the extension length of the predicted path to the projected length (to be called L-ratio) is 1.19 for path E and 1.12 for path A. But the ratio of the length of ITZ to the entire path (to be called I-ratio) is 88.2% for path E and 53.1% for path A.

The L-ratio, I-ratio, flexural strength and tensile strength of the experimental results are 1.15, 53%, 4.60–4.85 MPa and 7.07–7.28 MPa. Then path A is consistent and Ft for ITZ should be

about 5.35 MPa. Following the same procedure, Gf for ITZ should be about 125 N/m which produces the same predicted Gf as the experimental Gf (96–116 N/m).

4.4.5 Application of fractographic model

Though the authors' model cannot consider the continuity of the deformation and strain, to which the Finite Element Method (FEM) for the structural analysis is useful, this model has the ability to reveal some interesting aspects of the interface as mentioned above. One can apply the fractographic model for the simulation of improving Ft and Gf of the interface similarly with the help of FEM.

If one admits that Ft is one special value of Gf before localization of a crack, one can say the crack path is determined by a simple mechanism of the balance of Gf of the material near the interface. After localizing of the crack path, the fibre in PCM will take effect. The authors suppose that PCM, which has a low Gf in localizing (i.e., low Ft) but high Gf after localizing will have good performance.

In the authors' simulation, the location and the density of voids at a local region is a governing factor for the crack path, because the area ratio of void is only 2.8% whereas the ratio of the void in a crack path is 3 to 4 times of the area ratio. The void is a model for conglomerated calcium hydroxide, air bubbles, agglomerated fine aggregates, layer of bleeding and so on.

5 CONCLUSIONS

The four types of concrete prism specimens which were adhered at the centre with polymer cement mortar were tested. After the fracture mechanics test, fractographic analysis was conducted. The important findings are as follows:

- Macroscopic observation revealed the fractured surface is classified into seven parts; detached, concrete fractured, mortar fractured, PCM fractured (two types), ITZ and void. The authors predicted the local Ft (tensile strength) and local Gf (fracture energy) of the seven parts based on the macroscopic observations and multivariate statistical analysis.
- The authors proposed the fractographic model for the prediction of the crack path using the above mentioned local Ft and Gf. This model could predict the mechanical properties of the test results of which the interface is concrete-to-PCM or concrete-to-concrete.
- The model revealed some important aspects of the diversion of crack paths into PCM in the case of weak PCM and the decreasing of the mechanical properties in the case of a deeply

Table 14. Simulated results.

Mortar MPa	ITZ MPa	Path –	Ft [1] MPa	Ft MPa	Ft[1]/Ft –
	2.56	E	3.90	3.19	1.22
	4.03	E	5.10	4.59	1.11
7.50	4.20	X/A/E	5.20	4.75	1.09
	5.35	A	5.84	5.45	1.07
	6.00	A	6.20	5.80	1.07
	6.85	A	6.68	6.26	1.07

Note: Ft[1] is the local FT in [1] region, and Ft is the one for the entire region.

roughened surface applied to the placing joint. Considering the dowel effect of the aggregate which resists pull out from the matrix, Ft and Gf of ITZ for the monolithic case are proposed. With using them, Ft and Gf for the monolithic concrete is also correctly predicted.

- The model would be useful for the simulations prior to FEM analysis; for studying the balance of mechanical performance of PCM and concrete, the depth of roughening, the mix proportions of concrete to be placed for repair and so on.

REFERENCES

JASS 5. 2009. Placing joint. In Masuda Y. (eds), *JASS 5*: 267–269. Tokyo: AIJ.

JCI-SFR3. 2004. A method for evaluation of tension softening diagram of concrete. In Izumi I. (eds), *JCI standards*: 550–558. Tokyo: JCI.

Kurihara T, Ando T, Uchida Y, & Rokugo K. 1996. Evaluation of adhesive performance of construction joint in concrete by tension softening diagram. *Proc Ann Meet JCI* 18(2): 461–466.

Kurihara T, Nishida Y, Kamata T, & Rokugo K. 1998. Evaluation of the effect of surface roughening on the adhesion performance. *Proc Ann Meet JCI* 20(2): 1261–1266.

Murata J, Iwasaki N, & Kodama K. 1996. *Science and technology of concrete*. Sankaido: Tokyo.

RILEM Draft Recommendation. 1985. Determination of the fracture energy of mortar and concrete by means of three-point bend tests on notched beams. *Mater Struct* 18(106): 285–290.

Satoh A, Yamada K, & Ishiyama S. 2007. A discussion on tension softening characteristics and fracture process of concrete prism with a vertical placing joint. *Proc AIJ Tohoku Chap* 70: 49–55.

Satoh A, Yamada K, & Ishiyama S. 2008. A proposition of stress distribution model in section of concrete prism with a vertical placing joint. *Proc Ann Meet JCI* 30(1): 399–404.

Satoh A, Yamada K, & Ishiyama S. 2009. Relationship between fracture energy and fractured area of interface in placing joint of concrete. *Proc Ann Meet JCI* 31(2): 91–96.

Takase S, Kodama K, Kurihara T & Sato K. 2000. Adhesion characteristics of polymer cement mortar as repair and strengthening materials. *Proc Ann Meet JCI* 22(1): 319–324.

Taylor HFW. 1997. Analyzes of individual phases. In: *Cement chemistry. 2nd ed*: 201–204. London: Thomas Telford.

Uchida Y, Rokugo K, & Koyanagi W. 1991. Determination of tension softening diagrams of concrete by means of bending tests. *Trans JSCE* V-1(426): 203–312.

Concrete Solutions – Grantham, Mechtcherine & Schneck (eds)
© 2012 Taylor & Francis Group, London, ISBN 978-0-415-61622-5

Scaling resistance and application of cementitious repair mortars for concrete barriers

Wencui Yang, Yong Ge, Xiaoping Cai & Xiao Chen
Department of Road Materials Engineering, Harbin Institute of Technology, P. R. China

ABSTRACT: Liaoning Province is located in the northeast of China, where the concrete barriers along with highways and roads deteriorate severely due to deicer salt scaling. In this paper, cementitious mortars for repairing concrete barriers were investigated. After determining the dosage of copolymer powder, polyacrylonitrile fiber and sand-cement ratio by orthogonal tests, six cementitious mortars with or without air-entraining agent or silica fume were prepared and their strengh at 28 days and scaling resistance were investigated. Then two mortars were used for field application in Liaoning Province. The laboratory study results showed that the cementitious mortars with proper air content exhibited good scaling resistance and higher strength. Adding copolymer powder and polyacrylonitrile fiber also improved scaling resistance of the mortar. In spite of no obvious effect, silica fume improved scaling resistance of repair mortars when it worked with air-entraining agents. The two selected cementitious repair mortars generally performed well in the field application.

1 INTRODUCTION

Liaoning Province is one of three provinces in northeast China, where the climate is continental and has at least 3 or 4 months below 0°C and a fixed period of snow each year in winter. Therefore, concrete structures are subjected to the action of freeze-thawe cycles in most areas of Liaoning Province (Li et al. 2004). Furthermore, in highways and roads of cities, deicer salts are used in winter to make snow or ice thaw and to assure traffic is safe. Most of the highways and roads in Liaoning proveince have asphalt concrete pavements with many cement concrete affiliated constructions, such as cement concrete barriers, trench cover plates and bridge pavement expansion joints (Wu. 2010). Barriers are sometimes employed as a means of creating a barrier between a road and ditches, ravines, or other roadside elements that would be dangerous if a vehicle left the road. Concrete barriers with a height of about 0.8 m to 1.3 m are widely used, making it difficult for vehicles to cross into lanes and directly into the path of oncoming traffic. Deicer salts solution splashes barriers by spinning wheels when vehicles pass by. Therefore, surfaces of the concrete barriers, along with highways and roads, deteriorate severely due to deicer salt scaling, which is one of the major durability issues facing concrete in such climates (Valenza & Scherer. 2007). The scaling starts from the base of the barriers where deicer salts access first and then progress

and scatter to whole surface of the concrete barriers (Fig. 1). To avoid the scaling deterioration, granite stone plates are used to cover the concrete barriers at the bottom in several newly built highways. However, the deicer salt scaling still occurs above the stone plates during the winter after traffic opening (Fig. 2).

Many materials have been used to repair concrete deterioration, such as cementitious mortars or concretes, epoxy mortars and polymer-modified cement-based mortars. However, some of these materials did not perform adequately on concrete structures. For example, the epoxy mortars in general did not perform well because they were not thermally compatible with the base concrete (Ribeiro et al. 2003) and their bonding to the wet concrete surfaces was very poor.

On the contrary, cement-based mortars as well as polymer-modified cement-based mortars have demonstrated acceptable performance because of their compatibility with the base concrete and because they had a similar colour with the base concrete (Mirza et al. 2002). Moreover, high frost resistance is also necessary for repairing concretes subjected to severe climatic conditions.

In this paper, cementitious mortars with high scaling resistance for repairing concrete barriers in Liaoning Province were investigated. To improve the bond strength between repair mortar and concrete, a dispersible copolymer powder was used. Meanwhile, a polyacrylonitrile fiber was used to reduce cracks of the repair mortar

Figure 1. Severe scaling deterioration of concrete barriers in Liaoning Province.

Figure 2. Scaling deterioration above stone plates cover on the bottom of concrete barriers in Liaoning Province.

coat which is thin and can otherwise crack easily. The dosage of copolymer powder, polyacrylonitrile fiber and sand-cement ratio were determined by orthogonal tests. Then six cementitious mortars with or without air-entraining agent or silica fume were prepared and their strengh at 28 days and scaling resistance were investigated. After experimental research, two mortars were used to repair surface scaling of 20 meter long concrete barriers utilized on a bridge in Liaoning Province.

2 EXPERIMENTAL PROCEDURE

2.1 Materials

A Chinese standard 42.5 ordinary Portland cement and river sand with fineness modulus of 2.9 and apparent density of 2610 kg/m³ were used in the experiment. A saponin-type air-entraining agent and a naphthalene-type water-reducing agent were used. Silica fume was also used in the experiment, details of which are given in Table 1.

A dispersible copolymer powder, VINNAPAS® LL 4023N, produced by Wacker Polymer Systems (Nanjing) Co. Ltd was used, and its properties are shown in Table 2, taken from the manufacture's specification sheets. A polyacrylonitrile fiber whose properties are given in Table 3 was also used.

2.2 Orthogonal test

Orthogonal tests are mathematical methods to carry out multifactor experiments. They are based on the principle of statistics and orthogonal theory. There is a series of orthogonal tables in correspondence with different amounts of factors and values. In this paper, orthogonal tests was applied first to analyze the influence of these three factors, copolymer powder dosage,

Table 1. The properties of the silica fume.

Properties	
SiO_2 Content (%)	86
Specific surface area (m²/kg)	21000
Ignition loss (%)	3.5
Cl⁻ Content (%)	0.2
Bulk Density (kg/m³)	650
Water requirement (%)	110
Strength activity index at 28 days (%)	95

Table 2. The properties of the dispersible copolymer powder.

Properties	
Appearance	White powder
Bulk density (kg/m³)	470
Ash content (%)	11
Solids content (%)	98~100
Minimum film forming temperature (°C)	10
Particle size (µm)	<400

Table 3. The properties of the polyacrylonitrile fiber.

Properties	
Length (mm)	6
Fiber number (Denier)	1.9
Density (g/cm³)	1.18
Tensile strength (MPa)	372
Modulus of elasticity (MPa)	14600
Elongation (%)	17

sand-cement ratio and polyacrylonitrile fiber dosage, on the fluidity of mortar to determined their proper dosage. According to the orthogonal tables, an $L_9(3^4)$ orthogonal table was applied and the experiment schemes used are shown in Table 4.

2.3 Samples and testing programs

The fluidity of mortar was measured according to GB/T 2419–2005, "Test method for fluidity of cement mortar".

Prism specimens with a size of 40 mm × 40 mm × 60 mm for strength analysis and cube specimens with a size of 100 mm × 100 mm × 100 mm for scaling resistance test were prepared, and then they were cured at a temperature of 20 ± 2 °C with a relative humidity of 95%.

The mortar strengths were determined according to GB/T 17671-1999 "Method of testing cements-Determination of strength".

After 12 days curing, the cube mortar specimens bottom surface were immersed into 3.5 wt.% NaCl solution to about 4 mm~6 mm depth for 2 days. Tests of mortar specimens subjected to freeze-thaw cycles were carried out at the age of 14 days by a slow freeze-thaw method. One freeze-thaw cycle involved freezing at $(-15 \pm 2)°C$ for 16~18 hours, and then thawing at room temperature for 6~8 hours, which was similar to a natural freeze-thaw cycle in winter in Liaoning Province. During the freezing-thawing process, the bottom surface of the specimen was always immersed in 3.5 wt.% NaCl solution to about 4 mm~6 mm depth. The scaling of mortar specimens was monitored and recorded each 10 cycles. The scaling per unit area of specimen was used to evaluate scaling resistance of mortar subjected to action of freeze-thaw cycles and deicer salts solution. The specimen was considered a failure if its scaling exceeded 0.8 kg/m² according to the test procedure. Three specimens were measured for each mortar.

Table 4. The orthogonal table, $L_9(3^4)$, for the fluidity of mortar.

Levels	A Copolymer powder dosage (%)	B Sand- cement ratio	C Polyacrylonitrile fiber dosage (kg/m³)	D Blank
1	1.0	2.5	0.5	–
2	1.5	3.0	1.0	–
3	2.0	3.5	1.5	–

3 RESULTS AND ANALYSIS

3.1 Orthogonal test results

Fluidities of the specimens prepared in the orthogonal test and mean values of each factor are shown in Table 5. Taking the levels of the experimental factors as X-coordinate and the corresponding mean values of fluidity results as Y-coordinate, the trend curves showing the relationship between the considered factor levels and fluidities of mortars could be drawn as shown in Figure 3.

It could be seen from Table 5 that fluidity of mortar decreased more or less with the increasing of copolymer powder dosage, sand-cement ratio and polyacrylonitrile fiber dosage. Considering the differences between the maximum mean value and the minimum one of each factor, it is obvious that the most effective factor affecting fluidity of mortar is sand-cement ratio (Fig. 3). As sand-binder ratio increased, fluidity of mortar decreased. The average fluidity of three mortars with sand-cement ratio of 2.5 was 168.3 mm, which dropped to 115 mm when the sand-binder ratio was 3.5. Neither the copolymer powder dosage nor the polyacrylonitrile fiber dosage had any obvious influence on mortar fluidity, which could be ignored. Based on these results, the sand-cement ratio, copolymer powder dosage and polyacrylonitrile fiber dosage of the repair mortars were 2.5, 1.0% by mass and 1.0 kg/m³.

3.2 Scaling resistance of cement mortars

Six cementitious mortars with or without air entraining agents, polyacrylonitrile fiber, polymer powder and silica fume were prepared, and their mix proportions are shown in Table 6.

Table 5. Fluidities of mortars and mean value of each factor in correspondence with levels.

No.	A	B	C	D	Fluidity (mm)
1	1.0	2.5	0.5	–	185
2	1.0	3.0	1.0	–	135
3	1.0	3.5	1.5	–	115
4	1.5	2.5	1.0	–	165
5	1.5	3.0	1.5	–	140
6	1.5	3.5	0.5	–	115
7	2.0	2.5	1.5	–	155
8	2.0	3.0	0.5	–	135
9	2.0	3.5	1.0	–	115
K_1	145	168.3	145	146.7	
K_2	140	136.7	138.3	135	
K_3	135	115	136.7	138.3	
Difference of mean value	10	53.3	8.3	11.7	

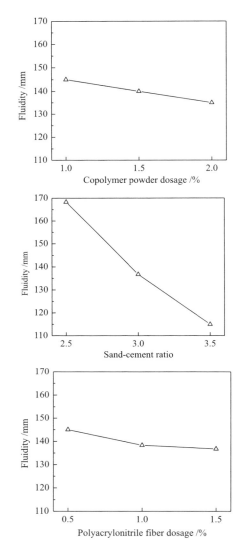

Figure 3. Effects of three factors on fluidity of mortars.

The sand-binder ratio, copolymer powder dosage and polyacrylonitrile fiber dosage were 2.5, 1% by mass and 1.0 kg/m³ respectively according to the results of orthogonal tests. The dosage of water was adjusted to keep the fluidity of each mortar in the range of 150 mm~160 mm with which mortars would have a good workability. Silica fume was used as partial replacement for cement by 5 wt.%. The properties, including bulk density, air content, flexural strength and compressive strength at 28 days of each mortar are given in Table 7.

The results in Figure 4 show an obvious effect of air-entrainment on improving the scaling resistance of cementitious mortars. The scaling of non air-entrained specimens increased quickly when the freeze-thaw cycles increased and reached the limit of 0.8 kg/m², which meant failure of mortar. The numbers of freeze-thaw cycles at failure of air-entrained mortar, PFA, SFA1 and SFA2, could be double or more of that of mortars without air-entraining agent.

Figure 4 shows the scaling of mortars subjected to freeze-thaw cycles in 3.5 wt.% NaCl solution. There was severe scaling on the surface of mortar specimens after a certain number of freeze-thaw cycles. Previous research has shown that sodium chloride which is usually used as deicing salt often exacerbates cementitious material damage originating from freezing-thawing (Pigeon et al. 1996 & Kejin et al. 2006). Besides creating the hydraulic pressure and the osmotic pressure, deicer chemicals generally increased the degree of paste saturation and keeps pores at or near maximum saturation, thus increasing the risk of frost damage (Valenza & Scherer. 2006).

Furthermore, the strength of air-entrained mortar didn't decrease when the air content was about 8% due to the water-reducing effect of the air-entraining agent. However, although the water-binder ratio has been decreased by 0.04 for SFA1 with high air content, the compressive and flexural strength at 28 days was decreased significantly. As in cementitious concrete (Chatterji. 2003), use of air-entraining agents properly in cementitious repair mortars was an important measure to

Table 6. Mix proportions of mortars.

Materials (kg/m³)	Series					
	PF	PFA	CS	SF	SFA1	SFA2
Cement	560	560	532	532	532	532
Silica fume	0	0	28	28	28	28
Sand	1400	1400	1400	1400	1400	1400
Water	265	237	250	265	239	237
Copolymer powder	5.6	5.6	0	5.6	5.6	5.6
Polyacrylonitrile fiber	1.0	1.0	0	1.0	1.0	1.0
Water reducer	2.8	2.8	2.8	2.8	2.8	2.8
Air entraining agent	0	0.07	0	0	0.1	0.08

Table 7. The properties of repair mortars.

Properties	Series					
	PF	PFA	CS	SF	SFA1	SFA2
Bulk density (kg/m³)	2016	1929	2045	2075	1814	1947
Air content (%)	4.4	8.7	3	1.5	14.3	7.8
Flexural strength (MPa)	5.5	5.9	7.0	7.4	3.2	7.6
Compressive strength (MPa)	48.7	52.3	80.0	68.0	39.7	67.0

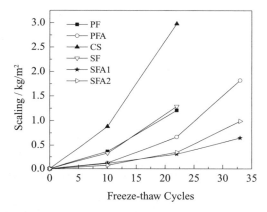

Figure 4. Scaling resistance of mortars subjected to freeze-thaw cycles and deicer salt solution.

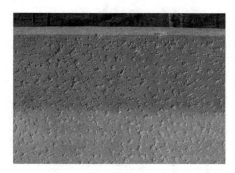

Figure 5. Surface of concrete barriers after roughening.

protect it from deicer scaling freezing-thawing in NaCl solution.

For the non air-entrained mortars, the water needed to have enough fluidity was more than that of the air-entrained mortars, while adding copolymer powder and polyacrylonitrile fiber also improved scaling resistance. For example, the numbers of freeze-thaw cycles at failure of SF were double that of CS. Polyacrylonitrile fiber which reduced initial cracks in mortar, increased resistance of cracking and shrinkage during the freeze-thaw process by helping to stop the growth of cracks (Kuder & Shah. 2010). Copolymer powder which is dispersed in the paste formed a copolymer network on some cracks, capilary surfaces and paste-aggregate interface (Afridia et al. 2003), resulting in decreasing the permeability of the mortar and reducing interfacial defects, which was also helpful to improve scaling resistance of the mortar.

The employment of silica fume led to higher compressive and flexural strengths of both air-entrained and non air-entrained mortars, due to its high pozzolanicity and filling pores of the paste by extremely small particles (Sabir. 1997). Comparing with PF, the scaling of mortar SF with silica fume and higher strength didn't reduce when subjected to freeze-thaw cycles. However, scaling resistance

was improved when silica fume worked with air-entrained agents.

3.3 Field application

Two cementitious mortars: PFA containing air-entraining agent and SFA2 containing air-entraining agent and silica fume were selected, based on the satisfactory results from the previous laboratory tests. They were used in repairing the surface of 20 meter long concrete barriers utilized on a bridge in Liaoning Province in September, 2010. The scheme and techniques of field application include the following actions:

(a) Surface roughening of concrete barriers (Fig. 5.); (b) Cleaning and wetting the background with water; (c) Daubing cement paste with high water cement ratio on the old concrete to enhance bond strength between it and the repair mortar; (d) Plastering the repair mortar with a thickness of about 10 mm. During this action, the repair mortar was plastered on concrete by three coats. For the first and second coats, after each was applied, pressing it with a rough trowel to create some roughness which can favor adhesion of the next coat (Fig. 6.); (e) Smoothing of the last coat with a trowel (Fig. 7.); (f) Curing the whole repair mortar coat by covering with plastic films (Fig. 8.).

The two mortars performed very satisfactorily on small-scale repairs on concrete barriers. All the patches showed good appearance at the end of application,

Figure 6. Pressing the repair mortar and creating roughness.

Figure 7. Pressing and smoothing of the last coat.

Figure 8. Curing of the repair mortar.

without cracks or disintegation. The repaired concrete barriers have now been applied for half a year. Generally, the appearance is quite good, so far.

4 CONCLUSIONS

The results of the laboratory study and field application led to the following conclusions:

The cementitious mortars with proper air content exhibited good scaling resistance in 3.5 wt.% NaCl solution and higher strength.

Adding copolymer powder and polyacrylonitrile fiber into cementitious repair mortars also improved scaling resistance.

No apparent effect of silica fume was observed on the scaling resistance of repair mortars. However, scaling resistance was improved when silica fume worked with air-entrained agents.

The two selected cementitious repair mortars generally performed well in the field application.

ACKNOWLEDGMENTS

The study was supported by National Nature Science Fund (No. 50778055).

REFERENCES

Afridia. M.U.K., Ohama. Y., Demurab. K. & lqbal. M.Z. 2003. Development of Polymer Films by the Coalescence of Polymer Particles in Powdered and Aqueous Polymer-modified Mortars. *Cement Concrete Research.* 33:1715–1721.
Chatterji. S. 2003. Freezing of Air-entrained Cement-based Materials and Specific Actions of Air-entraining Agents. *Cement and Concrete Research.* 25: 759–765.
Kejin. W., Daniel. E.N. & Wilfrid. A.N. 2006. Damaging Effects of Deicing Chemicals on Concrete Materials. *Cement and Concrete Composites.* 28: 173–188.
Kuder Katherine G. & Shah Surendra P. 2010. Processing of high-performance fiber-reinforced cement-based composites. *Construction and Building Materials.* 24: 181–186.
Li Ye, Yao Zukang, Sun Xuyi & Liu Chunchen. 2004. Quantification Research on the Frost Environment of Pavement Cement Concrete. *Journal of Tongji University (Natural Science).* 32(10): 1408–1412.
Mirza. J., Mirza. M.S. & Lapointe. R. 2002. Laboratory and Field Performance of Polymer-modified Cement-based Repair Mortars in Cold Climates. *Construction and Building Materials.* 16: 365–374.
Pigeon. M., Marchand. J. & Pleau. R. 1996. Frost Resistance Concrete. *Construction and Building Materials.* 10(5): 339–348.
Ribeiro. M.C.S., Reis. J.M.L., Ferreira. A.J.M. & Marques. A.T. 2003. Thermal expansion of epoxy and polyester polymer mortars-plain mortars and fibre-reinforced mortars. *Polymer Testing.* 22: 849–857.
Sabir. B.B. 1997. Mechanical Properties and Frost Resistance of Silica Fume Concrete. *Cement and Concrete Composites.* 19: 285–294.
Valenza. J.J. & Scherer. G.W. 2006. Mechanism for Salt Scaling. *Journal of American Ceramisite Society.* 89(4): 1161–1179.
Valenza. John. J. & Scherer. George. W. 2007. A Review of Salt Scaling: I. Phenomenology. *Cement and Concrete Research.* 37: 1007–1021.
Wu Liang. 2010. Investigation and Study on Typical Structure of Rural Highway Pavement in Northern Region of China. *Northern Communications.* (6): 20–23.

Repair of fire damage

Concrete Solutions – Grantham, Mechtcherine & Schneck (eds)
© 2012 Taylor & Francis Group, London, ISBN 978-0-415-61622-5

Basic techniques for the damage assessment of concrete members after fire

E. Annerel & L. Taerwe

Magnel Laboratory for Concrete Research, Faculty of Engineering and Architecture, Department of Structural Engineering, Ghent University, Ghent, Belgium

ABSTRACT: Generally, concrete structures behave very well during a fire. After a fire, it could be of economical interest to reuse the structure after appropriate repair based on reliable assessment of the strength properties. This paper demonstrates how the strength may be assessed from drilled cores by measuring the weight increase of the concrete after water immersion. Furthermore, the effect on the remaining strength of a change of heating rate, duration at target temperature, water cooling and post-cooling storage is studied. Considering the effect of the storage period, a stress/strain model is developed for both traditional and self-compacting concrete.

1 INTRODUCTION

Because damage to the concrete gradually appears during fire, it is in most cases possible to repair the structure after an adequate assessment. To do this in a systematic way, knowledge is necessary concerning residual material properties and methods to assess the strength.

The remaining mechanical properties after a fire are influenced by different parameters. First of all, the heating conditions, such as heating rate, duration at target temperature and the presence of an external load are of importance. The load ratio has a major influence, since this can enhance the remaining strength. Second, the cooling rate plays an important role, since quenching of the concrete into water introduces a thermal shock with additional strength loss. Finally, the post-cooling storage conditions are of influence. During the first weeks after fire, the strength further decreases due to the formation of new portlandite which is accompanied by a 44% expansion and leads to internal cracking. Afterwards, the strength may slowly recover which occurs faster for concretes stored under water. This paper studies these influences for different concrete types and presents a post-cooling stress/strain model.

Since the residual strength is temperature dependent, methods may be used to assess the strength indirectly by measuring the alteration in the material as a function of the temperature. Although several techniques are possible (Annerel & Taerwe 2007), this paper focuses on the increase of porosity as a function of the temperature measured with water immersion.

Once the temperatures and the strength properties are assessed, simplified calculations based on EN 1992-1-2 may be used to determine the residual capacity of concrete elements.

2 RESIDUAL STRENGTH

2.1 *Compressive strength reduction*

Table 1 summarizes the mix design of a Self-Compacting Concrete (SCC), a traditional vibrated concrete with siliceous aggregates (TC) and calcareous aggregates (TCk), as well as a High Strength Concrete (HPC). Cubes (150 × 150 × 150 mm) are cured for 4 weeks in an air-conditioned room at a RH > 90% and a temperature of 20 ± 1°C, after which they are stored at 60% RH and 20 ± 1°C for drying until testing age (>17 weeks). Two cubes are heated for each of the examined temperature levels (till 800°C), occurring at a heating rate of 3.5°C/min. The target temperature is kept constant for 750 minutes to obtain a uniform temperature distribution. The cubes are allowed to cool slowly in an oven (0.5°C/min), after which they are immediately tested for compression. It is noticed that higher heating rates will influence the compressive strength as thermal strains will be introduced due to difference in expansion between the outer and inner concrete.

Figure 1 shows the results in respect to the curves mentioned in EN 1992-1-2:2004 (EC2). Although, the experiments are after cooling and the values of the Eurocode consider the strength at high temperature, both are situated in each neighbourhood.

Table 1. Concrete mix design.

	SCC siliceous	TC siliceous	TCk calcareous	HPC siliceous
Sand [kg/m³]	782	640	663	650
Gravel 2–8 mm [kg/m³]	300	525	–	530
Gravel 8–16 mm [kg/m³]	340	700	–	720
Limestone 2/6	–	–	450	–
Limestone 6/20	–	–	759	–
Portland cement I 52.5 [kg/m³]	400	350	350	400
Water [kg/m³]	192	165	165	132
Limestone powder [kg/m³]	300	–	–	–
Superplasticizer 1 [l/m³]	2.90	–	–	–
Superplasticizer 2 [l/m³]	–	–	–	16.5
W/C [–]	0.48	0.47	0.47	0.33
Compressive strength 28d [N/mm²]	65.9	56.5	60.3	77.3

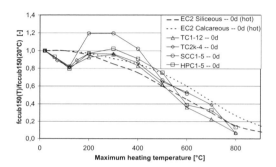

Figure 1. Residual compressive strength (0d = immediately tested after cooling, no post-cooling storage).

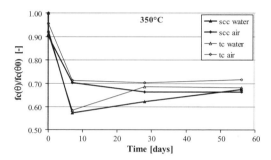

Figure 3. Further strength decrease and recovery during storage after heating ($\theta_0 = 20°C$).

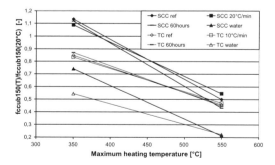

Figure 2. Influence of different test conditions on the residual compressive strength.

2.2 Effect of test conditions during heating

To determine the influence of the test conditions on the residual strength, TC and SCC 150 mm cubes were heated up to 350°C and 550°C. Under reference test conditions (section 2.1) the cubes were heated at a rate of 3.5°C/min, kept at the target temperature for 750 minutes and then cooled down in ambient air (Fig. 1). One of these conditions is altered while the others remain the same as the reference. The heating rate is increased to 10°C/min for TC and 20°C/min for SCC. The duration at the target temperature was 60 minutes and the cooling regime was modified into a rapid cooling by immersion under water. Figure 2 shows the effect of the different testing regimes on the residual strength (measured immediately after cooling). It appears that the cooling method is the most important parameter, resulting in an extra drop of the residual strength of 30 to 35%.

2.3 Effect of storage conditions after heating

Cubes (150 × 150 × 150 mm) were heated up to 350°C and 550°C, after which they were stored under water or in air for 7, 28 and 56 days. The test parameters are the same as the reference conditions mentioned before. Figure 3 illustrates that the strength decreases to a minimum around 7 days after heating and that it recovers from then on.

The strength recovery is faster for the cubes stored under water. The strength at 56 days is lower than the strength immediately after cooling as showed in Figure 1. Therefore, these results should be considered when evaluating the residual strength of a concrete member.

3 POST-COOLING STRESS/STRAIN MODEL

TC and SCC concrete cylinders with a diameter of 106 mm and a height of 320 mm are cast and stored for 4 weeks in an air-conditioned room at a RH > 90% and a temperature of $20 \pm 1°C$, after which they are stored at 60% RH and $20 \pm 1°C$ for drying for at least 12 months. The cylinders are heated to different target temperatures (20, 120, 200, 300, 400 and 500°C). No external load was applied before the specimens are tested for Young's modulus after a 12 weeks post-cooling storage at $20 \pm 1°C$ and 60% RH. Each temperature level is tested twice. From the experimental data, a model is developed (equation 1), which is a modification of Sargin's concrete strength model as published in EN 1992-1-1:2004.

$$\frac{\sigma_{c,T}}{f_{cm,T}} = \frac{k \cdot \eta - \eta^2}{1 + (k-2) \cdot \eta} \qquad (1)$$

With:

- $f_{cm,T}$ is the mean cylinder strength of the heated concrete
- $\eta = \varepsilon_{c,T} / \varepsilon_{c1,T}$
- $\varepsilon_{c,T}$ is the strain of the heated concrete corresponding to $\sigma_{c,T}$
- $\varepsilon_{c1,T}$ is the strain at peak stress of the heated concrete, corresponding to $f_{cm,T}$
- TC: $k = -7.61 \ 10^{-4} \cdot T + 1,459$
- SCC: $k = -5.46 \ 10^{-4} \cdot T + 1,271$

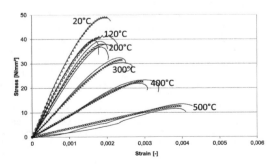

Figure 4. Stress/strain diagram of TC concrete after 12 weeks post-cooling storage.

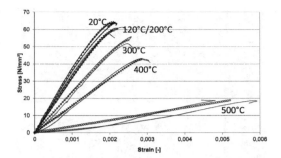

Figure 5. Stress/strain diagram of SCC concrete after 12 weeks post-cooling storage.

The loss of Young's modulus and compressive strength is included by defining the k-parameter as a function of temperature. The model not only considers the losses due to heating, but also the additional strength losses that may occur upon storage. Figures 4 and 5 illustrate the stress–strain diagram of the experimental and modelled data.

4 WATER IMMERSION

Heating of concrete introduces tensile stresses, resulting in cracks. Meanwhile, chemical alterations, such as dehydration and decarbonation, lead to the disappearance of the hydration products (Liu 2006), which increases the pore space (Fig. 6). Hence, these two effects cause an increase of the porosity when heating concrete. Notice that immersion of concrete under water will fill the pores and cracks with water. Then, the weight increase can be used to assess the internal damage due to heating.

The total water absorption can be defined as the difference in weight after storage under water and a reference weight, for instance the weight at uniform target temperature ($M_{0d,hot}$). After already 7 days, the curve representing the weight increase flattens. Under in situ circumstances, $M_{0d,hot}$ can be determined from a drilled core by drying it till constant mass. Drying is necessary to eliminate the moisture absorbed due to climatic exposure. Notice that the heated sample can be considered as reference, which is more convenient than searching for an adequate reference concrete that has not been exposed to fire. Newly formed hydration products which may fill some small cracks and thus may hinder the water absorption are neglected in this method. In laboratory conditions, this reference weight is measured during the test when the concrete is at target temperature or after cooling down to 60°C (Fig. 7).

Figure 8 illustrates the water immersion of half cubes (TC1-8, TC2k-1) and small discs (TC1-10)

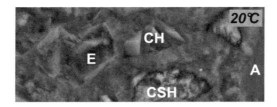

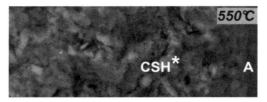

Figure 6. ESEM images (2000× magnification) of ordinary Portland concrete at 20°C and heated up to 550°C. (E = ettringite, CH = portlandite, A = aggregate, CSH* = fire altered CSH).

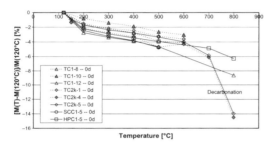

Figure 7. Weight loss due to heating (0d = immediately tested after cooling, no post-cooling storage).

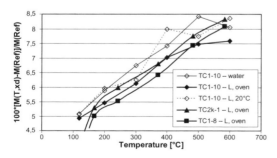

Figure 8. Water immersion of half cubes and small discs.

with Ø80 mm and 15 mm height. These results are transformed into percentages by dividing with the reference weight $M_{0d,hot}$. For the discs, different cooling methods are used: 1) slowly cooling in the oven ('L, oven'); 2) cooling outside the oven at ambient air ('L, 20°C'); 3) cooling by quenching with water ('Water'). The results on half cubes and small discs are comparable, as is visible on the graph for the water absorption of specimens slowly cooled in the oven.

5 CONCLUSIONS

– Post-cooling storage results in additional strength losses of up to 20–30% during the first weeks after heating. Afterwards, the strength may slowly recover which occurs faster for concretes stored under water. A strength recovery of up to 10% was found when storing for 56 days under water.
– The cooling rate is of major importance. Water cooling may induce an additional reduction of the compressive strength of 30 to 35%.
– The Sargin model from EN 1992-1-1 is modified into a post-cooling stress/strain model.
– Water immersion provides an adequate basis to assess the temperature history of concrete.

ACKNOWLEDGMENT

The authors would like to thank the Fund for Scientific Research in Flanders (FWO) for the financial support through the research grant "Damage assessment and estimation of the residual strength of concrete members after exposure to fire". The authors are thankful for the help of TNO Delft and TU Delft (Netherlands) for their contribution to the microscopic research.

REFERENCES

Annerel, E. & Taerwe, L. 2007. Approaches for the Assessment of the Residual Strength of Concrete Exposed to Fire. In Rodrigues J.P.C. et al. (ed.), *Proceedings of the International Workshop, Fire Design of Concrete Structures, From Materials Modeling to Structural Performance, Coimbra, 8th and 9th November, 2007.* Coimbra: Coimbra University.
EN 1992-1-2: 2004—*Eurocode 2: Design of Concrete Structures—Part 1-2: General Rules—Structural Fire Design.* Brussels: CEN.
EN 1991-1-1: 2004—*Eurocode 2: Design of concrete structures—Part 1-1: General rules and rules for buildings.* Brussels: CEN.
Liu, X. 2006. *Microstructural investigation of self-compacting concrete and high-performance concrete during hydration and after exposure to high temperatures,* PhD thesis. Ghent: Ghent University.

Concrete Solutions – Grantham, Mechtcherine & Schneck (eds)
© *2012 Taylor & Francis Group, London, ISBN 978-0-415-61622-5*

Behaviour of concrete containing lightweight expanded clay aggregates under high temperatures

H. Kew & T. Donchev
Kingston University London, UK

N. Petkune
University College London, UK

ABSTRACT: This study investigates the behaviour of concrete containing lightweight expanded clay aggregates (LECA) under high temperatures and compares the test data with the results for a control mix containing Thames Valley aggregates. The replacement of natural aggregates in concrete mixes was done at 50% and 100% by volume for concrete mixes with LECA. Concrete specimens were heated up to temperatures 100°C, 200°C, 300°C, 400°C and 500°C. Samples were allowed to cool down naturally to room temperature. After that, the maximum compressive and flexural strength were evaluated. The strength of concrete containing higher percentages of LECA gradually decreased for all temperature increments. The experimental study includes experimental data from testing samples with different percentage of lightweight aggregate, corresponding analysis and expressing views for applicability of the results.

1 INTRODUCTION

The purpose of this study was to investigate and compare compressive strength loss of concrete containing traditional concrete aggregate and lightweight aggregate.

An experimental program was carried out to study the behaviour of concrete containing various percentages of lightweight expanded clay aggregates (LECA) after exposure to high temperatures. After the concrete specimens were subjected to high temperature of 100°C, 200°C, 300°C, 400°C and 500°C their residual compressive and flexural strength was tested. Results were compared with the behaviour of a control mix containing Thames Valley aggregates.

The specific type of concrete lightweight aggregate- Lightweight Expanded Clay Aggregate (LECA)—was used in the investigation of the project.

2 BACKGROUND

According to BS EN 13055-1:2002, aggregates are defined as lightweight aggregates when their particle density does not exceed 2000 kg/m³ or loose bulk density is less than 1200 kg/m³. Lightweight aggregate is differentiated by the origin of its natural materials, by the thermal treatment, by manufacture or by processing of industrial by-products. The effect of high temperatures on

lightweight and normal concretes was investigated in this research. The differences in properties of the aggregates are the main factors affecting behaviour and strength results of concrete.

When the concrete is exposed to high temperature, its strength and Young's modulus decreases and microdefects appear at micro (less than 1 μm) and mesolevels (between 1 μm and 1 cm).

Different types of aggregates have various processes happening under high temperature. The majority of aggregates tend to be more or less stable until the temperature is about 500°C. For the non- siliceous aggregates, the temperature when reactions like transformation and decomposition will start is at about 600°C (Harmathy & Aleen 1973). Limestone (calcareous) aggregates experience decomposition of the carbonates, decarbonation at temperatures between 600°C and 900°C, when a significant amount of CO_2 is expelled. The chemical and physical changes happen not only to aggregates, but to hardened cement paste as well. When dehydration of hardened cement paste takes place, it changes porosity and water evaporates from aggregates (Bazant 1996).

The duration of the exposure affects the loss of the strength considerably as well. When the duration of the exposure is more than 1 hour, the concrete loses its strength significantly and the most significant strength loss happens when the exposure is between 1 and 2 hours. After the first hour of exposure, residual strengths of the concrete are approximately 80, 70, 60 and 30% at heating correspondingly to 200, 400, 600, 800°C. After two hours or more, residual strengths decrease to 70, 60, 45 and 25% at 200, 400, 600, 800°C (Bazant 1996). For the presented research, five hours exposure of the samples was adopted to allow uniform distribution of the temperature inside the samples and to allow estimation of long term heating effects and corresponding residual strength to be measured.

Various cooling regimes for concrete specimens were investigated by Peng et al. (2006) and it was concluded that when the concrete cools down with a rapid change of temperature under quenching in water or spraying water for more than 30 min, it experiences 'thermal shock' and severe damage. When concrete is exposed to a temperature of 200°C and cooled down under natural conditions, its compressive strength can be higher than when kept at room temperature. The activation of additional hydration of residual cement in concrete happens at elevated temperatures, it happens to a lesser degree when there are rapid cooling regimes like water spraying.

For the planned experiments a cooling regime at room temperature for 24 hours was accepted. In this way, any possible additional reduction of the strength due to rapid cooling was excluded and at the same time the chance of long term recovery with possible re-carbonation of the cement paste was avoided.

It is considered that if the concrete's temperature is not more than 300°C, the residual strength after cooling is not considerably changed (Concrete Society TR68 2008). When the concrete's temperature exceeds 300°C, it is assumed that concrete losses of strength are significant.

At high temperatures, the colour of the concrete changes to red/pink for the concrete containing most types of siliceous aggregates. However, the discoloration may not happen with all types of aggregates and concrete with aggregates containing ferrous salts is more likely to develop a pink hue colour. The colour of the concrete remains normal up to 300°C, and then it changes to pink. When the temperature in the concrete is above 600°C it becomes whitish grey. (Soutsos, 2010).

3 EXPERIMENTAL SET-UP

3.1 Materials

The materials used in this study were: portland cement- CEM1, sand, Thames Valley coarse aggregate and lightweight expanded clay aggregate (LECA). Table 1 shows the mix design for three different concrete mixes containing Thames Valley aggregates and Lightweight Expanded Clay Aggregates. The strength of the mixes was designed to be approximately 40 N/mm²

for the control mix with slump values between 30 and 60 mm.

Three sets of concrete mixes were cast containing Thames Valley aggregates and LECA. The replacement of natural aggregates with LECA in concrete mixes 2 and 3 was done correspondingly at 50% and 100% by volume. After the process of casting, samples were cured for 28 days and then heated to high temperatures.

Table 1. Concrete mix design.

	Mix 1: Control Mix	Mix 2: 50% LECA	Mix 1: 100% LECA
Cement, kg	63.51	63.51	63.51
Water, l	28.56	19.58	23.03
Sand, kg	63.24	63.24	63.24
Thames Valley, kg	171.09	85.54	–
LECA, kg	–	19.86	39.77

3.2 Materials testing

Prior to designing the concrete mix, testing of materials was conducted which included sieve analysis for three coarse aggregates and loose bulk density and particle density for the LECA. Sieve analysis was carried out for two types of aggregates namely Thames Valley aggregates and lightweight expanded clay aggregates. The experiment was conducted according to the procedure specified in the EN 933-1: 1997, EN 932-2:1999 and BS EN 12620:2002+A1:2008. To obtain the density of LECA, a loose bulk density measurement was carried out in accordance with the BS EN 1097-3:1998 and BS EN 932-2.

The determination of particle density for lightweight aggregates (LECA) was calculated according to the procedure specified in the EN 1097-6:2000.

Casting of the concrete specimens was carried out according to BS EN 12390-2:2000. The amount of water was adjusted to test fresh properties of concrete and get the required slump value. Cubes and mini- beams then were placed in the curing room for 28 days to achieve the required strength of the concrete. The curing room had a relative humidity of 95 percent and the samples were kept at 20°C.

3.3 Heating and cooling down process

Specimens were exposed to temperature levels of 20°C, 100°C, 200°C, 300°C, 400°C and 500°C. For each set of temperatures, 3 cubes (150 × 150 × 150 mm in size) and 2 mini beams (100 × 100 × 500 mm in size) were used to determine the residual compression and flexural strength.

The total amount of cubes and minibeams used for testing was 54 and 36 respectively.

The heating period was for 5 hours at each temperature increment to allow the concrete inside the samples to reach the required temperature. The dimensions of the furnace used for heating were 380 × 350 × 800 mm with a maximum heating capacity of 750°C. Taking into consideration the size and amount of concrete specimens, it was decided to place specimens of each concrete mix in three sets to reach the specified temperature. Specimens were weighed before and after heating to calculate moisture loss. After heating, specimens were left to cool down under natural conditions.

3.4 Determination of compressive and flexural strength

To determine the compressive strength of the cubes: sample preparation, spacing and loading were carried out according to BS EN 12390 3:2009. A compression testing machine conforming to EN 12390-4 was used for the experiment.

To calculate the compressive strength of the concrete, the Equation 1 was used:

$$f_c = \frac{F}{A_c} \tag{1}$$

Where f_c is the compressive strength in MPa (N/mm^2);

F—maximum load at failure, in N;

A_c—cross-sectional area of the specimen on which the compressive force acts, in mm^2

The test to determine the flexural strength was carried out according to BS EN 12390 5:2009. During the experiment the load was applied to specimens through two upper and two lower rollers, so as a result, the mini beams were subjected to four point bending.

Flexural Strength was calculated via Equation 2 as shown below.

$$f_{cf} = \frac{F \times 1}{d_1 \times d_2^2} \tag{2}$$

Where f_{cf} is flexural strength, in N/mm^2;

F—maximum load in failure, in N; I—distance between the supporting rollers, in mm;

d_1 and d_2—lateral dimensions of the specimen, in mm: d_1—width of the beam, in mm; d_2—depth of the beam, in mm.

4 RESULTS

4.1 Sieve analysis

Figure 1 shows particle size distribution for natural aggregates and LECA.

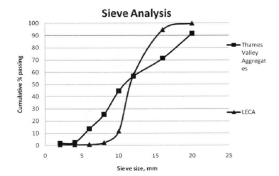

Figure 1. Aggregate size distribution.

4.2 Loose bulk and particle densities

The loose bulk density was calculated by testing three test samples and recording the mean value. The loose bulk density of the LECA was found as 0.379 Mg/m^3. The particle density was found in accordance with EN1097-6:2000 and is estimated as 0.631 Mg/m^3.

4.3 Slump test

The slump value was recorded as 60 mm for the control mix, 40 mm for Mix 2 and 30 mm for Mix 3.

4.4 Compressive strength

Figure 2 is presented overleaf.

Table 2. Compressive strength results in N/mm^2.

	MIX 1	MIX 2	MIX 3
20°C	44.4	41.0	30.7
100°C	41.6	38.4	27.1
200°C	39.4	34.8	24.1
300°C	35.3	27.3	22.8
400°C	29.4	19.6	17.8
500°C	14.0	12.3	15.8

4.5 Flexural strength

Table 3. Flexural strength results in N/mm^2.

	MIX 1	MIX 2	MIX 3
20°C	4.4	3.7	3.2
100°C	3.8	3.3	2.6
200°C	3.0	2.7	2.3
300°C	1.9	1.9	2.2
400°C	1.3	1.1	1.9
500°C	0.4	0.7	1.7

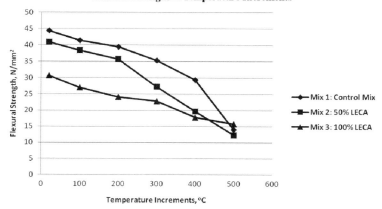

Figure 2. Compressive strength.

5 ANALYSIS

5.1 Residual strength reduction

Concrete mixes 1 and 2 showed similar compressive strength reduction after heating up to 500°C of about 70% of their initial strength. Significantly lesser loss of compressive strength was observed for mix 3, which was a loss of 48.5%. The change of the compressive strength is given on Fig. 4.

The largest flexural strength reduction experienced was for mix 1, which had a flexural strength of 4.0 N/mm^2—a 91% loss of initial concrete flexural strength. Concrete mix 2 had similar strength of about 3 N/mm^2 corresponding to 81% loss. Mix 3 containing 100% LECA showed the least flexural strength loss of about 47% of initial strength. The flexural strength change between unheated and heated to 500°C is given in Fig. 5.

5.2 Residual strength vs temperature increments

Concrete mixes containing Thames Valley aggregates and LECA demonstrated similar trends of a decrease in strength with an increase in temperature. A gradual decrease of strength was observed up to 300°C; at higher temperatures concrete specimens experienced a more severe and progressive decrease in strength.

For concrete mixes containing Thames Valley aggregates the loss of compressive strength was between 25% and 30% when specimens were heated up to 300°C. It was observed that a considerable loss of compressive strength happens when specimens are heated to the temperature higher than 300°C. For concrete mixes 1 and 2 loss in compressive strength was up to 70% when samples were subjected to a temperature

of 500°C which indicates that the major loss of strength (about 40%) happens between 300 and 500°C.

When specimens of mix 3 were exposed to high temperature, the reduction of compressive strength happened gradually compared to other concrete mixes. The more dramatic reduction of compressive strength which is observed for mixes 1 and 2 is not recognizable for mix 3.

A similar gradual decrease of the strength is observed for all 3 mixes from the results of flexural strength. The graph for flexural strength to temperatures for each of the mixes is close to linear (Fig. 3).

Specimens of concrete mix 1 had a flexural strength of about 0.4 N/mm^2 when they reached 500°C, which means they lost more than 90% of their initial strength. Mix 3 containing LECA had a value of 1.7 N/mm^2 with a 47% reduction of the initial flexural strength. As expected, the lightweight concrete had a better performance in high temperature loading than the concrete with natural aggregates.

5.3 Colour change

A change in colour with temperature was an indication of physical and chemical changes of aggregates used for concrete mixes.

The samples heated to 200°C maintained their original colour, while specimens heated to 300°C and 400°C changed to pinky hues and specimens exposed to 500°C changed to pink. At this level of heating, the samples with LECA aggregate obtained a rather more intensive coloring than the specimens with natural aggregates. The change of the color is connected with chemical

494

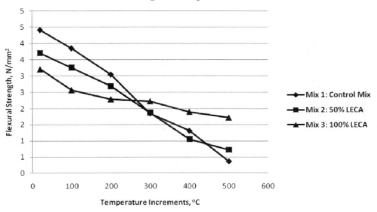

Figure 3.　Flexural strength.

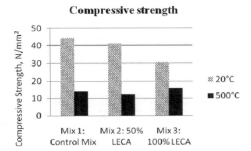

Figure 4.　Change of the compressive strength.

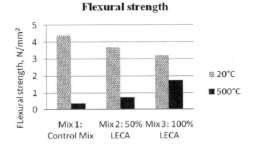

Figure 5.　Flexural strength change.

Figure 6.　Appearance of cracks (Mix 1).

Figure 7.　Appearance of cracks (Mix 2).

transformations of the siliceous and limestone aggregates at elevated temperatures.

5.4　Cracking and spalling

When specimens are exposed to high temperatures, they experience moisture loss due to increased pore pressure from evaporating water inside the concrete. This process results in an increase in internal stresses and therefore appearance of cracks.

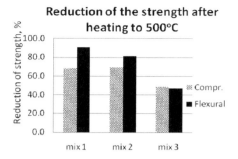

Figure 8. Strength reduction.

During the experiments, visible micro cracks on specimens appeared when temperatures of exposure were 400°C and 500°C. As the increase in moisture loss results in appearance of more excessive cracking, cubes heated to 500°C had a significant increase in number and size of cracks, compared to cubes exposed to 400°C as shown on Fig. 6 and Fig. 7.

6 CONCLUSIONS

When concrete is exposed to high temperatures, it undergoes changes in its chemical composition, physical structure and water content. These changes occur both in the hardened cement paste and in aggregates. It results in reduction of residual strength.

During the experiments, all types of samples from concrete mixes containing natural aggregates and lightweight expanded clay aggregates demonstrated reduction of their compressive and flexural strengths.

For specimens tested at temperatures between 20°C and 300°C, the reduction of the compressive strength was relatively small. However, when samples were exposed to temperatures higher than 300°C, a progressive and severe decrease in residual strength was measured.

Samples from concrete mix 2 (50% LECA) experienced significant reduction both for its compressive and flexural strength in a similar way to the samples from mix 1. However, the reduction of strength of the concrete containing 100% lightweight expanded clay aggregates was gradual for every temperature increment and to a significantly lesser degree.

Adding of 50% LECA aggregate did not improve the residual strength of the samples heated at 500°C significantly in comparison with samples from natural aggregates.

For both types of samples from mixes 1 and 2 the reduction of the flexural strength

was more significant than the reduction of the compressive strength (Fig. 8). For samples from mix 3 (100% LECA) the reduction for both types of strength was approximately the same. Those samples maintained approximately 50% of the strength of the control samples even after heating to 500°C.

The type of the aggregate used influences not only the difference of strength reduction but also affects the change in color. The colouration of samples containing Thames Valley aggregates and LECA aggregates was observed when specimens were exposed to the temperatures above 300°C. However the change of colour for the second type was more intensive.

In conclusion, investigations that were carried out showed that concrete with LECA had much better performance at higher temperatures than other concrete aggregates. However replacing 50% of natural aggregates with LECA by volume did not have a significant effect on the compressive and flexural residual strengths in comparison with specimens containing natural aggregates.

REFERENCES

Arpacıoğlu, U., Tanacan, L. & Ersoy, H.Y. (2008). *Effect of high temperature and cooling conditions on aerated concrete properties.* Construction and Building Materials.

Bazant, Z.P. & Kaplan, M.F. (1996). *Concrete at High Temperatures. Material Properties and Mathematical Models.* Harlow: Longman Group Limited.

BSI. *BS 8500–2:2006 Concrete –Complementary British Standard to BS EN 206-1—Part 2: Specification for constituent materials and concrete.* London.

BSI. *BS EN 1097-3:1998. Tests for mechanical and physical properties of aggregates —Part 3 an 6.* London.

BSI. *BS EN 12350-2:2009. Testing fresh concrete Part 2: Slump-test.* London.

BSI. *BS EN 12390-3:2009. Testing Hardened Concrete. Part 3: Compressive Strength of Test Specimens.* London.

BSI. *BS EN 12390-5:2009. Testing Hardened Concrete. Part 5: Flexural Strength of Test Specimens.* London.

Concrete Centre (2008). *Technical Report No. 68. Assessment of fire-damaged structures.* The Concrete Society.

Harmathy, T.Z. & Allen, L.W. (1973). *Thermal properties of selected masonry unit concretes.* Journal American Concrete Institution 70(2).

Peng, G.F., Bian, S.B., Guo, Z.Q., Zhao, J., Peng, X.L. & Jiang, Y.C. (2006). *Effect of thermal shock due to rapid cooling on residual mechanical properties of fiber concrete exposed to high temperature.*

Soutsos, M. (2010). *Concrete durability.* A practical guide to the design of durable concrete structures. London: Thomas Telford Limited. (in press).

Concrete Solutions – Grantham, Mechtcherine & Schneck (eds)
© *2012 Taylor & Francis Group, London, ISBN 978-0-415-61622-5*

Fire damaged concrete—the potential for on-going deterioration post-fire in concrete heated to temperatures of less than 300°C

M.A. Eden

Geomaterials Research Services (part of Sandberg LLP), London, UK

ABSTRACT: The damage to concrete resulting from fire is well documented in numerous laboratory studies as well as in reference publications such as Concrete Society Technical Report No. 68. Petrographic examination is the definitive method for measuring the depths damage of fire damaged concrete and can be used to establish depth/temperature profiles in fire damaged concrete. These techniques are essential in determining the depth of concrete that needs to be removed prior to repair. Petrographic studies of fire damaged concrete sometimes show evidence for on-going sulphate-induced expansion after the extinguishing of the fire in concrete heated to temperatures of less than 300°C. The potential for concrete expansion resulting from internal sulphate attack highlights the importance of the complete removal of all damaged concrete prior to concrete repair.

1 INTRODUCTION

Sulphate, usually in the form of calcium sulphate, is added to Portland cement during its manufacture principally to control setting time and to avoid flash setting (Taylor 1997). A typical modern Portland cement would contain of the order of 3 to 4% of sulphate as SO_3.

During the early stages of cement hydration the calcium sulphate reacts with the calcium aluminate and ferrite minerals in the hydrating cement grains slowing their hydration and forming hydrated calcium-sulpho-aluminate-hydrate compounds of which ettringite is an example. This reaction takes place over a short space of time and before the cement hydrates have fully hardened. The hydrated calcium aluminate sulphate compounds normally formed are accommodated within the structure of cement hydrates and form before the cement paste has hardened and without giving rise to expansion.

The hydrated calcium sulphate aluminate minerals normally present within cement paste in concrete are readily decomposed by heating. Temperatures in excess of around 65°C during curing are sufficient to inhibit the normal formation of ettringite during cement hydration in fresh concrete. Most cases of delayed ettringite formation (DEF) occur when concrete cured at elevated temperature is exposed to moisture. DEF can give rise to significant expansion and this expansion is associated with the expansive formation of ettringite within the hardened cement paste. The pattern of ettringite formation caused by DEF is distinctive under the petrological microscope and the ettringite associated with DEF characteristically occurs in peripheral cracks around aggregate surfaces as well and within cracks in the paste (St John, Poole and Sims 1998).

In fire damaged concrete there is the potential for the hydrated calcium alumina sulphate minerals to be decomposed due to heating leaving the sulphate compounds in the paste in a meta-stable form that can re-form as soon as there is a source of moisture and the temperature drops. Laboratory testing was carried out to confirm whether or not such expansion might occur and over what timescale that expansion might occur.

2 CASE STUDY

2.1 Site observations and background

The case study involves a fire-damaged concrete slab forming the floor of a building of predominantly timber construction. During the fire, the debris including burning timber from the fire accumulated on the concrete surface exposing the concrete to high temperatures for a period of in excess of 12 hrs. Five 70 mm diameter concrete cores were taken from representative locations across the area of the slab for petrographic examination in order to assess the severity and depth of fire damage.

2.2 Test methods

Concrete petrography is a widely accepted method of reliably determining depths of damage and depth/temperature profiles in fire damaged concrete. The concrete petrography testing was carried out in accordance with APG-SR2 (Eden 2010) and ASTM C856. The surfaces of each core were vacuum impregnated with epoxy resin prior to the preparation of longitudinal fluorescent resin-impregnated thin sections each measuring 50×75 mm. The thin sections were examined with a Zeiss petrological photomicroscope.

2.3 Visual evidence for fire damage

The surfaces of four out of the five cores had spalled and had exposed reddened flint gravel particles and surface-parallel cracking (Figure 1). Visible depths of fire damage along the sides of the cores ranged between 0 and 15 mm and the principal forms of fire-related alteration/damage visible without the microscope were aggregate reddening (indicative of temperatures of >300°C and surface-parallel fine cracking.

2.4 Petrographic assessment of fire damage

The concrete throughout the slab contained flint gravel and siliceous sand and had a binder that was based on a blend of Portland cement with PFA. There was little evidence to suggest that the concrete had deteriorated prior to the fire.

The thin sections showed evidence for concrete alteration to much greater depths than visible to the naked eye. The visual and petrographic measurements of the depths of fire damaged are summarized in Table 1. The principal form of alteration resulting from fire visible in the thin sections was surface-parallel microcracking. The development of surface-parallel microcracking and fine cracking is characteristic of damage caused by fire (Figure 2). Intense surface-parallel and sometimes

Figure 1. One of the core samples from the fire-damaged concrete slab with a spalled outer surface. The surface has exposed, reddened flint gravel particles and shallow surface-parallel fine cracking through both the aggregate particles and the paste.

Table 1. Depths of fire damage.

Sample	Visible cracking	Micro-cracking	Possible 300°C isotherm
	Depth, mm		
C1	15	20	8
C2	12	9	5
C6	0	22	7
C7	2	56	4
C8	12	21	3

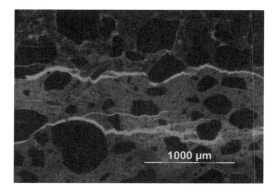

Figure 2. Fluorescent light photomicrograph of a thin section at a depth of about 3 mm below the outer surface showing the characteristic appearance of surface of the concrete slab heated to temperatures of >300°C.

reticulate cracking is often indicative of temperatures of >300°C.

A 300°C isotherm was identified at depths of between 3 and 8 mm on the basis of aggregate reddening and the occurrence of intense surface-parallel cracking in both the aggregate particles and paste. The lack of evidence for portlandite decomposition indicated that the temperatures reached in the uncarbonated paste along the surfaces were <400–450°C. No evidence was found for loss of carbonate from the carbonated paste along the surfaces indicating that the temperatures reached in the paste exposed at the surfaces were <600–900°C.

2.5 Petrographic assessment of post-fire alteration

Ettringite was found to be unusually abundant as microcrack fillings and void fillings in the paste throughout the depths of concrete affected by fire. The larger cracks were commonly lined with distinct needle-like crystals of ettringite. On a finer scale however ettringite was found to be abundantly present as microcrack fillings (Figure 3).

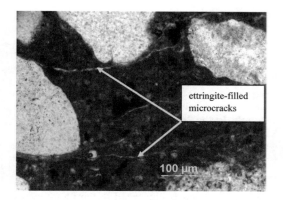

Figure 3. View showing the typical form of the ettringite-filled microcracks in paste in the fire damaged concrete. The microcracks are orientated approximately parallel with the outer surface of the sample.

Ettringite is readily decomposed by heating to temperatures of in excess of about 100°C and the ettringite observed in the thin sections would have therefore formed after the fire. It is very likely that the water used to extinguish the fire would have provided the necessary moisture for ettringite formation. The pattern of ettringite formation observed in the fire-damaged concrete is reminiscent of that seen in concrete affected by DEF.

3 LABORATORY INVESTIGATION

3.1 Introduction and test methods

Laboratory testing of a reference concrete containing flint gravel and siliceous sand in a Portland cement based paste was carried out to investigate the potential for post-fire expansion due to ettringite formation in fire-damaged concrete. The testing involved residual expansion core testing and petrographic examination of three tests specimens subjected to the regimes of heating and cooling as listed in Table 2 below.

The heat and quench test was intended to replicate the likely scenario of concrete being heated during a fire and then quenched during the extinguishing of the fire.

At the end of the period of expansion testing the causes of expansion were investigated petrographically in accordance with APG-SR2 and ASTM C856 using thin sections prepared from the expansion-tested samples. Polished surfaces were prepared from the test samples and these were examined with a Hitachi S570 scanning electron microscope fitted with an Oxford Instruments INCA energy dispersive X-ray microanalysis system calibrated with certified mineral standards.

3.2 Dimensional changes resulting from the heat treatment of the cores

The test samples showed distinct volume changes during their heat treatment as listed in Table 3. The control sample showed a slight expansion most likely due to swelling resulting from water absorption during the 24 hrs of water immersion. The heated and cooled sample showed a shrinkage of −0.035% which was most likely due to drying shrinkage during the heat treatment. The heat and quench core showed a negligible change in length during its cycle of heat treatment and quenching.

3.3 Residual expansion testing

Residual expansion testing was carried out at 38°C following the method given in Appendix H of the BCA Report on the Diagnosis of Alkali-Silica reaction over a period of 196 days. The method followed involves storage of the cores in a controlled damp environment at 100% relative humidity at 38°C.

The development of expansion in the cores during the testing is illustrated in Figure 4 and the test results are given in Table 4.

The control core showed no expansion other than that due to the initial thermal expansion.

The heated and cooled core showed an expansion intermediate between the control sample and the heated and quenched core and the expansion

Table 2. Test sample conditioning.

Test sample	Test regime
Control test sample	Core sample soaked in water for 24 hrs at room temperature.
Heated and cooled test Sample	Core sample heated to 200°C for 12 hours and then allowed to cool in air.
Heated and quenched test sample	Core sample heated to 200°C for 12 hours and then quenched in water.

Table 3. Dimensional changes during heat treatment.

Test sample	Length change during heat treatment%
Control test sample	0.011
Heated and cooled test Sample	−0.035
Heated and quenched test sample	0.004

ceased after about 80 days. It is likely that a significant proportion of this expansion resulted from the re-wetting of the core after its drying shrinkage.

The heated and quenched core showed a marked expansion with on-going expansion after 196 days. The expansion of this test sample was about double that of the heated and cooled core.

3.4 Post-expansion testing petrographic analysis and electron microscopy

A comparison of the results from the petrographic examination of the expansion-tested samples

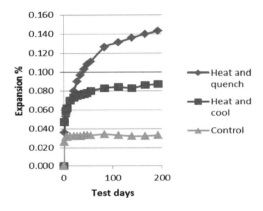

Figure 4. Graph showing the development of core expansion over time.

Table 4. Residual core expansion testing.

Test sample	Residual expansion after 196 days at 38°C%
Control test sample	0.033
Heated and cooled test sample	0.087
Heated and quenched test sample	0.143

is given in Table 3. The principal differences between the samples were in the degree to which the voids and pores in the cement paste were filled with ettringite. In the control sample there was much unfilled void space and pore space in the cement paste. In the "heat and cool" sample the amounts of unfilled void and pore space were substantially reduced relative to the control sample. In the "heat and quench" sample the void and pore space was generally completely filled with ettringite.

The "heat and quench" sample showed evidence for the development of ettringite-related expansive cracking in the paste and around aggregate surfaces and this is illustrated in the photomicrograph of the thin section given in Figure 5 and in the backscattered electron images of the polished surfaces given in Figure 6. No evidence was found for the development of expansive cracking relating to ettringite formation in the control sample or in the "heat and cool" sample.

None of the samples examined in thin section or with the electron microscope show evidence for the occurrence of alkali-aggregate reaction.

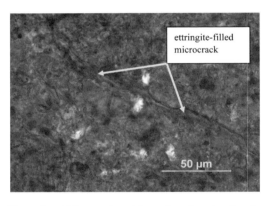

Figure 5. Oblique polars thin section view showing the typical form of the ettringite-filled microcracks in the "heat and quench" test sample.

Table 5. Summary of petrographic features of the residual expansion test samples.

Test regime	Void fillings	Crack fillings in the paste	Cracks on aggregate surfaces
	Relative ettringite abundance		
Control (water immersion)	Partial void fillings common	None found	None found
Heat and cool test sample	Most voids completely filled	None found	None found
Heat and quench test sample	Most voids completely filled	Sometimes present throughout the paste	Moderately abundant as microcrack fillings

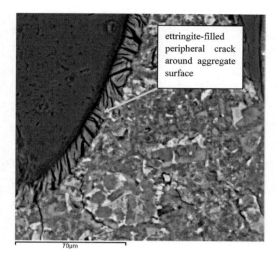

ettringite-filled peripheral crack around aggregate surface

70μm

Figure 6. Backscattered electron image of the polished surface prepared from the "heat and quench" test sample showing the development of ettringite in a peripheral crack around the surface of an aggregate particle.

4 DISCUSSION

The case study described is representative of several cases examined by the author where there appeared to be evidence for post-fire ettringite-related expansion in fire damaged concrete. In each case the concrete was exposed to heat for a prolonged period of time—typically >12 hrs.

The residual expansion testing carried out on the core samples heated to 200°C showed a clear potential for post-fire ettringite-related expansion where the heated concrete was quenched in water as would normally be the case with fire damaged concrete where the fire is eventually extinguished with water.

It is generally acknowledged that the most significant concrete weakening due to fire takes place at temperatures above about 300°C. The implication of the laboratory testing is that there is some potential for on-going expansion and weakening in fire damaged concrete heated to temperatures of much less than 300°C if the concrete is maintained in a damp environment post-fire for prolonged periods of time.

The potential for expansion demonstrated by the residual core expansion testing of the "heat and quench" test sample contrasts with the substantially lower expansion measured for the "heat and cool" test sample. This is likely to be related to the development of thermally induced cracking due to thermal shock in the "heat and quench" sample. It is regarded as probable that cracks generated by thermal shock in the "heat and quench"

test sample act as a focus for sites of ettringite formation in the paste and, once initiated, the on-going formation of ettringite and ettringite-related expansion.

5 CONCLUSIONS

The study highlights the importance of complete removal of the full depth of heat-damaged concrete in concrete exposed to fire.

In cases where the fire was prolonged and the concrete is likely to be in a damp environment after the fire a greater depth of surface removal may be necessary to achieve a long-term durable concrete repair.

The depth of the 300°C isotherm is often taken as being of primary importance in measuring the depth of significantly weakened fire-damaged concrete. It is commonly possible to visually recognize the depth of the 300°C isotherm on the basis of colour changes in the aggregate particles.

Visual assessments of depths of fire damage can however be misleading as it is not uncommon for significant concrete weakening to be found at much greater depths than the 300°C isotherm.

The study shows that there is a potential for ettringite-related post fire expansion in concrete heated to temperatures of much less than 300°C. The greatest risk of post fire expansion would be expected to occur where the fire-damaged concrete is in a damp environment after the fire.

Post fire expansion in fire damaged concrete has the potential to give rise to a failure of adhesion with a concrete repair should the full depth of heat-affected concrete not be fully removed at the time the repair is applied.

REFERENCES

ASTM C856-95. 1995. *Standard practice for petrographic examination of hardened concrete*. Philadelphia USA.
British Cement Association. 1992. *The diagnosis of alkali-silica reaction*.
Concrete Society. 2009. *Assessment and repair of fire-damaged structures*. Concrete Society Technical Report No. 68.
Eden, M.A. (ed.). 2010. *APG-SR2 Code of Practice for the Petrographic Examination of Hardened Concrete*. Available for download at www.appliedpetrographygroup.com
St John, D.A., Poole, A.B. & Sims, I. 1998. *Concrete petrography—a handbook of investigative techniques*. London: Arnold.
Taylor, H.F.W. 1997. *Cement chemistry*. Thomas Telford, London.

Concrete Solutions – Grantham, Mechtcherine & Schneck (eds)
© *2012 Taylor & Francis Group, London, ISBN 978-0-415-61622-5*

Flexural behavior of partially restrained beams of self compacting concrete exposed to fire flame

Ghalib Habeeb & Atheer Al-Juborry
College of Engineering, Babylon University, Iraq

ABSTRACT: The aim of this research was to evaluate the residual flexural strength of partial restrained Self Compacting Concrete (SCC) beams after exposure to fire flame with moderate and high intensity. The experimental program of the research consisted of preparation and testing of three SCC mixes: these mixes were different in fine to coarse aggregate ratio by weight (f/c), tested at the fresh state to achieve self compatibility and, then some of its mechanical properties were investigated before and after exposure to firing at 60 days age. The research also, included preparation and testing of 28 beam specimens, different in mix type, curing method, cover of reinforcement, and the degree of restraint of the beam ends. The flexural behavior of the SCC beams was investigated by the experimental determination of ultimate load, and the ultrasonic pulse velocity before and after the exposure to the fire operation.

1 INTRODUCTION

Fire is a great risk to human life, especially in the aftermath of vehicular, earthquake, and other extraneous accidents. When a concrete structure is exposed to fire, concrete experiences large volume changes resulting from thermal dilatation of aggregate, shrinkage of the cement paste, and spalling due to high thermal stresses combined with internal pore pressure buildup. During a fire, concrete structures suffer from severe degradation of mechanical and transport properties that may lead to expeditious reduction of the remaining service life. The level of thermal damage depends on the size of the structural member and the spatial and temporal fire conditions such as maximum temperature, heating rate, exposure time, and cooling rate. Therefore, it is very important to study the residual mechanical and transport properties after the concrete was subjected to high temperatures with different heating and cooling rates (Lee (J.), Yunping Xi, and Kaspar Willam2008).

1.1 Materials and experimental work

Ordinary Portland cement type I according to (BS12:1991).

The fine aggregate used in this experimental work, was tested according to BS EN 12620:2002, BS EN 12620:2002+A1:2008.The results showed that the fineness modulus was 2.8.

Rounded coarse aggregate of maximum size 14 mm was used. Grading, and the physical properties of this aggregate conformed to the (BS: 882:1992).

Water which used for the mix and curing in this work was tap water from the water-supply network system. Glenium-type 51 was used as super plasticizer.

Finely, crushed limestone was used as filler in this work, the mother rock of this filler was brought from the west desert of Iraq. The fineness of it can be described as 70% passing through sieve size 0.15 mm, and 30% passing through sieve size 0.075 mm.

Deformed steel wire of diameter 4 mm (fy = 441 MPa) was used as longitudinal and lateral reinforcement.

1.2 Components of SCC mixes

Three mixes of SCC were designed according to the first approach of (EFNARC, 2002) and achieved the requirements of the EPG recommendations (Project Group, 2005), The first mix contained a fine to coarse aggregate (f/c) ratio by weight equal to 0.9, the others two mixes contained f/c ratios = 1, and 1.1, Table (1) shows the components of the three mixes.

2 THE FRESH PROPERTIES OF SCC

The fresh properties of the SCC were tested by the procedure of hte EPG (European Project Group, 2005) for testing fresh SCC. Four characteristics were achieved by conducting four tests which were flowability, achieved by slump flow test, passing ability which was achieved by L box test, viscosity

Table 1. Components of SCC mixes.

Mix	f/c	Cement kg/m³	L.S kg/m³	F kg/m³	C kg/m³	W kg/m³	S.P l/m³	W/P
M0.9	0.9	480	120	760	844	200	6	0.33
M1	1	480	120	760	760	200	6	0.33
M1.1	1.1	480	120	844	760	190	7	0.32

which was achieved by T50 and V funnel tests, and segregation resistance which was achieved by no halo shape in the slump flow test, no visible segregation during handling or testing, and by controlling the average separated diameter of slump to not exceed the segregation border in the slump flow test.

3 THE HARDENED PROPERTIES OF SCC

3.1 Compressive strength test

Compressive strength test were conducted by standard cubes (150×150×150) mm which were prepared, and tested according to BS 1881:part:116:1983 at 60 days age.

3.2 Splitting tensile strength test

The splitting tensile strength was conducted according to the procedures of (ASTM C-496, 2002), using a cylinder with dimensions (Diameter 100, length 200 mm).

3.3 Static modulus of elasticity test

The static modulus of elasticity was conducted according to (ASTM C-469, 2002). By using cylinders specimens with dimensions (150 × 300) mm.

3.4 Modulus of rupture test

This test was conducted according to (ASTM C-78, 2002) by using Concrete prisms of dimensions (100 × 100 × 400) mm.

4 BEAM SPECIMEN PREPARATION

A steel deformed wire of 4 mm diameter was used to reinforce the beam specimens as a longitudinal (flexural) reinforcement and as lateral stirrups (shear) reinforcement. Beams were analyzed and designed according to the (ACI committee −318, 2005) for both flexural and shear requirements, the dimensions of beam specimens were (100 × 100 × 1000) mm. (28) beam specimens were cast in steel moulds, demoulded, cured, and then tested at 60 days age. Two beam specimens were considered as reference beams which were called (B1-20), the others beams differed from the reference in mix type, steel reinforcement cover, curing method, restraint of the ends. All types of beams were tested at 20°C, 300°C with moderate intensity, and, 300°C with high intensity as in Table (2).

4.1 Detail of reference beam specimens

The reference beam specimens were reinforced by longitudinal and stirrup reinforcement against flexural and shear failure respectively, cast from M1 (f/c = 1), demoulded and cured in water for 28 days, dried in air until 60 days age, its cover of reinforcement equal to 20 mm then, tested without any exposure to fire flame and, without any connection with the supports. All beam specimens were reinforced by relatively minimum flexural reinforcement as in Figure (1) to avoid the shear and the flexural-shear failure (satisfying pure flexural failure), in the same time to avoid bond failure by decreasing the diameter of wires and increasing the number of wires. Finally the mix was tested for passing ability of the SCC in practical application.

4.2 Partial restraint beam specimens

All beam specimens exposed to fire flame were supported during the firing and during the test by the same method. The supporting frame used during firing consisted of four steel angles with dimension 75 × 75 × 5 mm, forming a rectangular shape, and raised 30 cm by four legs. The supporting frame used during the test consisted of the parts shown in Figure (2). To satisfy the restraint of the ends for beam specimens and for changing the degree of restraint, holes were made in the steel angles (in both frames) and in the steel molds. Eight beam specimens (called B1S and B1D series) were provided with steel bolts Φ5 mm embedded inside them during the casting process. After drying, demoulding, curing, and before the firing or testing, the specimens were tied with the frame (in both cases) by inserting the bolts inside the holes and connecting it with the frame, then the frame including the specimen was carried and put inside the furnace or the testing machine for firing or testing respectively.

Table 2. Description of beams.

Beam notation	Deference from the reference beam	No
B1-20	Reference beam	2
B1-300M	Exposed to fire flame at 300°C with moderate intensity	1
B1-300H	Exposed to fire flame at 300°C with high intensity	1
B0.9-20	Cast from M0.9 (f/c = 0.9)	2
B0.9-300M	Cast from M0.9 (f/c = 0,9) and exposed to fire flame at 300°C with moderate intensity	1
B0.9-300H	Cast from M0.9 (f/c = 0,9) and exposed to fire flame at 300°C with high intensity	1
B1.1-20	Cast from M1.1(f/c = 1.1)	2
B1.1-300M	Cast from M1.1(f/c = 1.1) and exposed to fire flame at 300°C with moderate intensity	1
B1.1-300H	Cast from M1.1(f/c = 1.1) and exposed to fire flame at 300°C with high intensity	1
B1S-20	Connected with support by single bolt from each end	2
B1S-300M	Connected with support by single bolt from each end, and exposed to fire flame at 300°C with moderate intensity	1
B1S-300H	Connected with support by single bolt from each end, and exposed to fire flame at 300°C with high intensity	1
B1D-20	Connected with support by double bolts from each end	2
B1D-300M	Connected with support by double bolts from each end, and exposed to fire flame at 300°C with moderate intensity	1
B1D-300H	Connected with support by double bolts from each end, and exposed to fire flame at 300°C with high intensity	1
B1C-20	Cover of stirrup reinforcement = 10 mm	2
B1C-300M	Cover of stirrup reinforcement = 10 mm, and exposed to fire flame at 300°C with moderate intensity	1
B1C-300H	Cover of stirrups reinforcement = 10 mm, and exposed to fire flame at 300°C with high intensity	1
B1Cu-20	Cured at air by covering with wetted sheet for 7 days	2
B1Cu-300M	Cured at air by covering with wetted sheet for 7 days, and exposed to fire flame at 300°C with moderate intensity	1
B1Cu-300H	Cured at air by covering with wetted sheet for 7 days, and exposed to fire flame at 300°C with high intensity	1

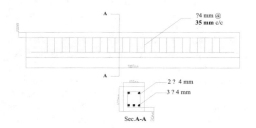

Figure 1. Detail of reference beam specimens.

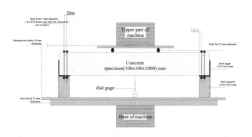

Figure 2. Restraint and test of beam specimens.

5 FIRING AND COOLING PROCEDURES

Fire processing was achieved inside a steel furnace with dimensions $750 \times 1200 \times 1200$ mm. The steel furnace was raised 750 mm from the ground and with hollows (from the upper surface for aeration, from the two sides for supplying the petroleum gas (methane) burner and supplying the temperature measured device respectively). The interior faces of the steel furnace were coated with a thin layer of green clay to protect the steel faces from the effect of high temperature. The specimens were subjected to direct fire flame from a set of methane burners inside the steel furnace. The temperature was measured by using two electrical thermocouples with digital monitors positioned at two different positions inside the steel furnace. After the temperature reached the target temperature (300°C), the firing operation was continued for 30 minutes. Then, the specimens were allowed to cool by air inside the steel furnace for 24 hours, after which those specimens were carried out from the steel furnace and tested.

5.1 Rate of heating and intensity of firing

In the present experimental study, SCC specimens were subjected to direct fire flame inside the steel furnace with a heating rate (30°C/min for high intensity, and 27°C/min for moderate intensity), the purpose was to subject the specimens to thermal sudden shock as in an actual fire. The temperature of the fire flame was measured and it was found to approximately 300°C, (the temperature was controlled by a divided gas regulator); after that the temperature of the fire flame was kept constant for 30 minutes. The distance between the upper point of the burner and the specimens was 100 mm, the thermocouples were positioned at a fixed distance from specimens of about 50 mm (this case represented the high intensity situation). To satisfy the moderate intensity situation, the distance between the burner and the specimens increased to 170 mm, the fire flame in the both situations touched the tip of the sensor of the thermocouples and the thermocouples stayed at fixed positions from the specimens.

6 ULTIMATE LOAD TEST

All beam specimens were tested according to the two point load method to subject the middle third of the beam to a pure bending moment without shear force. The frame which is shown in Figure (2) was used to support the beams inside the testing machine. The load was increased, the cracks were clarified by colored pen and, at the end, the ultimate load was recorded, which was defined as the load which is recognized by an excessive increase in deflection without any increase in the applied flexural load (Neville A.M. 1995).

7 ULTRASONIC PULSE VELOCITY TEST (UPV)

U.P.V testing was conducted for sixteen beam specimens before and after fire processing by using direct method with a grease couple to the concrete surface. The test was performed according to (ASTM C597, 2002) (Khoury, 2000).

8 RESULTS OF TESTS

8.1 Fresh properties of SCC

The three mixes (M0.9, M1, M1.1) of SCC were prepared, and then the fresh properties of each were evaluated by four tests, which were, Slump flow and T_{50} test, L-Box test, and V-Funnel test. The results of these tests and their acceptance limits according to (EFNARC, 2002) are shown in Table (3).

Table 3. Results of fresh properties of SCC.

Test type	Mix notation			Limits of EFNARC, 2002
	M0.9	M1	M1.1	
Slump flow (mm)	780	720	770	650–800
T50 (sec)	2.8	4.3	3.2	2–5
V-funnel (sec)	6.7	8.2	7.6	6–12
L-box (h2/h1)	0.95	0.88	0.9	0.8–1

8.2 Mechanical properties of SCC

The effect of exposure to fire flame on the mechanical properties of SCC can be generally summarized as the following:

1. All mechanical properties of SCC (compressive strength, splitting tensile strength, modulus of elasticity, and modulus of rupture) decreased when they were exposed to fire flame at 300co for 30 minutes, also they were decreased when the intensity of firing increased from moderate to high intensity as shown in Figures (3), (4), (5), & (6). And this can be attributed to the physicochemical changes in cement paste and aggregate and, the thermal incompatibility between them (Khoury, 2000).
2. For all the three mixes, the higher reduction in mechanical properties of SCC after the exposure to fire flame occurred in M1, and the lower reduction occurred in M1.1. This can be attributed to the increase of the f/c ratio causing a reduction in the Cement/Sand C/S ratio, and the decreasing C/S ratio decreases the coefficient of thermal expansion (Neville, 1995).
3. For all the three mixes, seemingly, the flexural strength was more sensitive to fire flame than the other mechanical properties of the SCC. This result can be attributed to the sensitivity to the loss in the moisture content of flexural strength specimens compared with that of the other mechanical properties: the drying of the specimen result in a reduction in the measured flexural strength.

8.3 Ultimate load results

Ultimate flexural load values were recorded for all beams (which were tested after the exposure to fire flame at 300°C with moderate and high intensity and which were tested without exposure to fire flame). The age of the firing or the direct test (without firing) was 60 days. Figures (7) to (10) show these results.

8.4 Ultrasonic pulse velocity (U.P.V) results

Figures (11) and (12) showed the effect of fire flame with different intensities on the U.P.V.

From the results, it can be seen clearly that burning had affected the U.P.V more than the ultimate load. This remarkable decrease in the U.P.V at burning can be attributed to the following two reasons:

1. The evaporation of the firmly adsorbed water on the gel crystals and the dehydration of the gel crystals themselves.
2. The formation of micro cracking which progressively propagates through the cement mortar and cement—aggregate interfaces. It is well established that micro cracking reduces appreciably the U.P.V. Micro cracking is inevitable due to drying shrinkage and differential thermal stresses.

9 CONCLUSIONS

Based on the test results obtained from the experimental works and after the evaluation of these results, the following conclusions can be summarized:

- All mechanical properties of SCC (compressive strength, splitting tensile strength, modulus of elasticity, and modulus of rupture) decreased when they were exposed to fire flame at 300co for 30 minutes, also they were decreased when the intensity of firing increased from moderate to high intensity.
- For all the three mixes (M0.9, M1, and M1.1) of SCC, the higher reduction in the mechanical properties of SCC occurred in M1, and the lower reduction occurred in M1.1, after the exposure to the fire flame at 300co for 30 minutes with moderate and high intensity of the firing operation.
- For all the three mixes of SCC, the flexural strength (modulus of rupture) was more sensitive to fire flame than the other mechanical properties of SCC.
- For all SCC beam specimens, ultimate load values were decreased and, deflection values were increased, after the exposure to the fire flame with moderate and high intensity.
- Increasing the f/c ratio decreased the residual ultimate load and, increased the residual deflection for the SCC beam specimens.
- The increasing of f/c ratio from 1 to 1.1 by increasing the fine aggregate content increased the residual ultimate load and, improved the residual deflection for the SCC beam specimens.

- Decreasing of cover of reinforcement and the period of the curing did not affect clearly the flexural properties of SCC beam specimens after firing.
- Increasing the degree of partial restraint of the ends of the SCC beam specimens improved the flexural behavior of SCC beams before and after the exposure to the fire flame with moderate and high intensity of firing.

REFERENCES

ACI Committee 318, *"Building Code Requirements for Structural Concrete"*, American Concrete Institute, 2005.

ASTM C469, *"Standard Test Method for Static Modulus of Elasticity and Poisson's Ratio of Concrete in Compression"*, American Society for Testing and Materials, 2002.

ASTM C496, *"Standard Test Method for Splitting Tensile Strength for Cylindrical Concrete Specimens"*, American Society for Testing and Materials, 2002.

ASTM C78, *"Standard Test Method for Flexural Strength of Concrete"*, American Society for Testing and Materials, 2002.

BS 12:1991 *"Specification for Portland Cement"*.

BS 1881: Part 116, *"Method for Determination of Compressive Strength of Concrete Cubes"*, British Standards Institution, 1989.

BS 882:1992 *"Specification for Aggregate from Natural Sources for concrete"*.

E.G., Bibm Organization, CEMBUREUAU Association, ERMCO Organization, EFCA Association and EFNARC, *"The European guidelines for self-compacting concrete"*, 2005.

EFNARC, *"Specification and Guidelines for Self-Compacting Concrete"*, The European federation dedicated to specialist construction chemicals and concrete systems, 2002.

European Project Group: E.G., Bibm Organization, CEMBUREUAU Association, ERMCO Organization, EFCA Association and EFNARC, *"The European guidelines for testing fresh self-compacting concrete"*, 2005.

Khoury (G.A.), *"Effect of fire on Concrete and Concrete Structures"*, Prog. Struct. Engng Materials Part 2, 2000.

Lee (J.), Yunping Xi, and Kaspar Willam, *"Properties of Concrete after High-Temperature Heating and Cooling"*, ACI Materials Journal/July-August 2008.

Neville (A.M.), *"Properties of Concrete"*, Five, and Final Edition, Wiley, New York and Longman, London, 1995.

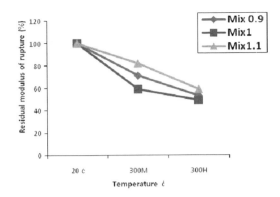

Figure 6. Relationship between residual modulus of rupture and exposure temperature.

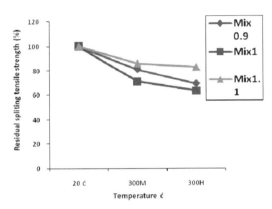

Figure 3. Relationship between residual compressive strength and exposure temperature.

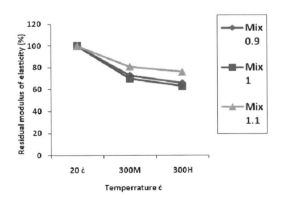

Figure 4. Relationship between residual splitting tensile strength and exposure temperature.

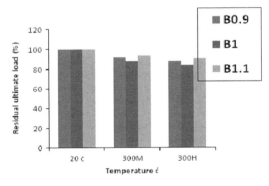

Figure 7. Relationship between residual ultimate load and exposure temperature for B0.9, B1, and B1.1.

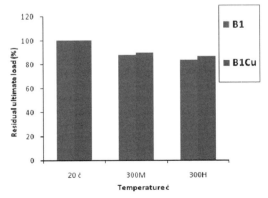

Figure 5. Relationship between residual modulus of elasticity and exposure temperature.

Figure 8. Relationship between residual ultimate load and exposure temperature for B1, and B1Cu.

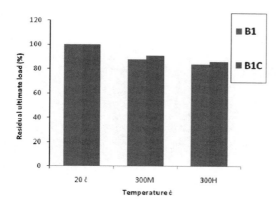

Figure 9. Relationship between residual ultimate load and exposure temperature for B1 and B1.

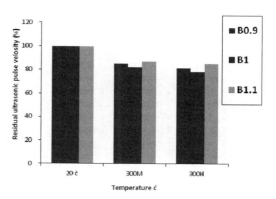

Figure 11. Relationship between residual U.P.V and exposure temperature for B0.9, B1, and B1.1.

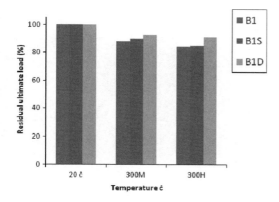

Figure 10. Relationship between residual ultimate load and exposure temperature for B1,B1S, and B1D.

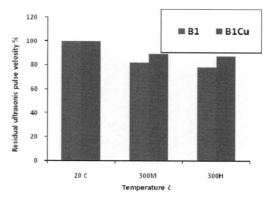

Figure 12. Relationship between residual U.P.V and exposure temperature for B1,B1Cu.

Concrete Solutions – Grantham, Mechtcherine & Schneck (eds)
© 2012 Taylor & Francis Group, London, ISBN 978-0-415-61622-5

Assessment of fire damage of an old RC structure

Gh. Petrovay & C. Mircea

Civil Engineering Faculty, Technical University of Cluj-Napoca, Romania

ABSTRACT: The paper refers to the fire resistance of RC structures, based on an investigation performed upon an old RC structure affected by a severe fire. The aim of the investigation was to identify the residual structural properties of the building, and to recommend the necessary repairs. Due to a lack of adequate regulatory guidance given by the Romanian norms, a methodology was conceived based on the ACI recommendations. The building had a RC structure and an envelope made of masonry. The investigation included: analysis of Fire Brigade reports; visual inspections of the structure, pachometer scanning of the structural members and drilled holes for identifying the reinforcing of the structural members exposed to fire; non-destructive and laboratory tests on drilled cylindrical core samples to determine the residual properties of the exposed elements and the actual properties of the non-exposed elements; numerical analysis for members; evaluation of results and elaboration of conclusions and recommendations.

1 INTRODUCTION

1.1 History of the structure

The structure that was the subject of the investigation described in the following chapters was a RC framed structure that was built during the 1900s in several stages. The construction started in 1927, the building initially had three stories (ground floor plus two stories). The height of the construction was modified in 1968, when a fourth story was added. In 1978, the ground floor columns underwent consolidation works due to an increase in local loads (heavy machinery) and the necessity for a larger seismic load bearing capacity.

In January 2007, the owner of the building was one of the leading Central and Eastern European furniture manufacturers. At the time of the fire, the company was using the upper three floors for storage and production, while the ground floor was being dismantled and the old industrial equipment removed by a specialized company.

1.2 Building description

The structure of the building was a three dimensional reinforced concrete structure, consisting of cast in situ reinforced concrete frames. The frames were placed along two orthogonal directions, with the main frames along the length of the building and secondary stiffening frames along the width.

The reinforced concrete frames had 19 equal 6.00 m spans along the longitudinal direction and 3 unequal spans along the transverse direction (one central 10.00 m span and two side 7.40 m

Figure 1. General view of the building.

spans). The total dimensions of the building were 119.25×24.82 m.

The slabs over the ground floor and the first two floors were one way monolithic RC slabs resting on secondary and main beams, while the roof was made of prefabricated RC cased elements.

The stairs connecting the four levels of the building were made of reinforced concrete. The exterior closing walls and the interior partition walls were made of ceramic masonry.

2 FIRE DEVELOPMENT AND CAUSES

2.1 Start and development of the fire

On January 9th 2007, the structure was subjected to a heavy fire that originated at around 9:30 AM on the ground floor, near the southern wall, approximately halfway along the length of the building. The fire extended from the origin along two directions, horizontal and vertical.

The horizontal development was facilitated by the presence of flammable materials stored in the building and the large open spaces not delimited by fire walls. The flames quickly spread through all of the ground floor.

The vertical development of the fire occurred due to the presence of technological openings in the RC slabs, these openings allowing the flames to easily pass to the first floor. The first floor was not as extensively affected as the ground floor, the fire damaging the structure and the objects inside only in the vicinity of these slab openings.

2.2 Causes and duration of the fire

After the fire was extinguished, a technical analysis was made by the local Fire Brigade (Inspectoratul pentru Situatii de Urgenta "Avram Iancu") in order to identify the causes of the fire. This report identified the most likely causes of the fire as either a lit cigarette improperly disposed of, or defective metal welding or cutting.

The rapid and violent spread of the fire was facilitated by the flammable materials stored in the area, such as sponge packages, textile residues, cardboard and wood.

During the intervention of the Fire Brigade, the source identification took approximately two hours due to the massive smoke emissions that led to very poor visibility. After the source was identified, two more hours were necessary to completely extinguish the fire.

Taking into account the time necessary for the firefighting equipment displacement and installation, the building was subjected to fire for a time interval of some 4 hours and 30 minutes.

2.3 Goals of the investigation

The owner of the building requested a complete technical evaluation of the RC structure in order to determine the load bearing capacity of the affected structural members. The investigation was conducted following these stages:

- Complete identification of the structural system.
- Identification of the construction materials used for the elements affected by fire and the determination of their physical characteristics before and after exposure to flames and high temperatures.
- Determination of the load bearing capacity of the affected elements.

- The complete inventory of affected structural members.
- The analysis of the structural state of the building.
- Necessary measures for repairing and consolidating the structure in order for the building to be safe for its occupants.

3 FIRE EFFECTS ON THE RC STRUCTURE

3.1 Fire effects on concrete

One of the advantages of concrete as a building material is its good behavior when in contact with flames or high temperatures. This is why concrete, together with masonry, are the most used materials for structural elements that might be subjected to fire. The behavior of concrete is far better that the behavior of the other two widely used structural materials, steel and timber.

However, when subjected to very high temperatures and/or direct fire action, concrete strength decreases. For temperatures up to 250°C, the variations in concrete compressive strength are negligible and irregular. For temperatures of up to 400°C, the concrete strength reduces, but during the cooling process, the material recovers almost completely, with no significant long term strength loss.

If exposed to temperatures above 400°C for longer periods of time, the concrete deterioration will also continue during the cooling process, resulting in a permanent alteration of the material characteristics.

The main factors that affect the behavior of concrete subjected to the action of fire are the following:

- Water content of concrete: This is the most important factor, as the strength loss in saturated concrete is higher than the strength loss in dry concrete.
- Water-cement ratio in concrete.
- Permeability of concrete.
- The heating rate (the speed at which temperature increases).
- Type of aggregates in concrete.
- The degree of loading in RC elements: Elements subjected to larger loads are more affected by fire than unloaded elements.

Under the effect of fire, concrete degradation occurs as dislocation of pieces of material. This phenomenon can occur in one of the following ways:

- Explosive expulsion of the outer layers: This occurs in the early stages of a fire, at temperatures around 100°C, when concrete pieces having the plane dimensions of 30–40 cm and the thickness of 1–2 cm are violently ripped from the concrete element. This leads to a reduction of the concrete cross section. For reinforced concrete elements, the phenomenon will be reduced to the expulsion of the reinforcement coverage layer, as the steel bars will stop its propagation towards the core of the element.

– Surface fragmentation: Small pieces of concrete (1–2 cm) are removed, leading to the exposure of reinforcement.
– Aggregate splitting: the aggregates in concrete break to pieces due to the tension induced by dilatation.
– Dislocation of edges and corners: This occurs in the late stages of a fire, at temperatures over 400°C. Concrete covering the steel reinforcement is removed due to tensile efforts and the element capacities are drastically reduced, thus compromising their strength and stability.
– Dislocation during cooling: This occurs for concrete elements containing aggregates that expand during the re-hydration that takes place while cooling.

3.2 Fire effects on steel

Significant strength losses for steel occur at temperatures exceeding 300°C. Between 300 and 400°C, the steel modulus of elasticity drops linearly, while at temperatures above 400°C, it reduces dramatically, following an exponential curve.

3.3 Fire effects on beams and columns

Figure 2 shows the influence of a fire acting from below on a continuous RC beam:

When fire acts from below, the temperature of the bottom of the beam increases, thus leading to dilatation. Because the bottom flange of the beam dilates while the top flange remains unchanged, the beam will tend to curve. This will lead to an increase in the support reactions and subsequently to an increase in support bending moments and a decrease in mid-span bending moments.

Both the support and span reinforcements may fail in this scenario: the bottom reinforcement due to the strength reduction caused by the high temperature and the top reinforcement due to the increase of the support bending moments. Practice has shown, however, that the support reinforcement will fail first, as the change of the bending moment distribution is significant.

The columns generally have a good behavior under fire, the main risk being the exposure of the reinforcement if the concrete cover layer has insufficient thickness. Exposure of steel bars will lead to a decrease of steel strength and modulus

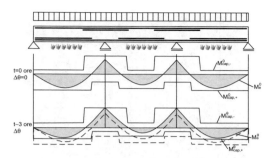

Figure 2. The effects of fire on a continuous beam.

of elasticity and subsequently a decrease in the column load bearing capacity.

3.4 Effects of the fire on the RC structure

The first step of the investigation was the determination of the building structural system and the complete identification of structural elements. After all the elements were located and their dimensions checked, the investigating team moved on to the next step, performing a complete inventory of the damage caused by the fire on the structural elements.

The most affected individual elements were the horizontal ones (beams and slabs) which were located directly above the fire. Out of the failure mechanisms of concrete presented in chapter 3.1, all but one were identified in the analysis of the damaged members. The phenomenon that did not occur was the splitting of concrete aggregates.

The degree in which the horizontal RC elements (beams and slabs) were affected was proportional with their distance to the origin of the fire.

The damage observed in the RC slabs could be roughly divided into 3 categories, according to the extent in which the element was affected. The slab presented in Figure 3 had minor damage of the bottom concrete surface.

The slab in Figure 4, situated closer to the origin of the fire, has the entire reinforcement coverage layer at the bottom expelled, the steel re-bars being fully exposed.

The slab in Figure 5 was situated directly above the area where the fire started, thus having a longer exposure compared to the previous two. The damage in this case was much more extensive, the concrete being removed along all the thickness of the slab and the steel reinforcements being fully exposed.

Most of the beams affected by the fire showed significant deteriorations at the bottom of the cross section, this area being closest to the flames and thus subjected to the highest temperatures.

Figure 3. RC slab with minor degradations of concrete.

Figure 4. RC slab with cover layer spalled.

Figure 5. RC slab with concrete fully removed.

The beam shown in Figure 6 had the cover layer for the bottom reinforcements completely removed.

3.5 Effects of the fire on the aspect of the materials in the structure

The influence of the high temperatures on concrete varied significantly from one area of the

Figure 6. RC beam with the bottom reinforcements completely exposed.

construction to another. In the areas where the temperatures were closest to the maximum values, the concrete suffered significant strength losses and became very brittle, pieces of the material easily coming off even after the elements cooled down.

The high temperature exposure also affected the steel bars. The damage recorded was only surface damage and no significant re-bar section variations were observed.

4 INVESTIGATIONS

4.1 In situ and laboratory investigations and results

Non-destructive and destructive tests were performed in order to determine the concrete characteristics for different sets of elements, both affected by the fire and unaffected.

The beams were subjected both to ultrasonic testing (Figure 7) and to distructive tests performed on extracted samples, in areas affected by the fire exposure and in areas not affected by fire. A general decrease in compressive strength was identified, a synthesis of the distructive test results being shown in Table 1 below. Even though the most affected individual elements were those directly above the fire (beams and slab over the ground floor), larger average strength losses occured in the beams above the 1st floor.

The reinforced concrete slab above the ground floor was not tested, as in the areas affected by fire exposure concrete quality was poor, with pieces of material easily detachable. The slab above the 1st floor was not tested, as the top face was not accessible due to the floor finishing layers at the 2nd floor.

The sectional dimensions of the columns were larger than the ultrasonic device measuring capacity, therefore ultrasonic testing was not possible for columns. Instead, cylindrical samples were extracted from RC columns (Figure 8) both affected and unaffected by fire and their compressive strength determined in an authorized laboratory.

The laboratory results regarding the variation of concrete compressive strength in columns were inconclusive. A direct relation between the position of the column with respect to the fire and the compressive strength of the tested specimen could not be determined, due to irregularity of the distructive test results.

The reinforcement quantities in the structural members were determined using two methods: pachometer testing (Figure 9) and exposure of the reinforcements by removing the concrete cover layer (Figure 10). The information regarding the reinforcement quantity in the structural member was further used in the numerical and analytical models presented at chapter 4.2. The strength losses in steel were determined only anilitically.

4.2 Numerical and analytical models

The numerical and analytical models used were based on the mathematical models for material behavior presented in *Guide for Determining the Fire Endurance of Concrete Elements and Standard Method for Determining Fire Resistance of*

Figure 7. Ultrasonic testing for determining the quality of concrete in beams.

Table 1. Average strength losses for beams.

Floor	Beams	ΔR
Above ground floor	Secondary beams	24.70%
	Main beams	28.00%
Above 1st floor	Secondary beams	30.00%
	Main beams	36.70%

Concrete and Masonry Construction Assemblies from the American Concrete Institute. Theoretical strength losses were calculated for materials (concrete and reinforcements) according to the applied temperature.

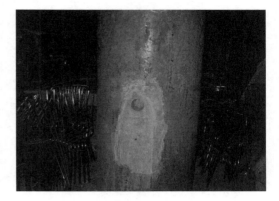

Figure 8. Cylindrical sample removed from central reinforced concrete column.

Figure 9. Pachometer testing of columns.

Figure 10. Column reinforcement exposure.

Figure 11 shows the variation of strength losses in concrete with respect to the concrete temperature. By corroborating the data in Figure 11 with the experimental data presented in Table 1, the temperature to which the structural elements were subjected can be deduced, in this case being around 450°C, close to the estimate value expressed by the Fire Brigade in their report of the incident.

Based on the this calculated value of the temperature, the steel strength losses were determined, as shown in Figure 12.

The numerical models were applied to the slabs, the secondary beams and the main beams. For each type of element, 6 hypotheses were considered, 3 for failure design and 3 for ULS design.

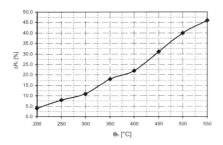

Figure 11. Variation of concrete strength losses with respect to the element temperature.

Table 2. Design hypotheses.

Hypothesis	Design type	Element status	Material characteristic considered
1	Failure	not affected	characteristic value
2	Failure	minimal damage	reduced characteristic value
3	Failure	maximal damage	reduced characteristic value
4	ULS	not affected	design value
5	ULS	minimal damage	reduced design value
6	ULS	maximal damage	reduced design value

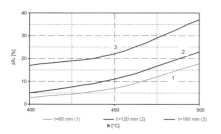

Figure 12. Variation of steel strength losses with respect to the element temperature.

5 CONCLUSIONS AND NECESSARY ACTIONS

5.1 *Conclusions*

Considering the results from the in situ testing, the laboratory testing and the analytic and numeric design, the effects of the fire upon the reinforced concrete structure can be comprehensively assessed.

The structure behaved well under the significant thermal load. There were no collapsed elements and the structural integrity and stability was never in danger. All the reinforced concrete structural elements fulfilled their load bearing role until the fire was completely extinguished.

However, the fire affected irreversibly the capacity of most of the structural elements situated in the areas that were exposed to high temperatures the longest. The concrete in the slabs was damaged, its compressive strength being drastically reduced. The main and secondary beams lost up to 40% of their initial capacity due to material degradation and cross section reduction.

The tests performed in the laboratory on concrete samples from the columns did not yield conclusive results. The distribution of the compressive strength of the tested specimens was highly irregular, independent of the position of the column with respect to the fire. Due to this irregularity, the behavior of the columns cannot be anticipated, thus making them unsafe.

5.2 *Necessary actions*

As most of the structural elements were affected by the fire and do not meet the strength and stability requirements of the design norms, the building will have to undergo extensive consolidation works in the areas affected by fire. These consolidation works will have to consider all the structural elements, which should be brought to their initial capacity.

REFERENCES

American Concrete Institute. 1989. Guide for Determining the Fire Endurance of Concrete Elements.
American Concrete Institute. 1997. Standard Method for Determining Fire Resistance of Concrete and Masonry Construction Assemblies.
Romanian Standards Association. 1977. STAS 10101/0—Actions upon structures—Classification and combination of actions for non-industrial and industrial structures.
Romanian Standards Association. 1990. STAS 10107/0—Civil and industrial buildings—Design and detailing of concrete, reinforced concrete and prestressed concrete structural members.

Concrete Solutions – Grantham, Mechtcherine & Schneck (eds)
© *2012 Taylor & Francis Group, London, ISBN 978-0-415-61622-5*

Assessing concrete repair after thermal exposure: Effect of aggregates on 3D response

G. Xotta, V.A. Salomoni & C.E. Majorana
Department of Structural and Transportation Engineering, Faculty of Engineering, University of Padua, Padua, Italy

ABSTRACT: Repairing strategies towards concrete structures subjected to exceptional actions such as fires, earthquakes, etc. require nowadays deeper knowledge on the behavior of concrete materials at the mesoscale level. Particularly, it appears fundamental to characterize aggregates (and specifically, their thermal properties when fire hazards are accounted for) to understand and model concrete behaviour in three-dimensional domains. The assessment of aggregate performance (and, correspondingly, concrete materials made of aggregates, cement paste and ITZ—interfacial transition zone-) is crucial for defining a realistic structural response as well as damage scenarios. Consequently, intervention strategies and repair procedures can be properly chosen and remediation guidelines can be effectively consistent when e.g. spalling phenomena are to be avoided. To this purpose the 3D F.E. code NEWCON3D has been adopted to perform meso-scale analyses of concrete elements characterized by aggregates of different types and different thermal conductivities. Damage maps allow for defining an appropriate concrete mixture for responding to spalling and for establishing repairing lines to recreate structural integrity under further loads.

1 INTRODUCTION

A thorough knowledge of concrete at the meso-scale level is nowadays essential if a more realistic response of concrete materials and structures under spalling is to be defined, so that a composite matter made of cement paste, aggregates and an Interfacial Transition Zone (ITZ) must be accounted for. Particularly, aggregates and their thermal properties have a crucial role in this exceptional scenario.

In fact, only after a deep comprehension of the response of these components under fire action, more appropriate and effective intervention strategies as well as repair procedures can be chosen.

For this reason, the effect of aggregates on the visco-damaged response of concrete at the meso-scale level is considered here; particularly, model B3 (Bazant & Baweja 2000; ACI Committee 2008) and Mazars' law (Mazars 1986; Majorana 1989; Pijaudier-Cabot et al. 1991) have been chosen and implemented in the 3D FE code NEWCON3D (Salomoni et al. 2009) when considering creep and damage, respectively.

As regards the viscous response, many experiments available in the literature have shown that in concrete the source of creep is the cement paste: aggregates do not creep in the range of stresses encountered in service. It is therefore reasonable to consider concrete as a composite formed by one aging viscoelastic phase (cement paste) and one elastic phase (aggregates) (Granger & Bazant

1995). Hence model B3, generally adopted to characterize the creep features of concrete, can be successfully used even to model cement paste creep alone.

Model B3 has been first validated within NEWCON3D to fit experimental tests at the macro-level (L'Hermite et al. 1965) and subsequently adopted to perform predictive creep and shrinkage analyses at the meso-level, where concrete is considered as a three-phase composite made of cement paste, aggregates and ITZ.

Additionally, the damaged behavior of concrete at the meso-level has been considered both to understand the influence of ITZ, the weakest region of the composite material, on the overall mechanical behavior and to define an appropriate concrete mixture for responding to spalling.

2 MODEL B3

Model B3 (Bazant & Baweja S. 2000; ACI Committee 2008) has been chosen for characterizing concrete creep and shrinkage; the model in fact shows good compatibility with experimental results and it is better theoretically justified if compared to previous creep models.

Differently from e.g. the approach making use of the double power law compliance function, B3 distinguishes between *basic creep* (time-dependent deformations where no moisture exchanges with the environment occur) and *drying creep* (additional creep strain accounting for drying). The compliance function at time t, caused by a unit one-axial constant stress applied at time t′, takes now the following form:

$$J = q_1 + C_0(t,t') + C_d(t,t',t_0) \tag{1}$$

where q_1 is the instantaneous strain due to unit stress, $C_0(t,t')$ the compliance function for basic creep, $C_d(t,t',t_0)$ the additional compliance function due to drying, t is the current age, t' is the age at loading and t_0 is the age at the start of drying.

The instantaneous strain may be expressed as:

$$q_1 = 1/E_0 \tag{2}$$

where E_0 is the asymptotic elastic modulus. The use of this modulus rather than of the conventional one E_{cm} is convenient because concrete exhibits pronounced creep even for short load durations. E_0 should not be regarded as a real elastic modulus, but merely as an empirical parameter considered as age independent.

The total basic creep compliance is given by:

$$C_0(t,t') = q_2 \cdot Q(t,t') + q_3 \cdot \ln\left[1 + (t-t')^n\right] + q_4 \cdot \ln\left(\frac{t}{t'}\right) \tag{3}$$

where $q_2 \cdot Q(t,t')$ is the aging viscoelastic compliance term, q_3 the non-aging viscoelastic term compliance parameter and q_4 is the aging flow compliance parameter. $Q(t,t')$ is an approximate binomial integral so expressed:

$$Q(t,t') = Q_f(t')\left[1 + \left(\frac{Q_f(t')}{Z(t,t')}\right)^{r(t')}\right]^{-1/r(t')} \tag{4}$$

that can be approximated using the formulas:

$$Q_f(t') = \left[0.086(t')^{2/9} + 1.21(t')^{4/9}\right]^{-1}$$
$$Z(t,t') = (t')^{-m} \cdot \ln\left[1 + (t-t')^n\right]$$
$$r(t') = 1.7(t')^{0.12} + 8 \tag{5}$$

where m and n are empirical parameters ($m = 0.5$; $n = 0.1$).

The additional creep due to drying is defined by:

$$C_d(t,t',t_0) = q_5 \cdot \left[exp\{-8H(t)\} - exp\{-8H(t')\}\right]^{1/2} \tag{6}$$

where q_5 is the drying creep compliance parameter whereas $H(t)$ and $H(t')$ are spatial averages of pore relative humidity:

$$H(t) = 1 - (1-h)S(t-t_c)$$
$$H(t') = 1 - (1-h)S(t'-t_c) \tag{7}$$

in which $S(t-t_c)$ and $S(t'-t_c)$ are the time functions for shrinkage calculated at the age of concrete t and at the age of concrete at loading t'.

This model allows for the prediction of the long-term behavior of concrete from short duration tests. Indeed q_1, q_2, q_3, q_4, q_5 parameters are determined by a series of experimental data by means of linear regressions. Bazant has provided for a series of relations, based on a statistical survey data of the database by RILEM, where such parameters are functions of cement content c, concrete mean compressive strength at 28 days f_{cm28}, water-cement ratio w/c, aggregate-cement ratio a/c, and ultimate shrinkage strain ε_{sh}. Typical expressions (referring to SI units) are:

$$q_2 = 185.4 \times 10^{-6} c^{0.5} f_{cm28}^{-0.9}$$
$$q_3 = 0.29(w/c)^4 q_2$$
$$q_4 = 20.3 \times 10^{-6}(a/c)^{-0.7}$$
$$q_5 = 0.757 f_{cm28}^{-1} \left|\varepsilon_{sh} \times 10^{-6}\right|^{-0.6} \tag{8}$$

The B3 model has been consequently implemented within NEWCON3D; as originally done when dealing with the double power law, it has been applied to the Maxwell-chain model at the basis of creep description. The formulation reported above for the creep function J(t,t′) (see Eqs. (1–8)) has been maintained but a change in the expression (6) of drying creep has been introduced, replacing the spatial averages of pore relative humidity $H(t)$ and $H(t')$ with the current relative humidity for every time step. Relative humidity is in fact one of the main variables, together with temperature and displacements, of the adopted numerical code; in this way such a substitution allows for a more precise definition of creep due to drying. Additionally, the coupled hygro-thermo-mechanical features of the code itself allows for a general better estimate of concrete response.

Then, as regards shrinkage, the formulations below for $S(t-t_c)$ and $S(t'-t_c)$, see ACI Committee (2008) have been adopted:

$$S(t-t_c) = \tanh\sqrt{\frac{(t-t_c)}{\tau_{sh}}}$$
$$S(t'-t_c) = \tanh\sqrt{\frac{(t'-t_c)}{\tau_{sh}}} \tag{9}$$

where τ_{sh} is the shrinkage half-time in days:

$$\tau_{sh} = 0.085 t_c^{-0.08} f_{cm28}^{-0.25} [2k_s (V/S)] \quad (10)$$

in which f_{cm28} is the mean compressive strength at 28 days, k_s the cross section shape-correction factor and V/S the volume-surface ratio.

It can be seen that S mainly depends by characteristics related to the geometry of the studied model but it is independent on the permeability of the different components, a property controlling humidity and hence drying creep evolution.

3 MAZARS DAMAGE MODEL

The damage model considered in NEWCON3D is the non-local Mazars' damage one. The stress-strain law is expressed as:

$$\boldsymbol{\sigma} = \boldsymbol{\Lambda}_0 (1 - D) \otimes \boldsymbol{\varepsilon}_e \quad (11)$$

where $\boldsymbol{\sigma}$ and $\boldsymbol{\varepsilon}_e$ are stress and strain tensors, D is the damage parameter and $\boldsymbol{\Lambda}_0$ the initial stiffness matrix of the material.

The response of the material takes the following form:

$$f\left(\varepsilon, \Lambda, K_0\right) = \tilde{\boldsymbol{\varepsilon}} - K(D) \quad (12)$$

where $\tilde{\boldsymbol{\varepsilon}}$ is the equivalent strain and $K(D)$ the hardening/softening parameter, initially equal to K_0.

Particularly, the response in traction or compression is described by the damage parameters D_t and D_c:

$$D = \alpha_t D_t + \alpha_c D_c, \quad D_t = F_t\left(\tilde{\varepsilon}\right) \ and \ D_c = F_c\left(\tilde{\varepsilon}\right) \quad (13)$$

$$F_i\left(\varepsilon_i\right) = 1 - \frac{(1 - A_i) K_0}{\tilde{\varepsilon}} - \frac{A_i}{exp\left[B_i\left(\tilde{\varepsilon} - K_0\right)\right]} \quad (i = t, c) \quad (14)$$

where α_t and α_c are weight coefficients and K_0, A_i and B_i are parameters that can be determined from experimental tests.

Considering a non-local approach, the model computes a variable $\bar{\varepsilon}$:

$$\bar{\varepsilon}(\underline{x}) = \frac{1}{V_r(\underline{x})} \int_V \tilde{\varepsilon}(\underline{s}) \alpha(\underline{s} - \underline{x}) dv \quad (15)$$

in which $\tilde{\varepsilon}$ is an equivalent strain, $\underline{x}$ the coordinate of the current Gauss point, $\underline{s}$ the coordinate of the generic Gauss point, α a weight function depending on the characteristic length l and V_r is the

characteristic volume. For further explanations, the reader is referred to (Mazars 1986; Majorana 1989; Pijaudier-Cabot et al. 1991).

4 CONCRETE AT THE MESO-SCALE LEVEL

Concrete has a highly heterogeneous microstructure and its composite behavior is exceedingly complex. For obtaining a deeper material understanding, theoretical studies based on micromechanics analysis of the interaction between various components of concrete have been developed for deducing its macroscopic constitutive behavior. However, microstructure and properties of the individual components of concrete and their effects on the macroscopic overall response have not been deepened enough; such aspects are now analyzed for simulating concrete behavior from the computational viewpoint (Wriggers & Moftah 2006).

As a composite material, concrete is a mixture of cement paste with aggregate inclusions of different sizes. The components of the heterogeneous material have different properties. The way they react on loading varies too. Variation in stiffness and strength of the components has influence on the global stiffness and fracture behaviour of the material. Different thermal expansion coefficients of the components results in internal stresses (*eigenstresses*) when the global temperature changes. Heat of hydration during hardening and temperature changes during fire are important features as well. Differences in porosity of the components influence the transport and even hygral dilation. Different chemical compositions have influence on internal reactions taking place inside the material, which can also be a function of ingress of species (Schlangen et al. 2007).

However, concrete is not just a two-phase composite; it has been found that the presence of grains in the paste causes a thin layer of matrix material surrounding each inclusion to be more porous than the bulk of the surrounding cement paste matrix. This layer is called the Interfacial Transition Zone (ITZ), which is known to play an important role in the properties of a concrete composite (Ollivier et al. 1995; Scivener et al. 2004). The ITZ has a layered structure, a lower density than the bulk matrix and it is more penetrable by fluids and gases (Scivener et al. 2004; Liao et al. 2004); therefore, the ITZ greatly influences the overall permeability of concrete (Garboczi et al. 1995). Additionally, due to its complex structure, the ITZ appears to be the weakest region of the composite material when exposed to external loads. Experiments have demonstrated that the elastic modulus of concrete is strictly related to the elastic modulus and volume fraction of ITZ regions (Zheng & Zhou 2006; Simeonov & Ahmad 1995). However, in the presence of low w/c ratios and/or fine mineral admixtures (e.g. silica fume), the ITZ may be absent or difficult to detect. Therefore, the ITZ is not necessarily an intrinsic feature of concrete but depends on factors such as the presence of admixtures, type of mixing, w/c ratio, etc (Garboczi et al. 2000).

As regards creep features, it is experimentally established that in concrete the only phase subjected to creep is the cement paste; aggregates have essentially an elastic response and cement paste consequently acts as an aging viscoelastic phase. So the cement paste is characterized by the aging viscoelastic compliance function $J(t,t')$; particularly, as previously shown, the compliance function here adopted is the one by model B3, being the physical basis of the assumptions used in its derivation which are valid also for mortar (Granger & Bazant 1995; Baweja et al. 1998).

5 THE MATHEMATICAL MODEL

Concrete is treated as a multiphase system where the voids of the skeleton are partly filled with liquid and partly with a gas phase. The liquid phase consists of bound water (or adsorbed water), which is present in the whole range of water contents of the medium, and capillary water (or free water), which appears when water content exceeds so-called solid saturation point S_{ssp}, i.e. the upper limit of the hygroscopic region of moisture content. The gas phase, i.e. moist air, is a mixture of dry air (non-condensable constituent) and water vapour (condensable gas), and it is assumed to behave as an ideal gas.

The approach here is to start from a phenomenological model, originally developed by Bažant and co-authors, in which mass diffusion and heat convection-conduction equations are written in terms of relative humidity, to an upgraded version in which its non-linear diffusive nature is maintained as well as the substitution of the linear momentum balance equations of the fluids with a constitutive equation for fluxes; moreover new calculations of thermodynamic properties for gaseous phases are implemented to include high ranges of both pressure and temperature. Additionally, Darcy's law is modified when describing gas flow through concrete. The proposed model couples non-linear material relations with experimental relations; to enhance its predictive capabilities, a predictor-corrector procedure is supplemented to enhance the convergence of the solution.

As regards the mechanical field and as previously stated, NEWCON3D couples shrinkage, creep, damage and plasticity effects under medium and high temperature levels.

For further details the reader is referred to (Salomoni et al. 2009).

5.1 The mechanical field

The constitutive relationship for the solid skeleton in incremental form can be written as

$$d\boldsymbol{\sigma}' = (1-D)\boldsymbol{D}_T(d\boldsymbol{\varepsilon} - d\boldsymbol{\varepsilon}_T - d\boldsymbol{\varepsilon}_c - d\boldsymbol{\varepsilon}_{lits} - d\boldsymbol{\varepsilon}_p - d\boldsymbol{\varepsilon}_{sh} - d\boldsymbol{\varepsilon}_0) \ (16)$$

where $\boldsymbol{\sigma}'$ is the effective stress, $\boldsymbol{D}_T$ is the tangent stiffness matrix, D is the chemo-thermo-mechanical damage, $d\boldsymbol{\varepsilon}_T$ is the strain rate caused by thermoelastic expansion, $d\boldsymbol{\varepsilon}_c$ is the strain rate accounting for creep, $d\boldsymbol{\varepsilon}_{lits}$ is the *load induced thermal strain* rate, $d\boldsymbol{\varepsilon}_p$ is the plastic strain rate, $d\boldsymbol{\varepsilon}_{sh}$ is due to shrinkage and $d\boldsymbol{\varepsilon}_0$ represents the autogeneous strain increments (e.g. due to chemical variations) and the irreversible part of the strain rates not contained in the previous terms.

Considering the effective stress definition, the macroscopic *linear momentum balance equation* for the whole medium may be expressed in the form

$$div(\boldsymbol{\sigma}' + p\boldsymbol{I}) + [(1-\varphi)\rho_s + \varphi S_w \rho_w + \varphi(1-S_w)\rho_g]\boldsymbol{g} = 0 \ (17)$$

with $\varphi = \varphi(T)$.

5.2 Finite element discretization

The application, within the numerical code NEWCON3D, of a standard finite element discretization in space of the *linear momentum, mass transfer and heat balance equations*, results in:

$$\begin{bmatrix} \mathbf{K} & \mathbf{HU} & \mathbf{TU} \\ \mathbf{L}^T & \mathbf{I} & \mathbf{TP} \\ \mathbf{0} & \mathbf{TH} & \mathbf{TS} \end{bmatrix} \begin{Bmatrix} \dot{\bar{\mathbf{u}}} \\ \dot{\bar{\mathbf{h}}} \\ \dot{\bar{\mathbf{T}}} \end{Bmatrix} + \begin{bmatrix} \mathbf{0} & \mathbf{0} & \mathbf{0} \\ \mathbf{0} & \mathbf{Q} & \mathbf{0} \\ \mathbf{0} & \mathbf{0} & \mathbf{TR} \end{bmatrix} \begin{Bmatrix} \bar{\mathbf{u}} \\ \bar{\mathbf{h}} \\ \bar{\mathbf{T}} \end{Bmatrix} = \begin{Bmatrix} \dot{\mathbf{f}} + \mathbf{c} \\ \mathbf{HG} \\ \mathbf{TG} \end{Bmatrix}$$
$$(18)$$

in which $\bar{\mathbf{u}}$, $\bar{\mathbf{h}}$ and $\bar{\mathbf{T}}$ are the nodal values of the basic variables.

6 NUMERICAL ANALYSES

6.1 Validation of B3 model

To validate the B3 Model within NEWCON3D, a series of tests by L'Hermite (L'Hermite et al. 1965) have been taken as reference; specifically, a $7 \times 7 \times 28$ cm^3 prism has been considered, with the same characteristics as reported in literature (see Table 1) and subjected first to basic creep only (specimen kept in water) and subsequently to

Table 1. Parameters used for validation of the homogeneous model (see Bazant & Kim (1992)).

Size of the sample [cm³]	3.5 × 3.5 × 1⌐
Elastic Modulus [MPa]	28522.1
f_{cm28} [MPa]	36.3
Cement Content [kg/m³]	350
Water Content [kg/m³]	171.5
Aggregate-cement ratio	4.82
Age at the start of dryng t_0 [d]	2
Age of loading t' [d]	7-28-90
Axial compressive stress [MPa]	9.07
Environmental Relative Humidity	50%
Environmental Temperature [°C]	20

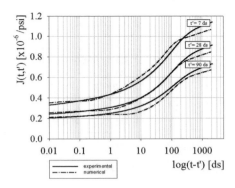

Figure 1. Comparison between compliance curves reported in Bazant & Baweja (2000) and obtained via NEWCON3D (dashed lines).

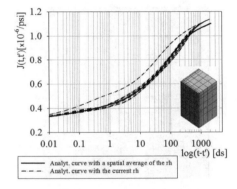

Figure 2. Comparison between analytical creep curves obtained with the spatial average relative humidity (solid line) and with the current relative umidity (dashed lines).

drying creep (specimen cured in water; at $t_0 = 2$ days exposed to drying).

The sample is additionally loaded by an axial compressive stress of 9.07 MPa; Figure 1 reports the curves of the compliance function (including drying creep), numerically obtained via the code NEWCON3D once Model B3 has been implemented. Three different loading times are considered (7, 28 and 90 days) and a comparison with the curves given by Bazant & Baewja (Bazant & Baewja 2000) is depicted, showing a good agreement between numerical and experimentally-based results.

Additionally, the spatial averages of pore relative humidity $H(t)$ and $H(t')$ within drying creep have been replaced with the current relative humidity obtained at each time step from the coupled **u**-H-T system of equations; hence, it has been possible to effectively estimate the humidity variation contribution on the creep term (Fig. 2).

6.2 *Numerical analysis of concrete at the meso-level with the presence of ITZ*

If concrete is studied as a composite material made of cement paste, aggregates and ITZ and the same test by L'Hermite (L'Hermite et al. 1965) as above is used for validating now the heterogeneous model, the only phase with an elastic behaviour is given by the aggregates, as reported in (Baweja et al. 1998; Granger & Bazant 1995).

The parameters used for the three different components are listed in Table 2; from the values it is possible to see that the ITZ is characterized by the the cement paste, instead the elastic modulus is half and the diffusivity double. As regards aggregates, if compared to cement paste, they are characterized by higher values for elastic modulus and thermal conductivity whereas diffusivity is nearly zero.

The sample is first subjected to basic creep only (specimen kept in water) and subsequently to drying creep (specimen cured in water; at $t_0 = 2$ days exposed to drying at 50% relative

humidity and 20 °C). The sample is additionally loaded by an axial compressive stress of 9.07 MPa at time $t' = 7$ days. The adopted discretization is reported in Figure 3.

In Figure 4 the change in relative humidity at different times for a section passing through an aggregate (red line in Figure 3) is depicted; from such curves a typical "barrier effect" exerted by the aggregate on the flux of humidity is evidenced, an effect which cannot be evidently caught when performing macro-scale concrete analyses. Consequently, some delay in drying can be noticed when comparing humidity fluxes of an homogeneous concrete sample (the results are not reported here for sake of brevity).

In Figure 5 the creep curves for two nodes belonging to ITZ (point 1) and to cement paste (point 2) are shown: a lower creep in proximity to the aggregate (point 1) is due to a "*stiffening effect*" caused by the presence of the aggregate, whereas just within

Table 2. Parameters for cement paste, aggregates and ITZ.

	Cement paste	ITZ	Aggregates
Elastic modulus [MPa]	20000	10000	67000
Poisson's ratio	0.2	0.2	0.2
Reference diffusivity along x,y,z [mm²/d]	20	40	0
Thermal conductivity along x,y,x [N/d K]	144288	144288	220320

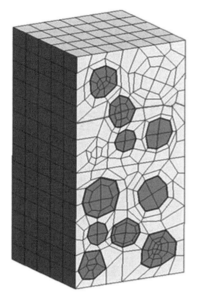

Figure 3. Mesh used to model concrete at the meso level, with ITZ.

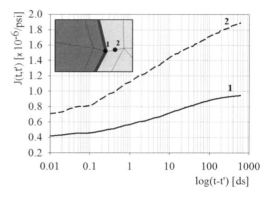

Figure 5. Creep functions for two nodes, one within ITZ and one within cement paste.

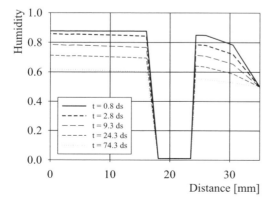

Figure 4. Relative humidity vs. distance at different times (section of Figure 3).

the cement paste such a reduction in deformation is not evidenced. Clearly, a more pronounced deformation, hence higher creep values, when farther from aggregates, is confirmed by the curves depicted in Figure 6: well within the cement paste the curves stabilize and show a mean trend as for point 4.

The same concrete sample ($3.5 \times 3.5 \times 7$ cm³, in symmetry conditions) has been further considered allowing a damage triggering effect; in this way a first estimate of the role of ITZ on the overall mechanical behavior of the concrete sample has been obtained, in view of defining an appropriate concrete mixture for e.g. responding to spalling under high temperature conditions. The sample is subjected to imposed displacements generating a compressive load and allowing for generating a typical damage response in a softening regime.

In Table 3 the adopted Mazars' parameters for cement paste and ITZ (an elastic behavior is assumed for aggregates) are listed, whereas the other hygro-thermo-mechanical parameters are those of Table 2.

Figure 7 describes the evolution of damage within the sample at different times for a typical section passing through an aggregate, ITZ, and cement paste. It can be clearly noticed that it is

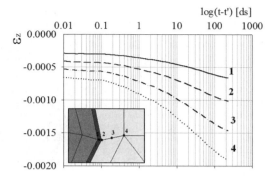

Figure 6. "Stiffening effect" maintained within cement paste.

Table 3. Parameters for the isotropic damage model by Mazars (cement paste and ITZ).

Parameter	Cement paste	ITZ
k_0	1×10^{-4}	1×10^{-5}
A_t	1.2	1.2
B_t	5000	5000
A_c	1	1
B_c	1000	1000
β	1	1

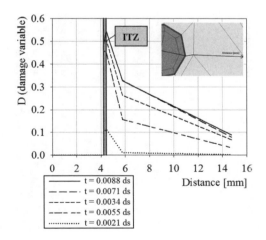

t = 0.0088 ds
t = 0.0071 ds
t = 0.0034 ds
t = 0.0055 ds
t = 0.0021 ds

Figure 7. Damage vs. distance along a section passing through the three phases (i.e., concrete components).

just ITZ that is strongly affected by damage due to its peculiar properties: the inefficient packing of cement grains within ITZ in proximity of aggregates makes it more porous and with a lower density than the bulk cement paste; so cracks essentially exploit this weak layer.

Hence the importance of considering ITZ when modeling concrete especially in nonlinear domains clearly comes out: without such a component e.g. damage contributions can't be evaluated, so possibly inducing an overestimation of concrete capability to respond to mechanical (and, particularly, thermo-mechanical) actions.

7 CONCLUSIONS

From the previous results, some key conclusions can be drawn.

First, the three-dimensionality of the geometric description of concrete at the meso-level can be now appreciated, since 2D or axis-symmetric sections often used in the past had not been able to describe with enough detail and realism the complex behaviour of concrete.

Then, creep of cement paste and ITZ, described by consolidated and complete models as that of B3 (carefully calibrated on the basis of well known experimental results like the ones given by L'Hermite) allows for catching the complex nature of creep, which is not only a matter of fluid flow and pressure dissipation but the result of chemical-physical reactions.

Again, the description of concrete as a composite material, in conjunction with fully coupled porous media analyses, allows for understanding the hygro-thermal and mechanical response of concrete, first of all in terms of hygral and thermal changes within a material where aggregate inclusions (encapsulated by ITZ concave volumes) appear with some statistical distribution (as originally described by Wittmann, even if without the ITZ effect (Wittman (1968)).

Hygral barriers due to the presence of aggregates can be seen only at this modelling level. On the other side, thermal conductivity properties dominate the thermal conduction within the sample.

Finally, from the mechanical viewpoint, the remarkable damage peak effect arising from the inclusion of ITZ, if compared with the less pronounced peak when ITZ is disregarded, is reported here. This result allows for a first explanation of specific phenomena linked to spalling, e.g. the generation of cracks driven by aggregates and the possible explosion of aggregates themselves.

Indeed, it is the weakness of ITZ together with the thermal properties of aggregates which seem mainly responsible for spalling scenarios.

REFERENCES

ACI Committee. 2008. Guide for Modeling and Calculating Shrinkage and Creep in Hardened Concrete. *ACI Report 209* 2R-08.

Baweja S., Dvorak, G.J. & Bazant, Z.P. 1998. Triaxial Composite Model for Basic Creep of Concrete. *J. Engng. Mech.* **124**(9): 959–965.

Bazant Z.P. & Kim J. 1992. Improved prediction model for time-dependent deformations of concrete: Part 1–7. Materials and Structures, **25**.

Bazant Z.P. & Baweja S. 2000. Creep and shrinkage prediction model for analysis and deign of concrete structures: Model B3. *Adam Neville Symposium: Creep and Shrinkage—Structural Design Effects*, ACI SP—194: 1–83.

Garboczi E.J., Bentz D.P. & Schwartz L.M. 1995. Modeling the Influence of the Interfacial Zone on the DC Electrical Conductivity of Mortar. *Adv. Cem. Bas. Mat.* **2**(5): 169–81.

Garboczi E.J., Bentz D.P. & Shane J.D. 2000. Effect of the interfacial zone on the conductivity of Portland cement mortars. *J. Am. Cer. Soc.* **83**(5): 1137–1144.

Granger L. & Bazant Z. 1995. Effect of Composition on Basic Creep of Concrete and Cement Paste. *J. Engng. Mech.* **121**(11): 1261–1270.

L'Hermite R., Mamillan M. & Lefèvre C. 1965. Nouveaux résultats de researches sur la déformation et la rupture du béton. *Ann. Inst. Batiment Trav. Publics* **18**: 323–360.

Liao K.Y., Chang P.K., Peng Y.N. & Yang, C.C. 2004. A study on characteristics of interfacial transition zone in concrete. *Cem. Con. Res.* **34**(6): 977–89.

Majorana C.E. 1989. Influenza del danno sul comportamento termoigrometrico e meccanico del continuo. *Giornale del Genio Civile*, **7–9**: 211–236 (in Italian).

Mazars, J.A. 1986. Description of Micro and Macroscale Damage of Concrete structures. *Eng. Frac. Mech.* **25**: 729–737.

Pijaudier-Cabot, G., Mazars, J. & J. Pulikowski 1991. Steel-concrete bond analysis with nonlocal continuous damage. *J. Struc. Engng. ASCE* **117**: 862–882.

Ollivier J.P., Maso J.C. & Bourdette B. 1995. Interfacial Transition Zone in Concrete. *Adv Cem. Bas. Mat.* **2**:30–38.

Salomoni V., Majorana C.E., Mazzucco G., Xotta G. & Khoury G.A. 2009. Multiscale Modelling of Concrete as a Fully Coupled Porous Medium, in: J.T. Sentowski (Ed.), *Concrete Materials: Properties, Performance and Applications*, Ch. 3, NOVA Publishers: 171–231.

Schlangen E., Koenders E.A.B. & Van Breugel K. 2007. Influence of internal dilation on the fracture behavior of multi-phase materials. *Engng. Frac. Mech.* **74**: 18–33.

Scrivener K.L., Crumbie A.K. & Laugesen P. 2004. The Interfacial Transition Zone (ITZ) Between Cement Paste and Aggregate in Concrete. *Int. Sci.* **12**: 411–421.

Simeonov P. & Ahmad S. 1995. Effect of transition zone on the elastic behavior of cement-based composites. *Cem. Con. Res.* **25**(1): 165–76.

Wittman F.H. 1968. Surface tension, shrinkage and strength of hardened cement paste. *Mat. Struct.* **1**(6): 547–552.

Wriggers P. & Moftah S.O. 2006. Mesoscale Models for concrete: Homogenisation and damage behavior. *Fin. El. An. Des.* **42**: 623–636.

Zheng J.J. & Zhou X.Z. 2006. A numerical method for predicting the elastic modulus of concrete made with two different aggregates. *J. Zhejiang Univ.—Sci. A* **7**(II): 293–296.

Service life modelling

Concrete Solutions – Grantham, Mechtcherine & Schneck (eds)
© 2012 Taylor & Francis Group, London, ISBN 978-0-415-61622-5

The application of simple modeling techniques to corrosion induced deterioration of reinforced concrete

J.P. Broomfield
Broomfield Consultants, East Molesey, Surrey, UK

ABSTRACT: In the present economic climate, many clients require more detailed exploration of the consequences of delaying repairs to structures. Also, when there are problems during construction, the implications with respect to the overall life of the structure need to be understood. This paper will explore some of the simpler mathematical models that the engineer can use without resorting to complex computing techniques. It presents some case histories where the application of simple models saved clients money while ensuring that a properly engineered solution was applied to the durability problems encountered.

1 INTRODUCTION

It has been estimated that approximately 50% of the resources of the construction industry in the developed world is being spent on repair and refurbishment rather than new construction (Matthews & Morlidge, 2006). Corrosion of steel in concrete is a primary cause of deterioration of the reinforced concrete built infrastructure so understanding the rate of deterioration due to corrosion of reinforcement in concrete is of increasing importance. Cost effective investigation and repair of reinforced concrete structures is therefore of increasing significance in sustaining economic growth. The NACE standard practice on inspection methods (NACE, 2008); the Concrete Society Reports 54 and 60 (Concrete Society, 2000 and 2004) and Broomfield (2007) give comprehensive overviews of inspection methods for determining the cause and extent of corrosion damage to reinforced concrete structures. However, there is little guidance in the literature or in national standards on how to apply these techniques to provide answers to owners' concerns in the current economic climate which can often be summarised as:

- How long can I leave it and what is the cost of deferring intervention?
- What is the lowest cost intervention option?
- What is the balance between lowest first cost against lowest life cycle cost?

One way of answering these questions is to collect quantitative survey data and use it to model how the structure will continue to deteriorate if there is no intervention. The owner can then understand the implications of deferring intervention, phasing repairs or using less than optimum corrosion control measures. In order to do this we

need practical models to back up engineering and financial decisions about maintaining individual structures and portfolios of structures.

2 MODELLING DETERIORATION RATES DUE TO REINFORCEMENT CORROSION

There are well established standards and models for durable design of new reinforced concrete structures (BSI 8500-1 2006, Bamforth 2004, CONTECVET 2001). These allow design engineers to evaluate the relative cost effectiveness of different corrosion mitigation options along with the optimum concrete mix design and cover for different exposure conditions. As they have been designed to be very conservative and to design structures of typically 50 or 100 year life, none of them have been fully field tested. Typically they are based on fairly long term data (more than a decade) of large samples at exposure sites. National and international construction codes are more prescriptive. For example the new Eurocode for design BSI 8500-1 (2006) has tables of reinforcement cover, cement types and water/binder ratios to achieve design lives of 25, 50 or 100 years in environments ranging from indoors and mild inland to extreme marine exposure conditions. NACE SP 0187 (2008) also gives an overview of these types of approaches.

A corrosion engineer dealing with reinforced concrete is more often dealing with existing structures rather than new build. If we are assessing a reinforced concrete structure that is already deteriorating we have the advantage that we are extrapolating our deterioration curve over a reasonable period of time and using data that actually relates to our structure and its environment. The simplest model of corrosion of steel in concrete was proposed by Tuutti (1982).

According to this simple model, there is an initiation period T_0 while the chlorides or carbon dioxide move through the concrete cover. The condition of the structure does not change assuming there are no other processes acting on it. Once the concentration of chlorides is sufficient to initiate corrosion or the carbonation front reaches the steel, the structure enters the corrosion propagation phase where the steel actively corrodes. There is no unit of damage on the Y axis in this model and it assumes a single cover depth.

The T_0 initiation phase is relatively straight forward to model. The carbon dioxide (CO_2) molecules and the chloride ions (Cl^-), dissolved in water, move into concrete by initial wicking or capillary action and then diffusion occurs, or at least a combination of transport mechanisms that can be approximated by (effective) diffusion through most of the cover thickness in reasonable quality concrete. Fick's laws of non steady state diffusion can be applied and effective diffusion coefficients can be derived from sampling actual structures in real field conditions or controlled representative concrete samples in either controlled exposure conditions or well monitored field exposure.

2.1 Modelling the corrosion initiation time T_0

Even after corrosion damage is observed, it can be important to determine the corrosion initiation time T_0 in order to work out how long the reinforcement has been corroding. The time to initiation is a function of the cover depth to the reinforcement, the concrete quality in terms of the diffusion coefficient of the cover concrete and the environment (e.g., the chloride exposure). These parameters will vary from point to point within the structure so the rate of degradation will vary around the structure as a function of the exposure conditions, cover depth and concrete quality. In some cases these may vary systematically for instance:

- A displaced reinforcing cage with low cover one side and high cover the other side.
- Saline water run down on a beam or column, e.g., from a leaking joint.
- A poorly cured concrete element during the construction process.

In other cases they will be more random due to the normal variability of the materials and construction process.

2.1.1 Carbonation induced corrosion

For carbonation induced corrosion, the carbonation depth is well defined, well understood and straight forward to measure. The carbonation front is a few millimeters wide. It is characterized by a drop in pH from about 13 to 8 and the passive layer on the steel decays at around pH 11. Phenolphthalein solution changes from clear to pink at pH 9.5 so within the practical accuracy of measurement in real concrete the depth of carbonation can be measured using suitable techniques such as the European test standard BSEN 14630 (2006).

The carbonation front moves at a rate defined in its simplest form by the equation:

$$x = kt^n \tag{1}$$

where x = depth; t = time; k is a constant and $n = \frac{1}{2}$ for most practical applications.

This equation has been developed by experiment and theory (Broomfield 2007). Predicted values of k in equation (1) and modification of the equation have been derived as a function of different concrete mixes to predict time to carbonation for new structures based on mix design and exposure (Bamforth 2004, CONTECVET 2001).

2.1.2 Chloride induced corrosion

Determining or predicting the initiation time for chloride induced corrosion is more complex than for carbonation for two reasons. The first is that there is no simply defined "chloride front" as there is a carbonation front. The chloride concentration increases with depth and increases with time according to the Fick's second law of diffusion:

$$C_{x,t} = C_i + (C_s - C_i)\, erf[(x/4tD_o)^{\frac{1}{2}}] \tag{2}$$

where Cl_s = Maximum (surface or near surface) chloride concentration; $C_{x,t}$ = Chloride concentration at depth x and time t; C_i = Minimum (background) chloride concentration; D_o = Chloride diffusion coefficient; $erf[y]$ = the error function of y.

To predict the time to development of a specific chloride concentration at a specific reinforcement depth, the chloride diffusion coefficient can be calculated from field measurements of the chloride profile. It is normal to take a minimum of 4 chloride samples with depth using a suitable standard method such as the European Standard for chloride measurement (BS EN 14629, 2007). The effective diffusion coefficient D_{eff} can then be determined. D_{eff} is the "measured" or "effective" diffusion coefficient value that allows for changes in transport rates due to other mechanisms than diffusion, and for changes in rates due to seasonal changes in temperature and moisture.

The error function Equation (2) can be approximated to a parabolic function within certain limits as shown by Poulsen (1990). This was used by

Broomfield (2005) to develop spreadsheets for calculating time to corrosion initiation for chlorides from a chloride profile.

2.2 Modelling the corrosion propagation time T_1

While it is essential to be able to predict the time from construction to corrosion initiation, it is also important to predict the time to actual damage on a structure, or its rate of progress. Once corrosion initiates, it proceeds by series of reactions that lead to the hydrated ferric oxide commonly known as rust. This material is known to have a volume approximately 6 to 7 times that of the consumed iron (or steel). While some of the expansive product will be accommodated in the pores and voids around the steel, eventually the available space will be filled and the oxide formation will lead to tensile stresses in the concrete cover leading to cracks. If cracks form between adjacent bars, this will lead to delamination and spalling of the concrete cover.

Once active corrosion has started it will lead to damage in terms of cracking, delamination and spalling of the concrete cover unless water saturated conditions occur in which case a non expansive corrosion product can occur (Broomfield 2007). Expansive corrosion product formation will lead to delamination and spalling of the concrete cover. In order to model this we need to know:

- when corrosion started;
- the average or effective corrosion rate;
- the amount of corrosion that will lead to cracking, delamination and spalling.

The damage rate will be a function of the following parameters:

- the corrosion rate of the steel;
- the cover depth;
- the bar diameter;
- the bar spacing;
- the concrete (tensile splitting) strength.

The instantaneous corrosion rate can be measured by several commercially available portable instruments (Broomfield 2007, Concrete Society 2004). These devices will give information on the rate of corrosion at the point and the time of measurement. They work by taking a reference electrode potential measurement (half cell) and then applying a current to shift the potential. The higher the corrosion rate, the higher the current required to achieve a given shift in potential.

Corrosion rate measuring devices are fairly slow to set up and to take measurements. To accurately measure the corrosion rate, they require determination of the area of steel below the sensor. This means that it typically takes 5 to 10 minutes per reading to locate the bars, determine their

diameters and take a reading. At the end of this process you have a set of readings taken on a single day when you really need to know how the corrosion rate has changed since corrosion initiated and how it will continue to fluctuate until repairs are carried out, i.e., the effective, average or typical corrosion rate.

Ideally one would embed permanent monitoring probes and take readings at regular intervals using suitable probes and monitoring equipment (Broomfield 2007). The next best option is to take readings at regular intervals (say 4 times a year for 3 or more years) with one of the portable instruments. A third option is to infer an average or typical corrosion rate from available readings and the final option, when corrosion rate measurements are not available, is to get an approximate corrosion rate from measurements of the chloride level at the reinforcement depth. Bamforth (2004) evaluated results from a series of exposure blocks with marine exposure and came up with the relationship:

$$CR = 0.6178 \ exp(1.45[Cl]) \tag{3}$$

where CR is the corrosion rate in μm/year; $[Cl]$ = chloride content by mass of cement at the reinforcement depth.

When exposure conditions are taken into account, this can be modified to:

- Wet rarely dry–
  $$CR = 0.84 \ exp(1.45[Cl]) \tag{4}$$
- Airborne sea salt/deicing salt, cyclic wet/dry
  $$CR = 0.54 \ exp(1.56[Cl]) \tag{5}$$
- Tidal type exposure
  $$CR = 0.46 \ exp(1.84[Cl]) \tag{6}$$

Based on extensive testing an empirical equation for corrosion induced cracking width (CONTECVET 2001), w is:

$$w = 0.05 + \beta[P_x - P_{xo}] \ for \ w < 1.0 \ mm \tag{7}$$

where $\beta = 10$ for top cast bars and 12.5 for bottom cast bars (on soffits); P_x is the radius loss for crack width w; P_{xo} is the radius loss needed for cracking to reach the surface and is derived as:

$$P_{xo} = (83.8 + 7.4c/\Phi - 22.6 f_{ct,sp})10 - 3 \ mm \tag{8}$$

where c is the cover depth and Φ is the rebar diameter and $f_{ct,sp}$ is the splitting tensile strength in MPa, which can be obtained through testing or from expressions linking compressive strength, tensile strength and splitting strength in the literature e.g., CONTECVET (2001).

We therefore have a procedure for determining the time from construction to corrosion initiation to cracking up to 1 mm wide at the surface from the following field survey data:

1. Half cell potential mapping (ASTM, 2009) to indicate the extent of corrosion initiation.
2. Chloride profiles (BS EN 14029, 2007), to determine concentration at cover depth and time to initiation.
3. Carbonation depths (BS EN 14030, 2006) to determine the rate of depassivation for carbonated structures.
4. Cover depths at chloride profile and/or carbonation depth measurement locations.
5. Bar diameters and chloride profile, carbonation depth and corrosion rate measurement locations.
6. Measurement of compressive strength, or determination/estimation from records.
7. Measurement of corrosion rates (Concrete Society 2004) or determination/estimation from exposure and chloride levels at the reinforcement depth using Equations (4), (5) and (6).

The procedure to determine the deterioration curve through to cracking is therefore:

A. Calculate the time to corrosion using the chloride profiles, carbonation depths and equations (1) or (2) or other suitable models.
B. Calculate the time from initiation to first cracking using the corrosion rates, cover depths bar diameters and compressive strengths using equations (4) to (7).
C. Calculate the time to up to 1 mm crack width (maximum) using equation (8).

2.3 Case study—A concrete floor slab in tidal marine ground conditions

The floor slab had been designed for a 50 year life with marine exposure using blended cement concrete, and controlled water cement ratio and 50 mm cover to the reinforcement. Unfortunately the concrete placed did not meet the specification and so the Author was asked whether it would meet the 50 year life or whether it needed to be removed and replaced at considerable expense and disruption to the construction program.

In order to determine the time to corrosion damage we required the contractor to take cores from the concrete floor slab as placed. These were subjected to accelerated (non electrical) chloride diffusion testing according to RILEM Report 12 (1995) at elevated temperature. The chloride profiles were used to calculate diffusion coefficients. These were compared with diffusion coefficients predicted by the mix design according to Concrete Society Technical Report 61 (Bamforth, 2004). The worst case (highest diffusion coefficient) mix design was

then used in the model to predict time to corrosion initiation and time to cracking. In all cases these exceeded 50 years. This saved the project considerable time and money.

3.4 Case study—Concrete structures suffering from carbonation induced corrosion

In this example an examination was carried out on a number of reinforced concrete buildings on a university campus (Broomfield 2005). The carbonation depths and cover depths were measured systematically and gave the distributions shown in Figure 1 for one particular building. From these results calculations of time to corrosion were made. The distribution with time is shown in Figure 2.

Figure 2 shows that the cracking, delamination and spalling observed at the time of survey of the façade had occurred only to a small percentage of bars which were suffering from low cover. These low cover bars were substantially corroding and therefore all damage was evident at the time of survey. The majority of bars had good cover and so calculations showed that they would not start to corrode for several decades. Therefore good quality repairs and the application of a suitable

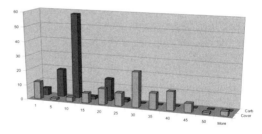

Figure 1. Cover depths (light bars) and carbonation depths (dark bars) for a reinforced concrete building façade. X axis is depth in mm, Y axis is % of readings.

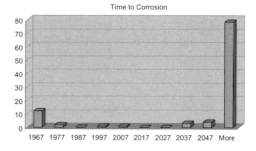

Figure 2. Time to corrosion for a reinforced concrete building façade showing percentage of bars (Y axis) starting to corrode in a given year (X axis).

anticarbonation coating would extend the life of the building at a modest cost.

3 MODELLING THE SPALLING RATE

Modelling the time to deterioration as the time to a 1 mm crack width at the surface may be suitable for design calculations of structures or parts of structures from the earliest stages of deterioration. CONTECVET (2001) also has a method which models deterioration in different elements and bar spacing which will not be discussed here.

Once corrosion damage has initiated, a method of modelling deterioration growth is needed. There are very few models in this area. One of the few was developed in the original Strategic Highway Research Program (SHRP 1994) where an "S" shaped deterioration curve was developed where the condition index at time t is given by:

$$S_t = 100/(1 + A. exp(-Bt)] \qquad (9)$$

where t = time; and A and B are coefficients derived from the condition at time of survey and from the initiation time. This is an analytical approach to Tuutti's model (Tuutti, 1982) where the vertical axis St is a condition index quantified as:

$$S = [CL + 2.5(Delam) + 7.5(Spall)]/8.5 \qquad (10)$$

where CL = percentage of area with bars above the corrosion threshold; $Delam$ = percentage of surface area delaminated; $Spall$ = percentage of surface area that has spalled.

The condition at initiation, $S_{To} = 1.2 = 10\%$ of bars above the threshold for corrosion with no spalling or delamination. The initiation time can be derived as described previously from Equations (2) or (3).

In the original report (SHRP 1994), the determination of CL required a high level of chloride measurement to determine the percentage area of the rebar mat that has exceeded T_0. The SHRP report recommends 10 chloride samples at rebar depth per member or per 450 m^2. It was typically aimed at bridge decks. However, a simpler alternative would be to carry out a half cell survey according to ASTM (2009) and either measure the percentage of the area with potentials more negative than −350 mV with respect to a copper/copper sulfate half cell or determine the threshold by correlation with a limited number of chloride measurements and/or with exposure of bars to correlate presence of rust with the half cell potential.

It is therefore feasible to write a simple spreadsheet program, conduct a fairly routine condition survey but with specified types and quantities of measurements and from that to predict the rate of deterioration of a corroding reinforced concrete structure. The parameters required are:

1. Year of Construction.
2. Year of corrosion initiation (calculated from the chloride profiles and/or carbonation depths).
3. Year of survey.
4. Percentage of bars (surface area) above the corrosion threshold (from ASTM C876, 2009).
5. Percentage of surface delamination measured.
6. Percentage of area of spalled concrete measured.

From this the deterioration, an "S" curve (Equations 9 and 10) is developed. The condition index can be determined for any given date. The condition index can also be "deconvoluted" or "deconstructed" into the percentage spalled and percentage delaminated at any given time.

According to the SHRP methodology the condition index can be deconvoluted as follows:

For $CL < 10\%$; $CL = S \times 5$; $DELAM = 0$; $SPALL = 0$

For $10\% < CL < 100\%$; $CL = S \times 5$; $DELAM = S \times 0.8$; and $SPALL = S \times 0.25$

For $CL = 100\%$; $CL = 100$; $DELAM = ((S \times 8.5)-100)/4.4$; $SPALL = S \times 0.25$.

3.1 Case study—concrete structures subject to marine exposure

A spreadsheet using equations (9) and (10) was used on the following set of survey data taken from a reinforced concrete structure in the tidal zone on the south coast of England:

- It was built in 1970
- It was surveyed in 2009
- At that time all chloride profiles showed chloride levels >0.4% by mass of cement at the reinforcement depth therefore $CL = 100\%$
- There was 5% spalling
- There was a further 5% delamination
- Date of corrosion initiation 1990 (10% at rebar depth) was calculated from chloride profiles using the website described in Broomfield (2005).

The spreadsheet was used to predict the deterioration index with time and allowed the index to be deconstructed into percentage of area actively corroding, delaminated and spalled. From these values the amount and cost of repair can be predicted at any point in the life of the structure, based on the amount of patching required. The curve is shown in Figure 3.

By carrying out life cycle cost analyses on the repair cost at different points on the deterioration curve, the optimum time for repair was determined and the costs of deferring repair were estimated.

Comparative UK costs for a range of repair and protection techniques can be found and used in a life cycle costing model (Broomfield 2005). The client is about to undertake trials of impressed current and galvanic anode system to determine the most cost effective treatment option.

3.2 Case study—A marine exposed culvert

In another example a far older reinforced concrete culvert type structure on a beach on the south coast of England built in the mid 1930s was given a limited surveyed in 2009 and found to have a very high level of chloride at the reinforcement, 8.4%

delamination and 2.6% spalls. This gave a condition index S of 17 at the time of survey. The deterioration index curve and its deconvolution indicated that the amount of spalling was increasing at a rate of about 7% per annum from 2000 to 2020. In this case the client is planning to undertake a more comprehensive survey to define the conditions and relevant structural issues before carrying out a full analysis to determine the most cost effective corrosion control method.

For this case, a number of parameters have been plotted in Figure 4. A simple linear extrapolation of the number of spalls and delaminations is plotted as suggested by Tuutti (1982) along with the condition index and the predicted percentages of depassivated steel (CL), and the percentages of delamination ($DELAM$) and spalling ($SPALL$) from the condition index.

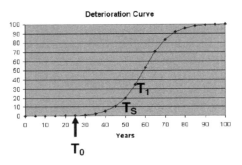

Figure 3. The deterioration curve (S_t in Equation 9) vs. time for a marine structure constructed in 1960 where corrosion initiated after 30 years and the condition index is 18 at the survey after 49 years. A condition index of 38 is projected in 2016.

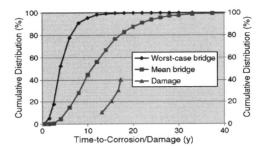

Figure 5. From Hartt (2010), Plot of Ti and corrosion-induced damage progression for untreated 1970s vintage bridge decks in New York state reinforced with BB, where "damage" is defined as the surface area percentage of spalls plus delaminations plus patches.

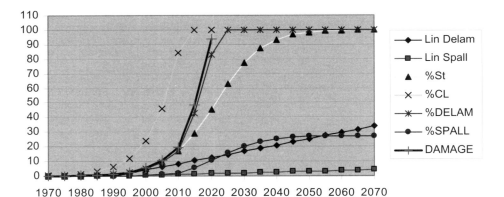

Figure 4. The deterioration curves from linear extrapolation and from the condition index curve. Lin Delam and Lin Spall are linear extrapolation of the percentage of delamination and spalling from time of corrosion initiation through survey measurement; %St, %CL, %DELAM and %SPALL are from equation 10.

It is notable that the condition index predicts a far more rapid rate of deterioration than linear extrapolation from T_0 straight through the survey measurements of delamination and spalling.

This rapid rise is similar to that found by Hartt (2010) when he considered the progression of the time to corrosion initiation assuming a Gaussian distribution of cover depths. His time to corrosion results, along with a sum of measured spalls delaminations and repairs from the structures is shown in Figure 5. This supports the modelling hypothesis that the deterioration rate accelerates as the corrosion threshold moves through the distributions of rebar cover depths.

4 CONCLUSIONS

1. The time to corrosion initiation can be predicted using chloride profiles, carbonation depths, and cover depth using well known diffusion calculation methods.
2. The time to early damage on a reinforced concrete structure can be estimated by determining the time to 1 mm cracking using corrosion rate measurements (or estimates) concrete strength, cover depth and bar diameter measurements.
3. Once corrosion damage is observed, its progression can be estimated from the degree of active corrosion of the steel, the percentage of spalling and the percentage of delamination that has already occurred.
4. These techniques can help in predicting deterioration rates, calculating life cycle costs of repairs and estimating the cost of deferring repairs.
5. Case studies have been presented where estimation of time to corrosion and rate of damage have led to cost effective repair solutions and the avoidance of major replacement works.
6. The time to cracking and the deterioration index calculations need further field validation to check their validity and their usefulness is providing structure owners with deterioration rates.
7. The distribution of reinforcement cover depths appears to have a strong influence on the rate of progression of damage.

REFERENCES

ASTM (2009). C876-09. *Standard test method for Corrosion Potential of Uncoated Reinforcing Steel in Concrete*, West Conshohocken, American Society for Testing and Materials.

Bamforth, P. (2004). "Enhancing reinforced concrete durability," Concrete Society Technical Report 61 Camberley, Concrete Society.

Broomfield, J.P. 2005. *"A Web Based Tool for Selecting Repair Options and Life Cycle Costing of Corrosion Damaged Reinforced Concrete Structures"* CORROSION/2005 Paper 05254 Houston, NACE International.

Broomfield, J.P. (2007). *Corrosion of steel in concrete, understanding, investigation and repair* 2nd Edition, London, Taylor and Francis.

BS EN 14629 (2007). *Products and systems for the protection and repair of concrete structures—Test methods—Determination of chloride content in hardened concrete* London, British Standards Institute.

BS EN 14630 (2006). *Products and systems for the protection and repair of concrete structures—Test methods—Determination of carbonation depth in hardened concrete by the phenolphthalein method*. London, British Standards Inst.

BSI 8500-1 (2006). *Concrete—Complementary British Standard to BS EN 206-1—Part 1: Method of specifying and guidance for the specifier* London, British Standards Institute.

Concrete Society (2000). Technical Report 54 *Diagnosis of deterioration in concrete structures*. Camberley, Concrete Society.

Concrete Society (2004). Technical Report 60 *Electrochemical tests for reinforcement corrosion*. Camberley, Concrete Society.

CONTECVET (2001). *A Validated Users Manual for assessing the residual service life of concrete structures: Manual for assessing corrosion-affected concrete structures*, Prepared by: Geocisa and Instituto Eduardo Torroja, British Cement Association, and CIB, Available from the Concrete Society Bookstore, Camberley, Concrete Society.

Hartt, W.H. (2010). Protocol for projecting time to corrosion of reinforcing steel in concrete exposed to chlorides *Corrosion* 66, (8), 086002-1 to 086002-12.

Matthews, S.L. Morlidge, J.R. (2006). "What's Wrong Concrete Repair—Solution or Problem?" Concrete Solutions: Proceedings of the 2nd International Conference, paper No. 1 St. Malo, France, (Garston, UK, BRE Press, 3–10.

NACE SP 0187 (2008). *Design Considerations for Corrosion Control or Reinforcing Steel in Concrete* Houston TX, NACE International.

NACE SP 0308 (2008). *Inspection Methods for Corrosion Evaluation of Conventionally Reinforced Concrete Structures*, Houston TX: NACE International.

Poulsen, E. *The chloride diffusion characteristics of concrete—approximative determination by linear regression analysis*. (Oslo, Norway, Nordic Concrete Research. Publication No. 1. 1990).

RILEM Report 12 1995. *Performance Criteria for Concrete Durability*, London, E & FN Spon 238–239.

SHRP 1994. Purvis, R.L. Babaei, K. Clear, K.C. & Markow, M.J. "Life-Cycle Cost Analysis for protection and rehabilitation of concrete bridges relative to reinforcement corrosion," Washington DC, Strategic Highway Research Program, National Academy of Sciences.

Tuutti, K. 1982. *Corrosion of steel in concrete* Stockholm, CBI Forskning Research.

Concrete Solutions – Grantham, Mechtcherine & Schneck (eds)
© 2012 Taylor & Francis Group, London, ISBN 978-0-415-61622-5

A critical examination of the chloride migration test to assess the resistance of concrete against chloride ingress

J.J.W. Gulikers

Ministry of Infrastructure and The Environment, Rijkswaterstaat Centre for Infrastructure, Utrecht, The Netherlands

ABSTRACT: In order to quantify the concrete quality with respect to chloride ingress a non-steady-state migration test has become very popular among commercial laboratories. In view of the increased application of this migration coefficient into service life prediction, a significant number of essential questions on the validity of the test can be raised based on a critical assessment of the underlying theoretical backgrounds describing transport due to migration. It has been established that the cell current and the duration of the test will result in major changes in the chemical composition of the catholyte in particular. These modifications of the exposure environment will undoubtedly have an impact on the chloride penetration rate and thus on the magnitude of the migration coefficient. Moreover, the chloride profiles determined by several researchers support the view that the theory underlying the migration test is to some extent questionable. Scientific research is required in the short term to clarify the theory and to assess the applicability of the chloride migration test, in particular for the intended use as input for service life design. Some of the problems associated with the migration test may be mitigated by introducing a stricter test procedure.

1 INTRODUCTION

Penetration of chloride ions from the exposure environment into the concrete cover is considered of major concern for the long-term durability of concrete structures with respect to reinforcement corrosion. Consequently, both the thickness and the quality of the concrete cover are considered of prime importance to prevent the occurrence of premature corrosion. The cover depth is specified in the design and can easily be measured non-destructively on site. In contrast the quality of the concrete cover is often given in qualitative terms by a combination of the maximum water to cement ratio, minimum cement content and curing conditions. However, mix design, i.e. type of cement, aggregate grading, and compaction are not addressed although these factors will undoubtedly have a serious impact on the achieved concrete quality. In order to include most of these effects on the resistance against chloride ingress a wide variety of test methods has been developed, the most common being the so-called bulk diffusion test e.g. according to NT Build 443 (1995). As this diffusion test is time-consuming, laborious and costly a number of alternative methods have been developed, the non-steady-state chloride migration test as performed to NT Build 492 (1999) being the most popular, as it is easy to perform and generally provides a result within 24 hours.

At present in several service life models the migration coefficient is introduced as one of the model parameters, e.g. in DuraCrete (2000) and the fib Model Code (2006). Although the migration test has gained enormous popularity in recent years, especially among commercial laboratories, there is serious concern on the validity of the theory supporting the migration test as well as on the influence of the test conditions on the overall result. This paper addresses some of these concerns in more detail.

2 DESCRIPTION OF THE CHLORIDE MIGRATION TEST

Tang (1995) introduced an accelerated non-steady state chloride migration test for concrete in which the penetration depth was used to determine the migration coefficient, D_{nssm}, being a quantified measure for the resistance against chloride ingress. Through the application of an electrical potential difference over a concrete sample chloride ions are forced to enter the porous material. After a certain test duration, the sample is axially split and a silver nitrate solution is sprayed on the split concrete surface. This results in the precipitation of white silver chloride revealing the achieved chloride penetration depth. The concrete quality is reflected in the chloride migration coefficient which is calculated from the penetration depth, taking into account the applied voltage and the test duration, according to:

$$D_{nssm} = \frac{RT}{zF} \cdot \frac{L}{U_{eff}} \cdot \frac{x_d - \alpha\sqrt{x_d}}{t} \tag{1}$$

where R = universal gas constant, [J/(K·mol)]; T = absolute temperature, [K]; z = valence (ionic charge) of a chloride ion, [–]; F = Faraday constant, [C/mol]; U_{eff} = net potential difference applied externally over the sample, [V]; L = thickness of the concrete sample, [m]; α = laboratory constant, [m$^{0.5}$], see Eq. (7); x_d = measured chloride penetration depth as made visible through silver nitrate, [m].

For most concrete qualities, the chloride migration test will provide results within 24 to 48 hours. Moreover, the chloride migration test requires simple equipment, is easy to perform, and the overall result, i.e. the chloride migration coefficient, D_{nssm}, is determined in a straightforward way. The test set-up is shown in Figure 1.

Usually, cast cylinders or drilled cores as to obtain test samples ∅100 mmm with a thickness of 50 mm. The overall voltage as indicated on the power source may range from 10 V for poor quality concrete to 60V for high quality concrete. Generally, the test duration will be such that a chloride penetration depth ranging from 15 to 30 mm will ensue.

It should be noted that the test samples are take at a depth of more than 20 mm from the cast concrete surface. Consequently, the samples and the test results obtained are not representative of the cover zone.

In NT Build 492 (1999) and Tang (1995) detailed information on the test procedure is provided, including a table indicating the most suitable combination of voltage and test duration to be applied depending on the concrete quality. The proposed combination is based on the cell current resulting from the application of a test voltage of 30 V, see Figure 2. Gulikers (2010) has performed a study on the theoretical backgrounds of the test and the

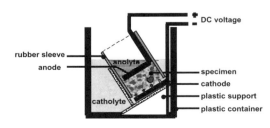

Figure 1. Experimental arrangement for the accelerated chloride migration test according to NT Build 492.

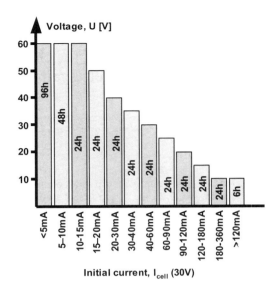

Figure 2. Test voltage and duration for concrete specimens according to NT Build 492, 1999.

potential application of the migration coefficient in practice and in this paper selected issues will be discussed.

3 THEORETICAL BACKGROUNDS

For the determination of the chloride migration coefficient D_{nssm} Eq. (1) plays an important role. This expression is derived from a differential equation which is considered to describe 1-dimensional transport of chloride ions in concrete due to the combined action of an electrical field (migration) and a concentration gradient (diffusion), as given in Tang (1995):

$$\frac{\delta c}{\delta t} = D \cdot \left(\frac{\delta^2 c}{\delta x^2} - \frac{zF}{RT} \cdot E \cdot \frac{\delta c}{\delta x} \right) \tag{2}$$

where c = chloride concentration, [mol/l], t = testing time, [s]; D = 'diffusion' coefficient, [m^2/s]; x = distance to the exposed concrete surface, [m]; z = 1; F = 96484 C/mol; R = 8,314 J/(K · mol); T = absolute temperature during the migration test, [K]; E = electrical field, [V/m].

It should be noted that for the further mathematical treatment, concrete is considered a sufficiently homogeneous porous material in which the solution contained in the pore network serves as the transport medium. The concentration refers to the concentration of free mobile chloride ions dissolved in the pore solution, i.e. physically and chemically bound chlorides are not included.

For fixed boundary conditions maintained during the complete exposure period, i.e. at the exposed concrete surface $c(x = 0;t) = c_o$ and assuming that initially the concrete material is not contaminated by chlorides, the mathematical solution is expressed by:

$$c = \frac{c_o}{2} \cdot \left[\exp(ax) \cdot erfc\left(\frac{x + aDt}{2\sqrt{Dt}}\right) + erfc\left(\frac{x - aDt}{2\sqrt{Dt}}\right) \right]$$
(3)

where $a = \dfrac{zFE}{RT}$ and $erfc(z) = (1-erf(z))$, i.e. the complementary error function.

In the accelerated non-steady-state migration test, the magnitude of the voltage applied across a concrete specimen is such that the contribution of diffusion to the transport process becomes negligible and thus can be discarded in the mathematical model. For this condition the mathematical expression can be simplified to:

$$c = \frac{c_o}{2} \cdot erfc\left(\frac{x - aDt}{2\sqrt{Dt}}\right)$$
(4)

In order to emphasize the origin of the 'diffusion' coefficient obtained from such an accelerated migration test, this calculated result is often referred to as D_{nssm} (non-steady state migration), D_{CTH} (Chalmers Tekniska Högskola) or D_{RCM}.
Figure 3 illustrates the concentration profiles obtained according to Eq. (4) for $U_{eff} = 30$ V, $L = 50$ mm and $D_{nssm} = 10 \cdot 10^{-12}$ m²/s for a test duration of 6, 12, 18 and 24 h. These theoretical chloride profiles are symmetric with respect to $x(c = c_o/2)$ and are quite distinct from the traditional diffusion profiles which are characterised by a gradual decrease of the chloride concentration with depth

An alternative way to demonstrate the (theoretical) effect of an electrical field on chloride ingress is illustrated in Figure 4 showing the development of the chloride concentration over time at a depth of 5, 10, 15, 20 mm, and 25 mm.
The chloride penetration profiles demonstrate an inflection point at a depth $x = x_f$ with:

$$x_f = a \cdot Dt$$
(5)

As it is difficult to determine the position of the inflection point an alternative method has been suggested by Tang (1995) to calculate the 'diffusion' coefficient by measuring the penetration depth x_d based on a simple colorimetric method. This method has been further elaborated resulting in a mathematical relationship between x_f and x_d given by:

$$x_f = x_d - \alpha\sqrt{x_d}$$
(6)

where:

$$\alpha = 2\sqrt{\frac{RT}{zF} \cdot \frac{L}{U_{eff}}} \cdot inverf\left(1 - \frac{c_d}{c_o}\right)$$
(7)

where c_d = concentration of free chloride at which the colour changes when using a colorimetric method; according to NT Build 492 (1999) $c_d = 0.07$ N.
The theory underlying the migration test predicts the occurrence of a chloride profile in which the free chloride ion concentration remains at a constant level c_o until a certain depth and then falls within a small distance to a negligible concentration. The value of c_o is assumed to be equal to that of the chloride concentration of the exposure solution. The occurrence of such a distinct chloride

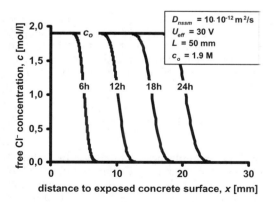

Figure 3. Theoretical (free) chloride profiles resulting from an accelerated migration experiment.

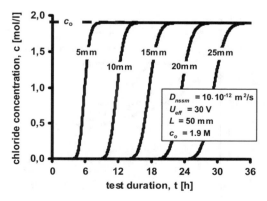

Figure 4. Development of the (free) chloride concentration at 5 fixed depths according to Eq. (4).

537

penetration front is essential for the interpretation of the test results as it allows a simplified method for the determination of the chloride penetration depth and the calculation of the migration coefficient.

If the theory is correct, an error in the value of c_d, the chloride concentration at which coloration occurs, will have only limited effect on the calculated value of the migration coefficient, D_{nssm}, provided the chloride penetration depth, x_d, is in excess of 20 mm. In view of this it should be noted that in NT Build 492 (1995) it is explicitly mentioned that for concrete made with ordinary Portland cement $c_d = 0.07$ N applies, however for other types of cements no quantitative indication for c_d is given.

However, there is some experimental evidence that this migration test does not result into such an ideal "tsunami" profile. The figures presented by Stanish (2002), Gruyaert et al. (2009), and Qiang (2009) clearly indicate that the measured chloride profiles do not demonstrate a sharp front, but in contrast more correspond to a diffusion profile. An example of the chloride profiles found by Qiang (2009) is presented in Figure 5.

If such a profile would be more representative for a chloride migration test then the theoretical basis for the calculation of the migration coefficient is invalid and thus it would pose doubt on the physical meaning of the migration coefficient and its application for service life modelling. An alternative theoretical model which results in major differences with the 'tsunami' profile is suggested by Krabbenhøft and Krabbenhøft (2008).

Moreover, it is argued by Gruyaert et al. (2009) that the coloration by spraying silver nitrate on a freshly split concrete specimen is dependent on the pH of the pore solution and thus the type of cement and presence of carbonation would affect the coloration. For chloride ingress characterised by a 'tsunami' profile the influence of pH on the penetration depth would be negligible, however, when a diffusion profile is valid the dependence on pH may further complicate the interpretation of the results obtained from a rapid chloride migration test by the colorimetric method.

4 TEST CONDITIONS

During the migration experiment one end of the concrete specimen is continually exposed to a chloride solution (catholyte) whereas the other end is in direct contact with a highly alkaline solution (anolyte). The implicit assumption is that the chemical composition of both the catholyte and the anolyte will remain constant throughout the complete duration of the test. However, both solutions may experience significant changes due to the occurrence of electrode reactions. These changes may affect the chloride penetration rate and consequently the overall result, i.e. the chloride migration coefficient D_{nssm}.

As tap water is used, the initial pH of the catholyte will be near neutral, i.e. $pH \approx 7.0$, although it reasonable to assume that upon contact with the concrete sample some leaching of hydroxyl ions from the pore solution will result in a gradual, although minor, increase of the alkalinity. At the moment the power source is switched on electrochemical reactions are induced at the cathode. According to Castellote et al. (2000) the predominant cathodic reaction will be the decomposition of water resulting in the consumption of electrons accompanied by the production of hydroxyl ions and the evolution of hydrogen gas, according to:

$$2H_2O + 2e^- \rightarrow 2OH^- + H_2\uparrow \qquad (8)$$

The introduction of hydroxyl ions into the catholyte will result in a gradual increase of the pH. For a sustained cell current I_{cell} it can be derived that, due to the electrode reactions at the cathode, the development of the pH of the catholyte over time is given by:

$$pH_c = 14 + \log\left[10^{-pH_{c,o}} + \frac{I_{cell} \cdot t}{F \cdot V_c}\right] \qquad (9)$$

(without the influence of migration of hydroxyl ions into the concrete specimen). Where $pH_c = pH$ of the catholyte solution, [–]; $pH_{c,o}$ = initial pH of the catholyte solution, [–]; t = duration of the migration test, [s]; $F = 96484$ C/mol; V_c = volume of the catholyte, [litre].

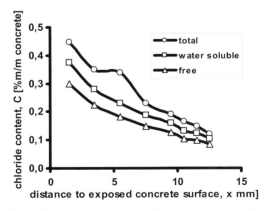

Figure 5. Measured profiles of total and free chloride content according to Qiang (2009).

According to NT Build 492 (1999) the anolyte is a 0.3 N NaOH solution, corresponding to an initial $pH = 13.47$. The predominant anodic reaction is expected to be decomposition of water according to:

$$2H_2O \rightarrow O_2\uparrow + 4H^+ + 4e^- \qquad (10)$$

Consequently, the anolyte will gradually become less alkaline due to the production of H$^+$-ions. The development of the pH of the anolyte over time resulting from the anode reactions only is given by:

$$pH_a = -\log\left[10^{-pH_{a,o}} + \frac{I_{cell} \cdot t}{F \cdot V_a}\right] \qquad (11)$$

where pH_a = pH of the anolyte solution, [–]; $pH_{a,o}$ = initial pH of the anolyte solution, [–]; V_a = volume of the anolyte, [litre].

The resulting theoretical development of pH over time for both the anolyte and catholyte is shown in Figure 6. With respect to the volume of the catholyte, some test arrangements used in laboratories use one common catholyte solution which is shared by 3 test set-ups. A few test arrangements use a volume of less than 1 litre for both the anolyte and the catholyte, and consequently the pH may demonstrate a more pronounced change over time.

According to Eq. (9) within 1h after switching on the power source the pH of the catholyte would theoretically shift from $pH = 7$ to pH-values in excess of 10. Such an increase is supported by the results presented in Castellote et al. (2000). On the other hand the pH of the anolyte will theoretically shift from its initial value $pH = 13.47$ to values well below 2. However, there is experimental evidence that the pH of the anolyte demonstrates only a minor shift to a lower pH and this seems to be in flagrant contrast with the result of the theoretical calculations. This can simply be explained by the fact that a significant amount of hydroxyl ions coming from the concrete pore solution will enter the anolyte forced by the electrical field. Ideally, there would be a balance between the production rate of H$^+$-ions and the inflow of OH$^-$-ions if it is assumed that hydroxyl ions are the single contributor to the ionic current. Consequently, a constant level of the pH of the anolyte would be maintained. In addition to the fact that other ions (both positively and negatively charged) will contribute to the ionic current, in due course the concrete layer in contact with the anolyte may become devoid of hydroxyl ions due to the sustained outflow. There is some visual evidence that for migration tests involving a high cell current ($I > 100$ mA) during a prolonged period of time, the concrete layer contacting the anolyte shows a distinct coloration. Moreover, the concrete quality will play a decisive role in passing a sufficient amount of hydroxyl ions per unit of time from the inner parts of the sample in the direction of the anolyte as to balance the consumption rate.

With respect to the catholyte it is implicitly assumed that, due to the high concentration of chloride ions, all of the ionic current is due to the transport of chloride ions. At least this assumption would be true for the near surface layer of the concrete sample being in direct contact with the catholyte and at the start of the experiment. However, in the course of time the concentration of hydroxyl ions in the catholyte increases strongly and this will result in an increasing competition with the chloride ions regarding transport of negatively charged ions into the concrete specimen. In this respect it should be noted that hydroxyl ions demonstrate a much higher mobility compared to chloride ions. As it is reasonable to assume that the chloride ion concentration in the catholyte will always be significantly higher than the hydroxyl ion concentration, this would imply that the contribution of chloride ions to the ionic cell current will remain far greater than that of the hydroxyl ions. However, there are some indications that this could be a premature conclusion. For most laboratories it appears to be common practice to use the catholyte solution several times before a freshly made solution is employed. Consequently, in adverse situations the pH level of the catholyte may eventually rise to values in excess of 13. As an example, in contrast to NT Build 492 (1999) in BAW Merkblatt (2004) the catholyte is defined as a 0.2 N KOH solution with 10% NaCl and consequently at the start of the migration test the pH

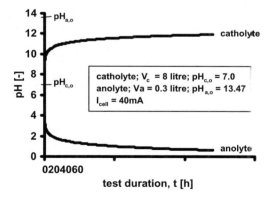

Figure 6. Theoretical development of the pH of the catholyte and the anolyte over time (without the effect of inflow of hydroxyl from the specimen into the anolyte).

of this solution would then amount to 13.3. The initial concentration of hydroxyl ions (0.2 N) in the catholyte solution is then just 10 times less than the concentration of chloride ions (2 N). Taking into account that the mobility of hydroxyl ions is approximately 2 times higher than that of chloride ions, it is anticipated that hydroxyl ions may contribute to approximately 20% of the total ionic current.

For reasons of simplicity in this discussion the contribution of other ions has been discarded. This implies that in practice a smaller amount of chloride will be forced into the concrete specimen and this supports the view that values for the migration coefficient obtained when using a catholyte solution according to NT Build 492 (1999) tend to be higher than the values obtained for similar concrete compositions when using a catholyte solution according to BAW Merkblatt (2004). The results presented in Gehlen (2000) seem to confirm this view.

5 CONCLUDING REMARKS

Serious doubt can be raised on the validity of the theoretical model supporting the chloride migration test as several researchers have measured chloride profiles that significantly differ from the 'tsunami' profile as predicted by the underlying theory used in NT Build 492 (1999). In view of the application of the chloride migration coefficient as an input parameter for service life modelling, experimental investigations are urgently required to validate the model as to obtain correct test results. In this respect, the model should take into account ionic transport by a number of species rather than only chloride. Moreover, the modifications of the exposure solution, in particular the catholyte, during the test should be included.

Regarding service life prediction it should also be noted that in real concrete structures chloride transport resulting from migration are rather uncommon in view of the absence of electrical fields. In real structures capillary suction will provide a significant contribution to chloride transport, particularly in the cover zone.

A more detailed description of the test procedure is needed to prevent the use of a wide range of exposure conditions which may eventually 'contaminate' the test result. According to Gulikers (2010) this may be accomplished by introducing a number of additional measurements prior, during and after the migration test.

In addition it should be noted that in an accelerated migration test, the mitigation of the transport process due to chloride binding is considered negligible as considerably more time is needed to establish complete binding. Consequently, it is likely that the actual resistance against chloride ingress may be severely underestimated for concretes containing supplementing cementitious materials, e.g. blast furnace slag.

REFERENCES

BAW. 2004. *Merkblatt Chlorideindringwiderstand* Karlsruhe (in German).

Castellote, M., Andrade C., and Alonso, C. 2000. Phenomenological mass-balance-based model of migration tests in stationary conditions—Application to non-steady-state tests', *Cem. and Con. Res.*, **30** (12) 1885–1893.

DuraCrete. 2000. *Final Technical Report*, Doc. BE95-1347/R17,Gouda, CUR.

fib, *Model Code for Service Life Design*, 2006, bulletin 34, Lausanne.

Gulikers, J. 2010. *Critical discussion on the chloride migration test*, Utrecht, Rijkswaterstaat.

Gruyaert, E., Van den Heede, Ph., and De Belie, N. 2009. Chloride ingress for concrete containing blast-furnace slag, related to microstructural parameters in Proc. of the 2nd Int. Workshop *Concrete Life'09*, PRO 66, Haifa, RILEM.

Gehlen, C. 2000. *Probabilistische Lebensdauerbemessung von Stahlbetonbauwerken*, Heft 510 Deutscher Ausschuss für Stahlbeton, Berlin (in German).

Krabbenhøft, K. and Krabbenhøft, J. 2008. Application of the Poisson-Nernst-Planck equations to the migration test', *Cem. and Con. Res.*, 38 (1) 77–88.

NT Build 443. 1995. *Hardened concrete: accelerated chloride penetration,* Espoo, nordtest.

NT Build 492. 1999. Chloride migration coefficient from non-steady-state migration experiments, Espoo, nordtest.

Qiang, Y. 2009. *Fundamental studies on test methods for the transport of chloride ions in cementitious materials*, University of Ghent.

Stanish, K. 2002. The migration of chloride ions in concrete, (University of Toronto, 2002).

Tang, L. 1995. *Chloride transport in concrete*, Publ. P-96:6 Göteborg, Chalmers University.

Concrete Solutions – Grantham, Mechtcherine & Schneck (eds)
© 2012 Taylor & Francis Group, London, ISBN 978-0-415-61622-5

Calculating the need for repair of concrete facades in the Finnish climate

A. Köliö & J. Lahdensivu
Tampere University of Technology, Tampere, Finland

ABSTRACT: There are approximately 44 million m² of concrete facades in Finland of which relatively young facades have required unexpected and extensive repair. New strategies for the repairing of existing concrete facades are needed. A model has been developed using a large pool of condition assessment data gathered over past 20 years to describe the degradation of concrete facades in Finnish climate and calculate the repair need of Finnish precast concrete facades of 1965–1995. Repair needs exist in 3/4 of the facades including mostly light coatings and patch repairs, but the continuing degradation will increase the need for more extensive repairs dramatically in the next 15 years. The total volume of needed repairs is assessed as €3.5 billion leading to prioritizing of repairs due to lack of resources. The average increase of repair need is 1.8% annually. This share has to be covered in order to maintain the present level of condition.

1   INTRODUCTION

This paper discusses a study where a new estimation was calculated for the repair need of existing concrete facades in Finland. The Finnish building stock consists of a total of 56,000 apartment houses that involves 44 million m² of concrete facade and 975,000 concrete balconies. Of these apartment houses nearly half have been built in the 1960s and 1970s due to increasing demand of urban apartments. This is the time when the use of prefabricated units in construction was being actively developed. Condition assessment systematics for concrete facades and balconies have been developed in Finland since the mid-1980s. Information on the degradation of concrete facades has been gathered and documented constantly in connection with every condition assessment. The condition assessment data of nearly a thousand facades has been gathered to a database for analysis.

This estimate is the first one that relies on a database of real measured data. The study includes prefabricated concrete facades and balconies of residential multi-storey buildings in Finland from 1965–1995. The repair need discussed here is induced by degradation of the structures and it does not include aesthetical, scheduled or other non-degradation related reasons to initiate facade repairs. In the absence of reliable statistics on facade renovation, the effect of annual repair activity is not included in the calculation. The increment of repair need is assessed in a situation where the facades degrade freely. This viewpoint gives

us information on the annual volume of repairs that is required to maintain the current condition of the building stock and how the repairs should be distributed over time. At the present, concrete facade repairs in Finland are often done using heavy cladding repairs including an added thermal insulation layer. This repair measure can often be overdimensioned in comparison to the degradation of the facade. This study is meant to prove, that the annual costs of facade renovation can be reduced significantly with a predictive strategy to facade renovation and by choosing repair measures according to the need.

2   DEGRADATION OF CONCRETE FACADES

2.1   Prefabricated concrete facades

The facades of buildings from 1965–1995 have been constructed using mainly similar prefabricated units consisting of an outer and inner layer of concrete and an insulation layer of mineral wool in between. The importance of frost durability of concrete was not truly recognized until 1980. However, concrete has occasionally been air-entrained to improve workability. The strength of concrete used has been approximately C20 and the thickness of the outer layer 40–85 mm. The outer layer is reinforced with a mesh and anchored to the inner layer with diagonal trusses travelling through the insulation layer. The most common type of

Finnish balcony after the late 1960s consists of a prefabricated frame, slab and parapet units that are assembled as a balcony tower. The parapet elements of balconies have rather heavy reinforcement. [Concrete Association of Finland, 2002].

2.2 Degradation mechanisms

The degradation of concrete structures is caused by simultaneous influence of environmental, structural and material factors. Degradation eventually results in cracking or spalling of concrete that reduces bearing capacity or bonding reliability of the structures. The harsh climate increases the requirements for durable materials. The major mechanisms in Finnish climate are corrosion of facade reinforcement due to carbonation and weathering of concrete [Pentti et al. 1998]. The presence of chlorides in facade structures is very rare.

Concrete reinforcement is protected from corrosion by the high alkalinity of concrete pore water. This alkalinity is, over time, neutralized by carbon dioxide in the surrounding air leaving the reinforcement susceptible to corrosion which, especially with shallow cover depths, leads to cracking or spalling of surrounding concrete. [Broomfield. 1997]. Structures are protected against corrosion by placing the reinforcement inside the structure using sufficient depths of concrete cover. The design values for concrete cover have been sufficient to withstand carbonation and tensile stresses caused by corrosion, but the deviation in construction has also resulted in very shallow concrete covers, even less than 5 mm.

Frost weathering is caused by the combined effect of temperature alterations and moisture. The freezing of water in fully saturated pores of concrete causes cracks if the tensile strength of concrete is exceeded by stresses from the freezing. [Pigeon & Pleau, 1995]. The importance of frost durability of concrete was not acknowledged in the 1960s and 1970s construction. Therefore many of the existing facades are prone to frost damage. The most effective way to protect concrete structures is to prohibit the entry of water to the structure, which is difficult concerning facade structures because of the constant exposure to the outdoor climate. Increase in the compressive strength makes concrete more dense decreasing the amount of water the pore structure is able to hold thereby improving frost durability. The requirement for compressive strength is less crucial, when sufficient air entrainment is used. Air entrainment of concrete creates protective pores in concrete where the pressure caused by freezing can escape. According to Finnish guidelines the coefficient for frost resistant concrete is ≥0.20. That is 20% of the pores in concrete are of the correct size to remain air filled in all conditions [Concrete Association of Finland, 2002].

2.3 Condition assessment and repair

The goal of condition assessments of facades is to find out the current state, rate and extent of damaging and the tendency of damage propagation in the future. The assessment is composed of the inspection of building designs and related documents, field investigation and laboratory analyses. The concrete association of Finland has published a manual for these assessments, which is used by practically every assessor. [Concrete Association of Finland, 2002]. The produced information is then used in planning of the facade repair work. Concrete facades and balconies can mainly be repaired by methods of three different magnitudes. Protective methods e.g. coatings are used for slowing down the advance of degradation, where patch repair is a traditional method used for repairing local damage caused by both weathering and corrosion. Properly made patch repairs together with protective coatings can extend the service life of concrete structures remarkably [Mattila, 2003]. If the damage is widespread, the patch repair method is substituted by different cladding methods that usually include an added thermal insulation layer. As a downside, the original structure and color of the facade cannot be preserved. It also is not applicable to balcony structures. Total renewal of the existing structure is arguable when large areas of the facade are extensively deteriorated.

3 THE DEGRADATION MODEL

3.1 The condition assessment database

According to earlier studies, the factors contributing to the degradation of Finnish buildings constructed using prefabricated units in 1965–1995 can be simplified and narrowed down to but a few major ones. This is mainly because of the tradition of using similar techniques in the fabrication of building elements. [Lahdensivu et al., 2010] The systematics of condition assessments have made it possible to gather and analyze data so that the same comparable information is available from each investigated building. The collected database consists of building identification information, geographical location, data from measurements and specific laboratory tests and repair measure recommendations given on the basis of the assessment. Data includes 947 buildings from 1960 to 1995 of nine different surface types of concrete facades that are brushed concrete (uncoated or painted), floated concrete, form surfaced concrete (uncoated or painted), exposed aggregate concrete, clinker surfaced, tile surfaced and white concrete.

3.2 The main principles

A degradation model for concrete facades and balconies has been developed from the basis of the assembled database including frost weathering of concrete and carbonation induced corrosion of reinforcement. These degradation mechanisms lead, depending on material properties and the extent of damage, to repair method proposals that include coating, patch repair, cladding, renewal or no repair need. Determining the correct repair measures is systematised with decision paths.

The repair needs caused by weathering or corrosion are first assessed as separate and then combined, weighing the heavier repair method over the lighter one. Because the model uses real measured properties of the facade materials it is arguable to claim that it represents the existing building stock accurately including e.g. errors made in construction. Because the values stored in the database represent the date of the condition investigation, it was essential to be able to advance the degradation to a desired date of examination. The damage propagation was modelled by setting different propagation times for different ranges of damaging related material properties.

3.3 Corrosion of reinforcement

Carbonation induced corrosion of reinforcement developes first through an initiation stage involving the carbonation process after which the actual corrosion starts in the propagation stage. In this study the end of service life of reinforcement is set to the end of the initiation stage i.e. the moment when carbonation has reached the reinforcement. This is a rather rough estimate because the service life of concrete structures is not yet compromised at that moment. With a lack of a reliable propagation stage model for reinforcement corrosion, the calculation at this point has to be acknowledged as an estimate on the safe side.

The model uses cover depths and carbonation depths derived from the condition assessment database according to building year. Different fabrication methods and deviation in the fabrication of elements create variation to the cover depth. Also the ingress of carbon dioxide to concrete varies. The amount of reinforcement in carbonated concrete, illustrated in Figure 1, is calculated by the publication *Condition investigation manual for concrete facade panels* [Concrete Association of Finland, 2002] first multiplying the total amount of reinforcement at a certain point (5 mm range)

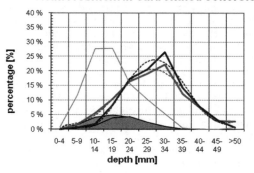

Reinforcement in carbonated concrete

Figure 1. The amount of reinforcement in carbonated concrete (area) and the distribution of reinforcement cover depths (on the right) and carbonation depths (on the left) in early 1970s brush surfaced concrete facades.

inside the structure with the percentage of carbonation depths that exceed the examination point, for we can be certain that this amount of reinforcement is located in carbonated concrete. To this value is then added the same amount of reinforcement multiplied with the percentage of carbonation depths at the examination point divided by two. The division by two is done because the values used are averages of each 5 mm range.

Carbonation advances in concrete first rapidly and then with decreasing speed. For modelling the concrete carbonation, the model uses the square root equation (1) introduced by Tuutti [1982].

$$x = k\sqrt{t} \qquad (1)$$

When the examination year is set to the model, it extends every measured value of carbonation depth using the equation. The intensity of carbonation is in the equation characterized with a carbonation factor k. The values of k are in this case derived from the condition assessment database. The result x is the carbonation depth in concrete and t is time in years, which in this case is the time from the building dates in the database to the examination year. After the advancement of carbonation the amount of reinforcement in carbonated concrete is recalculated.

3.4 Frost weathering of concrete

The pore structure of concrete is essential for the frost durability of concrete structures. Both the strength of concrete and air entraining alter the pore structure for better frost resistance. The condition assessment database, however, does not include information on the compressive strength forcing the use of pore structure measurement data.

Frost weathering is assessed through the amount of non-capillary pores of concrete and observed frost damage in the structures. Facades with protective pore coefficient, p_r values above 0.20 are considered intact and undamaged whereas values lower than 0.20 result in repair measures. The extent of repairs is then determined using the amount of visible frost damage. Extensive visual frost damage leads to cladding repairs or renewal of the old structure while local frost damage results in patch repairs and no visual damage leads to protective methods.

The progression of frost damage is modelled as the increment of visible damage over time. The value of p_r and the geographical location determines the progression speed. Damage does not advance in concrete with p_r values of over 0.20. The lower the value gets, the faster the progression is. The value of p_r is assumed constant over time, although over time there may occur reactions that fill pores e.g. the formation of ettringite. In the Finnish climate, the number of harmful freeze-thaw cycles is ca. 30–60 per winter season depending on the geographical location and year. Buildings located in coastal climates deteriorate remarkably faster than those located inland. The impact of material properties and location to the progression of frost damage is illustrated in Figure 2.

3.5 Utilization of the model

The model has been formed into a computer application to automate the calculation process. Because of the statistical nature of the examination, it can only be applied on a group of buildings, a certain area or a suburb. The case-specific properties of single buildings cannot be estimated, but in a larger group the properties even out. A preliminary survey of the building group has to be conducted for gathering input data. The model writes out the information for a certain year and surface type after which the information has to be adjusted to the surface type and age distribution of buildings on the area.

The model operates with input data that consists of the surface type and the age and geographical location of buildings. The age and quantity of balconies is needed if the assessment of balcony structures is to be included in the calculation. This information may be acquired by investigating the documents and drawings on the building group or by surveying the area. The analysis of repair needs is then carried out using this collected input data. These percentages of different repair alternatives are then converted to quantities and costs by multiplying them to the surveyed building group. An average type house is used in the converting calculations.

4 CALCULATION

To acquire the input data for the degradation model a sample of 496 concrete buildings was gathered in a survey. The sample was distributed in the localities of Helsinki, Turku, Tampere, Jyväskylä and Oulu. These localities are the five biggest growth areas in Finland and make 1/3 of the total quantity of prefabricated residential buildings. From the basis of calculations of the building stock of these five localities it is believed to be possible to make an estimation of the total repair need of these facades in Finland.

Information was gathered studying building design archives, surveying areas by foot and using internet searches. For determining repair expenses, average cost estimates from the year 2009 were input to the model: facade repairs 40–195 €/m² and balconies 5000–9000 €/balcony depending on the repair method. The same repair costs were used in calculation in every locality regardless of the changes in local price levels. This will bring forth the differences caused by the technical repair need over the local price level. This evaluation includes the costs of only the repair of the concrete facade. The calculation does not include e.g. the changing of windows that is typically done in connection with facade renovation.

5 RESULTS

5.1 Current situation

The results of the calculation in Figure 3 show that repair is needed to some extent in approximately 3/4 of prefabricated concrete facades of residential

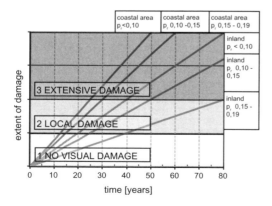

Figure 2. Progression of frost damage in relation with the material properties of concrete.

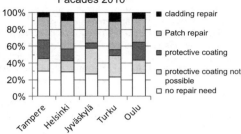

Figure 3. The calculated division of repair needs in prefabricated facades of residential buildings from 1965–1995 in Finland.

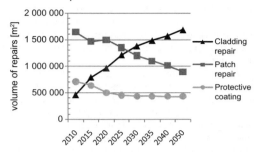

Figure 4. The calculated division of repair needs in prefabricated facades of residential buildings from 1965–1995 in Finland.

buildings from 1965 to 1995. The majority of these repairs are, however, light protective repairs or traditional patch repairs where the observed damage is local. The share of heavier cladding repairs is 5–10% of the examined facades, according to the differences in the five examined localities.

Protective coatings are considered problematic to apply on facades that have a rough surface e.g. exposed aggregate concrete. The share of these rough facade surfaces is considerably high in Finnish residential buildings. This means, that there is a share of about 20% of facades that need protective repair but there is not a suitable alternative available.

Of the concrete balconies, over 80% require repairs to some extent, of which approximately half can be repaired with protective coatings. Renewal is required in 12–19% of balconies.

The total volume of facade and balcony repairs in Finland is estimated according to these calculations 3.5 billion € including 43% from facade repairs and 57% from balcony repairs.

5.2 *Advancement in the future*

The propagation of degradation was also assessed with the model using a time span of 40 years, from 2010 to 2050. This time span was divided into five-year intervals for which the repair need of facades was calculated. The propagation of damage was assessed in a situation where annual repair activity is not taken into account and the facades degrade freely. The propagation of the need of different repairs is illustrated in Figure 4. The propagation is similar in all localities.

At the moment the share of light repairs covers the majority of repair needs. However, the need of heavier cladding repairs is currently beginning to develop and in approximately 15 years it will surpass patch repairs as the major repair method of these concrete facades: that is, if no measures

are taken. For balconies, the need for renewal increases rapidly in the next 15 years and there are, in all, few cases where lighter patch repairs or protective measures can be applied. This is because of the poor sustainability properties of concrete used in balcony structures mainly in 1960s and 1970s.

The average increase of the total volume of facade and balcony repairs is 1.8% annually if the effect of annual repairs is not included. This will approximately double the value of the repairs needed by the year 2050. The average increase of 1.8% makes 63 million € annually. This is the minimum volume of repairs that has to be taken annually to maintain the current state of the prefabricated concrete facades in Finland.

6 DISCUSSION

The model and the calculation of the repair need of prefabricated concrete facades are a step towards anticipatory property management where the aging and repair of different surfaced concrete facades can be prepared for. This predictive tool, being based on extensive real measured data, can be argued to represent the Finnish building stock rather accurately including, for instance, deviation in building quality showing as insufficient protective pore coefficient values or very little cover depths of reinforcement. The model works well for the precast concrete facades from 1965–1995. Buildings of that age have been constructed very much using the same techniques and the same kinds of building units fabricated the same way.

According to the calculation the most needed repairs at the moment are light coatings and patch repair. If no repair measures are taken, the share of heavier cladding repairs will increase rapidly and outstrip patch repairs by the end of 2025. Generally, these more extensive repairs needlessly add to the expense of repairs, if the same result could have been achieved with lighter repairs. By investing now to the protective repair of concrete facades, the progression of degradation could be remarkably slowed down. Still, these protective measures are not yet very common in concrete facade repair in Finland.

There is a remarkable share of rough exposed aggregate and tile surfaced facades in Finnish building stock. Currently there are no suitable protective measures available for anticipatory repair and slowing down the degradation of these facades and cladding repair is often chosen because of a lack of other alternatives as a safe method. The developing of protective measures also suitable for these rough facades should be taken into consideration.

REFERENCES

Broomfield, J. 1997, *Corrosion of Steel in Concrete*, E & F Spon, London.

Concrete Association of Finland. 2002, *Condition investigation manual for concrete facade panels,* Concrete Association of Finland, Helsinki (In Finnish).

Lahdensivu, J., Varjonen, S. & Köliö, A. 2010, *Repair strategies of concrete facades and balconies*, Tampere University of Technology, Structural Engineering. Research report 148, Tampere (In Finnish).

Mattila, J. 2003, *On the durability of cement-based patch repairs on Finnish concrete facades and balconies,* Tampere University of Technology, Structural Engineering. Publication 123, Tampere (In Finnish).

Pigeon M., Pleau R. 1995. *Durability of concrete in cold climates.* London. E & FN Spon. 244 s.

Tuutti, K. 1982, *Corrosion of Steel in Concrete,* Swedish Cement and Concrete Research Institute CBI Research 4:82, Stockholm.

Concrete Solutions – Grantham, Mechtcherine & Schneck (eds)
© *2012 Taylor & Francis Group, London, ISBN 978-0-415-61622-5*

Prediction of reliability of utility tunnel structures subject to dynamic loads

M. Kurgansky, V. Gaponov & S. Pavlov
ZAO "Triada-Holding", Moscow, Russia

ABSTRACT: More than 360 km of utility tunnels are under operation in Moscow at the moment. They are designated for laying central heating and water-supply pipes, electrical and telephone cables, etc. These tunnels are located mainly under streets with intensive traffic. Experience shows that tunnel structures subject to dynamic loads from traffic fail earlier than their design service life term. This can be explained partly by the fact that not always the would-be interaction between structures and environment is considered at the design stage as well as by intensive growth of street traffic.

Existing normative documents for design, construction, and repair of utility tunnels were approved long ago; they cannot give sufficient backup for the mentioned activities under quickly changing circumstances. That was one of the reasons why in 2008 we started our own theoretical and practical investigations based on continuous monitoring of utility tunnels structures. Our main goal was to establish the relationship between dynamic loads and the state of structures and as a result to develop new methods of structural analysis aimed at increasing reliability and service life of structures.

Good correlation between theoretical and practical results confirms the relevance of the chosen investigation techniques applied to studying structural behaviour, namely their mode of deformations and provides comprehensive backup for sustainable design.

1 INTRODUCTION

Utility tunnels in cities as well as the mains laid in them are subject to aggressive environmental impact. This causes accelerated wear of structures and also problems with tunnel waterproofing. Early failures of such structures can lead to serious consequences for infrastructure of whole city districts. Our inspection results show that under the streets where tunnels are subject, not only to static loads but also to dynamic ones, the number of structures in an emergency state is 1,5 times higher than in tunnel sections located farther from traffic routes (Shilin A, 2009). The rate of growth of the number of such tunnel sections depends on the duration of their operation period: the longer the period (and traffic intensity degree), the steeper the rate curve.

When designing a tunnel slab, traffic loads are introduced by way of increasing a static load value adding a live load value (weight of a HK-80 vehicle) to it (Regulations, 1979 and Technical Regulations, 1990).

The dynamic nature of the applied traffic loads is accounted for by introducing a special coefficient for the live load value; though the range of the coefficient application is limited by a particular structural depth equal to 0,4 m (Technical Regulations, 1990).

The relationship between the design load from a HK-80 vehicle onto the tunnel lining and tunnel depth as well as a particular design method is shown in Figure 1.

When the graph passes the point h = 0,4 m, the live load value goes down abruptly (21–26%, depending on the tunnel width). Pressure applied by a HK-80 vehicle onto 1 m^3 of tunnel roof slabs with various dimensions is different even if tunnel structures have the same depth.

The above mentioned effect comes in contradiction with the traditional idea on strain distribution as formulated by soil mechanics.

No special studies to define dynamic coefficients for live load calculation as applied to utility tunnel linings have been conducted.

It must be noted that our long-term experience in tunnel inspection revealed a stable trend of an accelerated wear of roof slabs in tunnels located under the streets, irrespective of their depth.

In 2007 the diagnostics department of our company started an extensive programme of operational state monitoring in utility tunnel sections subject to man-caused impact.

We were focused on roof slabs in tunnels constructed by cut-and-cover methods as the most representative from the viewpoint of corrosion wear. At the same time the state of these structural

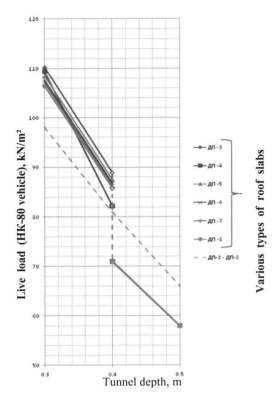

Figure 1. Relationship between live loads on tunnel roof slabs and tunnel depth as well as design procedure.

elements determines the safety level of a tunnel as a whole (Album of Working Drawings, 1963).

Accumulation of defects in roof slabs in the course of operation takes a long time and while the process is going on it is not so easy to predict the moment of structural failure due to deterioration.

It is known nowadays that minor defects in reinforced concrete structures are not always seen, nor do they cause any relevant deformations. That is why it is hard to detect them at early stages of structural operation.

Our studies have been conducted to evaluate and predict operational reliability of shallow tunnel structures.

The monitoring programme was executed in a number of utility tunnels in Moscow located under the main streets along the route of powerful military vehicles to the Red Square for the Victory Day parade (Technical Conclusion, 2008 and Report, 2008).

We decided to define roof slab reliability using the probabilistic method when we assume probabilistic values of structural materials parameters and loads as input data whereas calculations are based on relationships describing structural bearing capacity in accordance with the current design codes and regulations.

To define roof slab reliability in terms of their strength it was necessary to correlate particular values of dynamic loads to the changes in strength of structural materials.

As dynamic loading parameters we assumed their maximum (p_d^{max}) and minimum (p_d^{min}) values as well as the number of loading cycles (N).

Then the bearing capacity of the roof slabs can be expressed as

$$M_{ult} = f(R_s, R_b, A_s, h_o, b, p_d^{max}, p_d^{min}, N) \qquad (1)$$

The bearing capacity of ДП-type roof slabs (Album of Working Drawings, 1963) depending on cross-sectional dimensions and strength of reinforcement and concrete is defined according to Construction Code 2.03.01–84 "Concrete and Reinforced Concrete Structures" as

$$M_{ult} = R_s A_s h_o \left(1 - \frac{R_s A_s}{2 h_o R_b b}\right), \qquad (2)$$

where R_s is design value of reinforcement resistance (ultimate limit state);

A_s is cross-sectional area of reinforcement providing strength equal to the moment M_{ult};

h_o is effective depth of concrete;

R_b is design value of concrete resistance to uniaxial compression (ultimate limit state);

b is width of a T-beam rib;

N is the number of loading cycles.

With regard to (1) bearing capacity equations (2) can be expressed as follows:

$$M_{ult} = S R_s A_s h_o \left(1 - \frac{S R_s A_s}{2 h_o B R_b b}\right), \qquad (3)$$

where $S = f_1(p_d^{max}, p_d^{min}, N)$
and $B = f_2(p_d^{max}, p_d^{min}, N)$.

Thus the results of our theoretical studies we were able to formulate the bearing capacity equation for ДП roof slabs with regard to dynamic loading parameters (Kurgansky M., 2010):

$$
\begin{aligned}
M_{ult} &= S R_s A_s h_o \left(1 - \frac{S R_s A_s}{2 h_o B R_b b}\right) \\
&= \left(1 - \frac{1-\gamma_{ss}}{6} \cdot \lg N\right) R_s A_s h_o \\
&\quad \cdot \left(1 - \frac{(1 - \frac{1-\gamma_{ss}}{6} \cdot \lg N) R_s A_s}{(1 - \frac{1-\gamma_{b1}}{6} \cdot \lg N) 2 h_o R_b b}\right)
\end{aligned}
\qquad (4)
$$

Coefficients γ_{b1} and γ_{s3} are applied to calculate durability of reinforced concrete structures subject to repeated dynamic loading in accordance with Construction Code 2.03.01-84 "Concrete and Reinforced Concrete Structures" (*Construction Code*, 1984).

The relationship between the roof slab bearing capacity and loading cycles' variation coefficient helps to solve various issues connected with increasing the level of structural reliability.

Figure 2 shows how slab bearing capacity goes down with the increase of number of loading cycles (for ДП-3 roof slabs, see equation (4)).

Figure 3 presents the results shown in Figure 2 with regard to environmental impact.

After summing up and analyzing the results of our studies we came to the following conclusions:

1. References to dynamic loading impact on structural state in the current design codes and regulations for utility tunnels with reinforced concrete linings do not reflect the actual level of knowledge and experience.
2. There are no practical recommendations for designers and planners that can help in correct assessment of live loads impact on tunnel structural state.
3. Being subject to external repeated loading cycles, tunnel roof slabs are subject to forced vibrations.
4. Vibration amplitudes are not always proportional to the applied load values. Structures in tunnels located under the streets are subject to heavier deformations which by far exceed design limit values.
5. The dynamic nature of the loads was registered by all sensors installed at various depths (0,8–1,5 m); this confirms the necessity of applying special dynamic coefficients when calculating live loads impact on tunnels located deeper than the design value of 0,4 m.

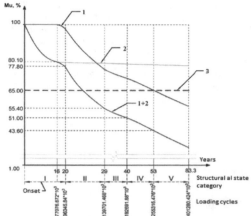

1 - loss of reliability due to aggressive environment impact
2 - loss of reliability due to dynamic loading
1+2 - loss of reliability due to combined impact of dynamic loading and aggressive environment
3 - loss of safety margin

Figure 3. Reliability of roof slab structures subject to dynamic loads from traffic and aggressive environmental impact.

6. Results of periodic inspections do not provide sufficient information on the time of structural deterioration onset. Neither do they create a relevant basis for design and reliability prediction, especially if we consider structures subject to combined impact of both dynamic loading and aggressive environmental impact.
7. To be able to analyze micromechanical processes as well the kinetics of defect accumulation in tunnel structures, it is necessary to monitor structural state continuously, especially if we consider structures subject to man-caused impact.
8. Method of structural reliability estimation with regard to the bearing capacity of tunnel structures proposed by us can be used for state assessment of the existing structures as well as for designing the new ones, the more so as the effective codes and regulations do not contain any relevant information on the matter.

REFERENCES

Album of Working Drawings for Utility Tunnels with Precast Reinforced Concrete Structures, 1963, Moscow.
Construction Code 2.03.01-84 "Concrete and Reinforced Concrete Structures", 1984, Moscow.
Kurgansky M., 2010 *Development of Estimation Procedure and Increasing of Reliability of Utility Tunnel Structures with Regard to Dynamic Loading*: Thesis, Dr. of Tech. Sciences, Moscow.

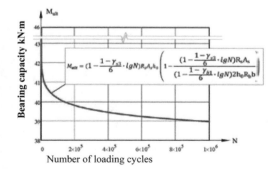

$$M_{edr} = (1 - \frac{1-\gamma_{s3}}{6} \cdot lgN)R_sA_s h_o \left(1 - \frac{(1-\frac{1-\gamma_{s3}}{6} \cdot lgN)R_sA_s}{(1-\frac{1-\gamma_{b1}}{6} \cdot lgN)2h_oR_bb} \right)$$

Figure 2. Roof slab bearing capacity vs the number of dynamic loading cycles.

Regulations on Design of Utility Tunnels, TSNII Promzdaniy Publishing House, 1979, Moscow.

Report on the Results of Research Study "Reliability Prediction for Structures in Tunnels Subject to Man-Made Impact with the Help of Structural State Monitoring", 2008, ZAO "Triada-Holding", Moscow.

Shilin A., et al. 2009. *Addendum to Regulations on Repair of Utility Tunnels with the Reinforced Concrete Linings*, Moscow: MSUM Publishing House.

Technical Conclusion on the Results of Atomized Monitoring of Operational State of Utility Tunnel Structures in the Centre of Moscow (Victory Day Parade), 2008, ZAO "Triada-Holding", Moscow.

Technical Regulations on Design, Construction, and Commissioning of Urban Utility Tunnels, 1990, Moscow.

Concrete Solutions – Grantham, Mechtcherine & Schneck (eds)
© 2012 Taylor & Francis Group, London, ISBN 978-0-415-61622-5

Service life prediction of underground concrete pipes subjected to corrosion

M. Mahmoodian & C.Q. Li
School of Engineering, University of Greenwich, UK

ABSTRACT: Concrete corrosion due to hydrogen sulfide attack is an inevitable prejudicious process in concrete sewer pipelines. A high rate of maintenance and repair costs and catastrophic consequences of a major sewer pipeline collapse lead asset managers to search for reliable methods for risk assessment and service life prediction of sewer systems. Furthermore, safety and risk assessment is gradually becoming a requirement for the design of new concrete sewers and for inspection, rehabilitation, upgrading, replacement, and demolition decisions of aging and deteriorated of concrete pipes.

This paper will present a case study on risk assessment of approximately 90 kilometer of concrete sewer pipes in California. A time dependent reliability method to predict the probability of failure for the system is proposed in the paper. The analytical results from the reliability method are verified by the Monte Carlo simulation method. The results are then utilized to estimate the expected remaining service life of the pipeline and determining the effects of maintenance and repair options on service life.

As will be seen, a time-dependent reliability method can be used as a rational tool for infrastructure managers to develop a risk-informed and cost-effective strategy in the management of sewer systems. By using a reliable tool for service life prediction of sewer pipes, resources for maintenance and rehabilitation can be allocated to those sewer facilities likely to present the greater risk of failure, prior to those facilities of lower risk, and hence a risk-cost optimized maintenance strategy can be achieved.

1 INTRODUCTION

Corrosion in the management of sewerage systems is one of the important factors for asset managers. Sulfide induced concrete corrosion is a time dependent process which considerably affects the lifetime of concrete sewers. Sulfide corrosion model has been introduced by Pomeroy (1976) and has been extended in ASCE Report No. 69 (1989).

For a sustainable development plan with scarce capital resources for concrete sewer maintenance, it is necessary to appropriately allocate funding and efforts with a thorough knowledge of sewer condition. It is vital for infrastructure managers to precisely predict the life expectancy of existing concrete sewers so that they can prioritize evaluation efforts and funding allocations.

To precisely predict life time of a concrete sewer pipe, uncertainties should be taken into account. Therefore instead of deterministic models, introduction and development of stochastic models should be considered.

In the case of steel pipes, various frameworks have been proposed to model the behavior of underground pipelines, using reliability-based concepts. Ahammed & Melchers (1997) developed a nonlinear limit state model for the analysis of underground pipelines subjected to combined stresses and corrosion. The reliability model was assumed to be a function of 20 independent random variables in order to study their effects. Camarinopoulos et al. (1999) used a combination of approximate quadrature analytical and Monte Carlo methods to evaluate the multiple integrals in their reliability analysis for cast-iron buried water pipes. They also used the model to assess the sensitivity of structural reliability to the variation of some important parameters such as wall thickness, unsupported length and external corrosion coefficient. Li et al. (2009) presented a methodology for predicting remaining life of underground pipes, subject to corrosion, with a mechanically-based probabilistic model by taking the effect of randomness into account in pipeline corrosion. They employed a Monte Carlo simulation to calculate the remaining life and its cumulative distribution function.

This paper intends to present a reliability based methodology for life time prediction of concrete sewers subjected to sulfide induced concrete corrosion. A stochastic model for wall thickness reduction is developed. To quantify the probability of failure due to corrosion, a time dependent reliability method is employed so that the time for sewer

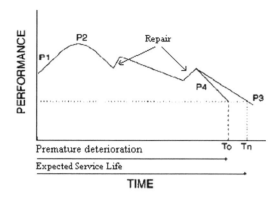

Figure 1. Conceptual relationship of performance service life and premature deterioration (Cheung and Kyle 1996).

failure can be determined with confidence. Factors that affect the rate of wall thickness reduction are also studied using sensitivity analysis.

By using the reliability as a measure of performance, repair and rehabilitation decisions can be made based on risk-cost analysis over the life time of the structure. The life-cycle performance of a typical structural component is illustrated in Figure 1. The beginning of the curve, labeled P1, represents the period shortly after installation. P2 is the optimum operation level. The performance is expected to decline from this point onward. Minor increases in performance can happen by conducting repairs and altering operations or maintenance practices. The system will have eventually deteriorated to an un-functional point (P3). The system is said to have deteriorated prematurely if the actual in-service life fail to meet specific expectation, such as design life.

In this paper a reliability-based methodology for the service life prediction and management of repair procedures of reinforced concrete pipes subjected to hydrogen sulfide corrosion is described.

2 FORMULATION OF SERVICE LIFE PREDICTION

According to ASCE manual NO. 69, one of the performance criteria related to the stability of concrete sewers is to control the wall thickness reduction under an acceptable limit (normally concrete cover). In the theory of structural reliability this criterion can be expressed in the form of a limit state function as follows:

$$G(d_{max}, d, t) = d_{max}(t) - d(t) \qquad (1)$$

where:

d : reduction in wall thickness due to corrosion, (mm)

d_{max} : Maximum permissible reduction in wall thickness (structural resistance or limit), (mm)

t : elapsed time.

d_{max} may change with time although in most practical cases it has a constant value prescribed in design codes and manuals.

With the above limit state function, the probability of failure of the concrete pipe due to the reduction of its wall thickness can be determined by:

$$P(t) = P[G(d_{max}, d, t) \leq 0] = P[d(t) \geq d_{max}(t)] \qquad (2)$$

Equation (2) is a typical upcrossing problem that can be solved using time-dependent reliability methods (Melchers 1999). In a time dependent reliability problem all or some of basic random variables are modeled as stochastic processes. For the above problem, the sewer failure depends on the time that is expected to elapse before the first occurrence of the stochastic process, $d(t)$, upcross a critical limit (the threshold, d_{max}) sometime during the service life of the sewer.

Therefore the probability of the first occurrence of such an event is the probability of failure during that time period. This is known as "first passage probability" which can be determined by (Melchers 1999):

$$P_d(t) = 1 - [1 - p_d(0)]e^{-\int_0^t v d\tau} \qquad (3)$$

where $P_d(t)$ is the probability of failure due to corrosion of the concrete wall at time $t = 0$ and v is the mean rate for the stochastic process $d(t)$ to upcross the threshold d_{max}. In many practical problems, the mean upcrossing rate is very small, so the above equation can be approximated as follows:

$$P_d(t) = p_d(0) + \int_0^t v d\tau \qquad (4)$$

The upcrossing rate in equation (4) can be determined from the Rice formula (Melchers 1999):

$$v = v_{d_{max}}^+ = \int_{\dot{d}_{max}}^{\infty} (\dot{d} - \dot{d}_{max}) f_{d\dot{d}}(d_{max}, \dot{d}) d_{\dot{d}} \qquad (5)$$

where $v_{d_{max}}^+$ is the upcrossing rate of the stochastic process $d(t)$ relative to the threshold $d_{max}(t)$; $\dot{d}_{max}$ is slope of $d_{max}(t)$ with respect to time t; $\dot{d}$ is the time—derivative process of $d(t)$; and $f_{d\dot{d}}()$ is the joint probability density function for d and $\dot{d}$.

552

An analytical solution to the above equation has been derived by Li and Melchers (1993), when d_{max} is deterministic, as follows:

$$v^+_{d_{max}} = \frac{\sigma_{\dot{d}|d}}{\sigma_d}\phi\left(\frac{d_{max}-\mu_d}{\sigma_d}\right)\left\{\phi\left(-\frac{\dot{d}_{max}-\mu_{\dot{d}|d}}{\sigma_{\dot{d}|d}}\right)\right. \tag{6}$$
$$\left. -d_{max}-\mu_d\,|\,d\sigma d\,|\,d\Phi - d_{max}-\mu_d\,|\,d\sigma d\,|\,d \right.$$

where ϕ and Φ are standard normal density and distribution functions, respectively; μ and σ denote the mean and standard deviation of random variables, represented by subscripts d and $\dot{d}$, and '|' denotes the condition. For a given Gaussian stochastic process with mean function $\mu_d(t)$ and auto-covariance function $C_{dd}(t_i, t_j)$, all the terms in the above equation can be determined, according to the theory of stochastic processes (Papoulis [1965] and Melchers [1999]).

With Equations (4) and (5) and considering that d_{max} is constant ($\dot{d}_{max} = 0$) the probability of failure would be:

$$P_f(t) = \int_0^t \frac{\sigma_{\dot{d}|d}(t)}{\sigma_d(t)}\phi\left(\frac{d_{max}-\mu_d(t)}{\sigma_d(t)}\right)\left\{\phi\left(-\frac{\mu_{\dot{d}|d(t)}}{\sigma_{\dot{d}|d}(t)}\right)\right. \tag{7}$$
$$\left. +\mu_d\,|\,d(t)\sigma dd(t)\Phi\mu_d\,|\,d(t)\sigma dd(t)d\tau \right.$$

To determine the probability of pipe failure due to its excessive wall thickness reduction, the key lies in developing a stochastic model for wall thickness reduction due to corrosion.

3 FORMULIZATION OF WALL THICKNESS REDUCTION DUE TO CORROSION

The rate of corrosion of a concrete wall of sewer pipes can be calculated from the rate of production of sulfuric acid on the pipe wall, which is in turn dependent upon the rate that hydrogen sulfide (H_2S) is released from the surface of the sewage stream. The average flux of H_2S to the exposed pipe wall is equal to the flux from the stream into the air multiplied by the ratio of the surface area of the stream to the area of the exposed pipe wall, which is the same as the ratio of the width of the stream surface (b) to the perimeter of the exposed wall (P). The average flux of H_2S to the wall is calculated as follows (ASCE No. 60, 2007):

$$\Phi = 0.7(su)^{3/8}j[DS](b/P') \tag{8}$$

where:
Φ: the average flux of H_2S to the wall
s: is the slope of the pipeline
u: is the velocity of the stream (m/sec)

j: is a pH-dependent factor for the proportion of H_2S
$[DS]$: Dissolved sulfide concentration (mg/l)
b: the width of the stream surface
P': perimeter of the exposed wall.

The average rate of corrosion (mm/year) can be calculated as follows (ASCE No. 60, 2007):

$$c = 11.5\,k\,\Phi(1/A) \tag{9}$$

where
c: the average rate of corrosion (mm/year)
k: Acid reaction factor
A: the acid-consuming capability of the wall material

Replacing Equation (8) in Equation (9) will result in:

$$c = 11.5\,k\times 0.7(su)^{3/8}j\cdot[DS](b/P')(1/A)$$
$$c = 8.05\,k\times(su)^{3/8}j\cdot[DS]\times\frac{b}{P'\cdot A} \tag{10}$$

Therefore the reduction in wall thickness in elapsed time t, is:

$$d(t) = c\cdot t = 8.05\,k\cdot(su)^{3/8}j\cdot[DS]\times\frac{b}{P'\cdot A}.t \tag{11}$$

To consider uncertainties about wall thickness reduction due to corrosion, a stochastic model is presented. Considering equation (11), basic random variables affecting thickness reduction includes: k, u, j, $[DS]$, b/P' and A.

The wall thickness reduction due to corrosion is a function of basic random variables as well as time. It can be expressed as:

$$d(t) = f(k,u,j,[DS],b/P', A, t) \tag{12}$$

It is assumed that statistical information of basic random variables is available. The mean function of d can be expressed as $\mu_d(t)$, and auto-covariance function for d (wall thickness reduction) would be (refer to Li and Melchers 1993):

$$C_{dd}(t_i,t_j) = \rho_d V_d(t_i)V_d(t_j)\mu_d(t_i)\mu_d(t_j) \tag{13}$$

where ρ_d is auto-correlation coefficient for $d(t)$ between two points in time t_i and t_j. V_d is the coefficient of variation. With $\mu_d(t)$ and $C_{dd}(t_i, t_j)$, other statistical parameters of $d(t)$ can be determined to solve Equation (7), Li (2005).

4 EXAMPLE APPLICATION

A comprehensive deterministic life time assessment has been carried out by Karl Kienow and

Kenneth Kienow (2001). They performed sulfide and corrosion modeling as part of screening analyses to support the prioritization of sewer evaluation efforts for a sewer inspection and evaluation in the City of Fresno, California. The project consisted of the inspection and evaluation of about 90 kilometer of concrete sewers in sizes ranging from 30 cm to 70 cm in diameter.

As specific information relative to flow quantity in the evaluation of the sewers was not available, modeling was based on assumed flow rates corresponding to relative depths (depth/diameter) of 0.2, 0.4, and 0.6, each occurring over a period equal to 1/3 of the age of the sewer.

Considering the data from Kienow's work, in the current study a reliability based method was performed for stochastic life time prediction of concrete sewers of 70 cm in diameter. Table 1 contains the input data used for sulfide and corrosion modeling for the California project. To change the deterministic situation to a stochastic condition, the coefficient of variation for every basic variable was assumed (column three in Table 1).

The probability of failure due to wall thickness reduction is computed using equation (7) and the results are shown in Figure (1). As can be concluded from this figure, the effect of a different correlation coefficient in the probability of failure is negligible, specially for the area of interest (acceptable probability of failure around 10 percent).

To estimate the probability of failure due to corrosion, a critical limit for the wall thickness reduction should be established. ASCE manual No. 69 considers exposure of reinforcement as a criterion for failure. Therefore the maximum acceptable limit for wall thickness reduction can be considered equal to the thickness of concrete cover. Figure (3) shows how different acceptable limits for the wall thickness reduction affect the probability of failure (when h/D = 0.2 and ρ = 0.2). This type of result

can be used as a guide for designing new concrete sewer pipes. It clearly shows how increasing the concrete cover (i.e., the cost of pipes production) affects the life time of the sewers. Therefore a sewer designer can economically estimate the design and choose the optimum concrete cover in the conceptual design stage.

4.1 Verification of the results

By using a Monte Carlo simulation (inverse transform method), equation (2) is solved and the results

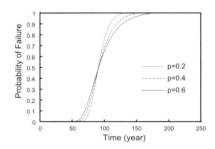

Figure 2. Probability of failure for different coefficients of correlation, ρ.

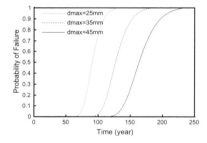

Figure 3. Probability of failure for different critical limits of wall thickness reduction, d_{max}.

Table 1. Values of basic variables.

Basic variables	Mean	Coefficient of variation
K	0.8	0.16
j	0.2	0.04
[DS]	1.5	0.2
u	0.6	0.12
b/P'	h/D = 0.2 b/P' = 0.36	0.072
	h/D = 0.4 b/P' = 0.55	0.11
	h/D = 0.6 b/P' = 0.71	0.14
A	0.18	0.018

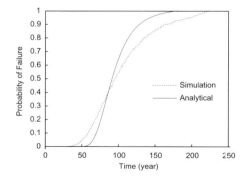

Figure 4. Probability of failure due to concrete corrosion by different methods.

can be compared with the analytical results in the previous stage (Figure 4). The comparison shows that the probability of failure as predicted by equation (7) is in a good agreement with the results from the Monte Carlo simulation, particularly for small probabilities which is of most practical interest.

5 SENSITIVITY ANALYSIS

For a complete reliability analysis it may be appreciated to assess the effect of different random variables on the lifetime of the sewer system. It is of interest to identify those variables that affect the wall thickness reduction most, so that more study can focus on those variables.

Concentration of dissolved sulfide [DS] and the sewage flow rate (presenting by h/D as relative depth) are two variables that are deemed to be of significance to concrete corrosion. The analytical model was run to study the effect of these variables on the probability of failure.

As can be concluded from Figure 5, change in sulfide concentration has a considerable effect on lifetime of the concrete sewer. Considering 10 percent of acceptable probability of failure, the lifetime increases from 50 to 105 years while sulfide concentration decreases from 2 mg/l to 1 mg/l. This is understandable since sulfide concentration is the main source of concrete corrosion in sewers.

Figure 6 also clearly shows the effect of sewage flow quantity on lifetime of the sewer. The relative depth of the flow (h/D) has a significant effect on corrosion rate of concrete and consequently the lifetime of the sewer decreases dramatically by increasing the relative depth.

5.1 The effect of repair on life time of the pipeline

To examine the consequences of repair actions on the lifetime of the sewer pipeline, the model was run assuming a complete repair of corroded

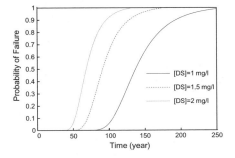

Figure 5. Effect of sulfide concentration on life time of the sewer.

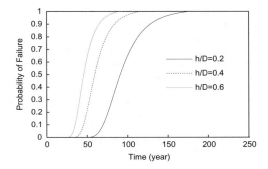

Figure 6. Effect of the relative depth on life time of the sewer.

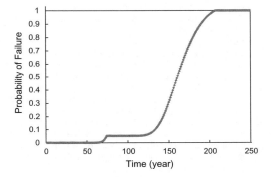

Figure 7. Effect of repair on life time of the sewer.

concrete wall in year 75. The illustrated results in Figure 7 show about 60 years increase in life time at the level of 10 percent acceptable probability of failure (Figure 7).

6 CONCLUSIONS

To predict the service life of concrete sewer pipes, a reliability based method was employed. Failure due to concrete corrosion was formulated and a stochastic model was proposed to consider uncertainties of basic random variables. A time dependent reliability method was employed to quantify the probability of failure so that the time for the sewer to be unusable due to excessive concrete corrosion can be determined with confidence. Sensitivity analysis showed that supplied concentration and relative depth of the fluid have significant effects on the service life of concrete sewer pipes. A Monte Carlo simulation was used to verify the analytical results with a relatively good agreement.

The study also demonstrated that reliability theory can be efficiently applied to repair and maintenance management of infrastructure as represented by sewer pipes.

It can be concluded that a time-dependent reliability method can be used as a rational tool for sustainable infrastructure management system to predict the life expectancy of existing concrete sewers. It helps asset managers to prioritize evaluation efforts and funding allocations for repairing concrete sewers and assists designers to optimize their structural design of sewer pipes by considering the effect of design parameters on the service life of concrete sewer systems.

REFERENCES

Ahammed, M. & Melchers, R.E. 1997. Probabilistic analysis of underground pipelines subject to combined stresses and corrosion. *Engineering Structures*, 19(12), 988–994.

Camarinopoulos, L., Chatzoulis, A., Frontistou-Yannas, S. & Kallidromitis, V. 1999. Assessment of the time-dependent reliability of buried water mains. *Reliability Engineering and System safety* 65, 41–53.

Cheung, M.S. & Kyle, B.R. 1996. Service life prediction of concrete structures by reliability analysis. *Journal of construction and building materials*, 10(1) 45–55.

Kienow, K.E. & Kienow, K.K. 2001. Inspection and Evaluation of Concrete Sewers 12 Inches to 27 Inches in Diameter, Inspection and Evaluation Report, Blair, Church & Flynn Consulting Engineers, for the City of Fresno, California.

Kienow, K.E. & Kienow, K.K. 2004. Risk management ... predicting your next concrete pipe sewer failure before it happens. *ASCE International Conference on Pipelines*, San Diego, California, USA.

Li, C.Q. 2005. Time dependent reliability analysis of the serviceability of corrosion affected concrete structures. *International Journal of Materials & Structural Reliability* Vol. 3, (2) 105–116.

Li, C.Q. & Melchers, R.E. 1993. Out-crossing from convex polyhedrons for non-stationary Gaussian processes. *Journal of Engineering Mechanics*, ASCE, 119 (11) 2354–2361.

Li, S.X., Yu, S.R., Zeng, H.L., Li, J.H. & Liang, R. 2009. Predicting corrosion remaining life of underground pipelines with a mechanically-based probabilistic model. *Journal of Petroleum Science and Engineering* 65(3–4) 162–166.

Manuals and Reports of Engineering Practice—No. 60. 2007. Gravity Sanitary Sewers, 2nd edition, American Society of Civil Engineers.

Manuals and Reports of Engineering Practice—No. 69. 1989. Sulfide in Wastewater Collection and Treatment Systems, American Society of Civil Engineers.

Melchers, R.E. 1999. *Structural reliability analysis and prediction*. Second Edition, John Wiley and sons, Chichester.

Papoulis, A. 1965. *Probability, random variables, and stochastic processes*. McGraw-Hill, New York, 304p.

Pomeroy, R.D. 1976. *The problem of hydrogen sulphide in sewers*. Clay Pipe Development Association.

Concrete Solutions – Grantham, Mechtcherine & Schneck (eds)
© 2012 Taylor & Francis Group, London, ISBN 978-0-415-61622-5

Repairing structures for nuclear facilities: A numerical approach by means of FEM and Monte Carlo techniques

B. Pomaro, V.A. Salomoni & C.E. Majorana
Department of Structural and Transportation Engineering, University of Padua, Padua, Italy

F. Gramegna & G. Prete
INFN, National Instiute of Nuclear Physics, National Laboratories of Legnaro (LNL), Viale dell'Università, Legnaro Padua, Italy

ABSTRACT: Concrete is commonly used as a biological shield against nuclear radiation. As long as, in the design of nuclear facilities, its load carrying capacity is required together with its shielding properties, changes in the mechanical properties due to nuclear radiation are of particular significance and they have to be taken into account in such circumstances.

The study presented here allows for reaching first evidence on the behavior of concrete when exposed to nuclear radiation, in order to evaluate the consequent effect on the mechanical field, by means of a proper definition of the radiation damage, strictly connected with the strength properties of the building material. This is expected to be of help to forecast a possible repair for concrete shielding within reasonable time spans, according to the serviceability of the nuclear structure.

Experimental evidence on the decay of the mechanical properties of concrete have allowed for the implementation of the required damage law within a 3D F.E. research code which accounts for the coupling between moisture, heat transfer and the mechanical field in concrete treated as a fully coupled porous medium.

The upgrade of the numerical model allows for assessing the durability of concrete under the effects of a radioactive environment; considerations on the ultimate strength resource of concrete cannot neglect the temperature rise due to the heat produced by radiation, which, in fact, is proved to represent the most serious source of damage for concrete.

The case study is represented by a next generation nuclear facility under design at the National Institute of Nuclear Physics (INFN), National Laboratories of Legnaro (LNL) in Padua (Italy): the SPES Project. The research structure is expected to produce neutron-rich unstable nuclei, called "exotic beams", by fission reactions of a primary radioactive proton beam on an uranium-carbonium target, in a dedicated underground bunker.

Contour diagrams and time evolution graphs of the most significant variables (temperature, humidity, displacements, damage parameter) are reported, for the practical scenario of the SPES Project, under an irradiation profile lasting approximately six months, i.e., a working rate of the facility for the production of the exotic species of 5000 hours per year, in order to limit the admissible exercise temperatures for concrete.

1 INTRODUCTION

With this work, a recently developed extension of a Finite Element (F.E.) code, NEWCON3D, that can perform fully coupled hygro-thermo-mechanical 3D analyses for cementitious materials, is outlined; the research code is applied to study the effects of nuclear radiation on a concrete shielding for the specific neutron source of the study case, in conjunction with a Monte Carlo code developed by CERN and INFN of Milan, Fluka, used to describe the radiation field (neutron fluence and deposited energy) which the mechanical field is dependent on.

In fact, radiation in the form of either fast and thermal neutrons, primary gamma rays or gamma rays produced as a result of neutron capture can affect concrete. Changes in the properties of concrete appear to depend primarily on the behavior of concrete aggregates that can undergo a volume change when exposed to radiation (Kaplan 1989). Radiation damage in concrete aggregates is caused by changes in the lattice structure of the minerals in the aggregates. Fast neutrons are mainly responsible for the considerable growth, caused by atomic displacements (Naus 2007), that has been measured in certain aggregates (e.g., flint). Quartz aggregates, made of crystals with covalent bonding, seem to be more affected by radiation than calcareous aggregates that contain a weaker ionic bonding (Hilsdorf et al., 1978). Neutron fluences of the order of $10^{19} n/cm^2$ (neutrons per square centimeter) and gamma radiation doses of 10^{10} rad seem to become critical for concrete strength (Hilsdorf et al., 1978; Naus 2007) and there is also evidence that a prolonged exposure to nuclear radiation significantly increases the reactivity of silica-rich aggregates to alkali (Ichikawa & Koizumi 2002).

The physical problem also requires the collateral effect to be taken into account, represented by the development of heat within the shielding, as a consequence of absorbed radiation, as long as the deposited power density is not negligible, i.e. for values of energy flux density below 10^{10} MeV/(cm^2 s).

Section 2 focuses on the main upgrade introduced in NEWCON3D to account for the effects of nuclear radiation on concrete via the definition of a new damage variable; specifically, an expression for radiation damage is suggested, based on experimental evidence; radiation damage is supposed to be acting together with the already implemented chemo-thermo-mechanical damage.

The numerical results are collected in Section 3. Neutron transport calculations can be held deterministically or stochastically (Harrison 1958; Shultis & Faw 1996); the former case implies solving numerically the Boltzman equation, an expression which establishes, in its general integro-differential time-dependant form, the neutron balance (production minus losses) in an arbitrary elementary volume. Since the unknown is the neutron flux, a spatially, directionally and energetically dependent quantity, the numerical resolution implies discretization in space, angles of propagation and energy of radiation. Since the early '90 s the Monte Carlo technique has bees improved to face the same problem and nowadays many physical phenomena have been implemented in Fluka (Fassò et al., 2005) or similar codes.

A proper interface between Fluka outputs, for the main physical quantities, and NEWCON3D has been developed here; this has allowed us to make coupled thermo-hygro-mechanical analyses for a slice of interest of the concrete shield, under a design neutron exposure spectrum. What is relevant is that the thermal effect due to radiation heat development is shown to be the most restrictive for the prescription of the duration of the neutron source compatible with the durability of the shielding material (approximately 6 months).

2 THE MATHEMATICAL MODEL

The F.E. model adopted to perform radiation-induced damage analyses is the 3D research code NEWCON3D (Schrefler et al., 1989; Baggio et al., 1995; Majorana et al., 1995, 1997, 1998; Majorana & Salomoni 2004; Salomoni et al., 2007a, 2007b, 2008). Concrete is here treated as a multiphase system where the micropores of the skeleton are partially filled with liquid water, in the form of bound or absorbed water and free or capillary water, and partially filled with a gas mixture composed of dry air (non-condensable constituent) and water vapour (condensable), supposed to behave like an ideal gas.

When higher than standard temperatures are taken into account, several phenomena are considered within the code, dealing with concrete as a porous medium: with heat conduction, vapour diffusion and liquid water flow in the voids.

As regards the mechanical field, the model couples shrinkage, creep, damage and plasticity effects within the constitutive law of the material, here developed starting from a thermodynamic approach.

2.1 Definition of radiation damage

As reported by available experimental data (Hilsdorf et al., 1978), a decay in the elastic modulus of concrete is to be expected due to nuclear radiation.

Figure 1 shows the effect of neutron radiation on the modulus of elasticity of concrete: the modulus of irradiated concrete E_c is given as a fraction of the modulus of companion specimens E_{c0}, neither irradiated nor temperature exposed.

The scattering of the experimental data is expected to be due to several reasons: different

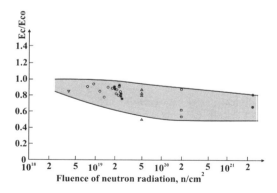

Figure 1. Modulus of elasticity of concrete after neutron radiation E_c related to modulus of elasticity of untreated concrete E_{c0} (Hilsdorf et al., 1978).

concrete making materials of the samples, different mix proportions of mortars, different specimens size, different cooling and drying conditions, impinging of fast or slow neutrons, possible simultaneous temperature exposure of specimens.

The available data are not sufficient to separate the effects of radiation and of heating of the samples (which in many cases are undergone in nuclear vessels conditions) however it seems reasonable to conclude that the strength loss is primarily due to neutron radiation, in analogy with similar graphs for the compressive and the tensile strength, for which a separation of the two effects was possible (Hilsdorf et al., 1978).

Therefore a neutron fluence lower than 10^{19} n/cm^2 is understood to be of some interest to appreciate a decrease in the Young modulus of irradiated concrete.

The lowest enveloping curve, for safety reasons, has been taken into account for describing the amount of damage due to radiation within NEWCON3D, in agreement with the effective stress theory (Kachanov 1958), and in conjunction with the already implemented forms of damage (i.e., thermo-chemical and mechanical); for their combination in the definition of a total damage parameter, see also (Mazars 1984, 1989; Mazars & Pijaudier-Cabot 1989, 1996; Gerard et al., 1998, Nechnech et al., 2001).

The enveloping curve is defined in a way that up to a neutron fluence of 10^{18} n/cm^2 the radiation damage is zero, then it increases with the neutron fluence and finally stabilizes at the maximum value of 50% of the E_c/E_{co} ratio. It was not necessary to extrapolate data in the numerical application.

3 NUMERICAL APPLICATION: FLUKA-NEWCON3D: A COMBINED APPROACH

3.1 Geometry of the problem and Fluka results

The case study takes its origin from the SPES Project that is currently being developed at the National Laboratories of Legnaro (Padua, Italy). The facility will be directed to the production of special radioactive heavy ion beams from a primary proton beam impinging on a target made of fissionable material, where fission reactions are expected to take place; the target therefore ideally represents a point-source of neutrons for the specific problem.

The target room is expected to be an underground bunker with wall thicknesses of the order of few meters, estimated by INFN with the aid of Monte Carlo simulations in order to keep the environment under 0,25 mSv/h ambient dose equivalent (INFN-LNL-224 Executive summary 2008),

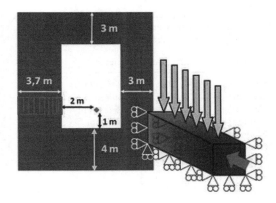

Figure 2. Geometry of the target cave for the SPES Project and static scheme of the model analyzed with NEWCON3D.

which is the limit dose prescribed by the national standard on radio-protection.

In Figure 2, a sketch of the geometry is reported: the point inside the room is the uranium carbide target; the neutron source is located at 1 m from the floor and 2 m from the directly impinged wall, which for safety reasons has been estimated 3.7 m thick.

The portion of concrete shielding modeled with NEWCON3D is the prism emphasized in figure, representing a typical wall portion directly exposed to neutron radiation. The prism has been restrained so to allow for dilations/contractions along the wall thickness only; selfweight has been neglected.

In this way the mechanical damage is expected to be zero, so that the only contributions to damage come from thermo-chemical effects or radiation.

The same geometry has been implemented in Fluka, in order to have an estimate of the main physical quantities affecting the problem, i.e. neutron fluence and energy power deposition. The former, which the decay in the Young modulus is a function of, is directly responsible for the quantification of radiation damage; the latter allows for determining the boundary conditions in terms of temperature, at the most exposed face of the wall.

The geometry in Fluka is assigned by means of elemental volumes (planes, spheres, parallelepipeds, regular prisms, ...) and Boolean operations between them (addition, subtraction, union) applied to describe "regions" made of different materials. Each portion of space needs to be assigned to one region only. As regards concrete, the chemical composition of an ordinary concrete in percentage by weight has been adopted (Table 1).

The target of fissionable material has the dimension of seven disks (of uranium and carbon compounds) for a total mass of 30 g, radius of 2 cm

Table 1. Assumed chemical composition for the ordinary concrete implemented in Fluka (Kaplan 1989).

Element	% by weight	Element	% by weight
Hydrogen	0.64	Phosphorus	0.09
Oxygen	45.36	Sulphur	0.09
Carbon	–	Potassium	0.64
Sodium	1.76	Calcium	13.05
Magnesium	3.66	Titanium	0.47
Aluminium	5.88	Iron	0.13
Silicon	20.90	Nickel	7.64

Concrete density [g cm^{-3}] 2.33

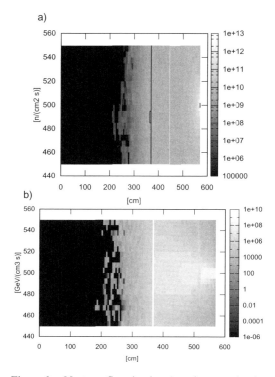

Figure 3. Neutron flux density a) and power density b) on the cutting plane of the directly exposed control volume.

and thickness of about 1.3 mm, which makes it like an ideal point-source of neutrons.

The impinging beam is assumed to start from an arbitrary point inside a vacuum pipe; thanks to the vacuum environment, it is therefore supposed to be delivered to the target as not attenuated. The characteristics of the primary proton beam come from the most serious exercise scenario designed by INFN for the SPES facility: a beam of energy 70 MeV, and electric current 300 μA. The stochastic simulation with Fluka has required 3 cycles per run, with 10^6 primary particles launched at each run, in order to reach acceptable statistics. The code makes a 3D analysis, though the visualization style is two-dimensional.

Fluka results are provided on a regular parallel-epiped grid, at the centre of mass for each element, the dimensions of which are determined by the required resolution for results. A regular grid of small elements 5 cm wide along each direction has been adopted for our study. A subsequent interface program has been additionally used to pass results from the centre of mass for each volume of the resultant grid to the FEM mesh implemented in NEWCON3D, based on the algorithm of the minimum distance.

In Figure 3 the results of the two physical quantities of interest are depicted, referring to the cutting plane of reference (Figure 2): neutron flux density [n/(cm^2 s)] and power density [GeV/(cm^3 s)].

The order of magnitude of the maximum neutron flux density is proved to be 10^{10} n/(cm^2 s); the maximum power density is 10^{10} GeV/(cm^3 s).

Neutron flux density, integrated in time of exposure to radiation (thus getting neutron fluence), is intended to enter NEWCON3D as the parameter directly affecting radiation damage, according to Figure 1; power density has been used to estimate the temperature field in concrete due to heat production by radiation, particularly to impose boundary conditions for temperature at the outer face of the parallelepiped modeled in NEWCON3D.

The temperature rise has been quantified via a transient thermal analysis and then applied as a variable boundary condition to the F.E. model. In Figure 4 the contour map of temperature for a neutron source working continuously for 6 months is shown.

The maximum value is encountered at the corner next to the source, where temperature after six months reaches nearly 70°C; the last picture shows, for the same critical node, a parabolic increase in time.

The thermal aspect is shown to be not negligible, which is in agreement with the prescriptions of ANSI/ANS-6.4-1985, according to which radiation heat and subsequent thermal effects are to be taken into account for energy flux densities (power densities) above 10^{10} MeV/(cm^2 s).

It is to be noticed that Figure 3b gives maximum values of the order of magnitude of 10^{10} GeV/(cm^3 s), where cm^3 are to be intended per volume of the small elements defined by the resolution of the results' grid (side of the cubes 5 cm), therefore one gets 5×10^{10} GeV/(cm^2 s), which is quite above the prescribed limit required to neglect thermal effects. In fact they are understood to be the main

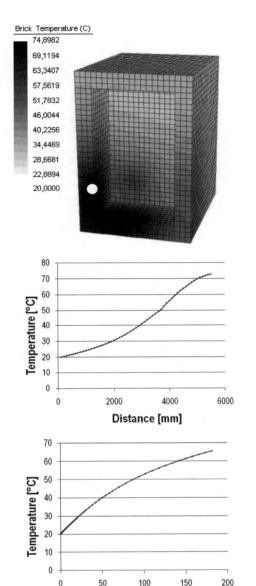

Figure 4. Temperatures in the portion of shielding surrounding the target after 6 months of work for the facility; point graphs refer to temperature vs. space and time.

Back-analyses with Fluka have been made in order to study the influence of radiation heat in the variation of water content of concrete, but no significant change in the neutron fluence has been envisaged; this has allowed us to conclude that the experimented deposited energies do not provide significant losses in the shielding properties of concrete; i.e., the slight variations in water content, due to radiation heat, have not been shown to affect the moderating capacity of concrete towards neutrons, namely due to the intrinsic hydrogen content given by its bound water.

3.2 Implementation into NEWCON3D

As already evidenced, the attenuation process of the incident radiation within concrete is a time-evolving phenomenon: neutron fluence [n/cm^2] is a flux density [$n/(cm^2\ s)$] integrated in the duration time of radiation, while power density [$GeV/(cm^3\ s)$] varies with the irradiation profile of the facility and in general it is due to a constant component, so called "*prompt radiation*", instantaneously provided when the facility works (zero otherwise) and a "*delayed*" component represented by the decay of radioactive particles, which is the time-variable amount.

Consequently, the problem is numerically treated as a time dependent process where radiation damage and temperatures at the boundary need to be calculated for several time steps.

The discretization is characterized by 4037 nodes and 800 elements, 20-node isoparametric brick elements; temperature is applied at the internal free prism surface.

Initial conditions are homogeneous and consider an internal relative humidity of 60% and a temperature of 20°C.

The results from the hygro-thermo-mechanical analysis are reported in Figures 5–9 (only a portion of the model is here shown); particularly, Figures 8 and 9 depict damage, longitudinal displacements, relative humidity and temperature, respectively, along the prism central axis and a parallel line at its border.

Relative humidity seems not to be much affected by the 6 months prolonged radiation, whereas temperature rise is understood to be of interest, leading to thermal gradients up to 50°C; for this reason the irradiation profile for the SPES facility should not exceed 5000 hours/year, i.e., nearly 7 months of continuous service, within the investigated exercise scenario (once specifics on the primary proton beam and geometry of the target cave are assigned).

As regards the results in terms of damage, this is intended to be due only to thermo-chemical effects, since the neutron fluence, for the investigated

cause for the stress state of the shielding, as will be evidenced by the thermo-hygro-mechanical analyses reported in the following.

The thermal analysis even justifies the working period of the facility assumed in the study, i.e., nearly 7 months, 5000 hours per year, resulting in longer durations being unacceptable for the material, due to the high temperatures reached.

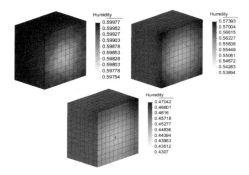

Figure 5. Contour maps of relative humidity after 1 hour, 1 week, 6 months [–].

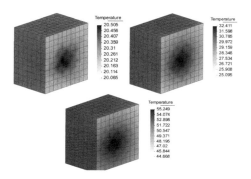

Figure 6. Contour maps of temperature after 1 hour, 1 week, 6 months [°C].

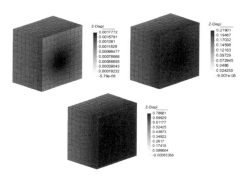

Figure 7. Contour maps of longitudinal displacements after 1 hour, 1 week, 6 months [mm].

time span, stays always under the critical value of $10^{19} n/cm^2$, which is expected to mark the beginning of the first evidence of damage by radiation in concrete; therefore, once more, the thermal aspect of the problem represents the most restrictive condition to prescribe the period of work for the facility as well as to define its structural integrity.

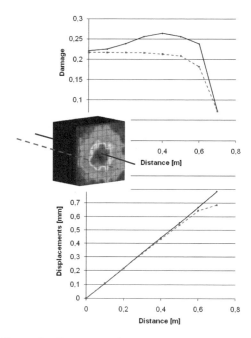

Figure 8. Damage and longitudinal displacements distribution after 6 months along the first 0.7 m wall thickness.

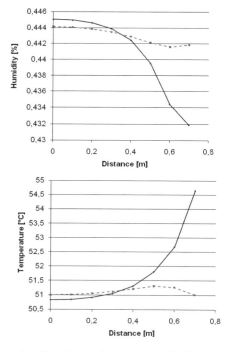

Figure 9. Humidity and temperature distribution after 6 months along the first 0.7 m wall thickness.

562

4 CONCLUSIONS

Nuclear radiation is known to affect the mechanical behavior of concrete above specific threshold quantities of radiation fluence. Even thermal collateral effects, due to heat production by absorbed radiation, can be of interest, thus requiring, for this kind of problem, a fully coupled hygro-thermo-mechanical approach to catch the response of concrete when employed as a shielding for nuclear facilities.

In this work the study case is represented by the SPES Project, an ongoing research project at INFN Laboratories in Legnaro (Padua, Italy) directed towards the production of neutron rich nuclei.

A collection of the most relevant experimental results on neutron irradiated concrete has allowed the definition of a radiation damage scenario, developed by means of a 3D F.E. research code assessing the coupled hygro-thermo-mechanical behavior of concrete.

Results from a Monte Carlo code developed by CERN and INFN have been properly interfaced to the numerical code in order to investigate the trend of humidity, temperature and mechanical quantities for the most exposed portion of the concrete shield.

Particularly, the numerical analyses have helped in identifying the maximum time span for continuous working of SPES as 5000 hours per year, to guarantee admissible thermal gradients for the material; in fact, thermal effects due to radiation appear as the most critical scenarios when defining safety exercise conditions.

Further steps in the research will be devoted to study the long term behavior of such kinds of structures, possibly assuming not continuous irradiation profiles, to quantify the delayed effect of the radiation decay after many cycles of work up to final decommissioning of the nuclear structure.

On the other hand, a meso-scale modeling of concrete is envisaged to be of interest, particularly for a more realistic representation of the building material, as well as for understanding the contribution of aggregates and interfacial transition zone (ITZ) in the characterization and definition of radiation shielding properties.

REFERENCES

Baggio, P., Majorana, C.E. & Schrefler, B.A. 1995. Thermo-hygro-mechanical analysis of concrete. *Int J Num Meth Fluids* 20: 573–595.

Fassò, A., Ferrari, A., Ranft, J. & Sala, P.R. 2005. CERN-2005-10, INFN/TC_05/11, SLAC-R-773 *FLUKA: a multi-particle transport code.*

Gerard, B., Pijaudier-Cabot, G. & Laborderie, C. 1998. Coupled diffusion-damage modeling and the implications on failure due to strain localization. *Int J Solids Structures* 35(31–32): 4107–20.

Harrison, J.R. 1958. *Nuclear reactor shielding.* Temple Press.

Hilsdorf, H.K., Kropp, J. & Koch, H.J. 1978. The effects of nuclear radiation on the mechanical properties of concrete. In Amer Concr Inst Special Publication SP 55-10: *Douglas McHenry International Symposium on Concrete and Concrete Structures*: 223–251. Detroit, Michigan.

Ichikawa, T. & Koizumi, H. 2002. Possibility of radiation-induced degradation of concrete by alkali-silica reaction of aggregates. *J of Nucl Sci Technol* 39(8): 880–884.

INFN-LNL-224 2008. *SPES Selective Production of Exotic Species: Executive summary.* A. Covello, G. Prete (eds), National Laboratories of Legnaro.

Kachanov, M.D. 1958. Time of Rupture Process under Creep Conditions. *Izvestia Akademii Nauk* 8: 26–31 (in Russian).

Kaplan, M.F. 1989. *Concrete radiation shielding: nuclear physics, concrete properties, design and construction.* John Wiley & Sons, New York.

Majorana, C.E., Saetta, A., Scotta, R. & Vitaliani, R. 1995. Mechanical and durability models for lifespan analysis of bridges. *IABSE Sym.: Extending the lifespan of structures*, San Francisco, CA, USA, aug. 23–25: 1253–1258.

Majorana, C.E. & Salomoni, V.A. 2004. Parametric analyses of diffusion of activated sources in disposal forms. *J of Hazard Mat* A113: 45–56.

Majorana, C.E., Salomoni, V.A. & Secchi, S. 1997. Effects of mass growing on mechanical and hygro-thermic response of three-dimensional bodies. *J Mat Process Technol* PROO64/1–3: 277–286.

Majorana, C.E., Salomoni, V.A. & Schrefler, B.A. 1998. Hygrothermal and mechanical model of concrete at high temperature. *Mat Str* 31: 378–386.

Mazars, J. 1989. Description of the behavior of composite concretes under complex loadings through continuum damage mechanics. In ASME. Lamb J.P. (ed.), *Proc. 10th U.S. National Congress of Applied Mech.*

Mazars, J. & Pijaudier-Cabot, G. 1989. Continuum Damage Theory – Application to Concrete. *J Engrg Mech ASCE* 115: 345–365.

Mazars, J. & Pijaudier-Cabot, G. 1996. From damage to fracture mechanics and conversely: a combined approach. *Int J Solids Structures* 33: 3327–42.

Nechnech, W., Reynouard, J.M. & Meftah, F. 2001. On modeling of thermo-mechanical concrete for the finite element analysis of structures submitted to elevated temperatures. In De Borst, Mazars, Pijaudier-Cabot & van Mier (eds), *Proc. Fracture Mech of Concrete Structures*: 271–278.

Naus, D.J. 2007. Primer on durability of nuclear power plant reinforced concrete structures: a review of pertinent factors. Oak Ridge National Laboratory, U.S. Nuclear Regulatory Commission Office of Nuclear Regulatory Research Washington, DC.

Salomoni, V.A., Majorana, C.E., Giannuzzi, G.M. & Miliozzi, A. 2008. Thermal-fluid flow within innovative heat storage concrete systems for solar power plants. *Int J Num Meth for Heat and Fluid Flow (Special Issue)* 18(7/8): 969–999.

Salomoni, V.A., Majorana, C.E. & Khoury, G.A. 2007a. Stress-strain experimental-based modeling of concrete under high temperature conditions. In B.H.V. Topping (ed.), *Civil Engineering Computations: Tools and Techniques*, Ch.14: 319–346. Saxe-Coburg Publications.

Salomoni, V.A., Mazzucco, G. & Majorana, C.E. 2007b. Mechanical and Durability Behavior of Growing Concrete Structures, *Engrg Comput* 24(5): 536–561.

Schrefler, B.A., Simoni, L. & Majorana, C.E. 1989. A general model for the mechanics of saturated-unsaturated porous materials. *Mat Str* 22: 323–334.

Shultis, J.K. & Faw, R.E. 1996. *Radiation shielding*. Prentice Hall PTR.

Concrete Solutions – Grantham, Mechtcherine & Schneck (eds)
© 2012 Taylor & Francis Group, London, ISBN 978-0-415-61622-5

Multi-physics numerical model for the repair of concrete structures

G. Sciumè
Department of Structural and Transportation Engineering, University of Padua, Padua, Italy
Laboratoire de Mécanique et Technologie, École Normale Supérieure de Cachan, Cachan, France

B.A. Schrefler
Department of Structural and Transportation Engineering, University of Padua, Padua, Italy

ABSTRACT: Experience has shown that repairs of concrete structures are often subject to premature cracking because the already dry and rigid substrate of the damaged structure contrasts the drying and self-drying contractions of the new material of restoration. In this paper a thermo-hygro-chemo-mechanical (THCM) model for concrete at early age is presented and used to analyze the behaviour of a real repair case taking into account casting and environmental conditions. The multi-physics mathematical model is a simplified version of COMES-HTC (developed a few years ago by Gawin, Pesavento & Schrefler, 2006). The THCM model for concrete at early age has been implemented in the French finite elements code CAST3M (developed by the CEA, *Commissariat c l'Energie Atomique* Français).

1 INTRODUCTION

During the last twenty years great progress has been achieved in the synthesis of special mortars and concretes for the repairs of damaged concrete structures. However these problems were always analyzed with a phenomenological and experimental approach, which typically can introduce errors when changing from laboratory specimens to real applications cases. The objective of this paper is to present a powerful numerical tool to study the thermo-hygro-chemo-mechanical behaviour of repairs taking into account the real casting and environmental conditions.

2 MATHEMATICAL APPROACH

The mathematical approach is a simplified version of the multi-physics model developed a few years ago by Gawin, Pesavento & Schrefler (2006). The unknowns of the numerical model are: capillary pressure P_c, temperature T and displacements **u**. The parameters of the model depend on two internal variables: the hydration degree and the mechanical damage.

2.1 Solidification model

The advancement degree of hydration of concrete Γ is defined as the ratio between the amount of water chemically combined at time t and that chemically combined at time $t = \infty$ if the material was kept in saturated conditions.

$$\Gamma_{(t)} = \frac{m_{(t)}^{hydr}}{m_\infty^{hydr}} \qquad (1)$$

The hydration process rate depends on the chemical affinity of the reaction, relative humidity and temperature. To calculate the hydration process rate, the following equation is used:

$$\frac{d\Gamma}{dt} = A_{(\Gamma)}\beta_{(h)}\exp\left(-\frac{E_a}{RT}\right) \qquad (2)$$

where $A_{(\Gamma)}$ = chemical affinity; E_a = hydration activation energy; R = universal gas constant and $\beta_{(h)}$ is a function of relative humidity (h).

The chemical affinity evolution used in the numerical model is a new analytical expression proposed by the authors and defined by four parameters A_i, A_p, Γ_p and α:

$$A_{(\Gamma)} = \frac{A_P\left[\dfrac{A_i}{A_P} + \sin\left(\dfrac{\Gamma_p + \Gamma - |\Gamma_p - \Gamma|}{2\Gamma_p} \cdot \dfrac{\pi}{2}\right)\right]}{\left[1 + \alpha\left(\dfrac{\Gamma - \Gamma_p + |\Gamma - \Gamma_p|}{2 - 2\Gamma_p}\right)^4\right]} - \left(\dfrac{A_i + A_p}{1 + \alpha}\right)\Gamma \qquad (3)$$

where A_i = initial affinity; A_p = the maximum value of the affinity function achieved for $\Gamma = \Gamma_p$; and α regulates the deceleration phase of the hydration process. Thanks to the meaning of its parameters this expression is really good to interpolate the experimental evaluations of the affinity function (Fig. 1).

Relative humidity plays an important role in the rate of the hydration process. Experimentally, it was shown that when the relative humidity decreases, the hydration process slows down, and if the relative humidity falls below a certain value, hydration stops. The curve $\beta_{(h)}$ in Equation (2) introduces the effect of relative humidity on the hydration process:

$$\beta_{(h)} = \frac{1}{1 + \left(a_h - a_h h\right)^4} \qquad (4)$$

For more details on the parameters of the numerical model see the reference paper of Gawin et al. (2006).

2.2 Thermal and hygral constitutive equations

The cement paste micro-structure is very complex. In the pores of the cement matrix, liquid water, vapour water and dry air are present (Fig. 2). Capillary pressure P_c in case of local thermodynamic equilibrium depends on the pressure of the liquid phase P_w and the gaseous one P_g: $P_c \approx P_g - P_w$

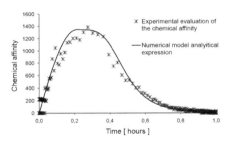

Figure 1.   Affinity curve for the numerical model.

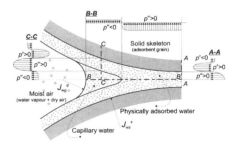

Figure 2.   Idealized representation of the micro-structure of a capillary pore.

The most important simplification of the presented model, compared to the reference mathematical formulation (Gawin, Pesavento & Schrefler), is the realistic assumption that in normal environmental conditions, gas pressure can be considered equal to the atmospheric one (0.1 MPa), and then it affects negligibly the value of capillary pressure. On the other hand the introduced assumption doesn't exclude a priori the presence of vapour pressure gradients and vapour diffusion.

So for the water mass balance equation there are two contributions:

$$\dot{m}_l = \nabla \cdot \left[K_{(P_c,T)} \nabla P_c\right] - \dot{m}_{vap} - \dot{m}_{hydr}$$

$$\dot{m}_v = \nabla \cdot \left[D_{(P_c,T)} \nabla P_v\right] + \dot{m}_{vap}$$

Adding the two previous equations eliminates the term $\dot{m}_{vap}$ and gives:

$$\dot{m}_w = \nabla \cdot \left[K_{(P_c,T)} \nabla P_c + D_{(P_c,T)} \nabla P_v\right] - \dot{m}_{hydr}$$

From $h = P_v / P_{vs}$ (P_{vs} = saturated vapour pressure) we can write the previous equation as function of the primary variables T and P_c:

$$\dot{m}_w = \nabla \cdot \left[\left(K + D P_{vs} \frac{\partial h}{\partial P_c}\right) \nabla P_c \right.$$
$$\left. + D\left(P_{vs} \frac{\partial h}{\partial T} + h \frac{\partial P_{vs}}{\partial T}\right) \nabla T\right] - \dot{m}_{hydr}$$

Multiplying ∇T for $\left(\nabla P_c \cdot \nabla P_c\right) / \left|\nabla P_c\right|^2$ (equal to 1) and doing some algebraic calculus gives:

$$\dot{m}_w = \nabla \cdot \left\{\left[\left(K + D P_{vs} \frac{\partial h}{\partial P_c}\right)\mathbf{1} + D\left(P_{vs} \frac{\partial h}{\partial T} + h \frac{\partial P_{vs}}{\partial T}\right) \right.\right.$$
$$\left.\left. \times \frac{\nabla T \otimes \nabla P_c}{\left|\nabla P_c\right|^2}\right] \nabla P_c\right\} - \dot{m}_{hydr}$$

where **1** is the identity matrix. For the case of concrete repairs there aren't important thermal gradients and so the contribution of the anisotropic matrix that depends on ∇T can be neglected. Then the thermo-hygro-chemical part of the numerical model is governed by the enthalpy balance equation and by the mass balance equations of water (simplified):

$$\left(\rho C\right)_{eff} \dot{T} = \nabla \cdot \left[\lambda \nabla T\right] + L_{hydr} \dot{\Gamma} \qquad (5)$$

$$\dot{m}_w = \nabla \cdot \left[\left(K + D_{mv} P_{vs} \frac{\partial h}{\partial P_c}\right) \nabla P_c\right] - \dot{m}_{hydr} \qquad (6)$$

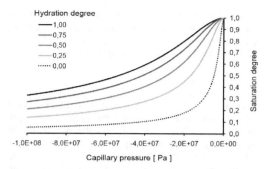

Figure 3. Desorption isotherm function that depends on the advancement degree of the hydration.

In the enthalpy balance equation (5) the loss of energy due to vaporization is not taken into account, because it has an irrelevant impact. These two equations are implemented and solved by using of the French finite element code Cast 3M developed by the CEA (Commissariat à l'Energie Atomique Français).

The desorption isotherm is intimately linked with the microstructure of cement paste, and changes with temperature. Experimentally it was seen that the effect of temperature begins to be significant above 85°C (Gawin et al., 2002). For this reason the used desorption isotherm (for repair simulations) doesn't depend on temperature. However its dependence on the degree of hydration is not negligible; so the analytical expression for the desorption isotherm is that proposed by Van Genuchten, modified by the authors to take into account the cement matrix degree of hydration.

$$S_w = \left\{ 1 + \left[\frac{P_c}{a} \left(\frac{\Gamma + \Gamma_p}{1 + \Gamma_p} \right)^{-c} \right]^{\frac{b}{b-1}} \right\}^{-\frac{1}{b}} \tag{7}$$

where a and b are the classical parameters of the Van Genuchten law, c and Γ_p are the new parameters introduced to take into account the hydration degree.

The boundary conditions are assumed to be of convective type. The convective heat flux q_t (Wm^{-2}) and convective water mass flux q_h (kg s^{-1} m^{-2}) are:

$$q_t = \varphi_t \left(T_s - T_{ext} \right) \mathbf{n}$$

$$q_h = \varphi_h \left(h_s - h_{ext} \right) \mathbf{n}$$

where φ_t and φ_h are the thermal and hygral convective coefficients; T_s = temperature on the surface (K); T_{ext} = ambient temperature (K); h_s = relative humidity on the surface; h_{ext} = ambient relative humidity and $\mathbf{n}$ is the normal unit vector to the surface (oriented towards the exterior).

2.3 Mechanical constitutive model

The mechanical behaviour of concrete is modeled by an elastic damage model coupled with creep, which includes the evolution of the mechanical properties with respect to the hydration degree (De Schutter & Taerwe 1996) and with respect to damage (Mazars 1986). The relationship between apparent stresses $\boldsymbol{\sigma}$, effective stresses $\tilde{\boldsymbol{\sigma}}$ (in the sense of damage mechanics), damage D, elastic stiffness tensor $\mathbf{E}$, elastic strains $\boldsymbol{\varepsilon}_{el}$, creep strains $\boldsymbol{\varepsilon}_{cr}$, shrinkage strains $\boldsymbol{\varepsilon}_{sh}$, thermal strains $\boldsymbol{\varepsilon}_{th}$ and total strains $\boldsymbol{\varepsilon}$ reads:

$$\boldsymbol{\sigma} = (1 - D) \tilde{\boldsymbol{\sigma}}$$

$$\dot{\tilde{\boldsymbol{\sigma}}} = \mathbf{E}_{(\Gamma)} \dot{\boldsymbol{\varepsilon}}_{el} = \mathbf{E}_{(\Gamma)} \left(\dot{\boldsymbol{\varepsilon}} - \dot{\boldsymbol{\varepsilon}}_{sh} - \dot{\boldsymbol{\varepsilon}}_{th} - \dot{\boldsymbol{\varepsilon}}_{cr} \right)$$

The Poisson ratio is assumed to be constant and the Young modulus E increases due to hydration as follows (De Schutter & Taerwe 1996):

$$E_{(\Gamma)} = E_\infty \left\langle \frac{\Gamma - \Gamma_0}{1 - \Gamma_0} \right\rangle_+^\beta \tag{8}$$

where Γ_0 = mechanical percolation threshold corresponding to the advancement degree of hydration below which the concrete has negligible mechanical properties (Young modulus, strength, etc.); it is kept constant and equal to 0.1, which corresponds to the usual value reported in the bibliographical analysis (De Schutter & Taerwe 1996). However it depends, in fact, on aggregates content, type of cement and water to cement ratio (Torrenti & Benboudjema). β is a constant equal to 0.62 according to De Schutter and $\langle \ \rangle_+$ is the positive part operator.

The damage D is linked to the elastic equivalent tensile strain $\hat{\varepsilon}$:

$$\hat{\varepsilon} = \sqrt{\langle \varepsilon_{el} \rangle_+ : \langle \varepsilon_{el} \rangle_+} \tag{9}$$

The damage criterion is given by (Mazars 1986):

$$f = \hat{\varepsilon} - \kappa_0 (\Gamma)$$

where $\kappa_0(\Gamma)$ is the tensile strain threshold.
Then $D = 0$ if $\hat{\varepsilon} < \kappa_0(\Gamma)$ and:

$$D = 1 - \frac{\kappa_0}{\hat{\varepsilon}} \left[(1 + A_t) \exp(-B_t \hat{\varepsilon}) - A_t \exp(-2B_t \hat{\varepsilon}) \right]$$

if $\hat{\varepsilon} > \kappa_0(\Gamma)$

567

where A_t and B_t are constant material parameters which control the softening branch in the stress–strain curve in tension. In the application cases presented in this paper only damage due to tension is considered (compressive stresses are very small as compared with the compressive strength).

The tensile strength evolution is (De Schutter & Taerwe 1996):

$$f_{t(\Gamma)} = f_{t\infty} \left\langle \frac{\Gamma - \Gamma_0}{1 - \Gamma_0} \right\rangle_+^{\gamma} \tag{10}$$

where $f_{t\infty}$ (Pa) is the final tensile strength (for $\Gamma = 1$), and γ is a constant equal to 0.46 according to experimental data.

The evolution of the tensile strain threshold is then computed from the evolution of tensile strength (Equation (10)) and Young modulus (Equation (8)):

$$\kappa_0(\Gamma) = \frac{f_t(\Gamma)}{E(\Gamma)} = \frac{f_{t\infty}}{E_\infty} \left\langle \frac{\Gamma - \Gamma_0}{\Gamma_\infty - \Gamma_0} \right\rangle_+^{\gamma - \beta} \tag{11}$$

The thermal strain ε_{th} is related to the temperature variation, due to the release of heat by hydration:

$$\dot{\varepsilon}_{th} = \alpha_{th} \dot{T} \mathbf{1} \tag{12}$$

The equation used to calculate the isotropic shrinkage contraction reads:

$$\dot{\varepsilon}_{sh} = \left(c_s \frac{1 - 2\nu}{E} S_w \right) \dot{P}_c \mathbf{1} \tag{13}$$

where c_s is a coefficient depending on cement matrix microstructure; S_w = saturation degree; $\mathbf{1}$ is the unit tensor and P_c is the capillary pressure.

The cement's hydration is accompanied by a decrease in volume which is equal to about 8,7% of the formed hydrates volume (LeChâtelier 1900). Before the development of a rigid mineral skeleton, this contraction produces only a small decrease in the external volume of cement paste. After the transition from semi-fluid state to semi-solid state ($\Gamma > \Gamma_0$), the decrease in volume due to hydration is incompatible with the admissible deformation of the solid skeleton. Thus, in the capillary pores initially saturated by water, there is the development of a volume of gas. This decrease of water saturation degree causes the autogenous contraction. The stoichiometry of the cement paste during hydration allows us to model the self-shrinkage mechanically by the mass balance of water (Equation (6)) and the shrinkage constitutive model (Equation (13)).

It will be shown in the numerical simulation that tensile creep is very important, since it relaxes the tension stresses and reduces cracking. The total creep strain has different components:

$$\varepsilon_{cr} = \varepsilon_{bc} + \varepsilon_{mc} + \varepsilon_{tc} + \varepsilon_{dc}$$

where ε_{bc} = basic creep; ε_{mc} = micro-creep strain that is intimately linked to microstructure and capillary pressure (Bazant 1988); ε_{tc} = thermal transient creep and ε_{dc} = drying creep.

Given that the objective of this work is to present the potential of the numerical tool qualitatively, for simplicity in the presented numerical simulation only basic creep is considered.

Usually models for basic creep are based on rheological elements (spring and dashpots): Kelvin-Voigt and Maxwell chains are combined in serial and/or parallel.

Here, three Kelvin-Voigt chains and one dashpot combined in a serial way are used (Fig. 4).

In order to respect the thermodynamic restrictions, an incremental constitutive relation for an aging spring is used.

Let us consider a Kelvin-Voigt unit i. The incremental equilibrium equation for the Kelvin cell is:

$$\dot{\tilde{\sigma}} = \dot{\tilde{\sigma}}_{sp}^i + \dot{\tilde{\sigma}}_{ds}^i$$

in which $\tilde{\sigma}_{ds}^i$ and $\tilde{\sigma}_{sp}^i$ are the effective stresses acting on the dashpot and the spring (in the Kelvin-Voigt unit i), respectively.

The behaviour law of the spring reads:

$$k_{bc}^i(\Gamma) \dot{\varepsilon}_{bc}^i = \dot{\tilde{\sigma}}_{sp}^i$$

where ε_{bc}^i is the elementary basic creep strain and k_{bc}^i is the stiffness of the spring in the Kelvin-Voigt unit i. The behaviour law of the dashpot reads:

$$\eta_{bc}^i(\Gamma) \dot{\varepsilon}_{bc}^i = \tilde{\sigma}_{ds}^i$$

where η_{bc}^i is the viscosity of the dashpot in the Kelvin-Voigt unit i.

The effect of age on basic creep is taken into account by relating the material parameters to the advancement degree of hydration. The relationships

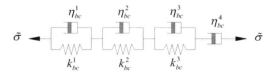

Figure 4.   Kelvin-Voigt elements for the prediction of creep strains.

proposed by De Schutter (1999) are slightly modified for the Kelvin-Voigt units (Benboudjema & Torrenti 2008):

$$k_{bc}^i(\Gamma) = k_{bc-\infty}^i \left(\frac{0.473}{2.081 - 1.608 \cdot \bar{\Gamma}} \right) \bar{\Gamma}^{-0.62}$$

$$\tau_{bc}^i = \frac{\eta_{bc}^i(\Gamma)}{k_{bc}^i(\Gamma)}$$

in which $\bar{\Gamma} = \left\langle (\Gamma - \Gamma_0)(1 - \Gamma_0)^{-1} \right\rangle_+$, $k_{bc-\infty}^i$ is the final stiffness (i.e., when $\Gamma = 1$) of the spring in the Kelvin-Voigt unit i. The retardation times τ_{bc}^i are assumed to be constant.

Combining the previous equations, we obtain a non-linear second-order differential equation for each Kelvin-Voigt element:

$$\tau_{bc}^i \ddot{\varepsilon}_{bc}^i + \left(\tau_{bc}^i \frac{\dot{k}_{bc}^i(\Gamma)}{k_{bc}^i(\Gamma)} + 1 \right) \dot{\varepsilon}_{bc}^i = \frac{\dot{\sigma}}{k_{bc}^i(\Gamma)}$$

This creep model was developed in Cast 3M by Benboudjema & Torrenti. For details on the numerical algorithm used to solve the differential equation see the reference paper (Benboudjema & Torrenti 2008).

3 NUMERICAL SIMULATION OF A REPAIRED SQUARE COLUMN

The restoration material of the presented case for simplicity is the same as that of the damaged column, in agreement with the old philosophy "repair like with like", in some situations followed still today. We study a square column restored with 5 cm of concrete. The case can be solved in double symmetry and 2D plane strain (Fig. 5). If a different material is used to repair a damaged concrete structure (Pellegrino et al., 2009) it is important to take this into account in the numerical simulation. Using Cast3M it is possible to join different materials and also to assign different mechanical properties to the interface, to take into account the treatment of the surface on which the repair will be applied.

3.1 Materials parameters

To define the material, many parameters are required. In the following tables all the material data and parameters used in the numerical simulation are classified by type.

Table 1. Mix of concrete.

Components	Value	Unit
Aggregates 12.5/25	783	kg/m³
Aggregates 5/12.5	316	kg/m³
Sand	772	kg/m³
Cement CEM II/A 52.5	350	kg/m³
Filler	0	kg/m³
Silica fume	0	kg/m³
Plasticizer	1.04	L/m³
Water	195	L/m³

Table 2. Thermal parameters.

Parameter	Symbol	Value	Unit
Convection coeff.	φ_t	3.0	W m⁻² K⁻¹
Conduction coeff. (dry)	λ	2.5	W m⁻¹ K⁻¹
Specific heat (dry)	c_t	750	J kg⁻¹ K⁻¹
Latent heat of hydr.	L_{hydr}	$107.6 \cdot 10^6$	J m⁻³
Activation energy/R	E_a/R	4000	K⁻¹

Table 3. Hygral parameters.

Parameter	Symbol	Value	Unit
Water dyn. viscosity (20°C)	μ_w	$1 \cdot 10^{-3}$	Pa·s
Water density (20°C)	ρ_w	1000	kg/m³
Convection coeff.	φ_h	$1.3 \cdot 10^{-12}$	kg s⁻¹ m⁻²
Parameter a in Equation (8)	a	$2.5 \cdot 10^7$	Pa
Parameter b in Equation (8)	b	2.08	–
Parameter c in Equation (8)	c	0.8	–
Parameter Γ_p in Equation (8)	Γ_p	0.1	%
Intrinsic permeability ($\Gamma = 1$)	K_∞	$1 \cdot 10^{-21}$	m²
Porosity ($\Gamma = 1$)	Φ_∞	0.135	%

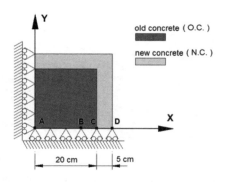

Figure 5. Geometry of the square column.

569

Table 4. Hydration constitutive model parameters.

Parameter	Symbol	Value	Unit
Percolation threshold	Γ_0	0.1	%
A_i in Equation (3)	A_i	256	1/s
A_p in Equation (3)	A_p	$5\cdot10^{-4}$	–
Γ_p in Equation (3)	Γ_p	0.765	–
α in Equation (3)	α	200	–
a_h in Equation (4)	a_h	5.0	–
$A_{\Phi\Gamma}$ for the porosity evolution law. (see Ref. [1])	$A_{\Phi\Gamma}$	0.061	–
$A_{K\Gamma}$ for the permeability law. (see Ref. [1])	$A_{K\Gamma}$	5.0	–

Table 5. Mechanical constitutive model parameters.

Parameter	Symbol	Value	Unit
Young modulus ($\Gamma = 1$)	E_∞	32.0	GPa
Tensile strength ($\Gamma = 1$)	$f_{t\infty}$	2.5	MPa
Poisson ratio	ν	0.25	–
c_s in Equation (13)	c_s	0.135	–
Thermal exp. coeff.	α_{th}	$1.2\cdot10^{-5}$	1/K
A_t Mazars law [9]	A_t	1.0	–
B_t Mazars law [9]	B_t	$17\cdot10^{3}$	–
Creep cell 1: spring ($\Gamma = 1$)	$k_{bc-\infty}^1$	$4.33\cdot10^{2}$	GPa
Creep cell 1: retardation time	τ_{bc}^1	0.3	days
Creep cell 2: spring ($\Gamma = 1$)	$k_{bc-\infty}^2$	$2.16\cdot10^{2}$	GPa
Creep cell 2: retardation time	τ_{bc}^2	3.0	days
Creep cell 3: spring ($\Gamma = 1$)	$k_{bc-\infty}^3$	43.3	GPa
Creep cell 3: retardation time	τ_{bc}^3	30	days
Creep cell 4: Single dashpot	η_{bc}^4	$1\cdot10^{30}$	GPa·days

3.2 Initial and boundary conditions

Environmental temperature and relative humidity are constant and equal to $T_{ext} = 12°C$ and $h_{ext} = 0.65$ respectively. It is assumed that the column to be repaired (O.C.) is in thermal and hygral equilibrium with the external environment. Constant exchange convective coefficients at the surface of concrete are assumed. On the two symmetry axes (see Figure 5) the heat and water mass fluxes are equal to zero. The advancement degree of hydration of the column to be repaired (O.C.) is considered equal to $\Gamma_\infty = 1$. For the new concrete (N.C.) we assume $\Gamma = 0.1$. Mechanical boundary conditions are those imposed by symmetry

Table 6. THC initial conditions.

	T	R.H	Γ
Column	12°C	0.65	1.00
Repair concrete	18°C	0.98	0.10

(see Figure 4). The following table summarizes the thermo-hygro-chemical initial conditions.

In the numerical simulation it is assumed that the repair is protected from drying during the first 12 hours.

3.3 THC solution

During the first 12 hours, in the repair concrete, relative humidity decreases due to self-drying, but is constant in space (Fig. 5).

After $t = 12$ h, repair is exposed to the external environment. Drying in the most superficial areas of repair will cause the inhibition of the hydration process (Figs. 7 and 8). Figure 6 shows temperature during the first 12 hours. At the beginning there is a decrease of the temperature in the repair, subsequently the heat generated by cement hydration causes a gradual increase of temperature that brings the system after 14 hours to a temperature of

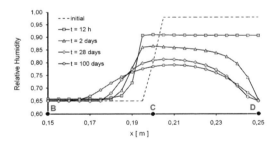

Figure 6. Relative humidity during 100 days from point B to point D.

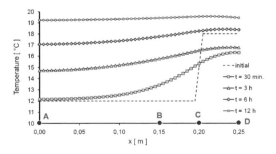

Figure 7. Temperature during 12 hours from point A to point D.

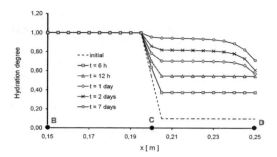

Figure 8. Advancement of hydration during 7 days from point B to point D.

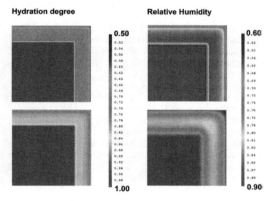

Figure 9. Hydration degree at 1 day and 2 days (left) relative humidity at 2 days and 100 days (right).

about 20°C. After 14 hours, the hydration process slows down and the system temperature decreases until it will be in thermal equilibrium with the external environment (after about a week).

3.4 Mechanical results

To identify the factors that determine the success of a repair, various mechanical calculations were made. In addition to installation and environmental conditions, the durability of a repair depends very much on the material mechanical properties, more precisely on Young modulus, tensile strength and also on tensile creep potential (Figs. 10 and 11).

When taking into account elastic damage, it is possible to evidence the cracking caused by the contraction of the new repair material prevented by the substrate. Using the elastic damage formulation, although the analyzed case is doubly symmetric, the mechanical solution is symmetric until a certain time step after which it loses its symmetry (Fig. 12). This is in agreement with what happens in reality where the original symmetric problem loses

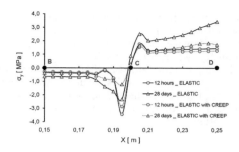

Figure 10. Stress σ_{yy} from point B to point D, with elastic computing.

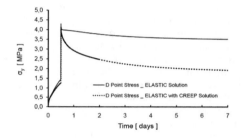

Figure 11. Time history of stress σ_{yy} for point D, with elastic computing.

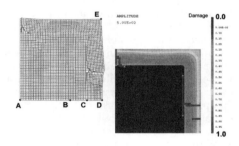

Figure 12. Deformed configuration and damage after 100 days, with elastic damage and creep computing.

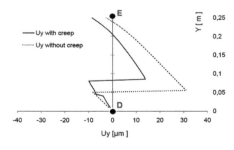

Figure 13. Displacement Uy along the line joining D and E after 100 days.

571

its symmetry after the appearance of the first crack. For this reason, it is important to consider that when a damage formulation is used, an imposed symmetry can distort the results.

The graph represented in Figure 13 gives some information on the crack's opening. With reference to Figure 12 the displacement Uy of the points along the line joining the nodes D and E are plotted.

4 CONCLUSIONS

The analyzed cases confirm that the factors influencing mainly the behaviour of repairs are: installation and environmental conditions, the repair's geometry and the material's properties.

With regard to the recovery material we have found that the intrinsic permeability, elastic modulus, tensile strength and creep are the properties that impact more on the success of a repair. The creep has a very important role because it relaxes the tensile stress (Figs. 9 and 10) and moderates crack phenomena. Figure 12 shows that when creep is taken into account in the numerical simulation, the maximum crack opening obtained is of 23 μm; if creep is not considered we obtain about 40 μm! These values of crack opening are very similar to those observed experimentally in the study of this kind of problem.

To succeed in simulating accurately the behaviour of a repair, the knowledge of the damaged structure's concrete and even more of the repair material is essential. Mechanical and thermal parameters do not pose important problems because they are easily found experimentally but hygral parameters are more difficult to estimate; in addition, all the properties vary with respect to the hydration degree of cement. Usually for this reason some of the necessary material parameters are not known. To solve this problem we are studying some microscale and meso-scale THCM models, which will allow for an estimate of the input parameters for the numerical model simply from the concrete's mix data (w/c ratio, aggregates, additives).

REFERENCES

Bazant, Z.P. 1988. Mathematical Modeling of Creep and Shrinkage of Concrete. *Wiley: Chichester.*

Benboudjema, F. & Torrenti, J.M. 2008. Early-age behaviour of concrete nuclear containments. *Nuclear Engineering and Design.*

De Schutter, G. & Taerwe, L. 1996. Degree of hydration based description of mechanical properties of early-age concrete. *Materials and Structures.*

De Schutter, G. 1999. Degree of hydration based Kelvin model for the basic creep of early age concrete. *Materials and Structures.*

Gawin, D., Pesavento, F. & Schrefler, B.A. 2002. Modelling of hygro-thermal behaviour and damage of concrete at temperature above critical point of water. *International Journal of Numerical and Analytical Methods in Geomechanics.*

Gawin, D., Pesavento, F. & Schrefler, B.A. 2006. Hygro-thermo-chemo-mechanical modeling of concrete at early ages and beyond. Part I: Hydration and hygro-thermal phenomena. *International Journal for Numerical Method in Engineering.*

Gawin, D., Pesavento, F. & Schrefler, B.A. 2006. Hygro-thermo-chemo-mechanical modelling of concrete at early ages and beyond. Part II: Shrinkage and creep of concrete. *International Journal for Numerical Method in Engineering.*

Mazars, J. 1986. A description of micro and macroscale damage of concrete structures. *Engineering Fracture Mechanics.*

Pellegrino, C., Da Porto, F. & Modena, C. 2009. Rehabilitation of reinforced concrete axially loaded elements with polymer-modified cementicious mortar. *Construction and Building Materials.*

Torrenti, J.M. & Benboudjema, F. 2005. Mechanical threshold of concrete at an early age. *Materials and Structures.*

Van Genuchten, M.Th. 1980. A closed-form equation for predicting the hydraulic conductivity of unsaturated soils. *Soil Science Society of America Journal.*

Strengthening materials and techniques/repair with composites

Concrete Solutions – Grantham, Mechtcherine & Schneck (eds)
© 2012 Taylor & Francis Group, London, ISBN 978-0-415-61622-5

Damage and repair quantification in reinforced concrete beams using vibration data

Ali Al-Ghalib, Fouad Mohammad, Mujib Rahman & John Chilton
School of Architecture, Design, and the Built Environment, The Nottingham Trent University, Nottingham, UK

ABSTRACT: A reinforced concrete (RC) 2 m long beam was loaded incrementally with a four-point bending static load. After each load step, the beam was tested with experimental modal analysis (EMA) under a free—free support condition. The collected natural frequencies, modal damping ratios, and mode shapes were measured and related to each load step. In addition, derived curvature along with the inertia bending moment associated with each load step were exploited to obtain the decrease in bending stiffness (EI). Subsequently, the severely damaged beam was repaired, retested with EMA, and new modal parameters were collected. At the final static load step, close to the complete failure stage, the midspan stiffness reduced by 52% compared to the intact beam stiffness. The increase in stiffness of the repaired beam was 43% compared with the stiffness of the beam at the final load step.

1 INTRODUCTION

Civil engineering infrastructure, because of its importance as a key utility of society, is subjected to regular periodic inspection and maintenance schemes. Some of these schemes may even be mandated by law (Brownjohn, 2007; Farrar & Worden, 2007). The efficiency of inspection schemes is only reliable, as long as they are able to detect problems likely to affect current or future performance of structures (Brownjohn, 2007). Competent monitoring techniques should have a positive impact on improvement of future design, and help to move towards a performance-based design philosophy (Brownjohn, 2007). In addition, they should reduce growth in construction needs and extend cyclic maintenance schemes (Farrar & Worden, 2007).

There are common technical challenges to the adaptation of inspection and monitoring systems. These challenges include identification of the features sensitive to small damage levels. For instance, in visual inspection, which is the most commonly named non-destructive (ND) assessment method in bridges; neither routine nor in-depth visual tasks are correctly identifying many types of defects (FHWA, 2001). Furthermore, most other local ND techniques are costly, subjective, qualitative, and often the suspected defect must be previously anticipated. Equally important, these local techniques are unable to predict useful information about the global degradation in safety and adequacy of a structure. As a result, the qualitative, time-consuming, and unreliable human factors are being replaced or supplemented by more measurable and automated systematic damage evaluation methods (Figueiredo et al., 2009; Brownjohn, 2007).

Vibration-based condition assessment methods have been studied widely and developed for the last 25 years as a structural health monitoring (SHM) tool for bridges (Owen et al., 2004). Even with the presence of their experimental errors, measurements from these methods give a more reliable representation for a tested structure than the simulated analytical model (Hwang & Kim, 2004). Stiffness coefficients of a structure could be directly determined by EMA without any need for analytical support, when the test and processing of data are planned and implemented well. No other testing method could provide such comprehensive information for actual structures (Zhengsheng et al., 2005). Although the methods of utilising vibration data seem straightforward, in principle, their effective application has proved remarkably challenging, because vibration tests are generally complemented by many issues related to creating accurate and repeatable measurements (Owen & Pearson, 2004). In addition, the extracted vibration data are difficult to interpret and relate to the location and size of damage. To that end, the usage of modal parameters to identify the amount of damage for concrete structures is still a subjective, and not necessarily, robust process (Wang et al., 2007; Kim & Stubbs, 2003).

In light of the difficulties in obtaining a robust modal damage identification scheme, this study utilised the primary features used to identify damage in structures, such as measured mode shape curvature, to quantify damage of a consecutively loaded RC beam.

The first objective of this work is to relate changes in vibration properties of a RC beam to a damage index defined as a decrease in bending stiffness. Linking between changes in stiffness and vibration data will provide a better understanding for the adequacy and remaining life of a structure.

The second objective is to evaluate the strength improvement in a severely damaged RC beam after a commonly made repair with carbon fibre-reinforced polymer (CFRP) is carried out. Whereas these two objectives were studied, the investigation also covered another current challenge in structural health monitoring (SHM).

The simulated numerical one-dimensional model for an undamaged beam stage was successfully validated with the measured model. The adopted methodology helps to construct any baseline model for a healthy structure, as a way to balance the shortage of information, which is critical in any damage identification process.

2 LABORATORY TESTS ON A CONCRETE BEAM

2.1 Description of the test beam

The project used a sample RC beam of 2.0 m length where the vibration data used in this study was collected. A reinforcing steel ratio of 1.1% was chosen to make the beam behaviour similar to those in normal construction. The dimensions and cross-section of the beam with all reinforcement details are shown in Figure 1. The concrete mix was designed to give a nominal cube compressive

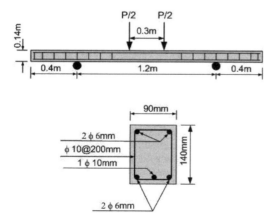

Figure 1. Typical dimensions and reinforcement details of the test beam.

Table 1. Specifications of concrete beam ($2000 \times 140 \times 90$ mm).

Density kg/m³	f_{ck} MPa (cube)	f_{ck} MPa (Cylinder)	f_{cn} MPa
2240	25.0	20.0	28.0

strength of 30 MPa and a total beam mass of 56 kg with a density $\rho = 2300$ kg/m³. Experimental static modulus of elasticity (E_s) was obtained using EC2 part 1–1 specifications (Eurocode, 2004) based on the mean cube concrete strength at 28 days (f_{cm}). The complete properties of this beam based on cubes made from each beam mix are given in Table 1.

After 28 days, the cubes made for the beam were tested, and the corresponding stiffness was determined. The dynamic modulus of elasticity (E_d) was estimated using the empirical formula proposed by Lydon and Balendran (Neville, 1995), and given as:

$$E_d = 1.205 E_s \qquad (1)$$

2.2 Experimental set up and procedure

The test beam was subjected to two symmetrical point loads at a separation of 0.3 m as a four-point bending loading, as shown in Figure 1. This procedure produced a middle zone of evenly distributed defects. As the width of the testing machine was smaller than the length of the beams, the span of the test beam was taken as 1.2 m and an overhanging distance of 0.4 m was left from each end. Then, each simply supported beam was subjected to five incremental load steps in order to produce controlled levels of damage. At the end of each static load step, the beam was unloaded, and the simple supports were replaced by freely supported conditions to carry out experimental modal analysis (EMA) on a completely freely supported beam.

2.3 Static test

The beam was loaded, as shown in Figure 1, statically to failure in five successive steps. Besides the initial intact state, five load steps were executed. The load steps were P = 3 kN, 6 kN, 10 kN, 13 kN and 16 kN. The last load step (step 5) corresponds to an almost completely damaged state or plastic yielding of the reinforcing bars. The theoretical failure load corresponding to the beam section, according to EC2 part 1–1 (Eurocode, 2004), is about 18 kN. At the end of each static load step, the beam surface was inspected visually to map out the crack distribution associated with that step. It was observed, that up to the 10 kN loading step, no apparent signs of defects appeared. Nonetheless, at the 16 kN loading, severe deterioration was developing in the area between supports. At the final static loading step, and just before the formation of plastic hinges, the process was stopped; the beams were dynamically tested then repaired. To repair the damage, the defective zone was strengthened by bonding external carbon fibre-reinforced polymer (CFRP-TORAYCA-FT 300B) layers of 500 mm long and 90 mm width. CFRP has become a well-known refurbishment material used in civil engineering over the past decade. Whereas using CFRP as a post-strengthening material in rehabilitation of concrete improves the strength, it does not have much effect on stiffness. In the current beam repair programme, the particular design of CFRP sheets is based on bending moment, where the maximum bending moment zone was strengthened with these sheets. The tensile modulus of this type of CFRP is 220 kN/mm^2, and it has a tensile strength of 3340 N/mm^2. High strength and moisture resistant epoxy (West System Epoxy) that is made of two separate parts, resin, and hardener, was used to glue the CFRP layers. The mixing ratio of 1 gram of hardener for every 5 grams of resin was used to guarantee a good cure. The combination should be mixed for around 120 seconds, and there is only less than 20 minutes before it turns into solid.

2.4 *Dynamic test*

In this study, the beam was tested under a free-free support condition by applying the excitation on the major axis, as shown in Figure 2. A freely supported testing model was chosen in order to remove the intervention of support rigidity (Ewins, 2000). In this test, each beam was suspended by two lightweight soft bungee cords attached at 0.23 L (0.46 m) from each end. Three accelerometers were mounted starting from the right end at

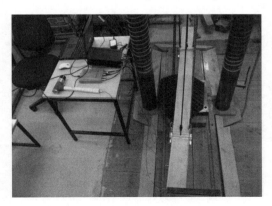

Figure 2. Concrete beam under free-free support condition.

stations 0.2 m apart. These three accelerometers were subsequently repositioned at three new locations in order to cover the entire beam length with a total of 11 measurement points. The beam was impacted and accelerations measured normal to the direction of the soft cords. In the case of roving accelerometers, the beam was impacted at a single unique location at the right-hand end of the beam. The DeltaTron® type 8208 impact hammer generated a dynamic force with a sensitivity of 0.22 mV/N containing frequency components up to 1000 Hz. Only the first four modes were covered with the current exciter. However, higher modes excitation is possible using a hammer with a tougher tip, which generates a high frequency loading function. The response measurements were collected using DeltaTron® 4514 accelerometers with sensitivities of 9.86 mV/g and a frequency range of 1–10 kHz. Accelerations were measured horizontally at every 0.2 m with accelerometers. Signals were captured using a four-channel data acquisition card with 4100 samples, taken at a rate of 8180 samples per second.

2.5 *Experimental modal analysis (EMA) and verification of results*

Experimental modal analysis (EMA) was utilised to describe the properties of the beam in terms of its modal parameters, which are the natural frequencies, modal damping, and mode shapes. For each measuring location, four force—and acceleration time histories were amplified, filtered, and then transformed into a frequency domain.

Frequency response functions (FRFs), which relate the response of the structure to an applied excitation were derived. Auto power spectra of the input excitation, $G_{ff}(\omega)$, and the cross power spectra between the excitation and the response, $G_{fx}(\omega)$, were utilised to obtain the system FRF, H(ω), for each measurement point as:

$$H_1(\omega) = \frac{G_{fx}(\omega)}{G_{ff}(\omega)} \qquad (2)$$

The coherence functions, which measure the correlation between the output and the input signals (Figueiredo et al., 2009), and are used as a data quality assessment tool, were obtained for the system FRF as:

$$\gamma^2(\omega) = \frac{\left|G_{fx}(\omega)\right|^2}{G_{ff}(\omega) \cdot G_{xx}(\omega)} \qquad (3)$$

Figure 3 shows the FRF at end (1) of the beam where the response at the same point (1), and its

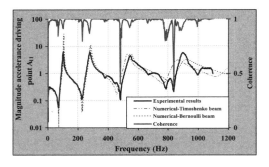

Figure 3. FRF and coherence functions from transducer 1 (right-hand end) when impact at 1 for intact beam.

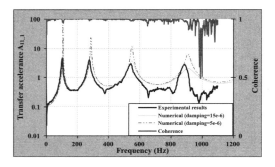

Figure 4. FRF and coherence functions from transducer 11 (left-hand end) when impact at 1 (right-hand end) for intact beam.

coherence function calculated from four ensemble averages. The quality of FRF measurements was verified through constant checking of features, including repeatability and reciprocity. In addition, as shown in Figures 3 and 4, a strong agreement was also achieved between each experimental FRF and its corresponding numerical FRF, after considering E_d and proportional damping in the Euler-Bernoulli beam model.

In the numerical simulation, shear deformation effects and dynamic modulus of elasticity control the shift in resonant peaks from the measured horizontal position. In contrast, proportional damping inclusion controls the magnitude of FRF, as shown in Figure 3 and Figure 4.

3 EXPERIMENTAL VIBRATION RESULTS

For each load step, the resulting driving point and transfer accelerances, at 11 measuring points along the RC beam, were generated. One driving acceleration function (FRF) gives information on the system modal frequencies and modal

damping, while a complete set of FRFs contain information regarding the mode shapes of the beam at the measured locations. The accelerance driving point $A_{1,1}(\omega)$ of the undamaged beam is given in Figure 3. In addition transfer accelerance function $A_{11,1}(\omega)$ of the undamaged beam is given in Figure 4. The simplest SDOF method for modal analysis, which treats the FRF data at the vicinity of a resonance frequency as SDOF, was adopted through this study (He & Fu, 2001). As shown in Figure 3 (or Figure 4), the first four mode shapes are obviously recognized, and the corresponding natural frequencies were 103.9 Hz, 281.7 Hz, 547.3 Hz, and 896.9 Hz for the intact beam. At the final load step (P = 16 kN), the first measured natural frequencies were 79.9 Hz, 241.7 Hz, 487.4 Hz, and 779 Hz. In addition, for the repaired beam, the first four natural frequencies were 89.9 Hz, 249.7 Hz, 509.4 Hz, and 811 Hz. The normalized drops in natural frequencies, for the first four modes, corresponding to each load step are shown in Figure 5.

As the RC beam in this study is a lightly damped structure, modal damping ratios (ξ) were experimentally estimated from the width of the resonance peak, which can be written as:

$$\xi_r = \frac{\omega_b - \omega_a}{2\omega_r} \qquad (4)$$

Where $(\omega_b - \omega_a)$ is the width of the resonance curve at half of the maximum power, and ω_r is the resonance frequency. The normalized measured modal damping ratios for the beam are given in Figure 6. For intact beam condition, the first four damping ratios were 3.42%, 2.59%, 2.22%, and 2.22%, respectively, while for the severely damaged beam (P = 16 kN), the damping ratios were 5.32%, 2.28%, 2.63%, and 2.19%.

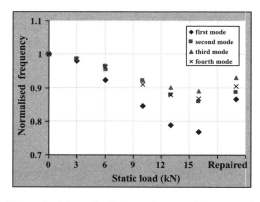

Figure 5. Normalised change in natural frequency for RC beam with respect to load steps.

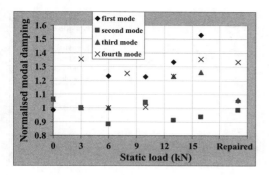

Figure 6. Normalised change in modal damping for the RC beam with respect to load steps.

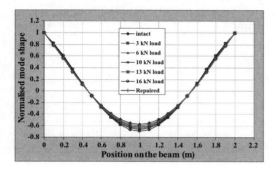

Figure 7. Progression of modal displacement of the first bending mode for successive loading steps.

The mode shapes for the first four modes were processed by using a simplified experimental modal analysis. In this approach, the response measurements are assumed to be dominated by resonant modes (Haritos & Owen, 2004). This assumption is reasonable for this beam sample, as the resonant frequencies are sufficiently separated (Haritos & Owen, 2004). A comparison of the first displacement mode shapes at different damage scenarios are shown in Figure 6. In general, the measured mode shapes agreed well with mode shapes of a freely supported beam, for both location of modal points and the symmetry or asymmetry of the corresponding mode shape. The mode shapes in the current study discriminate clearly between different conditions of the beam. In addition, they show the modified mode shape for the repaired beam, Figure 7.

4 CURVATURE MODE SHAPES

An alternative to using mode shape to obtain spatially distributed features sensitive to damage is that using mode-shape derivative, such as curvature.

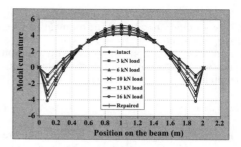

Figure 8. Progression of modal curvature of the first bending mode for successive loading steps.

Mode-shape curvature is calculated by numerically differentiating the deflection mode-shape vectors twice to obtain an estimate of the curvature.

Mode—shape curvature has proved more sensitive to small perturbations in the system than is the mode shape itself. In addition, for beam and plate-like structures, changes in curvature can be related to changes in strain energy, which is shown to be a sensitive indicator of damage (Farrar et al., 2001). In this study, the curvature mode shapes were investigated to find a better understanding about the distribution of damage. The curvature of the continuous deflection mode shape was obtained using a central difference approximation, which can be written as

$$\phi_i'' = \frac{\phi_{i+1} - 2\phi_i + \phi_{i-1}}{(\Delta x)^2} \tag{5}$$

Where Δx represents the length of the element and Φ is the displacement mode shape at a specific position. The calculated curvature of the measured first mode shape for each damage step is shown in Figure 8. Although the differences between curvature mode shapes appear clearer than in the mode shape (Figure 7) the curvature mode shapes do not heavily react to the damage, particularly at the points of inflection.

5 DAMAGE INDEX USING MOMENT-CURVATURE RELATIONSHIP

Existence of damage in RC beams produces almost even reduction in the stiffness over a definite length. The reduction in the stiffness leads to a subsequent increase in the absolute magnitude of the curvature (k), as shown in Figure 7, and can be defined mathematically as:

$$k = \phi'' = \frac{d^2\phi}{dx^2} = \frac{M}{EI} \tag{6}$$

579

Where M is the bending moment at a section, E is Young's modulus and I is the moment of inertia of the cross-section.

For free vibration analysis with damping neglected, the pseudo static force system can be written as:

$$K \phi = \omega_r^2 m \phi \qquad (7)$$

In which, the right-hand side of Equation 7 represents the modal inertia forces for specific mode (*r*) acting on the beam of stiffness *K* to create a displacement vector Φ.

For a continuous linear piecewise mode shape through the measurement points at location x_i, x_{i+1}, using the sign convention shown in Figure 9, the internal bending moment at section x_{i+1} (M_{i+1}), assuming that only the inertia load is acting on the beam, is given below (Maeck & De Roeck, 1999).

$$M_{i+1} = M_i + V_i(\Delta x) - \frac{1}{2} \int_{x_i}^{x_{i+1}} \omega_r^2 \rho A \phi(x)(\Delta x) dx \qquad (8)$$

Where ρ is the mass density, *A* is the cross-sectional area, *V* is the shear force, and *M* is the bending moment. In fact, the bending moments and shear forces are considered as experimentally measured, because the calculated inertia loads (ω_r^2 ρ A) are based on experimentally measured ω_r. Additionally, the displacement vector Φ is a measured mode shape.

The distribution of inertia shear forces and bending moments of the first mode at each damage state are shown in Figures 10 and 11, respectively. Slightly, less than perfect shear distribution was achieved. The slight lack of symmetry in the measured first mode shape caused a trivial shift in the shear distribution. Accordingly, the maximum bending moment values crept slightly from the midspan location.

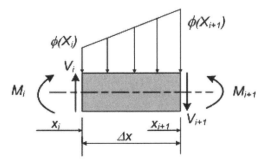

Figure 9. Internal pseudo static force system.

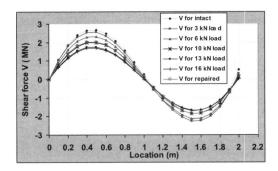

Figure 10. Shear forces for different loading steps based on first mode.

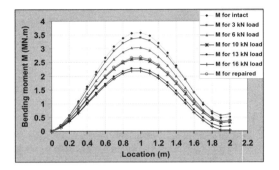

Figure 11. Bending moments for different loading steps based on first mode.

Next, by using the calculated modal bending moment distribution found from Equation 8, along with curvature corresponding to that mode, given in Equation 5, the dynamic bending stiffness (EI) can eventually be evaluated using Equation 6.

In general, the changes in the element system stiffness emerge as local changes in modal curvature. However, points of inflection, where the curvature changes from being concave to convex (or vice versa) result in a confusing interpretation. Additionally, support points, which appear as zero curvature points and points of inflection often, show larger changes of curvatures, of course, in addition to changes occurring due to the drop in EI. In this study, the maximum midspan decrease in the flexural stiffness, with respect to its initial value was calculated as an indication to the amount of damage that had occurred with each load step. The decreased EI was calculated based on the measured first mode shape, and given in Figure 12 and Table 2.

In this study, an effort was made to articulate the drop in flexural stiffness in terms of a scalar quantity. In general, there are no acknowledged measures of structural damage (Chen et al., 1995). However, an indicator of the level of deterioration

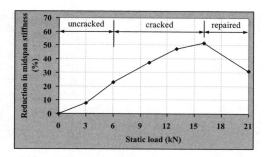

Figure 12. Reduction in midspan bending stiffness with the progress of load.

Table 2. Successive midspan stiffness decrease based on the moment-curvature ratio.

Load Step	BM* MN·m	k† 1/m	EI MN·m²	ΔEI‡%	D
Intact	3.58	4.172	0.858	0	0
3 kN load	3.40	4.301	0.791	7.81	0.08
6 kN load	3.04	4.596	0.661	22.96	0.23
10 kN load	2.63	4.883	0.538	37.30	0.37
13 kN load	2.28	5.052	0.452	47.32	0.47
16 kN load	2.19	5.291	0.414	51.75	0.52
Repaired	2.68	4.545	0.590	31.24	0.31

*BM = maximum midspan bending moment
†k = curvature
‡ΔEI = accumulated decrease in bending stiffness

that the structure arrived at, a damage size indicator (D) was suggested. The damage indicator (D) is set as the ratio of the difference in EI between any damage and intact stage to the EI of the intact stage, and given as:

$$D = 1 - \frac{EI_{damaged}}{EI_{int\,act}} \qquad (9)$$

Theoretically, the values of D vary between 0 and 1, with 1 for a complete failure stage and 0 for intact beam. Practically, for the current case study, a damage indicator of D = 0.52 indicates that the formation of a plastic hinge is very imminent, when P = 16 kN, as shown in Figure 12.

The successive percentage reduction in midspan EI with the static load was given in Figure 12 and Table 2. The progression of this reduction was almost linear. As a proof of accuracy, the theoretical EI of the intact beam is 0.843 MN · m², while the measured EI is 0.858 MN · m². Interestingly, EI at the midspan dropped by about 23% at the second load step (P = 6 kN), although no bending cracks were observed. However, at the final static

load step (P = 16 kN), close to the complete failure stage, the midspan EI reduced by 52% compared to EI of the healthy beam. At this stage, wide and spread cracks at the midspan zone were observed. Moreover, the midspan EI of the repaired beam increased by 43% compared to the severely damaged beam.

6 COMPARISON AND DISCUSSION OF RESULTS

Discrepancy of frequency with escalation of damage is shown in Figure 5. Frequencies were measured for the beam sample by imposing progressive load. As can be seen from Figure 5, the measured frequencies of the first mode decreased significantly responding to the increasing damage, suggesting that damage location affected remarkably the high stress zone of the first mode. However, the variation of frequency appeared less significant for higher modes, which can be attributed to the fact that the midspan cracked area is close to the modal nodes of these modes. The first four modal frequencies of the test beam are also shown as a function of load steps, Figure 5. Obviously, the modal frequencies decrease as the damage index increases. When the beam's sections were in the uncracked state (P = 6 kN), the first four frequencies decreased by 7.8%, 3.5%, 4.4%, and 3.8%, respectively, compared to the intact state. Interestingly, the damage index at this step was D = 0.23 (23% reduction in EI). The big differences in natural frequencies conclude that vibration-based methods are able to detect damage at its early stage, without any apparent visible change in the condition. At the final load step (P = 16 kN), when the beam is severely damaged and formation of a plastic hinge is imminent D = 0.52 (52% reduction in EI), the first four natural frequencies decreased by 23.1%, 14.2%, 10.9%, and 13.2, respectively, compared to the intact state. As the drop in natural frequencies of the severely damaged beam is quite big, vibration-based assessment methods could be recognizably utilised. Noticeably, as the damaged zone is repaired, the beam becomes stronger, and the properties are modified. The first four natural frequencies decreased, respectively, by 13.5%, 11.4%, 6.9%, and 9.6% compared to the undamaged stage. The damage index of the repaired beam was (D = 0.31), where the bending stiffness (EI) increased by 21% of the undamaged beam stiffness.

In Figure 6, variation in modal damping with evolution of damage is shown. Naturally, the presence of cracks in concrete structures often increases the damping.

Although estimation of damping includes relatively high errors, quite consistent modal damping measurements were collected in this project. At the severely damaged beam stage (P = 16 kN), the modal damping increased by 52.8%, 25.8%, 33.5%, for the first, third, and fourth mode, respectively, compared to the 3 kN load stage. Unusually, for the intact beam stage, damping ratios of the first four modes were higher than modal damping of the next step load (3 kN) beam stage. Others (Salawu & Williams, 1994) observed trends similar to this. As was seen in natural frequency trends, modal damping of the first mode increased significantly responding to the increasing damage. This would suggest that the damage location affected the high stress zone. Markedly, for the repaired beam, the first four damping ratios decreased by 47.3%, 20.1%, and 8.5% for the first, third, and fourth mode, respectively, from the severely damaged (16 kN) load stage. One unanticipated finding was the inconsistent damping ratios of the second mode, Figure 6, which can be accounted for the fact that modal damping of this mode is less likely to be influenced by damage.

Furthermore, an effort was made to locate and to estimate the size of damage, making use of the first mode shape and its curvature. The mode shapes of the beam at various levels of damage were generated by normalisation and shown in Figure 7. The anticipation was that with the development of cracks, the higher the level of damage the higher a beam will oscillate. Therefore, this phenomenon is reliably captured in this work, and can be seen in Figure 7. Unlike previous research, which suggested that mode shapes may change a little if the damage is widespread cracking in RC beams (Owen et al., 2004; Yeung & Smith, 2005), mode shapes in this study reliably detected the presence of damage and clearly discriminated between its levels. Even the modification produced on the severely damaged beam was remarkably identified through the first mode shape. However, changes in the curvature mode shape are more localised in the region of damage and even clearer discrimination of damage levels were achieved, Figure 8. Most importantly, using curvature mode shape in conjunction with inertia bending moment corresponding to the same mode shape has a valuable benefit. Dynamic stiffness associated with each damage state can be determined by using related curvature along with the distributed bending moment. The study managed easily to calculate numerically the drop in flexural stiffness associated with each load step.

7 CONCLUSIONS

In the current study, the frequency response functions along a progressively loaded RC beam were collected and numerically verified with an undamaged one-dimensional beam model. The extracted modal parameters were employed to discriminate between different levels of damage. Measured natural frequencies and damping ratios obviously detected early stage damage in the RC beam, and then discerned the local increase in damage as a function of loading step. Mode shapes and curvature mode shapes were also measured and tested through this study. Mode shapes were able to successfully recognize the increase in damage of the beam. At variance with previous work, which suggested that mode shapes might change little if the damage is widespread cracking in RC beams, mode shapes in this study reliably detected the presence of damage and clearly discriminated between its levels. Moreover, the refurbishment work done on the severely damaged beam was significantly captured by using both mode shapes and their curvatures.

Curvature mode shapes along with their calculated inertia bending moment distribution were exploited to obtain the decrease in midspan bending stiffness. The measured midspan stiffness of the intact beam was correctly validated with theoretical bending stiffness.

One possible advantage of this study is that, a consistent numerical simulation can be achieved once damping effect, shear deformation effects, and dynamic Young's modulus are considered. This is a very necessary step in many damage identification methods, as a complete as-built model for the undamaged structure is usually unavailable. Furthermore, in an experimental modal analysis, correlated measurements can be accomplished through testing laboratory-scale structures under a free-free support condition.

REFERENCES

Brownjohn, J.M.W. 2007. Structural Health Monitoring of Civil Infrastructure. *Philosophy Transactions of Royal Society*, Vol. 365: pp. 589–622.

Chen, H., Spyrakos, C. & Venkatesh, G. 1995. Evaluating Structural Deterioration by Dynamic Response. *ASCE, Journal of Structural Engineering*, Vol. 121, No. 8: pp. 1197–1204.

Eurocode Part 1–1, 2004. *Design of Concrete Structures, General Rules and Rules for Buildings*. European Committee for Standardization BS EN 1992-1-1: p. 29.

Ewins, D. 2000. *Modal Testing: Theory, Practice and Application*. England: Research Studies Press Ltd., Baldock, Hertfordshire.

Farrar, C., Doebling, S. & Nix, D. 2001. Vibration-Based Structural Damage Identification. *Philosophy Transactions Royal Society*, Vol. 359: pp. 131–149.

Farrar, C. & Worden, K. 2007. An Introduction to Structural Health Monitoring. *Philosophy Transactions of Royal Society*, Vol. 365: pp. 303–315.

FHWA NDE Validation Center 2001. *Reliability of Visual Inspection for Highway Bridges*. FHWA-RD-01-020, US Department of Transportation. Federal Highway Administration.

Figueiredo, E., Park, G., Figueiras, J., Farrar, C. & Worden, K. 2009. Structural Health Monitoring Algorithm Comprises Using Standard Data Sets. *Report LA-14393, Los Alamos National Laboratory*, US.

Haritos, N. & Owen, J. 2004. The Use of Vibration Data for Damage Detection in Bridges: A Comparison of System Identification and Pattern Recognition Approaches. *Journal of Structural Health Monitoring*, Vol. 3(2): pp. 141–163.

He, J. & Fu, Zhi-Fang. 2001. *Modal Analysis*. Oxford, England: Butterworth-Heinemann.

Hwang, H. & Kim, C. 2004. Damage Detection in Structures using a Few Frequency Response Measurements. *Journal of Sound and Vibration*, Vol. 270, issue 1: pp. 1–14.

Kim, J. & Stubbs, N. 2003. Non-destructive Crack Detection Algorithm for Full-Scale Bridges. *ASCE, Journal of Structural Engineering*, Vol. 129, No. 10: pp. 1358–1366.

Maeck, J. & De Roeck, G. 1999. Dynamic Bending and Torsional Stiffness Derivation from modal Curvatures and Torsion Rates. *Journal of Sound and Vibration*, Vol. 225, issue 1: pp. 153–170.

Neville, A.M. 1995. *Properties of Concrete*. England: Longman Group Limited.

Owen, J.S. & Pearson, R. 2004. The Use of Dynamic Data for the Structural Health Monitoring of Bridges. *Proceedings of 1st FIG International Symposium on Engineering Surveys for Construction Works and Structural Engineering*, Nottingham, United Kingdom: pp. 1–14.

Owen, J.S, Pearson, S.R, Tan, C.M. & Choo, B.S. 2004. Classification of Damaged and Modified Beams with Vibration Signatures. *Transportation Research Record 1814*, Paper No. O2-2504: pp. 135–144.

Salawu, O.S. & Williams, C. 1994. Damage Location Using Vibration Mode Shapes. *Proceeding of 12th International Modal Analysis Conference*: pp. 933–939.

Wang, X., Swanson, J., Helmicki, A. & Hunt, V. 2007. Development of Dynamic-Response-Based Objective Function for Finite-Element Modelling of Bridges. *ASCE, Journal of Bridge Engineering*, Vol. 12, No. 5: pp. 552–559.

Yeung, W.T. & Smith, J.W. 2005. Damage Detection In Bridges Using Neural Networks for Pattern Recognition of Vibration Signatures. *Journal of Engineering Structures*, Vol. 27: pp. 685–698.

Zhengsheng, L., Swanson, J., Helmicki, A. & Hunt, V. 2005. Modal Contribution Coefficients in Bridge Condition Evaluation. *ASCE, Journal of Bridge Engineering*, Vol. 10, No. 2 pp. 169–178.

Concrete Solutions – Grantham, Mechtcherine & Schneck (eds)
© *2012 Taylor & Francis Group, London, ISBN 978-0-415-61622-5*

Flexural behaviour of concrete beams reinforced with CFRP composites

Mustafa K. Ali
Institute of Sustainable Engineering, Cardiff University, Wales, UK

D.B. Tann
Department of Urban Engineering, London South Bank University, UK

A.I. Abu-Tair
Engineering Department, University of Glamorgan, Wales, UK

ABSTRACT: Steel reinforcement performs well when embedded in high quality concrete and protected from chlorides and or carbonation of the cover concrete; however, this does not always happen and reinforcement corrosion is by far the major cause of reinforced concrete deterioration requiring a significant repair and restoration budget. Fibre Reinforced Polymers (FRP) are extensively used to repair and strengthen structures suffering from corrosion or lack of strength and are also used to replace conventional steel reinforcement. The application of Fibre Reinforced Polymer (FRP) as an alternative to replace the conventional steel reinforcement can overcome corrosion problems. This paper presents an experimental study on the flexural behaviour of concrete beams reinforced with CFRP compared with steel reinforced concrete beams (control beams). Flexural behaviour was studied by testing all beams to ultimate load failure under four-point loading. The behaviour of these beams was investigated based on the load deflection characteristics, concrete strain distribution and cracking behaviour. The test results indicated that the CFRP section performed in the same manner as steel reinforcement. The reinforcing of such beams in shear was also investigated and the CFRP performed well.

1 INTRODUCTION

Current studies indicate that the use of advanced composites for structural applications is increased dramatically during the last decade and their use is expected to continue rising (Nanni, 2000). In the last decade, the use of FRP composites to reinforce concrete members has emerged as one of the most promising technologies in materials/structural engineering. There are a wide range of applications of FRP reinforcement that cover new construction as well as rehabilitation of existing structures. FRP systems for strengthening concrete structures are a practical alternative to traditional strengthening techniques such as steel plate bonding, section enlargement, and external post-tensioning.

Applications of FRP composites in civil/infrastructure engineering are diverse and may include internal reinforcement, structural elements, and externally bonded reinforcement (Nanni, 2000, CIRIA, 2002). For concrete reinforcement, the most popular forms of FRP are smooth and deformed bars (IStructE, 1997). FRP composites are light in weight (IStructE, 1997), therefore they are easier to transport and install. Also they are corrosion

resistant and perform well in terms of long term durability and maintenance cost (Concrete Bridge Development Group, 2000; Nanni 2000; CIRIA, 2002). In conjunction with that development, design standards have developed and designers now regard FRP as a viable alternative to the more traditional steel and concrete.

2 EXPERIMENTAL TEST PROGRAM

The focus of the structural tests was to investigate the flexural behaviour of CFRP RC Beams. Hence, a simultaneous investigation of cracking, strain and curvature behaviour was necessary (Aiello, 2000; Tann, 2001; Sooriyaarachchi, 2005). Moreover the CFRP was used for the main flexural reinforcement. A steel RC beam was used for comparison purposes. A total of seven concrete beams with 100 mm width, 200 mm height and 2600 mm length as shown in Figure 3, were tested under four-point loading until failure. Table 1 shows the mechanical properties of the CFRP strip used. Figure 4 shows the typical dimensions and reinforcement of the test models. The concrete mix used for casting

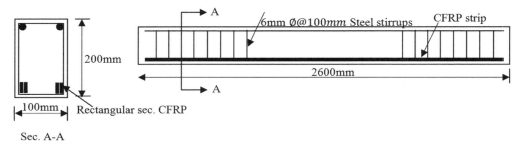

Sec. A-A

Figure 1. Beam dimensions and reinforcement details.

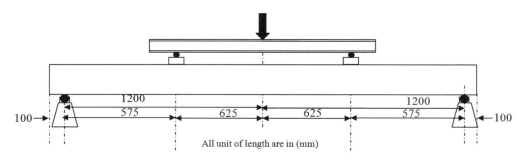

Figure 2. Loading configuration for all simply supported beams.

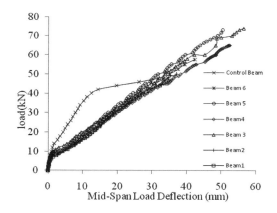

Figure 3. Load against mid-span deflection for all beams.

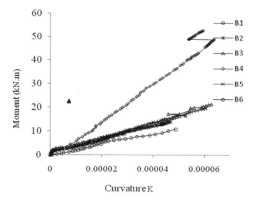

Figure 4. Moment against Curvature for all beams.

Table 1. Carbon plate properties.

CFRP	
Tensile strength (MPa)	4,900
Elongation at break%	2
Density (g/cm³)	1.8
Tensile modulus (kN/mm²)	230
Net thickness (mm)	1.2 & 1.7

the concrete was 0.5:1:2:4 for Water: Cement: Sand and Aggregate, respectively. The above mix complies with the comprehensive specification in BS5328 (BSI, 1991; BSI, 1985).

2.1 *Specimen preparation*

The first step in the laboratory work was the preparation of reinforcement for the six beams. The size of the main reinforcement in the control beam was 12 mm diameter. The main reinforcement on the other beams was CFRP plate size 10 mm × 1.7 mm and the lateral reinforcement was fabricated using 6 mm non-deformed bars. The tying method was chosen as the most common in industry to combine reinforcement together (Brown, 1993; Cosenza,1997). The manual operation was carried out by using pincers and a specific type of tying wire. The tying wire was black annealed (Soft) iron with a 2.0 mm diameter size. This wire was used to tie the main reinforcement and the shear link tightly together at intersection point and laps, thereby preventing relative movement of the bars and ensuring maximum rigidity (Brown, 1993) of the completed shell. In addition, wheel spacers were used to provide cover protection of the reinforcement bars and plate within the concrete (Concrete Society, 1998). Spacers used to provide maintaining cover in vertical members to the reinforcement nearest to the surface of the concrete (CIRIA, 1995). The wheel spacers were made from plastic with 15 mm thickness to ensure that the beams had enough cover with 15 mm.

3 ANALYSIS AND DISCUSSION

It was observed from the load deflection, as shown in Figure 3, that all the beam deflections (other than the control beam) seemed to follow a linear path up to the failure point. There were clear signs of failure. The CFRP internal reinforcement plate failed first and was accompanied with a rattling sound in the fabric and by partial snapping of the fibre. This was followed gradually by crushing of concrete in the compression zone which failed in the pure flexural zone of the last two beams only (B5, B6). In the first four beams (B1, B2, B3, B4) the failure mode was shear failure in the shear span even though the CFRP sheet strengthening was applied by one layer in beams (B3, B4) and two layers in beams (B5, B6). The beams (B5, B6) failed at higher load capacity 75 and 80 kN respectively as shown in Table 2. The ultimate loading of beams (B3, B4) were 81and 65 kN respectively. The reasons of the failure mode was in the flexural zone of the last two beams (B5, B6), because they were strengthened with two layers of CFRP sheet in shear zone.

From the moment-curvature graph as shown in Figure 4 all beams seemed to have followed a linear path up to the failure stage, and that mean all beams were in the elastic phase until they failed. In the same figure, a large energy absorption was also observed in the test of CFRP- reinforcement beams. The magnitude of this energy absorption depended on the failure mode (tension-or compression

Table 2. Summary of test results for B1–B6.

| Beam Ref. | Load at specific stages (kN) | | Ultimate load increase % | Deflection @ failure (mm) | Failure mode |
	First crack	Ultimate failure			
Control	12	48.9	–	31.7	SY-CC
B1	8	46.6	–	35.26	SH
B2	8	51.0	0.6	37.09	SH
B3	14	81.0	69.1	44.14	SH
B4	15	65.0	35.7	48.60	SH
B5	16	75.0	56.6	50.46	FC
B6	15	80.0	67	51.0	FC

Note: SY-CC = Steel yielding followed by concrete crushing; CC = Concrete crushing; SH = Shear Failure; FC = Flexural Failure Followed by concrete crushing.

controlled) (Hota et al., 2002; Achillides et al., 1997b & 2004).

When visible deformations occur on beams under a large load, ductility is considered as an important attribute that can provide the opportunity to take remedial action before failure occurs. In the context of such a structural member as a beam, the concept of ductility generally applies because of the inherent ductility, large deformations can become visible, giving ample warning of an impending structural failure (often elastic) without structural collapse. (Hota et al., 2002; Alkhrdaji et al., 2002; Benmokrane et al., 1996). From the comparison of moment curvature relationship, which is represented in Figure 4, it can be seen there was similarity of the behaviour for all beams. This is an indication of the reliability of the measured data as well as the applicability of the methods used. The only apparent slope change occurred at the initial concrete cracking stage at a moment of around 3–4.5 kN · m, and corresponding load 8–14 kN. After this initial change of slope in the moment-curvature curves, the beams behaved almost "linearly" until sudden failure. Moreover, this failure mode was very sudden and brittle in the laboratory test.

4 STRAIN DISTRIBUTION ACROSS SECTION DEPTH

The Demec (Demountable Mechanical Strain Gauge) stud groups were installed on both sides of the beam, at the early stage of the beam set-up. They were used to take readings of concrete strain development in the constant moment zone, throughout the depth of the beams. In addition, the concrete strain was measured at the top concrete fibre at midspan. The concrete strain increased noticeably.

It then increased with load at a somewhat fast rate, while the midspan crack widened and penetrated deeper into the section. These recordings were processed in tabulated and graphical form. All the graphs were made by uncorrected data entry as recorded; these graphs shows the strain variation at each load increment as shown in Figures (5–10). The purpose of the strain measurement through the depth of the beams was in order to demonstrate that the section strain profile is affected by several cracks (Benmokrane et al., 1996, Bischoff 2005a). As can be seen from the Figures (5–10) the distribution of concrete surface strain across the beam depth exhibited a near perfect linear vari-

ation, indicating that the plane section remained plane during the loading process.

It was clear in Figures (5–10) strain distribution graphs that the B3, B4, B5, B6 beams exhibited similar and greater strain than the B1, B2 beams. This is because the presence of existing cracks resulted in the neutral axis position being slightly moved upwards due to the loading process, which in turn led to a reduction of second moment of area. However, just before ultimate failure load, beams B3, B4, B5, and B6 showed similar values of strain at around 14500 microstrains. In all graphs at the pure bending zone, the strain value remains high for the most of the load duration.

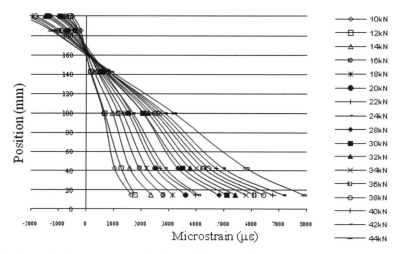

Figure 5.   Typical beam depths against strain for B1 at mid-span section.

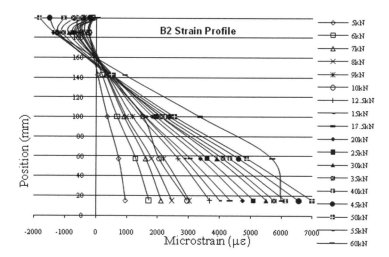

Figure 6.   Typical beam depths against strain for B2 at mid-span section.

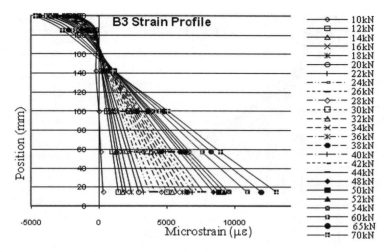

Figure 7.   Typical beam depths against strain for B3 at mid-span section.

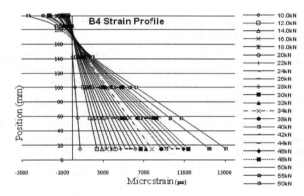

Figure 8.   Typical beam depths against strain for B4 at mid-span section.

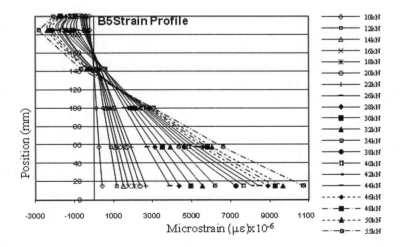

Figure 9.   Typical beam depths against strain for B5 at mid-span section.

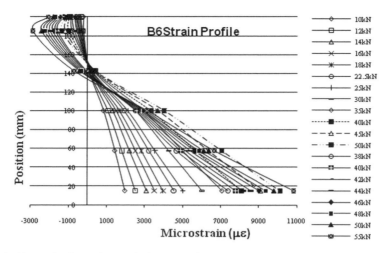

Figure 10. Typical beam depths against strain for B6 at mid-span section.

In addition, the strain in the mid-span tended to increase with loading more rapidly. This behaviour confirms that full composite action was ensured, with perfect bonding between the concrete and no deformed rectangular section of CFRP (Achillides et al., 1997a). The unexpected concrete strain in all the RC beams might have been caused by lack of concrete homogeneity. The variation in predicted and measured concrete strain may be related to the characteristics of cracks in terms of their width and penetration. The response of the compressive concrete zone may also be influenced by the suspected shear lag as it may enhance the localised effect of cracks.

5 CONCLUSIONS

When using FRP reinforcement that exhibits nonductile behavior, its use should be limited to structures that will benefit from properties such as its noncorrosive or nonconductive characteristic. Note The CFRP strip reinforced beams exhibited greater ductility at the earlier loading stage when compared with conventionally reinforced beams of similar configuration.

The deflection and flexural curvature followed an almost linear relationship with load up to failure, which indicates that the CFRP strip strain had more contribution to curvature than the concrete strain.

It can be reported with confidence that RC beams made with CFRP strips can significantly improve their ultimate load capacity. This observation agrees well with the conclusion of many researchers.

REFERENCES

Achillides, Z., Pilakoutas, K. and Waldron, P. (1997a), "Bond Behaviour of FRP Bars to Concrete," Proceeding of the Third International Symposium on Non-Metallic (FRP) Reinforcement for concrete Structures, Sapporo-Japan, Vol. 2, pp. 339–350.

Achillides, Z., Pilakoutas, K. and Waldron, P. (1997b), "Modelling of FRP rebar bond Behaviour," Proceeding of the Third International Symposium on Non-Metallic (FRP) Reinforcement for concrete Structures, Sapporo-Japan, Oct. 1997, Vol. 2, pp. 420–435.

Achillides, Z., Pilakoutas, K. and Waldron, P. (2004), "Bond Behaviour of Fiber Reinforced Polymer," Journal of composite for Construction, ASCE, Vol. 8, No. 2, pp. 170–180.

Aiello, M.A. and Ombres, L. (2000), "Load –Deflection Analysis of FRP Reinforced Concrete Flexural Members," Journal of composite for Construction, ASCE, Vol. 4, No. 4, pp. 160–170.

Alkhrdaji, T., Ombres, L. and Nanni, A. (2002), "Flexural Behaviour and Design of one –way concrete Slabs Reinforced with Deformed FRP Bars," Proceedings, 3rd International Conference on Advanced Composite Material in bridges and structures. Ottawa, Canada, Humar J. and Razaqpur A.G., Editors, 15–18, pp. 215–222.

Benmokrane, B., Chaallal and Masmoudi, R. (1996), "Flexural Response of concrete Beams reinforced With FRP Reinforcing Bars," ACI Structural Journal, Vol. 93, No. 1, pp. 45–55.

Bischoff, P.H. (2005a), "Reevaluation of Deflection Prediction for Concrete Beams reinforced with steel and Fiber reinforced polymer Bars," Journal of Structural Engineering, ASCE, pp. 750–760.

Brown, V.L. and Bartholomew, C.L. (1993), "FRP Reinforcing Bars in reinforced Concrete Members," ACI Materials Journal, Vol. 90, No. 1, pp. 34–40.

BSI (1991), BS 5328: Methods of specifying concrete mixes, part 2: Section 5, London, UK.

BSI (1985), "Structural Use of Concrete –Part 2: Code of practice for Special Circumstances (BSS8110-2:1985), including amendments No. 1, (1989) and 2 (2001)," British Standard Institution, p. 60.

CIRIA, (1995), "*Steel Reinforcement*" A guide for young construction professional, special publication 118, CIRIA, Westminister, London, UK.

CIRIA, (2002), "*Fiber reinforced polymer composites in construction*" C546, CIRIA, Westminister, London, UK.

Concrete Bridge Development Group, (2000), *The use Fibre composites in concrete bridges*, Technical Guide 3, Crowwthorne, Berkshire, UK.

Cosenza, E., Greco, C., Manfredi, G. and Pecce, M. (1997a), "*Flexural Behaviour of Concrete Beams Reinforced With Fiber Reinforced Polymer (FRP)Bars*," Proceeding of the Third International Symposium on Non-Metallic (FRP) Reinforcement for Concrete Structural, Sapporo-Japan, Vol. 2, pp. 463–470.

Concrete Society, (1998), *The spacers for reinforced Concrete*, report CS101, the Concrete Society, Technical Guide 3, Berkshire, UK.

Hota, V.S. GangaRao, P. and Vijay, V. (2006), Reinforced Concrete Design with FRP composites, UK.

IStructE (1997), "Interim Guidance on the Design of Reinforced Concrete Structures Using Fiber composites Reinforcement," SETO Ltd, London, pp. 115–118.

Nanni, A. (1993), "*flexural Behaviour and Design of Reinforced Concrete using FRP Reinforcement*," Journal of Structural Engineering Vol. 119, No. 11, pp. 3340–3360.

Nanni, A. 2000, "*FRP Reinforcement For Bridge Structures*", proceedings, Structural Engineering Conference, The University of Kansas, Lawrence.

Sooriyaarachchi, K., Pilakoutas, K. and Byars, E. (2005), "*Tension Stiffening behavior of GFRP-Reinforced Concrete*" Proceedings of the 7th International Symposium on Fiber-Reinforced Polymer Reinforcement for Concrete Structures, ACI, pp. 970–990, USA.

Tann, D.B. (2001), "Retrofitting of Mechanically Degraded Concrete Structures using Fibre reinforced polymer composites" Thesis (PhD), University of Glamorgan, UK.

Concrete Solutions – Grantham, Mechtcherine & Schneck (eds)
© 2012 Taylor & Francis Group, London, ISBN 978-0-415-61622-5

Safety of RC highway bridges strengthened with CFRP; flexural and shear limit states

O. Ali & D. Bigaud

LASQUO Laboratory, Angers University, Angers, France

ABSTRACT: The paper presents an analysis of durability factors of RC highway bridges strengthened with CFRP laminates. Durability factors are concrete cover and CFRP thickness. Three deterioration factors were considered. First, growth of live load with time. Second, resistance losses due to steel corrosion. Third, deterioration due to CFRP aging. Reliability analysis was performed for both flexural and shear limit states. The flexural limit state is controlled by three failure modes; concrete crushing, CFRP rupture and CFRP debonding. Monte-Carlo simulation was used to develop time dependent statistical models for steel area and live load extreme effects (bending moment & shear). Reliability is estimated in term of a reliability index β using FORM. For illustrative purpose, the reliability of RC bridge interior girder is evaluated under various traffic and corrosion environments. Bridge design options follow AASHTO specifications. The study work extends to calibrate a CFRP resistance safety factor which corresponds to two target reliability levels, $\beta_T = 3.5$ & 4.2.

1 INTRODUCTION

The safety of reinforced concrete bridges is strongly affected by many deterioration factors. The most important factor is reinforcement corrosion. Considerable research effort has been done to evaluate corrosion effects. It has been found that, corrosion causes reduction of steel properties (Cairns et al 2005), losses of bond between concrete and steel rebars, cracking, and spalling of concrete cover (Li et al 2006). Another factor of great importance is live load growth with time. Additional resistance through strengthening technique is required to compensate for losses in section resistance. Recently, carbon fibre reinforced plastic CFRP materials have used for the purpose of strengthening; laminates are externally bonded to the concrete tensile surface to produce additional bending or shear strength. In the last two decades, the flexural behaviour of CFRP strengthened RC beams has been studied in a significant number of studies. Different failure modes were observed, which can be classified in two types according to location. First, failure modes occur at position of maximum moment. Such modes are concrete crushing, CFRP mid span debonding, and CFRP rupture. Second, failure modes occur at plate ends. Herein, failure modes of the second type were neglected as they can be prevented using anchorage systems. In an early study proposed by Plevris et al (1995), the authors suggested a specific reduction factor ($\psi_{CFRP} \approx 0.8$) for the CFRP contribution

to strengthened element resistance. However, the study was limited to CFRP rupture failure mode. Recently, Pham & Al-Mahaidi (2008) discussed the reliability of strengthened beams considering all failure modes of the first type. Atadero & Karbhari (2007) studied the reliability of CFRP strengthened RC beams considering steel corrosion and CFRP durability. The authors focused on the importance of CFRP statistical properties on the CFRP safety factor. The present work aims to evaluate the reliability profile of CFRP strengthened RC beams and to compare the effect of durability factors (concrete cover & CFRP laminate thickness) on the service life of girders. Calibration of the partial safety factor for CFRP laminates is performed for both shear and flexural limit states.

2 CORROSION OF REINFORCEMENT BARS

2.1 Corrosion stages

The corrosion deterioration process can be divided into three stages; initiation, propagation before cover cracking, and after cover cracking. This classification corresponds to the variation of corrosion current in each stage (i.e. Bastidas et al 2008).

2.1.1 Corrosion initiation
In many studies, chloride attack has been considered as a diffusion process of moisture through voids

spread in concrete which is assumed to be relatively moist. 1D Fick's second law is chosen to represent the diffusion process:

$$\frac{\partial C_{(x,t)}}{\partial t} = D_{cl}\frac{\partial^2 C_{(x,t)}}{\partial x^2} \qquad (1)$$

where, C is the chloride ion concentration at a depth x in the concrete in the diffusion direction, t is the time and D_{cl} is the chloride diffusion coefficient in concrete which is taken as:

$$D_{cl} = D_{cl,ref} f_{cl1}(T) f_{cl2}(t) f_{cl3}(RH) \qquad (2)$$

where $D_{cl,ref}$ is a value of D_{cl} which corresponds to a reference temperature ($T_{ref} = 298$ K), at a critical relative humidity ($RH_c = 0.75$), and at a reference time ($t_{ref} = 28$ days). The three functions in (Eq. 2) were formulated by Val & Trapper (2008) as:

$$f_{cl1}(T) = \exp[U_c(1/T_{ref} - 1/T)/R] \qquad (3a)$$

$$f_{cl2}(t) = (t_{ref}/t)^{m_{age}} \qquad (3b)$$

$$f_{cl3}(RH) = [1 + (1 - RH)^4/(1 - RH_C)^4]^{-1} \qquad (3c)$$

where, T is the absolute temperature in (Kelvin), U_c ($=44.6 \pm 4.46$ kJ/mol) is the activation energy, R is the universal gas constant, m_{age} is the aging coefficient, and RH is the relative humidity. $D_{cl,ref}$ is influenced by mix proportions, curing, compaction ... etc, and can be expressed as (Vu & Stewart 2000):

$$D_{cl,ref} = 0.15 D_{H_2O}\frac{1 + \rho_c wc}{1 + \rho_c wc + \rho_c ac/\rho_a} \times \left(\frac{\rho_c wc - 0.85}{1 + \rho_c wc}\right)^3 \qquad (4)$$

where, D_{H_2O} is the chloride diffusion coefficient in an infinite solution ($=50491.08$ mm²/year for $NaCl$), ac is the aggregate-cement ratio, wc is the water cement ratio. ρ_c & ρ_a are mass densities of cement and aggregates respectively. Solution of (Eq. 1) gives chloride concentration in concrete as:

$$C(x,t) = C_s\left[1 - erf\left(\frac{x}{2\sqrt{D_{cl,ref}\cdot t}}\right)\right] \qquad (5)$$

where, erf is the error function and C_s is the chloride concentration at the concrete surface. In the present study C_s is evaluated as a function of the distance from the construction site to the coast (d in km) as expressed in the following empirical models reported in (Vu & Stewart 2000):

$$C_s(d) = \begin{cases} 2.95\ \text{kg/m}^3 & \text{if } d \le 0.1 \\ 1.15 - 1.81\log_{10}(d), & \text{if } 0.1 < d < 2.84 \quad (6) \\ 0.03 & \text{if } d > 2.84 \end{cases}$$

The corrosion initiation time (t_{ini}) corresponds to the time required for $C(x,t)$ to reach a threshold value C_{th} at the contact surface between concrete and steel as x equal the concrete cover. The term ($D_{cl,ref}\cdot t$) under the square root is calculated incrementally taking into account the change in chloride diffusion coefficient at each time increment according to temperature and humidity profiles (Luping & Gulkers 2007).

2.1.2 Corrosion current before cover cracking

In the current stage, deterioration takes place with the formation of corrosion current i_{corr}. Based on Faraday's law of electrochemical equivalence, the current density, of steel corrosion cell can be expressed as (Bastidas-Arteaga et al 2008):

$$i_{corr}(t) = \frac{n_{O_2} F D_{O_2}(t) C_{O_2}}{x(t)} \qquad (7)$$

where, n_{O_2} is the obtained electric number of oxygen molecules participating in chemical reaction ($n_{O_2} = 4$), F is Faraday's constant, C_{O_2} is the oxygen concentration on the surface ($C_{O_2} = 8.93 \times 10^{-10}$ mol/mm³), $x(t)$ (in mm) is the depth in concrete media that has chloride concentration equal to C_{th} & $t > t_{ini}$. $D_{O_2}(t)$ is the coefficient of oxygen diffusion in concrete. This latter parameter is considered as constant in this stage and can be expressed as (Bastidas-Arteaga et al 2008)

$$D_{O_2} = 3.1536 \times 10^5\left(\frac{32.15}{f'_{cu}} - 0.44\right)(\text{mm}^2/\text{year}) \qquad (8)$$

where, f_{cu} ($=f'_c/0.8$) is the concrete cube compressive strength in (MPa). It can be observed from (Eq. 7) that corrosion current decreases with the increasing the depth $x(t)$ of critical chloride concentration (see Fig. 1).

This concept simulates the actual corrosion process, as the corrosion rate decreases due to the

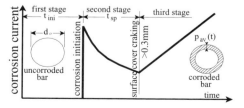

Figure 1. Time-variant corrosion rate.

formation of a rust layer around the corroded bar. This layer tends to expand with time, thus access of oxygen and moist are gradually delayed leading to a reduction in corrosion rate (Yuan et al 2009).

2.1.3 *Corrosion current after cracking*

Expansion of the accumulated rust layer around the steel bar with time induces internal radial compression stresses. These stresses take place when the rust layer fully fills the porous band around the bar. It is well known that embedded bars and the concrete cover behave as thick ring (Li et al 2006) as shown in (Fig. 2), where D is the bar diameter, c is the concrete cover, and d_o is the thickness of the porous band around the steel bar. The inner and outer radii of the thick ring are $a = (D + 2d_o)/2$ and $b = c + a$ respectively. The thickness of rust layer required to start compression radial stresses $P_s(t)$ can be determined as (Li et al 2006):

$$d_s(t) = \frac{W_r(t)}{\pi(d + d_o)}\left(\frac{1}{\rho_{rust}} - \frac{\alpha_r}{\rho_{st}}\right) \tag{9}$$

where α_r is a ratio expressing the molecular weight of steel divided by the molecular weight of corrosion products. The value of α_r depends on the kind corrosion products (0.523 for $Fe(OH)_3$ & 0.622 for $Fe(OH)_2$) an average value of α_r (=0.57) is assumed here as recommended by Lui & Weyers (1998), ρ_r is density of corrosion products, ρ_{st} is density of steel, and $W_r(t)$ is the mass of corrosion products (mg/mm) and can be determined as:

$$W_r(t) = \left[2\int_0^t 0.105(1/\alpha_r)\pi Di_{corr}(t)dt\right]^{1/2} \tag{10}$$

Obviously, the induced radial compression stresses are simultaneously accompanied by tensile strains in the tangential direction. The growth of tensile strains with time initiates radial cracks starting from the contact surface between the steel bars and concrete (see Fig. 2c). The time to severe cracking t_{sp} can be obtained through an analytical crack width model derived by (Li et al 2006). The model concludes the surface crack width is:

$$w_c(t) = \frac{4\pi d_s(t)}{(1 - v_c)(a/b)^{\sqrt{\kappa}} + (1 + v_c)(b/a)^{\sqrt{\kappa}}} - \frac{2\pi b f_{ct}}{E_{ef}} \tag{11}$$

where, v_c is the Poisson ratio of concrete, $\kappa(\leq 1)$ is the tangential stiffness reduction factor which takes into account the residual tangential stiffness of cracked concrete and is related to the average tangential strain at the cracked surface and concrete properties, and $E_{ef}(= 1/v_c+1)$ is the effective elastic modulus of concrete. The model is fully detailed in (Li et al 2006) and verified with experimental results in the same study. When the exposure time equals to the time to severe cracking (t_{sp}) additional access of oxygen and moist occur, where t_{sp} is the time required for the surface crack width to reach a critical value of 0.3 mm according to Bastidas-Arteaga et al (2008).

It is complex to model and predict corrosion rate activation due to cover cracking. Bastidas-Arteaga et al (2008) assumed that D_{O_2} becomes linearly time-dependent when $t > t_{sp}$. The authors consider that the oxygen concentration on the steel surface C_{nO_2} after t_n (with $t_n >>> t_{sp}$; e.g. $t_n = 500$ years) coincides with the oxygen concentration at the concrete surface C_{O_2}. They substitute these values into Fick's second law (Eq. 1) and it leads to $Dn_{O_2}(t)$, the oxygen diffusion coefficient at time t_n:

$$Dn_{O_2}(t) = c^2\left/4t_n\left[erf^{-1}\left(1 - \frac{C_{nO_2}}{C_{O_2}}\right)\right]^2\right. \tag{12}$$

where, c is clear concrete cover in mm. Finally, the time-variant oxygen diffusion can be taken as:

$$D_{O_2}(t) = \begin{cases} D_{O_2} & \text{if } t < t_{sp} \\ D_{O_2} + \left(\dfrac{D_{O_2} - D_{nO_2}}{t_{sp} - t_n}\right)(t - t_{sp}) & \text{if } t \geq t_{sp} \end{cases} \tag{13}$$

Herein, the oxygen diffusion coefficient is assumed to be temperature dependent according to (Eq. 3a). Activation energy U_{O_2} of oxygen diffusion was taken as (Pour-Ghaz et al 2009):

$$U_{O_2} = -505wc^2 + 484.5wc - 94; \quad \text{kj/mol} \tag{14}$$

The reduction in the diameter of corroded reinforcing bar ΔD in (mm) is evaluated according to the following equation (Val et al 2000):

$$\Delta D = 0.0232\int_{t_{ini}}^t i_{corr}(t)dt \tag{15}$$

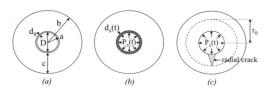

Figure 2. Scheme of corrosion induced cracking.

It is worth mentioning that corrosion did not affect the steel area only, but its action also extends to change the steel properties with time; yield strength, ultimate strength, ultimate strain (Cairns et al 2005). It can be assumed that yield strength is linearly proportional to the reduced cross-sectional area $A_s(t)$ such that (Stewart & Al-Harthy 2008),

$$f_y(t) = \left(1 - \alpha_y \frac{A_s(t)}{A_{so}}\right) f_{yo} \qquad (16)$$

where, f_{yo} and A_{so} are steel yield stress and area of un-corroded bar respectively. α_y is an empirical coefficient. Cairns et al (2005) review 12 experimental studies which report an average value of α_y up to 0.01. Herein α_y is taken equal to 0.005 according to recommendations given by Stewart & Al-Harthy (2008).

2.2 Time dependent steel area statistical model

The reference chloride diffusion coefficient $D_{cl,ref}$ is an important material parameter that has been considered as random variables in many studies (e.g. Stewart & Rosowsky 1998, Vu & Stewart 2000, Arteaga et al 2009). It is reviewed that, $D_{cl,ref}$ is influenced by many factors as presented in (Eq. 4) and is not significantly affected by the source of chlorides (Vu & Stewart 2000). In order to compute a probabilistic model for $D_{cl,ref}$ Monte-Carlo simulation was used to fit an overall statistical model. Deterministic values of ac, ρ_c, and ρ_a are presented in Table 1. Uncertainty in the value obtained using (Eq. 4) is presented in Table 2. Fitting results proposes that a generalized extreme value distribution best fits the simulated data with statistical parameters (scale = −0.1021, shape = 17.0195, location = 46.5274).

Table 1. Material constant (deterministic).

	Value	Units	Description
E_s	201300	MPa	Elastic steel modulus
γ_c	22	kN/m³	Specific weight of concrete
γ_p	18	kN/m³	Asphalt pavement specific weight
υ_c	0.2	–	Concrete Poisson ratio
d_o	0.0125	mm	Porous band thickness around bar
ρ_s	78.5	kN/m³	Density of steel
ρ_r	36	kN/m³	Density of corrosion rust
ρ_c	29	kN/m³	Density of cement
ρ_a	26	kN/m³	Density of aggregate
ac	5.14	–	Aggregate to cement ratio
m_{age}	0.13	–	Aging coefficient, Val & Tapper

Environmental variables (C_s, C_{th}, c,..., etc) reported in Table 2 were used to generate an environmental data set containing 5×10^5 cases using a Monte-Carlo random algorithm. Each case is simulated under the above described corrosion model to provide a time dependent steel area data set. Evaluation of steel damage using the proposed simulation could obviate many complicated differential calculations required for the FORM algorithm. Monthly profiles of temperature and relative humidity in the ranges (20–40°C) and (0.5–0.75) respectively were considered. Figure 3 shows simulation results at different ages (0, 50, 100 years) for concrete cover; $c = 45$ mm. Based on (Eq. 6), an extreme value of $C_s = 3$ is considered. It is shown from (Fig. 3) that the steel area density function changes with time from a normal distribution with two parameters $N(\mu, \sigma)$—assumed at initial ages—to a bimodal distribution which can be fitted with a five parameter distribution ($\mu_1, \sigma_1, \mu_2, \sigma_2, \rho$) according to Eq. (17).

$$f_{As}(x,t) = \rho_{(t)} \Phi(x, \mu_{1(t)}, \sigma_{1(t)}) - (1 - \rho_{(t)}) \Phi(x, \mu_{2(t)}, \sigma_{2(t)}) \qquad (17)$$

where, $\mu_{i(t)}$ is the mean value, $\sigma_{i(t)}$ is the standard deviation, $\rho_{i(t)}$ is the mixture ratio, and Φ is the normal density function. The observed density distribution obtained from the generation (Fig. 3) simulates the corrosion process in the nature, as there is a probability—decreases with time—that the steel rebar still be non-corroded.

3 LIVE LOAD MODEL

Statistical parameters for a single truck (heavy) weight were considered according to Vu & Stewart (2000) based on a truck data survey. It is assumed that the truck weight follows the normal distribution with initial mean ($\mu_w = 250$ kN) and standard deviation ($\sigma_w = 100$ kN). Gross truck weight distribution between axles and axle's configuration were adopted as for a standard HS20 truck reported in AASHTO. The nominal truck dynamic effect was taken as fraction of the gross truck weight; 0.15 for a single truck and 0.1 for two trucks side-by-side (Nowak et al 2001). Highway Traffic survey studies confirm that traffic load volume and weight continue to increase with time. Vu & Stewart (2000) suggested that the time dependent mean truck weight is $\mu_{w(t)} = \mu_w(1 + \lambda_m)^t$, standard deviation is $\sigma_{w(t)} = \sigma_w(1 + \lambda_m)^t$, and the average daily truck traffic is $ADTT_{(t)} = ADTT_{initial}(1 + \lambda_v)^t$, where λ_v is the annual increase in traffic volume ranges between (1–3% taken 2.3% as an average), λ_m is the annual increase truck weight ($\lambda_m = 0.005$), and $ADTT_{initial}$

Table 2. Random variables parameters.

Variable	Distribution	Units	Nominal	Bias[a](mean)	Cov[b](std[c])	Description (source)
f'_c	Normal	MPa	34.5	1	0.15	Compressive strength (Plevris et al 1995)
α_{ct}	Normal	–	0.3	1	0.15	Concrete tensile uncertainty (Val et al 2000)
f_y	Normal	MPa	414	(460)	(46.2)	Steel yield strength (Vu & Stewart 2000)
d_s	Normal	mm	700	(700 – 4.7)	(12.7)	Steel rebars depth (Plevris et al 1995)
b_c	Normal	mm	400	(400 + 2.54)	(3.658)	Beam width (Plevris et al 1995)
b_s	Normal	mm	350:10:370	1	(5)	Stirrup width (Duprat 2007)
e_c	Normal	mm	0	(0)	(5)	Stirrup eccentricity (Duprat 2007)
s	Normal	mm	200	1	0.1	Stirrup spacing (Duprat 2007)
$A_{s,intial}$	Normal	mm²	490.87	0.97	0.024	Initial rebars area (Atadero & Karbhari 2007)
c	Lognormal	mm	25:5:45	1	0.2–0.1	Lower concrete cover (Duprat 2007)
C_s—chloride	Lognormal	kg/m³	3.0	1	0.5	Surface concentration (Vu & Stewart 2000)
C_{th}—chloride	Uniform	kg/m³	0.9	1	0.19	Threshold (Bastidas-Arteaga et al 2009)
D_{c},—chloride	GEV	mm²/yrs	1	54.65	0.35	Diffusion coefficient (Vu & Stewart 2000)
$i_{current}$	Normal	–		1	0.2	Uncertainty in current (Vu & Stewart 2000)
^dE_f	Lognormal	GPa	51.7	1	0.2	CFRP modulus (Atadero & Karbhari 2007)
$^df_{f,u}$	Weibull	MPa	620.5	1	0.15	CFRP strength (Atadero & Karbhari 2007)
t_p	Lognormal	mm		1	0.05	CFRP thickness (Atadero & Karbhari 2007)
Wc	Normal	–	0.45	1	0.05	Water cement ratio (Atadero & Karbhari 2007)
Concrete weight	Normal	depend on analysis		1.05	0.1	(Val et al 2000)
Asphalt thickness	Normal	mm	90	1	0.25	(Val et al 2000)
Truck load w	Normal	kN	250	1	0.4	(Val et al 2000)
Impact factor (IL)	Normal	–	0.1	1	0.8	(Val et al 2000)
γ_v	Normal	–	1	1.15	0.125	Shear model error (Vu & Stewart 2000)
γ_m		–	1	See Figure 7		Flexural model error

Concrete crushing: Lognormal, CFRP debonding: Lognormal, and CFRP: rupture normal.
[a]Bias; mean/nominal, [b]cov; coefficient of variation, [c]std; standard deviation, [d]property decorrelated from CFRP thickness.

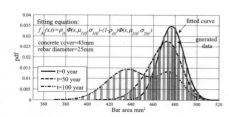

Figure 3. Corroded rebar area $A_s(t)$ density; $c = 45$ mm.

is the initial average daily traffic. *ADTT* can be assumed as a fraction of the total traffic flow, this fraction depends on the highway class (rural, urban ... etc) (AASHTO).

Extreme truck events (moment or shear) induced in girders are affected with four variables (Nowak 2004); first: truck model, second: impact factor, third: variation in transverse traffic position d_{lane} (see Fig. 4) through bridge lanes (for standard 3.6 m wide lane, d_{lane} is approximated by a lognormal

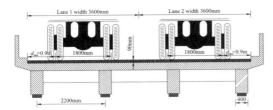

Figure 4. Bridge cross-section and trucks position.

distribution with coefficient of variation 0.33 and mean value 0.9 m. The fourth, multiple presence of fully correlated heavy truck side-by-side on bridge deck traffic lanes (2 lanes is assumed here).

Nowak (1993) observed that on average, about every 15th truck is on the bridge simultaneously with another truck (side-by-side). For each such simultaneous occurrence, it is assumed that every 10th time the trucks are partially correlated (with regard to weight) and every 30th time the trucks are fully correlated. For example if $ADTT = 250$ truck/day, there are $N = 5274, 607$, and 202 case/year of simultaneous none, partial, and fully correlated trucks respectively. The three levels of correlations assumed correspond to a correlation coefficient $\rho = 0, 0.5, 1$ respectively. Monte-Carlo random number generation was used to simulate daily traffic loads passing through each bridge lane in a way to get an extreme event statistical model. Simulation was implemented in three steps. First, for each day in the year, $ADTT$ trucks were randomly generated for each lane; the finite element program SAP2000 was used to determine each truck event, thus uncertainty due to girder distribution factors reported in bridges design codes could be minimized. As distribution factor statistical parameters (bias λ_d & variation coefficient cov_d) for simplified formulas (i.g. AASHTO specifications) and sophisticated methods (e.g. finite element and fried analysis) are $\lambda_d = 0.93$ & $cov_d = 0.12$ and $\lambda_d = 0.98$ & $cov_d = 0.07$ respectively (Nowak et al 2001). Recent field tests confirmed that the girder distribution could be treated as a normal random variable (Nowak et al 2001). A day extreme event is recorded and taken equal to the maximum of; (maximum event induced in the first lane, maximum event induced in second lane, and maximum of N summation of two events randomly chosen. The two chosen truck events must have zero interaction between the two trucks in the transverse deck direction). Second, extreme events—values for each day in the year—obtained in step 1 are averaged and their standard deviation is calculated. The third, Step 1 and 2 are repeated so that variation in parameters converges to chosen tolerances.

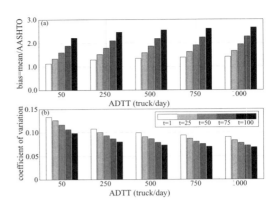

Figure 5. Live load bending moment statistics. t (years).

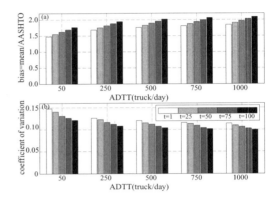

Figure 6. Live load shearing force statistics. t (years).

A statistical comparison between the effect of time and $ADTT$ on live load extreme events statistics for bending moments and shear are shown in Figures 5 and 6 respectively. It can be noted that the proposed model provides more accurate simulation for daily traffic loads rather than the model proposed by Nowak (1993) as the author neglected the effect of the $ADTT$ value and growth of traffic loads on the statistical parameters of live loads.

4 CFRP DEGRADATION

The long term performance of CFRP laminates is affected by field conditions (humidity, temperature, method of installation ... etc). Karbhari & Abanilla (2007) have extensively studied experimentally different sizes (2, 6, 12 layers) of CFRP specimens under various exposure conditions of accelerated tests ranging between two and three years. The authors also formulate a simplified durability model for the aging effect based on Arrhenius acceleration law. For a specific grade of FRP properties, strength and modulus can be expressed as

$$f_{fu}(t) = f_{fuo}(-3.366\ln(t) + 106.07) \quad (18a)$$

$$E_f(t) = E_{fo}(-0.418\ln(t) + 106.07) \quad (18b)$$

where, f_{fuo} is the initial FRP ultimate strength, E_{fo} is the initial FRP modulus, t is the time in days. The model was derived for wet layup carbon/epoxy for external strengthening. Assessment of predictive accuracy of the model shows reliable results of the model especially for long exposure time.

5 STRUCTURAL MODELLING

Flexural behavior is evaluated through sectional analysis of the concrete section. The concrete stress-strain constitutive relation was taken according to Model Code MC90 (CEB-FIP 1990). Steel bars present an elastic perfect plastic behavior while CFRP is assumed to be linear elastic. The flexural ultimate limit state is controlled by three failure modes. First; concrete crushing as maximum concrete strain reaches the ultimate strain. Second; FRP rupture as maximum FRP strain reaches rupture strain $(=f_{fu}(t)/E_f(t))$ of laminates. Third; FRP mid span debonding as maximum FRP strain reaches the FRP debonding strain. Many analytical models were proposed to evaluate debonding strain such as; ACI 440.2R-02, Fib Bulletin 14, Concrete Society TR 55, Chen & Teng (2001). 41 beams were studied experimentally by (Ashour et al 2004; Bogas & Gomes 2007; Aram & Czaderski 2008; Pham & Al-Mahaidi 2004; Teng et al 2003), all tested beams were simply supported and failed by intermediate crack debonding. Capacities of all the beams were calculated by inserting these models in beam section analysis. We compared the experimental and calculated ultimate capacities. It was found that Chen & Teng (2001) gives the best correlation (=0.958) between experimental and calculated. So, it is recommended to use this model in reliability analysis. The model can be briefly described by defining the limiting ultimate CFRP debonding strain $\varepsilon_{f,debonding}$:

$$\varepsilon_{f,debonding} = \alpha \beta_{fl} \beta_L \sqrt{f'_c / t_f E} \quad (19)$$

$$L_e = \sqrt{\frac{t_f E_f}{\sqrt{f'_c}}}; \quad \beta_f = \sqrt{\frac{2 - b_f/b_c}{1 + b_f/b_c}};$$

$$\beta_L = \begin{cases} 1 & \text{if } L > L_e \\ \sin(\pi L/2L_e) & \text{if } L < L_e \end{cases} \quad (20)$$

where, α is an empirical factor depends on the RC element type (=1 for beams), b_c is the beam width.

b_f, t_f, and E_f are FRP plate width, thickness, elastic modulus, respectively. L is the actual bond length.

Shear capacity V of RC beams is evaluated by adding the contribution of concrete V_c and internal steel stirrups V_s to the contribution of the externally bonded CFRP shear strips V_f according to

$$V = V_c + V_s + V_f \quad (21)$$

where steel and concrete contributions were calculated according to the ACI 440.2R-02 as

$$V_c = 0.17b_c d_s \sqrt{f_c} \quad (22)$$

$$V_c = A_{sv} f_y d_s / s \quad (23)$$

where b_c is the beam width, d_s is lower steel depth, A_{sv} is the steel stirrup area, s is the stirrup spacing. 12 analytical models were compared to calculate the CFRP contribution V_f. The models are reported in (SAS 2008; Khalifa & Nanni 2000; ACI 440.2R-02; Aprile & Benedetti 2004; Colotti et al 2005; Kim et al 2008). 84 beams were studied experimentally and fully detailed in (Sas 2008; Barros & Dias 2006; Jayaprakash et al 2008; Sundarraja & Ragamohan 2009; Taljsten & Elfgren 2000; Khalifa & Nanni 2000; Mosallam & Banerjee 2007; Diagana et al 2003; Kim et al 2008; Monti & Liotta 2007; Colotti et al 2005; Aprile & Benedetti 2004), all tested beams were simply supported and failed only by shear under four-point tests. The capacities of all the beams were calculated for the 12 models. The experimental and calculated ultimate capacities were compared. It was found that Triantafillou & Antonopoulos (2000) and Ye el al 2005 reported in SAS 2008 gave the best correlation $R = 0.947$ and 0.916 respectively between experimental and calculated capacities. The former model can be described as follows:

$$V_f = \varepsilon_{f,e} E_f \rho_f b_c d_s (\sin\theta + \cos\theta) \quad (24)$$

$$\varepsilon_{f,e} = \min\{65 \times 10^{-5} \ (f_c^{2/3}/E_f \rho_f)^{0.56}, \\ 0.17 \ \varepsilon_{f,u} \ (f_c^{2/3}/E_f \rho_f)^{0.3}\} \quad (25)$$

Where θ is CFRP aliment angle inclination, ε_{fu} is the ultimate CFRP strain, $\rho_f = 2b_{fv}t_{fv}/s_f$, b_f is shear CFRP strip width, t_{fv} shear strip thickness, s_f is strip spacing, E_f is CFRP modulus in GPa. The later model (Ye el al) can be described as follows:

$$V_f = K_f \tau h_{f,e}^2 b_{fv} (\sin\theta + \cos\theta)/s_f \quad (26)$$

599

$$K_f = \varphi_f \frac{\sin\theta\sqrt{E_f t_{fv}}}{\sin\theta\sqrt{E_f t_{fv}} + 0.3 f_{ct} h_{f,e}};$$

$$\tau = 1.2\beta_{fv} f_{ct} \qquad (27)$$

$$\beta_{fv} = \sqrt{\frac{2.25 - b_{vf}/s_f \sin\theta}{1.25 + b_{vf}/s_f \sin\theta}};$$

where φ_f is taken 1.3 for U-jacket scheme and 1 for side scheme, $h_{f,e} = z_t - z_b - h + 0.9 d_s$, z_t and z_b are the distances from beam compression face to top and lower edges of CFRP plates respectively.

6 RELIBILITY ASPECTS & APPLICATION

The ultimate limit state G of a RC section can be expressed as:

$$G = \gamma_m R(t) - S(t) = \gamma_m R(X_1, X_2, \ldots X_n) \\ -(\gamma_{DL} DL + \gamma_{LL} LL) \qquad (28)$$

where, γ_m random variable reflects the uncertainty in theoretical resistance, R is the resistance as a function of random variables X_i (geometric and material properties). S is expresses random loads. γ_{DL} and γ_{LL} are random variables expressing uncertainty in dead DL and live LL loads respectively. FORM was used to estimate the reliability index β which can be determined from a solution of constrained minimization; $\beta = (u^{*T} u^*)^{1/2}$ under $G = 0$, where u^* is the vector of the most probable design point in the standard normal space. Table 1, shows the statistical variables considered in the analysis. In order to take into account dependency between concrete compressive strength f_c and concrete tensile strength f_{ct}. It is assumed that f_{ct} can be expressed via f_c as $f_{ct} = \alpha_{ct} f_c^{2/3}$, thus f_c and the coefficient α_{ct} could be assumed independent (Val et al 2000). The gain in concrete properties with time was considered according to (CEB-FIP 1990).

Atadero & Karbhari (2009) and Atadero et al (2005) study experimentally and statistically the variability of CFRP properties (modulus E_{fu}, & strength f_{fu}) versus total thickness tp (represented by single layer thickness & number of layers). The studies conclude that E_{fu} & f_{fu} are statistically correlated with tp. Comparing FRP properties versus number of layers, it was proven that FRP number of layers has no effect on E_{fu}. While f_{fu} decreases with respect to number of layers by 0, 2, 11, and 23% (as average) for 1, 2, 3, and 4 layers respectively. It is considered here that f_{fu} decreases according to the latter decrement ratios. CFRP strength and modulus statistical distribution were fitted by the authors. Lognormal and Weibull distributions are the best descriptors for CFRP modulus and

strength respectively. The CFRP properties used in this study and reported in Table 2 were statistically decorrelated from thickness, single CFRP layer net thickness equal to 1.27 and 0.13 mm for flexural and shear limit state respectively. Plevris et al (1995) proposed an algorithm to evaluate section resistance model error uncertainty γ_m based on the Monte-Carlo simulation. The algorithm was limited to CFRP rupture failure mode only. For a certain concrete element if R and R_n are the actual and the nominal strength respectively, strengths were evaluated on the principle of a concrete stress block. A large number of simulations ($=5 \times 10^4$) are generated, for each simulation the strength bias ratio R/R_n is determined. The mean and the coefficient of variation of these ratios are calculated. In the present study, the algorithm was generalized for concrete crushing, debonding, and CFRP rupture failure modes using section analysis previously described instead of the principle concrete block. Different laminate layers are considered. Figure 7 shows statistical properties for model uncertainty. It is found that a lognormal distribution best fit biased ratios rather than the normal distribution assumed by the authors for both concrete crushing and CFRP debonding failure modes. However, a normal distribution best fit the bias ratios for the CFRP rupture failure mode.

Reliability analysis was used to check the reliability of a simple span bridge interior girder: span = 10 m & slab thickness = 0.25 m (see Figs. 4 and 8). The girder follows AASHTO recommendation. The altered LRFD design equation is;

$$\gamma_D DL + \gamma_w WL + \gamma_L LL \le \phi R_n(\ldots, \psi x_{FRP}) \quad (29)$$

where γ_D, γ_W, and γ_L are load factors for dead and wearing surface, and live load respectively. WL is the wearing surface load, ϕ is the general resistance factor, R_n is the nominal resistance, ψ is CFRP resistance factor, and x_{CFRP} is the CFRP contribu-

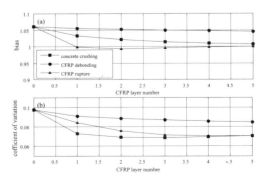

Figure 7. Model uncertainty statistics vs. CFRP layer number.

tion to resistance. The RC section should produce an initial reliability index: $\beta = 3.5$. It is assumed that the strengthening time corresponds to the time required for β to reach a minimum value: $\beta_{min} = 3$. Strengthening has to increase β to a value greater than a target value β_T. The choice of β_{min} and β_T values depend on cost, consequences of failure probability allowed, and required service life. According to the JCSS Model (2001), moderate consequences of failure and cost requires: $\beta_T = 4.2$. After strengthening, two options were considered. First, option I: corrosion will continue regardless strengthening effect on corrosion activity, as proven by Gadve et al (2009) that FRP strengthening has no significant effect on corrosion. Second, option II: corrosion is prevented, thus A_s statistical parameters don't change after strengthening. The CFRP resistance safety factor ψ_{CFRP} was calibrated. Two target reliability indices were considered: $\beta_T = 3.5$ & 4.2. A strength reduction safety factor algorithm was used to calculate ψ_{CFRP}; for assumed β_T index and ψ_{CFRP}, CFRP thickness is calculated incrementally according to (Eq. 6) even: $\beta = \beta_T$

7 RESULTS AND DESCOUSION

7.1 *Non-strengthened section*

First, when the considering live load effect (neglecting corrosion effect as a first step). Reliability analysis is performed for the girder detailed in the previous section. The results are plotted in Figures 9 and 10. It can be observed that the initial reliability index β is time dependent, as it decreases with increasing $ADTT$ value, moving from $ADTT = 1000$ towards $ADTT = 50$ truck/day causes a 14% drop in β. This can be explained by the effect of $ADTT$ on a live load extreme event induced in the girder.

This effect appears to be relatively small when compared with the effect of live load growth which plays an important role in girder safety versus time.

Considering the effect of corrosion in addition to live load model, reliability index profiles of the

Figure 8. Intermediate beam cross-section.

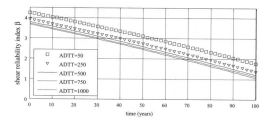

Figure 9. Shear β vs. time, growth of live load effect.

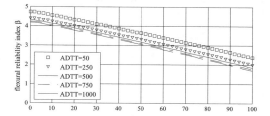

Figure 10. Flexural β vs. time, growth of live load effect.

most extreme cases ($c = 45$ mm & $ADTT = 50$ and $c = 25$ mm & $ADTT = 1000$) and ($b_s = 350$ mm & $ADTT = 50$ and $b_s = 370$ mm & $ADTT = 1000$) were plotted in Figures 11 and 12 for flexural and shear limit state respectively. It can be seen that the amounts of steel losses is likely more important than live load growth in reliability degradation.

Optimization of c versus strengthening time is plotted in Figures 13 and 14. For flexural, it is noted that relation between concrete cover and strengthening time is almost linear till $c = 45$. Cover effectiveness decreases after $c > 45$ especially for high $ADTT$ values. $ADTT$ and live load growth with time accelerate significantly strengthening time.

As shown in Figure 14 for Shear analysis, the relation between c and strengthening time is linear. Comparing Figures 13 and 14, it could be concluded that flexural cover is more effective than stirrups cover.

7.2 *Application of CFRP strengthening*

Reliability analysis was implemented for all the considered deterioration cases due to corrosion and live load growth. Option I and II were analyzed for both debonding and rupture failure mode after strengthening. For the flexural case; two layers of CFRP laminates with thickness equal to 1.27 mm per layer are applied. It is assumed that the laminate width equals 300 mm. For non end anchorage laminates it is found that the debonding failure mode is the control mode, rupture is yet to occur. Figure 15 shows the reliability of strengthened girder under the worst deterioration condition ($c = 25$ mm & $ADTT = 1000$ truck/day). It

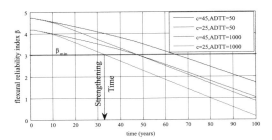

Figure 11. β vs. time, growth of live load & corrosion effect.

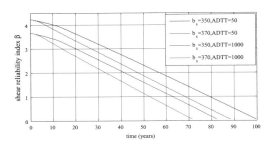

Figure 12. β vs. time, growth of live load & corrosion effect.

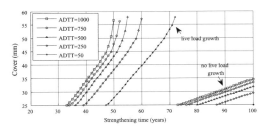

Figure 13. c vs. strengthening time, flexural limit state.

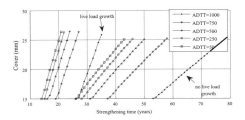

Figure 14. c vs. strengthening time, shear limit state.

could be observed that strengthening considering option II could maintain the concrete element in a reliable condition longer; this may reflect the effect of resistance losses due to reinforcement corrosion in option I. For shear; one CFRP laminates layer

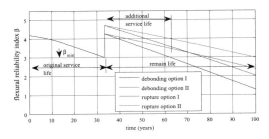

Figure 15. Flexural β of strengthened girder vs. time; $c = 25$ mm & $ADTT = 1000$ truck/day.

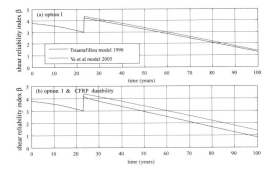

Figure 16. Shear β of strengthened girder vs. time; $b_s = 350$ mm & $ADTT = 500$ truck/day.

with thickness equal to 0.13 mm was bonded for each beam side with spacing equals to 250 mm. Laminate width equals to 100 mm. Reliability profiles are plotted in Figure 16. No significant effect is observed between the profile given by Triantafillou and Ye el al (§ 5, Eqs. 24–26). CFRP durability does not seem to fit the profile given by Ye el al model. So, Triantafillou 2000 model is assumed.

Optimization of CFRP thickness versus total service life was performed. End anchoraged and non-anchorage laminates are considered. For anchorage ends the model will be controlled by concrete crushing or CFRP rupture. While for non-anchorage ends, the model is served by concrete crushing, CFRP debonding and CFRP rupture. Laminate thicknesses were optimized for three level of deterioration after strengthening. First, option II. Second, option I. Third, option I in addition to CFRP durability. Results are plotted in Figure 17 for a flexural limit state. It can be seen that, the results (for anchorage and non-anchorage) are identical for small amounts of CFRP laminates. In this case it is observed that failure mode is independent whether the laminate ends are anchorage or not, as the CFRP rupture failure mode is the control one and CFRP debonding is yet takes place.

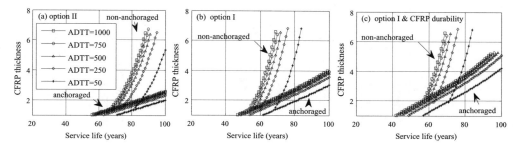

Figure 17. CFRP thickness (mm) vs. total service life, $c = 25$ mm. flexural limit state.

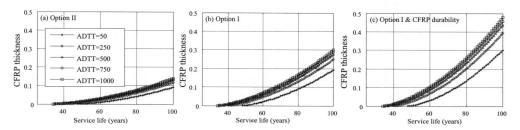

Figure 18. CFRP thickness (mm) vs. total service life, $b_z = 370$ mm. Shear limit state.

From the other side increasing laminate thicknesses considering debonding the CFRP is inefficient as in the CFRP rupture case especially when considering corrosion after strengthening (option I) and CFRP durability. CFRP laminate thickness is linearly proportional with total service life. It is also to be noted that, CFRP durability has a negligible effect in debonding failure mode while a significant effect is observed when anchoring laminates (CFRP rupture). This may return to two factors. First is the high contribution of CFRP in Eq. (29). Second is the dependency of rupture failure mode on both strength and modulus ($\varepsilon_{f,rupture} = f_{CFRP,u}/E_{CFRP}$) while modulus E_{CFRP} only affects debonding failure mode (see eq. 19). Although, CFRP rupture failure mode is significantly affected by CFRP durability, it gives a longer service life than debonding failure mode for the same CFRP amounts. It could be concluded that, for a certain desired service life rupture failure mode—anchorage ends—is safer, more economical in CFRP quantities, and more durable than debonding failure mode when use the same CFRP laminates thickness. Optimization results of CFRP thickness versus total service life for shear limit state are plotted in Figure 18. The figure reflects the importance of each degradation factor on service life especially CFRP aging and corrosion. From the other side the figure reflects the strengthening capability to enhance section service life as well as in anchorage end laminates for flexural limit state.

7.3 CFRP resistance safety factor calibration.

Table 3 presents CFRP resistance safety factor ψ_{CFRP} calibration results. The design value (x_d) of CFRP strength or modulus required for Eq. 24 is typically related to a certain percentile of test values as; $x_d = m_x(1 - n_d cov_x)$. Where m_x and cov_x are the mean and coefficient of variation of test results. n_d ($n_d = 3$ for ACI 440.2R-02, $n_d = 1.64$ Fib Bulletin 14, $n_d = 2$ Concrete Society TR 55) is constant specified by guidelines. Two target reliability indices were considered ($\beta = 3.5$ & 4.2). It could be observed that the CFRP safety factor depends on the target value, $ADTT$, steel losses and CFRP end anchorage system in the case of a flexural limit state. Small values of CFRP safety factors are recorded for small values of concrete cover ($c = 45$ mm) as strengthening time is delayed and the need of strengthening returns to live load growth as a principle deterioration factor followed by corrosion. It could be assumed that CFRP strengthening effectiveness in increasing and β is more significant for steel losses than live load growth.

Also it could be observed that for free design (no restriction in calculating CFRP amounts) non-anchorage CFRP laminates are more durable (≈ 1.1–2.7 times) than end anchorage laminates. The choice of target reliability index is very important in calibrating the CFRP safety factor. The recorded values of the CFRP safety factor ($\psi_{CFRP} = 1$; no factor required) correspond to design cases satisfying

Table 3. Summary of safety factor Ψ_{CFRP}, CFRP thickness t_p, and additional service life after strengthening L_{str} (years).

	Flexural; anchorage end; $c = 25$ mm				Flexural; non-anchoraged end; $c = 25$ mm				Shear limit state; $b_s = 370$ mm			
	$n_d = 0$	$n_d = 1$	$n_d = 2$	$n_d = 3$	$n_d = 0$	$n_d = 1$	$n_d = 2$	$n_d = 3$	$n_d = 0$	$n_d = 1$	$n_d = 2$	$n_d = 3$
$\beta_{target} = 4.2$												
$\Psi_{,ADTT=50}$	0.673	0.798	0.975	1	1	1	1	1	0.664	0.871	0.971	1.00
$\Psi_{,ADTT=250}$	0.571	0.687	0.841	1	0.960	1	1	1	0.546	0.731	0.815	0.92
$\Psi_{,ADTT=500}$	0.572	0.687	0.841	1	0.960	1	1	1	0.502	0.676	0.753	0.85
$\Psi_{,ADTT=750}$	0.562	0.668	0.817	1	0.939	1	1	1	0.467	0.640	0.715	0.80
$\Psi_{,ADTT=1000}$	0.547	0.655	0.801	1	0.923	1	1	1	0.452	0.624	0.692	0.78
t_p (mm)	1.85–1.85	1.85–1.85	1.85–1.85	2.28–1.89	4.02–3.01	5.08–3.05	6.67–4.06	9.94–6.07	0.12–0.12	0.12–0.12	0.12–0.12	0.13–0.12
L_{str} (I + dur)	21.6–20.9	21.7–20.9	21.6–20.9	28–21.5	30.6–27.2	33.0–27.3	36.3–30.3	39.4–34.8	25.0–23.9	23.3–22.1	23.3–22.2	22.3–22.2
L_{str} (II + dur)	33.3–32.5	33.4–32.4	33.4–32.4	47.9–37.8	48–43.2	51.5–43.4	52.3–47.6	52.3–53.8	39.2–39.4	39.4–39.9	39.7–40.1	47.3–40.1
$\beta_{target} = 3.5$												
$\Psi_{,ADTT=50}$	1	1	1	1	1	1	1	1	1	1	1	1
$\Psi_{,ADTT=250}$	1	1	1	1	1	1	1	1	1	1	1	1
$\Psi_{,ADTT=500}$	1	1	1	1	1	1	1	1	1	1	1	1
$\Psi_{,ADTT=750}$	1	1	1	1	1	1	1	1	1	1	1	1
$\Psi_{,ADTT=1000}$	1	1	1	1	1	1	1	1	1	1	1	1
t_p (mm)	1.29–1.07	1.5–1.25	1.81–1.5	2.28–1.89	4.02–2.45	5.08–3.05	6.67–4.06	9.94–6.07	0.07–0.04	0.10–0.06	0.11–0.08	0.13–0.09
L_{str} (I + dur)	13.2–9.3	16.3–11.9	20.9–15.6	28.0–21.5	30.5–25.3	33.0–27.3	36.3–30.3	39.4–34.8	17.2–11.4	20.5–14.1	22.6–15.8	22.3–17.6
L_{str} (II + dur)	20.5–14.8	25.3–18.8	32.3–24.5	47.9–37.8	48–40.3	51.5–43.4	52.3–47.6	52.3–53.8	27.7–20	35.4–26.7	38.6–29.5	42.8–32.6

I & II are first and second options considered. dur; durability.

the target index β_{target} with CFRP amounts less than the values presented in Table 3, but the need for these amounts of CFRP is to satisfy Eq. 24. This is more evident in the case of (β_{target} = 3.5) which corresponds to the AASHTO provision. This may reflect the over estimation existing in live AASHTO truck weight or its load factors in Eq. 29. Examining service life provided after strengthening L_{str} (see Fig. 15) in Table 3 confirms that strengthening with option II provides longer service life than option I and ranges between ($\approx$1.5 to 1.75 times) for flexural, lower ranges are observed for shear. Thus, it could concluded that strengthening with (β_{target} = 4.2) provides a better and more reliable index and service life than β_{target} proposed by the AASHTO provision with no significant differences in CFRP amounts required. Values of the CFRP safety factor that correspond to $n_d \geq 2$ require high amounts of CFRP for non-anchorage laminates, reasonable values were obtained for $n_d < 2$ which correspond to Fib Bulletin 14. So, it could be concluded that Fib Bulletin 14 provision is more conservative than ACI Committee 440 & Concrete Society TR55 especially for CFRP debonding failure mode.

8 CONCLUSIONS

Reliability analysis of CFRP strengthened RC concrete girder under aggressive environment is preformed. Flexural and shear limit states were considered. Flexural limit state is controlled by concrete crushing, CFRP debonding, and CFRP rupture. Live load model was considered time and Traffic dependent. Aging of CFRP after strengthening is considered. Results have shown that initial reliability index is affected by amount of traffic which passes through bridge lanes. It was found that strengthening with preventing corrosion after strengthening achieves longer service life not less than two times when considering corrosion after strengthening. The three deterioration factors are very significant in CFRP strengthened highway bridges safety located on coastal zones. The considered deterioration factors can be ordered according to their influence as corrosion, live load growth and CFRP durability. No significant effects are observed in service life after strengthening due to CFRP durability with debonding failure mode while significant effects are observed when anchoring laminates (CFRP rupture).

REFERENCES

ACI Committee 440, ACI 440.2R-02. 2002. Guide for the design and construction of extern ally bonded FRP system for strengthening concrete structures. Farmington Hills, MI: ACI.

Aprile, A., & Benedetti, A. 2004. Coupled flexural-shear design of R/C beams strengthened with FRP. *Composites: Part B* 35:1–25.

Aram, M.R., & Czaderski, C. 2008. Debonding failure modes of flexural FRP-strengthened RC beams. *Composites: Part B* 39:826–841.

Arteaga, E., Ressolette P., Chateauneuf, A., & Sanchez-Silva, M. 2009. Probabilistic lifetime assessment of RC structures under coupled corrosion deterioration processes. *Structural safety* 31:84–96.

Ashour, A.F., El-Refaie, S.A., & Garrity, S.W. 2004. Flexural strengthening of RC continuous beams using CFRP laminates. *Cement & Concrete Composites* 26:765–775.

Atadero, A.A., & Karbhari, V.M. 2008. Calibration of resistance factor for reliability based design of externally-bonded FRP composites. *Composites: Part B* 39:665–79.

Atadero, R.A., & Karbhari, V.M. 2009 Sources of uncertainty & desing values for field-manufactured FRP. *Composite Structures* 89:83–93.

Atadero, A.A., Lee, L., & Karbhari, V.M. 2005 Consideration of material variability in reliability analysis of FRP strengthened bridge decks. *Composites Structures* 70:430–443.

Barros, J.A.O., & Dias, S.J.E. 2006. Near-Surface-Mounted CFRP Laminates for Shear Strengthening of RC Beams. *Cement & Concrete Composites* 28:276–292.

Bastidas-Arteaga, E., Sanches-Silva, M., Chateauneuf, A., & Silva, M.R. 2008. Coupled reliability model of biodeterioration, chloride ingress and cracking for reinforced concrete structures. *Structural Safety* 30:110–129.

Bogas, J.A., & Gomes, A. 2008. Analysis of the CFRP flexural strengthening reinforcement approaches proposed in fib bulletin 14. *Construction & Building Materials* 22:2130–40.

Cairns, J., Plizzari, G.A., Du, Y., Law, D.W., & Franzoni, C. 2005. Mechanical Properties of Corrosion-Damaged Reinforcement. *ACI material journal* 102(4):256–64.

CEB-FIP, CEB-FIP, Model Code 1990. London: Thomas Telford Services Ltd.

Chen, J.F., & Teng, J.G. 2001, 'Anchorage strength model for FRP and steel plates bonded to concrete. *Journal of Structural Engineering* 127 (7):784–91.

Colotti, V, Bencardino, F., Spadea, G., & Swamy R.N. 2005. Shear behavior of reinforced concrete beams strengthened in flexural with bonded carbon fiber reinforced polymers laminates. *Can. J. Civ. Eng.* 32:812–824.

Concrete Society Technical Report 55. 2000. Design guidance for strengthening concrete structures using fiber composite material. Concrete Society, Crowthorne, UK.

Diagana, C., Li, A., Gedalia B., & Delmas, Y. 2003. Shear strengthening with CFF strips. *Engineering Structures* 25:507–516.

Duprat, F. 2007. Reliability of RC beams under chloride-ingress. Construction & Building Materials 21:1605–1616.

Fib bulletin 14, FIB TG 9.3 FRPEBR. 2001. Externally bonded FRP reinforcement for RC structures. Féderation international du béton (fib), Task Group 9.3 FRP, P.130.

Gadve, S., Mukherjee, A., & Malhotra, S.N. 2009. Corrosion of steel reinforcement embedded in FRP wrapped concrete. *Construction & Building Material* 23:153–161.

Jayaprakash, J., Abdul-Samad, A., Abbasovich, A.A., & Ali, A.A.A. 2008. Shear capacity of pre-cracked and non pre-cracked reinforced concrete shear beams with externally bonded by bi-directional CFRP strips. *Construction & Building Material* 22:1148–1165.

JCSS, Joint Committee of Structural Safety. 2001. Probabilistic Model Code. Internet Publication: www.jcss. ethz.ch.

Karbhari, V.M., & Abanilla, M.A. 2007. Design factors, reliability, and durability predictions of wet layup carbon/epoxy used in external strengthening. *Composites: Part B* 38:10–23.

Khalifa, A., & Nanni, A. 2000. Improving shear capacity of existing RC T-section beams using CFRP composites. *Cement & Concrete Composites* 22:165–174.

Kim, G., Sim, J., & Oh, H. 2008. Shear strength of strengthened RC beams with FRPs in shear. *Construction & Building Materials* 22:1261–1270.

Li, C., Melchers, R.E., & Zheng, J. 2006. Analytical model for corrosion-Induced Crack Width in Reinforced Concrete Structures. *ACI Structural Journal* 103(4):479–87.

Lui, Y., & Weyers, R.E. 1998. Modeling the Time-to-Corrosion Cracking in Chloride Contaminated Reinforced Concrete Structures. *ACI Material Journal* 95(6):675–681.

Luping, T., & Gulkers, J. 2007. On the mathematics of time-dependent apparent chloride diffusion coefficient in concrete. *Cement & Concrete Research* 37:589–595.

Nowak, A.F. 1993. Live load model for high way bridges. *Structural Safety* 13:53–66.

Nowak, A.F. 2004. 'System reliability models for bridge structures. Bulletin of the Polish Academy of Science. Technical Science, 52(4):321–328.

Nowak, A.S., Park, C., & Casa, J.R. 2001. Reliability analysis of prestressed concrete bridge girders: comparison of Eurocode, Spanish Norma IAP and AASHTO LRFD. *Structural Safety* 23:331–344.

Monti, G., & Liotta, M.A. 2007. Test and design equation for FRP strengthening in shear. *Construction & Building Materials* 21:799–809.

Mosallam, A.S., & Banerjee, S. 2007. Shear enhancement of reinforced concrete beams strengthened with FRP composite laminates. *Composites: Part B* 38:781–793.

Pham, H., & Al-Mahaidi, R. 2004. Experimental investigation into flexural retrofitting of reinforced concrete beams using FRP composites. *Composites Structures* 66:617–625.

Pham, H.P., & Al-Mahidi, R. 2008. Reliability analysis of bridge beams retrofitted with fibre reinforced polymers. *Composite Structures* 82:177–184.

Plevris, N., Triantafillou, T., & Veneziano, D. 1995. Reliability of RC members strengthened with CFRP Laminates. *Journal of Structural Engineering* 121(7):1037–44.

Pour-Ghaz, M., Isgor, O.B., & Ghods, P. 2009. The effect of temperature on the corrosion of steel in concrete. Part 2: Model verification and parametric. *Corrosion science* 51:426–43.

Sas, G. 2008. FRP shear strengthening of RC beams and walls. Licentiate thesis, Luleå University of Technology, Sweden.

Stewart, M.G., & Al-Harthy, A. 2008. Pitting corrosion and structural reliability of corrosion RC structures: Experimental data and Probabilistic analysis. *Reliability Engineering & System Safety* 93:373–82.

Stewart, M.G., & Rosowsky, D.V. 1998. Time-dependent reliability of deteriorating reinforced concrete bridge decks. Structural Safety 20:91–109.

Sundarraja, M.C., & Ragamohan, S. 2009. Strengthening of RC beams in shear using GFRP inclined strips—An experimental study. *Construction & Building Materials* 23:856–64.

Taljsten, B., & Elfgren, L. 2000. Strengthening concrete beams for shear using CFRP-materials: evaluation of different approach methods. *Composites: Part B* 31:87–96.

Teng, J.G., Smith, S.T., Yao, J., & Chen, J.F. 2003. Intermediate crack-induced debonding in RC beams and slabs. *Construction & Building* 17:447–462.

Val, D.V., Stewart, M.G., & Melchers, R.E. 2000. Life-Cycle Performance of RC Bridges Probabilistic Approach. *Computer-Aided Civil Infrastructure Engineering* 15:14–25.

Val, D.V., & Trapper, P.A. 2008. Probabilistic evaluation of initiation time of chloride-induced corrosion. *Reliability Engineering & System Safety* 93:364–372.

Vu, K.A.T., & Stewart, M.G. 2000. Structural reliability of concrete bridges including improved chloride-induced corrosion models. *Structural safety* 23:313–33.

Yuan, Y., Ji, Y., & Jiang, J. 2009. Effect of corrosion layer of steel bar in concrete on time variant rate. *Materials & Structures* 42:1443–1450.

Concrete Solutions – Grantham, Mechtcherine & Schneck (eds)
© *2012 Taylor & Francis Group, London, ISBN 978-0-415-61622-5*

Strengthening of rectangular reinforced concrete columns using fiber glass reinforced polymers

A.H. Elzanaty
RC structures, Cairo University, Egypt

H.M. Allam & A. Fawzi
RC structures, Housing and Building National Research Center, Egypt

ABSTRACT: Using FRP to strengthen columns by wrapping may be applied in many different ways and depends on highly qualified applicators and highly experienced workers. A new technique for strengthening rectangular reinforced concrete columns by GFRP laminates is introduced in this paper. This technique decreases the materials used and the man effort which leads to a decrease in the total cost of the strengthening process. A test program was undertaken taking into consideration this new technique and a comparison between the new and the traditional techniques. The variables of this experimental program were the aspect ratio, the characteristic compressive strength of the concrete and the strengthening technique. An experimental program was undertaken testing nine rectangular columns with total height 1560 mm and clear height 1000 mm and was classified into three groups depending on the characteristic compressive strength of the concrete. An analytical approach was used to predict the deformation behavior as well as the ultimate capacity of the strengthened rectangular columns.

1 INTRODUCTION

Due to the rapid increase in population and high demand, upgrading of structures, specially residential buildings, is required. Moreover, the increase of earthquake loads requires an increase in both the axial capacity and ductility of columns in addition to their flexural capacity. The major disadvantages of using the traditional techniques of bonding steel plates or enlarging the concrete section are corrosion of steel elements and the need for technical labour and heavy equipment for installing the repair materials. Furthermore, use of conventional methods for repair results in an increase of the column stiffness, and consequently increases the applied forces due to earthquakes. Significant research has been devoted to circular columns retrofitted with FRP and numerous models were proposed. FRP wrapping of existing circular columns has proven to be an effective retrofitting technique. In contrast, very limited data has been reported on rectangular columns retrofitted with FRP wrap, even though rectangular RC columns with aspect ratios up to one-to-five are commonly used in residential buildings. This paper studies a new technique to wrap the rectangular RC columns by decreasing the man effort in the strengthening process. This new technique depends on rounding the corners of the columns, roughening them, and attaching laminates by adding epoxy resin to these corners with a suitable overlap instead of roughening the entire column surface and attaching the laminates to the entire surface of the column. A test program was carried out in this study using the old and the new methods to compare the test results.

2 EXPERIMENTAL PROGRAM

The program consisted of testing nine RC rectangular columns with an overall height of 1560 mm, and clear height of 1000 mm divided into three groups depending on the characteristic compressive strength of the concrete.

The first group consisted of three rectangular columns (CRA1, CTA1, and CCA1) with a cross section equals to 200 × 300 mm and a characteristic compressive strength of concrete equals to 16 MPa. The longitudinal reinforcement of the columns was four 12 mm diameter bars, while the stirrups were 6 mm diameter bars every 166 mm. The specimen CRA1 was tested as a control specimen while the specimens CTA1 and CCA1 were strengthened by the old and the new techniques respectively. The second group consisted of three rectangular columns (CRP2, CTP2, and CCP2) with a cross section equals to 200 × 400 mm and a characteristic compressive strength of concrete equals to 23 MPa. The longitudinal reinforcement of the columns was six 12 mm diameter bars, while the stirrups were

Table 1. Properties of steel.			
Properties	Ø6	Ø8	Ø12
Yield stress (N/mm²)	342.36	517.78	433.4
Ultimate stress (N/mm²)	393.64	807.22	685.6
Mass per unit length (kg/m)	0.22	0.39	0.883
Ultimate stress/ Yield stress	1.15	1.56	1.58
Elongation (%)	36.3	24.4	16.3

Table 2. Properties of the GFRP laminates.	
Nominal thickness	0.17 mm / layer
Modulus of elasticity	35.4 GPa
Maximum elongation %	2.8%
Width of laminates	600 mm

The properties of the GFRP laminates are indicated in Table 2.

6 mm diameter bars every 166 mm. The specimen CRP2 was tested as a control specimen while the specimens CTP2 and CCP2 were strengthened by the old and the new techniques respectively. The third group consisted of three rectangular columns (CRB2, CTBP2, and CCB2) with a cross section equals to 200 × 400 mm and a characteristic compressive strength of concrete equal to 12 MPa. Details of the reinforcement were kept the same as the second group. The specimen CRP2 was tested as a control specimen while the specimens CTP2 and CCP2 were strengthened by the old and the new techniques respectively. For specimens CCA1, CCP2, and CCB2, paper sheets were attached as an insulator to the surface of the columns except for the corners. The properties of the steel bars are indicated in Table 1. All strengthened columns were wrapped with two layers of Glass Fiber Reinforced Polymers (GFRP).

3 APPLICATION OF GFRP LAMINATES

GFRP laminates were wrapped after the concrete had reached an age of 28-days. The wrapping procedure was applied as follows:

1. Preparation of concrete surface using a hammer and blower to remove the weak elements on the concrete cover.
2. Application of epoxy paste on the column surface to fill the irregularities on the surface.
3. Smoothing the surface of the epoxy paste.
4. Attaching the insulating paper sheets for specimens CCA1, CCP2, and CCB2.
5. Applying the first layer of GFRP laminates to the concrete surface using epoxy resin.
6. Rolling the GFRP laminates by special laminating-roller to ensure that the GFRP was saturated with the epoxy resin and there were no air voids between the fibers and the concrete surface.
7. Appling the second layer of GFRP laminates.
8. Rolling the second layer of the GFRP laminates.

4 INSTRUMENTATION

The specimens were instrumented to record the axial strain of the concrete, strain of both the longitudinal and transverse steel reinforcement, as well as strain of the GFRP laminates. The axial and transverse strains of the specimens were measured by two different methods. The first method was using electrical strain gauges. The data from strain gauges were collected using a data acquisition system and "lab view software". Three electrical strain gauges were installed on the steel reinforcement, as shown in Fig. 1; one strain gauge was installed on a stirrup and the remaining two strain gauges were installed on the longitudinal reinforcement. Three electrical strain gauges were installed on the GFRP laminates, as shown in Fig. 2, to measure its strain in the fiber direction.

Strains were also measured using Linear Variable Distance Transducers, LVDTs, which had different lengths; ±15, ±25 mm. The LVDTs were attached to the RC column using 8-mm fisher bolts. Four LVDTs were attached to each RC column to measure the longitudinal strains of the column, as shown in Fig. 2. One LVDT with length 200 mm was attached to the hydraulic jack to record the stroke of the jack.

5 RESULTS OF THE PROGRAM

All tests were conducted at the RC laboratory in the Housing and Building National Research Center, HBRC. It was found that the behavior of the load-strain curve for all the specimens was linear till about 70% of the maximum load then changed to non-linear till failure. The slope of the ascending part of the load strain curve was almost the same for each group of specimens, which indicates that the stiffness of the columns was almost not changed after strengthening. Load–longitudinal strain relationship of each specimens are shown in Figs. 3 to 5. The behaviour of each specimen can be summarized in Table 3.

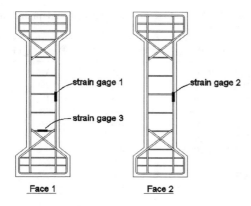

Figure 1a. Location of strain gauges on the steel reinforcement (First Group).

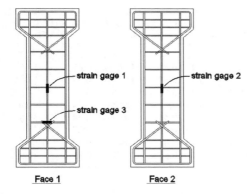

Figure 1b. Location of strain gauges on the steel reinforcement (Second and Third Group).

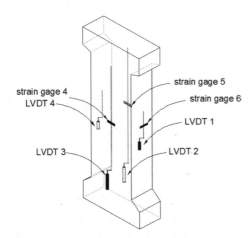

Figure 2. Location of LVDTs and strain gauges on the concrete surface and the GFRP laminates.

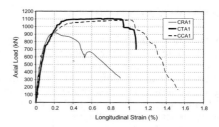

Figure 3. Load-Longitudinal strains relationships for specimens CRA1, CTA1, and CCA1.

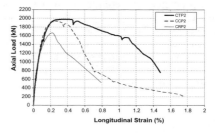

Figure 4. Load-Longitudinal strains relationships for specimens CRP2, CTP2, and CCP2.

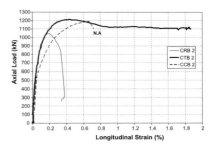

Figure 5. Load-Longitudinal strains relationships for specimens CRB2, CTB2, and CCB2.

Table 3. Effect of strengthening on the carrying capacity.

Specimen	$P_{max.}$ (kN)	Strain corresponding to $P_{max.}$	Max. Strain	Effect of Strengthening
CRA1	915	0.22%	0.91%	–
CTA1	1108	0.32%	1.08%	21.1%
CCA1	1091	0.40%	1.53%	19.2%
CRP2	1667	0.21%	0.79%	–
CTP2	1977	0.34%	1.48%	18.6%
CCP2	1937	0.26%	1.75%	16.2%
CRB2	1044	0.19%	0.38%	–
CTB2	1215	0.44%	1.88%	16.4%
CCB2	1188	0.67%	N.A.	13.8%

6 ANALYTICAL STUDY

Two analytical approaches based on the stress-strain characteristics of the concrete under a triaxial stress state were used to predict the deformation behavior as well as the ultimate capacity of the rectangular columns. The first model was presented by Mander et al. (1988) to predict the ultimate capacity of RC columns. Wang et al. (2001) and Fam and Rizkalla (2001) introduced the mechanical properties of CFRP in the model to predict the ultimate capacity of strengthened columns. The load-deformation behavior of each tested specimen is predicted and compared to the measured values. Hosny et al. (2002) proposed the second approach by replacing some factors in Mander et al.'s model.

For a slow (quasi-static) strain rate and monotonic loading, the longitudinal compressive concrete stress fc is given by:

$$f_c = \frac{f'_{cc}\, x r'}{r' - 1 + x^{r'}} \tag{1}$$

$$x = \frac{\varepsilon_c}{\varepsilon_{cc}} \tag{2}$$

$$\varepsilon_{cc} = \varepsilon_{co}\left[1 + 5\left(\frac{f'_{cc}}{f'_{co}} - 1\right)\right] \tag{3}$$

$$r' = \frac{E_{co}}{E_{co} - E_{sec}} \tag{4}$$

$$E_{CO} = 4700\sqrt{f'_{co}}\, MPa \tag{5}$$

$$E_{sec} = \frac{f'_{cc}}{\varepsilon_{cc}} \tag{6}$$

where:

f'_{cc} = Compressive strength of confined concrete.

ε_c = Longitudinal compressive concrete strain.

f'_{co} = Unconfined concrete strength.

ε_{co} = Strain corresponding to the unconfined concrete strength. (taken equal to 0.002).

E_{co} = Modulus of elasticity of unconfined concrete.

E_{sec} = Secant modulus of confined concrete at peak stress.

Hosny et al. (2002) presented a modified model to predict the resulting strain in the longitudinal direction and the inclined angle of the descending part. The approach adopts the same equations proposed by Mander et al. (1988). Different factors are proposed based on interpolation of the measured values for the tested fourteen columns. The modified model was presented by Eqn. 7 and

Table 4. The values of the measured and predicted maximum load.

Specimen	$P_{experimental}$ (kN)	$P_{analytical}$ (kN)	$(P_{exp} - P_{anal})/P_{exp}$
CRA1	915	839	8.3%
CTA1	1108	1245	−12.4%
CCA1	1091	1245	−14.1%
CRP2	1667	1509	9.48%
CTP2	1977	1919	2.9%
CCP2	1937	1919	0.9%
CRB2	1044	899	13.9%
CTB2	1215	1256	−3.4%
CCB2	1188	1256	−5.7%

Table 5. The values of the measured and predicted strain corresponding to the maximum load.

Specimen	$\varepsilon_{cc\text{-}exp}$ (%)	$\varepsilon_{cc\text{-}Mander}$ (%)	$(\varepsilon_{cc\text{-}Mander} - \varepsilon_{cc\text{-}exp})/\varepsilon_{cc\text{-}exp}$	$\varepsilon_{cc\text{-}modified}$ (%) Mander	$(\varepsilon_{cc\text{-}Modified} - \varepsilon_{cc\text{-}exp})/\varepsilon_{cc\text{-}exp}$
CRA1	0.22	0.24	9.1%	0.225	2.3%
CTA1	0.4	0.87	117.5%	0.47	17.5%
CCA1	0.4	0.87	117.5%	0.47	17.5%
CRP2	0.21	0.22	4.8%	0.22	4.8%
CTP2	0.34	0.54	58.8%	0.34	Equal
CCP2	0.26	0.54	107.7%	0.34	30.8%
CRB2	0.19	0.22	15.7%	0.22	15.7%
CTB2	0.44	0.81	84.1%	0.44	Equal
CCB2	0.67	0.81	21%	0.44	−34.3%

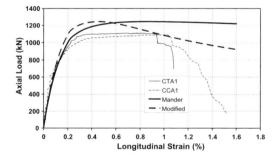

Figure 6. Load-Longitudinal strain relationship for specimens CTA1 and CCA1 (Experimental & Analytical).

Eqn. 8, which should replace equations Eqn. 2 and Eqn. 3, respectively.

The load-deformation behavior of each tested specimen is predicted by the two models and compared to the measured values, as shown in Tables 4, 5. This comparison is represented graphically as shown in Figs. 6 to 8.

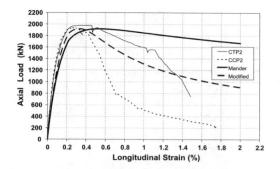

Figure 7. Load-Longitudinal strain relationship for specimens CTP2 and CCP2 (Experimental & Analytical).

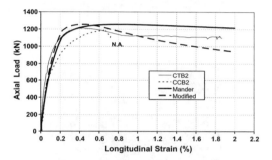

Figure 8. Load-Longitudinal strain relationship for specimens CTB2 and CCB2 (Experimental & Analytical).

Table 6. Energy absorbed and ductility factor.

Specimen	E_1	E_2	E_{total}	Ductility factor
CRA1	1.59	2.21	3.80	1.39
CTA1	2.44	8.15	10.59	3.34
CCA1	2.80	8.99	11.79	3.21
CRP2	2.68	1.48	4.16	0.55
CTP2	5.23	13.22	18.45	2.53
CCP2	3.94	4.39	8.33	1.11
CRB2	1.47	1.38	2.85	0.94
CTB2	4.39	16.46	20.85	3.75
CCB2	6.38	N.A.	N.A.	N.A.

7 ENERGY AND DUCTILITY

Ductility of RC columns can be represented by the area under the load-axial strain curve. This area provides information about the energy accumulated in the column under the applied load. In this research, the area under the curve representing the energy absorbed was calculated to a load up to 80% of the maximum load on the descending part of the curve, P80%, and was represented as E80%. A ductility factor was given by the ratio of two areas (E2/E1); the first area (E1) was calculated from zero load up to the maximum load, and the second area (E2) was calculated on the descending curve from the maximum load till 80% of the maximum load. Table 6 summarizes the areas under the load-axial strain curve, and the ductility factor for each specimen.

8 FAILURE MODES

Two failure modes were observed during the tests:

- Compression failure mode: this was a brittle failure mode observed clearly for the control specimens (CRA1, CRP2, and CRB2). At about 70% of the maximum load, a sound of aggregate sliding was heard then by continuing loading, an inclined crack occurred at the top third of the column as shown in Figs. 9, 12, and 15. The concrete cover at and around the crack spalled off and the longitudinal bars appeared to buckle between two stirrups.
- Rupture of GFRP laminates: this was a ductile failure mode observed for specimens CTA1, CCA1, CTP2, CCP2, CTB2, and CCB2. For specimens CCA1, CCP2, and CCB2, the failure occurred by rupture of the GFRP laminates at the middle of the long direction at the top third of the column as shown in Figs. 11, 14, and 17. For specimen CTA1, the failure occurred by rupture of the GFRP laminates near the corner at the top third of the column as shown in Fig. 10. For specimens CTP2 and CTB2, the

Figure 9. Failure of CRA1.

611

Figure 10.   Failure of CTA1.

Figure 12.   Failure of CRP2.

Figure 11.   Failure of CCA1.

Figure 13.   Failure of CTP2.

failure occurred by rupture of the GFRP laminates near the corner at the middle third of the
column as shown in Figs. 13 and 16. Generally,
failure of confined specimens was explosive and
was marked by rupture of the GFRP laminates.
There were some differences between the failure
features of specimens CTA1, CTP2, and CTB2

Figure 14.   Failure of CCP2.

Figure 15. Failure of CRB2.

Figure 17. Failure of CCB2.

and the concrete surface for specimens CTA1, CTP2, and CTB2 which firstly failed at the mid-width and then transferred to the adjacent location until the laminates rebounded from the concrete surface.

9   CONCLUSIONS

1. Using GFRP laminates in confinement of RC columns increases the carrying capacity and ductility.
2. The proposed technique saves effort in surface preparation and material cost.
3. It was found that the behavior of the load-strain curve for all the specimens was linear till about 70% of the maximum load then changed to non-linear till failure.
4. The slope of the ascending part of the load strain curve was almost the same for each group of specimens.
5. Bonding the GFRP laminates only to the corners slightly reduces the carrying capacity and ductility of the columns, but on the other side it decreases the material cost and effort compared with bonding the laminates to the entire surface.
6. The effect of strengthening on the ductility of the columns increases as the characteristic compressive strength of concrete decreases.
7. From the experimental and the analytical study it was noticed that the maximum actual

Figure 16. Failure of CTB2.

and that of specimens CCA1, CCP2, and CCB2. For specimens CTA1, CTP2, and CTB2, sound was heard during the early and middle stages of loading and a loud sound was heard at the ultimate load while for specimens CCA1, CCP2, and CCB2, sound was heard after the middle stages of loading. This phenomenon is due to increasing the shear interlocking between the laminates load reached in the control specimen, CRB2, recorded an increase of 13.9% more than the predicted maximum load. This increase led to the decrease in the calculated values representing the effect of strengthening on the carrying capacity of the specimens CTB2 and CCB2. Accordingly, the effect of strengthening on the carrying capacity increased as the characteristic compressive strength of concrete increases and this is not logical.

8. The effect of strengthening on the carrying capacity of the columns increases as the aspect ratio of the column cross section decreases.
9. The analytical models gave good agreement with the experimental results.

REFERENCES

Abdelhady Hosny, Hamdy Shahin, Amr Abdelrahman, and Tamer El-Afandy, (2002). "Strengthening of Reinforced Concrete Columns Using Advanced Laminates", *A Thesis Submitted in Partial Fulfillment for the Requirements of the Degree of Master of Science in Civil Engineering*, Ain Shams University, Faculty of Engineering, 2002.

Abdelhady Hosny, Hamdy Shahin, Amr Abdelrahman, and Tamer El-Afandy, (2002). "Uniaxial Tests on Rectangular Columns Strengthened with CFRP", *The Third Middle East Symposium On Structural Composites For Infrastructure Applications*, December 17–20, 2002, Aswan, Egypt, pp. 93–94.

Ahmad, S.H. and Shah, S.P., (1982). "Stress-Strain Curves of Concrete Confined by Spiral Reinforcement", *ACI Structural Journal*, Vol. 79, No. 6, November–December 1982, pp. 484–490.

Gebran Karam, and Mazen Tabbara, (2002). "Corner Effect On The Efficiency of Rectangular Concrete Columns With FRP Confining Wraps", *The Third Middle East Symposium On Structural Composites For Infrastructure Applications*, December 17–20, 2002, Aswan, Egypt, pp. 77–81.

Hassan, M. Allam, (2005). "Strengthening of Square Columns by a new technique", *The Ninth international conference on inspection appraisal repairs and maintenance of structures*, October 20–21, 2005, Fuzhou, China, pp. 159–166.

Mander, J.B., Priestley, M.J.N. and Park, R. Fellow, ASCE, (1988). "Observed Stress-Strain Behavior of Confined Concrete", *Journal of Structural Engineering, ASCE*, Vol. 114, No. 8, August, 1988, pp. 1827–1849.

Mander, J.B., Priestley, M.J.N. and Park, R. Fellow, ASCE, (1988). "Theoretical stress-Strain Model For Confined Concrete", *Journal of Structural Engineering, ASCE*, Vol. 114, No. 8, August, 1988, pp. 1804–1826.

Matthys, S., Taerwe, L. and Audenaert, K. (2000). "Tests on Axially Loaded Concrete Columns Confined by Fiber Reinforced Polymer Sheet Wrapping", *Fourth International Symposium on Fiber Reinforced Polymer Reinforcement for Reinforced Concrete Structures*, March 1, 2000, pp. 217–228.

Michel Samaan, Amir Mirmiran, and Mohsen Shahawy, (1998). "Model of Concrete Confined by Fiber Composites", *Journal of Structural Engineering, ASCE*, Vol. 124, No. 9, September, 1998, pp. 1025–1031.

Omar Chaallal, Munzer Hassan, and Mohsen Shahawy, (2003). "Confinement Model for Axially Loaded Short Rectangular Columns Strengthened with Fiber-Reinforced Polymer Wrapping", *ACI Structural Journal*, Vol. 100, No. 2, March-April 2003, pp. 215–221.

Paultre, P. and Légeron, F. (2008). "Confinement Reinforcement Design for Reinforced Concrete Columns", *Journal of Structural Engineering, ASCE*, Vol. 134, No. 5, May 1, 2008, pp. 738–749.

Richard Sause, Kent A. Harries, Stephanie l. Walkup, Stephen Pessiki, and James M. Ricles, (2004). "Flexural Behavior of Concrete Columns Retrofitted with Carbon Fiber-Reinforced Polymer Jackets", *ACI Structural Journal*, Vol. 101, No. 5, September-October 2004, pp. 708–716.

Saadatmanesh, H., Ehsani, M.R., and Li, M.W. (1994). "Strength and Ductility of Concrete Columns Externally Reinforced with Fiber Composite Straps", *ACI Structural Journal*, Vol. 91, No. 4, July-August 1994, pp. 434–447.

Scott, B.D., Park, R., and Priestley, M.J.N. (1982). "Stress-Strain Behavior of Concrete Confined by Overlapping Hoops at Low and High Strain Rates", *ACI Structural Journal*, Vol. 79, No. 6, November-December 1982, pp. 13–27.

Shamim A. Sheikh, (1982). "A Comparative Study of Confinement Models", *ACI Structural Journal*, Vol. 79, July-August 1982, pp. 296–306.

Shamim, A., Sheikh and Shafik, S. Khoury, (1997). "A Performance-Based Approach for the Design of Confining Steel in Tied Columns", *ACI Structural Journal*, Vol. 94, No. 4, July-August 1997, pp. 421–431.

Teng, J.G., and Lam, L. (2004). "Behavior and Modeling of Fiber Reinforced Polymer-Confined Concrete", *Journal of Structural Engineering, ASCE*, Vol. 130, No. 11, November 1, 2004, pp. 1713–1723.

Yung, C. Wang and José, I. Restrepo, (2001). "Investigation of Concentrically Loaded Reinforced Concrete Columns Confined with Glass Fiber-Reinforced Polymer Jackets", *ACI Structural Journal*, Vol. 98, No. 3, May-June 2001, pp. 377–385.

Concrete Solutions – Grantham, Mechtcherine & Schneck (eds)
© 2012 Taylor & Francis Group, London, ISBN 978-0-415-61622-5

FRP strengthening of shear walls with openings

K. Behfarnia
Isfahan University of Technology, Iran

A. Sayah & Sh. Eghtesadi
Saze Andishan Co., Iran

ABSTRACT: Concrete shear walls are one of the main lateral resisting members in buildings. The functional requirements like architectural and even mechanical requirements entail that openings have to be installed in structural walls. In this study, nonlinear static analysis was utilized to study the effects of Fiber Reinforced Plastic (FRP) on the ultimate load capacity of concrete shear walls with openings using the software ABAQUS. In order to verify the accuracy of the numerical model, a comparison was done between the results of experimental and numerical analysis of a concrete shear wall. Subsequent to verification of the Finite Element Model (FEM), the effects of creating cut-off openings as well as strengthening effects of applying FRP have been studied. Whereas the numerical results show good correlation between the FEM and the experimental results of RC shear walls, the numerical analysis represents a remarkable improvement in ultimate lateral load capacity of a shear wall with opening strengthened using fiber reinforced plastic. The results are obtained are presented in relative diagrams and tables.

1 INTRODUCTION

Earthquake resistant structures should be provided with lateral and vertical seismic force-resisting systems. Force-resisting systems should be capable of transmitting forces to the foundations. Continuity and regular transitions are essential requirements to achieve adequate load paths (Elnashai, 2008).

Concrete shear walls are one of the main lateral resisting members in buildings because of their high in-plane rigidity. The functional requirements like architectural and even mechanical requirements entail that openings have to be installed in structural walls. Generally, discontinuity regions in reinforced concrete wall like openings can cause stresses which cannot be classified in known patterns making the design difficult (Sas, 2008). Due to the high stress redistribution capability of concrete walls, creating small openings does not have a significant influence on the overall behavior of wall. However, creating large openings leads to significant reduction of wall rigidity and stiffness (Elnashai, 2008). Thus, adequate measures should be taken to counteract these reductions.

In the last decade, the use of Fiber Reinforced Polymers (FRP) to strengthen existing structures has increased remarkably. This is due to their excellent characteristics such as high resistance to chemical damages, durability, ease of installation and their high strength to weight ratio. A significant amount of research has been conducted on the use of fiber reinforced plastic for the strengthening and rehabilitation of reinforced concrete elements. However, there is little information on the strengthening of reinforced concrete shear walls. One of the first projects using FRP strengthening of RC shear walls was reported in 1997 (Ehsani,1997). They used FRP in order to retrofit a concrete building subjected to the 1994 Northridge earthquake.

Another study on FRP strengthening of RC shear walls has been carried out by Lombard et al. The purpose was to investigate the feasibility of CFRP strengthening and rehabilitation of reinforced concrete shear walls (Lombard, 1999). In his studies, four walls were tested in a quasi-static cyclic load sequence in predetermined load control steps up to the calculated yield load and then predetermined displacement control steps up to failure, respectively. The configuration of the CFRP strengthened system consisted of one or three sheets with fibers oriented either vertical or vertical and horizontal directions on both faces of the walls. Based on the test results, he developed an analytical model to predict the ultimate flexural capacity of plain reinforced concrete shear walls and walls strengthened or repaired with externally bonded fiber reinforced plastics based on the test results. Another study has been carried out by Sugiyama et al, where seismic behavior of non-structural reinforced concrete walls with openings strengthened using FRP composite sheets was studied (Sugiyama, 2000). He tested eight specimens of non-structural shear walls with the scale of 1/3. It was concluded that even if the bearing capacity of the non-structural walls increased, the global behavior of the frame remained the same. For a serviceability limit state (the deflection angle of doors and the residual crack width) a good enhancement was provided by the FRP strengthening.

Another extensive experimental study was conducted on the strengthening of low-slenderness reinforced concrete (RC) walls designed to modern code provisions (Antoniades, 2003). In this study the walls initially were subjected to cyclic loading to failure, and subsequently, conventionally repaired and then strengthened using FRP jackets. The results showed that the wall strengths increased from as low as 2 percent, to as high as 32 percent based on the anchorage conditions of the FRP strips. Li et al, analyzed the GFRP strengthening of shear walls in order to evaluate the accuracy of finite element method to predict the behavior of shear walls (Li, 2005). In this FEA model, a SPRING element was used to simulate the constraint deformation due to FRP; also, a damaged plasticity-based concrete model was used to simulate the behavior of concrete under cyclic loading. The conformity of numerical and experimental results indicated the ability of finite element method to predict the behavior of FRP strengthening of shear walls.

Despite these advances, more research is still required to study the structural behavior of strengthened walls with FRP, particularly with openings. Besides, most of the previous works only discussed experimental studies and analytical analyses but not finite element analysis and modeling. Consequently, in this study, the effects of applying FRP on the ultimate capacity of concrete shear walls with openings were investigated by using the finite element analysis software ABAQUS. In this paper, the numerical model is calibrated and verified with experimental data from laboratory tests of plane RC shear walls. After verification of the FEM model, the effects of creating cut-off openings as well as the strengthening effects of applying FRP have been studied.

2 FE MODELING AND MATERIAL MODELS

2.1 Overview of the experimental reference model

In this study, experimental results of one of the RC shear wall specimens tested by Lefas et al, is used to confirm the applicability of the proposed numerical models (Lefas et al, 1990). This wall was 750 mm wide, 750 mm high and 70 mm

thick and monolithically was connected to an upper and lower beam. The upper beam (1150mm long, 150 mm deep and 200 mm thick) functioned as both the element through which axial and horizontal loads were applied to the walls and as a cage for anchorage of the vertical bars. The lower beam (1150 mm long, 300 mm deep and 200 mm thick) was utilized to clamp the specimens down to the laboratory floor. The location of hydraulic jacks and the details of bar locations are shown in Figures 1a and 1b, respectively. The material properties and percentage of reinforcement are given in Table 1.

2.2 Finite element model

In this study, nonlinear analysis was utilized using the finite element analysis software ABAQUS. The

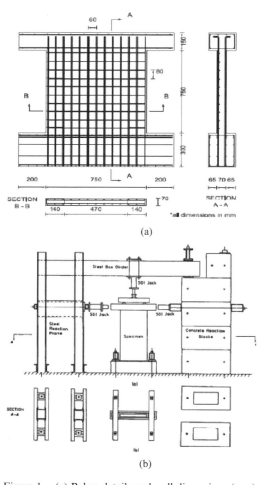

(a)

(b)

Figure 1. (a) Rebar details and wall dimensions (mm); (b) Test setup.

Table 1. Mechanical properties of materials.

Type	Yielding stress (Fy) and ultimate stress (Fu) of steel (MPa)			Cube strength of concrete (MPa)	Elastic modulus of concrete (MPa)	Tensile strength of concrete (MPa)
	Diameter	Fy	Fu			
SW-13	ϕ 4	420	490	40.6	27600	3.2
	ϕ 6.25	520	610			
	ϕ 8	470	565			

concrete wall was modeled using 8-node 3-D solid elements (C3D8R) which had three degrees of transitional freedom in each node. In the ABAQUS software, there are two possible ways to model reinforcement bars in three dimensional concrete elements. Reinforcement bars can be modeled either as an embedded rebar layer or as truss elements. The first method is better for regular distributed reinforcement (ABAQUS, 2008). However, considering arrangement of reinforcements in boundary elements, it is better to model discrete reinforcement in the form of two dimensional truss elements (T3D2) which are embedded in C3D8R solid elements (Sayah, 2010). The concrete behaviour of walls will be considered independent of the reinforcing bars. The effects associated with the rebar-concrete interface, like bond slip and dowel action, are not considered by this model. As a result, these effects may model approximately by introducing some "tension stiffening" into the concrete modeling (ABAQUS, 2008). External FRP reinforcement is modeled using 4-node shell elements with orthotropic behavior. It is worthwhile to mention that in ABAQUS STD analyses are performed using 8-Gauss integration points for solid elements and 4-Gauss integration points for shell elements, with 2-Gauss integration points over the thickness (ABAQUS, 2008). The boundary condition of the base of the wall was simulated as fixed end. In order to prevent out-of-plane displacement, proper roller supports were placed at the mid surface of the model. Moreover, in order to simulate the loading conditions of the control wall, a vertical pressure load was applied on the top beam to simulate the vertical load; lateral displacement was applied on a steel plate at the top beam to simulate the lateral displacement.

2.3 Material properties and constitutive models

This study involves modeling of steel reinforcing bars, concrete and FRP. However, constitutive models are available in the ABAQUS material library, but their input material properties and associated constitutive models are briefly discussed. For steel a bilinear model with strain hardening is used to determine the behavior of steel in tension and compression. Full bond between steel and concrete is assumed. The support plate which is used to apply the lateral displacement was considered to behave in a linearly elastic manner. The constitutive model used to analyse the concrete was a concrete damaged plasticity model which is a continuum, plasticity-based, damage model (ABAQUS, 2008). It assumes that the main two failure mechanisms of concrete are tensile cracking and compressive crushing. In addition, it assumes when the concrete specimen is unloaded from any point on the strain softening branch of the stress–strain curves, the unloading response is weakened which means the elastic stiffness of the material appears to be damaged (or degraded). The degradation of the elastic stiffness is characterized by two damage variables in tension and compression stress which can take values from zero, representing the undamaged material, to one, which represents total loss of strength. The model makes use of the yield function of (Lubliner, 1989), with the modifications proposed by (Lee & Fenves, 1998) to account for different evolution of strength under tension and compression. The yield surface is controlled by two hardening variables, one in tension and one in compression. For defining the yield function two parameters are required; first parameter, which reflects the behavior of concrete under biaxial stress conditions, is the ratio of initial equibiaxial compressive strength to uniaxial compressive strength σ_{b0}/σ_{c0}.

The concrete under combinations of biaxial stress exhibits behaviors which are different from those under uniaxial loading conditions by the effects of Poisson ratio and microcrack confinement (Hyo-Gyoung & Do-Yeon, 2001). In the biaxial compression state of stress, concrete exhibits an increase in compressive strength of up to 25 percent of the uniaxial compressive strength (Kupfer et al, 1969). In the equibiaxial state of stress, the concrete compressive strength (σ_{b0}) is approximately 1.16 times greater than the uniaxial concrete compressive strength (σ_{c0}). The second parameter is the ratio of the second stress invariant on the tensile meridian to that on the compressive meridian at initial yield for any given value of the first stress invariant such that the maximum principal stress is negative K_c the default values in ABAQUS is used 2/3. The concrete damaged plasticity model assumes nonassociated potential plastic flow. The flow potential G used for this model was the Drucker-Prager hyperbolic function. This flow potential, which is continuous and smooth, ensures that the flow direction is always uniquely defined. For this function, a couple of parameters must be defined; the uniaxial tensile stress at failure, the dilation angle w and the eccentricity ε which is a parameter that defines the rate at which the function approaches the asymptote. The default flow potential eccentricity values in ABAQUS is $\varepsilon = 0.1$. In order to reduce the mesh sensitivity of the FEM, the post-failure behavior of concrete in tension must be provided. This can help to account for the effects associated with the rebar-concrete interface such as bond slip.

The post-failure behavior can be defined by means of a stress–strain relationship or by applying a fracture energy cracking criterion. In this study, the behavior of concrete in tension is defined by means of trilinear stress–strain relation with an ascending branch until the first crack and a bilinear softening branch after cracking. The choice of these parameters is important and they should be calibrated to a particular case. In this study, the FRP is considered as a linear elastic material until failure and the interaction between the concrete and the FRP is modeled without considering debonding.

2.4 *Parameter to identify debonding in FE study*

In order to control the debonding in FRP, the effective FRP strain at failure is calculated by means of the equations provided by ACI 440 (2008). In addition, the FRP strain was controlled in each step of the analysis in order to identify debonding and rupture in the FEA study.

2.5 *Numerical procedure*

In this study, a displacement-controlled incremental loading method was adopted and an iterative solution procedure based on the modified Newton–Raphson method was employed in order to simulate nonlinear behavior of FEM using ABAQUS software.

3 VERIFICATION STUDY

The validity of the proposed material constitutive models for steel, concrete and FRP were verified by testing against experimental data. The results of the

verification study demonstrated that the numerical model fitted with acceptable accuracy the experimental results of the reference wall. For instance, the measured maximum lateral force and corresponding displacement in the reference wall were 330 kN and 8.88 mm, respectively (Lefas,1988). On the other hand, the numerical predictions obtained for maximum lateral force and corresponding displacement were 314 kN and 9.74 mm, respectively. Moreover, cracking patterns in the FE model fitted with the experimental results of the reference wall. It is worthwhile to mention that the concrete damaged plasticity model does not have the notion of cracks developing at the material integration point. However, in order to show cracking patterns we can show maximum principal plastic strain in FE analysis, because we can assume that cracking initiates at points where the tensile equivalent plastic strain is greater than zero. After verification of the finite element method with the proposed reference model, in order to study the effects of cut-off openings, several arrangements of square openings with a variety of dimensions were created in various heights in the reference wall model. The models were divided into three main groups; B, M, and T based on the opening location. Figure 2 shows the geometry of the wall and arrangements of openings. All models of group M had openings at the mid-height of the wall whereas models of group B, and T had openings at the bottom and top of the wall, respectively. The opening size was either L/4, L/3, or L/2 (L corresponded to the length of the wall); consequently, in the finite element model, the steel reinforcement intercepted by the opening was cut. Table 2 illustrates the details of openings and the analysis results.

The results show that creating an opening with the area equal to 11.11 percent of the total area of the wall will cause reduction in the ultimate capacity of wall from 9.8 percent (In model SW-L/4-T) up to 37.1 percent (In model SW-L/3-B).

Figure 2. The geometry of the wall and arrangements of openings.

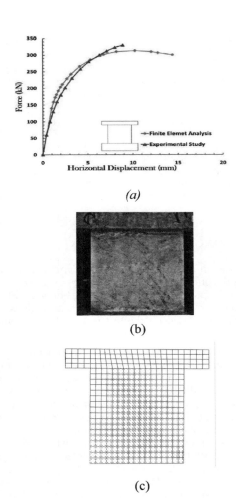

(a)

(b)

(c)

Figure 3. (a) Load–top displacement curve from experimental and numerical analysis of reference shear wall; (b) cracking patterns in reference wall; (c) cracking patterns in numerical model.

Table 2. Details and results of creating openings in the reference shear wall.

Model	Ratio of opening area to wall area (percent)	F_{max} (kN)	Capacity reduction (percent)
SW-L/4-B	6.25	228.64	27.1
SW-L/4-M	6.25	260.09	17.1
SW-L/4-T	6.25	282.99	9.8
SW-L/3-B	11.11	197.28	37.1
SW-L/3-M	11.11	214.10	31.8
SW-L/3-T	11.11	255.33	18.6
SW-L/2-B	25	130.95	58.3
SW-L/2-M	25	130.70	58.4
SW-L/2-T	25	119.65	61.9

Moreover, by increasing the area of openings from 11.11 percent to 25 percent, a capacity reduction from 58.3 percent to 61.9 percent was observed. Whereas in walls with small openings changing the location of the opening affected the wall capacity, in models with large opening, the wall capacity was not significantly affected by changing the location of the opening, because large openings change the integrity of the wall and change the wall behavior to a frame action in which the lateral load resisting behavior changes to one where overturning moments are resisted partially by an axial compression–tension couple across the wall piers rather than by the individual flexural action of the walls (Lu & Chen, 2005).

4 STRENGTHENING TECHNIQUE

The CFRP scheme used as external strengthening is shown schematically in Figure 4. The strengthening technique consists of unidirectional CFRP wraps with the fibers oriented horizontally for the top and bottom areas of the opening with the width of Y1/2 (Y1 is the opening height) and also two piers. The thickness of laminates used to strengthen the shear walls are C1, C2 and C3 which are equal to 0.05, 0.08 and 0.12 mm, respectively. Table 3 and 4 illustrates mechanical properties of the CFRP laminates and models names which are based on the location of the opening as well as the thickness of laminates, respectively.

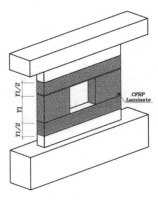

Figure 4. CFRP scheme used as external strengthening.

Table 3. Mechanical properties of CFRP plates.

Longitudinal elastic modulus (GPa)	281
Transverse elastic modulus (GPa)	7.71
Ultimate strain	0.015
Ultimate stress (MPa)	4215

Table 4. Results of CFRP strengthened models.

Model	F_s/F_{NS}	Model	F_s/F_{NS}	Model	F_s/F_{NS}
SW-L/4-B-C1	1.06	SW-L/3-B-C1	1.07	SW-L/2-B-C1	1.08
SW-L/4-B-C2	1.08	SW-L/3-B-C2	1.09	SW-L/2-B-C2	1.14
SW-L/4-B-C3	1.1	SW-L/3-B-C3	1.12	SW-L/2-B-C3	1.17
SW-L/4-M-C1	1.02	SW-L/3-M-C1	1	SW-L/2-M-C1	1.2
SW-L/4-M-C2	1.05	SW-L/3-M-C2	1.05	SW-L/2-M-C2	1.26
SW-L/4-M-C3	1.09	SW-L/3-M-C3	1.12	SW-L/2-M-C3	1.31
SW-L/4-T-C1	1.01	SW-L/3-T-C1	1.07	SW-L/2-T-C1	1.29
SW-L/4-T-C2	1.015	SW-L/3-T-C2	1.08	SW-L/2-T-C2	1.34
SW-L/4-T-C3	1.02	SW-L/3-T-C3	1.09	SW-L/2-T-C3	1.39

5 NUMERICAL RESULTS

The analysis results of the strengthened walls and the load versus top horizontal displacement curve are presented in Table 4. As can be seen, the effectiveness of the CFRP strengthening method in improving the capacity of walls is related to the thickness of laminates as well as the dimensions and location of openings in the walls. In this study, the lowest effect of CFRP strengthening was observed in the SW-L/3-M-C1 model (1%) which had a square opening with the dimension of 250 mm in the mid-height of the web strengthened with one layer of 0.05 mm CFRP laminate, and the highest effect was observed in the SW-L/2-T-C3 model (39%) which had a square opening with the dimension of 370 mm at the top of the wall strengthened with one layer of 0.12 mm laminate.

In the above table F_s/F_{NS} is the ratio of ultimate lateral load of the strengthened model to the ultimate lateral load of unstrengthened model.

Compared to the reference wall, the application of the fiber reinforced polymer sheets resulted in a 39 percent increase in ultimate load capacity of the models which had a large opening with the size of 25 percent of the total surface area of the walls. In the walls with the opening size of 11.11 percent and 6.25 percent of total surface area of the walls the maximum increase in capacity up to 12 percent was observed. As can be seen in Figure 6, in models with the area of 25 percent of total wall area, increasing the CFRP laminate thickness lead to increasing the maximum force and its corresponding displacement; while increasing the thickness of CFRP laminate, in models with smaller openings, mostly increased the displacement corresponding to the maximum force. It is worthwhile to mention that in all strengthened models, the failures of the walls were neither rupture nor debonding of the CFRP.

6 CONCLUSIONS

The main two objectives of this paper are studying the effects of creating openings in shear walls and the potential use of externally bonded CFRP sheets for strengthening of RC shear walls with openings. Based on the test results the following conclusions can be drawn:

1. Comparison between the experimental and numerical results indicated the ability of the finite element method procedure to give reasonable predictions for behavior of RC shear walls.
2. Creating openings with the area equal to 11.11 percent of the total wall area or less resulted in a load capacity reduction of about 37.1 percent.
3. The failures of RC shear walls with openings in which the load path is disrupted by openings were dependent primarily on the opening sizes and locations. However, increasing the area of openings up to 25 percent (large opening) of total area of the walls lead to a capacity reduction up to 61.9 percent. Moreover, in models with large openings, changing the location of the opening in the height of the walls did not have a significant effect on the wall ultimate load capacity. The primary reasons for this reduction is because the opening will changed the integrity of shear walls to a frame action in which the lateral load resisting behavior changed to one where overturning moments are resisted partially by an axial compression–tension couple across the wall system rather than by the individual flexural action of the walls.
4. Shear strengthening around the openings of RC shear walls can remarkably increase the wall capacity, based on the size and location of the opening. The capacity gain caused by FRP sheets was in the range of 1 percent to 39 percent. The capacity gain was highest (39 percent) when the opening was located at the top of the walls.

Only a strength gain of 6 percent was observed for the walls with bottom openings.

5. The failures of strengthened RC shear walls with openings, as well as unstrengthened walls, were dependent primarily on the thickness of FRP as well as the location and size of openings. In models with a large opening, increasing the CFRP plate thickness lead to increasing the ultimate load and its corresponding displacement; however, in models with smaller openings, increasing the thickness of CFRP plate mostly increased the displacement corresponding to the ultimate load.

6. CFRP strengthening had the highest effect on ultimate load capacity of models which had openings with the size of 25 percent of the total surface area of the walls in comparison to respective unstrengthened walls (up to 39 percent capacity increase). In the walls with the opening size of 11.11 percent and 6.25 percent of total surface area of the walls a maximum increase in capacity up to 12 percent was observed.

7. In all strengthened models, the failures of the walls were neither rupture nor debonding of the CFRP.

REFERENCES

ABAQUS 2008. Theory manual and users' manual, version 6.8.

ACI 440 2008. Guide for the design and construction of externally bonded FRP systems for strengthening concrete structures, ACI 440.2R-08, American Concrete Institute, Farmington Hills, MI.

Antoniades, K.K., Salonikios, T.N. & Kappos, A.J. 2003. Cyclic tests on seismically damaged reinforced concrete walls strengthened using fiber-reinforced polymer reinforcement. *ACI Structural Journal* 100(4): 510–518.

Ehsani, M.M. & Saadatmanesh, M. 1997. Fiber composites: An economical alternative for retrofitting earthquake-damaged precast-concrete walls. *Earthquake Spectra* 13(2):225–241.

Elnashai, A. & Sarno, L. 2008. Fundamentals of earthquake engineering. John Wiley: New York.

Hyo-Gyoung, K. & Do-Yeon, K. 2001. Nonlinear analysis of RC shear walls considering tension-stiffening effect. *Journal of Computers and Structures*, 79(1):499–517.

Kupfer, H., Hilsdorf, H.K. & Rusch, H. 1969. Behavior of concrete under biaxial stresses. *ACI Structural Journal*, 66(8): 656–666.

Lee, J. & Fenves, G.L. 1998. A plastic-damage model for cyclic loading of concrete structures, *J. Eng. Mech. ASCE*, 124:892–900.

Lefas, ID. 1988. Behavior of reinforced concrete structural walls and its implication for ultimate limit state design, Imperial College, University of London, PhD thesis.

Lefas, ID., Kotsovos, MD. & Ambraseys, N.N. 1990. Behavior of reinforced concrete structural walls: strength, deformation characteristics, and failure mechanism. *ACI Structure Journal*, 87(1):23–31.

Li, Z.J., Balendra, T., Tan, K.H. & Kong, K.H. 2005. Finite element modeling of cyclic behavior of shear wall structure retrofitted using GFRP. ACI-SP-230–74.

Lombard, J. 1999. Seismic Strengthening and Repair of Reinforced Concrete Shear walls using Externally Bonded Carbon Fiber Tow Sheets, Department of Civil and Environmental Engineering, Carleton University, Master of Engineering thesis.

Lu, X. & Chen, Y. 2005. Modeling of coupled shear walls and its experimental verification. *Journal of Structural Engineering*, 131(1): 75–84.

Lubliner, J., Oliver, J., Oller, S. & Onate, E. 1989. A plastic-damage model for concrete, *Int. J. Solids Struct.*, 25(3):299–326.

Sas, G. 2008. FRP shear strengthening of RC beams and walls, Department of Civil, Mining and Environmental Engineering, Luleå University of Technology, Licentiate Thesis.

Sayah, A.R. & Behfarnia, K. 2010. Study the effect of FRP composites on strengthening of shear walls with openings using nonlinear finite element analysis. 5th National Congress on Civil Engineering, Tehran.

Sugiyama, T., Uemura, M., Fukuyama, H., Nakano, K., & Matsuzaki, Y. 2000. Experimental study on the performance of the RC frame infilled cast-in-place non-structural RC walls retrofitted by using carbon fiber sheets. Proceedings, Twelfth World Conference on Earthquake Engineering, New Zealand Society for Earthquake Engineering, Silverstream, New Zealand.

Concrete Solutions – Grantham, Mechtcherine & Schneck (eds)
© 2012 Taylor & Francis Group, London, ISBN 978-0-415-61622-5

Using mineral based composites for shear strengthening concrete members

T. Blanksvärd & B. Täljsten
Luleå University of Technology, Luleå, Sweden

ABSTRACT: During the last two decades, strengthening concrete structures with epoxy bonded carbon fiber reinforced polymers (CFRP) has shown excellent results in increasing bearing capacity. However, there are some limitations with epoxy coated concrete surfaces, e.g., low permeability which may provoke freeze/thaw problems, poor thermal compatibility to the concrete substrate which makes epoxy coating more sensitive to the surrounding temperature and regulations when it comes to the security and health (allergic reactions) of applicators and third party users. In this respect, using mineral based composites (MBC) may overcome some of these challenges associated with epoxy bonded strengthening systems. MBC, in this context, refers to high strength fibers bonded to the surface using a mineral based bonding agent. This study examines the cracking behavior and strain development of shear MBC strengthened RC beams. The results show that using MBC as shear strengthening postpones the formation of macro-cracks and that a considerable strengthening effect is achieved by using MBC.

1 INTRODUCTION

1.1 Background

As time changes so does society and its structures. Time dependent factors such as degradation have a significant impact on the life span of structures. When dealing with concrete structures and reinforced concrete (RC) structures the types of degradation listed in the European standard EN 1504-9 (2008) categorize the causes of deficiencies into *defects in concrete* and *reinforcement corrosion*. All of these underlying reasons may ultimately result in concrete structures that have too low bearing capacity or multiple cracking enforcing it to be repaired or strengthened.

However, it is not only the degradation that may provoke strengthening measures. Other reasons might be; changes in structural use, the adoption of new design codes, safety etc.

When it comes to structural strengthening, the traditional ways include; adding or replacing embedded or external reinforcing steel bars, installing bonded rebars in preformed or drilled holes in the concrete, plate bonding, adding mortar or concrete, injecting cracks, voids or interstices, filling cracks, voids or interstices and prestressing (post tensioning). All of the above are part of principle 4 in the EN 1504–9 (2008), for protection and repair of concrete structures.

1.2 Strengthening concrete structures

Plate bonding (method 4.3 in EN 1504-9 (2008)) is a good alternative when it comes to strengthen concrete structures. Traditionally this has been done with epoxy bonded steel plates. This method requires heavy lifting and extensive mounting equipment due to the dead weight of steel. Another drawback when using steel is the corrosive properties which may reduce the life span of the strengthening system. During the last two decades a lot of research and development efforts have been made to develop strengthening systems utilizing fiber reinforced polymers (FRP). These FRPs are typically made of glass (G), aramid (A) and, most commonly in structural strengthening, carbon fibers (C). These fibers have a high strength/stiffness to weight ratio and are easy to apply.

These FRPs can be designed as laminates, sheets or bars mounted on the surface or as near surface mounted bars in the concrete cover (Oehlers et al., 2007; Nordin & Täljsten 2006). Although strengthening systems using epoxy as the bonding agent have shown good results in the form of bonding and application, there exist some drawbacks.

(a) There are regulations on how to handle the epoxy boding agents, based on the risk for eczema and toxicity of the components. (b) They have low permeability and diffusion of moisture out of concrete can be difficult, which for example can provoke freeze/thaw problems. (c) Poor thermal compatibility to the base concrete, which may cause unfavourable constraints. (d) The surface of the base concrete has to be free from water (dry) and the recommended temperature at the time of application and hardening should not be below 10 °C. (e) Depending on the amount of FRP coverage, it may also be difficult to assess the structure after strengthening.

Upgrading civil structures with mineral based composites gives a highly compatible repair and strengthening system with the base concrete. Mineral based composites (MBC) are in this paper used synonymously for upgrading with FRP materials together with a polymer modified or polymer reinforced cementitious bonding agent. Consequently, the use of these mortars should prevent some of the disadvantages with the organic resins such as epoxy.

1.3 Mineral based composites

Fibers utilized in combination with cementitious bonding agents can be designed in different ways. Up-to-date, some of the commonly used designs of fiber are unidirectional dry fibers, Wiberg (2003), textiles in the form of meshes made from woven, knitted or unwoven rovings of fibers in different directions, (Triantafillou & Papanicolaou 2006; Brückner et al., 2006) or FRPs where the fibers are assigned as a grid with two orthogonal directions, Blanksvärd (2007). The possibilities with the formability of the dry fibers and the textile meshes are much better than with an FRP grid where the fibers are embedded into a matrix. On the other hand, using dry fibers and non impregnated textiles has shown poor bond properties to the cementitious bonding agent which leads to inferior strength capacities compared to the impregnation of dry fibers with polymers, e.g., epoxy. Impregnation in this respect will give a much higher bond strength to the cementitious bonding agent compared to the use of non impregnated fibers. This is due to the low ability of the cementitious bonding agent to penetrate the dry fiber rovings, (Raupach et al., 2006; Shilang & He 2007). Considering the bond, it is therefore advantageous to use impregnated fibers than using dry fibers. It is also shown in Blanksvärd (2009) that using epoxy impregnated carbon fiber grids outperforms the use of dry textile carbon fiber strengthening systems.

In addition, there are also some uncertainties regarding the use of mortars as the bonding agent. These are primarily; (i) the bond in the transition zone between the mortar and the FRP and especially the bond between the base concrete and the mortar which can be influenced by drying shrinkage, (ii) Durability regarding fatigue. (iii) Influence on the structural performance regarding both micro and macro cracking of the structural system.

1.4 Investigated MBC system

Previous studies show that the use of MBC for shear strengthening reaches similar strengthening effects as the use of epoxy bonded carbon fiber sheets, Blanksvärd (2007). The MBC system used in this research contains a cementitious binder, a CFRP grid and a concrete surface primer.

Generally, the surface of the base concrete needs to be roughened in order to remove the cement laitance to achieve a good bond between the base concrete and the mortar. Examples of roughening techniques are sandblasting or water jetting. In laboratory environments, or on smaller defined surfaces, a hand lay-up method can be used to apply the MBC. Prior to mounting the MBC system the base concrete surface has to be primed using a primer product to prevent moisture transport from the wet mortar to the base concrete. The hand lay-up technique used in this study basically consists of the following; first a layer of mortar is immediately applied to the primed surface, next, the CFRP grid is placed on the first layer of mortar followed by an additional layer of mortar applied on the grid. A graphical representation of the hand lay-up MBC method, after sandblasting, is shown in Figure 1. For larger in-situ cases then the system can also be applied by spraying. In this respect the application is done in three main steps. First, non corrosive anchors and studs are mounted to the prepared concrete surface, these studs also acts as thickness gauges to ensure that the sought after thickness is achieved. Secondly, the CFRP grid is a mounted onto the studs and the grid are stretched to be leveled without any unevenness. Thirdly, the mortar is sprayed behind and onto the CFRP grid. The mortar is sprayed in such an amount that the sought after total thickness is achieved. When the outer layer of mortar has been sprayed then, where applicable, the mortar surface might be prepared into a desirable condition.

Figure 2 is showing the three main steps for in-situ application of the MBC system together

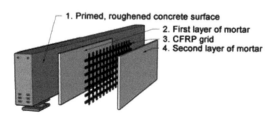

1. Primed, roughened concrete surface
2. First layer of mortar
3. CFRP grid
4. Second layer of mortar

Figure 1. Schematic overview of the MBC strengthening system.

Anchors and studs for clear distance

Mounting of CFRP Grid

Spraying mortar onto the pre-mounted CFRP grid

Finishing the surface preparation of the MBC system

Figure 2. In-situ application of the MBC system.

with a finishing surface treatment. The structure in Figure 2 is a silo which needed to be strengthened due to internal pressure from the silo content. In this case the silo was under reinforced and had significant cracking prior to strengthening with the MBC system. No cracks were visible after repeated loading and unloading of the strengthened silo. One advantage with the MBC system is that it is a transparent system when it comes to cracks inspected by eye. This study will also show crack propagation and monitoring tools for cracks and strains not visible to the naked eye.

1.5 Crack monitoring

It is off great interest to be able to monitor the composite action between the MBC systems and the concrete structure. One way of evaluating the composite action is to monitor the crack formations that progress in a shear strengthened structure during loading. However, monitoring the formation of cracks in concrete requires special monitoring tools. Firstly, the formation of cracks needs to be established. The formation of cracks does not start immediately but can be considered as an accumulation of micro-cracks while the load is increasing. When these micro cracks have created a certain level of damage, a macro-crack will form.

It is suggested in Hegger et al. (2004), based on experimental and theoretical investigations, that a non linear process is preceding the

formation of macro-cracks. It follows that the use of laser-interferometry and strain gauges on the stirrups can give an indication of the redistribution of forces before the appearance of macro cracks, by means of monitoring the linearity during the initial loading. Also for the post cracking behavior, it is shown that methods of photometric measurement make it possible to investigate the strain distributions prior to the formation of visible shear cracks (Lee & Al-Mahaidi 2008; Sonnenberg & Al-Mahaidi 2007). This paper will show the potential of postponing the formations of macro-cracks by the use of mineral based strengthening in shear.

2 EXPERIMENTAL INVESTIGATION

2.1 Materials

The materials used in this investigation concern two different concrete qualities corresponding to C35 and C55 in EN 1992-1-1, flexural and shear steel reinforcement, $\phi16$ and $\phi12$ respectively, an orthogonal CFRP grid and a polymer modified mortar as bonding agent. Table 1 shows the compressive and tensile properties for the different constituents, note that all properties are given as ultimate values accept for the steel reinforcement which is given as yield values. The values of the concrete and mortar are tested according to DIN EN 196-1 (2005). Values for the properties of the fibers in the CFRP grid, were as provided by the manufacturer.

2.2 Test set-up

In this investigation there were 11 reinforced concrete beams tested in total. All of the beams had a rectangular cross section. The chosen loading scheme for all specimens was 4-point loading, thus with two constant shear spans. All loading rates were deformation controlled to 0.01 mm/s. The experimental set-up, geometries and reinforcement scheme are recorded in Figure 3.

For monitoring convenience, the beam specimens were heavily shear reinforced in one span to ensure

Table 1. Mechanical properties of the materials used.

| Material | Tensile | | Compression |
	Stress [MPa]	Strain [‰]	Stress [MPa]
Concrete C35	2.8	–	48.9
Concrete C55	3.4	–	73.5
Mortar	3.0	–	65.6
Steel $\phi12$	601	2.84	–
Steel $\phi16$	555	2.79	–
CFRP grid	3800	15	–

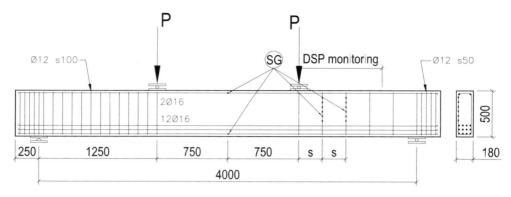

Figure 3. Test set-up including DSP and SG monitoring.

that the shear failure happened on the shear span with the lower shear capacity. Only one shear span was monitored and also strengthened. Common to all of the concrete beams is that they were heavily reinforced in flexure with 12 Ø16 mm steel bars at the bottom and two Ø16 mm at the top of the beam. The shear reinforcement constituted Ø10 mm stirrups with a distance 50 mm at the supports and Ø12 mm stirrups with the distance 100 mm in the heavily reinforced shear span. The densification of the shear reinforcement over the supports was designed to secure the anchorage of the longitudinal reinforcement. Further, the strengthened shear span of the beam specimens had three different designs of the shear reinforcement, which can be categorized as *no* shear reinforcement, stirrups with a distance *s* = 350 mm and stirrups with a distance *s* = 250 mm. The first category mainly distinguishes the behavior of the beam with no shear reinforcement and without the MBC system (reference beam). The other two mainly assess the influence of the interaction between the steel shear reinforcement and the MBC strengthening system.

2.3 Monitoring

A quite extensive measuring program was used to record the behavior of the tested beams. This includes monitoring the load with a load cell, Linear Variable Differential Transducers (LVDT) for measuring deflections and settlements, electrical foil strain gauges (SG) for local strain measurements and photometric strain measurement for global strain measurements. The loading was deformation controlled and the deformation rate was set to 0.01 mm/s, measured at the midpoint of the beam specimens. For a more detailed description of the experimental program the reader is referred to Blanksvärd (2007).

2.3.1 Strain gauge set-up

Two different types of SGs were used to measure strains on the CFRP grid and steel reinforcement. A gauge length of 5 mm was used (KFW-5-120-C1-11L3M2R) to measure strains on the steel reinforcement. In the case of measuring the strains on the CFRP grid the tows were quite narrow and a gauge length of 2 mm had to be used (KFWS-2N-120-C1-11L3M3R).

All beam specimens had SGs on the compressed and tensile longitudinal steel reinforcement at half span of the beam, see Figure 3. Twelve SGs were applied on the two stirrups closest to the load for beam specimens with shear steel reinforcement in the weakened or strengthened shear span. The set-up for the SG assessment is recorded in Figure 3.

To compare the CFRP strain to the strain in the steel stirrups, a similar assessment as for the SGs mounted on the stirrups was affiliated to the CFRP grid. By placing SGs on the steel stirrups, CFRP and using photometric strain measurement (see below) it was possible to compare strains in the steel stirrups (internal concrete) to strains in vertical CFRP tows (internal MBC) as well as strain fields obtained by the photometric strain measurements.

However, due to the design of the CFRP grid it was not possible to mount the SGs at exactly the same position as the steel reinforcement SGs. After casting the concrete beam specimens, the steel stirrups were located using a metal detector and the SGs were mounted onto the nearest vertical CFRP tow corresponding to the stirrup with SGs applied, leading to a maximum horizontal dislocation of 20 mm. The first SG on the stirrup and on the vertical CFRP tow was applied 170 mm from the bottom of the beam, just above the tensile reinforcement. The internal distance between the following SGs was then 50 mm, see also Figure 3.

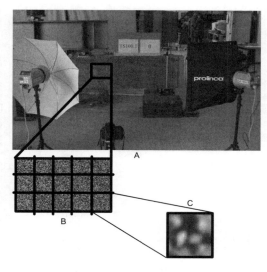

Figure 4. Set-up for the digital speckle pattern monitoring equipment. A) Equipment using camera and flashes, B) Part of the monitored surface, C) Sub-picture.

2.4 *Photometric measurement*

Traditional strain measurements using strain gauges only measure local strains, while photometric strain measurements can indicate the global strain behavior of a specific surface. Photometric monitoring is a non-contact measurement by taking photos of the area studied. The photos were taken prior to loading (reference) and at certain load steps using a digital resolution camera (Canon EOS 5D). Photos were taken at load steps every 5 kN.

The pictures were processed into a raw format grey scale) and trimmed so that only the investigated area remains. All photos were then analyzed by computer software based on speckle pattern correlation (DSP), developed at Luleå University of Technology (Carolin et al., 2004; Svanbro 2004). The photos were divided into different sub-pictures and their point of gravity was calculated, see Figure 4. The centre of gravity was then calculated for all individual sub-pictures. The accuracy becomes higher if the sub-pictures are chosen to be large. A large number of pixels within the sub-picture will also increase the accuracy of the positioning. Speckle pattern correlation analysis will find the same sub-picture in the second loading condition even if the pattern has deformed or moved. The size and the distance of the sub-pictures can be chosen as desired.

The strains are calculated by correlating the sub-pictures during loading to the unloaded reference. For the software to work properly and give adequate results, the photographed area needs to be

given pattern or divergent colors. In this case the strengthened area was given a random pattern by using an epoxy adhesive to adhere a mix of white and black sand.

Results from the speckle pattern correlation analysis can be plotted as shear strains, principal strains or strains in any arbitrary direction. In this study the accuracy of the strain measurements was 300 μ strain. The monitored surface was set to 880 × 500 mm, see Figure 3 and Figure 7.

3 EXPERIMENTAL RESULTS

The pre-cracking behavior of the strengthened and non strengthened specimens was observed by the monitored strains with a SG in the midpoint of the stirrups. Figure 5A and B shows the strain development in the stirrup 700 mm from the load for a beam specimen with concrete quality C35, without any strengthening system and having the MBC strengthening system. The first visual shear crack was formed at a shear force of 186 kN (without MBC) and 285 kN (with MBC). Figure 5B shows the initial part of the strains at lower loads in order to get a more detailed overview of the initial elastic behavior. Here the strains behave linearly up to a shear force of 57 kN (without MBC) and 79 kN (with MBC). Thereby the formation of macro-cracks initiates long before the appearance of the first visual shear crack. Comparing a beam specimen with the MBC strengthening system and a specimen with no strengthening, it is clear that the strengthening reduces strain levels in the stirrup for low shear forces and continues to do so for higher load levels.

The linearity at low load levels becomes harder to detect when the shear reinforcement is increased due to low strain levels in the stirrups in the initial load levels. This is shown in Figure 5C for a beam specimen with higher concrete quality (C55) and shear reinforcement ratio (s = 250 mm). Still, the strain in the stirrup for the MBC strengthened specimen has lower strains for the same shear load level compared to a non strengthened one. Thus, indicating that utilizing the MBC strengthening system will reduce strains as the loading prevails. This behavior was noticed for all specimens with and without strengthening for different concrete qualities and different steel shear reinforcement ratios.

Shear strengthening of a beam with MBC will reduce the strains in the stirrups compared to a non strengthened one. Thus, the vertical CFRP tows will attain and redistribute some of the above mentioned strains. Figure 6 shows the shear cracks and strains in the vertical CFRP tow at different shear loads. Here it is possible to see that there are strain

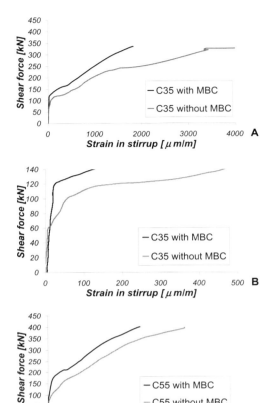

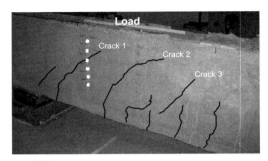

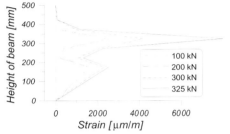

Figure 6. Above, shear crack propagation, white dotes indicates the location of the SGs on the CFRP grid. Under, strains monitored in the vertical CFRP tow located at 680 mm from the load.

Figure 5. Strains measured in stirrup with and without MBC for specimens with A) Concrete C35 S = 350 mm, B) Part of the initial strains in C35 s = 350 mm, C) Concrete C55 s = 250 mm.

concentrations in the vicinity of the formation of shear cracks.

The post cracking behavior and global strain distribution is monitored by the photometric measurement. Figure 7 shows the monitored principal strains at different load steps. The monitored area is shown in Figure 7 for beam specimens with a stirrup distance of 350 mm and concrete quality C35 both with and without the MBC strengthening system.

The load steps were taken at shear loads of 200 and 260 kN. By comparing the specimens with and without the MBC strengthening system, it is clear that the MBC system reduces the strains even for a load of 200 kN. When the load is increased the MBC system still reduces the principal strains at the load 260 kN compared to a non strengthened specimen. Further, the photometric strain

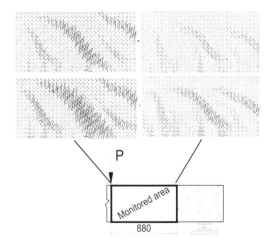

Figure 7. Photometric measurement of the principal strains for concrete quality C35 and s = 350 mm. A) Without MBC at 200 kN, B) With MBC at 200 kN, C) Without MBC at 260 kN, D) With MBC at 260 kN.

measurement indicated shear crack formations long before first visual appearance.

All of the recorded principal strains in Figure 7 have the same scale. Only the direction and relative size are given, for values on the principal strain the reader is referred to Blanksvärd (2007).

4 CONCLUSIONS

In the pre-cracking stage, macro-cracks preceded the formation of visual shear cracks. The formation of macro cracks appear at 31% of the first visual shear crack load for non strengthened specimens and 28% for strengthened specimens, when studying strains in the stirrups. Compared to a non strengthened speciment, MBC strengthening increased the macro-crack formation by 38% for specimens with concrete quality C35 and s = 350 mm and 35–67% for all C55 specimens. MBC had a better reduction of macro-cracking for specimens with low shear reinforcement ratios, most likely due to the close spacing of the carbon fibre tows in the CFRP grid. High reinforcement ratios transferred tensile stresses in a more continuous manner during the macro-cracking. This is explained by low strain levels in the stirrups in the initial load levels which made the transition between micro—and macro cracking less distinguished.

It as also noted from the strain gauge monitoring on the CFRP grid that there were high strain concentrations in the vertical tows close to the forming shear cracks. The strain concentrations in vertical CFRP tows in the vicinity of shear cracks indicates a good bond between the CFRP and the mortar. This bond-slip behavior will be the subject of future research.

The post cracking behavior was monitored by using photometric strain measurement. It was noted that strengthening with MBC reduces the principal strains for all load steps in comparison to a non strengthened specimen. It was also possible to detect shear crack formations before they were visually apparent.

Measurements from both traditional strain gauges together with photometric strain monitoring were in agreement. Using the photometric monitoring tools is an easy way to obtain useful strain fields on the surface not detectable by traditional strain gauges.

ACKNOWLEDGEMENTS

The research presented in this paper has been funded by several organizations. The Swedish National Road Administration, The Development Fund of the Swedish Construction Industry, Skanska AB and Sto Scandinavia AB.

REFERENCES

Brückner, A., Ortlepp, R. and Curbach, M. 2006. Textile reinforced concrete for strengthening in bending and shear. *Materials and Structures*, 39, 741–748.

Blanksvärd, T. 2007. *Strengthening of concrete structures by the use of mineral based composites*. Licentiate thesis 2007:15, Luleå University of Technology, Division of Structural Engineering.

Blanksvärd, T. 2009. *Strengthening of concrete structures by the use of mineral-based composites—System and design models for flexure and shear*. Doctoral thesis, Luleå University of Technology, Division of Structural Engineering.

Carolin, A., Olofsson, T. and Täljsten, B. 2004. Photographic Strain Monitoring for Civil Engineering. *Proc. in, FRP Composites in Civil Engineering, CICE 2004, Adelaide, Australia*, 593–600.

DIN EN 196–1. 2005. Methods of testing cement - Part 1: Determination of strength.

EN 1504-9:2008. 2008. Products and systems for the protection and repair of concrete structures—Definitions, requirements, quality control and evaluation of conformity—Part 9: General principles for the use of products and systems.

Hegger, J., Sherif, A. and Görtz, S. 2004. Investigation of pre- and postcracking shear behavior of prestressed concrete beams using innovative measuring techniques. *ACI Structural Journal*, 101(2), 183–192.

Lee, T.K. and Al-Mahaidi, R. 2008. An Experimental investigation on shear behaviour of RC T-beams strengthened with CFRP using photogrammetry. *Composite Structures*, 82, 185–193.

Nordin, H. and Täljsten, B. 2006. Concrete beams strengthened with prestressed near surface mounted CFRP. *Composites for Construction*, 10(1), 60–68.

Oehlers, D.J., Rashid, R. and Seracino, R. 2007. IC debonding resistance of groups of FRP NSM strips in reinforced concrete beams. *Journal of composites for construction*, 11(4), 401–409.

Raupach, M., Orlowsky, J., Büttner, T., Dilthey, U. and Schleser, M. 2006. Epoxy impregnated textiles in concrete—Load bearing capacity and durability. *Proc., the 1st international RILEM symposium: Textile reinforced concrete*, RILEM, Aachen, Germany, 55–66.

Shilang, X.U. and He, L.I. 2007. Bond properties and experimental methods of textile reinforced concrete. *Journal of Wuhan University—Materials Science Edition*, 22(3). 529–532.

Sonnenberg, A.M.C. and Al-Mahaidi, R. 2007. Investigation of dowel shear in RC beams using photogrammetry. *Magazine of Concrete Research*, 59(9), 621–626.

Svanbro, A. 2004. *Speckle interferometry and correlation applied to large-displacement fields*. Doctoral thesis 2004:05, Luleå University of Technology, Division of Experimental Mechanics.

Triantafillou, T.C. and Papanicolaou, C.G. 2006. Shear strengthening of reinforced concrete members with textile reinforced mortar (TRM) jackets. *Materials and Structures*, 39, 85–93.

Wiberg, A. 2003. *Strengthening of concrete beams using cementitious carbon fibre composites*. Doctoral Thesis, Royal Institute of Technology, Structural Engineering, 100 44 Stockholm, Sweden, p. 140. ISSN 1103-4270.

Concrete Solutions – Grantham, Mechtcherine & Schneck (eds)
© *2012 Taylor & Francis Group, London, ISBN 978-0-415-61622-5*

Behaviour of RC elements internally reinforced with BFRP at elevated temperatures

T. Donchev, P.L. Blanco & P.S. Shah
Kingston University, UK

ABSTRACT: This paper has been planned to reflect a study about the behaviour of internally reinforced concrete beams with Basalt Fibre Reinforced Polymer (BFRP) reinforcement at elevated temperatures. To investigate the effect of heating, 12 samples of small scale beams with dimensions $400 \times 100 \times 100$ mm were prepared. They were heated in an oven at 100, 200 and 300°C in a loaded condition.

The behaviour of the beams was investigated via two types of experiments—during heating and cooling in loaded condition including the processes of loading and unloading and 4-point bending test till achieving the ultimate load of the cooled samples. Information about the residual capacity and deformability of the heated minibeams is provided and analysed.

1 INTRODUCTION

In recent years an immense use of fibre reinforced polymer (FRP) bars has been recorded. One of the most important reasons for FRP materials to be increasingly used in the construction industry is their extreme endurance when exposed to high corrosive conditions. Their durability, high strength and light weight are additional reasons for such growing demand.

Many authors have recently investigated the performance of FRP composites under elevated temperatures. However, most of the research is focused on the use of FRP for strengthening of deteriorated concrete structures, with a very limited number of investigations on the performance of internal FRP reinforcement at high temperatures.

This research has been carried out in an attempt to understand the behaviour of RC beams internally reinforced with Basalt FRP (BFRP) rebars under high temperatures. A total of twelve small scale concrete samples were tested in two different types of experiments:

– Type 1: the first part of the test was carried out inside an oven, where beams were subjected to elevated temperature conditions (between 100 and 300°C) and constant load (1 KN), applied as a point load in the middle of the beam.
– Type 2: after cooling and unloading of the samples, a four point load testing in cooled condition was carried out till destruction.

The influence of temperature in BFRP internally reinforced beams is assessed in terms of maximum deflection during heating, residual deflections after heating in a loaded condition, failure load for heated and cooled samples, including strain development and crack appearance and progression.

2 BACKGROUND

FRP composites are constituted by a combination of fibres embedded in a resin matrix. While the fibres strengthen the composite, the matrix keeps the fibres together, acts as a medium transferring the loads from the fibres to the entire structure and prevents the environmental damage of the fibres (Cripps, 2002). According to GangaRao et al. (2007), the matrix is constituted by polymers, which can be classified into two main groups depending on their reaction to heat and pressure: thermosetting and thermoplastic. Based on the type of fibres some of the most used FRP materials could be classified as Glass FRP (GFRP), Carbon FRP (CFRP), Basalt FRP (BFRP) and Aramid FRP (AFRP).

Basalt fibres are produced by melting basalt rocks, which have to be fractioned into tiny particles and then rearranged into the form of fibres. The use of BFRP implies opportunity for a considerable saving since it is obtained through a single product process and it does not contain any additive apart from basalt rocks (Sim et al., 2005). According to Palmieri et al. (2009a, b) the growing use of BFRP is due to its many advantages such as resistance to corrosion, high strength and good performance against extreme temperatures and fire. Moreover, as Liu et al. (2006) stated, BFRP has a similar coefficient of thermal expansion to concrete, it is 2.5 times stronger than steel and 3.7 times lighter and has a higher final strain than carbon fibres. It promotes sustainable development since they do not produce waste while manufacturing and reduce the global warming generated by production of materials such stainless steel (Brik, 2003). Overall basalt fibres are cheaper than many other FRP materials, as they are made from widely available natural material.

FRP reinforced concrete structures behave quite differently in comparison with steel reinforced ones when exposed to normal and high temperatures. Under normal temperatures their performance has been widely proved as successful, but at elevated temperatures it is highly determined by the Glass Transition Temperature (T_g), at which the resin modifies its behaviour from glassy to rubbery. The value of T_g varies between 65 and 150°C, which are rather low if compared to fire temperatures (Palmieri et al., 2009a, b). Even though the bars are embedded in the concrete and the absence of oxygen prevents the burning of FRP, the resin softens, and when the FRP surface resin reaches T_g, the concrete-FRP bond is reduced and the resin cannot transfer effectively the tensile stresses to the fibres any longer. Consequently, the contact area between concrete and the bars surface could be considered as weak point, therefore requiring further research to be done (Naaman, 2003).

Tanano (1997) studied the effect of elevated temperatures on the mechanical properties of CFRP and AFRP reinforced concrete beams, demonstrating that both the tensile strength and elastic modulus of the bars decrease as the temperature rises, this reduction being more significant in the case of the tensile strength.

Abbasi & Hogg (2004) have concluded that GFRP bars under flexural load and in a heated condition could satisfy the minimum period of fire resistance, recommending a minimum cover of 70 mm for future design for fire protection.

Al-Zahrani et al. (2007) found that high temperature reduces both the tensile strength of GFRP bars and the flexural resistance of GFRP reinforced concrete beams, linearly to the exposure time period.

Wang et al. (2007) carried out an experiment to compare the strength of steel, CFRP and GFRP bars at high temperatures, and found that, for FRP reinforcing bars, the stress-strain diagram remained linear up to failure. However, the failure strength reduction is also linear, with a null value at 500°C. Moreover, it was concluded that 350°C is a critical temperature: when the temperature is lower, even though there is a some tensile strength reduction, stiffness remains almost invariable (90% of that at

room temperature). However, when temperature is higher than 350°C results are variable and it is not possible to guarantee that the bars will be strong enough, since the elastic modulus value suffers a sharp fall.

It can be concluded that FRP reinforced concrete structures are susceptible to elevated temperatures, suffering a significant deterioration of the mechanical properties as well as the bond in the concrete interface. As a result, a considerable reduction of the stiffness and the resistance is expected. There is a lack of sufficient experimental data on basalt FRP performance and on its residual capacity when used as a reinforcing material under high temperatures. The purpose of the current research has been to analyse the behaviour of small scale BFRP reinforced concrete beams under high temperatures and after cooling.

3 EXPERIMENTAL SET-UP

3.1 *Preparation of the samples*

A total of twelve mini beams were made using internal BFRP reinforcement. Three specimens were made for each temperature level: room temperature, 100°C, 200°C and 300°C, in order to study how the mechanical properties of BFRP reinforced elements are affected by elevated temperatures.

All twelve mini beams had the same dimensions of $400 \times 100 \times 100$ mm. The concrete used for these specimens was C25/30. All beams were provided with 10 mm cover for the reinforcement.

The reinforcement consisted of two steel bars at the top of 6 mm diameter, two BFRP 8 mm diameter bars as bottom reinforcement and six links made from 3 mm diameter steel bars, 60 mm apart. The dimensions and reinforcement of the samples are detailed on Figure 1.

The main mechanical characteristics for BFRP reinforcement are indicated in Table 1.

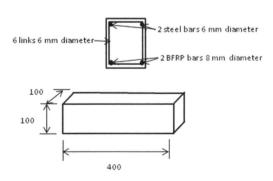

Figure 1. Samples dimensions and reinforcement.

Table 1. Materials properties.

Property	Description
Composition	BFRP bars with a sanded finish
Tensile strength	1200 MPa
Elastic modulus	50 GPa
Coefficient of thermal expansion	3.6×10^{-6} $1/°f$ (in the longitudinal direction)
Providers	Magmatech Ltd

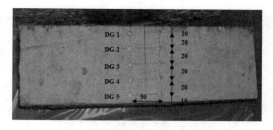

Figure 2. Demec gauge positions.

The measuring equipment used during the process of heating consisted of 3 thermocouples measuring the temperature in the oven, Demec gauges were used to measure the distribution of the strains at the beginning and at the end of the heating process (Fig. 2) and a deflection gauge measured vertical deformations during the process of heating (Fig. 3).

Five pairs of Demec gauge bases with 50 mm base length were attached to the front face of each reinforced beam. These gauge bases were installed along a vertical line at mid span in order to estimate the positioning of the neutral axis and the strain/stress distribution during the experiment.

3.2 Testing

The experimental programme included two types of experiments:

– Test at a fixed level of elevated temperature and static loading.
– Test of the cooled and unloaded samples in a four point loading scheme till destruction.

3.2.1 Type 1: Testing during heating

For this part of the experiment, the samples were heated inside an oven with a permanently acting static load. The beams were supported on a metal stand and load was applied via a steel hanging device in a three point bending scheme. A dial gauge was placed above the top of the oven, allowing taking readings of the deflection at mid span during the process of heating (Fig. 3).

Four stages of experimental work were carried out:

• Stage 1 (loading): increasing load was applied before heating from 0 to 1 KN in steps of 0.25 KN.
• Stage 2 (heating): the beams were heated at different temperatures (100, 200 or 300°C) and at constant load (1 KN).

DIAL GAUGE READER

MINI BEAM SUPPORTI NG FRAME

STATIC LOAD

Figure 3. Equipment used for Part 1 of the experiment.

• Stage 3 (cooling): immediately after the heating stage. Readings were taken every fifteen minutes.
• Stage 4 (unloading): 20 hours after cooling final reading in loaded condition is taken and the load was gradually removed following the same steps as for stage 1 in reverse order.

Readings from the demec gauges were taken at the beginning and during all stages of application of the static load and during the process of unloading after heating (stages 1 and 4).

3.2.2 Type 2: Testing till destruction in cooled condition

After exposing the samples to elevated temperatures and cooling, they were tested under a four point loading scheme, from 0 KN up to failure

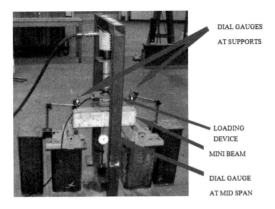

Figure 4. Equipment used for Part 2 of the experiment.

load, in steps of 2 KN. A hydraulic jack was used to generate the load, applied centrally through a reaction frame. The span was 380 mm and shear span was 165 mm.

A dial gauge was placed underneath the beam to record the deflection at mid span, and two dial gauges were located at the supports, in order to allow taking into account the deformations of the support devices (Fig. 4).

Readings from the demec gauges and dial gauges were taken at each level of loading.

4 EXPERIMENTAL RESULTS

4.1 *Type* 1 *experiments: Elevated temperature test*

4.1.1 *Stage* 1: *Static loading before heating*
The increase in deflection at mid span of the samples when loaded before heating was approximately the same for all the samples, with an average value of 1.00 mm deflection for 1 KN load.

An applied load of 1 KN during the heating is significantly less than the ultimate load and, as expected for this level of loading, the load/ deflection relation was close to linear.

4.1.2 *Stage* 2 *(heating)*
The heating was increased gradually at a rate of 5°C per minute till the corresponding level and kept at this level for 2 hours for 100°C samples, 3 hours for 200°C and 5 hours for 300°C samples to allow for uniform distribution of the temperature within the samples. Having in mind that the supporting frame was expanding with increase of temperature, final deflections at mid span were obtained via correcting the measured values with estimated temperature expansion of the supports. The deflection readings obtained during heating indicate that deflections gradually increased as

temperature increased for the initial stages of heating (during the first 105 minutes), presenting a parabolic behaviour. Probably the main reason for this relatively fast developing deflection was the exceeding of Tg and corresponding initial softening of the reinforcement.

Passing that stage, the deflections decreased gradually from the maximum level at 120 minutes for the 200°C and 300°C samples, which were exposed to longer periods of heating (Fig. 5). This effect could be explained considering the difference in coefficients of thermal expansion between the concrete and BFRP reinforcement. Having in mind that BFRP rebars have a lower coefficient of thermal expansion then concrete, further heating resulted in prestressing effects for the FRP reinforcement. In addition, a slightly higher coefficient of thermal expansion for the upper steel reinforcement at elevated temperatures could increase to a minor extent the above mentioned effect. The final deflection due to heating was between 1.2 and 1.4 mm, most of it developed at initial stages of heating.

The graph in Fig. 6 represents the maximum values of deflection reached during the heating stage for each temperature. Deflections were higher for 300°C samples, with an approximately linear rate

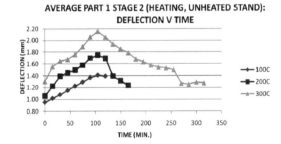

Figure 5. Stage 2 (heating): Deflection v time.

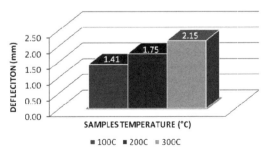

Figure 6. Maximum deflection during heating.

634

of increase as temperature rose. The maximum deflections during the process of heating were higher than the measured deflections at the end of the heating process for temperatures 200 and 300°C due to the "prestressing" effect.

4.1.3 Stage 3 (cooling)

The cooling process continued for 20 hours at room temperature to allow reduction to normal temperature for all parts of the samples. A significant increase of the deflection between the initial cooling stage and at the end of the cooling period (Fig. 7) was observed. As a possible explanation of this effect the elimination of the "prestressing" of BFRP reinforcement with reduction of the temperature could be considered. At the same time, the reduction of Young's modulus of the concrete due to heating may have contributed to the development of significant residual deflections.

In addition to the above effect, some plastic deformations in the FRP reinforcement during the heating process above Tg were probably influencing the deflections as well.

4.1.4 Stage 4 (unloading)

The unloading stage took place 20 hours after beginning of the cooling and the temperatures of the sample and the stand were the same as the room temperature. During the unloading stage, the deflection reduced as the load was progressively removed, with larger residual deflections for higher temperatures, ranging from 1.20 mm for 100°C to 1.59 mm for 300°C (Fig. 8).

Figure 9 presents the results of the residual deflection after unloading in a cooled condition. The deflection values were again higher for higher temperature, but they were smaller than the values of deflection in a loaded condition. Partial recovery of the shape of the mini beams after unloading indicated that a significant part of the residual deformations after heating under static load were elastic. The percentage of the elastic recovery of

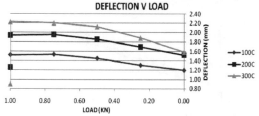

Figure 8. Stage 4 (unloading): Deflection v load.

RESIDUAL DEFLECTION AFTER UNLOADING V SAMPLES TEMPERATURE

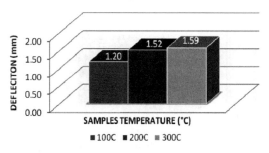

Figure 9. Residual deflection after unloading.

the samples varied between 21% for 100°C and 29% for 300°C. The higher value for samples heated to higher temperatures could be explained with higher reduction of the elastic modulus of the concrete and corresponding higher deformability at the same level of loading.

4.2 Type 2: Four point load test

4.2.1 Strain at demec gauge 5 v load

DG5 was the gauge in the lowest position and it reflected the magnitude of tensile stresses close to the bottom edge of the mini beams.

The graph in Figure 10 shows the average strain developed at the bottom positioned of Demec gauges (DG 5) for the different values of temperatures of preliminary heating. It is observed that the performance of all samples in the aspect of strain development at the bottom part was overall the same, with slightly higher values of deformation for the samples exposed to more elevated temperatures. Therefore, the performance of BFRP reinforcing bars does not seem to be dramatically affected by the effect of temperature which could be an indicator for a relatively small change in their deformability after heating up to 300°C and cooling.

RESIDUAL DEFLECTION AFTER COOLING V SAMPLES TEMPERATURE

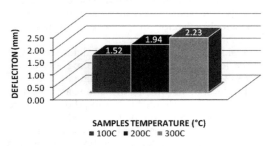

Figure 7. Residual deflection after cooling.

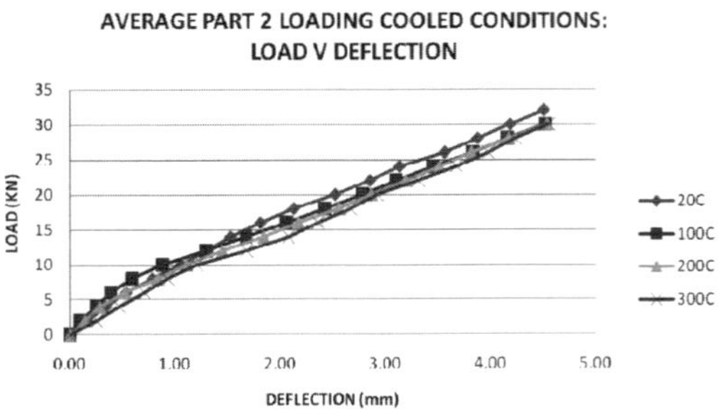

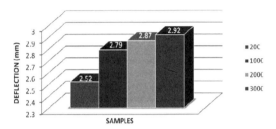

Figure 10.   Part 2 Demec gauge 5 strain v load.

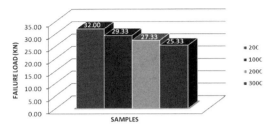

Figure 12.   Failure load v samples temperature.

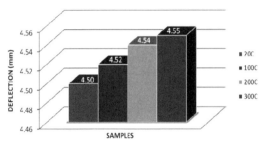

Figure 11.   Deformability 20 KN v samples temperature.

Figure 13.   Maximum deflection v samples temperature.

4.2.2   Deformability at 20 KN

The chart in Fig. 11 presents the level of deformability of the heated and cooled samples when the applied load was 20 KN. As expected, the samples subjected to a higher degree of heating had higher deformability. However the rate of increase of deflection reduced for higher values of temperature, with the maximum difference observable between the samples at room temperature and 100°C. The increase of deflection compared with the control samples was of 11% for 100°C, 14% for 200°C and 16% for 300°C.

This trend might be due to an additional curing of the polymer matrix and a consequential increase of the stiffness for those samples that were heated in Part 1 of the experiment.

4.2.3   Ultimate load

Figure 12 summarises the average failure load for different levels of temperature of heating in Part 1 of the experiment. As can be observed, the failure load decreased almost linearly from 32 to 25.3 KN.

Considering the level of heating applied, the performance of the samples was reasonably good, with a failure load being 92% of the initial capacity for 100°C (29.3 KN), 85% for 200°C (27.3 KN) and 79% for 300°C (25.3 KN) (Fig. 12).

4.2.4   Maximum deflection

Figure 13 presents the maximum deflection reached by the samples heated at different temperatures and tested in a cooled condition. The data registered is in a similar range in all cases, with an approximately linear rate of increase of the deflections as temperature rises. Those deflections are registered at different (ultimate) levels of loading.

5   CONCLUSIONS

– Maximum deflections during heating to temperature in the indicated range were limited due to pre-stressing effects and did not exceed the residual deflection in a loaded condition after heating and cooling.
– A significant part of residual deformations in the loaded condition after cooling was elastic and was reduced during unloading.
– The level of residual deformations after heating and cooling in loaded condition did not exceed 2.23 mm or approximately span/150.
– The level of residual deformations after heating up to 300°C in loaded condition, cooling and unloading was less than span/200.

- Deformability of samples heated and tested in a cooled condition increased by 29% for 300°C.
- A reduction of load capacity of samples heated to 300°C of 21% was observed.

ACKNOWLEDGEMENTS

The authors wish to acknowledge the company MagmaTech Ltd for sponsoring the research via providing BFRP reinforcement.

REFERENCES

Abbasi, A. & Hogg, P.J. 2004. Fire testing of concrete beams with reinforced plastic rebar. *Proceedings of Advanced Polymer Composites for Structural Applications in Construction, ACIC 2004*: 445–456.

Al-Zahrani, M.M. et al. 2007. High Temperature Effect on Tensile Strength of GFRP Bars and Flexural Behavior of GFRP Reinforced Concrete Beams. *Proceedings of 8th International Symposium on Fiber Reinforced Polymer (FRP) Reinforcement for Concrete Structures (FRPRCS-8), Patras, Greece, 2007.*

Brik, V.B. 1997. Basalt Fiber Composite Reinforcement for Concrete. *NCHR-IDEA Program Project Final Report, Transportation Research Board, Washington, DC, 1997.*

Brik, V.B. 2003. Advanced Concept Concrete Using Basalt Fiber/BF Composite Rebar Reinforcement. *Final Report for Highway-IDEA Project 86, Transportation Research Board, February 2003.*

Cripps, A. 2002. *Fibre-reinforced polymer composites in construction.* London: CIRIA 2002.

GangaRao, H.V. et al. 2007. *Reinforced Concrete Design with FRP Composites:* CRC press Boca Raton.

Liu, Q. et al. 2006. Investigation of Basalt Fiber Composite Mechanical Properties for Applications in Transportation. *Polymer Composites 2006*, available online in: Wiley InterScience

Naaman, A.E. 2003. FRP Reinforcements in Structural Concrete: Assessment, Progress and Prospects. *Proceedings of 6th International Symposium on Fiber Reinforced Polymer (FRP) Reinforcement for Concrete Structures (FRPRCS-6) Singapore, July 2003.*

Palmieri, A. et al. 2009a. Basalt Fibers for Reinforcing and Strengthening Concrete. *Proceedings of 9th International Symposium on Fiber Reinforced Polymer (FRP) Reinforcement for Concrete Structures (FRPRCS-9) Sydney, Australia, July 2009.*

Palmieri, A. et al. 2009b. Study of the Fire Behaviour of Structures Strengthened with NSM. *Proceedings of 9th International Symposium on Fiber Reinforced Polymer (FRP) Reinforcement for Concrete Structures (FRPRCS-9) Sydney, Australia, July 2009.*

Sim, J. et al. 2005. Characteristics of basalt fiber as a strengthening material for concrete structures. *Composites Part B: Engineering 36*: 504–512.

Tanano, H. 1997. Tensile Properties at High Temperatures of Continuous Fiber Bars and Deflections of Continuous Fibre Reinforced Concrete Beams under High Temperature Loading. *Non-metallic (FRP) Reinforcement for Concrete* Structures, Japan Concrete Institute, Vol. 2.: 43–50.

Wang, Y.C. et al. 2007. An Experimental Study of the Mechanical Properties of Fibre Reinforced Polymer (FRP) and Steel Reinforcing Bars at Elevated *Temperatures. Journal Composites Structures Part, Elsevier, Vol. 80, 2007*: 131–140.

Concrete Solutions – Grantham, Mechtcherine & Schneck (eds)
© 2012 Taylor & Francis Group, London, ISBN 978-0-415-61622-5

Rehabilitation of reinforced concrete beams with insufficient longitudinal reinforcement lap-splice length using FRP sheets

M.M. Sayed & T.M. Elrakib
Housing & Building National Research Center, Giza, Egypt

ABSTRACT: Experimental investigation was carried out to study the effect of both transverse and longitudinal FRP sheets on bond strength of longitudinal reinforcement in normal strength RC beams. Nine RC rectangular beams were tested in positive bending: five of them were strengthened by transverse FRP wraps in the defected splice region and one beam was strengthened by longitudinal FRP sheet and the other four beams were kept unstrengthened and considered as control specimens. The main parameters included were concrete compressive strength, type of FRP sheets, retrofitting length as a percentage of the lap splice and FRP configuration. The cracking behavior, failure modes, load-deflection relationships and the strains in the longitudinal steel were investigated. The effect of key parameters on the stiffness, ductility and ultimate load was evaluated. It was concluded that the transverse FRP confining system provided a new mechanism whereby most bars over the spliced region could be used more effectively in the stress transfer between steel and concrete leading to a more ductile failure mode combined with an increase in the ultimate load.

1 INTRODUCTION

Parameters affecting the bond strength between reinforcing bars and concrete may be summarized into three major groups. The first one is the components of the concrete mix such as: type of aggregates, additives, binding minerals and the level of concrete strength. The second group which is mainly corresponding to the reinforcing bar itself may be listed as bar diameter, bar surface specifications, bar surface coating, lap splice length and position of the reinforcing bars with respect to each other and to the concrete surface. The rest of the affecting parameters can be classified in the third group like the existence and amount of transverse reinforcement, temperature, corrosion level and the loading history.

According to Azizinamini et al. (1999) bond splitting failure of bars anchored in RC beams with small concrete cover takes place before all bar lugs participate in resisting the applied axial forces producing a non-uniform bond stress distribution. This non-uniform stress distribution is chiefly responsible for the lower bond stress achieved. Previous experimental researches reported in the literature have shown the most famous and effective methods for enhancing the bond strength in the lap splice regions of beams. Najjar, S., et al. (2002) concluded that the use of transverse reinforcement in the form of hoop stirrups can cause higher bond strength levels and more ductile bond

behavior leading to adequate bond strength with a relative shorter lap splice length. Meanwhile, experimental tests carried out by Harjli, M. et al. (1997), showed that the use of steel fibers in the concrete matrix increased both of the tensile strength and toughness of normal strength concrete resulting in higher bond strength and leading to a considerable improvement in ductility for the cases of splitting predominant failure through delaying the splitting failures. In addition, they reported that higher bond strength may be obtained for higher ratios of steel fibers in concrete. Jumma, G et al. (2001) studied the effect of fiber reinforcement on the behavior of lap splices in high strength concrete beams. Results of the study indicated the significance of steel fibers in improving the serviceability and the whole behavior of tested beams.

On the other hand, FRP composites have been used widely for the repair of deteriorated RC elements and they are also used to strengthen existing structures against shear and flexural failures, Sergio, F. et al. (2003) & Tarek, M.B. et al. (2005). FRP-laminated composites, consisting of carbon, aramid, and glass fibers, present significant advantages such as high-strength/weight ratio, light weight, ease of handling and application, elimination of falsework and heavy equipment, faster construction rates, and no corrosiveness. However, a limited number of studies were conducted to investigate strengthening RC beams, with defects in the lap splice zone, with FRP sheets. Bilal S. Hamed et al. (2004) examined the effect of confinement provided by FRP sheets on the bond strength of tension lap splices in high strength concrete beams. They tested ten beams in positive bending and concluded that FRP wraps were effective in improving the bond strength of the lap splices and the mode of failure. Also, they mentioned that more research is needed to study the effect of other key parameters like concrete strength, steel bar size and the application of longitudinal FRP sheets parallel to the beam axis.

2 RESEARCH SIGNIFICANCE

Insufficient anchorage length in flexural members generally results in premature, sudden brittle failures due to inadequate bond strength. The anchorage length may be considered inadequate due to a lower concrete strength, higher reinforcing steel yield strength, or small anchorage length relative to the design specified values. The external application of FRP sheets may well be a solution in case of such deficiencies as the FRP sheets develop a clamping force on the splice region. The literature review has indicated the scarcity of test data on this case. This study evaluates the use of FRP sheets as an alternative tool to enhance the bond strength, ductility and the mode of failure of tension lap splices anchored in RC beams. An experimental program comprising tests of 9 RC beams was conducted. Cracking behavior of the tested beams, mode of failure, load-deflection behavior and the strains in the longitudinal reinforcement are discussed. Moreover, the test results were analyzed and evaluated to demonstrate the effect of the key parameters on the ultimate load, stiffness and deflection ductility.

3 TEST PROGRAM

3.1 *Characteristics of laboratory specimens*

The experimental test program involved 9 RC beams 150 × 300 × 2200 mm designated as B1 to B9. The full splice length was determined according to Egyptian Code of Practice, ECP203-2007. Beams B1 and B2 had a full splice length according to the ECP. Beams B3 and B4 had a shortage in the lap splice length. Beams from B1 to B4 were kept unstrengthened and considered as control beams. On the other hand, Beams B5 to B8 were retrofitted with u shaped FRP sheets with different schemes in the defective splice region. Beam B9 was retrofitted with one layer of longitudinal CFRP sheet and it was also provided with 2-U wrap strips at both ends of the CFRP longitudinal sheet in order to prevent premature laminate debonding and concrete cover

delamination. The main test variables in this study included the concrete compressive strength, type of FRP (carbon and glass) and the configuration of FRP sheets in the splice region (transverse and longitudinal layers), Table 1. All beams were constructed in the lab of the Housing and Building National Research Center and tested under positive bending moment. Details of beams are shown in Figures 1–4. All beams were reinforced on both tension and compression sides with two longitudinal steel bars 12 mm diameter. To avoid shear failure, 8 mm steel stirrups were provided in the shear span for all beams at spacing 150 mm. The predetermined lap splice locations had no steel stirrups to eliminate their effect on the investigated bond strength. A concrete clear cover of approximately 25 mm was provided for all beams.

3.2 *Materials*

The longitudinal reinforcing bars had a measured yield stress of 570 MPa and stirrups had a measured yield stress of 300 MPa. The average

Table 1. Details of the tested beams.

Beam No.	Fcu MPa	Steel rft lap splice (Ls) mm	FRP* sheets	R.L**
B1	25	1.3 Ld = 750	–	–
B2	15	1.3 Ld = 960	–	–
B3	25	300	–	–
B4	15	300	–	–
B5	25	300	T-1CFRP	100% Ls
B6	15	380	T-1CFRP	100% Ls
B7	15	380	T-1GFRP	100% Ls
B8	15	380	T-1CFRP	200% Ls
B9	15	380	L-1CFRP	300% Ls

* T = transverse, L = longitudinal, 1CFRP = one layer of carbon Fiber Reinforced Polymer,
** R.L = retrofitting length

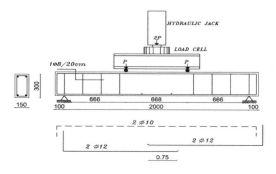

Figure 1. Reinforcement detail of beam B1 and test setup.

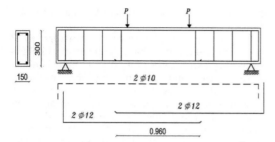

Figure 2. Reinforcement detail of beam B2.

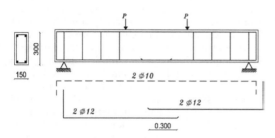

Figure 3. Reinforcement detail of beam B3 and B5.

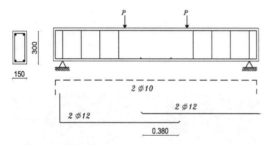

Figure 4. Reinforcement detail of beam B4, B5, B6, B7, and B8.

compressive strength Fcu measured at the time of testing was approximately 15 and 25 MPa. The mixture proportions for the two mixes were as shown in Table 2. FRP sheets used for confinement were unidirectional and were manufactured by S&P (Swiss company). The properties of the fibers and epoxy are listed in Table 3. The fiber-reinforced polymer sheets were applied on the beams at least 28 days after casting and 14 days before testing to allow full curing of the epoxy.

3.3 Strengthening technique

Special consideration was given to surface preparation before bonding the FRP sheets to the concrete surface according to the Egyptian Code for Fiber Reinforced Polymers, 208-2005. The surface was

Table 2. Mix proportions of the two concrete grades *.

Cement	Dolomite	Sand	Water	Fcu, MPa
300	1307	650	190	15
400	1400	700	145	25

* All quantities are in kg/m³.

Table 3. Mechanical properties of the used FRP sheets.

Type	t*	Tensile strength, MPa	Elongation at break%	Elastic modulus, GPa
CFRP	0.11	3900	1.55	240
GFRP	0.14	1700	2.88	65

t* = thickness of sheet in mm.

prepared by removing a layer of concrete of thickness 5–10 mm around the specimen at the predetermined locations by the use of manual hammer. A suitable grout (Sikadur41) was used in leveling the sides of the roughened locations and in rounding their sharp corners at least one day prior to the application of the FRP sheets then, all the loose particles were removed using compressed air or blower and the surface of the grout was mechanically smoothed. FRP sheets were spread and cut in the appropriate dimensions. Epoxy was prepared in accordance with manufacturer's directions. Finally the epoxy-saturated FRP sheets were wrapped around the perimeter of the section with a U shape in such a way that FRP fabrics were placed with an orientation perpendicular to the reinforcing bar axis except for beam B9. Each FRP layer was impregnated with resin using a steel roller and coated with epoxy adhesive. Beam B9 was strengthened using a different configuration as the CFRP fabrics were placed with an orientation parallel to the reinforcing bar axis. In addition, 2 U-wrap strips were provided at the both ends of the CFRP sheet to reduce the possibility of sheet debonding or concrete cover delamination.

3.4 Test setup and instrumentation

All beams were tested using a 2000 kN double portal, open reaction frame. Load was applied using a hydraulic jack of 400 kN capacity in compression. The hydraulic jack was attached to the cross girder of the double portal frame. The jack was equipped with a tension/compression load cell of ± 680 kN capacity to measure the applied load. The load was distributed equally by a spreader beam to two points along the specimen to generate a constant moment region at midspan. Beams were supported

Figure 5.   Test setup & instrumentation.

on 100 cm tall concrete pedestals so that the researchers could safely observe the bottom face of beams during the tests. Electronic strain gauges were bonded to both steel reinforcement and FRP sheets to measure the actual strain. A linear variable differential transducer (LVDT) with stroke ± 20 cm and sensitivity 0.1 mm was mounted at the bottom side of the midspan for each specimen, Figure 5. All beams were tested 14 days at least following the application of the FRP sheets. At each load stage, the electrical strain gauges, load cells and (LVDTs) voltages were fed into the data acquisition system. The voltage excitations were read, transformed and stored as microstrains, force and displacement by means of a computer program that runs under the Lab View software. However, the cracking pattern was monitored with each load stage. The test was continued after the ultimate load in order to evaluate the post peak behavior of the tested beams.

4   TEST RESULTS AND ANALYSIS

4.1   *General behavior and mode of failure*

The test specimens were loaded to failure and the observed behavior in terms of cracking, modes of failure and total load-deflection response were recorded. Generally, for all the unstrengthened specimens, two major flexural cracks initially appeared at the critical sections adjacent to the end of the lap splice zone and extended up to failure. By increasing the applied load, minor diagonal tension cracks appeared. For the control beams B1, B2 with full lap splice length and no FRP wrapping, failure occurred by yielding of steel followed by compression failure of the concrete at the midspan combined with splitting the concrete cover within the lap splice zone. For the other control beams B3, B4 with inadequate lap splice length and no FRP wrapping, failure occurred suddenly after the formation of longitudinal splitting cracks which initiated in the bottom cover of the tension side and the load had a noticeable drop. However, the failure could be classified as a pronounced brittle

mode and the steel reinforcing bars did not reach the yield point.

On the other hand, beams with transverse FRP sheets showed a noticeable enhancement in behavior as they exhibited a more ductile failure mode. It was noticed that the clamping force developed by the FRP sheets delayed the propagation of longitudinal splitting cracks which were observed in the bottom and side concrete cover within the splice region. After reaching the peak, the load dropped gradually as the deflection increased. The test ended when failure of FRP wraps occurred with rupture of sheets. Based on test observations, it could be said that FRP confining system provided a new mechanism whereby most bars over the spliced region could be used more effectively in the stress transfer between steel and concrete leading to a more ductile failure mode combined with a small increase in the ultimate load. However, the final mode of failure was a semi ductile-split one. However, B9 with longitudinal FRP sheets showed a relative increase in the ultimate load compared with B4 followed by a sudden drop after the formation of longitudinal splitting cracks, which initiated in the bottom cover of the tension side combined with a major flexural crack at the critical section adjacent to the end of the lap splice zone. Then, the applied load maintained constant with increasing deflection for a short period and finally a pronounced rupture of the longitudinal FRP sheets occurred, Figures 6–8.

Figure 6.   Failure of B1 (control beam with full lap splice).

Figure 7.   Failure of B4 (control beam with defected lap splice).

Figure 8.   Failure of B5 (T-1CFRP, RL = 100% Ls).

Figure 9.   Failure of B8 (T-1CFRP, RL = 200% Ls).

Figure 10.   Failure of B9 (L-1CFRP, RL = 300% Ls).

4.2   *Load-deflection behavior*

The applied load was plotted against the vertical deflection measured at midspan for all tested beams as shown in Figures 11 and 12. For beams B1, B3 and B5, a noticeable increase in the ultimate load and deflection of the strengthened beam B5 compared with the control beam B3 was found. The load-deflection history, after the ultimate load was reached, represents an indication of the improved ductility when FRP sheets were used. The load deflection relationship for beams B2, B4 and B6, shown in Figure 12, leads to the same observations. While the unstrengthened control beams with defective lap splice length experienced almost complete loss of resistance after reaching the ultimate load, the load of beams with transverse FRP sheets confining the lap splice zone dropped gradually. It was clearly observed that load-deflection relations for beams B1 and B2 represent the upper limit for all other specimens

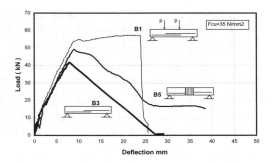

Figure 11.   Load deflection relationship for beams B1, B3, and B5.

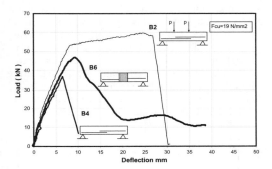

Figure 12.   Load deflection relationship for beams B2, B4, and B6.

Table 4.   Experimental results of the tested beams.

Beam No.	P_u (kN)	Δ_f mm	Δ_y mm	*$\varepsilon_u \times 10^{-6}$
B1	57.1	24.4	8.56	5100
B2	59.2	26.5	8.69	4000
B3	41.6	12.5	7.14	1993
B4	37.1	8.5	6.58	2712
B5	49.3	18.3	7.469	4334
B6	47.2	13.6	6.32	3370
B7	45.1	14.3	6.36	–
B8	59.5	23.5	8.55	4200
B9	43.9	12.3	8.2	1500

*ε_u = steel strain at ultimate load.

as well as load-deflection relations for beams B3 and B4 representing the lower limit. Ultimate load P_u, deflection at failure Δ_f, defection at yield Δ_y and steel strain at ultimate load ε_u for all of the tested beams are shown in Table 4.

4.3   *Strains in longitudinal steel reinforcement*

Strain measurements on the longitudinal reinforcing steel bars of most of the tested beams recorded tension steel strain values in the range of 2000 to 5000 μ_s at the ultimate load level which indicate that the longitudinal reinforcement developed yielding, where μ_s means micro strain = strain $\times 10^{-6}$.

The steel strain values for all tested beams, except for B3 and B9, were much higher than the yield strain $\varepsilon_y = 2000$ μs indicating that the longitudinal reinforcing steel of these beams entered the hardening range leading to ductile behavior. Figure 13 shows the strains developed in the longitudinal reinforcement for beams B1, B3 and B5 where Figure 14 shows the steel strain for beams B2, B4 and B6. As shown in these figures, the difference in the strain values between the control specimen B1 and the strengthened one, B5, was small and the strain of both recorded about 5000 μs at ultimate load, while the maximum strain of B3 hardly reached 1993 μs indicating that using FRP wraps allowed steel bars along the splice zone to participate more effectively in the stress transfer within the lap splice zone. By investigating Figure 14 for beams B2, B4 and B6, it was found that the steel strain of the unstrengthened beam B4 passed the yielding strain value and consequently,

it can be drawn that the lap splice length required by the provision of Egyptian Code, ECP203-2007, is conservative for reinforced concrete beams made of low quality concrete.

4.4 Stiffness and ductility

The stiffness of each beam was evaluated as the slope of the linear ascending part of the load deflection curve and presented in Table 5. It can obviously be noticed that the unstrengthened control beams (B3, B4) had relatively lower stiffness compared with those with full lap splice length (B1 and B2). Meanwhile, beams with U-shaped CFRP sheets (B5, B6 and B8) had approximately the same stiffness compared with unstrengthened control beams (B3, B4) indicating that the use of transverse FRP sheets did not affect the flexural stiffness of the strengthened beams. Referring to Table 5, using longitudinal FRP sheets in B9 resulted in an increase in the stiffness value as the CFRP directly contributed in the flexural strength of the tested beam.

Ductility is the ability of a RC member to sustain related large inelastic deformation without an important reduction in load resisting capacity. Many authors adopted the displacement ductility index, μ_Δ, to evaluate the ductility level of RC beams, Sergio, F. et al. (2003) & Tarek, M.B. et al. (2005). However, this index, μ_Δ, was used in the current study to calculate ductility of the tested beams using Equation 1 and as presented in Table 5.

$$\text{Displacement ductility index, } \mu_\Delta = \Delta_f/\Delta_y \quad (1)$$

where: Δ_f = Deflection at 80% of the ultimate load on the descending branch of the load-deflection curve, Δ_y = Deflection at yield load was calculated from the load-deflection curve as the corresponding displacement of the intersection of the secant stiffness at a load value of 80% of the ultimate lateral load and the tangent at the ultimate load.

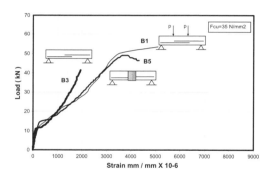

Figure 13. Load- steel strain relationship for beams B1, B3, and B5.

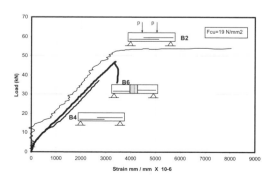

Figure 14. Load steel strain relationship for beams B2, B4, and B6.

Table 5. Stiffness and ductility of the tested beams.

Beam No.	Stiffness N/mm	$\mu_\Delta = \Delta_f/\Delta_y$
B1	6670	2.85
B2	6700	3.05
B3	6100	1.75
B4	5900	1.29
B5	5800	2.45
B6	6000	2.15
B7	5400	2.25
B8	6300	2.75
B9	6950	1.5

Ductility indices of the unstrengthened control beams B3 and B4 were lower than those for beams with full lap splice length B1 and B2. On the other hand, beams with U-shaped FRP sheets had a meaningful increase in the ductility indices compared with B3 and B4. For instance, using CFRP in beams B5 and B6 increased the displacement ductility indices by 40% and 66% compared to B3 and B4, respectively. Generally, it can be concluded that strengthening the lap splice defected beams B3 and B4 restored a noticeable part of their ductility.

5 EFFECT OF KEY PARAMETERS

5.1 *Effect of type of FRP*

Figure 15 and Table 4 show test results of beam B6 and B7. Both beams were identical in terms of concrete compressive strength, reinforcement ratio, and wrapping schedule and only the type of FRP was different. B6 was retrofitted by one layer of CFRP while B7 was retrofitted by one layer of GFRP. The ultimate load of B6 and B7 was 27% and 22% higher than that of the control beam B4 and lower than the ultimate load of control beam B2 by 20% and 23% respectively. In addition, the displacement ductility indices of B6 and B7 were increased by 66.66% and 74.42%, respectively compared with the ductility index of the defected beam B4 however, their ductility indices were lower than the ductility index of the control beam B2 by 29.50% and 26.22% respectively. The overall structural behavior of beams B6 and B7 showed that the type of FRP sheets, glass or carbon, confining the splice zone had no significant effect on load-deflection behavior or mode of failure.

5.2 *Effect of length of the strengthening zone*

The effect of length of the strengthened zone for the retrofitted beams can be discussed by comparing the behavior of beams B6 and B8 which were identical in all aspects except for the length of the strengthened region. Figure 16 presents the load deflection relation for B6 with a strengthened zone equal to 100% of the lap splice length and B8 with a strengthened length equal to 200% of the same lap splice length. Figure 11 shows the steel strain of beams B6 and B8 in comparison with control beams B2 and B4. Among the strengthened specimens, B8 recorded the highest value of ultimate load. The ultimate loads of the strengthened beams B6 and B8 were higher than that of the defected beam B2 by 27% and 60% respectively. In addition, the ultimate load of beam B6 was lower than that of the control beam B2 by 20%, whereas the ultimate load of the strengthened beam B8 was almost identical to the ultimate load of the control beam B2. Both beams B6 and B8 had post peak ductile behavior, however, the strengthened beam, B8, had a significant increase in both the ultimate load and ductility in comparison with beam B6. As shown in Tables 4, 5 the ultimate load and ductility index of beam B8 were higher than that of beam B6 by 26% and 27% respectively. The pronounced improved behavior of beam B8 in comparison with beam B6 indicate that the negative effect of the defective splice zone on the beam behavior practically extends beyond the lap splice area and the extension of the U-shape FRP wraps is practically required to maintain the structural behavior of the defected beam.

Regarding steel strain, the strain values of both beams B6 and B8 were higher than the yield strain value (2000×10^{-6}). However, the load steel strain relation of strengthened beam B8 was almost identical to the load steel strain of the control specimen B2. As seen in Table 4, the steel strain of beam B6 was lower than the steel strain of the control beam B2 by 15.75% whereas, the steel strains of the strengthened beam B8 and control beam B2 were almost identical, 4200×10^{-6} mm/mm and

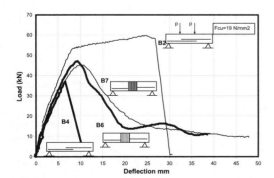

Figure 15. Load deflection relationship for beams B2, B4, B6, and B7.

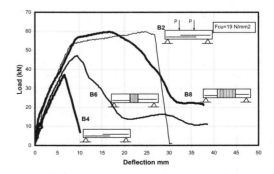

Figure 16. Load deflection relationship for beams B2, B4, B6, and B8.

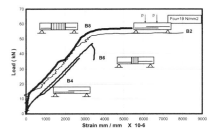

Figure 17. Load steel strain relationship for beams B2, B4, B6, and B8.

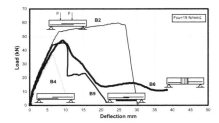

Figure 18. Load deflection relationship for beams B2, B4, B6, and B9.

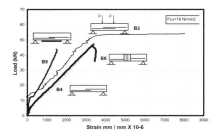

Figure 19. Load steel strain relationship for beams B2, B4, B6, and B9.

4000×10^{-6} mm/mm respectively. The similarity of load-strain behaviors of beams B8 and B2 indicates that extending the wrapping zone beyond the defected lap splice zone effectively helps the lapped reinforcement bars to reach their full capacity, Figure 17.

5.3 *Effect of strengthening method*

Figure 18 shows the load deflection relation for Beams B6 and B9 while Figure 19 shows the load steel strain for those beams. The results of the control beam B2 and the defective one, B4, were plotted in Figures 18, 19 to represent the upper and lower limit respectively. Comparison between B6 and B9 indicates that beam B9 had a relatively higher flexural stiffness: the flexural stiffness of beam B9 was higher than that of beam B6 by 16% but it was almost identical to the flexural stiffness of control beam B2. This previous result is attributed to the existence of the FRP sheet in the extreme tension concrete fibers of beam B9. The load deflection curve of beam B9 had a discontinuous part in the post peak zone and this was due to the mode of failure of this beam which was started by splitting tension crack in the lap splice zone followed by complete rupture of the FRP as seen in Figure 10.

Figure 18 and Table 4 show that the ultimate load of B6 and B9 was 27.00% and 18.60% higher than that of the control beam B4. The displacement ductility indexes were 1.29, 2.25, and 1.50 for B4, B6, and B9 respectively, indicating that using longitudinal FRP sheets added approximately nothing to the ductility index. In addition, the strain developed in the longitudinal reinforcement of beam B9 was lower than the yield strain (2000×10^{-6}), Figure 19. It could be concluded that wrapping of the beams by FRP in the lap-splice zone is more effective than strengthening them longitudinally in the tension side mainly from ductility point of view.

5.4 *Effect of concrete compressive strength*

Figure 20 shows the load deflection relation of beams B1, B2, B3, and B4. Beams B1 and B2 represent the control beams which had reinforcement lap splice lengths according to the provisions of the Egyptian code while, beams B3 and B4 represent defective beams which had 40% of the lap splice lengths assigned for beams B1 and B2, respectively. In addition, Figure 21 shows the load deflection of the retrofitted beams B5 and B6 in comparison with the control beams B1 and B2. Although the compressive strength of beam B2 (19 MPa) was lower than that of B1 (35 MPa) by 45.70%, the ultimate load was slightly higher than that of beam B1 by 3.50% in clear contradiction with the expected behavior. The previous behavior could be attributed to two reasons; the first is the lap splice length of beam B2 which was 960 mm longer than the distance between the two-point loads (600 mm) and consequently the beam actually contained four longitudinal steel bars at the constant moment region, the second is due to the fact that concrete compressive strength has a minor effect on the ultimate strength of the flexural members. The load deflection responses of the defective beams B3 and B4 were approximately similar regarding the flexural stiffness. However, beam B4 was more negatively affected by the shortage of lap splice length from the view point of ultimate load and ductility. Reducing the concrete compressive strength by 45.70% for beam B2 in comparison with B1 resulted in reduction of ultimate load and ductility by 10.90% and 26.30% respectively, which could conclude that Egyptian Code equation of calculating lap splice length is conservative

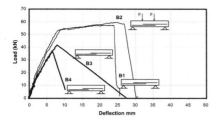

Figure 20. Load deflection relationship for beams B1, B2, B3 & B4.

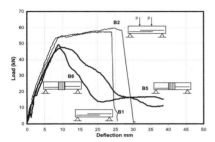

Figure 21. Load deflection relationship for beams B1, B2, B5 & B6.

for low quality concrete. The load deflection relations of the retrofitted beams B5 and B6 shown in Figure 21 support the previous conclusion. As shown in Figure 21, the retrofitted beams B5 and B6 had almost the same behavior although the ductility of beam B6 was slightly lower than that of beam B5 by 12%.

6 CONCLUSIONS

Within the range of the investigated parameters and properties of the materials used in this work, the following conclusions could be drawn:

- Wrapping the insufficient lap splice length zone of reinforced concrete beams that had either normal or low concrete strength by FRP is highly effective in enhancing both the ultimate load and mode of failure. A ductile mode of failure instead of brittle mode was observed for all wrapped beams. In addition, the load deflection flexural stiffness was almost the same for all the tested beams.
- None of the FRP U-shaped strengthened beams had experienced debonding or separation of the sheet at the end of the U-shape and based on the results of the tested beams, no special anchorage system is needed for bonding the FRP sheets on the concrete faces.
- Wrapping the beams in the lap-splice zone by glass fiber Reinforced polymer (GFRP) had comparable structural performance in comparison

with those beams wrapped by carbon fiber reinforced polymer (CFRP). In both cases, the mode of failure changed from brittle mode to ductile one and the enhancement in ultimate load and ductility were approximately the same.
- Increasing the CFRP strengthening length beyond the defective lap splice length zone completely restored the beam performance including ultimate load and ductility. In general, it is preferable to extend the strengthened zone beyond the defected lap splice region.
- Wrapping of the beams by (CFRP) in the lap splice zone was more effective than the strengthening of the beams longitudinally in the tension zone.
- The lap splice length as required by the provision of Egyptian Code, ECP203-2007, is conservative especially for low strength concrete however; shorter lap splice length negatively affects the beam ductility.

REFERENCES

Ashour, A.F., El-Refaie, S.A. & Garrity, S.W. 2004. Flexural strengthening of RC Continues Beams using CFRP Laminates. *Cement & Concrete Composites Journal*, 26: 765–775.

Azizinamini, A., Pavel, R., Hatfield, E. & Ghosh, S.K. 1999. Behavior of Lap Spliced Reinforcing Bars Embedded in HSC. *ACI Structural Journal*, Sep.–Oct. 96(5): 826–835.

ECFRP-208 2005. Egyptian Code for Fiber Reinforced Polymers. *Housing and Building National Research Center, Cairo, Egypt.*

ECP-203 2007. Egyptian Code of the Design and Construction of Reinforced Concrete Structures. *Housing and Building National Research Center, Cairo, Egypt.*

Hamed, B., Harajli, M. & Jumaa, G. 2001. Effect of Fiber Reinforcement on Bond Strength of Tension Lap Splice in HSC. *ACI Structural Journal, Sep.–Oct.*, 98 (5): 638–647.

Hamed, B., Soudki, K., Harajli, M. & Rteil, A. 2004. Experimental and Analytical Evaluation of Bond Strength of Reinforcement in Fiber-Reinforced Polymer-Wrapped high-Strength Concrete beams. *ACI Structural Journal, Nov.–Dec.*, 101 (6): 747–754.

Harajli, M. & Salloukh, K. 1997. Effect of Fibers on Development Splice Strength of Reinforcing Bars in Tension. *ACI Material Journal, Jul.–Aug.* 317–324.

Sergio, F. Brena, Regan, M.B., Sharon, L. Wood, & Michale E.K. 2003. Increasing Flexural Capacity of RC Beams using CFRP Composites. *ACI Structural Journal, Jan.–Feb.* 100(1): 36–46.

Tarek, M.B. & Mohamed, A.K. 2005. Strengthening of Continuous RC Beams Using CFRP Laminates. *The 7th International Conference on Multi-Purpose High Rise Towers and Tall Buildings*, Dubai, UAE.

Concrete Solutions – Grantham, Mechtcherine & Schneck (eds)
© 2012 Taylor & Francis Group, London, ISBN 978-0-415-61622-5

Strengthening of T section RC beams in shear using CFRP

E.E. Etman
Structural Engineering Department, Tanta University, Tanta, Egypt

ABSTRACT: Strengthening reinforced concrete RC beams in shear using Carbon Fiber-Reinforced Polymer (CFRP) has been found to significantly enhance the shear capacity of existing reinforced concrete beams. In previous studies, the use of steel plates bonded externally to RC beams was found to improve the shear performance of these beams. Most of the previous work was conducted on RC beams having rectangular sections. The main objective of this paper is to gain a better understanding and enhance the experimental database of shear behavior of RC T-beams strengthened with Externally Bonded Reinforcement (EBR) system. The present study encompasses some of the important parameters such as the EBR direction of fiber alignment, and strengthening materials made of carbon fiber sheets, steel plates or steel bars for shear strengthening. The contribution of the EBR to the shear capacity of the T beams was computed using three design codes and compared with the experimental output. A series of RC T-beams were experimentally tested where the CFRP and steel strips were carefully aligned and spaced. A reference T beam and a rectangular RC beam were tested as well to explore the effect of the internal shear reinforcement and the existence of the flange on the shear capacity of the beam.

1 INTRODUCTION

Repairing and upgrading existing concrete structures is becoming more obvious due to deterioration of Reinforced Concrete (RC), faults in design, mistakes in construction phases and/or changes in the uses of buildings. The need to lower the cost of maintenance, repair and strengthening techniques while extending the service life of the structures has resulted in new systems, processes, or products to save money and time. The Fiber-Reinforced Polymer (FRP) systems are recently used in the field of strengthening and restoration of buildings.

Numerous research projects have been conducted in the field of using FRP in flexure strengthening, repairing or upgrading (Etman and Beeby 2000, Etman 2004, and Khalil 2004). However, due to its complexity, shear strengthening with FRP, is relatively less documented, Abdelhak Bousselham and Omar Challal (2008). Recently, the interest and popularity in conducting research in the field of shear strengthening or repair has increased. This is clearly indicated by the number of studies devoted to this research field (Bousselham and Chaallal 2006a,b; Carolin and Täljsten 2005a,b; Cao et al. 2005; Zhang et al. 2005; Colotti et al. 2004; Chen and Teng 2003, E. Etman et al. 2001, Sharkawi and Etman 2007, Neil and Lees 2009). These studies, which are mostly experimental, have substantially enhanced the existing database.

The most commonly utilized Fiber-Reinforced Polymers (FRPs) are fibers made of Carbon (C) or Glass (G). These materials can be designed and used in the form of laminates, rods, dry fibers (sheets) adhesively bonded to the concrete, wet lay-up sheets mounted on the surface, or near surface mounted bars or laminate strips in the concrete cover, (Oehlers et al. 2007; Nordin 2003; Täljsten et al. 2003; Nordin and Täljsten 2006; Carolin and Täljsten 2003). The Carbon Fiber-Reinforced Polymer (CFRP) materials have a high potential for manufacturing effective strengthening systems to increase the flexural or shear strength of RC beams. The CFRP have a very low weight to volume ratio, are immune to corrosion, and possess high tensile strength.

For shear strengthening of RC beams, it is common in research to use sheets bonded to either side faces or to sides and soffit of a beam (Externally Bonded Reinforcement (EBR) technique) in continuous or discrete arrangements. The use of CFRP sheets in such applications has been the most researched and applied shear strengthening system (Khalifa and Nanni 2000). If anchorage systems are not used (Sato et al. 1997; Khalifa and Nanni 2000), or if CFRP configurations do not embrace the element to strengthen (Adhikary et al. 2004), experimental research has shown that the maximum tensile stress that can be introduced in the CFRP materials, when the EBR technique is applied is, in general, a small percentage of the tensile strength of the material, since premature debonding of the CFRP is the mandatory failure mode (Bousselham and Chaallal 2004).

In an attempt at developing a more effective technique for structural shear strengthening, De Lorenzis and Nanni (2001) proposed the Near-Surface Mounted (NSM) technique. A nearly constant thickness of the two adhesive layers binding the laminate to the concrete is assured, and the ratio between the bond perimeter and the area of cross section for the laminates is, theoretically, higher than the ratio for round bars. The influence of both the percentage and inclination of the laminates, as well as the effect of beam depth on the performance of the NSM technique for the shear strengthening of small rectangular RC beams without internal stirrups, was recently studied (Barros and Dias 2006).

This paper presents an experimental investigation to study the behaviour of T section RC beams strengthened in shear. The main parameters explored were the effect of the use of different materials for strengthening, configuration of the strengthening application using strips at different spaces and the orientation direction of the strengthening strips.

2 EXPERIMENTAL PROGRAM

The experimental program involved testing of 10 full-scale RC beams. Nine of them were of T-sections and the last had a rectangular section to assess experimentally the contribution of the flange to the shear strength of the T section. In this way, its effect can be isolated and in this case only the contribution of the strengthening scheme is determined. The seven specimens, (to be strengthened), had a similar default internal shear reinforcement design to assure failure in shear after strengthening. To guarantee that shear failure would occur only within the left side shear span of the beam (L_L), internal shear reinforcement

(stirrups) were increased in the right side shear span (L_R). Stirrups 6 mm spaced at 50 mm were applied in the right side shear of the beam "L_R", against almost no stirrups (6 mm@500 mm) in the left side shear span "L_L". All tension and compression reinforcement were kept the same for all specimens. In addition to two reference beams, a T section beam (TR1) and a rectangular section beam (RR3), both having the same internal reinforcement and concrete dimensions, except that the flange was omitted for the R section, were tested. Details of internal reinforcement and geometry of tested specimens are described in Figure 1 and Table 1.

For the purpose of comparison, a fully, internally beam, reinforced in shear was considered in this research called (TR2). Figure 2 shows the concrete dimensions and the details of reinforcement for the tested beam.

All specimens were cast using concrete having a characteristic compressive strength of 21 MPa. Compression reinforcement, stirrup reinforcement as well as external steel plates were made of steel grade 240/350, however, the tension reinforcement was made of high tensile steel 360/520. The CFRP sheets used for external strengthening had an ultimate tensile strength of dry fibers 4300 N/mm², modulus of elasticity 238 GPa and ultimate strain at break 1.7%. A wet lay-up technique was used to bond the sheets to the concrete. Epoxy adhesive was used to bond the CFRP sheets. The epoxy had a tensile strength 30 N/mm², modulus of elasticity 3.8 GPa and 0.9% elongation at break.

2.1 Details of strengthened specimens

Six T-section specimens were strengthened externally in shear using either Carbon Fiber Reinforced Polymer (CFRP) sheets strips or steel plate strips. Horizontal, vertical and inclined configurations were used for the proposed external shear strengthening

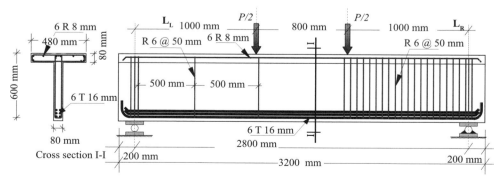

Figure 1. Concrete dimension and RFT details for tested beams.

Table 1. Details of the tested beams.

| Description and beam notation | Shear reinforcement system for the left shear span L_L | | | | |
	Internal shear reinforcement	External shear reinforcement	Percentage %	Spacing (S) mm	Orientation angle (Θ_f)
Reference T-sec. (TR1)	Steel stirrups R6@500 mm	N/A	0.14	500	90
Reference T-sec. (TR2)	Steel stirrups R6@5 mm	N/A	1.41	50	90
Reference R-sec. (RR3)	Steel stirrups R6@500 mm	N/A	0.14	500	90
Strengthened T-Sec (TSCV)	Steel stirrups R6@500 mm –	– 11 strip of CFRP sheets (0.11 × 25 mm²) on both beam sides	0.14 0.08	500 90	90 90
Strengthened T-Sec (TSCH)	Steel stirrups R6@500 mm –	– 2 layers, 5 strips of CFRP sheets (0.11 × 25 mm²) on both beam sides	0.14 N/A	500 100	90 0
Strengthened T-Sec TSCI	Steel stirrups R6@500 mm –	– 11 strip of CFRP sheets (0.11 × 25 mm²)on both beam sides	0.14 0.11	500 90	90 60
Strengthened T-Sec (TSSV)	Steel stirrups R6@500 mm –	– 11 steel strip (1.25 × 25 mm²) on both beam sides	0.14 0.07	500 90	90 90
Strengthened T-Sec (TSSH)	Steel stirrups R6@500 mm –	– 5 steel strips (2.5 × 25 mm²) on both beam sides	0.14 N/A	500 100	90 0
Strengthened T-Sec (TSSI)	Steel stirrups R6@500 mm –	– 11 steel strip (1.25 × 25 mm²) on both beam sides	0.14 0.10	500 90	90 60
Strengthened T-Sec (TSSB)	Steel stirrups R6@500 mm –	– 11 steel bars (73.5 mm²) on both beam sides	0.14 0.08	500 200	90 90

systems, In addition to one T-section specimen that was strengthened externally through the use of vertical steel bars. The internal shear reinforcement in the left L_L side was kept constant at 0.14% while in the right L_R side, it was kept at 1.41%. The external shear strengthening ranged between 0.07% and 0.10%. The percentage of internal shear reinforcement was calculated using the following equation:

$$\rho_{sw} = \frac{A_{sw}}{b_w S} \times 100 \qquad (1)$$

where:
A_{sw} = area of web reinforcement for one stirrup
b_w = beam width
S = spacing between stirrups.

The external CFRP shear strengthening percentage was calculated using the following equation as stated by Salvador J. E. Dias and Joaquim A. O. Barros (2008):

$$\rho_{fw} = \frac{2\,t_f\,b_f}{b_w S_f \sin\theta_f} \times 100 \qquad (2)$$

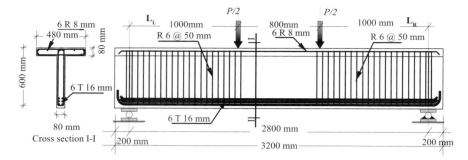

Figure 2. Concrete geometry and reinforcement details of TR2.

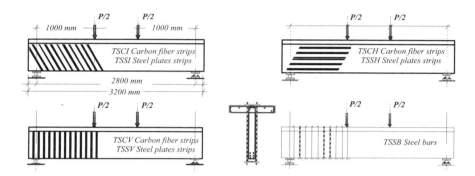

Figure 3. Configuration of proposed strengthening technique.

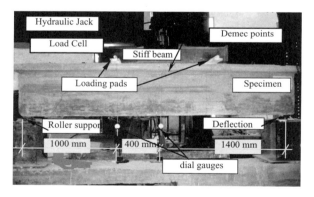

Figure 4. Test setup and instrumentation.

However, the equation can be used for external steel strengthening with the following modification:

$$\rho_{fw} = \frac{2\,t_f\,b_f}{b_w S_f \sin\theta_f} \times \frac{f_y}{f_t} \times 100 \qquad (3)$$

Where

t_f = thickness of external strengthening strips (CFRP sheets or steel plates)

b_f = width of external strengthening strips (CFRP sheets or steel plates)

S_f = spacing of external strips

Θ_f = orientation angle of external strips

f_y = yield strength of steel plates
f_t = ultimate tensile strength of CFRP sheets.

The details of external strengthening are shown in Figure 3.

2.2 *Test setup and instrumentations*

The beams were tested in four-point bending. The load was applied with a hydraulic jack. To avoid local failure under the loading pads, the size of the loading pads was taken as 130 mm long by 520 mm wide, to cover the width of the flange of the beam and extend 20 mm from each side as recommended by Neil A. Hoult and Janet M. Lees (2009). Deflections were measured using 2 mechanical dial gauges of accuracy 0.01 mm spaced as shown in the Figure. Strain gauges were also placed at the mid height of the internal steel stirrups. The test set up is shown in Figure 4.

3 TEST RESULTS AND DISCUSSIONS

Figure 5 shows the load deflection relationships of reference beams TR1, TR2 and RR3. Both TR1 and TR2 (T section beams) showed almost 50% less deflection than RR3 (reference rectangular section beam) at about half the ultimate load of beam RR3. This is mainly attributed to the existence of the flange in the T-section that resulted in a higher stiffness than the R-section. The existence of the flange showed 29% increase in the shear capacity of the section compared to the R-section. The internal shear reinforcement in beam TR2 showed about 16% increase in the shear capacity than reference beam TR1.

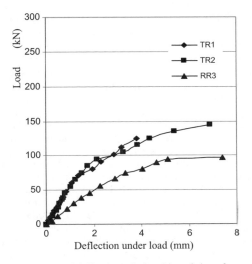

Figure 5. Load deflection relationships of the reference tested beams.

Figure 6 shows the relationship between loads and deflections of specimens strengthened externally using either CFRP strips or steel strips or bars, bonded vertically, horizontally or inclined at 60°. In this figure, a comparison of the load-deflection relationships between reference and strengthened specimens is presented.

It is easily noted that at about 50% of the ultimate load of the reference beam TR1, there were no evident difference in deflection between the strengthened and reference beams. However, after the beginning of the first shear crack, the effect of different strengthening configuration was clear in the form of less deflection at the same load level. However, the effect of type of strengthening on the loads deflection relationship was slightly different. All the nine tested beams initially had approximately similar stiffness. However, the stiffness of the tested beams began to diverge between 70 and 80 kN as shown in Figure 6. This was to be expected since the shear cracks began to appear for the reference beam TR1 at this load. The control specimen TR1 had the largest reduction in stiffness after cracking due to the absence of any additional external shear reinforcement to delay and minimize crack openings and thus reduce deflections in tested beams.

The unstrengthened control specimen TR1 failed in shear at load (P) = 125 kN. All strengthened specimens showed higher failure load and lower deflection. However the increase in ultimate load and the reduction in deflection was the lowest for tested beams with a horizontal orientation of strengthening while it exhibited the highest increase in ultimate load and lowest deflection with tested beams having inclined orientation of strengthening.

Specimens strengthened with different materials, CFRP or steel plates, having the same orientation showed that the use of CFRP strips demonstrated minimal increase in ultimate load and a minor reduction in deflection capacity of the tested beams. For the vertical orientation, specimen TSCV failed at (P) = 231 kN and showed 5% increase in ultimate load when compare with TSSV which failed at 220 kN. Quite to the contrary, the maximum deflection of TSCV was 5.25 mm which was about 7% lower than that exhibited by TSSV (5.65 mm). For the horizontal orientation, specimen TSCH exhibited 215 kN ultimate load which was 4.87% higher than TSSH that failed at 205 kN. The difference in deflection was almost negligible. For specimens with the inclined strengthening orientation, specimen TSCI showed 12% and 4.5% higher ultimate load and deflection, respectively, than TSSI.

It can be also noted that the external shear strengthening delayed the occurrence of the first

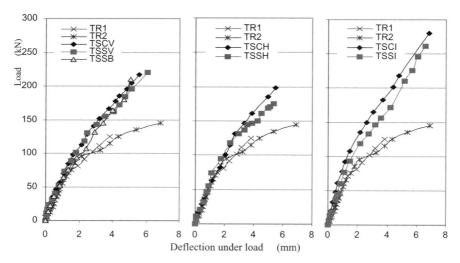

Figure 6. Load deflection relationships of the strengthened tested beams.

shear cracks. Beams strengthened externally with CFRP strips showed higher first shear crack load compared to specimens strengthened externally with either steel strips or bars. On the other hand, the orientation of the strengthening again showed that it had a positive effect on delaying the first shear crack: the inclined orientation demonstrated the ultimate delay in the first shear crack. To assess exactly the contribution of each type of strengthening to the ultimate shear capacity of the section, the tested beams were reinforced and strengthened to fail in shear. This explains why there was no significant difference in the mode of failure.

The maximum load attained by each specimen as well as the percentage increase in capacity, the maximum mid-span deflection, the first shear crack load and the failure modes are given in Table 2. The maximum mid-span deflection is taken as the maximum deflection measured while the applied load was still within 5% of the maximum load.

From Figure 7, it can be seen that the orientation of the external strengthening affects the ultimate load and deflection of the tested specimens. The load capacity of specimen TSCI was 280 kN which was 21% higher than TSCV that failed at 231 kN and 30% higher than TSCH that failed at 215 kN. The same trend was noted with specimens externally strengthened with steel strips. The specimen TSSI which failed at 250 kN exhibited 13.6% higher failure load than TSSV that failed at 220 kN, while TSSI with the inclined orientation of strengthening illustrated 22% higher failure load than TSSH with the horizontal strengthening strips which failed at 205 kN.

Figure 8 shows the shear crack of the different tested specimens. The first shear crack load seems to be affected dramatically by the external shear strengthening reinforcement. When increasing the internal shear reinforcement in specimen TR1 for the left shear span L_L to be the same as the maximum contained in the right shear span L_R, the increase in first shear crack load was 5.9% compared to reference beam TR1. However, using bonded external strips demonstrated an increase in the shear crack load that ranged between 27.1% and 85% than the reference beam TR1.

The effect of the used strengthening material is easily identified. It is evident that the use of carbon fiber strips was more efficient than using the steel strips, whatever the orientation of the strips. The use of CFRP strips in specimens TSCV and TSCI showed 16.6% and 5.3% higher improvement in first shear crack load compared to specimens TSSV and TSSI, respectively. This was not the same trend with specimen TSCH that exhibited 22% less shear crack than TSSH. This seems to be a result of premature local debonding of the horizontal CRFP strips at the plane of the intersection between shear crack and the CFRP strips.

Also the orientation of the external strengthening displayed noticeable difference in its effect on the first shear crack load. The minimum increase in shear was noted for the specimens with horizontal orientation of strips (TSCH and TSSH) and ranged between 27.1% and 34.6% than TR1. On the other hand, specimens TSSI and TSCI that were externally strengthened with bonded inclined strips exhibited a higher first shear crack load of 80.7% and 85%, respectively, compared to TR1.

Table 2. Summary of the tested specimens' results.

| Specimen | Ultimate capacity | | Maximum mid-span deflection (mm) | First shear crack | | Failure mode |
	Ultimate load (kN)	% increase versus TR1		Load (kN)	% increase versus TR1	
TR1	125	–	3.62	70.8	–	Shear failure
TR2	145	16	6.10	75.0	5.9	Shear + Local bearing failure
TSCV	231	84.8	5.25	107.0	59.6	Shear failure
TSSV	220	76.0	5.65	113.0	51.1	Shear failure + debonding
TSSB	210	68.0	4.92	96.0	35.6	Shear failure
TSCH	215	72.0	5.33	90.0	27.1	Shear failure + local debonding
TSSH	205	64.0	5.37	95.3	34.6	Shear failure with debonding
TSCI	280	124.0	6.70	131.0	85.0	Shear failure with debonding
TSSI	250	100.0	6.41	128.0	80.7	Shear failure + local debonding

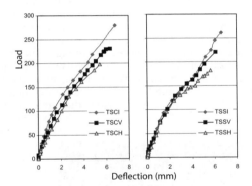

Figure 7. Effect of the orientation of strengthening material on load-deflection relations.

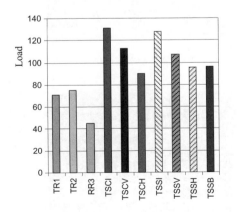

Figure 8. The first shear crack load for different tested specimens.

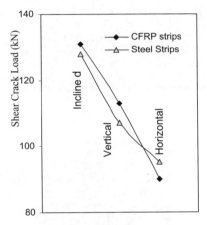

Figure 9. Effect of the type and orientation of strengthening material on shear crack load.

The middle improvement in first shear crack load was attained by the vertical bonded strips TSSV and TSCV as it showed 51.1% and 59.6% compared to TR1, as shown in Figure 9.

3.1 Effect of the type and orientation of strengthening material on shear crack load

The existence of the bonded external shear reinforcement seems to hinder effectively the first shear crack and consequently enhances the shear force carried by aggregate interlock. This result correlates well with shear models that suggest aggregate interlock is the primary shear force carrying mechanism in the concrete such as the Modified Compression Field Theory (MCFT) (Vecchio and Collins 1986). Although it is not bonded, the existence of external vertical bars in TSSB compared to the steel strips in tested specimen TSSV showed similar efficiency regarding shear crack and failure loads.

4 FAILURE MECHANISM

The failure mechanism, displayed by either strengthened or reference T specimens, was mainly identical to the typical failure mechanism used for the shear analysis of the rectangular reinforced concrete beams. The failure shape of the specimen with rectangular section is shown in Figure 10. The difference between the rectangular and the Tee section is that the diagonal tension crack that

Figure 10.   Failure of tested Specimen RR3.

formed in the web extended to the longitudinal bars where it began running along the length of these bars towards the support, instigating dowel action. The other tip of the crack extended to the flange–web interface. Near failure, the externally bonded strips started to debond as shown in Figure 11. The strips with shorter anchorage beyond the crack line were noted to debond before other strips. Specimens strengthened with bonded strips showed only one major shear crack extending between the loading line and support, as shown in Figure12. However, specimen TSSB that was strengthened with external unbonded bars displayed more than one major crack as depicted in Figure 13. Specimen TSCH that was strengthened with CFRP horizontal strips was noted to have earlier debonding started at the tips of the cracks as shown in Figure 14.

At failure, the previous mentioned specimens exhibited a crack on the edge of the flange. This crack appeared to correspond to a diagonal tension splitting of the flange. The crack on the edge of the flange continued on the under-side of the flange to meet with the diagonal tension crack at the flange–web interface as one continuous crack. As the load approached the ultimate load, the crack at the flange–web interface started to propagate into the underside of the flange at an angle inclined to the transverse directions of the beam. In some specimens, at the failure load, this crack on the underside of the flange continued along the length of the

Figure 11.   Samples of failure by debonding of strips as depicted in tested beams (TSCV) and (TSCI).

Figure 12.   One major shear crack.

Figure 13.   Two major cracks.

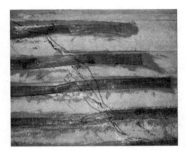

Figure 14.   Failure of tested beam TSCH.

span. In addition it was also noted that cracking appeared on the top surface of the flange.

5   STRAIN IN STIRRUPS

The strain carried by the stirrups is taken as a tool that represents the amount of strains carried by the strengthening strips. Figure 15 shows the strain in the stirrups for the reference beams TR1, TR2 and RR3. It is clear that differences in strain values in stirrups of the three specimens are minimal especially at the very low stages of loading. This is because the stirrups only start to carry loads after the cracking of concrete in shear. Once the concrete cracked in shear, it seems that stirrups started to carry the shear strains however, the specimens were not able to carry any noticeable extra loads. With a closer look, it may be noted that the existence of the flange (T section compared to R section) increased the strain capacity of the beam.

The effect of using different strengthening materials and strengthening orientation on the strain carried by stirrups are shown in Figures 16 and 17 respectively. In Figure 16-a, specimens TSSV, TSCV and TSSB (that were strengthened in the vertical direction using steel strips, CFRP strips or steel

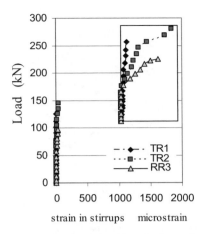

Figure 15.   Load strain relationships of reference beams.

bars respectively) showed almost no difference in stirrups' strains up to the shear cracking of TSSB. Once the shear crack appeared in TSSB, the strain in the stirrups of beam TSSB was higher than that of TSSV or TSCV up to failure. This seems to be a result of bonding the strengthening strips which in turn hindered the growth of shear cracks and carried part of the strain instead of the internal stirrups. It may also be noted that the strains carried by the stirrups in TSCV was lower than that carried by the stirrups in specimen TSSV, which in turn shows that the CFRP strips in TSCV carried more strain than the steel strips in TSSV up to failure. From Figure 16-b, it can be concluded that using steel horizontal strips in specimen TSSH performed better than that in specimen TSCH regarding the strain carried by the strips. This may be attributed to the early debonding of the horizontal CFRP strips; besides that the properties of steel strips are isotropic while it is orthotropic for the CFRP strips (knowing that the strength of the CFRP strips is only in the direction of fibers). Aligning the strips in the inclined direction (nearly perpendicular to the shear main crack) directed us to a conclusion that the CFRP strips in TSCI sustain extra share from the strains than that carried by the steel strips in specimen TSSI, as shown in Figure 16-c.

From the above discussion, it could be concluded that CFRP strips performed better than the steel strips in the vertical and inclined direction, however steel in the horizontal direction was superior than CFRP horizontal strips. It is obvious that, applying strips in the inclined direction carries more shear strain than in the vertical or horizontal direction. This was clear for the CFRP strips however; the difference was not distinguishable with the use of steel strips. This conclusion is noticeable in Figure 17.

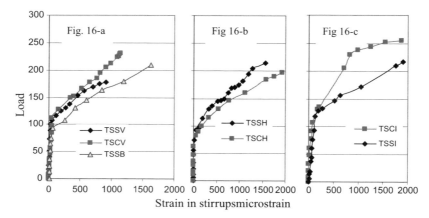

Figure 16. Effect of strengthening technique on strain in stirrups.

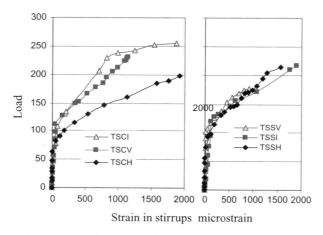

Figure 17. Effect of strengthening orientation on strain in stirrups.

6 CONCLUSIONS

An experimental program was carried out on T cross-section RC beams that were shear strengthened with bonded CFRP or steel strips and unbonded bars. The study was developed to differentiate between the efficiency of strengthening the T section using CFRP or steel. The study also aimed to distinguish the effect of the orientation of strengthening. From the obtained results the following conclusions can be pointed out:

- All strengthened specimens showed lower deflection values than the control specimens after the formation of the first shear crack.
- The existence of the flange showed a 29% increase in the shear capacity of the section compared to the rectangular beam. The internal shear reinforcement in beam TR2 showed about

16% increase in the shear capacity compared to specimen TR1.

- All strengthened specimens exhibited increase in the ultimate load ranging between 64% and 124%. From the strengthening material point of view, the CFRP strips, generally, showed higher ultimate load than steel. This was clear for the vertical and inclined orientation however, the horizontal CFRP strips demonstrated less increase in the ultimate load than the steel horizontal strips. This conclusion may also be drawn for the shear crack load.
- Regardless of the strengthening material (either CFRP or steel), the configuration with inclined strips was the most effective among the adopted shear strengthening orientations. In general, beams strengthened with inclined strips provided increase in the shear strengthening efficacy

larger than those assured by vertical strips. This is justified by the orientation of the shear failure cracks that had a tendency to be almost orthogonal to the strips. The use of horizontal strips demonstrated the least efficiency.

- The load carrying capacity of the beams strengthened with bonded CFRP strips was conditioned by the concrete tensile strength, since the loss of shear strengthening efficiency occurred when the strips debonded with some concrete pieces attached to the debonded length.
- The use of external unbonded vertical steel bars for shear strengthening is a very easy and applicable technique: it showed 68% and 35.6% increase in the ultimate load and shear crack load, respectively.
- Design codes should consider the contribution of the flange of the T section on the shear capacity in analysis as the existence of the flange demonstrated 29% higher shear capacity than the rectangular beam.

REFERENCES

Bousselham, A., and Chaallal, O. (2006a). "Behavior of RC T-beams Strengthened in Shear with CFRP: An Experimental Study." ACI Struct. J., 103(3), 339–347.

Bousselham, A., and Chaallal, O. (2006b). "Effect of Transverse Steel and Shear Span on The Performance of RC Beams Strengthened In Shear with CFRP." Composites, Part B, 37(1), 37–46.

Bousselham, A. and Challal, O. (2008). "Mechanisms of Shear Resistance of Concrete Beams Strengthened in Shear with Externally Bonded FRP" Journal of Composites for Construction, 12(5), 499–512.

Cao, S.Y., Chen, J.F., Teng, J.G., Hao, Z., and Chen, J. (2005). "Debonding in RC Beams Shear Strengthened with Complete FRP Wraps." J.Compos. Constr., 9(5), 417–428.

Carolin, A., and Taljsten, B. (2005a). "Experimental Study of Strengthening for Increased Shear Bearing Capacity." J. Compos. Constr., 9(6), 488–496.

Carolin, A., and Taljsten, B. (2005b). "Theoretical Study of Strengthening for Increased Shear Bearing Capacity." J. Compos. Constr., 9(6), 488–496.

Colotti, V., Spadea, G., and Swamy, R.N. (2004). "Analytical Model to Evaluate Failure Behavior of Plated Reinforced Concrete Beams Strengthened for Shear." ACI Struct. J., 101(6), 755–764.

Chen, J.F., and Teng, J.G. (2003). "Shear Capacity of Fiber-Reinforced Polymer-Strengthened Reinforced Concrete Beams: Fiber Reinforced Polymer Rupture." J. Struct. Eng., 129(5), 615–625.

Dias, S. and Barros, J. (2008). " Shear Strengthening of T Cross Section Reinforced Concrete Beams by Near-Surface Mounted Technique" Journal of Composites for Construction, 12(3), 300–311.

Etman, E. and Beeby, A. (2000). "Interfacial Bond Stress Distribution Along A Composite Plate Bonded to A Reinforced Concrete Beam; Experimental Investigation and Parametric Study". Journal of Cement & Concrete Composites, Vol. 22, pp. 281–291.

Etman, E., Zaher, F. and Beeby, A. (2001) " Experimental Study of Shear-Strengthened Beams" 7th International Conference on Inspection, Appraisal, Repairs & Maintenance of Buildings & Structures, 11–13 September 2001: Nottingham, United Kingdom, pp. 313–319.

Etman, E. (2004), "Behavior of Reinforced Concrete Continuous Beams Repaired and/or Strengthened Under Load Condition". 4th International Conference on Advanced Composite Materials in Bridges and Structures. Calgary, Alberta, Canada July 20–23.

Hoult, N. and Lees, J. (2009). "Efficient CFRP Strap Configurations for The Shear Strengthening of Reinforced Concrete T-Beams" Journal of Composites for Construction, 13(1), 45–52.

Khalil, A. (2004)," Strengthening of RC Continuous Beams in Sagging and Hogging Moment Regions Using CFRP," Scientific Bulletin of Ain-Shams University, Egypt, V.39, No. 1, pp. 75–98.

Sharkawi, A. and Etman, E. (2007). "Effect of Shear Strengthening on The Flexural Behavior of RC Simple Beams Strengthened Externally With FRP Laminates" Twelfth International Colloquium on Structural and Geotechnical Engineering, Ain Shams University, Faculty of Engineering, Department of Structural Engineering, 10–12 Dec. 2007, Cairo – Egypt.

Vecchio, F.J., and Collins, M.P. (1986). "The Modified Compression-Field Theory for Reinforced Concrete Elements Subjected to Shear." ACI Struct. J.,83 (2), 219–231.

Zhang, Z., Hsu, C.-T.T., and Moren, J. (2005). "Shear Strengthening of Reinforced Concrete Deep Beams Using Carbon Fiber Reinforced Polymer Laminates." J. Compos. Constr., 8(5), 403–414.

Concrete Solutions – Grantham, Mechtcherine & Schneck (eds)
© 2012 Taylor & Francis Group, London, ISBN 978-0-415-61622-5

Concrete repair and strengthening with ultra ductile micro-mesh reinforced mortar

C. Flohrer & M. Tschötschel
HOCHTIEF Construction AG, Mörfelden-Walldorf, Germany

S. Hauser
DUCON GmbH, Mörfelden-Walldorf, Germany

ABSTRACT: For rehabilitation of industrial floors or bridge deck overlays in most cases cost effective and high potential repair materials are needed. The application of ultra ductile micro-mesh reinforced abrasive resistant and impervious high strength mortar has the advantage to work with thin layers (2–5 cm) of this repair material. The high ductility of the repair system can be achieved by using micro-reinforcement mats with slurry infiltration. The damaged surface can be left in place and doesn't have to be demolished and disposed of because of the crack bridging properties of the micro-mesh reinforced mortar. Several examples of repaired floors or slabs will be presented. The ultra ductile material is also used for the repair of waste areas or extremely loaded floors with impervious overlays. Besides having high compressive and flexural strength, it is an extremely ductile material, expansion joints are not necessary. Also for strengthening of columns, increasing resistance against blast or earthquake, the micro-mesh reinforced mortar will be applicable. The ductile behaviour of the material allows the application of thin repair layers at the surface of the columns. For new buildings the material can be used as permanent formwork. Examples of strengthening of columns and protection of columns against high blast impact as well as further applications are presented.

1 MATERIAL

1.1 *Composition and material characteristics*

DUCON® stands for DUctile CONcrete and represents the combination of a high-performance or ultra-high-performance concrete and a micro-reinforcement from steel wire meshes (Fig. 1), developed by Hauser. The micro-reinforcement is uniformly distributed all over the cross section which results in a homogenous composition of the composite material (Hauser 1999, Hauser & Wörner 1999). It consists of multiple layers of meshes with variable mesh width (between

6 mm and 35 mm) which are 3-dimensionally connected. Table 1 shows the most important material characteristics.

1.2 *Production*

Production is based on the placement of the pre-fabricated micro-reinforcement and the infiltration of the concrete slurry (Fig. 2).

Between 1 Vol.-% and 10 Vol.-% of microreinforcement are embedded, typically, 6 Vol.-%.

Due to the fine mesh size of the microreinforcement, the crack width can be reduced to

Figure 1. Self-compacting high-strength concrete + Microreinforcement.

Table 1. Material characteristics.

Type	Value
Compressive strength	90–180 N/mm² (cube)
Flexural strength	16–75 N/mm²
Tensile strength	9–20 N/mm²
Shear strength	3–16 N/mm²
Modulus of elasticity	>35.000 N/mm²
Thickness	≥10 mm–500 mm
Ductility factor	>10

Figure 2. Slurry infiltration process.

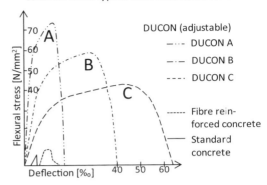

Figure 3. Stress-deflection diagram for three different adjustments.

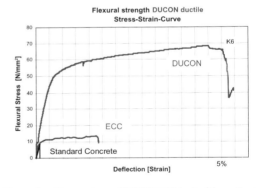

Figure 4. Four-Point-Bending-Test of a DUCON member, thickness 25 mm.

values of $w < 0.1$ mm which qualifies DUCON as an impervious material. Thus, DUCON can be executed with a small concrete cover of a few millimetres compared to 20 to 50 mm of standard reinforced concrete.

1.3 Flexural strength and ductility

One major benefit of DUCON is that the material performance is programmable. Various setups and qualities of the micro-reinforcement (e.g., steel characteristics) allow the adaption of the material performance to the specific application. Figure 3 shows a stress-deflection diagram from flexural bending strength tests (Fig. 4) with three different possible adjustments A, B, C in comparison with standard concrete and typical fiber-reinforced concrete. Note that the curves for standard concrete (grey) and fiber-reinforced concrete (blue) are shifted horizontally for a better legibility.

Besides having high compressive and flexural-strength, the properties can thus be adjusted to achieve an extremely ductile material. The ductility and its high strength are the key characteristics for high energy absorption of high speed dynamics and dynamics in combination with large deformations.

Compared to other ductile materials DUCON provides a high load bearing capacity at the same time (Fig. 4). The specimen as shown in Fig. 4 had a maximum deflection at a failure of 75 mm at 540 mm span. These characteristics are required for building protection for example against explosion and earthquake. Figure 5 shows a comparison of the flexural behavior of DUCON in comparison with a typical *Engineered Cementitious Composite* (*ECC, Wang & Li 2006*) and a standard concrete.

Whereas "ECC has approximately half the flexural strength of Ductal (another ultra-high performance concrete) but 20 times its tensile ductility" (Smock 2007), DUCON exhibits even more than twice the tensile ductility of ECC and more than 4 times its flexural strength.

Figure 5. Comparison of DUCON (blue) with an *Engineered Cementitious Material* (ECC, green) and standard concrete.

2 DYNAMIC PROPERTIES

2.1 Blast resistance

Figures 6 and 7 demonstrate the resistance of DUCON against close range and contact charges compared to reinforced concrete (RFC) at the same thickness of 150 mm (RTL TV broadcasting, 2004). The reinforced concrete failed, the blast wave

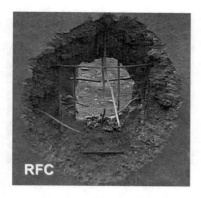

Figure 6. Reinforced concrete fails under contact charge. Full penetration + fragment projectiles.

Figure 7. DUCON remains stable, no penetration nor fragment projectiles, 85% of the cross section stays intact.

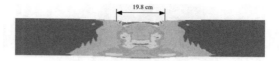

Figure 8. Finite-element simulation of DUCON under contact charge load.

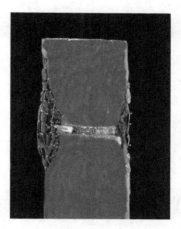

Figure 9. DUCON panel, thickness 100 mm, resists a armor piercing Wolfram-Carbit Penetrator at a speed of 840 m/s.

penetrated the panel and in addition created fragment projectiles. DUCON resisted the blast test and no penetration or fragments could be observed.

Several blast tests at the Fraunhofer Institute for the US Military (Schuler & Mayrhofer 2004, Schuler & Mayrhofer 2007, Marchand 2007) proved that the blast resistance of DUCON is at least twice as good as that of ordinary reinforced concrete, which means it can be executed at half the thickness and in addition it does not spall.

The 3-dimensional micro-reinforcement keeps the structural integrity of the concrete and avoids spalling and fragment projectiles. The material properties of DUCON have been recently implemented into a finite element code for high-speed dynamics (Fig. 8) (Gebbeken & Greulich, 2006).

2.2 Ballistic resistance

According to the blast resistance DUCON proved a comparable performance in ballistic resistance.

It reaches the resistance of reinforced concrete with less than 50% of the thickness. Moreover, the special 3-dimensional micro-reinforcement allows a structural integrity of the concrete and avoids spalling.

Figure 9 shows that a 10 cm thick DUCON panel absorbed an armor piercing bullet (Wolfram-Carbit penetrator at a speed of 840 m/s) while RFC needed to be 24 cm. Bullet tests resulted in a PM7 (highest requirement level of European code) for a thickness of only 80 mm.

Further Military test series (Marchand 2007) proved that a 10 cm DUCON-panel also resists high velocity fragments of propeller drilled weapons, like Mortars in combination with explosion.

3 RECENT STANDARD APPLICATIONS

3.1 Fragmentation protection for blast loading

Figure 10 shows an application of a DUCON layer (thickness 15 mm) acting as an integrated "safety-net" on the bottom of a reinforced concrete slab (thickness 300 mm). The tests performed proved the effectiveness of DUCON to maintain the structural integrity of the slab under blast loading. This application has been used several times to protect

Figure 10. DUCON panel, thickness 15 mm, acts as an integrated "safety-net" on the bottom of a reinforced concrete slab.

Figure 11. DUCON wall, thickness 250 mm, acts as protective element in front of an embassy.

the server room of high security data centers in Europe. It was also used for the concrete walls.

3.2 *Blast protection wall and blast protection facade*

In these applications, DUCON has been used as protective walls and secondary facades in front of endangered buildings. Walls have a typical thickness of 100 mm to 250 mm, façade elements a typical thickness of 40 mm to 150 mm. The DUCON panels are prefabricated elements and can be easily transported and installed. Figure 11 shows an embassy in Europe protected by a DUCON wall.

3.3 *Architectural applications*

Beside thin plates for tables, façade panels or counter tops, recently also structural elements have been produced. Figure 12 shows an application as an entrance portal, height 4,50 m, span 4,50 m with a thickness of only 80 mm to 100 mm. The portal was pre-fabricated and installed on site.

Figure 12. Entrance portal of DUCON, height 4,50 m, span 4,50 m, thickness 80 mm to 100 mm.

4 REPAIR APPLICATIONS

4.1 *Blast protection columns*

Here, three types of production have been applied; a retro-fitting of existing columns with external formwork (Fig. 13), without external formwork (using Ducon mortar as plaster, Fig. 14) or tube columns made of DUCON used as integrated formwork (Fig. 15). They have been applied for earthquake protection (Zekaria 2001) and for blast protection (Schuler & Mayrhofer 2007).

4.2 *Impervious and abrasive resistant overlays*

Based on the high performance material characteristics of DUCON, impermeability, durability, freeze-thaw resistance and corrosion resistance in combination with crack control DUCON has been tested for the International Code Council (ICC) approval which was obtained for the applications on the US market. These characteristics are well suited for applications of thin impervious overlays on top of existing or damaged flooring or concrete structures.

Figure 16 shows an application at a chemical plant where 7.500 m² of damaged and cracked concrete slab could be quickly repaired by a 25 mm DUCON overlay and a time- and cost consuming demolition and reconstruction of the concrete could be avoided.

Thin members of concrete for free-form applications are another future possibility as the microreinforcement can be adapted to any shape by hand.

4.3 *DUCON as structural overlay*

The existing concrete slab of the Main Train Station of Frankfurt has been damaged and a structural retrofit of the slab has been necessary. Reinforcement of the slab from below has been impossible, due to mechanical installations.

Figure 13. Retro-fitting of existing columns for earthquake protection with external formwork.

Figure 16. DUCON overlay, 25 mm, applied on an existing cracked concrete slab of a chemical plant.

Figure 14. Retro-fitting of existing columns using DUCON-mortar as a surface-formwork.

Figure 17. Repair and strengthening of concrete slab—Train station Frankfurt.

Figure 15. DUCON tubes used as integrated formwork for reinforced concrete columns.

Figure 18. Placement of MicroMat repair—train station Frankfurt.

The existing floor fill (60 mm) has been replaced by 60 mm DUCON. DUCON now performs as retrofit of the existing concrete slab and carries the structural loads (Figs. 17 and 18). The advantage is that due to the replacement of the gypcrete the granite stone cover could be executed 2 days after the installation of DUCON and the DUCON overlay didn't change the height of the former floor set-up.

4.4 DUCON as high performance overlay

Heavy duty off-set printing machines are sensitive to tilting and deformation of the foundation, which leads to loss of print quality. In addition crack propagation of the surface has to be avoided.

For this specific project DUCON replaced the existing floor fill and performed as a retrofit of

Figure 19. Installed MicroMat and infiltrated slurry.

Figure 20. Installation of heavy duty printing machine—2 days after execution of overlay.

the existing concrete slab, as energy absorption for dynamic loads and as a crack controlled foundation for the printing machine (Figs. 19 and 20).

5 CONCLUSIONS

DUCON, a very ductile composite material of concrete and steel, shows excellent material properties and a large spectrum of applications. Its high energy absorption allows applications for blast and ballistic protection without fragmentation at approximately half the thickness of ordinary reinforced concrete.

The ductile behavior of the material allows applying thin repair layers at the surface of columns and slabs for strengthening and increasing the earthquake resistance.

Future applications and research should also consider the stability behavior of the material, e.g., for shells and thin membranes and should develop new connection.

DUCON® = registered Trademark of Ducon GmbH.

REFERENCES

Blastow, M. 2006. High performance product testing goes ballistic, *Concrete Products*, 10/2007: 36–39.
Gebbeken, N. & Greulich, S. 2005. Expert opinion and structural design of blast wall, Universität der Bundeswehr, report.
Gebbeken, N. & Greulich, S. 2006. Expert opinion on structural design of a blast wall, Universität der Bundeswehr, report.
Hauser, S. 1999. DUCON und SIMCON NEU ein innovativer Hochleistungsbeton, PhD-thesis, Darmstadt University of Technology.
Hauser, S. & Wörner, J.-D. 1999. DUCON ein innovativer Hochleistungsbeton Teil 1: Grundlagen. *Beton-und Stb*, 1999: 66–75.
Hauser, S. & Wörner, J.-D. 1999. DUCON ein innovativer Hochleistungsbeton Teil 2: Bemessung. *Beton-und Stb/* 1999: 141–145.
Hauser, S. & Wörner, J.-D. 1999. DUCON, a durable overlay, Rilem HPFRCC International Symposium Mainz, May 1999.
Hauser, S. & Wörner, J.-D. 1999. Hochleistungsfaserbeton, Materialeigenschaften und Anwendungen, In *Festschrift zum 60. Geburtstag von Herrn Prof. Falkner*, TU Braunschweig, 1999.
Hofmann, P. et al. 2007. Toughened throughout. Microreinforced concrete gets blast resistance as its first assignment, *Concrete International* 29 (12).
Holschemacher, K. & Tue, N.V. (eds). Sanierung und Verstärkung von Massivbauten. Bauwerk Verlag GmbH, Berlin.
Marchand, K. 2007. Ballistic and Blast Tests of DUCON Panles for Department of Defense at deployed operation bases (DOBs) Overhead Cover Applications. Protection En gineering Consultants, report, July 12th, 2007.
Miller, S. 2007. Explosion in blast resistant construction, *Masonry Construction Journal*, 10/2007: 1–5.
Reymendt, J. 2006. Instandsetzung von Betonbauteilen beim Umgang mit wassergefährdeten Stoffen. In: Dehn F., Klaus.
RTL TV broadcasting 2004. Blast tests DUCON vs. RFC Seminar of THW and Firemen.
Schuler, H. & Mayrhofer, C. 2004. Stoßrohrprüfung von Platten aus DUCON, Fraunhofer Ernst Mach Institute, August 2004.
Schuler, H. & Mayrhofer, C. 2007. Untersuchung von mikrobewehrten Betonstützen bei Explosionseinwirkungen, Fraunhofer Ernst Mach Institute, Report, June 2007.
Smock, D. 2007. Bendable Concrete Protects Against Hurricanes. *Reed Business Information, Reed Elsevier*, November 11th, 2007.
Wang, S. & Li, V.C. 2006. High-Early-Strength Engineered Cementitious Composites. *ACI Material Journal*, March–April 2006: 97–105.
Zekaria, A. 2001. Seismic retrofitting of reinforced concrete columns using SIMCON jackets, PhD-thesis, Darmstadt University of Technology.

Concrete Solutions – Grantham, Mechtcherine & Schneck (eds)
© 2012 Taylor & Francis Group, London, ISBN 978-0-415-61622-5

Applied research and recent developments on composite material technology for structural strengthening

E. Fyfe
Fyfe Co LLC, San Diego (CA), US

M. Karantzikis & C. Kolyvas
Fyfe Europe S.A., Athens, Greece

ABSTRACT: In the last two decades Advanced Composite Systems (ACS), which are commonly referred to as FRP systems, have been introduced in the construction industry as a promising new technology for structural strengthening. This paper presents not only about FRP systems but also the supplementary materials and techniques leading to the use of a broader name of the system as ACS. Some individuals and companies have been really stayed at the forefront of these new ACS developments all these years. Especially in the recent years, when the ACS entered a first maturity age, new applications, new concepts and superior installation methods have been investigated, researched, developed and adopted for real case studies.

In this paper, firstly the recent research and development advancements for the fire protection of FRP strengthened systems will be discussed. This passive protection material has been tested under load in fire laboratories providing promising results. The issue of glass transition temperature of the epoxy resins used in ACSs has also been investigated hereinafter. Another topic that will be covered in this paper will be the mechanical anchorage of ACS on bond critical applications. Recent tests for example, as will be discussed in the paper, show the advanced performance of "U-shape" ACS for beams shear strengthening when anchored with Fibrwrap® anchors. Finally, a newly launched material for the strengthening and repair of historical monuments and relevant test campaigns will be presented in detail.

1 PASSIVE FIRE PROTECTION OF FRP

Fire is one of the major concerns regarding the use of FRP under service loads because of the sensitivity of the epoxy to high temperatures. Many efforts in the last decade have taken place to develop a passive fire protection system for FRP. Following extensive full scale, under load testing in Canada and the USA, the AFP (Advanced Fire Protection) system has been approved as the first FRP fire protection system. The system is already available internationally since 2004 while the second generation of the system is currently under development. Selective results of the tests and a brief system description are presented herein.

It is known that the mechanical properties of the epoxy resins used in FRP degrade at high temperatures. Therefore, gradual loss of strength and bonding of the FRP is expected in the case of a fire event. As a result the engineers should ensure that the service temperature remains below a certain level and assume complete loss of the FRP strengthening during a fire event, unless a suitable fire protection system has been installed to protect the FRP in such cases.

Extensive fire endurance experiments have been conducted by Kodur et al. (Kodur et al., 2006) on full scale loaded specimens, consisting of FRP-retrofitted columns, beams and slabs in accordance with ASTM E-119. All assemblies were retrofitted with carbon or glass FRP and covered with the AFP system. The system consists of a noncombustible, zero flame spread, spray-applied fire insulation layer, covered by a surface hardening sealing compound. The insulating component's thermal conductivity is about 0.082 W/m °C, whereas for gypsum plaster it is approximately 0.25 W/m °C at room temperature. The AFP thickness can be varied to obtain several fire endurance performances.

Columns achieved, when tested to ASTM E-119 fire endurances, greater than 4 hours under the retrofitted service loads. The AFP thickness varied from 32 mm to 57 mm. It is evident from the temperatures recorded at various locations (Fig. 1) that a good level of thermal insulation is provided by the AFP system.

All T-beam assemblies retrofitted with carbon FRP and protected with AFP thickness 25 mm to 38 mm, achieved fire endurances above 4 hours under retrofitted service loads. Based on the

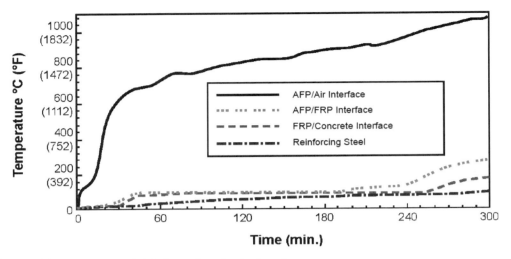

Figure 1. Temperatures recorded during testing of a circular column.

Figure 2. Application of AFP System on FRP strengthened beams (Fyfe Company).

results of these tests, standard fire ratings have been developed through Underwriters' Laboratories (UL) for insulated FRP retrofitted beams and columns. These rated assemblies are listed in the UL directory.

A new series of tests are under way for developing a new Super-AFP system with advanced performance (smaller required thickness) suitable for external use as well.

2 DEVELOPMENT OF EPOXY RESINS FOR HIGH WORKING TEMPERATURES

By now, lots of investigations have been done to reveal the evolution of the mechanical properties of FRP with temperature (Foster and Bisby, 2005). High temperature is a major concern regarding strengthening applications in warm climates or where the working temperature is exceptionally high (e.g. industry). In such cases, conventional epoxies fail to meet the requirements. A new generation of epoxy resins for high temperatures have been developed (Tyfo® S-T Epoxy) that are characterized by especially high Glass Transition (T_g) and Critical Temperatures (T_c). Part of the development study is presented below.

All studies show that the mechanical properties of FRP at elevated temperature are dominated by the properties of the polymer matrix (epoxy). As known, the structural role of epoxy in FRP is to hold the fibers in place and transfer stresses among them. Softening due to elevating temperature of the epoxy will lead to decrease of the mechanical properties of FRP, as the softened epoxy will not effectively transfer the force between fibers. The fibers will fail at different strain levels because of minor waviness and misalignment further reducing the mechanical properties of the FRP.

Further studies on the properties of epoxy show that after its curing, a cross-linking structure is created, and therefore the epoxy cannot be molten anymore but only softened. The temperature at which epoxy changes from brittle (glass) to soft (rubbery) form is the T_g. As the temperature gets close to the T_g the polymer matrix starts to soften and exhibit a lowered modulus. With the further increase in the temperature, the matrix becomes softer, until the matrix shows a temperature-independent modulus (rubbery modulus). Above the T_g, the epoxy still possesses a low degree of modulus and strength. This characteristic is very important for the much higher T_c of FRP in tension. T_c is defined as the temperature at which FRP loses 50% of its tensile strength and can no longer support the applied load.

Correspondingly, the variation of the mechanical properties of the FRP with temperature is similar to the epoxy. As the temperature increases, the mechanical properties slowly decrease. As the temperature gets close to T_g, the mechanical properties start to dramatically decrease. At much higher temperatures, the mechanical properties become temperature independent until the occurrence of severe degradation of the epoxy or the interfaces. If the tensile strength of the FRP at the latter stage is higher than 50% of the original strength, then the T_c of the FRP will be much higher than the T_g of the epoxy.

While developing the new generation of epoxy resins the major concern was to create a polymer matrix for FRP used for structural strengthening that would be characterized by an exceptionally high T_g and even higher T_c. The result was Tyfo® S-T Epoxy that possesses a T_g of 101 °C, while the FRP (Tyfo® Composite System) formed with that epoxy possesses an even higher T_c of 260 °C. As a result, the new material is capable to conform with demanding design requirements set by structural strengthening needs at exceptionally high ambient temperatures (e.g. warm climates, industrial plants etc.).

3 ANCHORING TECHNOLOGY OF FRP WITH FIBER ANCHORS

Mechanical anchorage of FRP on bond critical applications has always been a subject of utmost importance. Mechanical steel anchors should be avoided due to stress concentrations and galvanic corrosion problems (Tavakkolizadeh and Saadatmanesh, 2001) when in contact with FRP. Fully compatible anchors made out of fibers (Fibr™ Anchors) have been developed and tested extensively. Recent tests revealed the advanced performance of "U-shape" FRP for shear strengthening of T-beams when anchored with Fibr™ Anchors. Testing further proved that anchoring of FRP applied to columns for flexural enhancement is possible by application of Fibr™ Anchors at the footings or joints.

A typical lay out of a Fibr™ Anchor is shown in Figure 3. Fibr™ Anchors made of special types of glass, carbon or glass/carbon (hybrid) fibers have been developed and patented by the Fyfe Company in the USA in the 1990's. The diameter, length and shape of anchors vary depending on the design requirements. Special types, such as pre-cured, pre-saturated, pinned have been produced and installed in special applications. The anchors are forced in a predrilled hole of specific diameter and depth, filled with epoxy in concrete, wood or masonry. Anchor fibers are splayed out

between the FRP layers in a pattern as per the design detail and cured with the FRP system as one monolithic system.

Recent T-beam shear testing conducted in the Structural Materials Laboratory (SML) in the University of Patras (UPatras), with the support of the Fyfe Company, showed the enhanced performance of the strengthened beams when Fibr™ Anchors were used to anchor the "U-shape" FRP. In Figure 4 the maximum load under which the beams failed in shear is shown: non-strengthened beam (105 kN), strengthened with non-anchored "U-shape" FRP (147 kN) and strengthened with Fibr™ anchored "U-shape" FRP with two different configurations of anchorage (169 kN, 228 kN).

The load carrying capacity increased almost 50% (228 kN/147 kN) comparing anchored versus non-anchored "U-shape" FRP and almost 120%

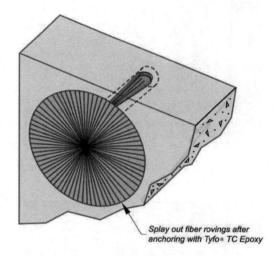

Splay out fiber rovings after anchoring with Tyfo® TC Epoxy

Figure 3. Fibr™ Anchor lay-out (Fyfe Company).

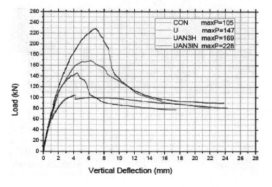

Figure 4. T-beams shear strengthened with FRP, (Structural Materials Laboratory—University of Patras).

Figure 5. Fibr™ Anchors on a beam after testing and removing the FRP system (Structural Materials Laboratory—University of Patras).

Figure 6. Anchorage in the foundation (Fyfe Company).

Figure 7. Anchorage through walls (Fyfe Company).

(228 kN/105 kN) comparing strengthened with Fibr™ anchored "U-shape" FRP versus a non-strengthened beam. Papers will be published soon, by the SML-UPatras with more detailed information on the work done.

A series of full scale tests have been further conducted on flexural strengthening of columns with FRP properly anchored with Fibr™ Anchors into the foundation (Fig. 6). The results showed that a proper configuration of large diameter and length Fibr™ Anchors can effectively transfer the stresses under monotonic or cycling loading from the vertical FRP layers into the foundation, in the joints or through the joints to the next floor.

Special cases of Fibrwrap® applications are always under consideration such as the ones shown in Figure 7. Special design guidelines for Fibr™ Anchors systems have been developed by the Fyfe Company for all cases.

4 COMPATIBLE REINFORCED MORTAR SYSTEMS FOR STRENGTHENING OF HISTORIC MASONRY STRUCTURES

New composite systems with inorganic matrices have been developed in recent years. These, so-called RM (Reinforced Mortar) Systems or TRM (Textile Reinforced Mortar) Systems, have the advantages of being fully compatible to heritage structures and possessing excellent fire resistance by eliminating the use of epoxy. Research has been contacted, mainly in Europe, and some sample projects have been already completed.

RM Systems comprise of an inorganic mortar (matrix) which can be cement or non-cement based and an open weaved (EP) biaxial fabric as reinforcement which may consist of carbon, AR-glass (alkali resistant) or basalt fibers. The EP fabric usually has a balanced architecture of main fibers in 0°/90°. Important characteristics of the EP fabrics are the stability at the joints and the coating of the fibers. Tests have shown that a coated joint-stable EP fabric has a much better performance compared to an uncoated one with loose joint stability. The coating is a special thin layer high-temperature resistive coating. Bitumen, PVC and other similar fiber coatings can create weak links, at the boding between matrix and EP fabric, and performance in case of a fire event is questionable. Special fiber type anchors (Fibr™ Anchors) have been developed and tested for enhanced bonding of the system to the substrate, especially when a non-cement low property mortar is used as matrix of the RM system.

Basalt fiber EP fabrics have advantageous characteristics because of their lower cost compared to carbon and AR-glass, higher technical properties than AR-glass and good resistance in an alkaline environment. The durability with time of a RM system used on a heritage structure is an important feature and more tests and studies have to be performed on this topic.

Figure 8. Application of RM Basalt system at the Structural Materials Laboratory in University of Patras (Operha Project).

Figure 9. Out of plane cycling flexural testing in the Structural Materials Laboratory, University of Patras (Operha Project).

The main features of RM systems are that they are totally compatible and consistent in physical characteristics (e.g. texture, color) to the substrate; they are a relatively reversible technique compared to FRP and other traditional methods (e.g. shotcrete); they

Figure 10. Strengthening a vault of a Romanesque church in Spain (Operha Project).

posses excellent fire resistance and are environmental friendly. RM systems may also be used for strengthening of non-heritage masonry structures as well as concrete members for contact critical applications (e.g. column wrapping).

Extensive research and testing have been performed in the Operha Research Project (OPERHA, 2008) funded by the European Union. The main objectives of the Operha were to set the standards and develop a strengthening system compatible with heritage structures. The laboratory research was followed by real life applications on listed monuments. One example is presented in Figure 10.

5 CONCLUSIONS

Use of high-technology composite materials in structural rehabilitation and improvement has been of increasing interest during the last two decades due to the decreasing cost of the material and the increasing availability of research on the use and effects of these materials on structural components. This paper discusses key issues in advanced composites focusing on practical applications on structures. One of the main issues in rehabilitation of existing structures against static service loads is the protection of the composites against fire, something that has attracted intensive research in last years and has been discussed in detail in this paper. The other important issue is the temperatureat which the epoxy resin changes its structural properties significantly, the relevant aspects of which have been summarized above.

Composite anchors have also been a subject of this paper due to their increasing use in practical projects. Finally, possible use of advanced composites in intervention projects for historical structures have been discussed by proposing a new material which is also being verified by extensive laboratory tests.

REFERENCES

Foster, S. & Bisby, L. 2005. High temperature residual properties of externally-bonded FRP systems. In the 7th Annual Symposium on Fibre-Reinforced-Plastic Reinforcement for Concrete Structures (FRPRCS-7).

Kodur, V., Bisby, L. & Green, M. 2006. FRP retrofitted concrete under fire conditions. Concrete International 28(12).

OPERHA: Open and Fully Compatible Next Generation of Strengthening System for the Rehabilitation of Mediterranean Building Heritage. 2008. www.operha.eu.

Tavakkolizadeh, M., Saadatmanesh, H. 2001. Galvanic corrosion of carbon and steel in aggressive environments, *Journal of Composites for Construction*, Vol. 5, No. 3.

Concrete Solutions – Grantham, Mechtcherine & Schneck (eds)
© 2012 Taylor & Francis Group, London, ISBN 978-0-415-61622-5

Flexural behavior of CFRP-strengthened and corroded reinforced concrete beams

M. Hussein

Department of Structural Engineering, Tanta University, Tanta, Egypt

ABSTRACT: An experimental program has been carried out to investigate the structural behavior of RC beams strengthened with carbon-fiber-reinforced polymer (CFRP) strips and exposed to a corrosive environment. A total of eight beams (200 × 300 × 2000 mm) were tested. Three beams were CFRP strengthened and corroded, three beams were CFRP strengthened and kept at room temperature, one beam was unstrengthened and corroded, and one beam was neither strengthened nor corroded. Three different strengthening schemes were applied: (I) externally bonded CFRP strip with two U-shaped CFRP sheet end anchorages; (II) externally bonded CFRP strip with four U-shaped CFRP sheet anchorages distributed along the beam span, and (III) Near Surface Mounted CFRP Strips (NSMS). The mass loss of the steel reinforcement in the test beams due to corrosion was about 5%. For the used three schemes, the experimental results showed that the ultimate strength of the CFRP strengthened uncorroded beams increased by about 24, 28, and 37% respectively above the predicted strength of a similar unstrengthened-uncorroded beam; however, weakening of the concrete cover near to the anchorage zones caused by corrosion cracks significantly reduced the corroded beams' flexural capacity. The recorded flexural strength gain decreased to 10%, 17% and 29% for the used three schemes respectively above the predicted strength of a similar unstrengthened-corroded beam.

1 INTRODUCTION

Fiber Reinforced Polymer (FRP) materials are currently produced in different configurations and are widely used for the strengthening and retrofitting of concrete structures and bridges. Their strength-to-weight ratio, durability in adverse environments, and high fatigue strength make them a good choice for civil engineering application (Bonaldo et al. 2008, Neal 2000, Petrou et al. 2008, Kim et al. 2008, Lam and Teng 2001, Seim et al. 2001, Tumialan et al. 2007, Quattlebaum et al. 2005, Tan et al. 2004, Triantafillou 1998, Teng et al. 2000). The reinforcement of existing reinforced concrete beams and slabs with Fiber Reinforced Polymer (FRP) materials bonded to their soffit may be needed for different reasons: improve the maximum load capacity (strengthening criterion), or limit the width and the distribution of cracks in concrete (durability criterion). Also, Carbon Fiber Reinforced Polymer (CFRP) wrapping can be used to enhance the bond of corroded reinforcing steel bars in concrete (Badawi and Soudki 2005, El Maaddawy and Soudki 2005, Soudki et al. 2007). However, the one major practical difficulty associated with RC structures strengthened with externally bonded CFRP strips is that any possible degradation of their concrete cover may affect the composite action between the

CFRP strengthening strips and the concrete. Thus, corrosion of reinforcing steel presents a problem for CFRP-strengthened structures for two reasons. First, as steel corrodes there is a corresponding reduction in the cross-sectional area that may not be significant except with pitting corrosion ACI (1996a). Second, the corrosion products occupy a larger volume than the original steel and exert substantial tensile forces on the surrounding concrete, causing it crack and spall off. The expansive forces caused by steel corrosion can cause cracking and spalling of the concrete cover and hence loss of composite action between the CFRP strengthening strips and the substrate concrete.

Many researchers have attempted to characterize the performance of corrosion-damaged RC beams (Al-Sulaimani et al. 1990, Andrade et al. 1993, Almusallam et al. 1996, Broomfield 1997, Cabrera 1996, Niu and Wu 2006, Val and Melchers 1997, Val 2007, Val 2005); however, very little information is available in the literature on the structural behavior of such beams strengthened with FRP strips.

This paper presents the experimental results of a study that was undertaken to address the effect of main steel corrosion on the load carrying capacity and ductility of CFRP-strengthened RC beams with different strengthening configurations.

2 EXPERIMENTAL PROGRAM

2.1 Description of test beams

Eight RC beams were constructed. Each beam was 2000 mm long with 200×300 mm rectangular cross section and reinforced by two 12-mm-diameter bottom longitudinal deformed reinforcing bars, two 8-mm-diameter top longitudinal plain bars, and 6-mm-diameter plain stirrups spaced at 70 mm. A typical clear cover of 20 mm was used around the stirrups. Four beams were corroded, whereas the other four beams were not corroded to serve as control beams. Typical dimension and reinforcement details for the RC beams are illustrated in Figure 1.

2.2 CFRP strengthening schemes

In accordance with ACI Committee 440 recommendations, six specimens were strengthened with CFRP strips. The strengthening schemes are demonstrated in Figure 2.

2.2.1 Strengthening scheme I

This scheme included bonding 25 mm wide 1,700 mm long CFRP stripe with fibers oriented parallel to the beam axis (the longitudinal direction) to the tensile face of the RC beam. Two CFRP sheets, each 100 mm wide, with their fiber oriented in the transverse direction (i.e., perpendicular to the specimen axis), were then wrapped over the beam cross section at both ends of the CFRP strip. These sheets were placed so that they covered the beam width and ran up both beam sides. The purpose of these U-sheets was to prevent the CFRP strips from prematurely peeling off the concrete surface (i.e., to provide an anchorage) (Garcez et al. 2008).

2.2.2 Strengthening scheme II

This scheme is similar to scheme I but, the RC beam section was wrapped with two additional 100 mm wide U-shaped CFRP sheets distributed along the beam span.

2.2.3 Strengthening scheme III

This scheme included strengthening the beam using two CFRP strips inserted into grooves cut at the bottom surface of the beam. The strips, as provided by the manufacturer had a nominal width of 50 mm and a total thickness of 1.2 mm. In order to

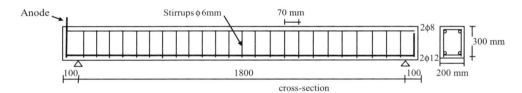

Figure 1. Typical dimensions and reinforcement details of test beams.

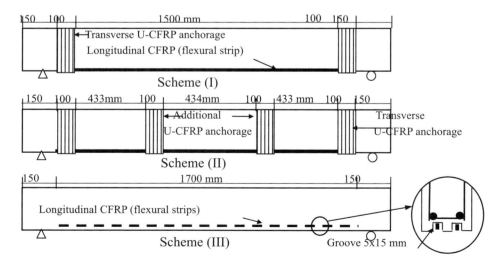

Figure 2. CFRP strengthening schemes.

insert the strip within a typical concrete cover used for concrete members, the strips were cut into four equal parts each, 12.5 mm wide. Using a concrete saw, approximately 5 mm wide and 15 mm deep grooves were cut into the bottom surface of the beams (Hassan and Rizkalla 2003). The grooves were injected with epoxy adhesive to provide the necessary bond with the surrounding concrete. The strips were carefully placed into the grooves to ensure that they were completely covered with the epoxy. The CFRP strengthening schemes are shown in Figure 2 and a summarized description of the test program is given in Table 1.

2.3 Material properties

The 28-day compressive strength (cylinder strength) of the concrete used was on average 25 MPa. Two 12 mm diameter steel bars having a yield tensile strength of 441 MPa were used for flexural reinforcement, while 6 mm diameter steel bars having a yield strength of 245 MPa were used as vertical stirrups. The principal mechanical properties of the strengthening materials provided by the manufacturer are shown in Table 2.

Table 1. Description of test beams.

Beam description	Uncorroded beams		Corroded beams	
	Name	A_{CFRP}	Name	A_{CFRP}
Control	B	–	B-c	–
Beams strengthened using scheme I	B-I	30 mm²	B-I,c	30 mm²
Beams strengthened using scheme II	B-II	30 mm²	B-II,c	30 mm²
Beams strengthened using scheme III	B-III	30 mm²	B-III,c	30 mm²

Table 2. Principal mechanical properties for strengthening materials provided by the manufacturer.

Type	CFRP strips	CFRP sheets	Epoxy for strips	Epoxy for sheets
Tensile strength, Mpa	2800	3500	30	30
Modulus of elasticity, Gpa	165	230	12.8	21.4
Failure strain,%	1.7	1.5	1.0	4.8
Shear strength, Mpa	–	–	30.0	15.0

2.4 Accelerated corrosion process

During the corrosion process, the beams and copper plates were placed in a small tank filled with NaCl solution (concentration = 3%) which covered only the beams' bottom third, as shown in Figure 3. Accelerated corrosion was carried out by impressing an electric current through the main longitudinal bottom reinforcing bars of about 300 mA. The copper plate acted as the cathode for this corrosion process, whereas the tension reinforcing bars acted as the anode. During construction of the specimens, the tension reinforcing bars were extended about 60 mm out of each specimen from one end to facilitate connecting to the power supply. A DC galvanostatic power supply was used to provide the current desired. To estimate the approximate time needed for about 5% mass loss associated with this corrosion process, Faraday's law was used. Many researchers have shown Faraday's law to provide a reasonably accurate approximation of the actual degree of corrosion (El Maaddawy and Soudki 2005, Soudki et al. 2007). This law relates the mass loss to the corrosion current and the time of the corrosion process by the following relation:

$$\Delta m = (I\ t\ M)/(z\ F)$$

where Δm is the mass loss, I the corrosion current (A), t the time of the corrosion process (s); M the atomic weight of iron (55.847 g/mol), z the ion charge (assumed 2 for Fe $\rightarrow$ Fe²⁺ + 2e⁻), and F the Faraday's constant (96,487 As).

Applying this law, the time need for about 5% mass loss of the steel reinforcement in the test beams was estimated to be about 20 days.

At the completion of the loading tests, sections of rebar were removed using a diamond tipped saw from each beam measuring approximately 250 mm in length. The removed rebar sections were then submerged into 10% Diammonium Hydrogen Citrate solution for 24 hours. Then, the rebar sections were cleaned and the rust was completely removed. The average mass loss of the steel rebars extracted from the corroded beams was about 5%.

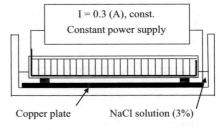

Figure 3. Setup for accelerated corrosion process.

Figure 4. Control beam after corrosion.

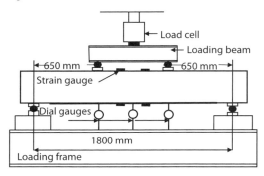

Figure 5. Test setup and instrumentation.

2.5 *Test setup and instrumentation*

All the beams were loaded in four-point bending. The load was applied using a hydraulic actuator through a spreader steel beam to the specimen. Each specimen spanned 1,800 mm and was loaded symmetrically about its centerline at two points 500 mm apart. A load cell was attached to the loading actuator to record the applied load. Two strain gauges were bonded to the top concrete surface of each specimen at two points, each 100 mm from the mid-span, to record the compression strain in the extreme concrete fibers. Two strain gauges were bonded to the CFRP flexural strengthening strips each at 100 mm from the mid-span. The instrumentation used to monitor the behavior of the beams during testing is shown in Figure 5.

3 TEST RESULTS AND DISCUSSION

By the end of the accelerated corrosion process, significant deterioration was observed for the unstrengthened beam B-c, where corrosion was uniform along the beam length. Visible continuous longitudinal cracks up to 0.8 mm wide were observed at the bottom reinforcing bar location. No cover spalling was noticed for all unstrengthened—corroded beams. The same distribution of corrosion cracks was observed for the strengthened beams B-I,c and B-III,c. For the CFRP-strengthened beam provided with 4 U-shaped CFRP sheets B-II,c some concrete cracking was observed. But their width was only about 0.4 mm, which is 50% of the width of the cracks observed for the unstrengthened specimen. This can be ascribable to the confinement provided by the transverse U-sheets stirrups wrapping the cross section, which would limit the development of corrosion cracks.

A total of eight RC beams categorized in two groups were tested as given in Table 1. The main objective of the present work is to address the effect of main steel corrosion on the flexural behavior of CFRP-strengthened RC beams with different strengthening configurations.

3.1 *Ultimate loads and modes of failure*

A considerable enhancement in strength was observed for all the CFRP-strengthened uncorroded beams as shown in Table 3. It can be seen that the ultimate load increased about 24, 28 and 37% in beams B-I, B-II and B-III, over the control beam B respectively. However, comparing the load carrying capacity of the corroded beams, it is clear that the recorded enhancement was not as much as in the case of the uncorroded beams (that is, 10, 17 and 29% above the predicted strength of a similar unstrengthened—corroded beam for the used three strengthening schemes respectively). This can be attributed to degradation of the shear strength of the substrate concrete caused by propagation of corrosion cracks near to CFRP strengthening strips. It seems that confinement provided by the U-shaped CFRP anchorages may have helped prevent early debonding.

Unstrengthened control beams B and B-c failed, as expected, in flexure with extensive yielding of the tension steel, followed by crushing of the concrete in the compression zone. The failure mode of all externally bonded CFRP-strengthened beams (B-I, B-I,c, B-II, and B-II,c) was by CFRP debonding, which started near the center of the span. Large cracks and debonding of the strips closer to the center span were the only indications that failure was imminent. Given that all failures initiated at midspan, it might be concluded that the U shaped CFRP anchorages were effective, and helped prevent premature failures by CFRP peeling off, which typically starts at beam endings, due to shear cracking growth. The examination of the fracture surface of the strengthened beams

Table 3. Test results.

Beam	f_c' MPa	Failure load (kN)	Ultimate strain CFRP (µε)	Ultimate deflection (mm)	M_u (kNm)	$M_{0.001}$ (kNm)	ϕ_u (km^{-1})	$\phi_{0.001}$ (km^{-1})	$\dfrac{M_{0.001}\,\phi_{0.001}}{M_u\,\phi_u}$
B	25.0	135	–	42.20	87.75	45.61	165.4	53.2	5.98
B-I	25.5	168	8000	20.10	109.20	76.44	28.2	11.1	3.63
B-II	25.5	174	9500	22.10	113.10	71.71	32.6	12.8	4.02
B-III	24.8	185	12000	27.60	120.25	69.15	38.8	14.5	4.65
B-C	24.8	126	–	48.20	81.90	46.91	180.1	56.2	5.59
B-I,C	25.1	138	4880	26.80	89.70	63.61	24.0	11.5	2.94
B-II,C	25.0	147	6500	27.10	95.55	64.91	28.0	12.4	3.32
B-III,C	24.8	163	9400	29.70	105.95	69.86	34.8	13.1	4.03

raised the possibility that the debonding failure was caused by differential displacements in crack tips. The development of a crack in the concrete substrate might produce high strain concentration points in the CFRP, initiating a local debonding, which then progresses along the beam (Fig. 6). Beams B-III and B-III,c strengthened with NSMS failed also due to debonding of the CFRP strips. Debonding was observed at both ends of the strips as well as at the midspan. This was attributed to shear stress concentration at the cutoff point as well as at the vicinity of flexural cracks. However, final debonding of the CFRP strips was always controlled by the high shear stress at the strips' cutoff points. Examination of the failure surface after the load had been removed showed shear failure in the concrete substrate, which appeared at the level of the steel reinforcement, with the adhesive and the CFRP strip remaining intact (Fig. 7).

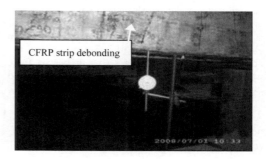

CFRP strip debonding

Figure 6.   Failure of beam B-I,c.

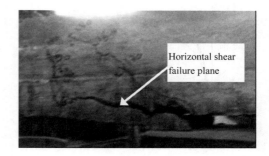

Horizontal shear failure plane

Figure 7.   Failure of beam B-III,c.

3.2 Deflection

Figures 8 and 9 show the measured load-deflection response for the tested beams. For uncorroded beams the control beam had the largest deflections at mid-span. Bonding CFRP strips to beam, however, reduced their deflections. The strengthened beams showed the usual elastic and inelastic parts of their deflection but failed at significantly less final deflections than the unstrengthened control beam. Comparing deflection behavior for corroded and uncorroded strengthened beams, it is clear that the enhancement provided by the CFRP strengthening strips at the service and ultimate limit states was significantly affected by steel corrosion. The effect of main steel corrosion used in the present work is evident in these figures, as both the corroded beams' stiffness especially in inelastic part of their load-deflection behavior and the ultimate strength were decreased compared to the uncorroded beams.

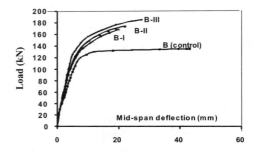

Figure 8.   Load-deflection response of the uncorroded beams.

3.3 Ultimate strain in CFRP strengthening strips

The maximum tensile strain experienced by the CFRP strips at failure load of each beam, are shown in Table 3 and Figure 10. For the three used schemes, the experimental results showed that the reduction in the maximum tensile strain experienced by the CFRP strips caused by main steel corrosion at the failure load was about 64%, 52% and 38% respectively. Also, the CFRP strips in all the beams were understressed, and the maximum utilization of the strength of strips for uncorroded beams was observed for beam B-III (that is, 80% of the ultimate strength of the strip), CFRP strengthening strips in uncorroded beams B-I and B-II were able to develop a stress of 53% and 63% of their ultimate strength respectively.

The maximum utilization of the strength of strips for corroded beams was observed for beam B-III,c (that is, 49% of the ultimate strength of the strip),CFRP strengthening strips in beams B-I,c and B-II,c were able to develop a stress of 19% and 30% of their ultimate strength respectively.

3.4 Ductility

The Canadian Highway Bridge Design Code (Canadian Standards Association (CSI) 2000),

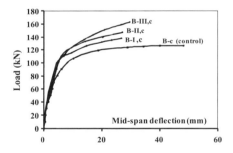

Figure 9. Load-deflection response of the corroded beams.

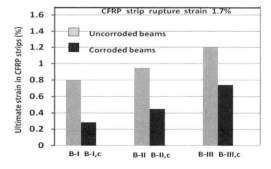

Figure 10. Ultimate strain in the CFRP strips.

based on the work of Jaeger et al. 1977, assesses the ductility of FRP-strengthened sections with a Performance Factor (PF) equal to $M_u\phi_u/(M_{0.001}\phi_{0.001})$, where M and ϕ are the beam moment and curvature and the subscripts u refer to the ultimate state, and 0.001 to the service state that corresponds to a concrete maximum compressive strain of 0.001. This performance factor must be greater than 4 for rectangular sections and greater than 6 for T sections.

Table 3 lists the values of the performance factors for each of the tested beams. According to the CSI (2000) recommendations, the performance factor should exceed 4 to prevent the occurrence of sudden failure in the strengthened flexural members. As seen in Table 3, the performance factor of all CFRP-strengthened uncorroded beams are lower than the value obtained for the control beam (5.98). However, the performance factor of CFRP-strengthened uncorroded beams B-II (4.02) and B-III (4.65) was higher than the minimum acceptable value according to CSI (2000) recommendations. The effect of steel corrosion used in this study was to decrease the performance factor of all tested beams. The greatest reduction in performance factor of the CFRP-corroded beams was obtained in beam B-I,c (20%), followed by beams B-II, c and B-III,c exhibiting decreases in the performance factor of 17 and 13% respectively. As can be seen in Table 3, the use of the NSMS technique enabled corroded beam B-III,c to attain a performance factor of 4.03, which, according to CSI (2000) recommendations, is adequate to guarantee satisfactory ductility.

4 CONCLUSION

This paper presented the results of an experimental program investigating the flexural behavior of control and CFRP-strengthened reinforced concrete beams subjected to a corrosive environment. Based on the test results, the following conclusions are provided to guide further research and development:

1. In general, the results of this experimental study showed that the load carrying capacity of CFRP-strengthened RC beams that are experiencing flexural reinforcement corrosion was significantly affected by weakening of the concrete cover caused by corrosion cracks. Reduction in load carrying capacity caused by 5% corrosion was increased from 7% for the unstrengthened beams to 18% for CFRP strengthened beam B-I; however, strengthening beam B-III with the same amount of CFRP strips but using the NSMS technique reduced the reduction in load carrying capacity to 12%.

2. For the used three strengthening schemes, the experimental results showed that the ultimate strength of the CFRP strengthened-uncorroded beams increased by about 24%, 28% and 37% respectively above the predicted strength of a similar unstrengthened-uncorroded beam, however, the recorded enhancement in the load carrying capacity of corroded beams was not as much as in the case of uncorroded beams (that is, 10%, 17% and 29% respectively above the predicted strength of a similar unstrengthened-corroded beam).

3. The CFRP strips in all test beams were under-stressed, and the maximum utilization of the strength of strips for uncorroded beams was observed for beam B-III (that is, 80% of the ultimate strength of the strip). The CFRP strips in uncoroded beams B-I and B-II were able to develop a stress of 53% and 63% of their ultimate strength respectively; however, the maximum utilization of the strength of strips for corroded beams was observed for beam B-III,c (that is, 49% of the ultimate strength of the strip). CFRP strips in beams B-I,c and B-II,c were able to develop a stress of 19% and 30% of their ultimate strength respectively.

4. Longitudinal cracking was observed after corrosion for both strengthened and unstrengthened specimens; however, the crack width for the strengthened beams using scheme II was about 50% of that measured for the unstrengthened specimen. This can be ascribed to the confinement provided by the transverse U-sheet stirrups wrapping the cross section, which would limit the development of corrosion cracks.

5. According to the Canadian Highway Bridge Design Code (Canadian Standards Association 2000) ductility criterion, both the corroded and uncorroded beams that strengthened using NSMS fulfilled the criterion, whereas the corroded beams that were strengthened using externally bonded CFRP strips did not (Beams B-I,c and B-II,c).

REFERENCES

American Concrete Institute (ACI). 1996a. Corrosion of metals in concrete, *ACI 222r-96*, Committee 222, Detroit.

American Concrete Institute (ACI). 2002. Guide for the design and construction of externally bonded FRP systems for strengthening concrete structures. *ACI 440.2 R-02*, Farmington Hills, Mich.

Al-Sulaimani, G.J., Kaleemullah, M., Basunbul, I.A. & Rasheeduzzafar. 1990. Influence of corrosion and cracking on bond behaviour of reinforced concrete members. *ACI Struct. J.*, 87 (2): 220–231.

Andrade, C., Alonso, C. & Molina, F.A. 1993. Cover cracking as a function of rebar corrosion: Part I—Experimental test. *Mat. and Struct.*, 26: 453–464.

Almusallam, A.A., Al-Gahtani, A.S., Aziz, A.R., Dakhil, H.F. & Rasheeduzzafar 1996. Effect of Reinforcement Corrosion on Flexural Behavior of Concrete Slabs. *J. Mat. Eng.*, 8 (3): 123–127.

Bonaldo, E., Oliveira de Barros, J.A. & Lourenco, P.B. 2008. Efficient strengthening Technique to Increase the Flexural Resistance of Existing RC Slabs. *J. Compos. Constr.*, 12 (2): 149–159.

Broomfield, J.P. 1997. Corrosion of steel in concrete: Understanding, investigation and repair, E&FN Spon, London.

Badawi, M. & Soudki, K. 2005. Control of corrosion-induced damage in reinforced concrete beams using carbon fiber-reinforced polymer laminates. *J. Compos. Constr.*, 9 (2): 195–201.

Canadian Standards Association 2000. Canadian Highway Bridge Design Code. *Section 16, Fiber-reinforced Structures*, Rexdale, Ont., Canada.

Cabrera, J.G. 1996. Deterioration of concrete structures due to reinforcement steel corrosion. *Cement and Concrete Compos.*, Barking, U.K., 18: 47–59.

El Maaddawy, T. & Soudki, K. 2005. Carbon-Fiber-Reinforced Polymer Repair to Extend Service Life of Corroded Reinforced Concrete Beams. *J. Compos. Constr.*, 9 (2): 187–194.

Garcez, M., Meneghetti, L. & Filho, L. 2008. Structural Performance of RC Beams Poststrengthened with Carbon, Aramid, and Glass FRP Systems. *J. Compos. Constr.*, 12 (5): 522–530.

Hassan, T. & Rizkalla, S. 2003. Investigation of Bond in Concrete Structures Strengthened with Near Surface Mounted Carbon Fiber Reinforced Polymer Strips. *J. Compos. Constr.*, 7 (3): 248–257.

Jaeger, L.G., Mufti, A.A. & Tadros, G. 1997. The concept of the overall performance factor in rectangular section reinforced concrete members. *Proc. 3rd Int. Symp. on Non-Metallic (FRP) Reinforcement for Concrete Structures*, Vol. 2, Sapporo, Japan: 551–559.

Kim, Y.J., Longworth, J.M., Wight, R.G. & Green, M.F. 2008. Flexural of Two-Way Slabs Strengthened with Prestressed or Nonprestressed CFRP Sheets. *J. Compos. Constr.*, 12 (4): 366–374.

Lam, L. & Teng, J.G. 2001. Strengthening of RC Cantilever Slabs Bonded with GFRP Strips. *J. Compos. Constr.*, 5 (4): 221–227.

Neal, k.w. 2000. FRPs for structural rehabilitation: A survey of recent progress. *Prog. Struct. Eng. Mater.*, 2 (2): 133–138.

Niu, H. & Wu, Z. 2006. Effects of FRP-Concrete Interface Bond Properties on the Performance of RC Beams Strengthened in Flexure with Externally Bonded FRP Sheets. *J. Compos. Constr.*, 18 (5): 723–731.

Petrou, M.F., Parler, D., Harries, K.A. & Rizos, D.C. 2008. Strengthening of Reinforced Concrete Bridge Decks Using carbon Fiber-Reinforced Polymer Composite Materials. *J. Bridge Engrg.*, 13 (5): 455–467.

Quattlebaum J.B., Harries, K.A. & Petrou, M.F. 2005. Comparison of Three Flexural Retrofit Systems under Monotonic and Fatigue Loads. *J. Bridge Eng.* 10 (6): 731–740.

Seim, W., Horman, M., Karbhari, V. & Seible, F. 2001. External FRP Poststrengthening of Scaled Concrete Slabs. *J. Compos. Constr.*, 5 (2): 67–75.

Soudki, K., S. El-Salakawy, E. & Craig, B. 2007. Behavior of CFRP Strengthened Reinforced Concrete Beams in Corrosive Environment. *J. Compos. Constr.*, 11 (3): 291–298.

Tumialan, J.G., Vatovec, M. & Kelley, P.K. 2007. Case Study: Strengthening of Parking Garage Decks with Near-Surface-Mounted CFRP Bars. *J. Compos. Constr.*, 11 (5): 523–530.

Tan, K.H. & Zhao, H. 2004. Strengthening of Openings in One-Way Reinforced-Concrete Slabs Using Carbon Fiber-Reinforced Polymer Systems. *J. Compos. Constr.*, 8 (5): 393–402.

Triantafillou, T.C. 1998. Strengthening of Structures with advanced FRPs. *Prog. Struct. Eng. Mater.*, 1, 126–134.

Teng, J.G., Lam, L., Chan, W. & Wang, J. 2000. Retrofitting of Deficient RC Cantilever Slabs Using GFRP Strips. *J. Compos. Constr.*, 4 (2): 75–84.

Val, D.V. & Melchers, R.E. 1997. Reliability of Deteriorating RC Slab Bridges. *J. Struct. Engrg.*, 123 (12): 1638–1644.

Val, D.V. 2007. Deterioration of Strength of RC Beams due to Corrosion and Its Influence on Beam Reliability." *J. Struct. Eng.*, 133 (9): 1297–1306.

Val, D.V. 2005. Effect of different limit states on life-cycle cost of RC structures in corrosive environment. *J. Infrastruct. Syst.* 11 (4): 231–240.

Concrete Solutions – Grantham, Mechtcherine & Schneck (eds)
© 2012 Taylor & Francis Group, London, ISBN 978-0-415-61622-5

Using steel fibred high strength concrete for repairing normal strength concrete beams and slabs

I. Iskhakov & Y. Ribakov
Ariel University Center of Samaria, Israel

K. Holschemacher & T. Mueller
Leipzig University of Applied Sciences, Germany

ABSTRACT: Steel Fibred High Strength Concrete (SFHSC) is an effective material that can be used for repairing concrete elements. The design of Normal Strength Concrete (NSC) elements that should be repaired using SFHSC can be based on general concepts for design of two-layer beams, consisting of SFHSC in compressed zone and NSC without fibres in the tensile one. It was previously reported that such elements are effective when their section carries rather big bending moments. Steel fibres added to high strength concrete increase its ultimate deformations due to the additional energy dissipation potential contributed by the fibres. By changing the fibres' content, a required ductility level of the repaired element can be achieved. Providing proper ductility is important for design of structures to dynamic loadings. The current study discusses experimental results that form a basis for finding optimal fibre content yielding the highest Poisson coefficient and ductility of the repaired elements' sections. Some technological issues as well as distribution of fibres in the cross section of two-layer bending elements are investigated. The experimental results, obtained in the frame of this study, form a basis for general technological provisions, related to repairing of NSC beams and slabs using SFHSC.

1 INTRODUCTION

Repair of concrete structures can be classified as restoring the original structural shape and strengthening the damaged members with inadequate load bearing capacity. There are different techniques available for retrofitting and strengthening of various reinforced concrete structural elements. The methods were developed due to different causes, such as inadequate maintenance, overloading of the reinforced concrete member, corrosion of the steel reinforcement and other reasons.

These methods include steel plate bonding, external pre-stressing, section enlargement, and reinforced concrete jacketing. Although these techniques can effectively increase the element's load bearing capacity, they are often susceptible to corrosion damage which results in failure of the strengthening system (Banu and Taranu, 2010). Strengthening by section enlargement can be performed by adding a new concrete layer to the structural element. The most important issue in this case is to ensure proper bonding between the concrete of the existing element and that applied for its strengthening.

Thanoon et al. (2005) have studied the structural behavior of cracked reinforced concrete one-way slabs, repaired using different techniques. Five techniques were used for the purpose of repair: cement grout, epoxy injection, ferro-cement layer, carbon fibre strip and section enlargement. The slabs were loaded up to failure. The efficiency of different repair and strengthening techniques and their effects on the structural behavior were analyzed. All repair techniques were found to be able to enhance the structural capacity of cracked concrete slabs.

Ultra High Performance Fibre Reinforced Concrete (UHPFRC) has also low permeability, making it suitable for rehabilitation of existing concrete structures (Oesterlee et al., 2009). A thin layer of UHPFRC, cast on an existing normal strength concrete element, increases its load bearing capacity and serviceability. Comprehensive experimental studies on the behaviour of UHPFRC with additional bar reinforcement were also recently performed.

The development of this idea for rehabilitation of concrete structures has been presented and validated by means of further applications (Bruhwiler and E. Denarie, 2008). It combines protection and resistance functions of UHPFRC with NSC. The rehabilitated structures have significantly improved durability. Full scale realization of the concept in

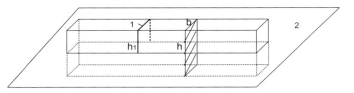

Figure 1. A general view of a roof beam and slab: 1—uncovered part of the beam, 2—roof slab.

realistic site conditions demonstrated its potential for wide applications.

A similar problem appears in roof beams, in which a part of their section comes above the slab, as shown in Figure 1. This uncovered part of the beam is subjected to an aggressive surrounding environment. As a result, the compressed zone of the beam's section is usually locally damaged. For repairing of such beams a recently developed idea of two-layer bending elements can be successfully applied (Iskhakov and Ribakov, 2007). In such beams the damaged part (see position 1 in Fig. 1) is proposed to be replaced by a Steel Fibred High Strength Concrete (SFHSC).

It was shown that the optimal Fibre Weight Ratio (FWR) can be selected based on the ductility level requirements (Iskhakov and Ribakov, 2011). As follows from the previous research, steel fibres have little effect on beams' elastic deformations, but increase the ultimate ones, due to the additional energy dissipation potential of fibres. Providing proper ductility is important for design of structures to seismic, wind and other dynamic loadings. Therefore, calculation of fibre content for such elements is important, like that of reinforcing steel bars for normal RC beams.

In the current study, a method for obtaining the class of SFHSC and the load bearing capacity of the beam after retrofitting are proposed. With this aim experimental investigations were carried out. SFHSC cubic and cylindrical specimens as well as short two-layer beams, made of NSC in the tensile zone and SFHSC in the compressed one, were tested. These experimental results together with those, obtained by Bruhwiler and E. Denarie (2008) and Oesterlee et al. (2009), show a promising way for using SFHSC for repairing damaged beams and slabs.

2 AIMS AND SCOPE

The current research is aimed at studying the load bearing and deformation behaviour of SFHSC. Dependence of fresh SFHSC properties on addition of fibres is investigated. Affect of steel fibres on hardened concrete properties, like compressive, splitting tensile and flexural tensile strength, is also studied. Influence of different fibre types and contents on stiffness and deformations characteristics of SFHSC is investigated too.

Technological aspects of casting the SFHSC layer of two-layer beams were studied, using small scale beams. Such aspects like fibre distribution in the SFHSC layer and interaction between the SFHSC layer and the NSC one were investigated.

The experimental results allow proper selection of the most efficient fibre type and content. It also allows more economical expenditure of steel. As a result, the cost of fibre reinforced elements will decrease, making them more attractive for practical applications.

3 EXPERIMENTAL PROGRAM

The experimental program includes four stages. During the first stage, the influences of geometry and tensile strength of fibres on compressive and splitting tensile strengths of HSC were studied. For this reason cubic specimens with fibre contents of 0, 20, 40 and 60 kg/m³ were tested.

The second stage was aimed to study the Poisson deformations in cylindrical SFHSC specimens. These deformations are associated with the energy dissipation ability of the element that corresponds to its ductility level. The same fibre contents as in the first stage were used.

The third stage was aimed at testing short SFHSC beams with reinforcing bars. The beams were prepared using the most appropriate type and content of fibres, according to the results of the first two stages.

The fourth stage was aimed at testing short two-layer beams without reinforcing bars in order to study technological aspects and fibre distribution in the SFHSC layer.

Three different fibre types were selected: two straight fibre types with end hooks having different ultimate tensile strength (F1, F2) and one corrugated fibre type (F3). The properties of the selected steel fibre types, used for the HSSFRC mixtures, are shown in Table 1.

All types of fibres had the same aspect ratio $\lambda = l_f/d_f = 50$, where l_f, and d_f are the fibre length and diameter, respectively. Fibre types F1 and F3

Table 1. Steel fibre types.

Description	Fibre type		
	F1	F2	F3
Shape	Straight	Straight	Corrugated
Surface	Plane	Plane	Plane
Cross-section	Circular	Circular	Circular
Anchorage	Hooked ends	Hooked ends	Continuous

Parameters	Units	Values		
l_f	mm	50	50	50
d_f	mm	1	1	1
f_t	MPa	1100	1900	1100
n_f	kg^{-1}	3150	3100	2850

were normal-strength fibres with a tensile strength f_t of 1100 MPa. F2 was a high-strength fibre with a tensile strength of 1900 MPa. The value n_f represents the number of fibres per kg. In all cases the modulus of elasticity was 200000 MPa.

The plane concrete mixture included the following components:

- composite Portland cement with portions of granulated slag and limestone between 6 and 20% with a density of 3.05 kg/dm^3 and a fineness of 4660 cm^2/g;
- fly ash with specific gravity of 2.3 kg/dm^3 and grain sizes between 2 and 290 µm;
- polycarboxylic ether-based superplasticizer with a density of 1.07 kg/dm^3;
- long-term retarder, based on phosphonic acid with a density of 1.17 kg/dm^3;
- natural sand with a fraction size of 0 to 2 mm;
- two different types of gravel with a fraction size of 2 to 8 mm and 8 to 16 mm.
- Sand and gravel had a specific gravity of 2.65 kg/dm^3.

The concrete compressive and splitting tensile strengths were measured for six cubes with an edge length of 150 mm for each fibre type and content. Additionally, the elasticity modulus was investigated on three cylinders with a height of 30 cm and a diameter of 15 cm. At the second stage, for each fibre content, three cylinders were cast. The specimens were tested 28 days after casting.

At the third stage, four-point bending tests were carried out. For this reason HSC and SFHSC beams with a cross section of 150×150 mm and a length of 700 mm were cast. For each fibre content 18 beams were cast. 12 of them were with two different steel bar reinforcement ratios (6 with 0.25% and 6 with 1.0%) and 6 beams without steel bar

reinforcement. Additionally, stirrups (Ø6) were attached only at the supports to hold the bar reinforcement. The longitudinal steel bars were Ø6 and Ø12 mm and yield strength of 500 MPa.

4 EXPERIMENTAL RESULTS

4.1 Cubic specimens

Average compressive strengths in cubic specimens with different fibre types and contents are given in Table 2. Following this table, for normal-strength fibre types (F1 and F3) the SFHSC the strength increased up to FWR = 40 kg/m^3 and decreased for FWR = 60 kg/m^3. For high strength fibres (F2) the SFHSC compressive strength showed similar values for all fibre contents. Hence, based on the current experimental results, FWR = 40 kg/m^3 is the optimal fibre content.

Average tensile splitting strengths in the tested specimens are presented in Table 3. The strength increased for all fibre types proportionally to the fibre content. The strength for fibre type F1 was the highest, compared to other fibre types. Specimens with fibre type F3 showed the lowest splitting strength. For all fibre types the highest tensile splitting strength reached its maximum value, when FWR was equal to 60 kg/m^3.

Steel fibres take the tensile stresses that yield cracks in the concrete matrix. To guarantee sufficient section ductility of fibred concrete elements, required to withstand design loadings, proper fibre contents should be used. Following Table 3, increasing the fibre content provides higher Plastic Energy Dissipation (PED). However,

Table 2. Compressive strength of cubic specimens, MPa.

Type of fibres	Fibre content, %			
	0	20	40	60
F1		86.8	91.2	88.1
F2	86.1	91.4	91.4	92.6
F3		86.1	95.3	93.4

Table 3. Splitting tensile strength of cubic specimens, MPa.

Type of fibres	Fibre content, %			
	0	20	40	60
F1		5.1	5.6	6.2
F2	4.2	4.8	5.0	5.8
F3		4.8	4.9	5.1

FWR = 0

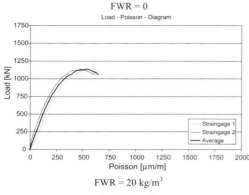

FWR = 20 kg/m³

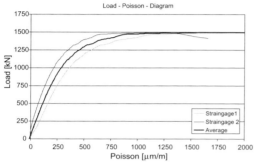

FWR = 40 kg/m³

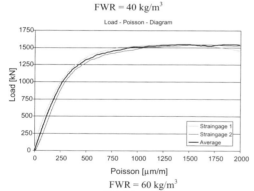

FWR = 60 kg/m³

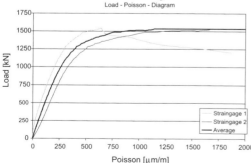

Figure 2. Poisson deformations vs. applied load for specimens with different FWR.

it is not recommended to increase the fibre content insufficiently, because of technological aspects and from the economical viewpoint. Hence, optimal fibre content should be applied.

Summarising the above presented results and taking into account the economical aspects, the fibre content value of 40 kg/m³ was selected as an optimal one. It should be mentioned that the option for improving compressive strength is preferable for repairing of existing beams and slabs, compared to the tensile splitting one, because SFHSC is effective for repairing mainly the compressive zone of bending elements.

4.2 Cylindrical specimens

The concrete, used for these specimens, had a compressive strength of about 90 MPa. It was previously demonstrated that steel fibres have little effect on elastic deflections, but the ultimate deflections of the section increase due to additional plastic energy dissipation potential (Iskhakov and Ribakov, 2008).

In the frame of the tests, longitudinal and Poisson deformations were measured. Two strain gauges were used for measuring Poisson deformations. Figure 2 shows the test results for the F1 type fibre weight ratios that were applied in the frame of this study (0, 20, 40 and 60 kg/m³).

As follows from the figure, up to about half of the ultimate load capacity, the specimens' behavior was elastic. After reaching the ultimate load value, all specimens exhibited plastic behavior from the Poisson deformations' viewpoint. Such behavior yields opening of longitudinal cracks in the cylindrical specimens. For fibred specimens, the ultimate deformations were 1.5 … 2 times higher, compared to those without fibres.

The energy dissipated during loading and unloading of cylindrical specimens with different FWR is given in Table 4. As follows from the table, the maximum energy dissipation (and correspondingly maximum ductility) was obtained for FWR = 40 kg/m³. Further increase of FWR yielded a significant decrease in PED. Similar results were obtained also from the viewpoint of longitudinal

Table 4. Energy, dissipated in cylindrical specimens with different FWR.

Fibre Content, kg/m³	Dissipated energy, kN · m/m
0	0
20	1.075
40	1.632
60	0.310

deformations. It proved the efficiency of the previously selected FWR value of 40 kg/m³.

It is known that energy dissipation and Poisson deformations are related to the element's ductility. As these characteristics become higher, the ductility parameter increases, accordingly. Based on tests, it should be concluded that the required ductility level can be calculated as a function of FWR.

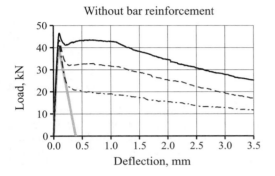

Without bar reinforcement

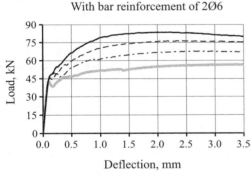

With bar reinforcement of 2Ø6

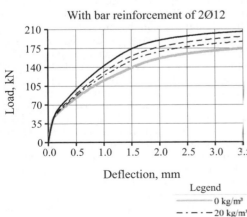

With bar reinforcement of 2Ø12

Legend
― 0 kg/m³
― · ― · ― 20 kg/m³
― ― ― ― 40 kg/m³
――――― 60 kg/m³

Figure 3.   Load—deflection behavior of tested beams.

This may form a basis for further development of existing design provisions regarding using SFHSC for repairing RC beams and slabs.

4.3   Short one-layer SFHSC beams

The influence of different fibre content and type as well as various bar reinforcement on the behaviour of HSC and SFHSC beams was studied. Six beams for each fibre content were tested. F1 type fibres were used. Figure 3 shows typical load-deflection curves for different fibre contents and steel bar reinforcement.

As follows from this figure, all specimens demonstrated higher loads in the elastic–plastic range as the fibre content became higher. The bearing capacity was also increased. The tests demonstrated that the PED significantly grows, as the fibre content became higher.

In specimens without bar reinforcement, the load in the elastic-plastic range decreased. For beams with 2Ø6 bar reinforcement in that range the load was almost constant. When 2Ø12 reinforcement bars were used, the load increased.

It should be noted that additional experiments, carried out by the authors in the frame of this study, have shown no significant difference in behaviour of specimens with bar reinforcement and this was observed for fibres with normal and high tensile strength (type F1 and F2, respectively). For specimens with fibre F3 with 2Ø6 mm the loading rate at 3.5 mm was clearly lower, compared to that in specimens with straight fibre types.

Figure 4.   A net for evaluation of fibres' distribution in a fractured section of a beam.

Table 5. Average distribution of fibres in the compressed section zone.

Section side	Row	Specimen no.											
		1				2				3			
		Column				Column				Column			
		C1	C2	C3	C4	C1	C2	C3	C4	C1	C2	C3	C4
Left	R2	7	1	1	2	3	–	1	3	1	–	2	1
	R1	2	3	2	2	1	2	1	1	1	–	–	–
Right	R1	2	–	4	–	–	–	3	1	–	4	–	–
	R2	3	2	–	3	3	1	4	2	1	2	3	–

The experiments show that the initial crack load is slightly influenced by the fibre content. According to the test results for beams with fibre content of 60 kg/m³, an initial crack load was higher than in specimens with lower fibre contents. It is especially relevant for the specimens without bar reinforcement.

It should be mentioned that the tested short beams had different failure modes. Specimens with a bar reinforcement ratio of 1% or lower (2Ø12 or no reinforcing bars, respectively) failed in shear or compression. The same failure mechanism was observed for specimens with low fibre contents (0 and 20 kg/m³). For fibre contents from 40 to 60 kg/m³ primary compression failure was observed.

4.4 Short two-layer beams

Three two-layer beams with FWR = 30 kg/m³, tested in the current study, consisted of SFHSC in the compressed zone and NSC in the tensile one. No reinforcing bars were used at this stage. As mentioned above, the experiments were aimed at studying the fibre distribution in the SFHSC layer. The depth of NSC and SFHSC layers were equal to the half of the beam section height.

The dimensions of the beams were 150 × 150 × 700 mm. The beams' production included two stages. At the first stage, a normal strength concrete mixture was produced and the tensile zone of the beams was cast and vibrated for 15 sec. The second stage included producing an SFHSC mixture and casting the beams' compressed zone. After that the beams were also vibrated for 15 sec.

The beams were subjected to four-point loading. In order to analyse the fibre distribution in the compressed zone of fractured sections (after the beams' failure), each fractured section was divided into four rows (R1 ... R4) and four columns (C1 ... C4) of cells with an edge length of 3.75 cm (Fig. 4). It should be mentioned that fibred concrete was used just in the two upper rows R1 and R2 (compression zone), but for convenience the grid was placed on the whole section, as shown in the figure.

The obtained results of fibre distribution density are summarized in Table 5. Following this table, it seems that the fibre distribution is higher in the HSC layers that are close to the neutral axis of the section (rows R2). However, the total number of fibres in the left and right section sides for all tested specimens was 37 and 36, respectively. Hence, the average number of fibres in these sides was almost the same (12 and 12.3, respectively). It is very important for repairing of beams and slabs, as uniform fibre distribution provides a higher quality covering layer and yields more effective utilization of the elements' compressed zone.

5 CONCLUSIONS

SFHSC is used for repairing normal strength concrete elements. The design of such elements is based on concepts developed for two-layer beams, consisting of SFHSC in the compressed zone and NSC without fibres in the tensile one.

High strength concrete is known as a brittle material. Addition of steel fibres increases ultimate deformations in the post-cracking elastic-plastic range of the repaired elements and provides supplementary energy dissipation potential in the structure.

Short SFHSC beams with bar reinforcement demonstrated higher loads in the elastic–plastic range as the fibre content became higher. The tests demonstrate that the plastic energy dissipation significantly grows, as the fibre content becomes higher. In specimens without bar reinforcement the load in the elastic-plastic range decreases.

The required ductility of the repaired element depends on the fibre content. Experimental results, obtained in this study, provided the optimal fibre content and type, yielding the highest Poisson coefficient that is directly related to the required ductility level.

686

The distribution of fibres in the cross section of two-layer beams was studied experimentally. It was shown that the fibres are distributed uniformly in the SFHSC layer. This is very important for the repair of beams and slabs, because such distribution provides a higher quality of the SFHSC layer and yields more effective utilization of the elements' compressed zone.

The obtained results form a basis for general design and technological provisions, on repairing of NSC beams and slabs using SFHSC in their upper part.

REFERENCES

Banu, D. and Taranu, N. 2010. Traditional Solutions for Strengthening Reinforced Concrete Slabs, Buletinul Institutului Politecnic Din Iasi, Publicat de Universitatea Tehnica "Gheorghe Asachi" din Iasi, LVI (LX), Fasc. 3.

Bruhwiler, E. and Denarie, E. 2008. Rehabilitation of Concrete Structures Using Ultra-High Performance Fibre Reinforced Concrete, *Proceedings of the Second International Symposium on Ultra-High Performance Concrete,* 5–7 March 2008, Kassel, Germany.

Holschemacher, K., Mueller, T. and Ribakov, Y. 2010. Effect of steel fibres on mechanical properties of high strength concrete. *Materials and Design*, 31 2604–2615.

Iskhakov, I. and Ribakov, Y. 2007. A design method for two-layer beams consisting of normal and fibred high strength concrete. *Materials and Design*, 28: 1672–1677.

Iskhakov, I. and Ribakov, Y. 2008. Two-layer prestressed beams consisting of normal and steel fibreed high strength concrete. *Materials and Design*, 29: 1616–1622.

Iskhakov, I. and Ribakov, Y. 2011. Two-Layer Beams from Normal and Fibreed High Strength Concrete, *6-th International Structural Engineering and Construction Conference,* Zurich, Switzerland, 21–26 June.

Oesterlee, C., Bruhwiler, E. and Denarie, E. 2009. Structural Behaviour of Composite Elements Combining Reinforced Ultra-High Performance Fibre-Reinforced Concrete (UHPFRC) and Reinforced Concrete, *Beton und Stahlbetonbau*, 104(8): 462–470 (in German).

Schnabl, S., Saje, M., Turk, G. and Planinc, I. 2007. Analytical Solution of Two-Layer Beam Taking into Account Interlayer Slip and Shear Deformation, *Journal of Structural Engineering*, 133 (6): 886–894.

Thanoon, W.A., Jaafar, M.S., Razali, M. Kadir, A. and Noorzaei, J. 2005. Repair and structural performance of initially cracked reinforced concrete slabs, *Construction and Building Materials*, 19 (8): 595–603.

Concrete Solutions – Grantham, Mechtcherine & Schneck (eds)
© 2012 Taylor & Francis Group, London, ISBN 978-0-415-61622-5

Improving the flexural performance of reinforced concrete one-way slabs

K.K. Shadhan, A.S.A. Al-Ameeri & N.H. Ali
College of Engineering, University of Babylon -Babylon-Iraq

ABSTRACT: This research presents an experimental study on flexural strengthening of reinforced concrete one-way slabs with two different systems. The first system is a conventional concrete overlay and the second system uses Carbon Fiber Reinforced Polymer (CFRP) strengthening. The suggested combination between the two systems is also studied. The experimental investigation was conducted using six small size one-way slab specimens. All slabs were tested to failure under simply supported conditions. Both strengthening systems increased the flexural strength and reduced the deflections and crack widths of the strengthened slabs. Two modes of failure were observed: debonding and rupture of the CFRP reinforcement. A significant increase in ultimate flexural capacity ranging from 13% to 139% was registered in all the strengthened slabs, as compared to the control slab. The slab which was strengthened with the suggested combined strengthening system exhibited the highest efficiency.

1 INTRODUCTION

The need for strengthening reinforced concrete structures to the original or a higher performance level due to mechanical damage, mistakes in design and/or construction works, functional changes or reinforcement corrosion has become common and necessary for economic reasons. It may also be necessary to strengthen old reinforced concrete structures as a result of damage in the structure due to environmental stresses or military operations.

In the past, reinforced concrete slabs were strengthened by conventional methods such as concrete overlay, span shortening and externally bonded steel reinforcement. Today there are several types of CFRP strengthening systems and techniques available to strengthen reinforced concrete slabs. The suitability of each system depends on the type of structure that shall be strengthened. Therefore, it is essential for engineers to understand the consequences of the design choice in terms of efficiency and failure mechanism for different systems before further attempts are carried out (Tan 2003).

Applying a concrete overlay is a conventional strengthening technique. The additional concrete overlay increases the lever arm of the resisting moment of the concrete section (Aprile et al., 2007). Detachment between the bare concrete and the new concrete overlay was observed during the tests, see Figure (1-a).

Many researchers have conducted experimental and analytical studies on concrete slabs strengthened in flexure using FRP strengthening systems (for example; Alkhrdaji et al., 1999, Tan 2003, and Costeira et al., 2007). The results have shown that externally bonded FRP sheets may be used to rehabilitate the entire behavior of slabs. However, one limitation in strengthening slabs is that the failure behavior at the ultimate load may become non-ductile, see Figure (1-b).

(1-a): Detachment of concrete overlay (Aprile et al., 2007)

(1-b): CFRP debonding (Tan, 2002) [1]

Figure 1.   Failure mode of strengthened RC one-way slab.

The main objective of this research is to study and compare the efficiencies of the conventional concrete overlay and relatively new CFRP strengthening systems. The suggestion of a combined system from these two systems has become necessary.

2 EXPERIMENTAL PROGRAM

This experimental study consisted of casting six reinforced concrete one-way slabs. Each slab had a 300 mm × 60 mm cross section. The flexural reinforcement of these slabs consisted of 5-Ø6 mm in the main direction and Ø6 mm @ 100 mm in the transverse direction. The flexural reinforcement ratio is 0.84% and is below the maximum reinforcement ratio allowed under the current ACI 318-05 code (2005). Figure (2) shows the cross section and the reinforcement details for the bare slab specimens.

2.1 Concrete materials

2.1.1 Cement
Ordinary Portland cement of Tasluja-Bazian mark (CEM1) was used in casting all the specimens. The cement was stored in air-tight plastic containers to avoid undue exposure to the atmosphere Physical and chemical composition and properties for the cement are given in Tables (1) and (2), respectively.

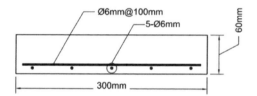

Figure 2. Cross-section of bare concrete slab.

Table 1. Physical properties for cement.

Property		Result	Iraqi specification limits (I.Q.S. 5/1984)
Fineness by air permeability method (Blaine)		348 m²/kg	≥230 m²/kg
Initial setting		125 min.	≥45 min.
Final setting		230 min.	≤600 min.
Soundness (Autoclave Method)		0.28%	≤0.8%
Compressive strength	3-day age	22.8 MPa	≥15 MPa
	7-day age	31.5 MPa	≥23 MPa

Table 2. Chemical analysis and compound composition for cement.

Oxides	Content, %	Iraqi specification limits (I.Q.S. 5/1984)
CaO	62.31	–
SiO$_2$	21.28	–
MgO	2.77	–
Fe$_2$O$_3$	3.60	–
Al$_2$O$_3$	5.31	–
SO$_3$	2.45	Not more than 2.8% if C3 A more than 5%
Free Lime	1.06	–
L.O.I	1.73	Not more than 4%
I.R	0.85	Not more than 1.5%
L.S.F	0.87	0.66%–1.02%
		Compound composition
C3S	39.61	–
C2S	31.13	–
C3 A	8.52	–
C4 AF	10.95	–

The properties conformed to the Iraqi Specifications Limits (I.Q.S. 5/1984).

2.1.2 Fine aggregate
Al-Akhaider natural sand was used as the fine aggregate. The sand was sieved at a sieve size of 4.75 mm to get rid of coarse aggregate. The sand was then washed and cleaned with water several times, later it was spread out and left to dry in air, after which it was ready for use. The grading of the sand conformed to the requirements of Iraqi Specifications Limits (I.Q.S. 45/1988) as shown in Table (3). Also, the physical properties of the fine aggregate are shown in Table (4).

2.1.3 Coarse aggregate
Crushed gravel from the Al-Nibaey region was used throughout this work with a maximum size of 14 mm to account for concrete cover. The gravel was washed and cleaned with water several times and left to dry in air. Table (5) shows the grading of aggregate and the limits specified by Iraqi Specifications (I.Q.S. 45/1988). Physical properties of the coarse aggregate are shown in Table (6).

2.1.4 Mixing water
Ordinary tap water was used for casting and curing all the specimens.

2.1.5 Concrete mix design
During the design phase of the experimental program 20–30 MPa concrete compressive strength was chosen for the bare slab to mimic an older reinforced concrete one-way slab that would be subject to strengthening. High strength concrete (greater

Table 3. Grading of fine aggregate.

Sieve size (mm)	Passing (%)	Iraqi specification limits (I.Q.S. 45/1984)
10	100	100
4.75	99	90–100
2.36	85	75–100
1.18	68	55–90
0.60	46	35–59
0.30	14	8–30
0.15	2	0–10

Table 4. Physical properties of fine aggregate.

Properties	Test results	Iraqi specification limits (I.Q.S. 45/1984)
Grading Zone	Second	–
Fineness Modulus	2.80	–
Sulfate content (SO$_3$)	0.38%	Not greater than 0.5%
Materials finer than sieve No. 200, %	2%	Not greater than 5%

Table 5. Grading of coarse aggregate.

Sieve size (mm)	Passing (%)	Iraqi specification limits (I.Q.S. 45/1984)
20	100	100
14	99	90–100
10	85	50–85
5	68	0–10

Table 6. Physical properties of coarse aggregate.

Properties	Test results	Iraqi specification limits (I.Q.S. 45/1984)
Specific gravity	2.60	–
Bulk density	1650 kg/m^3	–
Sulfate content (SO$_3$)	0.09%	Not greater than 0.1%
Materials finer than sieve No. 200, %	3%	Not greater than 3%

than 42 MPa) may be used for concrete overlay strengthening. Two different concrete strengths are obtained by using different cement content and water to cement ratios. The proportion of the two mixtures is presented in Table (7).

2.1.6 Concrete cylinders

To obtain a measure of the compressive strength of concrete, five cylinders (200 × 100) mm were cast from the concrete of each slab specimen. Three cylinders were tested in uniaxial compression for each slab specimen at the same time to obtain the compressive strength using an ELE Testing Machine (Capacity 200 Ton) in accordance with ASTM C39/C39M-05) (2005). The remaining two cylinders were tested for indirect tension by applying a line load along the 200 mm long side to obtain the splitting tensile strength in accordance with ASTM C496/C496M-04 (2005). The cylinder test results are summarized in Table (8).

2.2 Steel reinforcing bar

For all slab specimens, two sizes of steel reinforcing bars were used. Values for yield and ultimate strength are given in Table (9).

2.3 Concrete overlay process

Concrete overlay is a conventional strengthening technique. The additional concrete overlay increases the lever arm of the resisting moment of the concrete section. Here, a 30 mm thick concrete

Table 7.

Table 8. Test results for concrete cylinders.

	Bare slab		Overlay	
Specimen	Compressive strength (MPa)	Tensile strength (MPa)	Compressive strength (MP)	Tensile strength (MP)
UP-0	31.8	2.5	–	–
UP-1	31.5	2.5	–	–
RP-0	32.3	2.3	40.4	2.6
RP-1	31.1	2.4	43.0	2.8
RP-2	32.5	2.4	43.5	2.8
RN-2	31.8	2.3	48.9	2.9

Table 9. Reinforcing steel properties.

Diameter	Yield strength (MPa)	Yield strain	Ultimate strength (MPa)	Ultimate strain
6 mm	708	0.0034	740	0.051
4 mm	715	0.0032	750	0.054

layer were used as the concrete overlay. The minimum steel reinforcement was used (Ø4 mm @ 100 mm) for each direction. To prevent shear failure at the interface between the old concrete (bare RC slab) and the concrete overlay, Quickmast®-108 (epoxy bonding agent) was applied after superficial cleaning and concrete dust suction. Figures (3) and (4) show the concrete overlay details.

2.4 CFRP strengthening process

When loaded in tension, CFRP fibers do not exhibit any plastic behavior before rupture. SikaWarp®Hex-230C carbon fibers were used as

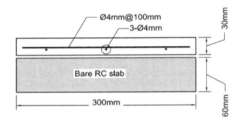

Figure 3. Reinforcement details of the concrete overlay.

flexural strengthening. The most crucial part of any strengthening application is the bond between the FRP and the surface to which the FRP is bonded. Proper bond ensures that the force carried by the structural member is transferred effectively to the FRP (Al-Mahaidi, 2003). Before the CFRP was applied to the soffit of the slabs, the surface of the concrete is ground using an electrical hand grinder to expose the aggregate and to obtain a clean sound surface, free of all contaminants such as cement laitance and dirt, see Figure (5). Then, Sikadur®-330 (two-part epoxy impregnation resin) was used in this work for the bonding of the CFRP sheet. The impregnation resin was mixed in 1:4 ratio by volume until it was uniform and spread to areas where the CFRP sheet has contact.

A two-part adhesive (black and white) was mixed in the required proportions, until the color was a uniform grey, and then applied with a special tool to the concrete surface to a thickness of 1.5 mm. The adhesive was also applied to the CFRP sheet to the same thickness. The CFRP sheet was then placed on the concrete, epoxy to epoxy, and a rubber roller was used to properly seat the CFRP sheet by exerting enough pressure so the epoxy was forced out on both sides of the

(4-a): Application of Quickmast®-108

(4-b): Casting of concrete overlay

Figure 4. Concrete overlay process.

(5-a): Grinding for concrete surface

(5-b): Final setting of CFRP

Figure 5. CFRP strengthening process.

CFRP sheet and the adhesive line did not exceed 2 mm in thickness.

The mechanical properties of carbon fibers and impregnation resin are taken from manufacturing specifications (Sika, 2005) and as shown in Tables (10) and (11), respectively.

2.5 Specimen identification and strengthening schemes

In order to identify the test specimens with different strengthening schemes, the following designation system is used:

- Concrete overlay: (R) for specimen with concrete overlay and (U) for specimen without concrete overlay.
- Loading type: (P) for positive moment and (N) for negative moment.
- Number of CFRP strengthening layer strips: (1) or (2).

Table (12) illustrates the specimen identification system used based on the specimen identification pattern described above.

As seen in Table (12) slab specimen UP-0 is not strengthened and directly subjected to the test loading to assess the structural performance of the control specimen. All of the remaining specimens are strengthened with concrete overlay and/or CFRP strengthening in order to evaluate the structural performances of the upgraded systems. Slab specimens UP-1 and RP-0 provided a comparison

Table 10. Technical properties of CFRP sheets (from manufacturer).

Properties	SikaWarp® Hex-230C
Tensile strength (MPa)	>3500
E-modulus (GPa)	230
Elongation at break (%)	>1.5
Width (mm)	50
Thickness (mm)	0.13

Table 11. Technical properties of impregnation resin (from manufacturer).

Properties	Sikadur®-330
Tensile strength, MPa	>30
Bond strength, MPa	Concrete fracture
E-modulus, GPa	4.5
Open time, min.	30 (at + 35°C)
Full cure, days	7 (at + 35°C)
Mixing ratio	1:4

Table 12. Slab specimens characteristics.

Specimen	Specimen cross section	Notes
UP-0		No concrete overlay No CFRP strengthening
UP-1		No concrete overlay 1-CFRP sheet strengthening applied to the bare concrete
RP-0		Concrete overlay No CFRP strengthening
RP-1		Concrete overlay 1-CFRP sheet strengthening applied to the bare concrete
RP-2		Concrete overlay 2-CFRP sheet strengthening applied to the bare concrete
RN-2		Concrete overlay 2-CFRP sheet strengthening applied to the concrete overlay

between the CFRP strengthening and concrete overlay techniques. The remaining two slab specimens (RP-1 and RP-2) are used to assess the effect of the amount of CFRP reinforcement. Finally, slab specimen RN-2 was tested with the restored concrete surface downside, in order to simulate the behavior of concrete slab sections at the supports and subjected to negative bending.

2.6 Test setup

All of the slab specimens were finally subjected to three-point tests up to failure. The load was applied making use of a 200 Ton capacity Universal Testing Machine. The distance between the specimen supports was 800 mm, see Figure (6). Deflection of the slab specimens was measured at mid-span using a dial gauge with travel distance of 50 mm and accuracy of 0.01 mm. To observe crack development, beam specimens were painted white with emulsion paint before testing. Cracks were traced by pencil.

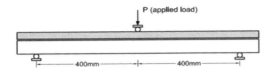

Figure 6. Test setup for slab specimens.

3 EXPERIMENTAL RESULTS

The main objective of the current research work is to investigate the two different strengthening systems on the flexural behavior of reinforced concrete one-way slabs. Test results were analyzed based on load-deflection curves, first cracking load, cracking behavior, ultimate load, failure modes and ductility.

3.1 Load-deflection curves

The load vs. deflection curves for all the slab specimens are shown in Figure (7). Generally, it can be observed that the load versus mid-span deflection response can be divided into three stages of behavior.

The first stage was characterized by an approximately linear relationship between the load and the mid-span deflection. During this stage of behavior, the section was uncracked and both the concrete and steel, in addition to the CFRP sheet, behave essentially elastic.

The second stage represents the behavior beyond the initial cracking of the composite section where the stiffness of the slab was decreased as indicated by the reduced slope of the load versus mid-span deflection curve. The end of this stage was distinguished when the main steel reinforcement started to exhibit inelastic behavior.

The third stage was characterized by a decreasing slope of the curve, where the tension steel reinforcement reaches the strain hardening stage.

The first crack was observed in control slab specimen UP-0 immediately after applying the load at 2.6 kN and yielded after a load of 15.3 kN was placed. The control slab continued to deform thereafter. The same behavior was observed for slab specimen UP-1. The maximum deflection prior to failure for these specimens was 12.7 mm and 10.4 mm, respectively.

1. The influence of the concrete overlay on the stiffness of the slab was clearly observed in slab RP-0. Slab RP-0 showed higher stiffness than the control slab until it reached 22.9 kN, at which point the internal steel reinforcement started to yield. It exhibited a lower deflection as compared to the control slab at the same load level. The maximum deflection prior to failure was 4.6 mm.

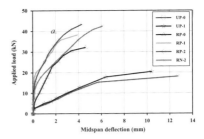

Figure 7. Load vs. Mid-span deflection curves.

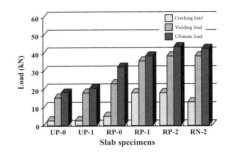

Figure 8. Comparison between slab specimens at different loading stages.

Slab RP-1 and slab RP-2 behaved similarly, with roughly linear response and stiffness greater than the control slab. They started to crack at 17.8 kN and yielded after a load of 35.7 kN was placed. Slab specimens RP-1 and RP-2 showed an increase in first cracking load of 6.8 times, when compared with the control slab specimen UP-0. The maximum deflections for these slabs prior to failure were 3.9 mm and 4.3 mm, respectively. Finally, slab RN-2 started to crack at 12.7 kN. After that, it is exhibited a lower stiffness as compared to Slabs RP-1 and RP-2. The maximum deflection prior to failure was 6.1 mm.

Comparison between slab specimens at different loading stages are presented in Figure (8). It is observed that the slab which was strengthened with the suggested combined (concrete overlay plus CFRP composites) strengthening systems (i.e., slab specimens RP-2 and RN-2) exhibited the highest efficiency.

3.2 Ultimate load and mode of failure

A measure of the efficiency of different systems can be obtained by considering the mode of failure and the failure loads of the slabs. Results are presented in Table (13) and Figure (9). The control slab specimen UP-0 behaved in expected fashion under flexural loading. As loads increased, flexural cracks increased in number, width and depth. Failure of the control slab was by yielding of steel followed by crushing of the concrete at the compression fiber, see Figure (9-a).

Slab specimen UP-1 showed an increase of only 13% in ultimate load capacity when compared to the control slab specimen, and this limited increase in percentage gain in strength is due to the reduced amount of CFRP laminate used. Failure of this slab was by CFRP rupture in mid span and occurred at 20.4 kN. The crack pattern after the failure of this slab is shown in Figure (9-b).

Slab specimen RP-0 showed a reduction of deflection compared to the control slab. No sign of detachment between the bare slab and the concrete overlay was observed. The failure load was 32.1 kN, which was 77% higher than that of the control slab. Failure of the test specimen was by yielding of steel followed by crushing of the concrete at the compression fiber in the concrete overlay. The crack pattern after failure of this slab is shown in Figure (9-c).

Slab specimen RP-1 failed in a sudden and brittle manner caused by rupture of CFRP at the mid span. The failure load was 38.2 kN, which was 111% higher than that of the control slab. The ruptured remains of carbon fiber sheet at both ends of the slab were still attached firmly to the concrete substrate. Figure (9-d) shows the crack pattern after the failure of slab RP-1.

In slab specimen RP-2, the formation of flexural cracks that occurred as a result of the yielding of the steel reinforcement generated high stresses in the CFRP plate across the cracks. Since the concrete could not maintain the interface shear and normal stresses, the CFRP plates snapped from the concrete substrate. The failure load was 43.3 kN, which was 139% higher than that of the control slab. This relatively high percentage in ultimate load

gain was due to the fact that slab specimen RP-2 was strengthened with the combined strengthening system. The crack pattern after the failure of this slab is shown in Figure (9-e).

Slab specimen RN-2 resulted in 134% increase in its ultimate load capacity when compared with

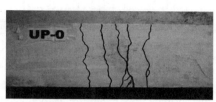

(9-a) Slab UP-0

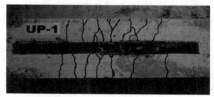

(9-b) Slab UP-1

(9-c) Slab RP-0

(9-d) Slab RP-1

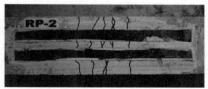

(9-e) Slab RP-2

(9- f) Slab RN-2

Figure 9. Crack patterns after failure for the slab specimens.

Table 13. Ultimate load capacity and failure mode.

Specimen	Ultimate load, kN	Increase in ultimate load, %	Failure mode
UP-0	18.1	N/A	Typical flexural failure
UP-1	20.4	13	CFRP rupture at mid-span
RP-0	32.1	77	Typical flexural failure
RP-1	38.2	111	CFRP rupture at mid-span
RP-2	43.3	139	CFRP debonding at mid-span
RN-2	42.4	134	CFRP rupture at mid-span

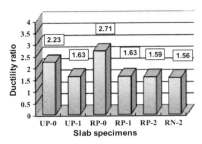

Figure 10.   Ductility ratio for the tested slabs.

control slab specimen UP-0. Failure of the test specimen was by CFRP rupture at the mid span. The crack pattern after the failure of this slab is shown in Figure (9-f).

3.3   Ductility ratios

The ductility of a flexural member can be defined as its ability to sustain inelastic deformation without loss in its load carrying capacity prior to failure and can be expressed as the ratio of ultimate deformation to deformation at yield. Here, deflection will be used as the primary measurement of ductility. The ductility ratio values for the slab specimens are presented in Figure (10) and it can be seen that the ductility ratio of the slab specimens decreases significantly.

4   CONCLUSIONS AND RECOMMENDATION

Based on the results obtained from the experimental work, the following conclusions are presented:

1. For the tested slab externally strengthened with CFRP strengthening system, the ultimate flexural load is increased by 13%. No increase in cracking load. The ductility ratio is decreased by 27% when compared with the control slab. These results may be attributing to the reduced amount of CFRP composites.
2. The concrete overlay strengthening system exhibited a significant increase in ultimate and cracking loads. These increases reached up to 77% and 100%, respectively. Also, the ductility ratio is increased by 22% when compared with the control slab.
3. Substantial increase in flexural efficiency was observed when the slabs strengthened with the suggested combined strengthening system. The increase in ultimate load reaches up to 139% and 134% for RC one-way slabs strengthened in positive and negative flexural bending, respectively. These slab specimens showed an increase in first cracking load of 7 and 5 times,

respectively, when compared with the control slab specimen.
4. The recorded ductility ratios for slab specimens strengthened with the combined strengthening system are 1.56–1.63. These values present reduction by 30%–27% when compared with the control slab.
5. Further studies should focus on expanding the experimental database of reinforced concrete slabs strengthened with CFRP composites and concrete overlay techniques through full scale experimental tests and on long-term performance.

REFERENCES

Al-Mahaidi, R. "Use of FRP Composites for Strengthening of Concrete Buildings and Bridges" Monash University, Melbourne, Australia, 2003.
Alkhrdaji, T., Nanni, A., Chen, G. and Barker, M. "Upgrading the transportation infrastructure: solid RC decks strengthened with FRP" Concrete International: Design and Construction,1999, Vol. 21, No. 10, pp. 37–41.
American Concrete Institute, ACI Committee 318, (2005), "Building Code Requirements for Structural Concrete (ACI 318-05) and Commentary (ACI 318R-05)", American Concrete Institute, Farmington Hills, MI.
American Concrete Institute, Committee 440 (2002). ACI 440.2R-02, "Guide for the Design and Construction of Externally Bonded FRP Systems for Strengthening Concrete Structures" p. 45.
Aprile, A., Pela, L. and Benedetti, A., "Repair and Strengthening with FRP of Damaged Bridge R/C Slabs", University of Patras, Greece, 2007.
ASTM C 39/C39M-05(2005). "Standard Test Method for Compressive Strength of Cylindrical Concrete Specimens", 2005 Annual Book of ASTM Standards, Vol.01.01, ASTM, Philadelphia, PA.
ASTM C 496/C496M-04 (2005). "Standard Test Method for Splitting Tensile Strength of Cylindrical Concrete Specimens", 2005 Annual Book of ASTM Standards, Vol.01.01, ASTM, Philadelphia, PA.
Costeira, P., Juvandes, L. and Figueiras, J., "Behavior of RC Slabs Strengthened by Externally Bonded CFRP Systems", University of Patras, Greece.2007.
IQS 5-1984. "Portland Cement", Central Organization of Standardization Quality Control-IRAQ.
IQS 45-1988. "Aggregates from natural sources for concrete and building construction", Central Organization of Standardization Quality Control-IRAQ.
Sika (2005). "Sikadur 330-Two Part Epoxy Impregnation Resin", Technical Data Sheet, Edition 2, (web site: www.sika.co.id).
Sika (2005). "SikaWrap230C-Woven carbon fiber fabric for Structural Strengthening", Technical Data Sheet, Edition 2, (web site: www.sika.co.id).
Tan, K.Y. "Evaluation of Externally Bonded CFRP Systems for the Strengthening of RC Slabs" MSc. Thesis, University of Missouri-Rolla, 2003.

Concrete Solutions – Grantham, Mechtcherine & Schneck (eds)
© *2012 Taylor & Francis Group, London, ISBN 978-0-415-61622-5*

Time-dependent behaviour of CFRP-strengthened reinforced concrete beams

M. Kaminski & E. Kusa
Institute of Building Engineering, Wroclaw University of Technology, Wroclaw, Poland

D. Demski
MC-Bauchemie, Wroclaw, Poland

ABSTRACT: Nowadays the strengthening of reinforced concrete structures with steel plate bonding techniques are being replaced by Fiber Reinforced Polymer (FRP) laminates. A lot of studies focused on short-term and static behaviour of FRP-strengthened concrete elements but only a few on long-term responses. The aim of this paper is to compare two strengthening methods: the CFRP strip bonding technique and Near Surface Mounted reinforcement (NSM CFRP). It presents results of experiments performed on five bonding concrete beams, under sustained load. The first beam was not strengthened, two of them were strengthened at the beginning of the experiment and the rest were pre-cracked before being strengthened. The results confirmed that time dependent behaviours are different when beams are strengthened by CFRP strips or NSM CFRP. It was shown that CFRP reinforcement has a positive influence on the long term behaviour of strengthened beams.

1 INTRODUCTION

The strengthening of existing civil concrete structures or their rehabilitation is necessary when elements are damaged. The same situation occurs when an increase in load capacity is required. The most popular strengthening technology for reinforced concrete beams was steel plates. This technique consists in externally bonding plates to concrete using epoxy adhesive. This method is effective and convenient but also has some disadvantages, which could be eliminated using FRP laminates. Steel can corrode in contrast to the FRP materials. Carbon Fiber Reinforced Polymer strips are lighter than steel plates and easier in manipulating at the construction site. In the case of the upgrading of very long elements steel plates may generate some problems with transport. The steel plates have limits in their delivery lengths as opposed to the composite materials. This is the reason why the strengthening of building structures with the external composites, bonded to the concrete surface with an epoxy resin adhesive, is more and more often chosen as the way of increasing the load bearing capacity of concrete elements subjected to bending, shearing and compression. The results of experimental tests proved that the concrete elements strengthened in flexure with the externally bonded composites demonstrated a limit of crack development and width, as well as an increase of the beam's stiffness

and load bearing capacity. The effectiveness of the strengthening of the bending capacity depends on the percentage of the ordinary reinforcement, on the distribution of the bending moments along the span of a beam, the number of layers of the composite reinforcement, the stiffness of the layers, and the distance of the end of the composite from the support of the beam.

A huge amount of studies that have been conducted on FPR-strengthened concrete elements have contained static and short-term response data. Little work has been carried out dealing with the long-term behaviour. Carbon Fiber Reinforced Polymer (CFRP) is a quite new material and the rheological behaviour of structural materials has always been significant in civil engineering, that's why it's important to study their long-term characteristics. Several studies have been done to determine the long-term behaviour for CFRP laminates and epoxy adhesive used for external FRP strengthening of reinforced concrete structures. Ascione et al. (2008) investigated the creep behaviour of CFRP strips by about 500 days at a constant temperature and noticed that carbon fibers are effective in limiting the primary creep strains of CFRP laminates. They concluded that this composite with high longitudinal Young modulus and high fiber volume fraction highlighted limited creep strains.

Experimental investigations of creep of epoxy adhesive at the concrete-FRP interfaces was made by Meshgin et al. (2009). This paper focused on time-before-loading, which is defined as the time period between the time of application of epoxy and the loading time. Nine specimens were tested under laboratory conditions controlled to constant temperature. Studies have been conducted for about nine months and have shown that as time-before-loading decreases, ultimate creep deformation increases. More recently, the creep behaviour of adhesives has also been considered by Ferrier et al. (2010). In that paper, short and long-term creep tests were performed on FRP/concrete bonded interfaces, using concrete specimens strengthened by four different CFRP systems. They noticed that epoxy systems used in construction exhibit low glass transition temperature values as opposed to epoxy formulations used for aeronautical applications. Their work was focused on this characteristic and proved that creep behaviour is correlated to the glass transition temperature value of the polymer. The value of this temperature should be higher than 55 °C in order to limit creep effects in the adhesive joint. Another solution is to maintain the service temperature of the structure to at least 15 °C less than than the glass transition temperature. Mazzotti and Savoia (2005) in their work about long-term properties of bond between concrete and FRP, which lasted for about 200 days, found that due to very high shear stresses at the adhesive and concrete cover level, creep phenomena may be highly non linear close to the loaded end. Hence, compliance increase at the beginning of the anchorage is much higher than for from it.

Investigations into the time-dependent behaviour of reinforced concrete elements strengthened with externally bonded CFRP strips were made by several research centers. Pelvris and Triantafillou (1994) reported that increasing the CFRP area fraction decreased both the immediate and the creep deflections. In a study by Chami et al. (2009), higher than typical service load levels were applied to better assess the influence of sustained loads on long-term creep induced deflections. These loads several times reached the cracking moment of the beam. The authors conducted research for about a year and found that the FRP laminates installed on the tension side of a concrete beam increased its ultimate strength and decreased the initial deflection. However, their influence on the long-term deflections was negligible, especially under low levels of sustained load. The influence under higher levels of loading was restricted to decreasing the instantaneous stress and strain in the compressed concrete. Muller et al. (2007) performed various bending relaxation tests on four reinforced concrete beams with or without strengthening with composite strips. The first beam had no composite

reinforcement, the second one was strengthened before testing. The third beam was pre-cracked before strengthening and the fourth beam, which was in fact the first beam, was unloaded after 57 days of relaxation, repaired after three months of resting and finally tested again in relaxation. The main conclusions of the study were that a period of loading before strengthening lead in this case to a lower tensile stress in the composite and the state of cracking had an influence on the time-dependent behaviour of reinforced concrete beams, depending on whether the beams were cracked before strengthening.

2 EXPERIMENTAL PROGRAM

2.1 Testing parameters

The main purpose of this study was to compare two strengthening methods: CFRP strip bonding technique and Near Surface Mounted reinforcement (NSM CFRP). It presents results of experiments performed on five bonding concrete beams under sustained load. All beams were strengthened except the last one—control beam (B0). Two of them were strengthened at the beginning of the experiment in two different ways (B1, B2). Beams B3 and B4 were pre-cracked before being strengthened. Two beams were strengthened using the NSM CFRP method (B1, B3) and the last two using external CFRP plates (B2, B4). All beams were loaded, then after cracking beams (B0, B3, B4) two of them were strengthened. The next day, the value of the load was doubled. It exceeded the design value of the cracking load by about 100%.

2.2 Materials

2.2.1 Steel reinforcement

The longitudinal reinforcement was made of ribbed steel bars of nominal diameter 12 mm. The stirrups were made of diameter 6 mm. Out of each kind of the steel applied to reinforcement of the beams, specimens were taken in order to test the strength characteristics. The test was carried out in the UFP.

Lipsk machine (Fig.1), additionally equipped with an elongation recording with the measurement base of 60 mm. Based on computer readings, the tensile strength (f_t), elasticity modulus (E_s), and the yield strength (f_{sy}) were defined (Table 1).

2.2.2 Concrete

During concrete work, beams, cylindrical specimens 113 mm in diameter and 350 mm height, cubic specimens of a 150 mm and beams with dimensions of

Figure 1.   Reinforcing bar after failure.

Figure 3.   Beams specimen in testing machine.

Figure 2.   Cubic specimen in testing machine.

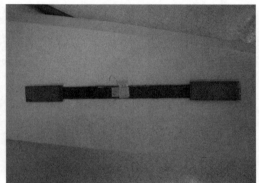

Figure 4.   CFRP specimen.

Table 1.   Characteristic of steel reinforcement paper.

Mean results	f_t MPa	E_s GPa	f_{sy} MPa
φ6	500	187	426
φ12	636	190	499

Table 2.   Strength characteristics of concrete samples.

	$f_{c,cube}$ MPa	f_c MPa	E_c GPa	f_{ct} MPa
Results	41.58	34.39	30.54	5.01
	35.86	34.67	28.59	4.85
	34.80	30.05	32.57	4.84
	–	35.25	30.62	4.68
	–	30.36	31.69	4.71
	–	31.80	30.34	5.05
	–	–	28.73	–
	–	–	33.82	–
Mean results	37.41	32.75	30.86	4.86

$150 \times 150 \times 700$ mm were produced. The compression strength of the cubic specimens were defined ($f_{c,cube}$), while on cylindrical specimens the compressive strength (f_c) and the modulus of elasticity (E_c) were defined (Fig. 2). Tensile strengths were defined on beams (f_{ct}) (Fig. 3). The concrete strength characteristics of each beam was determined using the ZD 100 VEB Lipsk test machine (Table 2).

2.2.3   CFRP materials

The strips MC-Bauchemie type MC-DUR CFK 160/2400 were tested in the press type UFP 400 VEB Lipsk. Eight specimens 250 mm long and 15 mm wide (Fig. 4) were cut out of the strips of nominal width 100 mm. Up to both ends of each specimen aluminium flat plates 15 mm wide, 50 mm long and

5 mm thick were bonded, in order to anchor the specimens in the jaws of the test machine. The test was carried out in the UFP Lipsk machine (Fig. 5) (Table 3).

For bonding the CFRP strips, a two-component epoxy adhesive MC-Bauchemie, MC-DUR 1280 was used. The component type A (epoxy resin) and type B (hardener) were in a mass proportion of A:B = 4:1.

2.3 Specimens

The reinforcing steel skeletons for the beams and concrete were produced in BETARD Company in Dlugoleka, nearby Wroclaw. The beams had 150 × 250 × 3300 mm dimensions (Fig. 6). Casting was carried out in a horizontal upside down position in timber formwork. Concrete in the beams and specimens was compacted with a poker vibrator.

For convenience, the beams were placed upside down during the installation of the CFRP laminates. In order to obtain proper adherence of the adhesive to the concrete, the surface of the beams where a strip was to be bonded was polished and cleaned of loose particles and dust. The strips were cut to fit the defined length with a face grinder. Next the composite and concrete surfaces were degreased with rag dampened in a thinner. The two-component adhesive was supplied in two separate containers, then mixed together in the proper proportions.

Adhesive was applied along the strip and beam, then the strips were put on the beam and pressed down. The excess adhesive from both sides of the strip was removed. CFRP strips of dimensions 1.4 mm thick and 100 mm wide were bonded to the beams B2, B4.

Six longitudinal grooves of 20 mm in depth and 6 mm wide were cut in the beams B1, B3 (strengthened with NSM). Afterwards the grooves were cleaned and degreased and then filled with the adhesive. The main CFRP strips of 100 mm wide were cut into six equal parts and inserted into the six grooves on each beams. The beams had been strengthened in the upside down position in order to facilitate access to the strengthened surface. All beams were stored in a special tent in the laboratory hall. In the tent a constant temperature of 20 °C and humidity of 60% was maintained.

2.4 Test setup

The test stand was constructed of a steep frame structure. The frame used a four-point configuration, with a clear span length of 3100 mm. The beams were tested in a normal and upside down position with simple supports. The elements were loaded with two concentrated forces which were applied with hydraulic servomotors. Afterwards they blocked the springs by tightening screws on the frames (Fig. 8).

Deflections were measured using dial gauges every day during the first week, every 3 days during the next week, and finally one day a week.

The tests are still in progress.

Figure 5.   CFRP strip after failure.

Table 3.   Strength characteristic of CFRP strip.

	CFRP width	CFRP thickness	CFRP area	Tensile strength	Modulus of elasticity	Ultimate tensile strain
	b_f	t_f	A_f	f_{fu}	E_f	e_{fu}
	mm	mm	mm²	GPa	GPa	%
Values supplied by the manufacturer	–	1.4	–	≥2.950	≥167.000	≥1.67
Values found in the laboratory	15.0	1.4	21.0	2.339	177.189	1.32

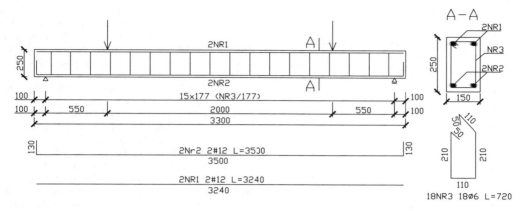

Figure 6. Steel reinforcement of beams.

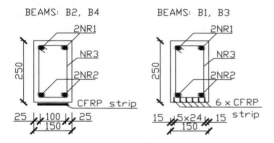

Figure 7. CFRP strengthening configurations.

Figure 8. Test setup.

3 EXPERIMENTAL RESULTS

3.1 *Crack widths*

For the concrete beams (B3, B4) the cracking moment varied from 4.25 to 4.75 kNm. The crack widths were measured immediately after loading, and then monitored throughout the test period.

For all the long-term creep tests, the crack width was equal to or less than 0.1 mm. The beams which were precracked had wider cracks than beams cracked after strengthening. The beam without strengthening (B0) had a large crack width of 0.5 mm.

3.2 *Static tests*

First beams B3 and B4 were cracked using a different test-setup (force about 17–19 kN), later removed from the research stand and moved to the proper test-setup. Prior to the long-term test, beams were loaded with a force about 20 kN, then after cracks reached width 0.1 mm, beams B3 and B4 were strengthened. The next day, when the adhesive had hardened, the beams were loaded to about 40 kN and the results of deflections were noticed. As we can see in Table 4, the deflection of the beam without reinforcement was increased, despite constant force, however, the deflection of the beams B1 and B2 remained unchanged. On the other hand deflection in beams B3 and B4 decreased due to the adhesive and activation of the CFRP strip to work. Differences in loading were dependent on whether the beams were placed normally or upside down which is whether it was a lower or upper beam. Differences in deflection between the beam B0 and the beams B3 and B4 were caused by the earlier cracked beams.

3.3 *Long-term deflections*

The deflections of the upper beam were measured by dial gauges installed on the top and on the middle of the beam. Gauges on the lower beam were installed on the bottom and on the middle of the beam. All beams had gauges installed under the forces and supports too.

Table 4. Experimental results for static tests on beams.

	Applied load	Experimental moment	Deflection
	kN	kNm	mm
B0	20	5.00	3.68
	20*	5.00	3.75
	40	10.00	12.74
B1	23	5.75	3.99
	23*	5.75	3.99
	43	10.75	8.58
B2	23	5.75	4.05
	23*	5.75	4.05
	43	10.75	8.52
B3	20	5.00	6.25
	20*	5.00	2.84
	40	10.00	7.28
B4	20	5.00	5.96
	20*	5.00	-1.53
	40	10.00	4.24

*Measured values of the second day.

Figures 9–13 presents the long-term deflections of tests. All these beams were cast from the same concrete batch and reinforced with the same reinforcement ratio. It is well known that the higher load levels increase short-term and long-term deflections.

According to Table 4, it can be concluded that the application of CFRP strips caused a significant reduction in short-term deflections. However, the impact of CFRP on long-term deflection was smaller than on the immediate deflection.

Comparing Figures 10 and 11, which represents the lower beams deflection, we can see that strengthening by the NSM CFRP method caused higher deflections than the traditional way of strengthening by CFRP strip. Both were under sustained loads of 43 kN.

Looking at the upper beams (Figs. 12 and 13) we can reach the same conclusion, namely, that the NMS CFRP method was less efficient in reducing deflections. These beams were under sustained

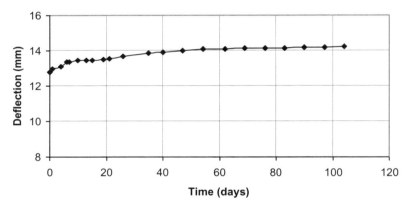

Figure 9. Long-term deflections of concrete beam (B0) without CFRP strengthening.

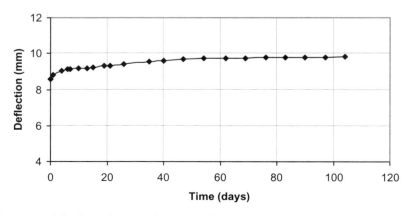

Figure 10. Long-term deflections of concrete beam (B1) with NSM CFRP strengthening.

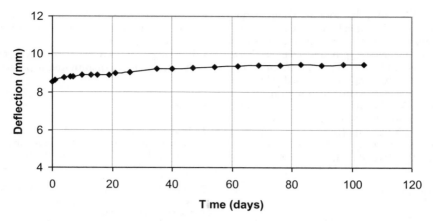

Figure 11.   Long-term deflections of concrete beam (B2) with CFRP strip strengthening.

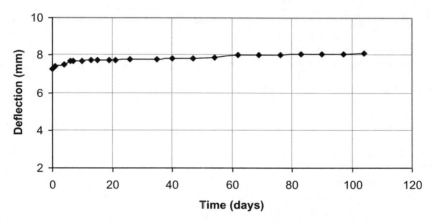

Figure 12.   Long-term deflections of concrete beam (B3) cracked before NSM CFRP strengthening.

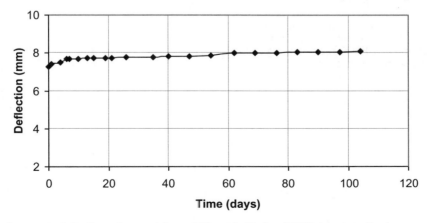

Figure 13.   Long-term deflections of concrete beam (B4) cracked before CFRP strip strengthening.

loads of 40 kN. Both methods of strengthening had the same cross-sectional area of CFRP strip.

Both Figures 10 and 12 present the long-term deflections for beams strengthening using the NSM CFRP method but on the Figure 12, beam B3 had been cracked before being strengthened. This comparison shows that the strengthening under load of the pre-cracked beams lead to a greater reduction of deflections. The same situation was found between beams B2 and B4 (Figs. 11 and 13) which were strengthened using CFRP strip externally bonded with the flexural surface.

4 CONCLUSIONS

The aim of this paper was to compare two strengthening methods: CFRP strip bonding technique and Near Surface Mounted reinforcement (NSM CFRP). Five reinforced concrete beams were tested under four-point bending. The influence of a composite strengthening on the time dependent behaviour of such structures has been studied. One of the beams was not strengthened. Two of them were strengthened with composite strips bonded to their tensile surface. The first beam was strengthened without had being cracked, the second one was pre-cracked before strengthening. The two others were strengthened with NSM and the first of them was strengthened without being cracked and the second one was pre-cracked before strengthening. The main conclusions of the study can be summarized as follows:

- These data confirm the efficacy of carbon fibers in limiting the deflections from short-term load.
- Both type of strengthening proved effective in limiting the crack propagation and the crack width.
- The NMS CFRP method was less efficient in reducing short and long-term deflections than strengthening using CFRP strip externally bonded.
- The results confirmed that time dependent behaviours are different when beams were strengthened by CFRP at the beginning of load or after the beam was cracked.

- It can be revealed that CFRP reinforcement had a positive influence on the long term behaviour of strengthened beams.
- It is suggested to repeat similar tests to confirm the results of the quantitative aspects.

REFERENCES

Ascione, F., Berardi, V.P., Feo, L., & Giordano, A. 2008. An experimental study on the long-term behaviour of CFRP pultruded laminates suitable to concrete structures rehabilitation. *Composites: Part B* 39(2008): 1147–50.

Chami, G.A., Thériault, M. & Neale, K.W. 2009. Creep behaviour of CFRP-strengthened reinforced concrete beams. *Construction and Building Materials* 23(4): 1640–52.

Ferrier, E., Michel, L., Jurkiewiez, B. & Hamelin P. 2010. Creep behaviour of adhesives used for external FRP strengthening of RC structures. *Construction and Building Materials* (in press).

Mazzotti, C. & Savoia, M. 2005. Long term properties fo bond between concrete and FRP. Chen & Teng (eds), *Bond behaviour of FRP in structures; Proc. intern. symp. 7–9 December 2005.* Hong Kong, China.

Meshgin, P., Choi, K-K. & Reda Taha, M.M. 2009. Experimental and analytical investigations of creep of epoxy adhesive at the concrete-FRP interfaces. International Journal of Adhesion & Adhesives 29(2009): 56–66.

Muller, M., Toussaint, E., Destrebecq, J.F. & Grédiac, M. 2007. Investigation into the time-dependent behaviour of reinforced concrete specimens strengthened with externally bonded CFRP-plates. *Composites: Part B* 38(2007): 417–28.

Pelvris, N. & Triantafillou, T.C. 1994. Time-dependent behaviour of RC members strengthened with FRP laminates. *J Struct Eng, ASCE* 120(3): 1016–42.

Ramana, V.P.V., Kant, T., Morton, S.E., Dutta, P.K., Mukherjee, A. & Desai, Y.M. 2000. Behaviour of CFRPC strengthened reinforced concrete beams with varying degrees of strengthening. *Composites: Part B* 31, 461–70.

Concrete Solutions – Grantham, Mechtcherine & Schneck (eds)
© 2012 Taylor & Francis Group, London, ISBN 978-0-415-61622-5

Behaviour of damaged RC beams repaired with NSM CFRP rods

A. Kreit, A. Castel & R. Francois
Université de Toulouse; UPS, INSA, LMDC (Laboratoire Matériaux et Durabilité des Constructions), France

F. Al-Mahmoud
Nancy I University—IUT Brabois, France

ABSTRACT: The deterioration of reinforced concrete RC structures due to continual upgrading of service loads has resulted in a large number of structures that need repair. In this paper, an experimental program presented studies the possibility of using a Near Surface Mounted (NSM) CFRP rod to repair RC beams damaged by overloading. Several beam specimens were built. Some specimens were repaired after preloading condition and the other ones were repaired under sustained load. One beam specimens were strengthened by composite rods before loading. The main goal of this work is to investigate the influence of initial load and sustained load on flexural behaviour of RC beams repaired with an NSM CFRP rod system. The main experimental parameters include different levels of damage and sustained load. Test results in the current study show that the maximum load-carrying capacity of repaired beams at different levels of sustained load generally performed very close to that of the initially strengthened beam. Beams repaired at higher levels of sustained load failed by crushing of concrete, because there is an important level of compression strain in concrete due to sustained load.

1 INTRODUCTION

The repair of structurally deteriorated reinforced concrete structures becomes necessary as the structural element ceases to provide satisfactory overloading, strength, and serviceability. Various methods are available to repair or strengthen those structures. External bonding of steel plates to damaged reinforced concrete structures is one of these methods and has been shown to be quite an efficient and a well-known repair or strengthening technique. It has been largely studied in France (L'Hermite 1967), (Bresson 1971) and intensive research performed in the beginning of the eighties (Theillout 1983) resulted in French rules concerning their design (SOCOTEC 1986).

In recent years, the use of composite materials represents an alternative to steel as it can avoid the corrosion of the plate. FRP materials have better mechanical, physical and chemical properties than steel. The applications of FRP materials for retrofitting or strengthening existing concrete structures have been growing rapidly throughout the world (U. Meier et al. 1992; Steiner 1996; Nanni 1997; Katsumata et al. 2001; Grace et al. 2003; Al-Mahmoud et al. 2009). Several organizations, including ACI Committee 440 (2000); ISIS Canada (2001); Fib Bulletin 14 (2001); The Concrete Society (2004); and JBDPA-Japan (1999), are developing extensive design guidelines for

the use of carbon fiber reinforced polymer (CFRP), indicating that the process of standardization is underway (Keller 2003).

The use of FRP materials for repairing infrastructure damaged by overloading is very recent. Several experimental studies have focused on the use of CFRP sheet for the repair of load-damaged RC beams (Arduini et al. 1997; Bonacci et al. 2000; Shahawy et al. 2001; Yeong-soo et al. 2003). A few studies were focused on the strengthening of preloaded structural members (Arduini et al. 1997; Norris et al. 1997; Sharif et al. 1994; Shin et al. 2003). No codes and standards have consistently taken the influence of preload levels or sustained loads into account, because there is not enough experimental data for investigating the influence of the preload level on flexural performance.

FRP rods used to repair or strengthen RC structures are currently emerging as a new technology to increase their bending or shear strength. The FRP rod requires a groove to be cut in the concrete cover, a technique known as Near Surface Mounted reinforcement (NSM). NSM FRP technology could be particularly attractive to strengthen structures in bending areas subjected to negative moment, to mechanical damage or environmental attack. Compared to externally bonded FRP reinforcement, the NSM system has a number of advantages, which are:

1. NSM bars are protected by the concrete cover and so are less exposed to accidental impact and mechanical damage;
2. The amount of site installation work may be reduced, as surface preparation other than grooving is no longer required;
3. NSM bars can be more easily anchored into adjacent members to prevent debonding failures;
4. NSM reinforcement is less prone to debonding from the concrete substrate;
5. The aesthetic of the strengthened structure is virtually unchanged.

Some studies dealing with NSM FRP rod technology for reinforced concrete strengthening are already available, including shear and flexural strengthening (De Lorenzis et al. 2000; Hassan et al. 2003, Hassan et al. 2004; Yost et al. 2007), development length, bond and failure modes (Al-Mahmoud et al. 2006, Al-Mahmoud et al. 2009; Cruz et al. 2004; De Lorenzis et al. 2004, De Lorenzis et al. 2002), strengthening or repair of infrastructure damaged by steel corrosion (Sherwood et al. 1999; Soudki et al. 2000; Kreit et al. 2010).

This paper presents the results of experimental studies concerning the flexural repair of preloaded RC beams by one NSM CFRP rod under different levels of sustained load (0, 45% and 65% of nominal flexural strength of the non-strengthened control beams) at the time of repairing, which is an important practical aspect to be considered in standardized repair techniques and deals with the flexural behaviour of those repaired beams and especially with the failure modes.

2 SUMMARY OF RELATED STUDIES

When structures require the application of FRP strengthening in the field, they are generally not new structures and hence have some form of existing damage. These structures can be damaged by long-term sustained overloading, by being overloaded by a large single event (such as an earthquake), or have lost capacity over time due to material degradation and are no longer capable of sustaining the service loads required. It is therefore important to not only conduct tests on specimens with similar cracked conditions, but also to know the specific effects these cracks have on strengthening behaviour.

The present work is geared toward evaluating the use of NSM CFRP rods to repair load-damaged RC beams that has received little attention in experimental research. In this regard, it is important to note that most of the research on the effect

of sustained loads on ultimate load-carrying capacity has been conducted on the technology of strengthening of concrete structures using externally bonded FRP composites.

One published article (Yeong-soo & Chadon 2003) focused on the effect of sustained load on the flexural behaviour of repaired RC beams. Yeong-soo & Chadon (2003) tested six beams strengthened with CFRP laminates subjected to different sustained loads. The levels of sustained load at the time of strengthening corresponded to 0%, 50% and 70% of nominal flexural strength of the non-strengthened RC beam. Results of the experiment showed that sustained load levels at the time of strengthening had more influence on deflections of beams at the yielding and at ultimate stage than the ultimate strength of the beam. In the test, all strengthened beams failed by rip-off rather than tensile rupture of CFRP laminates; hence, it was difficult to judge the effect of strengthening at different levels of sustained load on the ultimate strength of those beams.

Shahawy et al. (2001) conducted a study on eight full-scale 6.1 m (20 ft) long RC T-girders. A control girder with no wrap and a reference girder with two layers of CFRP wrap were tested up to failure in one run for comparison purposes. The girders were preloaded up to 65%, 85% and 117% of the control yield moment and locked and strengthened with two layers of CFRP wrap before resuming the loading up to failure. The results demonstrated the effectiveness of the externally bonded CFRP in repairing load-induced damage in the RC beams. The level of preload prior to installation of CFRP did not affect the overall behaviour of the wrapped specimens.

Bonacci & Maalej (2000) tested one beam, which was named B3, to study the effect of sustained load on the performance of a member reinforced with CFRP. In Bonacci's test, three cycles of load between 45 kN and 90 kN were applied, after which the load was held constant at 45 kN for a period of 1 week to allow application of CFRP. CFRP debonding failure mode was observed. The test results show that two layers of CFRP external reinforcement gave beam B3 strength gains of 28% over the control beam B2, which was strengthened with two layers of CFRP at zero load.

Arduini & Nanni (1997) studied the behaviour of precracked beams strengthened with CFRP sheets. Their experimental program included short and medium-length RC beams that were preloaded and cracked prior to the application of the FRP. Only two specimens were maintained under load during the application and curing of the FRP. The results showed that specimens that were precracked showed lower ultimate capacity and stiffness than their virgin counterparts. For damaged specimens, a specimen repaired without sustained load had an average strength increase of 24% (over the control), while a specimen repaired under sustained vertical load had a strength increase of only 16% (over the control). Because failure was controlled debonding of the FRP, there was not a substantial difference in ultimate capacity of the specimens.

3 EXPERIMENTAL CONTEXT

In this work, 5 RC beams were tested. All beams were 3 000 mm long, and had 150 mm wide, 280 mm high cross sections. All beams were tested in four-point bending over a simple span. The main flexural reinforcement consisted of two 12 mm deformed bars with a sectional area of 226 mm² and a steel ratio of 0.67% was used (Fig. 1). Two 6 mm round bars with a sectional area of 56.5 mm² were used as top reinforcement (Fig. 1). Shear reinforcement consisted of 6 mm-diameter round steel stirrups spaced at 150 mm (Fig. 1). The beams were reinforced in this manner to prevent shear failure and to isolate the flexural behaviour from shear behaviour. Figure 1 shows the dimensions and the reinforcement arrangement of the specimens.

Variables in the test plan included different preload levels and sustained loads at the time of repair. One beam strengthened by one NSM CFRP rod was used as initially strengthened specimen P0-0 and the other four beams were preloaded and repaired in flexure using the same system under different levels of sustained loads (0, 45% and 65% of nominal flexural strength of the non-strengthened control beam "32.8 kN·m") at the time of repairing. The nominal flexural strength of the non-strengthened control beam was calculated by assuming an equivalent concrete compressive stress block as given in the EuroCode-2 (1992). The test specimens are summarized in Table 1. Specimens are labeled as P (p—s), where p, and s stand for the preload level (P = 0, 45% and 65% of nominal flexural strength of the non-strengthened control beams), and sustained loads at the time of repairing (S = 0, 45%, 65%, of nominal flexural strength of the non-strengthened control beams) respectively.

4 MATERIALS

4.1 *Properties of concrete*

One type of concrete, BO40, was used. The properties of the hardened concrete (compressive strength, tensile strength and instantaneous elastic modulus) were measured at 28 days on concrete cylinders (diameter = 110 mm, height = 220 mm). The specimens were removed from their moulds 24 h after casting and stored for 28 days in a confined room (T = 20° C, RH = 60%). The tensile strength was obtained from splitting tests. Table 2 shows the mechanical properties of the concrete measured at 28 days for all beams and at 7 days for the filling materials.

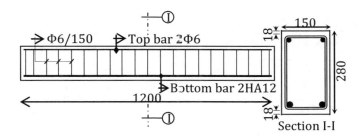

Figure 1. Lay-out of the reinforcement (all dimensions in cm) for all beams.

Table 1. Specimen and experimental parameters.

Beam	Pre-load	Sustained load	Load history
P0-0	None	None	0 → Failure
P45-0	45% (15 kN·m)	None	0 → 15 kN·m → 0 → Repairing with NSM CFRP → Failure
P45-45	45% (15 kN·m)	45% (15 kN·m)	0 → 15 kN·m → Sustained loading → Repairing with NSM CFRP → Failure
P65-0	65% (21.6 kN·m)	None	0 → 21.6 kN·m → 0 → Repairing with NSM CFRP → Failure
P65-65	65% (21.6 kN·m)	65% (21.6 kN·m)	0 → 21.6 kN·m → Sustained loading → Repairing with NSM CFRP → 0 → Failure

4.2 Properties of steel

The yield strength, ultimate tensile strength and modulus of elasticity of the steel bars were 600 MPa, 650 MPa, and 210 000 MPa respectively. A typical stress-strain relationship for a steel reinforcing bar is shown in Figure 2. Results for the yield strength, ultimate tensile strength and elastic modulus of steel bars are presented in Table 3.

4.3 Properties of CFRP rods

The CFRP rod was made in France by the Soficar Company. Al-Mahmoud et al. (2007) tested three specimens in axial tension to measure their mechanical characteristics. The brittle failure started with splitting and ended with rupture of

the rod. Table 3 shows the strengths and the elastic modulus obtained; the manufacturer's mechanical characteristics of the CFRP rods are also presented (Fig. 2). To modify the surface of the initially smooth rods in order to enhance the bond with the filling material, a surface sanding treatment was applied. The smooth CFRP rods were coated with 0.2/0.3 mm-size sand by sprinkling it on to a thin layer of freshly applied epoxy resin.

4.4 Properties of filling material

One filling material was studied: epoxy resin. After 7 days, the compressive and tensile strengths were 83 and 29.5 MPa respectively. The elastic modulus was 4 940 MPa as shown in Table 2.

Table 2. Mechanical characteristics of the concrete and filling material.

Material	Concrete beams after 28 days	Epoxy resin after 7 days
Compression strength (MPa)	47.5	83
Traction strength (MPa)	3.8	29.5
Elastic modulus (MPa)	38 000	4 940

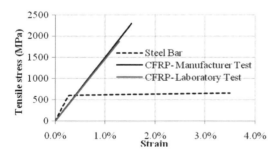

Figure 2. Typical tension stress–strain curves of steel reinforcement bar and CFRP rods.

Table 3. Mechanical characteristics of steel bars and CFRP rods.

Material		Yield strength (MPa)	Ultimate strength (MPa)	Elastic modulus (GPa)
Steel bars		600	650	210
CFRP rods	Manufacturer test	_	2.300	150
	Laboratory test	_	1.875	145.9

5 EXPERIMENTAL PROGRAM

5.1 Repair procedure by Near Surface Mounted technique

The NSM CFRP rod was installed by making two cuts in the concrete cover in the longitudinal direction at the tension side of the specimen beam as shown in Figure 3a. A special concrete saw with a diamond blade was used. The remaining concrete lug formed by the sawing was then removed using a hammer and hand chisel so that the lower surface became rough (Fig. 3b). The groove was cleaned using air-brushing to remove dust, debris and fine particles so as to ensure proper bonding between the resin and the concrete. Then, the groove was half filled and the CFRP rod was placed inside it and pressed lightly. This forced the resin to flow around the CFRP rod. More resin was applied to fill the groove and the surface was leveled (Fig. 3c).

As a result, the CFRP rod was placed in the middle of the cross-section in the tension area, as shown in Figure 12. The total length of the CFRP rod was 2 700 mm with 6 mm of diameter, which means that the repair was stopped just before the supports. In practice, it may be impossible to access the zone located above the supports. The beam was

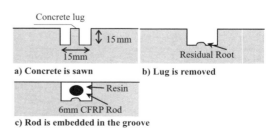

Figure 3. Installation of NSM CFRP rod.

tested after one week to check the filling material strength. The groove was 15 mm deep (only 18 mm of concrete cover for beams) and 15 mm wide (around twice the rod diameter) (Al-Mahmoud et al. 2006).

All specimens were tested in four-point loading.

5.2 Testing procedure

For each beam, each longitudinal steel bar was instrumented with two electrical resistance strain gauges. In addition, each test beam repaired with one NSM CFRP rod was instrumented with three strain gauges as shown in Figure 4. Each beam was instrumented with linear voltage displacement transducers (LVDT's) to measure the midspan deflection.

Over a 2800 mm simple span, the two load points were offset 600 mm from the midspan of the beam, as shown in Figure 4. One control beam was strengthened with one NSM CFRP rod (P0-0) and tested to failure for evaluating cracking, yielding, and ultimate loads. The other four beams were preloaded to 12 kN·m before repairing and the cracking patterns of each one were drawn with the exact locations of the flexural transverse cracks. Two beams were loaded additionally until the desired level of preload (45%-15 kN·m and 65%-21.6 kN·m of nominal flexural strength of the non strengthened control beams) for (P45–0 and P65–0). The other two beams were unloaded and then reloaded in a four-point flexure to expectable loads (45%-15 kN·m and 65%-21.6 kN·m of nominal flexural strength of the strengthened control beams) for (P45-45 and P65-65) by coupling each beam with the other support beam, when the preload reached the desired levels of sustained load, the load was held constant for a period of

1 week to allow for application and curing of the NSM CFRP rod.

6 EXPERIMENTAL RESULTS AND DISCUSSION

6.1 Load–deflection curves and failure modes

The experimental results obtained from the tests for all beams are summarized in Table 4. This table gives cracking moments M_{cr} and preloading moments (M_{pre}) before repair of the beams as well as the moments and deflection at yielding of steel and ultimate. Moment–midspan deflection responses for the beams are shown in Figures 5 and 6.

For ease of interpretation, the unloading-reloading cycles are not shown in the moment-midspan deflection curves (with the exception of the initially strengthened beam P0-0). Figure 7 reports the failure modes obtained in the experimental program and the Figures 8–11 present the evolution of crack patterns under sustained load and at failure load.

6.2 For beam P45

Figure 5 shows moment–midspan deflection curves of initially strengthened beam P0-0, and repaired beams P45-0, P45-45. The beam P0-0 developed flexural tensile cracks in the constant moment region at a moment of 10 kN·m. The tensile reinforcing steel of the beams P0-0, P45-0, and P45-45 yielded at moments near 32.7, 30, and 25.5 kN·m respectively. Beams P0-0, P45-0, and P45-45 failed at moments of 49.3, 45.9, and 43 kN·m respectively.

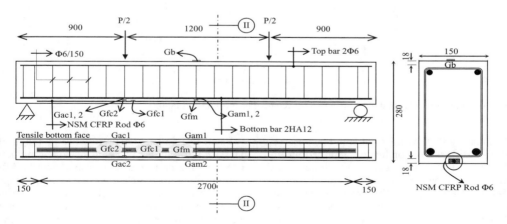

Figure 4.   Details of repairing beams (dimensions in mm).

Table 4. Summary of test results.

Beam	Before repair Moment (kN·m)		Stiffness (N/mm)	After repair Moment (kN·m)		Deflection (mm)		Stiffness (N/mm)		Modes of failure
	M_{cr}	M_{pre}	S_{0y}	M_y	M_u	δ_y	δ_u	S_y	S_u	
P0-0	–	0	–	32.7	49.3	17.8	67	7243	905	Pullout of the NSM CFRP rod followed by concrete crushing + localized spalling of the concrete cover
P45-0	6	15	7120	30.2	45.9	11.8	71	6137	775	Pullout of the NSM CFRP rod at the rod-epoxy interface followed by concrete crushing
P45-45	5.6	15	7125	25.5	43.1	10.8	75	6087	767	
P65-0	5.8	21.6	7145	30.7	45.5	14.5	70	5665	808	
P65-65	6	21.6	7140	27.7	43.1	12.7	74	5666	795	Concrete crushing

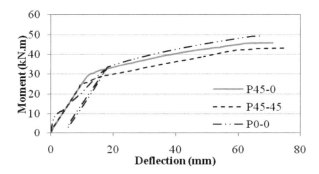

Figure 5. Moment-midspan deflection curves for repaired beams P45 and P0-0.

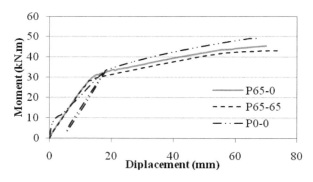

Figure 6. Moment-midspan deflection curves for repaired beams P65 and P0-0.

Comparing P0-0 with P45, it could be observed that the stiffness of preloaded repaired beams P45 was a little lower before the longitudinal steel yielding level (15.3% and 16% for P45-0 and P45-45 respectively), and the P45 repaired beam's stiffness was also lower after the longitudinal steel yielding level (14% and 15% for P45-0 and P45-45 respectively).

Beam P45-45 was repaired with one longitudinal CFRP rod under 15 kN·m sustained moment. The cracking pattern is shown in Figure 9. After strengthening, the cracks that had been developed up to the sustained load level propagated continuously upward in the constant moment region of the beam and new diagonal cracks were formed in the shear span region of beam as the additional

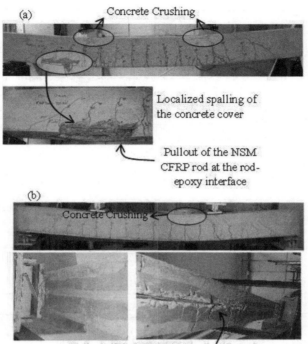

Figure 7. Failure of beams repaired with NSM CFRP rod. (a) for P0-0; (b) for P45-0, P45-45 and P65-0; (c) for P65-65.

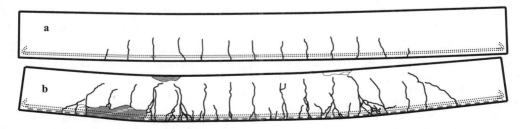

Figure 8. Crack patterns of the initially strengthened beam P0-0 (a) at service load 12 kN·m, (b) at failure load.

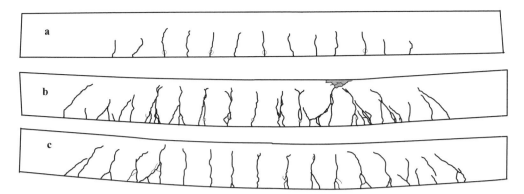

Figure 9.   Crack patterns of repaired beams P45 at failure load (a) at service load 12 kN·m, (b) at failure load for P45-0, (c) at failure load for P45-45.

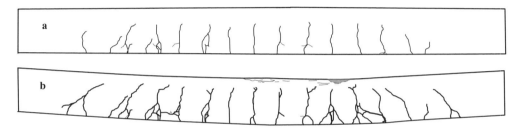

Figure 10.   Crack patterns of the beam P65-0 (a) under sustained load, (b) at failure load.

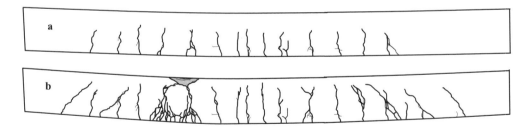

Figure 11. Crack patterns of the beam P65-65 (a) under sustained load, (b) at failure load.

load was applied beyond 30 kN·m. However, there was no appearance of new bending cracks between the existing cracks. By comparison of P45-45 with P45-0, similar behaviour and failure modes were also observed when the load of the repaired beam was increased up to failure.

Finally, the failure of beam P45 occurred after yielding of the tension steel by the pullout of NSM CFRP rod due to debonding at the interface between the CFRP rod and the resin (splitting of resin) following a crushing of concrete in the extreme compression fiber as shown in Figure 7b. This failure mode of pullout of the NSM CFRP rod was also reported in the literature (Al-Mahmoud et al. 2007).

The same failure mode occurred for P0-0 accompanied by localized spalling of the concrete cover as shown in Figures 7a and 8. By comparing P0-0 with preloaded beam P45, it can be observed that P0-0 failed at a load higher than the preloaded beam P45 (7% and 12.6% for P45-0 and P45-45 respectively) and the preloaded beam P45–0 failed at load slightly higher than preloaded beam P45-45 (6%).

6.3   For beam P65

Figure 6 shows moment–deflection curves of initially strengthened beam P0-0, and repaired beams P65-0 and P65-65. The tensile reinforcing steel of the beams P0-0, P65-0, and P65-65 yielded at moments near 32.7, 30.7, and 27.7 kN·m respectively. The beams P0-0, P65-0, and P65-65 failed at moments of 49.3, 45.5, and 43.1 kN·m respectively.

By comparing P0-0 with preloaded repaired beam P65, it can be observed that there is a significant difference in the stiffness before the longitudinal steel yielding level (21.8% for P65-0 and P65-65), and P0-0 stiffness is higher than preloaded repaired beam P65 after the longitudinal steel yielding level (11% and 12% for P65-0 and P65-65 respectively).

Beam P65-65 was repaired with one longitudinal CFRP rod under 21.6 kN·m sustained load. Cracks had formed as the sustained load was applied as shown in Figure 11 and these cracks were denser than those in beams P45 (Fig. 9). After strengthening, the cracks that had been developed up to the sustained load level propagated continuously upward in the constant moment region of the beam and a number of additional cracks were formed as the additional load was applied beyond 30 kN·m corresponding with new diagonal cracks that were formed in the shear span region of beam as the additional load was applied beyond 30 kN·m. The failure of beam P65–65 occurred after yielding of the tension steel by crushing of concrete in the extreme compression fiber and no slip of the NSM CFRP rod end was observed, as shown in Figure 7c. It can be observed that the P65-0 has the similar behaviour and failure mode when the load of repaired beam was increased up to failure where the P65-0 was failed after yielding of the tension steel by the pullout of NSM CFRP rod (splitting of resin) following a crushing of concrete as shown in Figures 7b and 10.

The effect of preloading can be observed by comparing P0-0 with preloaded beams P45-0 and P65-0. Obviously, the preloaded beams are less rigid after the longitudinal steel yielding phase and also its ultimate capacities are lower.

On the other hand, the effect of sustained load can be observed by comparing P45-0 and P65-0 with P45-45 and P65-65. The ultimate capacities of preloaded beams repaired under sustained load are slightly lower (5%) than that repaired without sustained load and the differences in the stiffness between these beams are insignificant. Also, the effect of sustained load at high level can be observed by comparing the failure mode of P65-65 with P0-0, P45, and P65-0, where the beam repaired with higher level of sustained load was failed by crushing of concrete in the extreme compression fiber.

Prior to cracking, the flexural behaviour for all repaired beams was similar to that of the non-strengthened beam in the elastic phase.

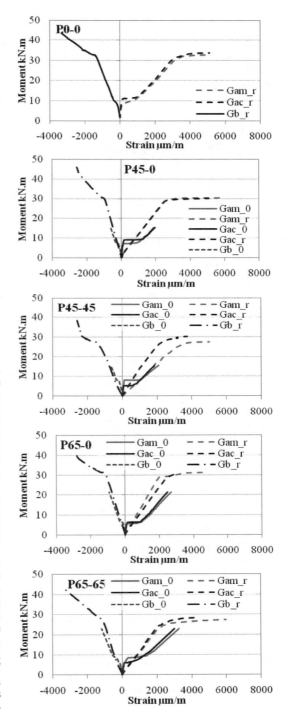

Figure 12. Moment–strain curves of bottom steel and top concrete for beams. (0) before repair by NSM CFRP rod and at preloaded level (r) after repair by NSM CFRP rod and at failure moment.

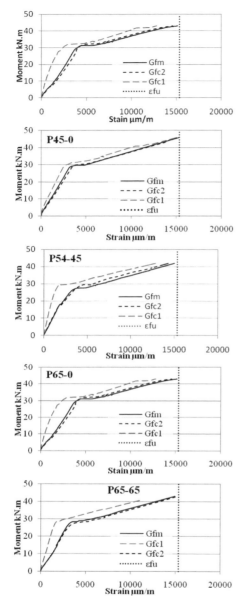

Figure 13. Moment–strain curves of CFRP rod for all beams.

This behaviour indicates that using NSM FRP reinforcement does not contribute to increase the stiffness and strength in this phase.

6.4 *Relationship of moments and strains*

The relationships between the applied moment and the strains recorded in the strain gauges glued onto the bottom steel, top surface of concrete and CFRP rod (Fig. 4) are depicted in Figures 11 and 12. Figure 11 shows the moment–strain curves of the bottom steel (Gam, Gac), and top concrete at midspan (Gb) before and after being repaired with NSM CFRP rod for all beams, Figure 12 shows the moment–strain curves of CFRP rod (Gfm, Gfc1, Gfc2) for all beams.

It can be observed that, after steel yielding, the strain in the CFRP rod (Fig. 12) increased at a much faster rate as indicated by the reduced slope of the curve. This is due to the fact that, after the rebars yielded, the CFRP rod alone resisted further increments of the tensile component of the internal moment couple. In the majority of the repaired beams some CFRP rods reached tensile strain values close to the ultimate rupture strain of the CFRP rod ($\cong 1.53\%$) as shown in Figure 13, showing this repairing technique has a high level of effectiveness.

For all levels of preloading in which damage due to cracking was induced, stress concentrations were observed in the CFRP rod at the crack location due to loss of continuity in the concrete material at that point causing all the tension force to be carried by the steel and the CFRP rod, however, as the strengthened specimen approached ultimate load, extensive new distributed cracks formed leading to more uniform distribution of strain in the CFRP rod.

7 CONCLUSIONS

Four RC beams repaired with one NSM CFRP rod at different levels of sustained load and one initially strengthened beam were tested. Two failure modes were obtained. Some useful conclusions are summarized as follows:

- When a beam is repaired at a higher level of sustained load, the *failure mode* by crushing of concrete will most likely occur because there is an important level of compression strain in the concrete due to the sustained load;
- The maximum *load-carrying capacity* of repaired beams at different levels of sustained load in this study generally performed very close to the same as the initially strengthened beam;
- The beams repaired at higher levels of sustained load had a lower *stiffness* than those of beams repaired at lower levels;
- When a beam is repaired at a higher level of sustained load, the *deflection* at maximum load capacity of the repaired beam hardly increased compared to that of the initially strengthened beam. When strengthened at 65% of the nominal flexural strength of the non-strengthened

714

control beam, its deflection may increase up to 10% more than that of the initially strengthened beam;

• The *ultimate strength* of RC beams repaired with NSM CFRP rod is very close regardless of load history at the time of repairing.

Finally, it may be concluded that a beam subject to external loading at the time of repairing may be rehabilitated with the technique NSM CFRP rod, neglecting the effect of existing external loads on both the maximum flexural load-carrying capacity and the deflection of the reinforced concrete beam to be repaired.

REFERENCES

ACI Committee 440. 2000. Guide for the Design and Construction of Externally Bonded FRP Systems for Strengthening Concrete Structures. *ACI 440.2R-02*.

Al-Mahmoud, F., Castel, A., François, R., & Tourneur, C. 2006. Anchorage and tension-stiffening effect between near-surface mounted fibre-reinforced polymer rods and concrete. *2nd International RILEM Symposium on Advances in Concrete through Science and Engineering*.

Al-Mahmoud, F., Castel, A., François, R., & Tourneur, C. 2007. Effect of surface pre-conditioning on bond of carbon fibre reinforced polymer rods to concrete. *Cement &Concrete Composites* 29(9): p.677–689.

Al-Mahmoud, F., Castel, A., François, R., & Tourneur, C. 2009. Strengthening of RC members with near-surface mounted CFRP rods. *Composite Structures* 91(2): p.138–147.

Arduini, M., & Nanni, A. 1997. Behavior of Precracked RC beams strengthened with carbon FRP Sheets. *Journal of Composites for Construction, ASCE* 1(2): p.63–70.

Bonacci, J., & Maalej, M. 2000. Externally bonded fiber-reinforced polymer for rehabilitation of corrosion damaged concrete beams. *ACI Structural Journal* 97(5): p.703–711.

Bresson, J. 1971. L'application du béton plaqué. *Annales de l'ITBTP*: p.278.

Cruz, J.M.S., & Barros, J.A.O. 2004. Bond Between Near-Surface Mounted Carbon Fiber-Reinforced Polymer Laminate Strips and Concrete. *Journal of Composites for Construction, ASCE* 8(6): p.519–527.

De Lorenzis, L., Lundgren, K., & Rizzo, A. 2004. Anchorage Length of Near-Surface Mounted Fiber-Reinforced Polymer Bars for Concrete Strengthening—Experimental Investigation and Numerical Modeling. *Structural Journal* 101(2): p.269–278.

De Lorenzis, L., & Nanni, A. 2002. Bond between near surface mounted FRP rods and concrete in structural strengthening. *ACI structural Journal* 99(2): p.123–132.

De Lorenzis, L., Nanni, A., & La Tegola, A. 2000. Flexural and Shear Strengthening of Reinforced Concrete Structures with Near Surface Mounted FRP Rods. Dans 521–528. Ottawa, Canada.

EuroCode–2. 1992. Design of concrete structures—Part 1-1 General rules and rules for buildings.

Fib Bulletin 14. 2001. *Externally Bonded FRP Reinforcement for RC Structures*. Lausanne, Suisse: International Federation for Structural Concrete.

Grace, N.K., & Sayed, G.A. 2003. Construction and Evaluation of Full-Scale CFRP Prestressed Concrete DT-girder. Dans 1281–1290. Singapore.

Hassan, T., & Rizkalla, S. 2003. Investigation of Bond in Concrete Structures Strengthened with Near Surface Mounted Carbon Fiber Reinforced Polymer Strips. *American Society of Civil Engineers—Journal of Composites for Construction* 7(3): p.248–257.

Hassan, T., & Rizkalla, S. 2004. Bond Mechanism of NSM FRP Bars for Flexural Strengthening of Concrete Structures. *ACI Structural Journal* 101(6): p.830–839.

ISIS Canada. 2001. Design Manuals Parts 1–4. *Intelligent Sensing for Innovative Structures*.

JBDPA-Japan. 1999. Seismic Retrofitting Design and Construction Guidelines for Existing Reinforced Concrete (RC) Buildings with FRP Materials. *Japan Building Disaster Prevention Association*.

Katsumata, H., Kimura, K., & Murahashi, H. 2001. Experience of FRP Strengthening for Japanese Historical Structures. Dans 1001–1008. New York, USA.

Keller, T. 2003. Use of Fibre Reinforced Polymers in Bridge Construction. Switzerland. Zürich: IABSE.

Kreit, A., Al-Mahmoud, F., Castel, A., & François, R. 2010. Repairing corroded RC beam with near-surface mounted CFRP rods. *Materials and Structures* 43(9).

L'Hermite, R. 1967. L'application des colles et résines dans la construction. Le béton àcoffrage portant. *Annales de l'ITBTP*: p.239.

Meier, U., Deuring, M., Meier, H., & Schwegler, G. 1992. Strengthening of Structures with CFRP Laminates: Research and Applications in Switzerland. *Advanced composite materials in bridges and structures, Canadian Society of Civil Engineers*: p.243–251.

Nanni, A. 1997. Carbon FRP Strengthening: New Technology Becomes Mainstream. *Concrete International, American Concrete Institute* 19(6): p.19–23.

Norris, T., Saadatmanesh, H., & Mohammad, R.E. 1997. Shear and flexural strengthening of R/C beams with carbon fiber sheets. *Journal of Structural Engineering, ASCE* 123(7): p.903–911.

Shahawy, M., Chaallal, O., Thomas, E.B., & Adnan, E. 2001. Flexural strengthening with carbon fiber-reinforced polymer composites of preload full-scale girders. *ACI Structural Journal* 98(5): p.735–743.

Sharif, A., AI-Sulaimani, G.J., Basunbul, I.A., Baluch, M.H., & Ghaleb, B.N. 1994. Strengthening of initially loaded RC beams using FRP plates. *ACI Structural Journal* 91(2): p.160–168.

Sherwood, T., & Soudki, K.A. 1999. Confinement of Corrosion Cracking in Reinforced Concrete Beams with Carbon Fibre Reinforced Polymer Laminates. *ACI-SP-188 on Non-Metallic (FRP) Reinforcement for Concrete*: p.591–603.

Shin, Y.S., & Lee, C. 2003. Flexural behavior of RC beams strengthened with carbon fiber-reinforced polymer laminates at different levels of sustaining load. *ACI Structural Journal* 100(2): p.231–239.

SOCOTEC. 1986. Recueil béton armé, Démolitions—Réparations—Renforcements, Tôles collées: justification par le calcul.

Soudki, K.A., & Sherwood, T. 2000. Behaviour of Reinforced Concrete Beams Strengthened with CFRP Laminates Subjected to Corrosion Damage. *Canadian Journal of Civil Engineering* 27(5): p.1005–1010.

Steiner, W. 1996. Strengthening of Structures with CFRP Strips. *Advanced Composite Materials and Structures*: p.407–417.

The Concrete Society. 2004. *Design guidance for strengthening concrete structures using fibre composite materials.* Camberley: The Concrete Society.

Theillout, J.N. 1983. *Renforcement et réparation des ouvrages d'art par la techniquedes tôles collées.* PhD Thesis. Ecole Nationale des Ponts et Chaussées.

Yeong-soo, S., & Chadon, L. 2003. Flexural behavior of reinforced concrete beams strengthened with carbon fiber-reinforced polymer laminates at different levels of sustaining load. *ACI Structural Journal* 100(2): p.231–240.

Yost, J.R., Gross, S.P., Dinehart, D.W., & Mildenberg, J.J. 2007. Flexural behavior of concrete beams strengthened with near-surface-mounted CFRP strips. *ACI structural journal* 104(4): p.430–437.

Concrete Solutions – Grantham, Mechtcherine & Schneck (eds)
© 2012 Taylor & Francis Group, London, ISBN 978-0-415-61622-5

Strengthening of reinforced concrete beam-column joints using ferrocement

B. Li & Eddie S.S. Lam

Department of Civil and Structural Engineering, The Hong Kong Polytechnic University, Hong Kong

ABSTRACT: Evidences from previous earthquakes have shown that failure in beam-column joints may cause disastrous collapse of structures, especially for buildings without seismic provisions. To extend the life span of beam-column joints, strengthening is required and this can be effectively achieved using ferrocement. Ferrocement is a composite material of wire mesh embedded in various mortars. It is bonded to the beam-column joints for strengthening. In this study, four 2/3 scale reinforced concrete interior beam-column joints, including one control specimen and three specimens strengthened by the proposed method, were constructed and tested under cyclic loading. The specimens were without transverse reinforcement and designed to be shear deficient, but complied with previous design codes in Hong Kong. Three types of mortar were selected as the variable parameters for the strengthening scheme while the same wire mesh was adopted. The experimental results indicated that the proposed strengthening method is effective to enhance the ultimate loading capacity, stiffness and energy dissipation. In addition, the strength of mortar has a crucial influence on strengthening.

1 INTRODUCTION

Beam-column joints in a reinforced concrete frame structure have been recognized as critical members transferring forces and bending moments between beams and columns. The change of moments in beams and columns across the joint region, under horizontal loading, induces high shear forces in the joint as compared with adjacent members. This also aggravates bonding conditions for the longitudinal reinforcement of beams and columns in the joint region. Therefore, shear failure and bonding deterioration were traditionally considered as primary failure modes of beam-column joints in moment resisting frame structures (Paulay & Priestley 1992).

Evidence from previous earthquakes has shown that the failure of beam-column joints may cause disastrous collapse of structures (EERI 1999, Huo et al. 2009, EERI 2010, Kam 2011). Figure 1(a) shows some damaged beam-column joints observed in the Wenchuan earthquake that took place on 12th May 2008. Figure 1(b) shows unreinforced beam-column joints that failed in shear which is possible a failure mechanism of the Pyne Gould Corp Building in Christchurch earthquake recently. In fact, particular attentions has been paid to strengthening beam-column joints in the last forty years. Hakuto et al. (2000) and Pampanin et al. (2002) illustrated poor performance of typical interior beam-column joints

designed without transverse reinforcement in the joint core (i.e. designed to gravity action only, similar to those commonly found in Hong Kong). As such, strengthening of beam-column joints in existing buildings is inevitable.

Since 1970s, a large number of research projects have been devoted to strengthening or repairing of beam-column joints in reinforced concrete frame structures. For instance, Popov & Bertero (1975) repaired interior beam-column joints using epoxy injection and concrete in the early 1970s. Subsequently, various kind of techniques or methods, mainly including concrete or steel jacketing, epoxy injecting and FRP composite wrapping etc., have been developed. In response to the situation that more buildings are facing different degrees of deterioration, there is great progress on methods for strengthening or repairing beam-column joints. Concrete jacketing, the most common technique, has been introduced and investigated by Hakuto et al. (2000), Wang & Hsu (2009). Even though this method has been identified as an effective method for enhancing strength, stiffness and ductility, it could be limited to application due to space requirements. Recently, Wang & Hsu (2009) improved concrete jacketing method by simplifying the construction procedure. Use of steel jacketing for strengthening has also been proved to be effective to upgrade beam-column joints (Ghobarah et al. 1997). Recently, use of FRP for strengthening beam-column joints has acquired

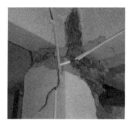

(a)

(b)

Figure 1. Damaged beam-column joints in (a) Wenchuan earthquake (Huo et al. 2009) and (b) Christchurch earthquake (Kam 2011).

numerous achievements (Ghobarah & Said 2002, Pantelides et al. 2008, Lee et al. 2010). Alternatively, mortar embedded with wire mesh, known as ferrocement, is proposed in this study for strengthening interior beam-column joints in reinforced concrete structures.

Ferrocement is defined by ACI committee 549 in the report on ferrocement as "a type of thin wall reinforced concrete commonly constructed of hydraulic cement mortar reinforced with closely spaced layers of continuous and relatively small size wire mesh. The mesh may be made of metallic or other suitable materials" (ACI 1997). Ferrocement exhibits a number of mechanical characteristics different from concrete, such as high strength to weight ratio, crack resistance, durability, impact resistance and ductility. Furthermore, ferrocement is able to achieve these properties through a thin panel reinforced in two directions to protect the reinforcement. Thus, ferrocement is an ideal material for strengthening structural members. Cao et al. (2008) strengthened beam-column joints using mortar reinforced with high strength steel wires. Wang et al. (2006) strengthened Zheng Cheng Gong Memorial in Xiamen by ferrocement. Ho & Lam (2010) strengthened full-scale columns using high performance ferrocement. The effect of variation of mesh density and strength of mortar to confinement action was investigated. Test results have shown that ferrocement is effective to enhance the axial load carrying capacity of columns.

In this study, a new approach using ferrocement with embedded diagonal reinforcement is proposed to strengthen interior beam-column joints. Four 2/3 scale interior beam-column joints were constructed and tested under reversed cyclic loading. Performance of specimens with or without strengthening was compared in terms of ultimate loading capacity, stiffness and energy dissipation. The main objective of this study is to investigate the feasibility of strengthening interior beam-column joints by the proposed method.

2 CONDITIONS OF BEAM-COLUMN JOINTS IN HONG KONG

Hong Kong has been recognized as an area with moderate seismic risk. However buildings in Hong Kong have been traditionally designed without seismic provisions (Lam et al. 2002). Buildings in Hong Kong were designed in accordance with British Standards and Hong Kong codes without taking seismic provisions into account. Wind load was considered as the only lateral force in the design of buildings. In terms of beam-column joints in reinforced concrete structures, no specific requirement was provided in the previous design code of Hong Kong. Consequently, beam-column joints were had a lack of transverse reinforcement in the design. This situation was changed after the publication of the Code of Practice for Structural use of Concrete (CoP 2004) which introduced specific detailing of beam-column joints. The design criteria for beam-column joints in the code were mainly based on those specified in New Zealand design code NZS 3101 (Wong & Kuang 2008). The code requires the joint should assure enough strength to resist the most adverse loading case from adjoining members. It specifies requirements for transverse reinforcement for horizontal shear, vertical shear and confinement. However, the above is still in accordance with non-seismic consideration. Therefore, shear strength of beam-column joints in a typical Hong Kong building could be inferior to that of a seismically designed building. The behavior of beam-column joints designed according to present code may be vulnerable and fail under seismic action.

Secondly, buildings in Hong Kong are facing the problem of aging. More than 18,000 reinforced concrete buildings have been constructed during the past 30 years, and pressingly, most of them are facing different degrees of degradation. For instance, the Buildings Department of the HKSAR Government received roughly 7,300 dangerous building reports annually during the past decade (Law et al. 2010). In the next ten years or so, more than 500 buildings will reach their design life, i.e. 50 years. Proper maintenance and repair is necessary if we want to extend the usable life of buildings, in particular those constructed in or before 1960s. The collapse of a 55 year old 5-story building on 29th January 2010 in Hong Kong, has raised further concern by the public urging proper repair/restoration of the old buildings. In general, there will be an increasing number of buildings facing the problems of aging, deterioration and substandard-designed.

Thus, beam-column joints in Hong Kong are facing possible deficiency in seismic resistance as well as deterioration of material. Strengthening of old buildings, especially beam-column joints is necessary both to extend the life span and to improve the seismic behavior.

3 STRENGTHENING SCHEME

In this study, strengthening of an interior beam-column joint was achieved by ferrocement with embedded diagonal reinforcement as shown in Figure 2. Ferrocement enhances shear capacity and provides confinement for the joint core. Firstly, ferrocement with wire mesh properly folded along the dotted lines and cut along solid lines is installed to replace the concrete cover in the beam-column joint region (Fig. 2(a)). In this study, two layers of wire mesh were installed in the joint region. Welded square mesh was adopted in this study. The mesh had an average wire diameter of 1.45 mm and width of spacing at 13.23 mm in both directions. Cement-based mortar of average 7-day cube strength 33 MPa was used for specimen S1. The ratio of binder to sand was 1:2.5 by weight, and 15% of cement was replaced by PFA. Meanwhile, two types of high performance mortar were adopted for specimen S2 and S3. One was a cementitious based fiber reinforced mortar and the other, epoxy-based mortar. Measured cube strengths of the two mortars on the day of testing were 34.7 MPa and 71.6 MPa respectively. Secondly, four diagonal reinforcing bars (two in each diagonal direction) of 10 mm diameter were installed in the joint for specimen S1 and 12 mm diameter for specimens S2 and S3. The ends of the diagonal reinforcement were effectively anchored to the main reinforcement of the beams to reduce the force to be transferred to the joint. The measured yield stress of the diagonal reinforcement was about 800 MPa.

When specimen S1 was subjected to cyclic loading, delimination of ferrocement was observed before failure. Improvement was made to specimens S2 and S3 by installing expansive anchors between concrete and the ferrocement panel. The arrangement of anchors is shown in Figure 3(a). Anchors are installed between ferrocement and concrete to

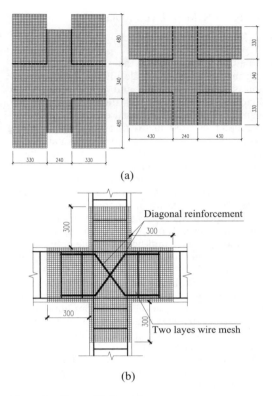

(a)

(b)

Figure 2.   Strengthening scheme.

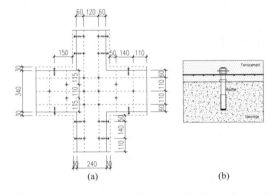

(a)   (b)

Figure 3.   Arrangement of anchors (a) front view and (b) details of an anchor.

improve bonding behavior as well as to facilitate ease of fixing the wire mesh. This is also recommended in the Technical Specification for strengthening concrete structures using grid rebar and mortar (CECS-242 2008). Each anchor had a length of 65 mm with 40 mm embedded in the concrete and 25 mm protruded out of the concrete. A typical detail of an anchor is shown in Figure 3(b).

4 EXPERIMENTAL PROGRAM

4.1 *Specimens*

To evaluate efficiency of the proposed strengthening method, four 2/3 scale interior beam-column joints were constructed and tested under cyclic loading. The first one was the control specimen, namely C1, which was based on typical reinforcement details used in existing buildings in Hong Kong. Three strengthened specimens, namely S1, S2 and S3, were strengthened using cement-based mortar, cementitious based fiber reinforced mortar and epoxy-based mortar respectively. All specimens had the same dimensions and reinforcement arrangement as shown in Figure 4.

The specimens replicate the lower stories of a building. The ends of the specimens coincide with the mid-span and mid-height of the actual frame structure. The columns were 2.385 m high and 300 mm by 300 mm in cross-section. The distance from the horizontal loading point to the upper face of the beam was 1.000 m, which is equal to the distance from the pin of the bottom hinge to the bottom face of the beam. The main reinforcement comprised 12 T16 bars (or 2.7% main reinforcement ratio). The beams were 2.700 m long and 300 mm by 400 mm in cross-section. The distances between the beam support and the column face was 1.000 m. The same reinforcement (4 T16 bars) were provided as top and bottom steel (or 1.35% main reinforcement ratio). The transverse reinforcement comprised R8 rectangular ties at 150 mm spacing and started at 50mm from the faces of beam and column. The joints had no transverse reinforcement and were prone to shear failure when subjected to cyclic loading.

As stated in the above, the ratio of column depth to diameter of main reinforcement in beams was $h_c/d_b = 300/16 = 18.75$, which does not satisfy the ratio of 20 as recommended by ACI-ASCE 352. Moreover, the beams had a larger moment capacity as compared with the columns, which is also not in accordance with the current code of practice. The above are typical joint details in frame structures in Hong Kong.

The measured cube strengths of concrete for specimens C1 and S1 and for specimens S2 and S3 on the day of test were 46.1 MPa and 48.85 MPa respectively. The measured yield strengths of the main reinforcement and the transverse reinforcement were 540 MPa and 410 MPa, respectively.

4.2 *Test setup and loading routine*

The test setup is shown in Figure 5. The specimens were tested by a displacement control multi-purpose testing system with a maximum vertical loading capacity of 10,000 kN and a maximum horizontal loading capacity of 1,500 kN. The bottom of the specimen was hinged. Both ends of the beam were supported by rollers to allow horizontal movement.

Axial load was first applied at the top and was kept constant throughout the loading test. Afterwards, cycles of horizontal displacement were applied at the top by displacement control. First of all, the yield displacement Δ_y was determined as follows. The specimen was subjected to progressive increase in the horizontal load up to 75% of the nominal moment capacity of the columns. The corresponding tip displacement at the top was recorded and extrapolated to determine the yield displacement of the column Δ_y. Afterwards, the displacement ductility factor μ (ratio of actual displacement to yielding displacement) was used to control the loading cycles.

Each loading cycle was repeated twice until the horizontal load dropped to 85% of its maximum value. The loading routine is shown in Figure 6.

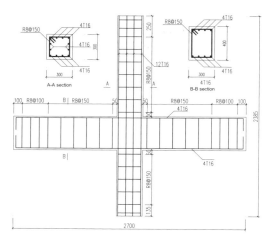

Figure 4.   Details of specimens.

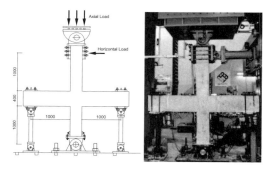

Figure 5.   Test setup for beam-column joint.

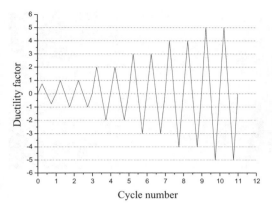

Figure 6. Loading routine.

It is to be noted that a high axial load was applied at $0.6f_c'A_g$ which is consistent with the common range of axial load from 0.5 to 0.7 for columns in Hong Kong (Lam et al. 2000). Complementarly, Su & Wong (2007) pointed out that the axial load ratio for columns can be 0.87 at ultimate conditions through conducting a survey study in Hong Kong for 17 existing buildings.

5 EXPERIMENTAL RESULTS

5.1 *General behavior and failure modes*

The crack pattern of specimen C1 is shown in Figure 7(a). After applying the axial load, one vertical crack in the joint and several flexural cracks in the beams were observed. When the displacement at the column tip reached 17.4 mm, a second vertical crack was observed. Occurrence of vertical cracks in the joint is attributed to the deformation of the main reinforcement of the column without shear hoops under the high level of axial load. This is also supported by bulging in the joint at the final stage of the test. Meanwhile, diagonal cracks appeared at the corner of the joint when the horizontal displacement reached 17.4 mm. With further increase in the horizontal displacement, diagonal cracks propagated due to diagonal tension. Moreover, obvious diagonal cracks were observed on both sides of the joint. With opening and closing of diagonal cracks under cyclic loading, spalling of concrete cover in the joint along the diagonal direction occurred. Although the moment capacity of the columns was similar to that of the beams, cracks were not observed on the column. This is attributed to the high level of axial load in the columns that reduced tensile strain in the columns. The final crack pattern consisted of

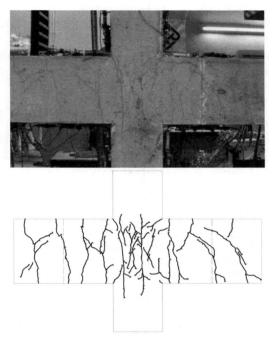

(a)

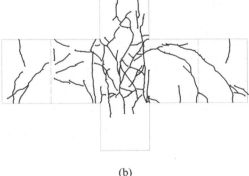

(b)

Figure 7. Crack patterns of specimen (a) C1 and (b) S1.

two vertical cracks along the main reinforcement of the columns, diagonal cracks in the joint and flexural cracks in the beams.

The formation of cracks in strengthened specimen S1 was improved due to the better crack control ability offered by the ferrocement. However, once the ultimate tensile strain of the ferrocement was attained, cracks propagated. When the horizontal displacement reached its fourth cycle of 8.7 mm, an obvious diagonal crack was observed. In the next cycle of 17.4 mm, diagonal cracks formed in the other diagonal direction, and several inclined cracks occurred in the column. Subsequently, cracks propagated in the joint region. At the horizontal displacement of 26.1 mm, spalling of mortar was observed outside the wire mesh in the upper column. This is probably caused by inconsistent deformation between the parent substrate and ferrocement under high axial load. Diagonal cracks in the strengthened specimen also appeared earlier than that of the control specimen. This may be attributed to the low strength of mortar. It is worth noticing that delamination of the ferrocement and bulging of the main reinforcement of the column occurred. The main reinforcement buckled due to inadequate confinement. Nevertheless, ferrocement offered some degree of confinement to the joint, though ferrocement in the joint region spalled off at the advanced stage of the loading. Another apparent observation was that cracks were distributed more uniformly in the case of specimen S1. This serves to demonstrate that ferrocement has a good ability to control cracks.

For specimen S2, using cementitious mortar for strengthening, more cracks were observed in the strengthening area as shown in Figure 8(a). This is contributed to the low strength of the cementitious mortar as compared with the concrete. After applying the axial load, several cracks were observed mainly in the joint region. As horizontal displacement increased, cracks appeared in the strengthening area. When the horizontal displacement reached 17.4 mm, several flexural cracks were observed in the unstrengthened part of the beam whereas the cracks in the joint were still propagating. The number of cracks in the joint region increased rapidly and mortar outside the wire mesh began spalling. At the advanced stage of loading, many cracks were formed: they propagated and joined together. Ferrocement exhibited bulging accompanied by delamination of the strengthening layer in the joint. Inconsistent deformation between the parent substrate and ferrocement could be the reason for cracking and spalling of specimen S2. Finally, failure of the ferrocement

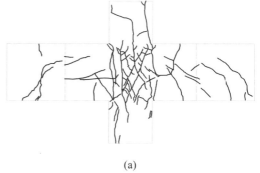

(a)

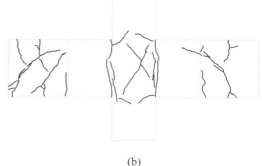

(b)

Figure 8. Crack patterns of specimen (a) S2 and (b) S3.

in the joint occurred and it resulted in obvious increase in vertical deflection of the column. This is attributed to the fact that ferrocement cannot provided adequate confinement to the joint. Deterioration of the joint strength under cyclic loading decreased axial load carrying capacity of the column. Similar to specimen S1, several cracks were formed in the strengthening area of the column but did not propagate substantially. In general, cracks in specimen S2 formed early and rapidly with severe failure in the joint.

Specimen S3, strengthened by epoxy-based mortar, showed excellent performance in crack resistance. As shown in Figure 8(b), lesser cracks were formed in the strengthening area. In the initial stage of the horizontal loading, cracks were mainly formed in the tensile zone of the beams and the interface between beam and column. Moreover, as cracks in the interface developed, cracks in the unstrengthened beam ceased to propagate. This indicated that failure at the interface of beam to column triggered joint shear failure. Subsequently, cracks on edges of the joint developed in terms of width and length as the horizontal displacement increased. It is worth noticing that no cracks had formed in the joint until the horizontal displacement reached 43.5 mm at the eleventh cycle. Two diagonal cracks were formed throughout the joint when the lateral displacement was 43.5 mm and 60.9 mm respectively. As compared with specimens S2 and S3, diagonal cracks in specimen S3 were formed later due to the use of high strength mortar. Furthermore, cracks were not observed in the strengthened area of beam. This proves that ferrocement is effective in strengthening the beams. When the cracks were connected together in the joint at the final stage of the displacement cycle, bulging of the ferrocement was observed and delamination occurred in the joint only. Bonding between the ferrocement and the joint performed well due to the use of anchors. In fact, delamination of the ferrocement was not caused by failure of anchors but by shear failure of the concrete in the joint. In general, fewer cracks were observed in specimen S3 as compared with specimens S1 and S2 and the cracks were mainly in the joint and unstrengthened area of the beams.

As shown in Figure 9, failure modes of the specimens were generally similar and were due to insufficient shear strength in the joint and buckling of main reinforcement of the columns. Buckling of main reinforcement of the strengthened specimens occurred in the final stage of the tests due to joint shear failure. For specimen S1, delamination of ferrocement occurred at the joint and

(a)

(b)

(c)

Figure 9. Failure of beam-column joints (a) specimen S1, (b) specimen S2 and (c) specimen S3.

the adjacent area. Debonding of ferrocement was observed in most of the strengthened area. This means that bonding between the ferrocement and the joint was poor and insufficient. Specimen S3, strengthened by high performance mortar, failed at the joint but there was debonding in the beam and column. In specimens S2 and S3, good bonding was achieved between the ferrocement and concrete in beams and columns. This proves that anchors provided at the interface had significantly improved the bonding.

5.2 Hysteretic behavior

The horizontal load-displacement relationship of the column tip for control specimen C1 and strengthened specimens S1, S2 and S3 are shown in Figure 10. Specimens C1, S1, S2 and S3 exhibited ultimate horizontal loads of 84.3 kN, 92.4 kN, 82.1 kN and 101.0 kN in the pull direction at displacements of 25.4 mm, 23.2 mm, 17.89 mm and 35.05 mm respectively. In the push direction, specimens C1, S1, S2 and S3 had ultimate horizontal loads of −84.7 kN, −90.1 kN, −79.6 kN and −96.0 kN at displacements of −25.35 mm, −17.40 mm, −17.5 mm and −34.85 mm respectively. Here, positive and negative signs represent pull and push directions respectively. As compared with control specimen C1, the ultimate horizontal load was enhanced by 9.6% in the pull direction and 6.4% in the push direction for specimen S1 while it was enhanced by 19.8% in the pull direction and 13.3% in the push direction for specimen S3. This is attributed to the strengthening scheme, which enhanced shear capacity of the joint.

However, the ultimate horizontal load of specimen S2 decreased by 2.6% in the pull direction and 6.0% in the push direction. This is mainly attributed to the strengthening mortar applied to specimen S2, which exhibited a lower strength as compared with the concrete. Inconsistent deformation between the strengthening layer and the concrete substrate also reduced the horizontal load carrying capacity of specimen S2. Although the mortar used for strengthening specimen S1 had relatively low strength, it had an elastic modulus compatible to the concrete. Comparing the performance between specimens S2 and C1, diagonal reinforcement had little contribution on strengthening.

A summary of the test results is shown in Table 1. As shown in Table 1, the improvement in load carrying capacity of specimen S3 was two times larger than that of specimen S1. Using ferrocement with high strength mortar had a significant effect on enhancing the load carrying capacity of the joint.

5.3 Energy dissipation

Energy dissipation is a key factor reflecting the ability to survive during an earthquake. It is calculated from the area of lateral load-displacement loops at each cycle of horizontal displacement. Cumulative energy dissipation for control specimen and strengthened specimens are shown in Figure 11. It is apparent that the energy dissipation capacity was enhanced for all strengthened specimens. In other words, if the same energy dissipation is required during an earthquake, specimen S1, S2 and S3

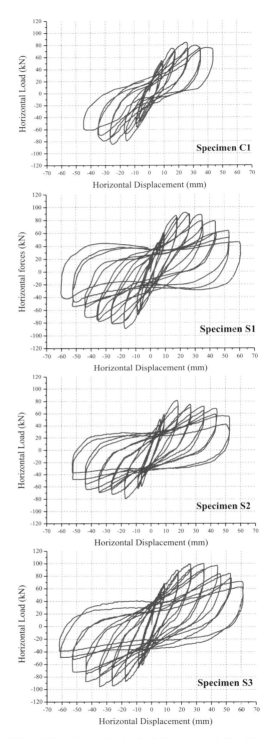

Figure 10.   Column tip load-displacement relationship.

Table 1. Summary of test results.

Specimen		Ultimate load (kN)	Corresponding displacement (mm)	Improvement in load carrying capacity
C1	Pull	84.3	25.40	0.0%
	Push	−84.7	−25.35	0.0%
S1	Pull	92.4	23.20	+9.6%
	Push	−90.1	−17.40	+6.4%
S2	Pull	82.1	17.89	−2.6%
	Push	−79.6	−17.50	−6.0%
S3	Pull	101.0	35.05	+19.8%
	Push	−96.0	−34.85	+13.3%

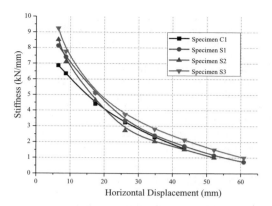

Figure 12. Relationship between stiffness degradation and horizontal displacement.

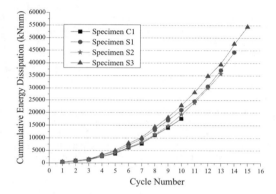

Figure 11. Energy dissipation of (a) each cycle, and (b) cumulative at each cycle.

would have had smaller horizontal displacements as compared with specimen C1. Strengthened specimens sustain a larger increase in energy dissipation as the horizontal displacement increases. Specimen S3 strengthened by epoxy-based mortar showed the best ability to dissipate energy as compared with the other strengthened specimens. Energy dissipated by specimen S2 strengthened by cement-based mortar was in between that of specimen S3 and S1. It can be found that the capacity of energy dissipation increased with increasing strength of mortar.

5.4 Stiffness degradation

The stiffness of a specimen is determined at each loading cycle by secant modulus, i.e. the line passing the origin to the point of interest. It represents resistance of a structural member to deformation. The results of all specimens are plotted in Figure 12. Strengthened specimens exhibited higher stiffness at the initial stage of the loading cycle. This can be

attributed to the use of ferrocement and diagonal reinforcement in the joint region. Furthermore, it can be found that stiffness increased when high strength strengthening material was used. However, the stiffness of specimen S2 decreased quickly as compared with the other strengthened specimens. It was even lower than that of the control specimen. It seems that the strengthening mortar for specimen S2 could not deform consistently with the parent substrate and spalling occurred at an early stage of the loading cycle. Meanwhile, specimen S3 showed the highest stiffness and reduction in stiffness and was similar to specimen C1. The stiffness of specimen S1 was significantly higher than that of specimen C1 but lower than that of specimen S3. In general, loss of stiffness can be attributed to deterioration of concrete in the joint region.

6 CONCLUSIONS

An experimental program was conducted to evaluate the improvement in strengthening interior beam-column joints by ferrocement embedded with diagonal reinforcement. Based on the observations and experimental results of four interior beam-column joint specimens, the following are concluded.

- The proposed strengthening scheme for interior beam-column joints was effective to enhance seismic performance in terms of ultimate strength, energy dissipation and stiffness.
- Strength of mortar was a vital factor for achieving higher ultimate strength, better energy dissipation and higher stiffness.
- Modes of failure of four specimens were due to buckling of the main reinforcement in the

columns accompanied by shear failure in the beam-column joints. Improved confinement to the main reinforcement in the joint will have to be provided.

- Bonding between the joint and ferrocement wasimproved significantly when anchors were installed at the interface.
- All strengthened specimens were able to sustain load carrying capacity after cracking due to the confinement action provided by the ferrocement.

ACKNOWLEDGEMENTS

The authors are grateful to the financial support from The Hong Kong Polytechnic University and the Research Grants Council of Hong Kong (RGC No: PolyU 5206/08E). The authors would like to thank the technical assistance provided by the Heavy Structural Laboratory of the Hong Kong Polytechnic University.

REFERENCES

ACI 549R. 1997. *Report on Ferrocement.* ACI Committee 549, 1997.

ACI-ASCE 352. 2002. *Recommendations for design if beam-column connections in monolithic reinforced concrete structures.* Joint ACI-ASCE Committee 352, Farmington Hills, Mich.

Cao, Z., Li, A., Wang, Y.Y., Zhang, W. & Yao, Q. 2007. Experimental study on RC space beam-column joints strengthened with high strength steel wire mesh and polymer mortar. *Journal of Southeast University (Natural Science Edition)* 37(2): 235–239. (In Chinese).

CECS 242. 2008. *Technical specification for strengthening concrete structures with grid rebar and mortar.* China Association for Engineering Construction Standardization. China Planning Press.

CoP 2004. *Code of Practice for Structural Use of Concrete 2004.* Second Edition, The Government of the Hong Kong Special Administrative Region.

EERI. 1999. Learning from earthquake The Chi-Chi, Taiwan Earthquake of September 21, 1999. *EERI Special Earthquake report, Earthquake Engineering Research Institute.* 12P.

EERI. 2010. EERI preliminary report on the 2010, M7.2 EL Mayor-Cucapah earthquake. *Editor: Jorge Meneses, Earthquake Engineering Research Institute.* 125P.

Ghobarah, A., Aziz, T.S. & Biddah, A. 1997. Rehabilitation of reinforced concrete frame connections using corrugated steel jacketing. *ACI Structural Journal* 94(2): 283–293.

Ghobarah, A. & Said, A. 2002. Shear strengthening of beam-column joints. *Engineering Structures* 24(7): 881–888.

Hakuto, S., Park, R. & Tanaka, H. 2000. Seismic load tests on interior and exterior beam-column joints with substandard reinforcing details. *ACI Structural Journal* 97(1): 11–25.

Ho, I.F.Y. & Lam, S.S.E. 2010. Strengthening Reinforced Concrete Columns by High Performance Ferrocement. *Proc. Joint Conf. of 7th Int. Conf. on Urban Earthquake Engng. & 5th Int. Conf. on Earthquake Engng.,* March 3–5, 2010, Tokyo Institute of Technology, Tokyo, Japan.

Huo, L., Li, H., Xiao, S. & Wang, D. 2009. Earthquake damage investigation and analysis of reinforced concrete frame structures in Wenchuan earthquake. *Journal of Dalian University of Technology* 49(5): 718–723. (In Chinese).

Kam, W.Y. 2011. Preliminary report from the Christchurch 22 Feb. 2011 6.3MW earthquake: Pre-1970s RC and RCM buildings, and precast staircase damage. *Field report.* 6P.

Lam, S.S.E, Wu, B., Wong, Y.L., Chau, K.T. Chen, A. & Li, C.S 2000. Ultimate drift of rectangular reinforced concrete columns in Hong Kong when subjected to earthquake action. *Seismic study for Hong Kong, Construction Industry Development Studies and Research Center,* 48P.

Lam, S.S.E., Xu, Y.L., Chau, K.T., Wong, Y.L. & Ko, J.M. 2002. Progress in earthquake resistant design of buildings in Hong Kong. *Structural Engineering World Congress,* Oct 9–12, 2002, Yokohama, Japan.

Law, C.K., Chui, E.W.T., Wong, Y.C. & Ho, L.S. 2010. The Achievements and Challenges of Urban Renewal in Hong Kong. Hong Kong. Study Report, March, 2010.

Lee, W.T., Chiou, Y.J. & Shih, M.H. 2010. Reinforced concrete beam–column joint strengthened with carbon fiber reinforced polymer. *Composite Structures* 92(1): 48–60.

Pampanin, S., Calvi, G.M. & Moratti, M. 2002. Seismic behavior of RC beam-column joints designed for gravity loads. *12th European Conference on Earthquake Engineering,* London. Sep, 2002. 726.

Pantelides, C.P., Okahashi, Y. & Reaveley, L.D. 2008. Seismic rehabilitation of reinforced concrete frame interior beam-column joints with FRP composites. *Journal of composites for construction, ASCE,* 12(4): 435–445.

Paulay, T. & Priestley, M.J.N. 1992. *Seismic Design of Reinforced Concrete and Masonry Buildings.* John Wiley & Sons, Inc.

Popov, E.P. & Bertero, V.V. 1975. Repaired R/C members under cyclic loading. *Earthquake Engineering and Structural Dynamics* 4(2): 129–144.

Su, R.K.L. & Wong, S.M. 2007. A survey on axial load ratios of structural walls in medium-rise residential buildings in Hong Kong. *The HKIE Transactions* 14(3): 40–46.

Wang, Y.C. & Hsu, K. 2009. Shear Strength of RC Jacketed Interior Beam-Column Joints without Horizontal Shear Reinforcement. *ACI Structural Journal* 106(2): 222–232.

Wang, Y.Y., Yao, Q.L., Gong, Z.G., Chen, Y.M., Xie, Y.R. & Chen, Z.M. 2005. Application of Strengthened Technology by composite cover combined with high strength wire cable mesh and polymeric Mortar in Zheng Chenggong Memorial Strengthened Engineering. *Building Structures* 35(8): 40–42. (In Chinese).

Wong, S.H.F. & Kuang, J.S. 2008. On the design of RC beam-column joints to Hong Kong concrete code 2004. *The HKIE Transactions* 16(3): 48–55.

Concrete Solutions – Grantham, Mechtcherine & Schneck (eds)
© 2012 Taylor & Francis Group, London, ISBN 978-0-415-61622-5

Engineered Cementitious Composite as a durability protective layer for concrete

Y. Lin, L. Wotherspoon & J.M. Ingham
Department of Civil and Environmental Engineering, University of Auckland, Auckland, New Zealand

A. Scott
Department of Civil and Natural Resources Engineering, University of Canterbury, Christchurch, New Zealand

D. Lawley
Reid Construction Systems, New Zealand

ABSTRACT: Engineered Cementitious Composite (ECC) shotcrete is a sprayable cement composite reinforced with synthetic fibres that exhibits a strain-hardening characteristic when subjected to load. The ductile behaviour of ECC makes it an ideal repair material for concrete structures as the strains that arise from thermal expansion of the original concrete structure can be accommodated.

Four tests were conducted to assess the suitability of ECC as a durability protective layer for concrete structures exposed to marine environments. The tests were conducted to determine the voids percentage, electrical resistance, capillary suction rate and chloride diffusion coefficient of the material. Six ECC mix designs and a 40 MPa concrete were tested. Results indicated that the optimum ECC mix design reduced the apparent chloride diffusion coefficient by 90.8% compared with a 40 MPa concrete, indicating that ECC is suitable as a durability protective layer for concrete.

1 INTRODUCTION

1.1 Background

Reinforced concrete bridge construction in New Zealand became common after the 1950s. Due to the nature of design and construction practice during this period, many of the bridges now have insufficient cover concrete compared to the current New Zealand concrete code (NZS 2006). As a result of insufficient specified cover thickness and lack of supplementary cementitious material, many bridges now exhibit signs of reinforcement corrosion. To extend the service life of these deteriorated bridges, immediate remediation is necessary and can be categorised into two procedures: firstly, removal of existing chloride ions and replacement of damaged steel reinforcement; and secondly, the application of new cover concrete to delay future chloride ingress. This study focused on the second step and investigated the effectiveness of sprayed Engineered Cementitious Composite as a cover concrete for repair work.

1.2 Engineered Cementitious Composite

Engineered Cementitious Composite (ECC) is a cement composite reinforced with synthetic fibres. ECC exhibits a strain-hardening characteristic when subjected to tension through the process of matrix micro-cracking and the transfer of forces through any fibres that bridge the crack. The strain-hardening characteristic means that when applied to an existing concrete substrate, the differential volume change between the existing structure and the ECC can be accommodated by the ECC without spalling of the substrate. As a result of the strain capability, the effectiveness of ECC as a repair material has been thoroughly investigated in previous studies such as those conducted by Kanda et al. (2003), Li et al. (2000) and Lim & Li (1997).

ECC is classified into two categories: self compacting cast ECC, and sprayed ECC. In this study the focus was on sprayed ECC because it is a more economical application method as it does not require setup of formwork. A typical mix design of sprayed ECC is shown in Table 1, revealing that

Table 1. Sprayed ECC mix design.

Materials	kg/m^3
300 μm Sand	640
Cement	800
Fly ash	240
Water	374
Fibre	26
Additives	0.3

ECC does not have any large (>300 μm) aggregates in its constituent material. Because of the use of fine materials, ECC is able to achieve a denser structure than conventional concrete, making it more resistant to chloride ion ingress.

2 MATERIALS

Six different ECC mix designs and a 40 MPa concrete were produced and subjected to durability testing, with detailed descriptions of each mix design provided in the following subsections. An M-tec duo-mix 2000 dry mixer was used to mix and spray the ECC shotcrete (see Figure 1).

To simulate the spraying process that would take place for repair work on existing concrete structures, all ECC mixes were sprayed into a 1 m high × 1 m long × 100 mm deep box that was placed vertically against a wall (see Figure 2). The ECC mix was sprayed into the box and then left standing vertically for 24 hours before the ECC panel was extracted from the mould and covered with a plastic sheet with the temperature maintained between 23 ± 2°C. The concrete panel was cast directly into the box mould resting flat on the ground. All samples were cured and tested at 56 days. Prior to testing, the panels were removed from curing and each panel was cut to obtain the samples required for different tests (see Figure 3).

2.1 ECC-S

ECC-S is the standard ECC shotcrete provided by the supplier, where S stands for standard. The main constituents are identical to that listed in Table 1. The mix proportions are also similar to those used by Kim et al. (2003). ECC-S has been previously used by Lin et al. (2010) as a strengthening material for masonry walls where bond to clay brick masonry surfaces was achieved without the use of any bonding agents or physical anchorages.

2.2 ECC-IFA

ECC-IFA has identical constituents to ECC-S with the exception that the fly ash ratio was increased to 40% of the cement content, compared to 30% in ECC-S. The code IFA stands for Increased Fly Ash. Fly ash content was increased because the fly ash particles are small (ranging between 0.5 μm–100 μm), such that an increase in the amount of fly ash within the mix results in an increase in density, and therefore potentially a more impermeable composite.

2.3 ECC-CH

ECC-CH is similar to ECC-S, with the only modification being that half of the fly ash has

Figure 1. M-tec duo mix 2000.

Figure 2. Spraying ECC into box.

Figure 3. Panel cut up to extract samples.

been replaced with calcium carbonate. Calcium carbonate provides the same physical function (as a filler) as does fly ash in ECC. However, fly ash and calcium carbonate do not share the same chemical function, as calcium carbonate acts as nucleation centres for cement particles and accelerates hydration, as oppose to fly ash which hydrates significantly slower. The primary reason for replacing half of the fly ash with calcium carbonate was to reduce cost, as calcium carbonate is a cheaper local material in New Zealand. The fly ash used in the mix was imported due to particle size consistency requirements, which was not available in fly ash produced in New Zealand.

2.4 ECC-Si

ECC-Si has a silane based water repellent added to the ECC-S mix. The silane based water repellent is typically used as a surface coated chloride resistance barrier and the effectiveness has been verified in SINTEF (2008). However, in the case of ECC-Si the water repellent was spread within the whole composite instead of just coated on the surface. The effectiveness of incorporating silane water repellent in the ECC mix was previously tested on cast mixes of ECC by Martinola et al. (2002), where a 90% reduction in the capillary suction was measured when water repellent was added to the mix.

2.5 ECC-Zn

ECC-Zn is the same mix as ECC-S but with a Zinc Stearate metallic soap additive added to the mix design. The metallic soap has a hydrophobic (water repelling) nature and also provides a lubricating effect, which would reduce the chemical bond between the fibres and the cement matrix and therefore potentially provide increased strain capacity.

2.6 ECC-RH

ECC-RH is an alternative ECC mix (as opposed to ECC-S) provided by the supplier. The main objective when using this mix is to be able to achieve thicker shotcrete layers in a short amount of time (less than 5 minutes as reported by the supplier). The code designation RH stands for Rapid Hardening. The main differences between the constituent materials in ECC-RH and ECC-S is that fly ash was completely replaced with calcium carbonate, and an increased amount of accelerators was used.

2.7 OCM-40

OCM-40 stands for Ordinary Concrete Mix, with an actual compressive strength of 40 MPa. The concrete mix was provided by a local ready mix concrete supplier with the mix being designed identical to that used for a 40 MPa structural concrete.

3 TEST METHODOLOGIES

Four durability tests were conducted to assess the performance of ECC as a chloride resisting barrier. The tests conducted were the ASTM C642 void test (ASTM 2006), ASTM C1585 sorptivity test (ASTM 2004a) and ASTM C1556 bulk diffusion test (ASTM 2004b). The test sequence listed above also indicates the relative time taken to conduct each test, from shortest to longest. The first two tests are indicative tests that provide a fast and economical method to determine the chloride resistance of the material. However, results of the indicative tests are only valid when they are consistent with the bulk diffusion test, which measures the chloride penetration depth in the sample directly.

3.1 ASTM C1202 resistivity test

The determination of the concrete resistivity involves applying a known alternating current across the specimen and measuring the voltage. The concrete resistivity is determined by dividing the measured resistance by the depth of the specimens and then multiplied by the cross sectional area. The 100 mm diameter by 50 mm deep test specimens were preconditioned prior to testing according to the vacuum saturation method outline in ASTM C1202 (1997).

3.2 ASTM C642 density, absorption and voids in hardened concrete

The ASTM C642 test measures the amount of air voids within a hardened concrete. The process involves oven drying a sample with a minimum volume of 375000 mm^3 (in this study cubes with volume of $75 \times 75 \times 75$ mm each were used) until constant mass was achieved (less than 0.5% of change in mass within a 24 hour period). After the samples had been oven dried and the mass recorded, they were immersed in cold water until constant mass was achieved and the mass recorded. Lastly, the samples were placed in boiling water for 5 hours and left to cool for 14 hours and the final mass recorded. The change between oven dried mass and mass after immersion in boiling water defines the amount of voids within the hardened concrete.

3.3 ASTM C1558 sorptivity test

The ASTM C1585 sorptivity test measures the capillary suction rate of cement composites. Capillary suction is one of the three dominant mechanisms by which chlorides are transported into concrete. Cube samples were used in the sorptivity test, using the same dimensions as the samples used in the void test. Cube samples were extracted from the panels and each sample was placed in an environmental chamber for 15 days, where the temperature was maintained at $50 \pm 2°C$, and a saturated solution of potassium bromide was placed within the oven to control the relative humidity (RH) at $80 \pm 5\%$.

Once removed from the environmental chamber, each surface of the cube (except the top and bottom) was sealed. A plastic sheet was placed around the top surface and tightened with elastic bands, while the bottom surface remained uncovered. The uncovered surface was then placed in contact with water, with the setup as illustrated in Figure 4.

3.4 *ASTM C1556 bulk diffusion test*

The ASTM C1556 bulk diffusion test determines the apparent chloride diffusion coefficient (the rate of chloride ingress) of the cement composite. As with the void and sorptivity tests, cube samples were extracted from the panels. With the exception of the bottom surface, all other surfaces of the samples were coated with polyurethane to prevent chloride ingress from surfaces other than the bottom surface. Samples were then immersed in a saturated solution of calcium hydroxide until constant mass was measured, following which the samples were immersed in NaCl solution with a concentration of 3.5% for a period of 35 days.

After the samples were removed from the NaCl solution, the polyurethane coating the surface was ground off and samples were placed in a lathe. Layers were then ground off the sample at two millimetre increments and the powders collected (see Figure 5). Ten layers were ground off each sample such that the maximum depth after grinding off all layers was 20 mm.

After all samples were ground off and collected, they were filtered through a 600 μm sieve so that the larger aggregates particles were removed to limit possible contamination from previous depth increments during grinding.

Powder weighing 4 ± 0.05 g was extracted from each of the samples, with the ASTM (2003) method of extraction being adopted, where samples were poured into a cone shape. The cone mass was then measured and cut into equal portions. The benefit of adopting this method was that the particle size distribution was consistent between the used and unused samples. When 4 g were poured directly out of the sample container then it was likely that only the lighter particles would be analysed.

After 4 g was measured from a sample and placed in a beaker, the total acid soluble chloride concentration was determined by means of potentiometric titration with 0.1 M of silver nitrate. The chloride concentration against depth plot was then produced to determine the apparent diffusion coefficient.

3.5 *Four point bending test*

In addition to the durability tests, a four-point bending flexural test was conducted on bar samples to demonstrate their flexural response when subjected to load. The samples tested were 500 mm long × 50 mm wide × 25 mm thick and were cut out

Figure 5. Grinding layers of bulk diffusion samples.

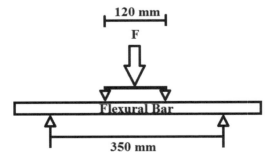

Figure 6. Flexural test setup.

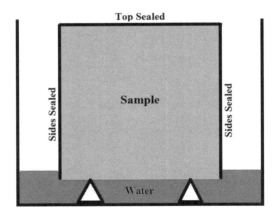

Figure 4. Sorptivity test setup.

of the panels with the loaded face parallel to the panel surface. The bar samples were simply supported on a 350 mm span and loaded 60 mm on each side of the centre of the bar. A schematic of the test setup is shown below in Figure 6.

4 RESULTS

4.1 *Resistivity results*

The results of the resistivity test along with the coefficent of variance (CoV) are shown in Table 2, indicating that with the exception of ECC-RH, there was no significant difference in the electrical resistance of the ECC mixes and the 40 MPa concrete mix. These results suggest that the chloride resistance of these mixes are similar.

4.2 *ASTM C642 density, absorption and voids in hardened concrete results*

Void test results are presented in Table 3, showing that the majority of ECC-mixes had a void percentage between 21.0 to 25.0%, which was relatively high compared to the 12% void percentage of the 40 MPa concrete. Studies conducted by Bharatkumar et al. (2001) have also found the void percentage of high performance concrete (with 28 day compression strengths varying between 33.5 to 40.9 MPa) to be within the ranges of 10.2 to 12.0%, verifying the percentages measured in this test.

The higher percentage of voids measured in the ECC mixes was likely a result of the spraying process. As ECC is sprayed onto the wall, air is trapped within the mix material, and when the material has hardened the air remaining within the composite becomes the voids. However, there were fundamental differences in the characteristics of the voids, it was visually observed that the ECC mix voids were smaller and more uniformly distributed across the sample, while the voids in the concrete sample were significantly larger and more concentrated.

Mix ECC-Zn had the lowest void percentage of 4.5%, and from observation there was no distinct

Table 2. Resistivity test results.

| Mixes | Average resistivity | | |
	kohm.cm	CoV
ECC-S	4.5	0.04
ECC-IFA	5.7	0.08
ECC-CH	4.9	0.07
ECC-Si	6.3	0.05
ECC-Zn	5.5	0.03
ECC-RH	2.2	0.09
OCM-40	5.1	0.20

Table 3. Voids test results.

| Mixes | Average void | |
	%	CoV
ECC-S	24.6	0.01
ECC-IFA	25.0	0.06
ECC-CH	21.4	0.01
ECC-Si	21.0	0.06
ECC-Zn	4.5	0.02
ECC-RH	22.3	0.01
OCM-40	12.0	0.03

difference between the physical appearance of ECC-Zn and other ECC mixes. The metallic soap incorporated within the ECC-Zn mix was effective in repelling water, so even though the voids existed, water could not penetrate into the sample.

The results of the void test indicate that ECC-Zn may have the best performance in resisting chloride penetration, while other ECC mixes have worse performance than concrete. It can also be observed that the results from the ECC-Zn mix were not in agreement with the results from the resistivity test, where ECC-Zn indicated a similar chloride resistance to the other ECC mixes and the concrete mix. The low resistance measured for the ECC-Zn mix was possibly due to the metallic additive that was incorporated in the mix being conductive and thus lowering the electrical resistance of the sample.

4.3 *ASTM 1558 sorptivity test results*

From Table 4 it is clear that the ECC-Zn mix had the lowest initial and secondary sorptivity. It was also physically identified that ECC-Zn was the only mix where no water vapour was observed on the top surface of the sample (where a clear plastic sheet was used to prevent water from escaping), indicating that the amount of water uptake into the sample was minimal.

4.3.1 *Correlation between total void percentage and sorptivity*

The difference in the voids percentage measured for all the mixes was of similar level to the difference in sorptivity rate measured for all the mixes. This observation suggests that there is a relationship between void testing and the sorptivity test. The results from the two tests are plotted against each other in Figure 7, indicating a linear relationship between the two test results with a regression of 90.5%. For each percentage point increase in the total voids, the sorptivity increases at a rate of 0.0014 mm/√min.

Table 4. Sorptivity test results.

Mixes	Initial sorptivity		Secondary sorptivity	
	mm√min	CoV	mm/√min	CoV
ECC-S	0.039	0.13	0.013	0.10
ECC-IFA	0.033	0.23	0.010	0.14
ECC-CH	0.027	0.5	0.0083	0.06
ECC-Si	0.025	0.09	0.0080	0.14
ECC-Zn	0.0027	0.14	0.0031	0.10
ECC-RH	0.036	0.34	0.016	0.30
OCM-40	0.019	0.30	0.0063	0.29

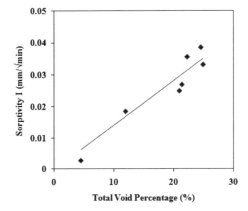

Figure 7. Relationship between sorptivity and total void percentage.

4.4 *ASTM 1556 bulk diffusion test results*

The averaged chloride profiles for all the mixes are shown in Figures 8 to 14, indicating that with the exception of ECC-RH, the chloride level declined significantly between the surface in contact with the chloride solution and a depth of approximately 10 mm from the surface. In contrast to the rapid decline of chloride level with depth of the ECC mixes, the concrete specimen exhibited a more gradual decline in chloride level, indicating that it was less effective at resisting chloride ion ingress.

From the chloride profiles obtained, the average apparent diffusion coefficient of each mix was determined and is shown in Table 5, suggesting that results from the bulk diffusion test do not correspond to the results obtained from the indicative tests. All the ECC mixes had a lower apparent chloride diffusion coefficient than that of concrete, indicating that ECC is more resistant to chloride ingress than is concrete. In the indicative tests only ECC-Zn showed better performance than concrete.

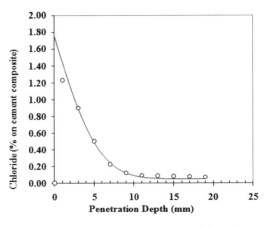

Figure 8. Averaged chloride profile for ECC-S mix.

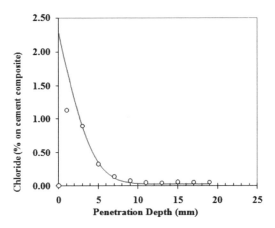

Figure 9. Averaged chloride profile for ECC-IFA mix.

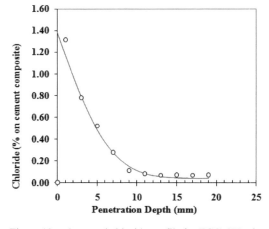

Figure 10. Averaged chloride profile for ECC-CH mix.

732

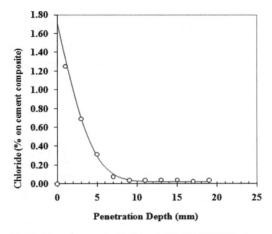

Figure 11. Averaged chloride profile for ECC-Si mix.

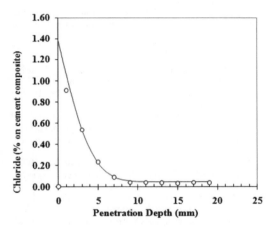

Figure 12. Averaged chloride profile for ECC-Zn mix.

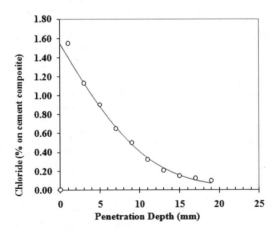

Figure 13. Averaged chloride profile for ECC-RH mix.

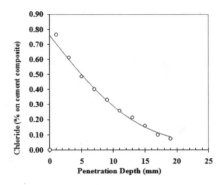

Figure 14. Averaged chloride profile for OCM-40 Mix.

Table 5. Bulk diffusion test results.

| Mixes | Apparent diffusion coefficient | |
	10^{-12}m^2/s	CoV
ECC-S	3.2	0.22
ECC-IFA	2.0	0.47
ECC-CH	4.1	0.16
ECC-Si	2.0	0.13
ECC-Zn	1.7	0.31
ECC-RH	13.4	0.81
OCM-40	19.0	0.30

With the exception of ECC-RH, all ECC mixes had an apparent chloride diffusion coefficient of approximately an order of magnitude lower than the concrete mix, with mix ECC-Zn having the best performance. While mixes ECC-IFA and ECC-Si also had a comparable apparent diffusion coefficient to ECC-Zn, ECC-Zn demonstrated the lowest void percentage and capillary suction rate in the indicative tests. Therefore it was determined that ECC-Zn should be selected as the ECC mix to be used as a chloride resisting barrier for concrete structures.

4.5 *Four point bending test results*

The averaged flexural response of the six samples extracted and tested from each mix design is shown in Figure 15 and it can be observed that the capability for the ECC samples to resist load with increasing displacement were significantly higher than the concrete samples, meaning that the energy absorption of the ECC mixes were also significantly greater.

A photograph of the tension surface of a loaded bar is presented in Figure 16, showing that several micro cracks occurred as opposed to a single localized crack.

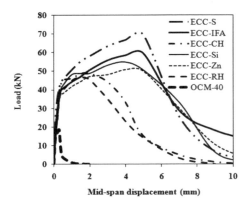

Figure 15.   Flexural response of all mixes.

Figure 16.   Micro-cracks observed on ECC bars.

5   CONCLUSIONS

ECC is effective as a chloride resistant barrier when compared with 40 MPa concrete. The standard ECC mix has a chloride diffusion coefficient that is less than 20% of the diffusion coefficient of concrete. The diffusion coefficient further reduced to 10.5% of the corresponding concrete value when either the fly ash was increased or silane water repellent was added. ECC was most effective when metallic soap was incorporated in the mix design, reducing the diffusion coefficient to 8.9% of the concrete diffusion coefficient.

The two indicative tests (void and sorptivity) cannot be used alone to determine the chloride resistance of a material, but they can be used as a quality assurance test if a correlation is established with the bulk diffusion test. There is also a positive correlation between the ASTM C642 void test and the ASTM C585 sorptivity test.

ACKNOWLEDGEMENT

The authors would like to thank David Nevans, Richard Leary, Gareth Williams and Mason Pirie from Reid Construction Systems for their assistance in producing the ECC samples. The authors would also like to thank Mike Botherway from Atlas Concrete for providing the concrete sample used in this study and Steve Lowery for cutting of the samples. Lastly the authors would like to thank the Foundation for Research, Science and Technology for the funding of this study.

REFERENCES

ASTM (1997). Standard Test Method for Electrical Indication of Concrete's Ability to Resist Chloride Ion Penetration. *ASTM C1202-97*. Philadelphia, American Society for Testing and Materials.

ASTM (2003). Standard Practice for Reducing Samples of Aggregate to Testing Size. *ASTM C702*. Philadelphia, American Society for Testing and Materials.

ASTM (2004a). Standard Test Method for Measurement of Rate of Absorption of Water by Hydraulic Cement Concrete. *ASTM C1585-04*. Philadelphia, American Society for Testing and Materials.

ASTM (2004b). Standard Test Method for Determining the Apparent Chloride Diffusion Coefficient of Cementitious Mixture by Bulk Diffusion. *ASTM C1556-04*. Philadelphia, American Society for Testing and Materials.

ASTM (2006). Standard Test Method for Density, Absorption, and Voids in Hardened Concrete. *ASTM C642-06*. Philadelphia, American Society for Testing and Materials.

Bharatkumar, B., Narayanan, R. Raghuprasad, B. and Ramachandramurthy, D. (2001). Mix proportioning of high performance concrete. *Cement and Concrete Composites* 23(1): 71–80.

Kanda, T., Saito, T., Sakata, N. and Hiraishi, M. (2003). Tensile and Anti-Spalling Properties of Direct Sprayed ECC. *Journal of Advanced Concrete* 1(3): 269-282.

Kim, Y., Kong, H.-J. and Li, V. (2003). Design of Engineered Cementitious Composite Suitable for Wet-Mixture Shotcreting. *ACI Materials Journal* 100(6): 511–518.

Li, V.C., Horii, H., Kabele, P., Kanda, T. and Lim, Y. (2000). Repair and retrofit with engineered cementitious composites. *Engineering Fracture Mechanics* 65(2-3): 317–334.

Lim, Y.M. and Li, V. (1997). Durable repair of aged infrastructures using trapping mechanism of engineered cementitious composites. *Cement and Concrete Composites* 19(4): 373–385.

Lin, Y., Lawley, D. & Ingham, J.M. (2010). Seismic Strengthening of an Unreinforced Masonry Building Using ECC Shotcrete. *8th International Masonry Conference, 4–7 July 2010*. Dresden, Germany: 1–10.

Martinola, G., Bauml, M.F. and Wittmann, F. (2002). Modified ECC Applied as an Effective Chloride Barrier. *JCI International Workshop on Ductile Fiber Reinforced Cementitious Composites (DFRCC)—Applcations and Evaluation*, Takayama, Japan.

NZS (2006). Concrete Structures Standard Part 1-The Design of Concrete Structures. *NZS 3101:2006*. New Zealand Standards. Wellington, New Zealand.

SINTEF Building and Infrastructure. (2008). Effect of Surface Treatment on Chloride Ingress and Carbonation in Concrete Structure—State of Art. Oslo: 1–38.

Concrete Solutions – Grantham, Mechtcherine & Schneck (eds)
© 2012 Taylor & Francis Group, London, ISBN 978-0-415-61622-5

Three-dimensional modeling of externally repaired beams using FRP sheets during short and long term loading

G. Mazzucco, V.A. Salomoni & C.E. Majorana

Department of Structural and Transportation Engineering, University of Padua, Padua, Italy

ABSTRACT: In the last few years FRP technology has been developed to repair damaged concrete structures. This investigation analyzes the complex mechanism of stress-strain evolution at the FRP interface, during different loading programs (short or long-term loadings), until complete debonding. This study has been performed by means of a three-dimensional approach within the context of damage mechanics. The adhesion properties have been reconstructed through a contact model incorporating an elastic-damaged constitutive law, relating inter-laminar stresses acting in the sliding direction. A F.E. code (FRPCON3D) has been developed, incorporating a numerical procedure accounting for Mazars' damage law inside the contact algorithm able to describe the delamination process even considering different surface preparation techniques. The long term behaviour of such composite structures has been studied by means of two visco-elastic formulations: i) B3 law has been considered for modelling concrete; ii) a micromechanical approach has been implemented for the FRP component.

1 INTRODUCTION

In the last few years externally bonded fiber reinforced polymer (FRP) technology has been successfully used, particularly for the recovery of existing damaged structures. This method, generally used in civil engineering practice for repairing and increasing the strength of masonry and concrete materials, can be subjected to delamination phenomena: a brittle rupture localized in the first concrete layer close to FRP, named the *interface zone* (Figure 1).

The bonding mechanism between two components of a composite structure is a very complex subject ruled by a series of factors, among which are: chemical-physical binding during the gluing phase, type of surface preparation, the components' strength and stiffness, etc. In the literature, several studies of stress field evolution at the interface, obtained in closed forms (Liu & Zhu 1994; Smith & Teng 2001) and via numerical models (Salomoni et al., 2011; Bruno & Greco 2001; Ascione 2009; Coronado & Lopez 2007) can be found.

Figure 1. Delamination in a bending beam.

Generally, the delamination process in bending beams is influenced by shear stress concentration at the joint, normally experimentally evaluated by single or double shear tests (Pellegrino et al., 2008; Mazzotti et al., 2009) or bending tests (Pellegrino et al., 2008).

The contribution of surface preparation in concrete beams (before FRP bonding) to increase strength, as proposed in (Iovinella 2009; Toutanji & Ortiz 2001; Mazzucco 2011), is a new aspect which can be considered for a deeper understanding of the delamination mechanism. Different techniques of surface preparation aim to increase concrete roughness at the interface zone, allowing for a better bonding with FRP and an increasing strength under ultimate limit loads.

A three-dimensional finite element code has been specifically developed to simulate debonding processes, influenced by surface preparation, by means of a contact-damage algorithm (Salomoni et al., 2011; Mazzucco 2011) able to represent the entire delamination progression under short or long term applied loads. Transient analyses to simulate long term effects have been carried out considering visco-elastic materials characterized by different compliance functions, for concrete materials (by using B3 theory (Bazant & Baweja 2000)) as well as for FRP materials (by using a micromechanical theory developed in (Ascione et al., 2003). For additional details on long term analyses, see (Mazzucco 2011).

2 DELAMINATION PROCESSES

Delamination is a progressive detachment of FRP reinforcement from concrete surfaces after exceeding the joint strength. Experimental evidence (Iovinella 2009; Pellegrino et al., 2008) establishes that delamination normally affects a thin layer of concrete close to FRP sheets (i.e., at the interface), due to the fact that the maximum shear stress of concrete is smaller than the adhesive's one.

From a numerical point of view, the interface can be represented with a physical constant thickness (t_a) known as the adhesive layer or, as previously stated, the interface zone (Ascione 2009; Coronado & Lopez 2007; Mazzotti et al., 2009), where the mechanical characteristics are assumed equal to the FRP matrix. In standard practice, the concrete surface is subjected to mechanical treatments for enhancing asperities (i.e., concrete roughness) close to the plane of FRP bonding, hence increasing adhesion properties (Figure 2).

At the interface, the real adhesive thickness, depending on the concrete surface roughness, is not constant along the joint, hence it appears as more appropriate to assume t_a as the average asperity height (Figure 3), so including concrete and adhesive as well.

If the interface zone is assumed to be composed by adhesive and concrete (i.e., asperities), necessarily homogenized, a constitutive tensor can be associated:

$$\mathbf{D}^C = \mathbf{D}^C(V_c, V_a)$$
$$D_{ij}^C = \frac{D_{c,ij}V_c^{\%} + D_{a,ij}V_a^{\%}}{V_c^{\%} + V_a^{\%}} \qquad (1)$$

Figure 2. Concrete surfaces after different surface preparation techniques.

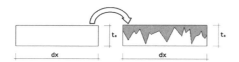

Figure 3. Asperities inclusion at the interface.

where V_c is the volume of asperities, V_a the volume of adhesive, $V_k^{\%}$ the volumetric percentage of k-material (k = a, c) and $D_{k,ij}$ are the constitutive tensor components of k-material.

3 CONTACT MODEL

FRP-concrete bonding at the interface has been numerically modeled by means of the contact mechanics theory. If considering two bodies, Ω^s and Ω^m, e.g., representative of concrete and FRP (Figure 4 a), two surfaces can be identified, Γ^s (named *slave*) and Γ^m (named *master*), where contact is possible. The closed contact condition is achieved and the two bodies are in contact if the contact surface $\Gamma^c = \Gamma^s \cap \Gamma^m \neq 0$ (Figure 4 b).

Contact is defined considering the fundamental conditions (Wriggers 2006):

i. Non-penetration conditions:

$$\left(\bar{\mathbf{u}}^S - \mathbf{u}^m\right) \cdot \mathbf{n} + g \geq 0 \quad on \ \Gamma^c$$
$$g = \left(\bar{\mathbf{X}}^S - \mathbf{X}^m\right) \cdot \mathbf{n} \quad on \ \Gamma^c \qquad (2)$$

where $\mathbf{u}^i$ (with $i = m,\ s$) are the displacement vectors, $\mathbf{X}^i$ the vectors' position in the reference configuration, g the gap function (the distance between two points in contact) and $\mathbf{n}$ the normal vector (Figure 4 b).

ii. Action-reaction conditions:

$$\mathbf{t}^s + \mathbf{t}^m = 0 \quad on \ \Gamma^c \qquad (3)$$

where $\mathbf{t}^i$ are the stress vectors.

– Kuhn-Tucker conditions:

$$\left[\mathbf{t} - \left(\mathbf{D}^C : \boldsymbol{\varepsilon}\right)\mathbf{n}\right]\left[\left(\bar{\mathbf{x}}^s - \mathbf{x}^m\right) \cdot \mathbf{n}\right] = 0 \quad on \ \Gamma^c \qquad (4)$$

where $\mathbf{D}^C$ is the constitutive tensor and $\boldsymbol{\varepsilon}$ the strain tensor of the interface (which has a physical volume, as explained in the previous Section).

In the developed three-dimensional numerical code, characterized by quadratic brick elements

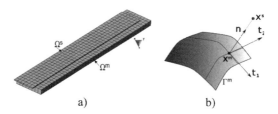

Figure 4. a) FRP and concrete in contact; b) Contact definition.

(20 nodes), master and slave surfaces have been defined by the faces of brick elements (Figure 5). The closed contact condition has been considered in the contact pair, defined through a slave node and a master point where the gap function g is evaluated.

The master point in a contact pair is chosen as the point with a minimum distance from the slave node x^m; generally it does not coincide with a master node but with a generic point belonging to Γ^n (Figure 4 b). If the gap function value is less than a minimum distance, the contact is defined as closed. To describe concrete-FRP adhesion by means of a contact algorithm, the minimum distance for considering closed contact has been assumed equal to the asperity height t_a.

To associate stress and strain tensors to the interface zone at each slave node (and for every contact pair), an element with volume $\Delta V = \Delta x \cdot \Delta y \cdot t_a$ has been considered, where the base $S = \Delta x \cdot \Delta y$ is geometrically defined by mesh discretization and the volume's height has been assumed equal to t_c (Figure 6).

The strain tensor has been obtained by considering linear displacement variations inside ΔV (Smith & Teng 2001); the stress field at the interface between FRP and concrete has been defined by slave and master displacement components for

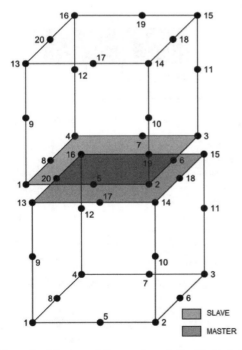

Figure 5. Master and Slave surfaces defined in the brick elements.

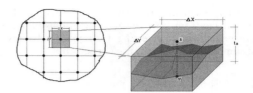

Figure 6. Typical *interface* volume evaluated at every contact pair (asperity plus adhesive).

every contact pair (u^s, v^s, w^s, u^m, v^m, w^m), so that the constitutive relationship can be defined:

$$\boldsymbol{\sigma} = \mathbf{D}^C : \boldsymbol{\varepsilon} \qquad (5)$$

4 DAMAGE MODEL

A contact procedure alone is not sufficient to simulate the stress-strain evolution at the contact zone during delamination processes. Considering that the detachment between FRP and concrete occurs in the first concrete layer closed to the joint, to represent the loss of adhesion, Mazars' damage law (Mazars 1986) has been associated to the contact algorithm. The damage variable d has been assumed as a sum of two components accounting for compressive and tensile contributions (d_i):

$$d = \alpha_t d_t + \alpha_c d_c \qquad (6)$$

where α_i are the parameters depending on the strain measure defined in (Mazars 1986).

Variables d_i have been calculated as:

$$d_t(\tilde{\varepsilon}) = 1 - \frac{\varepsilon_0(1 - A_t)}{\tilde{\varepsilon}} - \frac{A_t}{\exp^{Bt(\tilde{\varepsilon} - \varepsilon_0)}}$$

$$d_c(\tilde{\varepsilon}) = 1 - \frac{\varepsilon_0(1 - A_c)}{\tilde{\varepsilon}} - \frac{A_c}{\exp^{Bc(\tilde{\varepsilon} - \varepsilon_0)}} \qquad (7)$$

where the material parameters A_i, B_i, ε_0 must be defined experimentally.

Since the mechanical characteristics of the interface zone during delamination are dependent on the damage variable d, the tensor $\boldsymbol{D}^C$ is correspondingly modified by damage, i.e., $\boldsymbol{D}^C = \boldsymbol{D}^C(d)$. Hence delamination occurs if, during loading, the damage variable assumes a unit value at a contact pair: the contact is consequently open.

In this way bonding/debonding phenomena are driven by the evolution of damage at the interface.

As a first approximation, an orthotropic constitutive tensor has been chosen, with a Poisson's coefficient equal to zero, so to obtain a diagonal interfacial constitutive tensor by supposing that the effects from transversal contractions/dilations are negligible. If referring to a principal stress/strain reference system, Eq. (5) becomes:

$$\begin{bmatrix} \sigma_{11} \\ \sigma_{22} \\ \sigma_{33} \end{bmatrix} = \begin{bmatrix} D_{11}^C(1-d) & 0 & 0 \\ 0 & D_{22}^C(1-d) & 0 \\ 0 & 0 & D_{33}^C(1-d) \end{bmatrix} \begin{bmatrix} \varepsilon_{11} \\ \varepsilon_{22} \\ \varepsilon_{33} \end{bmatrix}$$

(8)

5 LONG-TERM EFFECTS

Long term effects in a composite material are generally characterized by the sum of the single component contributions. Considering concrete structures repaired by externally bonded FRP sheets, the whole viscous response is ascribed by the behaviour of concrete as well as FRP. Consequently, the evaluation of compliance functions in the viscoelastic constitutive model must be differentiated according to the treated component.

5.1 Creep definition for concrete

Long term effects in concrete materials have been evaluated considering the B3 model developed by Bazant & Baweja (1995). This model, often adopted for modeling concrete creep, has been shown to have good compatibility with experimental results. The compliance function J at time t can be found considering a unit uniaxial constant stress applied at time t' with the following form:

$$J(t,t') = q_1 + C_0(t,t') + C_d(t,t',t_0)$$

(9)

where q_1 is the instantaneous elastic part; $C_0(t,t')$ represents basic creep (the creep part independent of humidity variations) and $C_d(t,t',t_0)$ drying creep (dependent on humidity variations). Time t_0 is the age at the start of drying.

5.2 Creep definition for FRP

FRP itself is a composite material, composed by fibers (of different natures) embedded in an adhesive matrix (Figure 7).

Generally, fibers are less viscous than the matrix and global creep effects in FRP depend on the percentage in volume of fibers $V_f^\%$ with respect to the percentage in volume of adhesive matrix $V_a^\%$. In Figure 8 the experimentally obtained compliance function is shown (Mazzucco 2011) referring to carbon fibers and an epoxy matrix adhesive. The "combined" curve represents the global compliance function for CFRP materials, in which the effects of fibers in the matrix are evidenced.

Numerically, the creep behavior of FRPs has been evaluated via a micromechanical model developed by Ascione et al. (2003), characterized by the rheological scheme of Figure 9.

Compliance functions have been defined for fibers and for matrix as:

$$J_m(t,t') = \left[c_{1,m} + c_{2,m}(t-t')\right] + c_{3,m}\left(1-e^{\frac{(t'-t)\frac{c_{4,m}}{c_{3,m}}}}\right)$$

$$J_f(t,t') = \left[c_{1,f} + c_{2,f}(t-t')\right] + c_{3,f}\left(1-e^{\frac{(t'-t)\frac{c_{4,f}}{c_{3,f}}}}\right)$$

(10)

where the subscript m refers to the adhesive matrix and f to fibers. The four parameters $c_{i,m}$ and $c_{i,f}$ (with i = 1–4) must be experimentally defined, referring to the two springs and the two dashpots of Figure 9.

The global creep behavior for FRP materials can be obtained as:

$$J_{mf}(t,t') = V_f^\% J_f(t,t') + V_m^\% J_m(t,t')$$

(11)

where J_{mf} represents the total creep effect in FRPs corresponding to the "combined" curve reported in Figure 8.

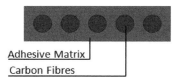

Figure 7. Components of CFRP materials.

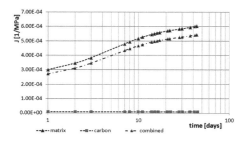

Figure 8. Compliance functions for CFRP components.

Figure 9. Rheological scheme for the micromechanical model.

6 MODELS AND RESULTS

6.1 Delamination evolution

Numerical analyses have been carried out to first calibrate and then validate the contact-damage procedure against available experimental results (Iovinella 2009). The setup of the single shear test (Figure 10) consisted of a $100 \times 100 \times 300$ mm concrete prism connected to a 50 mm wide sheet of carbon fiber-reinforced polymer (CFRP).

The models have been constructed making use of the research code FRPCON3D; the discretization (half sample, symmetry condition) is characterized by 7759 nodes and 1168 quadratic brick elements, each with 20 nodes and 27 Gauss points (Zienkiewicz & Taylor 2000). The contact interface has been defined by 300 quadratic master and slave elements with 8 nodes and 9 Gauss points each (Figure 11).

Several types of surface preparation have been considered with different asperity heights (see Table 1).

Under an increasing applied load, the elastic state is overcome at the interface and subsequently delamination starts; the damage evolution of Figure 12 is representative of the delamination process, characterized by a typical shear stress distribution (Figure 13).

A comparison between experimental and numerical results in terms of ultimate loads has hence confirmed the correctness of the adopted procedure (Table 1).

6.2 Long term effects

Experimental bending tests on concrete beams reinforced by CFRP sheets under long term loads (Mazzucco 2011) have been additionally considered for validating the model.

The bending test setup is reported in Figure 14, where $100 \times 100 \times 600$ mm concrete prisms have been strengthened by 50×400 mm carbon fiber sheets (their thickness has been evaluated to be 0.165 mm). Creep measures have been obtained in terms of interfacial strains vs. time, using one dimensional strain gauges bonded to the FRP sheet.

The numerical simulations have accounted for a viscous behaviour for the considered materials: specifically, model B3, by Bazant & Baweja (2000) has been chosen to representing concrete creep and a micromechanical model by Ascione et al. (2003) for FRP sheets. The reference mechanical characteristics have been experimentally obtained (Mazzucco 2011).

The analyses have been carried out taking into account the double symmetry of the experimental sample; the discretizations have considered 16235 nodes, 3208 brick elements and 200 master and slave elements, Figure 15.

Figure 10. Experimental setup, single shear test.

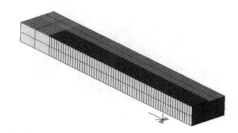

Figure 11. Numerical discretization for single shear test.

Table 1. Experimental and numerical ultimate limit loads with different surface preparation techniques.

Surface preparation technique	Asperity height t_a [mm]	Experimental ultimate load [kN]	Numerical ultimate load [kN]
Sandblasting	2.7	25.31	25.89
Hammering	2.4	23.48	22.98
Brushing	1.6	17.62	15.85

Figure 12. Damage evolution.

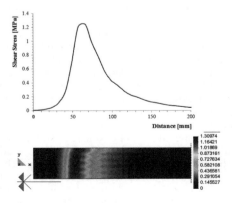

Figure 13. Interface shear stresses.

Figure 14. Creep test setup.

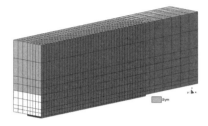

Figure 15. Sketch of the numerical model used for long term analyses.

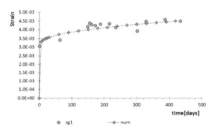

Figure 16. Experimental and numerical results in terms of strain vs. time relative to one of the strain gauges.

A typical curve of strain evolution in time is depicted in Figure 16.

7 CONCLUSIONS

Composite beams made of concrete strengthened by FRP sheets have been investigated considering short and long term applied loads, starting from already available experimental evidence and referring to a specifically developed 3D numerical code. The whole system (concrete plus FRP and adhesive) has been represented via three different physical objects: the concrete base, the interface zone composed of adhesive and concrete asperities, and the strengthening bonded FRP strip. The adhesion between layers has been modelled by means of a contact model whose elastic-damaged constitutive law relates interlaminar stresses acting in the sliding direction. Long term effects have been studied considering appropriate compliance functions (B3 model for concrete and a micromechanical model for FRP). The research 3D F.E. code has

demonstrated to be able to simulate delamination processes and long term stress-strain evolution. By comparing the numerical results with those of a wide experimental investigation, in terms of both ultimate loads and strain vs. time, it has been shown that such an approach is able to catch delamination from a three-dimensional point of view and its evolution during the entire loading process.

REFERENCES

Ascione, F. 2009. Ultimate behaviour of adhesively bonded FRP lap joints. *Comp. Part B* 40:107–115.
Ascione, L., Berardi, V.P. & D'Aponte, A. 2003. Il Comportamento a lungo termine dei materiali compositi fibrorinforzati: un modello micromeccanico. *XXXII Congresso AIAS, Salerno, Italy* (in Italian).
Bazant, Z. & Baweja, S. 2000. Creep and Shrinkage prediction model for analysis and design of concrete structures: Model B3. *Adam Neville Symposium: Creep and Shrinkage—Structural Design Effects, ACI SP-194, A*, Al-Manaseer Ed., Am. Concr. Inst., Farmington Hills, Michigan 1–83.
Bruno, D. & Greco, F. 2001. Mixed mode delamination in plates: a refined approach. *Int. J. Solids Struc.*, 38: 9149–9177.
Coronado, C.A. & Lopez, M.M. 2007. Damage Approach for the Prediction of Debonding Failure on Concrete Elements Strengthened with FRP. *J. Comp. Constr.* 11(4): 391–400.
Iovinella, I. 2009. *Influenza dei trattamenti superficiali sull'efficacia del rinforzo esterno in FRP*. PhD Thesis, Napoli, Italy (in Italian).
Liu, Z. & Zhu, B. 1994. Analytical solutions for R/C beams strengthened by externally bonded steel plate. *J. of Tongji University* 167–176.
Mazars, J.A. 1986. Description of Micro and Macroscale Damage of Concrete structures. *Eng. Frac. Mech.* 25: 729–737.
Mazzotti, C., Savoia, M. & Ferracuti, B. 2009. A new single-shear set-up for stable debonding of FRP–concrete joints. *Constr. Buil. Mat.* 23:1529–1537.
Mazzucco, G. 2011. *Experimental and Numerical analysis of bond behaviour between concrete and FRP*. PhD Thesis, Trento, Italy (in Italian).
Pellegrino, C. Tinazzi, D. & Modena, C. 2008. Experimental Study on Bond Behavior between Concrete and FRP Reinforcement. *J. Comp. Constr.* 12(2): 180–189.
Salomoni, V.A., Mazzucco, G., Pellegrino, C. & Majorana, C.E. 2011. Three-dimensional modelling of bond behaviour between concrete and FRP reinforcement. *Eng. Comp.* 28(1): 5–29.
Smith, S.T. & Teng, J.G. 2001. Interfacial stresses in plated beams. *Eng. Struct.* 23(7): 857–71.
Toutanji, H. & Ortiz, G. 2001. The effect of surface preparation on the bond interface between FRP sheets and concrete members. *Comp. Struc.* 53: 457–462.
Wriggers. P. 2006. *Computational Contact Mechanics*. Berlin, Springer-Verlag.
Zienkiewicz, O.C. & Taylor, R.L. 2000. *The Finite Element Method, The Basis*. Oxford, Butterworth-Heinemann.

Concrete Solutions – Grantham, Mechtcherine & Schneck (eds)
© 2012 Taylor & Francis Group, London, ISBN 978-0-415-61622-5

Strengthening/retrofitting of masonry by using thin layers of Sprayed Strain-Hardening Cement-Based Composites (SSHCC)

V. Mechtcherine, A.-E. Bruedern & T. Urbonas
Technische Universität Dresden, Institute of Construction Materials, Dresden, Germany

ABSTRACT: This paper presents an overview of ongoing research at the Institute of Construction Materials of TU Dresden on the subject of strengthening of masonry by means of highly ductile cementitious materials with short polymeric fibres, so-called strain-hardening cement-based composites (SHCC). SHCC compositions with 1.8% and 2% by volume of PVA fibre were developed on the basis of appropriate rheological experiments on fresh concrete with subsequent spraying and of mechanical tests on hardened material samples produced both by spraying and casting. Afterwards, specimens built of three bricks (triplets) and reinforced with thin layers of sprayed SHCC were monotonically loaded in a deformation-controlled regime in order to investigate the strengthening effect of the applied SHCC layers. The results obtained from these experiments showed, that the static load bearing capacity of such triplets increased significantly, along with even more pronounced augmentation in energy absorption with a remaining high carrying capacity even at high deformations. In further laboratory tests, masonry walls were reinforced on both sides with sprayed SHCC layers and later subjected to cyclic shear loading. An evident increase in mechanical performance was observed in comparison to reference masonry walls with no strengthening layers. Additionally, two surface treatment methods (impregnation with water repellent agents and priming) were investigated for the effect on water absorption of the masonry surface, bond strength between masonry and applied SHCC layer, and finally, the workability of SHCC straight after its application (when finishing). The Karsten tube method was used to evaluate the surface water absorption for the chosen surface treatment methods in comparison to a reference brick face. Surface tension tests showed that impregnation with water repellent agents reduce the surface water intake, weakening the bond strength of the two materials. Priming, on the other hand, achieved a reduction in surface water absorption, an increase in bond strength and easier finishing of the sprayed composite.

1 INTRODUCTION

The improvement of overall mechanical performance of existing masonry buildings in general and their earthquake resistance in particular, is a challenging task. Current research activities in this area are concentrated mainly on the use of fibre-reinforced polymer strips, see e.g., Krevaikas & Triantafillou (2006). The present paper investigates an alternative method for the strengthening of masonry with a thin layer of wet sprayed strain-hardening cement-based composites (SHCC).

SHCC describes a group of fibre-reinforced, cement-based composites which exhibit quasi-ductile and, moreover, strain-hardening behaviour due to the bridging of fine multiple cracks by short, well-distributed fibres (Li 1993, Mechtcherine & Schulze 2005). Such composites behave favourably under tensile loading, showing strain capacities of up to 5%, i.e., they can absorb and dissipate huge amounts of energy before complete failure. Advantageous behaviour with respect to shear

forces as well was demonstrated by Kanda et al. (1998). In this project a thorough investigation was carried out in order to develop an SHCC mixture with good rheological properties in its fresh state (good sprayability and rapid stiffening) as well as superior mechanical performance when hardened (primarily high ductility and high shear resistance). The variable parameters were the fibre content, the amount and type of superplasticiser as well as some other components for steering particular material properties.

After a careful investigation, a few mixtures were selected for the final set of experiments. Masonry triplet specimens comprised of three bricks were sprayed with, on average, 10 mm thick SHCC layers and, 28 days later, tested for their behaviour under shear stress. Furthermore, thin layers of sprayed SHCC were used to reinforce the masonry walls to be assessed afterwards in cyclic shear loading tests. The obtained load-deformation curves would allow a first estimation of the strengthening effect of an SHCC layer applied onto masonry structures. In addition, two types of surface treatment methods, i.e., impregnation with water resisting/repelling agents and priming, were used respectively to investigate the water absorption by the masonry surface, the bond quality between masonry and the SHCC as well as the workability of the SHCC layer following its application onto masonry walls (especially when finishing).

An evident benefit of this strengthening approach is the possibility of using a common wet-spraying procedure with its easy application of a thin SHCC-layer, even on complex geometries.

2 MATERIALS AND TEST METHODS

2.1 Development of SHCC compositions

The starting point for developing SHCC compositions suitable for the strengthening of masonry was a composition developed by Mechtcherine and Schulze (2005).

In order to achieve the desired behaviour of concrete in both the fresh and hardened states, several changes were undertaken in the reference mixture. In the first step, the amount of superplasticiser (SP) and the fibre content were adjusted. The addition of superplasticiser was considerably reduced in order to yield a consistency favourable to its spraying. Subsequently, the effect of the addition of calcium aluminate cement was tested, which was used in the mixture as replacement for small portions of Portland cement. The addition of calcium aluminate cement ensures quicker hardening (Bruedern et al., 2008).

In addition, an air-entraining agent was used in one of the mixtures. The air bubbles should improve the frost resistance of SHCC. Furthermore, fine air voids act as micro-defects which trigger the multiple cracking of SHCC, see also Mechtcherine et al. (2010).

To be able to exclude the inappropriate compositions as well as to test the quality of mixtures, simple slump flow tests were performed. Sprayability of the SHCC was tested only with mixtures that showed promising results. The fine-tuning of the compositions was performed using a MARS high-precision rheometer.

Table 1 presents the compositions of SHCC with 1.8% and 2% of PVA fibre by volume, designated as S1.8 and S2.0, respectively. S1.8 mixtures were investigated by Bruedern et al. (2008) and S2.0 compositions were studied at a later stage by Schubert (2011). The increase in the fibre content from 1.8% to 2% was possible after some improvements had been made to the spraying equipment (using an altered nozzle geometry and mortar pump setup).

Finally, the presented S1.8 and S2.0-based mixtures were selected for testing the mechanical properties of the SHCC (compressive, tensile and flexural strength) and behaviour under loading with regard to the strengthening of masonry (triplet shear tests as well as tests on wall elements).

2.2 Spraying tests

A DURAPACT 326S spraying machine was used to test the sprayability of the mixtures with the base compositions S1.8 as shown in Table 1. The wet spraying method was applied without the addition of admixtures via the nozzle. Alongside the necessity for testing the sprayability of the chosen mixtures, the spraying served as the production method for specimens used in subsequent mechanical testing. This sample production approach was crucial since the properties of the material can vary significantly due to the method of application; i.e., test results for samples produced by casting would not be necessarily valid for material applied by spraying (due to the orientation pattern of the fibres inside the matrix and some other phenomena).

2.3 Surface treatment and water penetration test

To reduce masonry water suction from the sprayed SHCC layer and also to investigate the methods to steer the bond properties between the masonry and SHCC, different surface treatment methods were tested. Masonry surface treatment changes its properties, first of all the water absorption, subsequently influencing the bond strength between

Table 1. Compositions of the SHCC matrices.

SHCC	S1.8	S1.8-CA03	S1.8-LP10	S2.0	S2.0-WC
	[kg per m³]				
Cement CEM I 42.5 HS	327	315	358	323	505
CA-cement	–	10	–	–	–
Fly ash	766	766	572	755	614
Quartz sand 0.06/0.2 mm	546	546	598	539	534
Water	342	342	291	337	334
SP 1	3.2	3.2	–	–	–
SP 2	–	–	8.9	–	–
SP 3	–	–	–	7.7	8.0
VA underwater compound	3.2	3.2	3.5	3.2	3.2
PVA fibre	23.4	23.4	21.1	26	26
Air-entraining agent	–	–	0.46	–	–

the substrate and strengthening layer as well as the water content in the applied SHCC layer and, therefore, impacting on the rheological behaviour of the material after application.

Two methods of surface treatments were selected for the masonry specimens: a) using water resisting/repelling agents, i.e., impregnation (IMPRG) and priming (PRM). The Karsten tube method was used to examine water absorption of the masonry surface, after applying different surface treatment methods.

2.4 Mechanical tests

Mechanical tests were performed for specimens produced from SHCC compositions both by spraying (S1.8, S1.8-CA03 and S1.8-LP10) and casting (S2.0, S2.0-WC).

Three-point bend tests were carried out for material compositions which showed the most favourable rheological behaviour in the slump flow and spraying tests. For the material mixtures with 1.8% fibres small beams (160 mm × 40 mm × 40 mm) were cut from the plates produced by spraying and later tested at the ages of 7 and 28 days.

To examine the strain-hardening behaviour of the mixtures, uniaxial tension tests were performed on prisms (290 mm × 40 mm × 40 mm) cut from the material plates produced by spraying. In the case of specimen production by casting, tension tests were performed on dumbbell shaped prisms with the smallest cross-section of 24 mm × 40 mm and a length of 250 mm. In addition, compression tests were carried out on cubes (40 mm × 40 mm × 40 mm) fabricated from sprayed mixtures and cubes (100 mm × 100 mm × 100 mm) made from casting of SHCC.

Earlier mentioned improvements to the spraying equipment followed by the increase of PVA fibre content in SHCC mixtures, as investigated by Schubert (2011), conditioned the difference in the size of produced specimens selected for mechanical testing in comparison to the test series by Bruedern et al. (2008). Further experiments with directly comparable mechanical tests on specimens, produced both by spraying and casting, are envisioned in the near future as part of the ongoing research work.

2.5 Bond strength test

The bond strength testing was necessary to evaluate the composite action of a multilayer system (masonry, surface treatment, SHCC cover).

A test machine Type DYNA Z6 was used to test the specimens at the age of 28 days.

Firstly, on average, an 11 mm deep groove with a diameter of 50 mm was cut in the surface of a masonry triplet. Having a typical thickness of 10 mm for the SHCC layer, this groove of 11 mm depth, presumably, would enable the failure to occur in the masonry, bonding zone or SHCC layer. There were two cases for setting of the groove on the surface of the triplet: a) within the region of a brick, and b) centred over the joint between the bricks.

2.6 Triplet test

The procedure to determine the initial shear strength of the masonry as described in DIN EN 1052-3 was utilized in order to estimate the strengthening effect of the SHCC layer when applied on a masonry wall. A 3DF format solid brick in accordance to DIN EN 771-1 along with lime cement masonry mortar MGII were chosen for the production of the testing units.

The assessment process consisted of testing triplet specimens, with the outside bricks standing on supports and the middle brick pressed down until the connection collapsed.

The test setup, as shown in Figure 1, included two concrete blocks serving as the supports and fixed 105 mm apart from each other on a steel beam.

The external bricks were positioned on the concrete blocks and fixed with a vertical screw. A steel plate with slightly smaller dimensions than the brick was put on the top of the middle brick (without any contact to the strengthening layer) to distribute the load applied by a ZWICK Z1200 testing machine.

One triplet comprised three masonry bricks cut to the size of 117 mm × 74 mm × 90 mm, and connected with, on average, a 12 mm thick regular joint mortar. An SHCC layer was applied on one side of the triplet (whose brick surfaces were not affected by cutting) by spraying (mixtures S1.8, S1.8-CA3, S1.8-LP10). A roller and trowel were used to ensure approximate distribution of the layer to a thickness of 10 mm. Finally, specimens were sealed with plastic and stored at a temperature of 20°C, and tested at an age of 28 days.

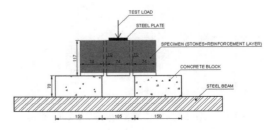

Figure 1.   Test setup for triplet tests.

2.7 Shear tests of masonry elements

Shear testing on the masonry elements was performed to validate the strengthening effect of SHCC layers on a larger scale. The thickness of the fabricated masonry walls was 175 mm in order to fit into the chosen shear testing device and to remain within its load capacity (Figure 2). The bricks in the wall were laid in a stretcher bond. The wall surface was 1.25 m × 1.00 m (width × height). Rigid RC beams were fixed to the top and bottom of the wall to guarantee its uniform shear loading (Figure 2).

As for triplets, solid bricks of format 3DF in accordance to DIN EN771-1 and lime cement masonry mortar MG2 were used in the production of the walls.

SHCC layers were sprayed on both surfaces with an average thickness of 10 mm. Wooden planks were placed along the side faces of the wall to control layer thickness and simplify the finishing of the surface by smoothing.

Cyclic, horizontal shear loading was applied (F_H in Figure 2). The tests were controlled by the displacement s_H of the upper RC beam. The displacement of the RC beam was increased stepwise by approximately 1 mm in both directions until failure of the wall occurred. The shape of the time-displacement curve was sinusoidal. For each new displacement level three load cycles were performed, cf. Figures 9 and 10. The vertical load F_v of 150 kN was kept constant during the entire test. This load simulated the self-weight of the building structure above the considered masonry element.

The wall was equipped with 12 LVDTs as shown in Figure 2. These LVDTs were mounted on both sides of the masonry element.

3 EXPERIMENTAL RESULTS

3.1 Sprayability of the mixtures

The results of sprayability for mixtures with good workability can be summarized below:

– The best sprayability was observed for SHCC mixtures with slump flow values between 150 and 160 mm as measured according to the DIN EN 1015-3.
– The maximum possible fibre content in SHCC depends on the type of the spraying apparatus and nozzle geometry.

3.2 Three-point bend tests

Figures 3 and 4 demonstrate the results of bending tests only for three sprayed material mixtures, all containing 1.8% fibres. The tests were

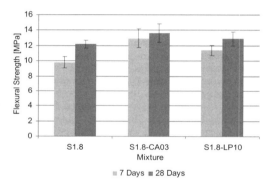

Figure 3. Average flexural strength of sprayed SHCC with different compositions at ages of 7 and 28 days, respectively, and standard deviation for 6 specimens per mixture and age.

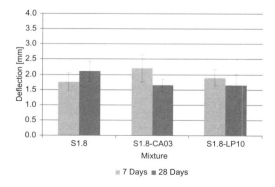

Figure 4. Ultimate deflection of sprayed SHCC with different compositions at ages of 7 and 28 days, respectively, with standard deviation for 6 specimens per mixture and age.

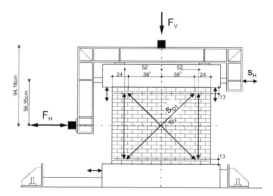

Figure 2. Test setup for shear tests on wall elements (dimesions are given in cm). The small arrows represent LVDTs for measurement of deformations.

performed at specimen ages of 7 and 28 days, respectively.

As can be seen from Figure 3, all mixtures show very similar values for flexural strength at the age of 28 days. The difference was more pronounced at the age of 7 days, where the mixture containing 3% of calcium aluminate cement showed the highest flexural strength. This result may be, at least partly, traced back to a faster hardening of the calcium aluminate cement when compared with Portland cement.

While an increase in the flexural strength over time could be monitored for all mixtures, the tendency was opposite for two of the three compositions in respect to ultimate deflection. Only the base mixture S1.8 showed an augmentation in this parameter.

3.3 Results from compression and tension tests

The mechanical characteristics of SHCC as obtained from the compression and tension tests for specimens produced by spraying and casting are given in Table 2.

In respect to the compressive strength specimens produced by casting, the S2.0 mixture delivered considerably lower values in comparison to the similar compositions of the S1.8-series. This could be explained mainly by different methods of fabrication (casting/spraying) and different specimen sizes (size effect) which lead to the differences in the fibre orientation and the degree of compaction and therefore affect the mechanical performance. On the other hand, in tension tests, the S2.0-composition delivered the highest value of strain capacity, which can be traced back to the increased fibre content in combination with a relatively moderate matrix strength. The increase in strength of the matrix by increasing the cement content of the SHCC (mixture S2.0-WC) caused a decrease in the strain capacity.

Table 2. Mechanical properties of the selected mixtures (with standard deviation given in parentheses).

Mixture	Compressive strength MPa	Tensile strength MPa	Strain capacity %
S1.8	48.4 (1.8)	3.02 (0.02)	1.3 (0.1)
S1.8-CA03	47.7 (4.6)	2.93 (0.32)	0.8 (0.2)
S1.8-LP10	43.7 (2.8)	3.11 (0.22)	1.2 (0.4)
S2.0*	27.9 (0.3)	3.58 (0.14)	2.0 (0.4)
S2.0-WC*	45.0 (0.7)	3.80 (0.07)	0.8 (0.2)

*Samples were manufactured by casting. Specimen size and shape were also different to those used for S1.8-series (see 2.4).

3.4 Results from triplet tests

Three tests were performed for each parameter combination. Table 3 shows the average values and the standard deviations of the maximum load and the deformation at failure attained during these tests. As can be seen, both parameters increased by nearly an order of magnitude when triplets were strengthened with a layer of sprayed SHCC.

Figure 5 shows representative load-deformation curves obtained from the failure tests on triplets with and without a strengthening layer, respectively. It is obvious that the static shear load bearing capacity of the masonry element under test as well as its energy absorption capacity increased with at least a factor of 6 due to the application of a thin SHCC layer.

3.5 Results from bond strength test and water absorption test

The bond strength test provided information about bond behaviour between the SHCC layer and the masonry. Moreover, from this investigation also

Table 3. Average results of the triplet test (with standard deviation given in parentheses).

Specimen type and mixture	Maximum load [kN]	Deformation at failure [mm]
Without strengthening layer	2.2 (0.6)	0.25 (0.04)
With 10 mm S1.8	18.4 (1.5)	3.50 (0.66)
With 10 mm S1.8-CA03	16.5 (2.0)	2.20 (0.60)
With 10 mm S1.8-LP10	13.1 (2.0)	2.10 (0.50)

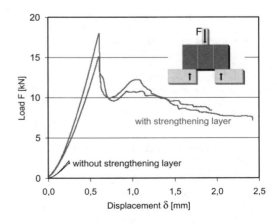

Figure 5. Typical load-deformation curves obtained from the triplet tests with and without strengthening layer, respectively.

745

the place of failure (masonry, bond zone or SHCC layer) could be determined. Higher composite action between masonry and SHCC was observed, when the fracture occurred in masonry, while there was a weaker bond when the failure happened in the bond zone.

Figure 6 represents values of the bond strength for two SHCC recipes S2.0 and S2.0-WC. Three surface treatment cases were considered: no treatment (reference), priming and impregnation.

In addition, Table 4 demonstrates the representative bond strength values shown for an S2.0-WC composition for test-cylinders centred over the brick and joint between the masonry units. These two different testing regions were chosen to find out if there were any significant variations in the bond strength at the brick surface and at a joint. A variation in values would point firstly to a possible delamination region occurring in the area of lower bond strength. The results, however, showed that the bond strength between the masonry and SHCC layer was more or less evenly distributed.

The test values, quite obviously, verified that impregnation with water repellent agents leads to a decrease in adhesion force at the masonry surface and consequently to a weak composite action between the masonry and strengthening layer of SHCC. As a result, this leads to a low bond strength.

The results from water absorption test using Karsten tube method (Karsten 1992) are shown in Figure 7.

Based on these observations, it can be stated that surface treatment methods diminishes the water absorption by masonry from the applied SHCC coating and, because of this, reduces the dehydration of the strengthening layer, consequently improving the surface finishing by smoothing right after the application of SHCC.

3.6 Spraying of SHCC layers on wall elements and shear test

Two masonry elements were strengthened on both sides by means of sprayed SHCC layers (mixtures S2.0 and S2.0-WC) to adapt the techniques of spraying and surface smoothing. Spraying was performed as a wet process (Figure 8). A conventional mortar pump was used to pump the fresh SHCC.

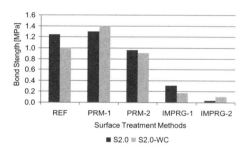

Figure 6. Bond strengths for specimens with different methods of surface treatment (REF = reference, PRM = priming and IMPRG = impregnation).

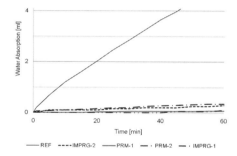

Figure 7. Masonry water absorption of 3 cm² area according to Karsten.

Table 4. Bond strength for mixture S2.0-WC for different surface treatment methods and regions of the masonry specimen.

Surface treatment	Bond strength (all, 10 tests) [MPa]	Bond strength (brick, 6 tests) [MPa]	Bond strength (joint, 4 tests) [MPa]
REF	1.01 (0.24)	1.03 (0.27)	0.97 (0.23)
PRM-1	1.40 (0.33)	1.52 (0.31)	1.23 (0.30)
PRM-2	0.91 (0.47)	0.87 (0.60)	0.99 (0.25)
IMPRG-1	0.18 (0.23)	0.15 (0.31)	0.22 (0.14)
IMPRG-2	0.11 (0.18)	0.00 (0.00)	0.27 (0.18)

Figure 8. Spraying of SHCC layer onto the surface of a masonry element.

The shear tests on the masonry elements were performed approx. 56 days after application of the SHCC layers using a wet-spraying procedure.

Figure 9 shows the representative test results for the non-strengthened reference masonry element and Figure 10 presents the corresponding data for the element reinforced with the SHCC combination S2.0-WC when no surface treatment method was used. Both diagrams display the controlled displacement s_H of the upper RC beam in time, the resulting shear force F_H and the diagonal deformation s_{D1} (cf. also Figure 2).

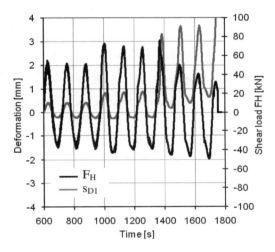

Figure 9. Shear load F_H and diagonal deformation s_{D1} of the reference masonry element.

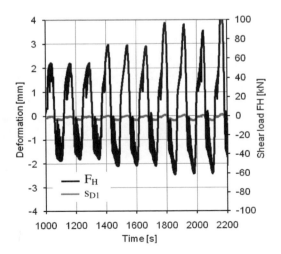

Figure 10. Shear load F_H and diagonal deformation s_{D1} of the masonry element strengthened with a SCHH-layer (S2.0-WC).

It can be seen, that reference wall reached failure at approximately $s_{D1} = 3$ mm and $F_H = 75$ kN, while the strengthened wall, on the other hand, resisted a shear load F_H of nearly 100 kN, showing virtually no diagonal deformation s_{D1}, thus, meaning no material damage occurred at this stage.

A shear test of the first wall strengthened with S2.0-WC composition of sprayed SHCC was stopped at the end of the deformation cycles with amplitude of 4 mm. Again no visible surface damage of the SHCC layer could be observed. At this point the oscillation of the hydraulic jaw became too pronounced. No damage to the strengthened masonry element could be achieved because of the obviously insufficient stiffness of the shear load frame. For future testing the use of a more rigid frame is foreseen.

4 SUMMARY

Several SHCC compositions suitable in strengthening masonry by spraying were developed during this investigation. To adjust the development of the rheological properties in time, a small portion of the Portland cement was replaced by calcium aluminate cement and the type of superplasticiser was varied. One of the mixtures was modified using an air entrainment agent.

Mechanical performance was estimated on sprayed material compositions using three-point bend tests. Subsequently, uniaxial tension and compression tests were performed on specimens made from sprayed and cast SHCC mixtures. The results showed the strain-hardening behaviour of the sprayed mixtures. Finally, the strengthening effect of the sprayed SHCC layer on masonry was estimated by means of shear tests on triplets. These experiments showed that the shear load bearing capacity and the energy absorption capacity of masonry increased by an order of magnitude due to the application of, on average, a 10 mm thick SHCC layer.

The shear test on the masonry wall element strengthened with layers of the S2.0-WC combination of SHCC on both sides showed significant increase in stiffness, load bearing capacity, and deformability in comparison to masonry walls without strengthening. The tests could not be performed up to failure of the wall elements because of the insufficient stiffness and strength of the test setup in use. A stiffer and stronger machine will be used in the following test series.

Investigation of the composite action between the masonry and SHCC showed that surface treatment methods change the surface properties, including the water absorption. While the workability (finishing) of the SHCC layer straight after application improved independently of the particular surface treatment method, primer PRM-1 demonstrated the augmentation in both bond strength and surface impermeability parameters. Surface treatment using water repellent agents, on the other hand, decreased the adhesion force at the surface, minimising the water intake nearly to zero. As a result the bond between the masonry and the strengthening layer was very weak.

Along with the foreseen improvements to the test setup for investigating masonry walls strengthened on both sides with wet sprayed SHCC layers, there are plans to further explore the possibility to use the strain-hardened cement-based composite for improvement of overall mechanical performance of existing masonry buildings and moreover their behaviour under dynamic loading in particular.

REFERENCES

Bruedern, A.-E., Abecasis, D. & Mechtcherine, V. 2008. Strengthening of masonry using sprayed Strain Hardening Cement-based Composites (SHCC). *Seventh Internation RILEM Symposium on Fibre Reinforced Concrete: Design and Applications*: 451–460.

Kanda, T. Wantanabe, S. & Li, V.C. 1998. Application of pseudostrain hardening cementitious composites to shear resistant structural elements. *Fracture Mechanics of Concrete Structures* 3: 1477–1490.

Karsten, R. 1992. *Bauchemie: Handbuch für Studium und Praxis*. Verlag C.F. Müller GmbH, Karlsruhe.

Krevaikas, T.D. & Triantafillou, 2006. Computer aided strengthening of masonry walls using fibre-reinforced polymer strips. *Materials and Structures*: 93–98.

Li, V.C. 1993. From mechanics to structural engineering—The design of cementitious composites for civil engineering aplications. *Structural Mechanics and Earthquake Engineering* 10(2): 37–48.

Mechtcherine, V. 2006. Testing Behaviour of Strain Hardening Cement-based Composites in Tension—Summary of recent research. *High-Perfomance Fibre Reinforced Cementitious Composites* 5: 13–22.

Mechtcherine, V. & Schulze, J. 2005. Ultra-ductile concrete—material design concept and testing. *CPI Concrete Plant International* 5: 88–89.

Mechtcherine, V., Bruedern, A.-E. & Butler, M. 2010. Strengthening of masonry elements using sprayed Strain-Hardening Cement-based Composites (SHCC). *8th International Masonry Conference Dresden*.

Schubert, A. 2011. *Untersuchung des Verbundverhaltens von Verstärkungsschichten aus hochduktilem Beton (SHCC) zu dynamisch belastetem Mauerwerk*. Project thesis at the Institute of Construction Materials, TU Dresden (in German).

Concrete Solutions – Grantham, Mechtcherine & Schneck (eds)
© 2012 Taylor & Francis Group, London, ISBN 978-0-415-61622-5

A comparative study for shear strengthening techniques of reinforced concrete beams using FRP

A.M. Morsy, N.H. El-Ashkar & K.M. Helmi
Construction & Building Engineering Department, Arab Academy for Science,
Technology & Maritime Transport, Alexandria, Egypt

ABSTRACT: This paper presents the results of a pilot testing program that was undertaken to study the feasibility of strengthening RC beams in shear using FRP reinforcement internally embedded in holes drilled through the depth of the beam. Five similar beams were tested in this program, a control beam without strengthening, and three beams strengthened using externally bonded CFRP sheets, NSM CFRP strips and embedded CFRP and GFRP rods. The specimens strengthened with externally bonded sheets and internally embedded CFRP reinforcement had a 30% increase in their shear capacity while the specimens strengthened with NSM strips and internally embedded GFRP reinforcement had a 60% increase in their shear capacity, compared to the control specimens. The results thus confirm the feasibility of the proposed technique.

1 INTRODUCTION

Strengthening Reinforced Concrete (RC) structures with Fiber Reinforced Polymers (FRP) has been studied and successfully implemented in field applications since the early 1990's. In addition to the superior properties of FRP, such as high strength to weight ratios and corrosion resistance, strengthening RC structures with FRP in most cases is easier and requires less labour and time than conventional materials. FRP has been used in strengthening RC columns and beams both in flexure and in shear. For the strengthening of RC beams in shear, typically carbon or glass fiber sheets are externally bonded to the sides or the sides and bottom of RC beams forming a U wrap using an epoxy adhesive. Another method for strengthening RC members with FRP is the Near surface mounting (NSM) technique, where grooves are cut in the concrete cover and FRP rods or thin plates referred to as strips are installed inside these grooves and bonded using an epoxy adhesive. Strengthening RC beams in shear with FRP round rods was studied by De Lorenzis & Nanni, (2001), Rizzo & De Lorenzis (2009), and Tanarslan, (2011), while Barros & Dias (2006), Rizzo & De Lorenzis (2009) and Dias & Barros (2010) studied strengthening RC beams in shear with CFRP strips. For the NSM technique the amount of site installation work may be reduced, as surface preparation other than grooving is no longer required e.g., plaster removal is not necessary; irregularities of the concrete surface can

be more easily accommodated. Additionally the FRP is protected by the concrete cover and therefore is less prone to accidental damage and vandalism (De lorenzis & Teng 2007). Furthermore the studies by Rizzo & De Lorenzis (2009) and Dias & Barros (2010) have shown that shear strengthening of RC beams using the NSM technique is more efficient than using the externally bonded technique. However the amount of FRP that could be used with the NSM technique is limited by the concrete cover available to accommodate the grooves. Additionally there is the possibility of damaging the main reinforcement during cutting the grooves due to the lack of proper concrete cover resulting from the misplacement of the reinforcement during construction.

The authors therefore suggest another technique for strengthening RC beams in shear, where holes are drilled through the depth of the beam and then FRP round bars are embedded in the holes using epoxy adhesive. This technique has the same advantage as the NSM technique; in addition the embedment of the FRP bars inside the beams will improve the ascetics since there will be no surface grooves on the sides of the beam. The presence of the reinforcement inside the beam may also improve the bond behavior of this system due to the confinement effect

The details and results of a pilot test program that was undertaken to examine the feasibility of this technique are presented in the following sections.

2 EXPERIMENTAL PROGRAM

Five specimens were tested in this program, a control specimen, and four specimens strengthened using three different techniques. The following is a description of the specimens and the materials used.

2.1 Description of the beams

Five reinforced concrete beams were tested in this program. The specimens had a cross section of 160 mm × 300 mm, and a total length of 2.40 meters. The specimens were designed to fail in shear at one side (The weak side). For flexure reinforcement, four 22 mm deformed bars arranged in two layers were used as bottom reinforcement, while two 22 mm deformed bars were used as top reinforcement. The shear reinforcement for the strong side consisted of 10 mm stirrups spaced at 50 mm, while the shear reinforcement for the weak side consisted of 6 mm bars with a spacing of 150 mm. Figure 1 shows the reinforcement details of the beams.

2.2 Test specimens

Five identical beams constructed as mentioned in the previous section were tested in this program. The first specimen "Control" was a control specimen without any strengthening. The second specimen "EB" was strengthened in shear using CFRP sheets externally bonded to the sides and bottom of the beam forming a U wrap. A single layer of 60 mm wide sheets with a spacing of 150 mm was used to strengthen this specimen. Figure 2 shows the strengthening of the EB specimen. The third specimen "NSM" was strengthened in shear using NSM CFRP laminates mounted inside grooves cut in the concrete cover of both sides of the beams. 1.2 × 15 mm strips with a spacing of 75 mm were used to strengthen this specimen. Figures 3 and 4 illustrate the strengthening of specimen NSM. The fourth and fifth specimens "IER-G" and "IER-C"

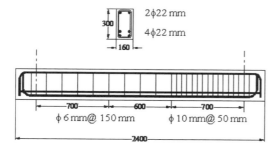

Figure 1. Reinforcement details of the specimens.

Figure 2. Strengthening of specimen EB.

Figure 3. Cutting grooves for specimen NSM.

Figure 4. Installing FRP strips in specimen NSM.

Figure 5. Drilling of holes for specimen IER-G.

were strengthened using 12 mm Glass and Carbon FRP bars embedded in circular holes drilled through the depth of the beams respectively. All the bars had a spacing of 150 mm. Figures 5 to 7 show the preparation work for specimen IER-G.

The configuration of the specimens was chosen so all specimens would have an equal amount of material. Table 1 provides a summary of the details of the specimens used in this program.

2.3 *Material properties*

The concrete used in these tests had a strength of 20 MPa based on testing 100 mm cubes. The steel bars used for the flexure reinforcement and the stirrups on the strong side had a nominal yield strength of 360 MPa, while the bars used

for reinforcing the weak side had a nominal yield strength of 240 MPa. Sikawrap 230 C carbon fiber sheets were used for the EB specimen. 1.2 mm thick MBrace S&P CFRP laminates manufactured by BASF were used for the NSM specimen. 12 mm V-Rod FRP bars manufactured by Pultral Inc. were used for IER specimens. Sikadur 330 epoxy adhesive was used for the CFRP sheets while Sikadur 31 CF epoxy adhesive was used for all the other specimens.

2.4 *Test setup and instrumentation*

All specimens were tested under four point bending. The span of the beams was 2.0 m and the distance between the loads was 0.6 m. The shear span for both sides was 0.7 m which is larger than 2.5 times the depth of the beam to avoid effects of arching action. Three dial gauges were used to measure the deflection at midspan, and both loading points. A strain gauge was mounted on the second stirrups after the support at the weak side. Long strain gauges were also mounted on the concrete surface at a 45° angle as shown in Figure 9. In addition strain gauges were also mounted on the second sheet, laminate and bar after the support for specimens EB, NSM and IER-C respectively. Loading was applied manually through a hydraulic pump to two hydraulic jacks at increments of 10 kN, at which time readings from the dial gauges and strains were manually recorded. Figures 8 and 9 show the test setup for the specimens.

Figure 6. Installing of reinforcement in specimen IER-G.

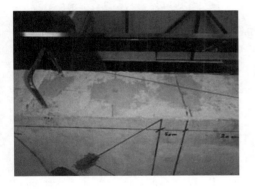

Figure 7. Specimen IER-G after strengthening.

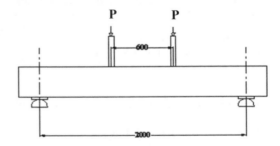

Figure 8. Test setup.

Table 1. Specimen details.

Specimen	Strengthening technique	Material	Dimensions of material	Spacing
Control	None			
EB	Externally bonded sheets	CFRP	60 mm wide sheets (One Layer)	150 mm
NSM	Near surface mounted strips	CFRP	1.2×15 mm strips	75 mm
IER-C	Internally embedded reinforcement	CFRP	12 mm Bars	150 mm
IER-G	Internally embedded reinforcement	GFRP	12 mm Bars	150 mm

Figure 9.   Test setup.

3   TEST RESULTS

3.1   *Specimens' behavior and failure modes*

All specimens failed in shear and all of the strengthened beams failed due to debonding. The following sections provide a description of the specimens' behavior during testing. Table 2 presents a summary of the test results "the loads for one jack only".

3.1.1   *Control specimen*

For the control specimen the first visible crack appeared at a load of about 70 kN. The crack extended from the point of loading to the support in the weak side. As loading progressed, the crack widened, and another major crack appeared in addition to several minor ones as seen in Figure 10. The specimen failed at a load of 100 kN. Although the failure was brittle it was less sudden than in the case of the other specimens.

3.1.2   *Specimen EB*

The first visible crack appeared at a load of 78 kN between the sheets. As loading progressed, cracks widened then the specimen finally failed in a brittle manner at a load of 130 kN after debonding started at the second sheet after the support. Then with further loading the failure occurred progressively one sheet at a time.

Post failure examination of the specimen showed a similar crack pattern to the control specimen as seen in Figure 11. It was noticed that the bonding failure took place in the concrete thin layer adjacent to the sheet, not in the adhesive epoxy.

3.1.3   *Specimen NSM*

The first visible crack appeared at a load of 80 kN. Discontinued small cracks appeared between the strips as the loading progressed. The specimen failed suddenly in an explosive manner at a load

of 155 kN, as the concrete cover containing the strips debonded from the beam's inner core as seen in Figure 12. After removing the concrete cover a similar crack pattern to the control specimen could be seen in the concrete core as seen in Figure 13. It was noticed that no de-bonding occurred between the CFRP laminates and the concrete.

Table 2.   Failure and first crack loads.

Specimen	First crack load (kN)	Failure load (kN)
Control	70	100
EB	78	130
NSM	80	155
IER-C	70	138
IER-G	70	160

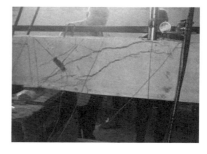

Figure 10.   Crack pattern of control specimen.

Figure 11.   Failure and crack pattern of specimen EB.

Figure 12.   Failure of specimen NSM.

Figure 13.   Crack pattern of specimen NSM.

Figure 14.   Crack pattern of specimen IER-G.

3.1.4 *Specimen IER-G*

The first visible crack appeared at a load of 70 kN at the loading point at a steeper angle than in the case of the control specimen. This can be related to the crack arresting action of the embedded bars which altered the cracking pattern compared to the control specimen.

Several other cracks appeared and widened as the loading progressed, although at steeper angle as seen in Figure 14. Failure occurred suddenly at a load of 160 kN due to the de-bonding at the thin layer of concrete adhered to the GFRP bars. No de-bonding between the GFRP bars and the epoxy adhesive was observed and a thin concrete layer was noticed to be fully attached to the GFRP bar as seen in Figure 15.

Figure 15.   GFRP bar after failure of specimen IER-G.

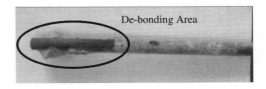

Figure 16.   CFRP bar after failure of specimen IER-C.

3.1.5 *Specimen IER-C*

Specimen IER-C behaved in a similar manner to specimen IER-G where the cracks occurred in a steeper form than the control specimen. However, the specimen failed suddenly in a brittle manner at a load of 138 kN. It can be seen that this specimen failed 14% lower than IER-G. After removing the concrete cover, it was noticed that the beam failed due to the de-bonding action of CFRP bars. On the contrary from the IER-G specimen the de-bonding took place between the bar's coating and its inner fiber core not in the thin concrete layer adjacent to the CFRP bar. This can be related to a manufacturing weak bond between the fiber core and its friction cover as seen in Figure 16.

3.2 *Deflection behavior*

Figure 17 shows the mid-span deflection behavior of all specimens. From this figure it can be concluded that the load-deflection behavior of all tested beams seemed similar up to the maximum load. This means that the stiffness of the beams seemed not to be affected by any type of shear strengthening. This can be due to the use of the

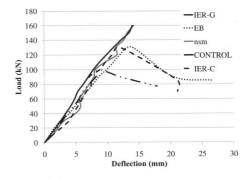

Figure 17.   Deflection behaviour.

same main reinforcement configuration and beam cross section for all the tested beams which governs the flexural behavior. This means that the flexural behavior governed the mid-span deflection behavior and the shear strengthening did not affect this behavior. The figure shows a softening behavior for the control specimen and this is consistent with the less brittle fracture behavior of the control beam compared to the other strengthened beams. All the other four beams failed catastrophically in brittle manner and the failure was explosive, which hindered capturing the post peak behavior in some specimens and only allowed recording two or three points in the softening part of the curve.

3.3 Strain behavior

3.3.1 Steel stirrups
Figure 18 shows the load vs. strain in the second stirrup after the support. It can be seen that the strain in the stirrups for the control sample started to pick up the stirrup's load at an early loading stage and the rate of strain increase was much higher than all the other strengthened beams. On the other hand it is apparent from this figure that the stirrups for all the shear strengthened specimens were not activated at small loads until cracking started occurring, after which the stirrups were activated and strain increased. Also it can be noticed that both the strengthened specimens using drilled method IER-C and IER-G had much lower stirrup strain compared to the other strengthened and control specimens, which indicate that the CFRP bars and GFRP bars carried most of the shear forces than its stirrups, this is due to the higher modulus of elasticity of FRP bars compared to the steel stirrups.

3.3.2 Concrete strains
Figure 19 shows the load vs. concrete strains for control specimen and specimens NSM and EB. The figure shows that the control specimen had a gradual increase in the strain rate as the loading progressed beyond about 18 kN. The higher value of concrete strain for the control specimen is due to cracks forming in the measuring range of the strain gauge.

On the other hand, the other two specimens had an almost similar stiffness to each other until about 75 to 80% of their failure load. The strains in the concrete at failure for these specimens were much smaller than that of the control specimen. This may be related to the change in crack pattern for those strengthened specimens that lead the crack to move away from the measuring rage of the strain gauge

3.3.3 Strains in strengthening FRP materials
Figure 20 shows the load vs. strain in the second sheet for specimen EB. The sheets seemed not to be activated until the load reached about 40 kN. The strains then increased at a high rate until about 120 kN where debonding started occurring and the strains dropped dramatically.

Figure 21 shows the load vs. strain for the second strip for specimen NSM. The FRP material seemed to be activated at the start of the test and the rate of strain increase seemed to be constant until the concrete cover de-bonding started to occur prior to failure.

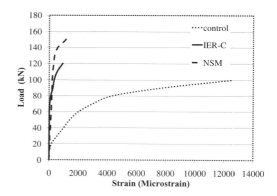

Figure 19.   Concrete strain behaviour.

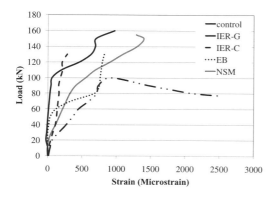

Figure 18.   Steel stirrup strain behaviour.

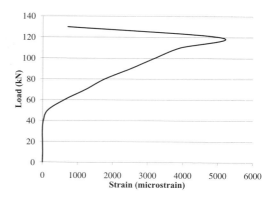

Figure 20.   Strain behavior of CFRP sheet in specimen EB.

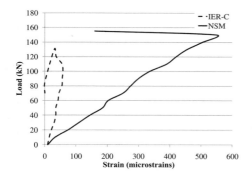

Figure 21. FRP strain behavior of specimens IER-C and NSM.

4 DISCUSSION OF RESULTS

The test results show that the load at which the first crack appeared was not affected by the IER strengthening technique, and was slightly increased when the beam was externally reinforced by the EB and the NSM techniques. Visual observation of the specimens during testing showed that the EB and the NSM techniques covered or prevented surface cracks from appearing. This could be also concluded from the small strains on the concrete surface compared to the control specimen (Fig. 19). For the IER technique on the other hand surface cracks were more visible, this in some situations is more desirable as it provides a warring of imminent failure or the existing of an overload.

The test results have also shown that all shear strengthening techniques significantly enhance the shear capacity of the beams. The NSM and the IER techniques provide better results than the EB technique. It is worth noting that for the same amount of strengthening material, two grooves at the sides of the beam had to be cut at a spacing of 75 mm for the NSM technique versus drilling one hole at the center of the beam every 150 mm in the IER technique. Although the use of CFRP reinforcement for IER strengthening yielded a smaller increase in the shear capacity this was due to the de-bonding between the coating and the internal fiber core of the bar. Therefore by enhancing the manufacturing technique for the CFRP and increasing the bond strength between the fiber core and the friction coating, the IER-C technique will yield at least the same shear strengthening capacity as the IER-G technique. This means also that a different surface treatment for the CFRP bar may produce better strengthening capacity. It is worth noting that the

use of GFRP bars for this technique, which are more economical, yielded slightly better results than the NSM technique and had a 50% more strength enhancement over the EB technique.

5 CONCLUSIONS AND FUTURE WORK

Based on the results of this experimental program the following conclusions and recommendations for future work could be made;

- Using internally embedded FRP reinforcement IER for strengthening RC beams in shear is feasible.
- Using the internally embedded strengthening technique can provide the same strength enhancement as the NSM technique and twice that of the EB technique.
- Using external strengthening techniques prevents or hides surface cracks while for the IER technique surface cracks are more visible.
- The IER technique yields an enhancement in the shear strength equal to in one case and double in another to the EB technique, and equivalent to the NSM technique in one case.
- Further research is needed to study the de-bonding behavior of IER and the effects of the different parameters like the bonding agent, angle of inclination of the IER, the spacing between the IER … etc. on its behavior.

REFERENCES

Barros, J.A.O. & Dias, S.J.E. 2006. Near surface mounted CFRP laminates for shear strengthening of concrete beams. *Cement & Concrete Composites.* 38: 276–292.

De Lorenzis, L. & Nanni, A. 2001. Shear strengthening of reinforced concrete beams with NSM fiber-reinforced polymer rods. *ACI Structural Journal.* 98(1):60–68.

De Lorenzis, L. & Teng, J.G. 2007. Near-surface mounted FRP reinforcement: an emerging technique for structural strengthening. *Composites: PartB.* 38(2):119–143.

Dias, S.J.E. & Barros, J.A.O. 2010. Performance of reinforced concrete T beams strengthened in shear with NSM CFRP laminates. *Engineering Structures.* 32: 373–384.

Rizzo, A. & De Lorenzis, L. 2009. Behavior and capacity of RC beams strengthened in shear with NSM FRP reinforcement. *Construction and Building Materials* 23: 1555–1567.

Tanarslan, H.M. 2011. The effects of NSM CFRP reinforcements for improving the shear capacity of RC beams. *Construction and Building Materials* 25: 2663–2673.

Concrete Solutions – Grantham, Mechtcherine & Schneck (eds)
© 2012 Taylor & Francis Group, London, ISBN 978-0-415-61622-5

Repairing reinforced concrete rectangular columns using ferrocement laminates

S.M. Mourad & M.J. Shannag
King Saud University—Riyadh- Saudi Arabia

ABSTRACT: This research investigates the performance of ferrocement laminates made of high strength mortar and non-structural welded wire meshes (WWMs) in strengthening and repairing reinforced concrete column specimens with rectangular cross sections (150 mm × 250 mm) and height of 1000 mm. The ferrocement laminates were applied on unloaded and preloaded columns with 60%, 80% and 100% of its axial capacity. The overall response of the tested specimens under axial compression was investigated in terms of load carrying capacity, axial stress and strain, lateral displacement, and ductility. Test results indicated that ferrocement jackets made of 2 layers of non-structural WWMs have a promising performance. An increase of about 25% and 20% in axial load carrying capacity and axial stiffness respectively, was observed in strengthened columns. The repaired preloaded columns with 60% and 80% of its ultimate load carrying capacity, showed about 20% and 15% increase in its axial load carrying capacity respectively.

1 INTRODUCTION

Much of the concrete infrastructures from the 1950s to 1970s is now deteriorating at an accelerating rate (Shah & Balaguru, 1984). The early stages of deterioration were regarded as superficial, requiring surface patch repairs. Now deeper and more extensive deterioration, combined with other deficiencies, makes it necessary to carry out repairs which are structurally effective. Furthermore, upgrading of design standards, and increased safety requirements, necessitates the need for developing new and effective construction materials for repair and strengthening of existing structures.

One of the major requirements for upgrading or repairing existing reinforced concrete structures is to increase their columns capacities to withstand larger expected loads and/or repair damaged columns to restore their original strength. Different techniques are available for increasing existing column capacities: (Priestley et al., 1994, Masukawa et al., 1997, Xiao et al., 1999). However, such techniques differ in their advantages and disadvantages. There has been increasing activity with ferrocement construction throughout the world including many countries such as USA, Canada, Australia, China, India, Thailand, Mexico, and Indonesia (Shah & Balaguru, 1984, Naaman, 2000). The availability of its materials in most developing countries, no skilled labor required and it being suitable for both prefabrication and self-help construction could lead ferrocement to become one of the most inexpensive and attractive alternative technique for strengthening and rehabilitation of existing and damaged concrete structures.

Many researchers have emphasized the potential uses of ferrocement laminates in repair and rehabilitation of concrete structures. Rosenthal, (1986), Winokur & Rosenthal, (1982), have demonstrated an innovative use of ferrocement as columns after conducting a preliminary test program. Razvi & Saatcioglu, (1989) investigated the behavior of small scale reinforced concrete square columns specimens when Welded Wire Fabric was used as lateral reinforcement to confine the concrete core of the column. Various combinations of WWF and tie reinforcement have been used as confinement steel. It was shown from the experimental results that the use of WWF as confinement reinforcement improves concrete strength and ductility very significantly. Ferrocement encased short circular and square concrete columns with unreinforced and reinforced cores were investigated by Kaushik et al. (1990). It was observed that the ferrocement encasement increases the strength and ductility of columns for both axial and eccentric loading conditions. Another interesting piece of research work was done by Ahmad et al. (1990), to investigate the possibility of using ferrocement as a retrofit material for masonry columns: the study demonstrated that the use of ferrocement coating strengthens brick columns significantly and improves their cracking resistance.

A preliminary investigation into repair of short square columns using ferrocement was conducted by Nedwell et al. (1990). It was found that the use of a ferrocement retrofit coating increased the apparent stiffness of the columns and significantly improved the ultimate load carrying capacity. Ganesan & Anil (1993) investigated the strength and behavior of short reinforced concrete square columns confined with ferrocement jackets having different ratios of lateral reinforcement and volume fraction of mesh reinforcement. The investigation revealed that the strength and strain at peak load could be enhanced by using ferrocement as confinement. A proposed method presented by Fahmy et al. (1999), for repairing reinforced concrete square columns using ferrocement laminates as a viable economic alternative to the highly expensive conventional jacketing methods, demonstrated that irrespective of the pre-loading level or the mesh type, better behavior and load carrying capacity for all test specimens could be achieved compared to their original behavior.

It can be noted that ferrocement laminates have been proven by many researchers as being an effective repair technique for different structural elements in providing additional strength and ductility, in addition to being a low cost repair technique as compared to others. However, the availability of Welded Wire Meshes (WWMs) conforming to the ACI committee 549, (1988), can alter the choice of using such techniques. Using other types of WWMs manufactured for non-structural purposes that are available commercially in the local market, may be an alternative solution for using ferrocement laminates. Also, it can be noted that limited research exists on the performance of reinforced concrete rectangular columns strengthened with ferrocement laminates.

The main objective of this study is to investigate the performance of ferrocement jackets containing two layers of non-structural Welded Wire Meshes (WWM) encapsulated in high strength mortar, when applied on reinforced concrete rectangular column specimens subjected to axial loads. The behavior of both damaged and preloaded columns after repairing them with ferrocement jackets is evaluated in terms of strength gain, ductility and failure modes.

2 EXPERIMENTAL PROGRAM

The experimental program consisted of testing one-third scale rectangular (150 mm × 250 mm) column specimens with a height of 1000 mm in three phases as follows; *Phase 1:* Control column specimens without any preloading and without ferrocement jackets, *Phase 2:* Jacketed column speci-

mens without any preloading but with ferrocement jackets, and *Phase 3:* Strengthened preloaded column specimens include columns strengthened with ferrocement jackets after preloading them with 60%, 80% and 100% of their ultimate axial strength.

The number and designation of the rectangular reinforced concrete column specimens are given in Table 1. The details of reinforcements and dimensions of the rectangular reinforced concrete column specimens are shown in Figure 1. The ferrocement jacket used in the experimental program was the same for all column specimens and consisted of two layers of WWM wrapped around the column and encapsulated in high strength mortar.

2.1 materials properties

The materials used in preparing the concrete mix included ordinary Portland cement (ASTM Type I), crushed limestone coarse aggregate with a maximum size of 10 mm, an absorption capacity of 1.5%, an oven dry bulk specific gravity of 2.60, a mixture of washed sand and natural silica sand with an absorption capacity of 1.5% and 0.1% and an oven dry bulk specific gravity of 2.56

Table 1. Number and designation of tested rectangular column specimens.

No. of specimens	Designation*	Preload (%)	Ferrocement jacket
2 (control)	RC1 RC2	0	None
2	RJ1 RJ2	0	2 layers of Welded Wire Mesh encapsulated in high strength mortar
2	RP-60 RP-80	60% 80%	
2	RP-100-1 RP-100-2	100%	

*RC: Rectangular Control,
RJ: Rectangular Jacketed,
RP:Rectangular Preloaded to different levels.

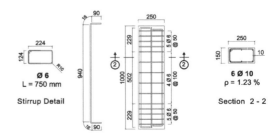

Figure 1. Reinforcement details of column specimen.

and 2.52 respectively, and tap water. The concrete mix used consisted of 300 kg/m³ Portland cement 700 kg/m³ crushed limestone, 600 kg/m³ washed sand, 450 kg/m³ silica sand, and 195 kg/m³ free water. The concrete mix was designed in order to obtain a target mean cylindrical compressive strength of 25 MPa after 28 days. It was intended to use and investigate the effectiveness of using non-structural WWM as a low cost material in rehabilitation and upgrading reinforced concrete columns The WWM used in the jackets had square openings of (12 × 12 mm) and wire diameter of 0.94 mm Tensile tests were performed on three coupons and the wire yield strength was determined in accordance with ACI committee 549 (1988). The average yield strength was 385 MPa at a yield strain of 0.0037, and the average ultimate tensile strength was 524 MPa, while the average modulus of elasticity was 106 MPa.

Different mixes of mortar were designed and prepared in order to develop high strength and flowable mortar: (Alshannag & Mourad, 2009). The materials used in preparing mortar specimens include locally available ordinary Portland cement (ASTM Type I) with a specific gravity of 3.15, natural silica sand with a specific gravity of 2.60 and a fineness modulus of 1.65, silica fume and fly ash were in powder form with a specific gravity of 2.2 and 2.3 respectively. Superplasticizer of a melamine formaldehyde sulfonated superplasticizer type with a specific gravity of 1.21 was incorporated in all mixes to maintain the same degree of workability. The mortar mix proportions were 1: 2: 0.15: 0.05: 0.4: 0.04 by weight of type I cement, silica sand, silica fume, fly ash, water and superplasticizer, respectively. The mortar mix achieved a compressive strength of 63 MPa and tensile strength of 5 MPa after 28 days and a flow of 132% as measured by flow table test according to ASTM standards (ASTM C230).

2.2 *Preparation of specimens*

The longitudinal reinforcement and stirrups were previously prepared and placed in wooden moulds specially made for the rectangular column specimens. One strain gauge was attached at the middle of each of the two diagonally longitudinal reinforcement bars of each column, in order to determine the strains in the longitudinal bars as well as to ensure perfect verticality of the column with minimal eccentricity during testing. In addition two strain gauges were attached to the middle stirrup of the column to determine the lateral strains in the stirrups and to be compared with those pasted on the concrete surface. The moulds were oiled and placed on the vibration table at a low speed while the concrete was poured. After casting

the specimens were covered with wet burlap in the laboratory at 23°C and 65% relative humidity. The specimens were demoulded after two days and wrapped with damp cloth for14 days. The control and preloaded column specimens were prepared for testing after 28 days from casting, while other column specimens were tested after applying the ferrocement jackets. The ferrocement jackets were prepared using two layers of Welded Wire Meshes (WWM) and covered with a flowable high strength mortar jacket using specially designed moulds. The ferrocement jackets were applied to the unloaded column specimens after 28 days from the day of casting. While the ferrocement jackets were applied to the preloaded and failed columns after being tested to 60%, 80% and 100% of their axial capacity. Before applying the ferrocement jackets all column specimens were sand-blasted to roughen their surfaces for a better bond between the concrete surface and the applied mortar layer. Two horizontal strain gauges were placed at the two opposite sides of the concrete column at its mid height, in order to determine the lateral strains at the concrete surface. The process of wrapping the WWM around the specimen included attaching the edge of the mesh to the surface of the specimen using a high adhesive bonding paste known as Sikadur-31, and then wrapping the two layers of WWM around the column specimen. The joints of the mesh were secured at different locations together using double thin steel wires that are commonly used in tying reinforcing bars. To maintain the integrity of the WWM layers and to increase its attachment to the column specimens, the bonding paste of Sikadur-31 was applied at four spots along the height and clamped to the specimen until it

Figure 2. Final form of the specimen after wrapping the WWM.

Figure 3. Final form of the column specimens after applying the ferrocement jacket.

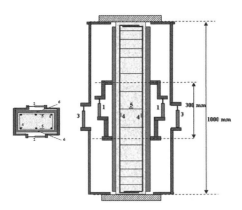

Figure 4. Different instrumentation used in column test.

hardened. Figure 2 shows the final form of the specimen after wrapping the WWM. It can be noticed that the ends of the WWM layers were 20 mm away from the ends of the concrete columns, since it was decided that the ferrocement jackets should not reach the ends of the specimens so that it only provided confinement without applying any vertical compression loads on the ferrocement jackets. The wrapped concrete column was placed in prepared oiled wooden moulds that had a spacing of 20 mm around the specimen except at ends to allow pouring the mortar. The mortar mix was poured around the column specimens, and the sides of the wooden moulds were vibrated to ensure the full penetration of mortar around the WWM. The specimen's top surface was finished and covered with damped cloth for two days, and covered with damped cloth for another 14 days after removing the moulds. The jacketed column specimens were kept uncovered to dry in the laboratory environment until testing. Figure 3 shows the final form of the column specimens after applying the ferrocement jacket.

2.3 Instrumentation and test setup

Instrumentations was used not only to measure the axial and transverse displacements and strains but also to verify those measurements. A special steel-frame setup was used to mount the LVDTs on the specimen. The different items of instrumentation used are shown in Figure 4 as follows:

1. Two vertical LVDTs at gauge length of 300 mm at the middle third of the column specimen, to measure the axial displacements and strains.

2. Two horizontal LVDTs across the column cross section to measure the transverse displacements and strains.
3. Two vertical LVDTs at a gauge distance equal to the total specimen height (1000 mm), to measure the total displacement of the specimen as well as to verify the axial strains.
4. Two strain gauges glued on the middle of the longitudinal reinforcements at opposite corners to measure the axial strains in the steel as well as to determine the axial stress in the longitudinal bars.
5. Two strain gauges glued on the two legs of the middle stirrup of the column, to measure the lateral strains in the stirrups and to compare it with the lateral strains of the column cross section.
6. Two horizontal strain gauges glued on the column concrete surface, to measure the concrete lateral strain and to compare it with the lateral strains of the ferrocement jacket and the stirrups.

The column specimen was placed on the floor of the AMSLER compression machine with a capacity of 10,000 kN. Careful attention was paid to ensure the verticality of the column during the test to obtain perfect centric loading on the column. Both bottom and top ends of the column were leveled horizontally using a thin layer of gypsum before placing the rigid steel plates at the ends of the column. Steel jackets were clamped and bolted together to increase the confinement and to prevent premature failure at column ends. All instrumentation was connected to the data acquisition system. The test was carried out under displacement control at a rate of 0.5 mm per minute, and the readings of all the instrumentation were taken at approximately each 5 seconds until the end of the test.

3 DISCUSSION OF TEST RESULTS

The measured data for each column specimen was collected and analyzed in order to obtain the axial stresses and strains in the concrete and reinforcement, as well as axial and lateral deformations. Axial stresses in the concrete were obtained after subtracting the axial loads taken by the longitudinal reinforcement. The axial strains were obtained from the measured axial displacements that were obtained from the average readings of the LVDTs. Figure 5 shows the comparison of axial load-axial displacement relationships for the tested specimens, while Figure 6 shows the corresponding axial concrete stress-axial strains relationships for the same specimens. Table 2 summarizes the values of ultimate loads achieved, maximum stresses reached in the concrete and the initial axial stiffness of each specimen as well as the corresponding percentages of increases as compared to the control specimens.

It can be observed that the jacketed specimens (RJ1) and (RJ2) reported significant increase in both load carrying capacity and axial stiffness as compared to the control specimens (RC1) and (RC2): the increases were about 25% and 20% respectively. It can be noticed that the strengthened

Table 2. Results of tested specimens.

	Ultimate load		Ultimate axial stress in concrete		Initial axial stiffness	
	(kN)	% *	(MPa)	% *	(MPa)	% *
RC1	1088	–	24	–	25,200	–
RC2	1117	–	25	–	24,950	–
RJ1	1380	125.1	33	134.7	29,900	120.1
RJ2	1382	125.4	34	135.0	29,850	120.0
RP-60	1327	119.0	32	128.0	27,370	110.0
RP-80	1276	114.0	30	120.0	25,760	103.3
RP-100-1	1056	95.0	24	97.0	23,930	96.0
RP-100-2	1047	96.0	25	104.0	24,100	96.0

* The percentage is computed based on the results of control specimens.

preloaded column specimens RP-60 and RP-80 recorded higher load capacities as compared to the control RC1 and RC2, with increases about 20% and 15% respectively. Such increases in load capacities indicate that the ferrocement jackets were able to provide sufficient confinement to the concrete section that resulted in increasing the ultimate axial stresses in the concrete by about 28% and 20% respectively. It is worth mentioning that such increases were almost certainly due to the confinement offered by the ferrocement jackets, since the jackets were not reaching the end of specimens. An insignificant increase in axial stiffness was observed for the preloaded specimens. Strengthening the failed columns RP-100-1 and RP-100-2 restored almost their original capacity with approximately the same axial stiffness but with less ductility, as compared to the control specimens RC1 and RC2. No significant change was observed in the maximum axial strains of the strengthened preloaded column specimens as compared to those of the control column specimen. However, the strengthened failed columns RP-100-1 and RP-100-2 recorded less axial strains as compared to those of the control columns due to the existence of minor cracks in the original concrete column. Figure 7 shows the axial load-lateral displacement relationship of the tested specimens. The effect of ferrocement jackets in reducing the lateral deformation of the column section, except for strengthened failed columns, can be easily observed in Figure 7.

The column failure was initiated by vertical hairline cracks at the middle part of the control specimen and in the mortar of ferrocement jackets at the middle portion of the jacketed column specimens. The vertical cracks became visible at about 90% to 95% of the ultimate load. The number and width of these cracks started increasing with the increase in axial load until the specimen reached its failure load. The control specimens exhibited

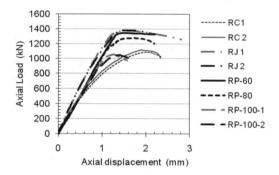

Figure 5. Axial load-axial displacement relationships of the tested specimens

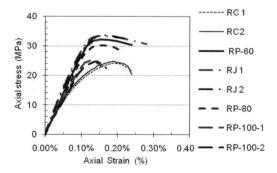

Figure 6. Axial stress-axial strains relationships for the tested specimens.

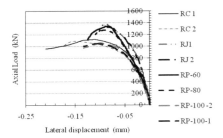

Figure 7. Axial load-lateral deformation relationship of the tested specimens.

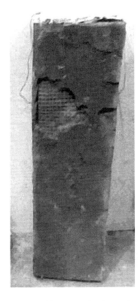

Figure 8. Typical Failure mode for column specimens with ferrocement jackets.

sudden brittle failure mode whereas the jacketed specimens exhibited a gradual ductile failure mode. The failure in jacketed specimens was mainly caused by the failure of WWM at the corners of the specimen that resulted in the separation and bulging of the mortar layer from the specimen. Figure 8 shows the typical failure mode for column specimens with ferrocement jackets.

4 CONCLUSIONS

Based on the test results of this investigation the following conclusions can be drawn:

1. Test results indicated that ferrocement jackets made of 2 layers of non-structural Welded Wire Mesh (WWM) and applied on rectangular reinforced concrete column specimens have a promising performance in increasing its load carrying capacity, stiffness and enhancing its failure mode.
2. Test results indicated that strengthening reinforced concrete rectangular columns of 150 mm × 250 mm and a height of 1000 mm, with the same ferrocement jackets showed about 25% and 20% increase in axial load carrying capacity and stiffness respectively.
3. Test results indicated that repairing similar reinforced concrete columns of rectangular cross section preloaded up to 60% of their ultimate load carrying capacity, with the same jackets showed about 20% and 10% increase in axial load carrying capacity and stiffness respectively, compared to control columns.
4. Test results indicated that repairing similar reinforced concrete columns of rectangular cross section preloaded up to 80% of their ultimate load carrying capacity, with the same jacket showed about 15% and 3.3% increase in axial load carrying capacity and stiffness respectively, compared to control columns.

ACKNOWLEDGEMENTS

The authors would like to acknowledge the support received from the research center of college of engineering at King Saud University, and the assistance of the technicians at the structures and materials laboratories of the Civil Engineering department.

REFERENCES

ACI Committee 549, 1988, Guide for the design, construction, and repair of ferrocement, ACI Structural Journal Vol. 85: 325–351.

Ahmed, T., Ali, S. & Choudhury, J. 1990. Experimental study of ferrocement as a retrofit material for masonary columns, In Proceedings of the Fifth International Symposium on Ferrocement, Nedwell and Swamy (eds.): 269–276.

Alshannag, M. & Mourad, S. 2009. High Strength Ferrocement Laminates for Structural Repair, Research Report No. 48/1428, College of Engineering Research Center, King Saud University.

Fahmy, E., Shaheen, Y. & Korany, Y. 1999. Reparing reinforced concrete columns using ferrocement laminates, Journal of Ferrocement, Vol. 29, No. 2: 115–124.

Ganesan, N. & Anil, J. 1993. Strength and behaviour of reinforced concrete columns confined by ferrocement, Journal of Ferrocement, Vol. 23 No. 2: 99–108.

Kaushik, S., Prakash, A. & Singh, A. 1990. Inelastic buckling of ferrocement encased columns, In Proceedings of the Fifth International Symposium on Ferrocement, Nedwell and Swamy (eds.): 327–341.

Masukawa, J., Akiyama, H. & Saito, H. 1997. Retrofiting of existing reinforced concrete piers by using carbon fiber sheet and aramid fiber sheet, Proceedings of the Third International Symposium on Non-Metallic (FRP) Reinforcement for Concrete Structures: 411–418.

Naaman, A. 2000. Ferrocement and laminated cementitious composites, TechnoPress 3000, Ann Arbor, Michigan: 372.

Nedwell, P., Ramesht, M. & Rafei-Tanhanaki, S. 1990. Investigation into the repair of short square columns using ferrocement, In Proceedings of the Fifth International Symposium on Ferrocement, Nedwell and Swamy (eds.): 277–285.

Priestley, M., Sieble, F., Xiao, Y. & Verma, R. 1994. Steel jacket retrofitting of reinforced concrete bridge columns for enhanced shear strength-Part II: Test results and comparison with theory: ACI Struct J 91: 537–51.

Razvi, S. & Saatcioglu, M. 1989. Confinement of Reinforced Concrete Columns with Welded Wire Fabric, ACI Structural Journal, 86: 615–623.

Rosenthal, I. 1986. Precast Ferrocement Columns, Journal of Ferrocement, 16: 273–284.

Shah, S. & Balaguru, P. 1984. Ferrocement, in New reinforced concrete, R.N. Swamy, Editor, Blackie and sons limited, Glasgow: 5–24.

Winokur, A. & Rosenthal, I. 1982. Ferrocement in Centrally loaded Compression Elements, Journal of Ferrocement, 12: 357–364.

Xiao, Y., Wu, H. & Martin, G. 1999. Prefabricated composite jacketing of RC columns for enhanced shear strength. ACI Struct J 125: 255–264.

Concrete Solutions – Grantham, Mechtcherine & Schneck (eds)
© *2012 Taylor & Francis Group, London, ISBN 978-0-415-61622-5*

Residual strength of CFRP strengthened beams after heating and cooling

D. Petkova & T. Donchev
Kingston University London, UK

ABSTRACT: The residual flexural strength of small-scale CFRP strengthened RC beams is presented in this paper. Seven groups of samples were heated uniformly to different temperatures up to 300°C. The minibeams were loaded in four-point bending configuration and tested to complete failure of the samples. The results of the local deformations in the concrete beam and CFRP laminate are presented. An intermediate debonding was observed as the most common mode of failure.

1 INTRODUCTION

The choice of using FRP materials to increase the capacity of structural elements leads to an improved system utilising the high strength of the new material with no significant increase in the dead load or potential corrosion. The effect of elevated temperatures on the strength of fibre reinforced polymer (FRP) strengthened reinforced concrete (RC) members has been found to have a significant influence on the performance of the strengthened system. Investigations of the effect of elevated and high temperatures and fire have been limited in most cases to fire studies with significant effects after a few minutes of exposure. Little is known about the residual properties of FRP strengthened systems after heating to elevated temperatures and cooling. More research in this area could be used to assess strengthened systems after heating to elevated temperatures.

2 BACKGROUND

The structural adhesives exhibit properties typical for polymers (Mays and Hutchinson, 1992). The thermal properties of polymers are mainly defined by two temperatures:

- glass transition temperature (T_g)—where the composite begins to soften and exhibits rubber-like behaviour;
- decomposition temperature (T_d)—above which the reduction of stiffness and strength is irreversible.

Karadeniz et al. (2007) investigated different equations for determining the coefficient of thermal expansion of fibre reinforced polymers α in longitudinal and transverse directions. The best agreement with experimental results was obtained from values expressed by the elastic moduli, the Poisson's ratios and volume fractions of the fibres and the matrix.

Existing investigations on the behaviour of FRP materials and FRP strengthened systems have been mainly focused on the effect of fire on the system performance. Keller et al. (2005) investigated cellular samples cut from a bridge deck exposed to fire conditions where two types of experiments were carried out: for charring and for liquid cooling. After a few minutes of exposure, colour changes in the glass FRP material were observed form brownish to black, followed by flames and decomposition of the resin. Later, Keller et al. (2006a, b) and Bai et al. (2008) summarized the work of the investigation to model the thermal and mechanical behaviour of the liquid- cooled and non-cooled GFRP slabs.

Green et al. (2006) reported a study of the behaviour of FRP wrapped columns in three main extreme conditions, including fire exposure. Temperature levels were recorded at the interface between FRP and concrete, which exceeded the T_g of the FRP. It was concluded that the insulation delayed the burning of the FRP strengthening and reduced the internal temperature of the column so that the load capacity of unstrengthened columns was intact.

Carbon/epoxy FRP system and glass/epoxy FRP system were used in a study by Kodur et al. (2006) on the fire endurance of insulated FRP strengthened and control columns. The tests were carried out in a full-scale column furnace. All five columns were tested under axial compressive load which was maintained at a constant value until failure or up to 5 h of fire exposure. The temperature at the level of the FRP maintained 100°C (4 h of exposure) due to the effect of the insulating system. The authors suggested that in a fire situation the reliability of the strengthened system would depend on a critical temperature, which conservatively could be accepted as the Tg of the FRP.

Zhou & Tan (2007) investigated the performance of glass FRP strengthened beams subjected to temperatures up to 800°C. The small scale samples were strengthened with GFRP sheet and were divided in groups where 3 of the groups had an additional protective layer. The samples were heated following the ASTM E-119 standard curve. The authors observed shear and flexural-shear modes of failure for the unprotected samples and shear for the rest of the groups. It was concluded that the effect of elevated temperatures resulted in a substantial decrease in the stiffness and ultimate strength for samples heated above 600°C.

Eighteen rectangular beams 127 mm by 254 mm and 1219 mm length were strengthened with two layers of CFRP sheets for flexure and GFRP sheets for shear in the study by Weber & Kachlakev (2007). The samples were heated to 150°C and then tested under 3-point bending. The authors concluded that above the T_g of the resin, the strengthened system had reduced stiffness and the ultimate capacity of the beam was determined by the behaviour of the internal reinforcement. The strain of the strengthening material was found to decrease with increase in temperature which was attributed to relaxation of the concrete-FRP interface. The ultimate capacity of the samples was reduced by 46% at 150°C temperature.

3 METHODOLOGY

3.1 Preparation of samples

Twenty one C20/25 concrete strength minibeams with a standard size of $100 \times 100 \times 500$ mm reinforced with 4 mild steel rebars with 6 mm diameter in the longitudinal direction and 7 stirrups of 3 mm diameter were prepared. The minibeams were strengthened with 20 mm wide 1.2 mm thick CFRP laminate. To ensure good bonding between the beam and the laminate the side of the concrete where the strengthening laminate was to be attached was given a preliminary treatment. A thin layer of the surface of the minibeam was removed using steel brushes, the roughened concrete was vacuumed and then Structural adhesive "Epoxy plus" from Weber was applied. The plates were cut to 400 mm length and 20 mm width, cleaned and then attached to the concrete surface. The excess adhesive was removed and the samples were left to cure for 7 days.

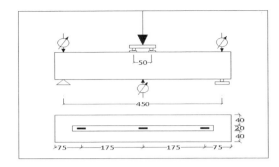

Figure 1. Loading scheme and position ER strain gauges.

3.2 Heating of samples

The samples were heated under a static point load of 1 kN individually to a specified temperature. Seven groups of three samples were exposed to a temperature of 50°C, 100°C, 150°C, 200°C, 250°C or 300°C. The air temperature in the oven was measured at three different levels with thermocouples and an additional thermocouple inside a control beam was used to measure the temperature at the core of the sample. After the uniform heating, the samples were left to cool to room temperature and then tested.

3.3 Test set-up

After heating and cooling, the minibeams were tested under four point loading, where the distance between the applied forces was 50 mm and the distance between the supports was 450 mm (Figure 1). The deflection was measured with three dial gauges—one at midspan of the beam and two above the supports. Three electro-resistant (ER) strain gauges were also attached to the laminate which was bonded to the bottom side of the beam.

The load was applied incrementally 1 kN every 10 min until the failure of the minibeams. After the initial debonding of the laminate, the load was applied until the beam could not sustain any further increase.

4 EXPERIMENTAL RESULTS

4.1 Group 20°C

4.1.1 Testing, cracking and failure load
Sample #20-1, where 20 represents the temperature and 1 represents the first tested sample of the group, was loaded to 19 kN when a brittle shear crack developed in the right half of the beam. The crack propagated through the bottom side of the beam reaching the concrete- adhesive interface

and then propagated to the end of the laminate. Another type of failure started to develop in the left half at the subsequent reloading which resulted in a flexural—shear crack at 23 kN. On the lower face of the beam the crack propagated to the concrete-adhesive interface and then to the left end of the laminate. To find the maximum load of the system the beam was reloaded until at 24 kN no further increase was possible.

Beam #20-2 failed in a more gradual manner. Flexural cracks were observed at 13 kN which continued to propagate upwards. Cracks started to propagate at 17 kN towards the adhesive on the strengthened face on the left side of the beam but at a later stage did not lead to delamination. Failure occurred in the right half of the beam at 23 kN when the crack propagated to 10 mm from the top of the beam and complete delamination was achieved between the adhesive and concrete interface.

The last beam of the group #20-3 exhibited similar behaviour to sample #20-2. Flexural cracks developed at 16 kN and they continued to propagate to 18 kN when a flexural-shear crack was formed in the left side of the beam which quickly propagated almost to the top surface. Delamination occurred at 20 kN followed by drop of the load to 15 kN. The maximum load the beam could then sustain was 24.5 kN.

4.1.2 Deflection

The deflections of the three samples are shown on Figure 2. Beam #20-1 deflected to 0.38 mm at 19 kN before it reached its failure load. The further increase in load resulted in significant increase in the deformation due to the cracked section and the development of a new failure mode in the left half of the beam until at 23 kN the ultimate load of the beam was reached. The deflection at

the last stage was 2.04 mm. Beam #20-2 exhibited a gradual deflection up to the maximum load of 22 kN when the deflection reached 0.86 mm. The load-deflection curve for beam #20-3 consisted of 2 main branches: up to 19 kN the increase was gradual to 0.72 mm, when a "jump" to 2.17 mm occurred caused by the formation of a flexural-shear crack. The maximum deflection of 2.91 mm for the beam was measured at 24 kN.

4.1.3 Strain of laminate

Strain gauge 3 (beam #20-1) registered a sudden increase to 401 microstrain at 19 kN at the right end of the laminate before a shear crack was formed. The delamination which occurred at 19 kN only led to debonding of 20–30 mm from the end of the laminate and at further load increase the gauge registered negative values. Thus, ER gauge 2 continued to register an increase up to 22 kN when the maximum strain of 1745 microstrain was recorded. The left strain gauge did not detect high deformations at the end of the laminate although a value of 89 microstrain was recorded at 22 kN prior to the formation of the flexural-shear crack and subsequent delamination.

ER gauge 2 of beam #20-2 revealed a gradual increase up to the maximum load when a strain of 2472 microstrain was reached (Figure 3). The strain gauges at the ends of the laminate exhibited slight increase in the deformations above 17 kN when significant crack development was observed. Maximum strains for ER gauge 1 and ER 3 prior to failure were 285 microstrain and 207 microstrain respectively.

ER gauge 2 of beam #20-3 reached a maximum value of 2451 microstrain prior to the delamination at 19 kN. Strain increase was observed for ER gauge 1 from 16 kN when flexural cracks occurred

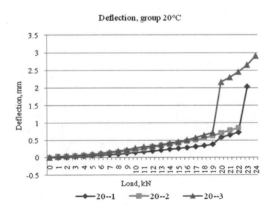

Figure 2.   Load-deflection diagram, group 20°C.

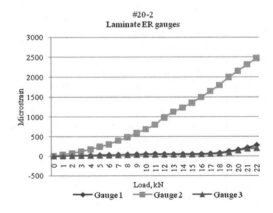

Figure 3.   Load-strain diagram, laminate ER gauges, sample #20-2.

to 19 kN with a maximum value of 405 microstrain prior to the delamination. The maximum value for ER gauge 3 was also measured at 19 kN with a value of 197 microstrain.

4.2 Group 50°C

4.2.1 Testing, cracking and failure load

Sample #50-1 developed flexural cracks at 15 kN of which one continued to propagate upwards with the increased loading. The crack had propagated at 18 kN almost to the top when delamination between the adhesive and the concrete occurred. The system then held a load of 11.5 kN and was further increased to 22.2 kN when the maximum load was reached.

Sample #50-2 exhibited similar behaviour to sample #50-1. Flexural cracks were formed at 15 kN but most of them did not propagate further. A major crack had developed on the left side of the beam when the load reached 18 kN. The crack had propagated through the tension side of the beam to the interface between the adhesive and the concrete. Delamination followed and the load was reduced to 12.9 kN. The beam was then reloaded and at 23.7 kN the maximum load was reached.

Sample #50-3 developed flexural cracks when the load reached 14 kN. The cracks were developed almost symmetrically about the centre line of the beam and at further increase all of them propagated vertically. At 20 kN delamination at the left side of the beam was observed followed by reduction of the load to 12.9 kN. The system was then able to sustain a maximum load of 22.6 kN.

4.2.2 Deflections

Beam #50-1 exhibited a gradual increase in the deflection up to 18 kN when delamination occurred (Figure 4). Prior to failure, the deflection of the beam was 0.64 mm. The following loading resulted in a significant increase in the deformation of the beam to 2.5 mm when the load reached 21 kN. Similar behaviour was observed for the deformation of beam #50-2. The beam had deflected to 0.63 mm at 17 kN before delamination occurred. The subsequent loading of the system resulted in a deflection of 3.1 mm when the maximum load was reached at 23 kN. Beam #50-3 was loaded to 20 kN with a deflection of 0.73 mm before delamination was observed. The maximum deflection which was recorded at 22 kN was 3.26 mm.

4.2.3 Strain of laminate

The deformations recorded by strain gauges attached to the laminate of beam #50-1 reached their highest values at 17 kN (Figure 5). A strain of 2065 microstrain was recorded by the strain gauge at the midspan of the beam before the failure load

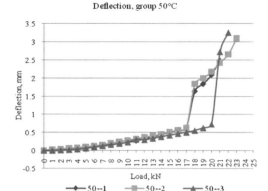

Figure 4. Load-deflection diagram, group 50°C.

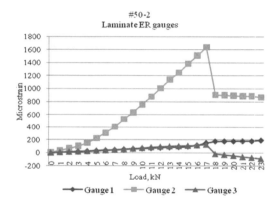

Figure 5. Load-strain diagram, laminate ER gauges, sample #50-2.

was reached. The strain gauge at the left end of the laminate registered an increase to 192 microstrain at 17 kN until delamination occurred. The strain gauge at the right end of the laminate was gradually increasing during the loading process and it reached 115.5 microstrain prior to delamination. Further loading did not lead to any increase in deformations in the laminate.

The strain of ER gauge 2 at 17 kN was 1640.5 microstrain for beam #50-2 (Figure 5). The measured strains at the left and right end of the laminate were similar and only at 17 kN was a slight increase to 149.5 microstrain observed at the left side. The right strain gauge reached a maximum value of 125.5 microstrain before failure.

Beam #50-3 was loaded to 20 kN when maximum values for the three strains were measured. At midspan the strain reached a value of 2346.5 microstrain prior to failure. The left and right strain gauges registered similar deformations up to 14 kN. At 20 kN ER gauge 3 reached a strain of 402 microstrain.

4.3 Group 100°C

4.3.1 Testing, cracking and failure load
Sample #100-1 developed shear and flexural cracks at 16 kN. The shear crack caused the delamination at the left end of the laminate and a reduction of the load to 13.4 kN. The further load increase resulted in the formation of new flexural cracks. The maximum load which the system reached was 21.9 kN.

The second beam of group 100°C formed flexural cracks at 15 kN which continued to propagate vertically up to 18 kN. At 21 kN a new flexural-shear crack was formed which resulted in the delamination at the left side of the beam. The load dropped to 15.9 kN and was then gradually increased to 22.7 kN when the ultimate capacity of the system was reached.

Sample #100-3 formed one flexural crack at the midspan of the beam which continued to propagate vertically to 12 kN. When the load was increased to 13 kN a new inclined crack was formed in the right half of the beam which led to a brittle diagonal crack. The right side of the laminate and adhesive layer had then separated from the concrete and the load dropped to 1.2 kN. The beam was then reloaded to 2.3 kN when the maximum capacity of the beam was reached.

4.3.2 Deflections
Beam #100-1 deflected to 0.44 mm at 15 kN before the beam failed due to formation of a shear crack (Figure 6). The beam was subsequently reloaded and 1.26 mm was measured as the maximum deflection. Beam #100-2 reached 0.97 mm deflection at 20 kN prior to failure. The following reloading of the beam led to a significant increase in the deflection to 3.17 mm. The last sample of the group failed at a lower load compared to the other samples of the group at 13 kN with gradual increase in the deflection to 0.86 mm prior to failure.

4.3.3 Strain of laminate
The strain measured by ER strain gauge 2 of beam #100-1 gradually increased to 15 kN recording a value of 1362 microstrain before failure occurred at the left side of the sample. Relative increase in the deformations was registered by ER gauge 1 at 9 kN and a maximum value of 358 microstrain was reached at 15 kN. The further load increase caused the strain at midspan to continue to grow and the maximum value reached 1933 microstrain. The strain of ER gauge 3 indicated a gradual increase in the deformation to a maximum 323 microstrain.

Flexural cracks were observed on beam #100-2 at 15 kN when the strain of the laminate at midspan reached a value of 1553.5 microstrain (Figure 7). The further increase in the load resulted in a steeper growth of the strain and the deformation reached a value of 2411 microstrain at 20 kN before the beam failed. The left and right strain gauges both registered an increase in the deformations above 16 kN. ER gauge 1 reached 570 microstrain prior to delamination at 21 kN whilst ER gauge 3 registered a lower deformation of 320.5 microstrain.

Beam #100-3 registered a significantly higher rate of deformation with increase in the load above 6 kN at midspan. The strain at 6 kN was 283 microstrain whilst at 13 kN the deformation was more than 10 times higher—2454 microstrain—mainly due to the flexural crack which occurred at an early stage of the loading and continued to propagate with increase in the load. ER gauge 3 registered higher deformations at the right end of the

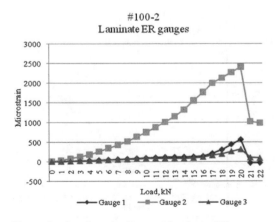

Figure 7. Load-strain diagram, laminate ER gauges, sample #100-2.

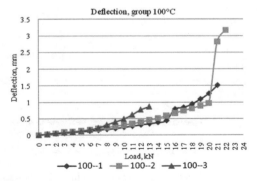

Figure 6. Load-deflection diagram, group 100°C.

laminate which reached a value of 445 microstrain at 13 kN.

4.4 Group 150°C

4.4.1 Testing, cracking and failure load

Sample #150-1 developed vertical cracks at 9 kN and 13 kN. One of the cracks continued to propagate upwards up to 15 kN when delamination at the interface of the adhesive and concrete occurred. The load was then reduced to 11.5 kN. The maximum capacity of the beam was reached at 21.5 kN.

Sample #150-2 was loaded to 7 kN when the first vertical cracks were formed. More cracks occurred at 10 kN and 14 kN when one of the cracks continued to propagate vertically up to 18 kN. After the delamination, the load dropped to 13.2 kN and was further increased to the maximum load of 22.9 kN.

Sample #150-3 failed at a lower load of 11 kN. Vertical cracks were observed at 10 kN and an increase by 1 kN led to a formation of a brittle flexural crack and the load was reduced to 0.8 kN. The maximum capacity of the system was then reached at 2.2 kN.

4.4.2 Deflection

The deflection of beam #150-1 was increasing gradually up to 14 kN when, due to a flexural-shear crack, a "jump" of the deflection was observed (Figure 8). The deflection prior to failure load was 0.44 mm and at maximum load of 20 kN it reached 2.16 mm. Beam #150-2 failed at a higher load of 17 kN due to a flexural crack when the deflection reached a value of 0.69 mm. The deflection was increasing gradually up to 14 kN when a flexural crack started to propagate upwards leading to failure at 17 kN and a subsequent jump of the

deflection of the beam. Ultimate load was then reached at 22 kN with a deflection of 2.6 mm. Beam #150-3 failed at a significantly lower load due to a flexural-shear crack at 11 kN. The maximum deflection for the sample prior to failure at 10 kN was 0.5 mm.

4.4.3 Strain of laminate

Strain gauge 2 of beam #150-1 registered a gradual increase in the deformations at midspan of the beam up to 14 kN when the reading reached 1374 microstrain. Further increase in the load led to delamination. The strain gauge at the right side of the beam registered a gradual increase in the deformations up to 14 kN when a value of 46.5 microstrain was reached. The strain measured at the left side of the laminate was lower: 22 microstrain at 14 kN, due to the cracking of the adhesive after the heating and cooling of the samples.

Beam #150-2 was loaded to 17 kN prior to failure load was reached (Figure 9). The strain measured at midspan of the beam increased to 1499 microstrain before the formation of a flexural crack. The strain measured at the right side of the laminate gradually increase up to 14 kN and with further increase the rate of growth was higher resulting in 503 microstrain prior to failure. The strain at the left side increased to 2 kN before the failure load was reached with a maximum strain of 111 microstrain. A change of the deformation at the midspan of beam #150-3 was observed at 7 kN and the maximum of the strain was measured prior to failure of the beam. At 10 kN the deformation reached 1614 microstrain before a flexural- shear crack was formed. The strain measured at the left and right end of the laminate reached values of 50 and 67 microstrain respectively at 10 kN.

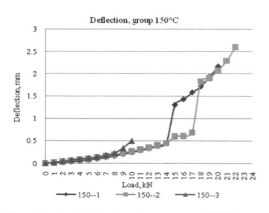

Figure 8. Load-deflection diagram, group 150°C.

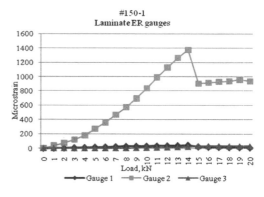

Figure 9. Load-strain diagram, laminate ER gauges, sample #150-1.

4.5 Group 200°C

4.5.1 Testing, cracking and failure load

Sample #200-1 developed a vertical crack at 9 kN which had also propagated through the adhesive layer. The load dropped to 7 kN and was then increased. The crack continued to propagate vertically and delamination was observed at 17 kN between the laminate and the adhesive although no reduction of the load was registered. The maximum load was then reached at 22.6 kN.

Vertical cracks were observed on sample #200-2 at 9 kN but they did not propagate at further load increase. A new crack was formed at 12 kN to 30 mm from the top surface which also resulted in a crack through the adhesive. The load dropped to 8 kN and the sample was then reloaded to 18 kN when delamination between the adhesive and the laminate occurred. The maximum load of the system was reached at 21.3 kN.

The last sample of the group formed few vertical cracks at 10 kN one of which propagated to 30 mm from the top at 11 kN. The development of the crack led to delamination between the adhesive and the concrete mostly due to an existing crack from the heating of the system. The load dropped to 9 kN and was then further increased until the maximum load of 23.1 kN was reached.

4.5.2 Deflections

The deflection of beam #200-1 (Figure 10) increased gradually up to 8 kN before a flexural crack developed. The deflection reached a value of 0.24 mm before a "jump" in the values occurred due to the further load increase. Maximum load was reached at 22 kN when the deflection was 3.35 mm. Beam #200-2 was loaded to 12 kN when a flexural crack was formed; prior to failure 0.4 mm deflection was measured. The ultimate capacity

of the system was then achieved at 18 kN when the deformation reached 2.42 mm. The last sample of group 200°C failed at 11 kN with a gradual increase in the deflection to 0.33 mm prior to the formation of a flexural crack. The ultimate load was then achieved at 22 kN when the deflection reached a value of 2.74 mm.

4.5.3 Strain of laminate

Gradual increase in the strain at midspan to 5 kN was recorded for beam #200-1 followed by a higher rate of growth of the strain, reaching 588 microstrain prior to the cracking of the beam at 9 kN. A slight increase was recorded up to 20 kN. Both the left and right ER strain gauges registered an increase in the deformation up to 8 kN when 60 microstrain and 70 microstrain were measured respectively by ER strain gauge 1 and ER strain gauge 3.

Beam #200-2 exhibited similar behaviour to sample #200-1 (Figure 11). The deformation measured prior to the formation of a flexural crack at 12 kN at midspan was 952 microstrain. The ER strain gauges 1 and 3 registered little increase in the deformation at the ends of the laminate with a value of 7 and 37 microstrain respectively at 11 kN. Compressive strains were registered by ER strain gauge 1 due to the delamination when the load was increased.

At the midspan of beam #200-3, the strain gradually increased to 5 kN and, with further increase in the load, a higher rate of deformation was registered. The strain reached 1137 microstrain at 10 kN. ER strain gauges 1 and 3 registered little increase in the local deformations to 24 microstrain at the right end of the laminate. At the left end of the laminate, no significant strain readings were recorded due to existing thermal cracks.

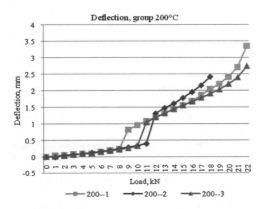

Figure 10. Load-deflection diagram, group 200°C.

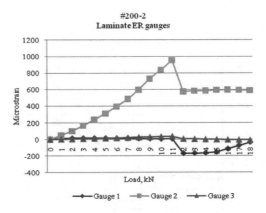

Figure 11. Load-strain diagram, laminate ER gauges, sample #200-2.

4.6 Group 250°C

4.6.1 Testing, cracking and failure load

The first cracks on sample #250-1 were formed at load 6 kN with an approximate length of 20 mm. At 9 kN one of the cracks propagated to 20 mm from the top and to the adhesive layer on the strengthened side. Delamination was observed between the adhesive and concrete. Then the crack propagated upwards and the width of the crack increased. The maximum load which was achieved was 19 kN.

Sample #250-2 developed one crack at 5 kN which propagated to 20 mm from the top at 6 kN. Delamination between the laminate and the adhesive occurred. The load was then increased which resulted in opening of the crack including through the adhesive layer. The maximum load was recorded at 17 kN.

The last sample of the group #250-3 developed a crack at 5 kN which later propagated at 8 kN and delamination between laminate and adhesive followed. The load was reduced to 7.1 kN and then the beam was reloaded to the maximum load of 20.2 kN.

4.6.2 Deflections

Beam #250-1 was loaded to 9 kN when delamination occurred and the deflection increased from 0.309 mm at 8 kN to 0.69 mm at 9 kN (Figure 12). Maximum load was reached at 19 kN when the deflection was increased to 2.89 mm. Beam #250-2 failed at 7 kN due to a flexural crack and delamination. At 6 kN the deflection increased to 0.18 mm and at maximum load of 17 kN the deflection reached 3.45 mm. The last sample of the group reached a deflection of 0.27 mm before the beam failed at 8 kN due to formation of a crack and delamination. At 20 kN the deflection reached 0.28 mm.

4.6.3 Strain of laminate

The strain measured at midspan of beam #250-1 gradually increased to 8 kN when a value of 677 microstrain was measured. Delamination occurred when the load was increased by 1 kN. The local deformations measured at the ends of the laminate registered little increase due to existing thermal cracks between the concrete and the adhesive layer.

Beam #250-2 exhibited similar behaviour to the previous sample with a failure load at 6 kN (Figure 13). At midspan the local deformation reached a value of 777 microstrain before failure due to a flexural crack occurred. At the left and right end of the laminate no significant increase in the strain was registered due to existing thermal cracks.

At 7 kN, the strain at midspan reached a value of 668 microstrain before a crack was formed in the right half of the beam #250-3 followed by delamination. The local deformations measured at the ends of the laminate registered no increase due to thermal cracks between the laminate and the adhesive layer.

4.7 Group 300°C

4.7.1 Testing, cracking and failure load

Sample #300-1 failed at a low level of loading. At 4 kN a flexural crack occurred almost though the full height of the beam followed by mixed laminate-adhesive-concrete delamination. The load was reduced to 1.2 kN and then at 1.5 kN the maximum load was reached.

The first cracks appeared on sample #300-2 at 5 kN which propagated upwards at 8 kN and 9 kN symmetrically about the central axis of the beam. Delamination was observed at 9 kN on the left side of the beam. The further increase in the load led to the further propagation of the cracks until at 19.8 kN the maximum load was reached.

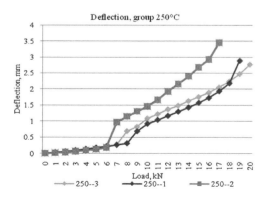

Figure 12.   Load-deflection diagram, group 250°C.

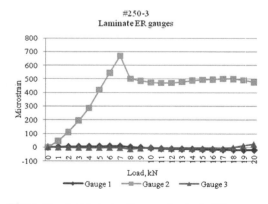

Figure 13.   Load-strain diagram, laminate ER gauges, sample #250-3.

The last sample of group 300 developed short flexural cracks at 6 kN. At 7 kN, another crack had developed which resulted in a reduction of the load to 6.3 kN and complete delamination. The crack then propagated upwards up to 11 kN. Maximum load was reached at 21.2 kN.

4.7.2 *Deflection*

Beam #300-1 failed at a very early stage of the loading at 3 kN (Figure 14). Beam #300-2 failed at a higher load of 8 kN due to a flexural crack when the deflection reached a value of 0.5 mm. The deflection was increasing gradually up to 5 kN when the first flexural cracks were observed and the maximum load was then reached at 19 kN, with maximum deflection of 2.71 mm.

Beam #300-3 failed when the beam was loaded to 7 kN with a deflection reading of 0.17 mm before delamination occurred. The load was then increased and reached 2.55 mm at 19 kN.

4.7.3 *Strain of laminate*

The strain measured at midspan for beam #300-1 increased to 176 microstrain when the load reached 3 kN. A load increase by 1 kN led to a vertical crack at midspan and delamination occurred. The local deformations measured at the ends of the laminate registered no increase due to thermal cracks between the concrete and the adhesive layer.

At the midspan of beam #300-2 the local deformation measured gradually increased to 5 kN until the first cracks were formed and with further increase in the load to 8 kN a maximum strain of 694 microstrain was registered. ER strain gauge 1 registered no increase in the local deformations and ER gauge 3 detected compressive strains from 5 kN to 9 kN. The concentration of the stresses at the right end of the laminate was caused by the cracks developed during the heating process and the following peeling action at the ends.

The strain measured at midspan of beam #300-3 increased gradually up to 6 kN before the beam failed due to a flexural crack and delamination. The strain continued to increase when the system was reloaded up to 16 kN which was attributed to residual local deformation above the failure load of the system. Both the left and right ER strain gauges registered no increase in the local deformation.

5 ANALYSIS OF THE EXPERIMENTAL RESULTS

The delamination load decreased gradually for samples from room temperature to 300°C (Figure 16). The average load for group 20°C was 20 kN and for group 300°C the average load was 5.6 kN, thus a reduction of 70% was found for the temperature range of 20°C to 300°C.

The reduction of the ultimate load with increase in temperature after initial delamination had occurred was less steep. A more significant effect was observed with samples heated to 250°C and 300°C. For group 250, the average ultimate load was 18.6 kN and 13.7 kN while at room temperature the average ultimate load was reached at 23 kN (Figure 17).

The effect of the temperature on the strain in the laminate was found to be more pronounced

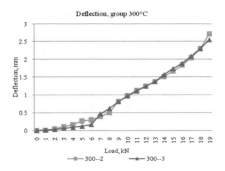

Figure 14.   Load-deflection diagram, group 300°C.

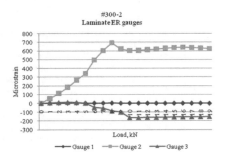

Figure 15.   Load-strain diagram, laminate ER gauges, sample #300-2.

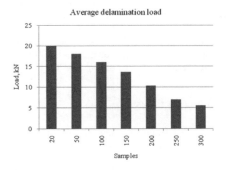

Figure 16.   Average delamination load for heated and cooled minibeams, groups 20–300°C.

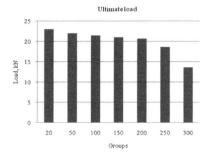

Figure 17. Average ultimate load for minibeams heated to elevated temperatures, groups 20–300°C.

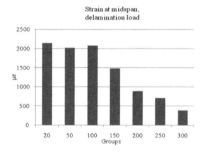

Figure 18. Strain at delamination, groups 20–300°C.

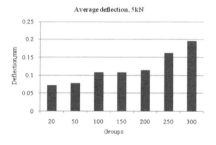

Figure 19. Deflection at 5 kN, groups 20 to 300°C.

for temperatures above the Tg of the laminate and gradually decreasing to 300°C indicating reduced stiffness of the system (Figure 18).

The deflection of the system showed gradual increase from room temperature to 100°C and a steep increase for groups above 200°C (Figure 19).

6 CONCLUSIONS

As a result of the experimental work and analysis the following conclusions are drawn:

- After heating up to 300°C and cooling the strengthened minibeams failed due to interfacial debonding.

- The deformability of the heated samples increased with increase in the temperature.
- The decrease of delamination load was proportional to the increase in temperature.
- The heating had a more pronounced effect on the delamination load than on the ultimate load.
- The effect of heating caused a reduction of the delamination by 70% at 300°C.

ACKNOWLEDGEMENTS

The authors would like to thank Weber for the supplied materials and help.

REFERENCES

ASTM E119.2007. Standard test methods for the fire tests of building construction and materials.
Bai, Y., Vallee, T. & Keller, T. 2008. Modelling of thermal responses for FRP composites under elevated and high temperatures. *Composites Science and Technology* 68: 47–56.
Green, M.F., Bisby, L.A., Fam, A.Z. & Kodur, V.K.R. 2006. FRP confined concrete columns: Behaviour under extreme conditions. *Cement & Concrete Composites* 28: 928–937.
Karadeniz, Z.H. & Kumlutas, D. 2007. A numerical study on the coefficients of thermal expansion of fiber reinforced composite materials. *Composite Structures* 78: 1–10.
Keller, T., Tracy, C. & Zhou, A. 2006a. Structural response of liquid-cooled GFRP slabs subjected to fire. Part I. Material and post-fire modeling, *Composites: part A* 37: 1286–1295.
Keller, T., Tracy, C. & Zhou, A. 2006b. Structural response of liquid-cooled GFRP slabs subjected to fire. Part II: Thermo-chemical and thermo-mechanical modeling, *Composites,* part A 37: 1296–1308.
Keller, T., Zhou, A., Tracy, C., Hugi, E. & Schnewlin, P. 2005. Experimental study on the concept of liquid cooling for improving fire resistance of FRP structures for construction, *Composites Part A* 36: 1569–1580.
Kodur, V.K.R., Bisby, L.A. & Green, M. 2006. Experimental evaluation of the fire behaviour of insulated fibre-reinforced-polymer-strengthened reinforced concrete columns, *Fire Safety Journal* 41: 547–557.
Mays, G.C. & Hutchinson, A.R. 1992. *Adhesives in civil engineering,* Cambridge University press, UK.
Weber, B. & Kachlakev, D, 2007. High temperature durability of reinforced concrete beams strengthened with carbon fiber-reinforced polymers-an experimental study, *Proc. FRPRCS-8 symposium, Patras, Greece*: 3–28.
Zhou, Y. & Tan, K.H. 2007. Behaviour of FRP strengthened beams subjected to elevated temperatures, *Proceedings of the FRPRCS-8 symposium, Patras, Greece*, 3–29.

Concrete Solutions – Grantham, Mechtcherine & Schneck (eds)
© 2012 Taylor & Francis Group, London, ISBN 978-0-415-61622-5

Strain hardening cement-based composites for repair layers on cracked concrete surfaces

C. Wagner & V. Slowik

Leipzig University of Applied Sciences, Germany

ABSTRACT: Strain Hardening Cement-based Composites (SHCC) have proved to be suitable materials for covering layers on cracked concrete surfaces. Because of the material's high tensile strain capacity such repair layers are capable of bridging considerable crack opening displacements in the substrate. In laboratory experiments, mortar with Polyvinyl Alcohol (PVA) fiber reinforcement served as test material. Experimental results concerning the crack bridging behavior of SHCC repair layers on concrete surfaces are presented. It could be shown that layers with a thickness of about 30 mm can withstand crack opening displacements of up to 0.6 mm in the concrete substrate. The applicability of SHCC repair layers could also be demonstrated in a pilot application.

1 INTRODUCTION

In covering layers on cracked concrete surfaces, crack opening displacements in the substrate may lead to local strain concentrations and, eventually, to the failure of the respective layer. Repair layers made of strain hardening cement-based composites (SHCC), however, have proved to be comparatively resistant to this type of loading. Because of their high deformability, these materials are capable of bridging cracks with comparatively high opening displacements in the substrate.

Strain hardening cement-based materials are characterized by a high tensile strain capacity when compared to conventional cement-based materials. This behavior may be attributed to the formation of numerous closely spaced cracks. During the formation of these cracks, the tensile stress is increasing or at least constant. This so-called strain hardening behavior may be achieved by the addition of about 2% by volume of polyvinyl alcohol (PVA) fibers having a comparatively high modulus of elasticity when compared to other synthetic fibers. The fibers are capable of bridging the cracks. The tensile stress transferred between the crack surfaces will even increase while the crack is opening. As a result, new cracks are formed under increasing total strain. This explains the formation of numerous parallel and closely spaced cracks in such materials. At a certain strain level, damage localization occurs, i.e., one of the cracks continues to open while the other cracks are being closed, and the tensile stress will start to decrease. When this happens, the maximum tensile strain of this particular material is reached. Strain hardening

cement-based composites (SHCC) with PVA fibers may undergo a maximum tensile strain of up to 5%. For the same mortar without PVA fiber reinforcement, the tensile strain at maximum load would amount to about 0.01% only.

Figure 1 shows an example of a tensile stress-strain curve for SHCC. The maximum tensile strain, i.e., the strain at maximum load, amounts to about 2.5%. The maximum and average crack widths are also shown. Because of the high number of individual cracks, their width is comparatively small before damage localization occurs. This fracture behavior results in a very good durability of the material.

In several studies conducted worldwide, the applicability of SHCC as a repair material was tested or the material has already been used in corresponding pilot projects (Rokugo et al., 2005, Kunieda & Rokugo 2006, Wagner et al., 2008).

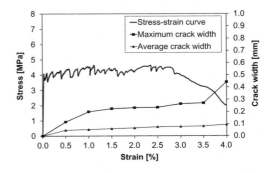

Figure 1. Stress and crack widths versus strain under uniaxial tension.

In addition to the high strain capacity, the cement-based repair layers provide the advantage of being compatible with the concrete substrates from the physical point of view.

The authors' motivation for the present work was to quantify the crack bridging capability of repair layers made of a strain hardening cement-based composite. The mechanical behavior of such repair layers does not only depend on the uniaxial fracture properties of the material but also on the layer thickness and on the interface properties. Because of the complexity of the problem, experimental methods had to be applied. Laboratory investigations were undertaken the results of which will be presented in the following.

Furthermore, the results of a five-year observation of SHCC repair layers applied under site conditions are presented.

2 LABORATORY EXPERIMENTS

2.1 Material

The material optimization was aimed at the highest possible strain capacity on one hand and at a good workability under site conditions on the other hand. In addition, the crack widths had to be small in order to ensure sufficient durability of the material. According to expert opinions published in the literature, a critical permeability with respect to concrete durability is reached when crack widths exceed a threshold value between 50 μm and 100 μm (Wang et al., 1997, Lepech & Li 2009). It is assumed that through wider cracks a larger amount of harmful gases and liquids may penetrate into the material. A review of SHCC design and testing was published by Mechtcherine & Schulze (2005).

Table 1 contains the material composition for the fiber reinforced mortar used in the laboratory experiments. The fiber content was 2.2% by volume. PVA fibers from Kuraray, Japan, with a length of 8 mm and a diameter of 0.04 mm were used.

Table 1. Material composition for laboratory experiments.

Material	Content by mass
Cement CEM I 42.5 R	1.00
Fly ash	2.30
Quartz sand (0 ... 0.5 mm)	0.40
Quartz powder (0 ... 0.1 mm)	1.00
Water	1.10
Superplasticizer	0.04
Stabilizer*	0.015
PVA fibers (length 8 mm)	2.20% by volume

* Woermann underwater compound.

2.2 Uniaxial tension tests

For the determination of the stress-strain curves for the previously specified material, uniaxial (direct) tension tests were carried out. Figure 2 shows the experimental setup for these tests.

Dog-bone shaped specimens with a length of 250 mm and a minimum cross-section of 40 mm × 40 mm were glued between steel platens. The inner part with constant cross-section had a length of 100 mm.

The tests were performed in a comparatively stiff 600 kN loading frame under displacement control. A more detailed description of the experimental setup may be found in Wagner (2007).

2.3 Four-point bending tests of reinforced concrete beams with SHCC repair layer

Steel reinforced beams made of normal concrete were loaded in four-point bending up to a moment larger than the cracking moment. In this way, a cracked concrete surface was created. Then, a SHCC layer was applied to the cracked surface, i.e., to the underside of the respective beam, and the beam was subjected to four-point bending again. During this repeated loading, the preexisting cracks in the reinforced concrete beam were opened and the crack bridging behavior of the SHCC layer could be studied.

Of particular interest was the evolution of the crack widths in the SHCC layer. Multiple cracking

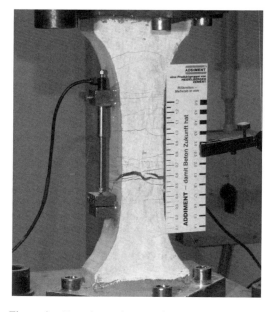

Figure 2. Experimental setup for the direct tension tests.

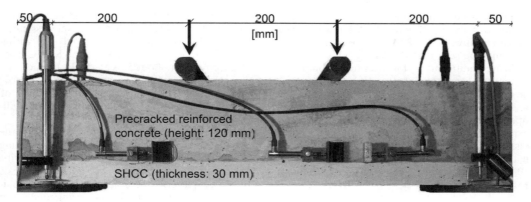

Figure 3. Four-point bending test of a reinforced concrete beam with SHCC repair layer at the bottom side.

and small crack widths in the repair layer would indicate an improved durability with respect to the untreated cracked concrete surface.

It has to be pointed out that the SHCC repair layers investigated here are not intended to strengthen or retrofit concrete members. Because of their comparatively low tensile strength, these materials are not suitable for significantly increasing the load carrying capacity of structures. As stated before, the application of SHCC layers is aimed at the bridging of cracks which results in an improved durability of the concrete structure.

Six reinforced concrete beams with rectangular cross-section were tested. The length of the beams amounted to 700 mm, the width to 150 mm, and the height to 120 mm. In order to obtain large crack widths during the preloading of the uncoated beams, only two reinforcement bars with a diameter of 6 mm and a concrete cover of 30 mm were inserted in the tension zone of each beam. The experimental setup and a reinforced concrete beam with applied SHCC repair layer at the bottom are shown in Figure 3. During the four-point bending tests, the deflection of the respective beam and the opening of three initial cracks resulting from preloading were measured continuously.

2.4 Zero-span elongation tests

An alternative way of investigating the crack bridging effect of SHCC layers are so-called zero-span elongation tests, see Figure 4. They allow the simulation of the opening of a single crack. The specimen consists of two concrete cubes $(70 \times 70 \times 75 \text{ mm}^3)$ placed on top of each other. The joint between the cubes serves as an artificial crack. The end faces of the specimen are glued to rotationally rigid steel platens. By displacing them the artificial crack is opened or closed. In the experiments reported here, on two opposite sides

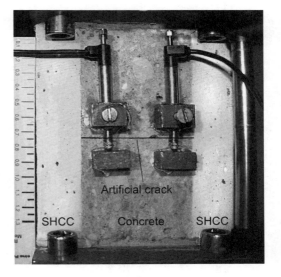

Figure 4. Experimental setup for the zero-span elongation tests.

faces of the cubes a 2.75 cm thick SHCC layer was applied, see Figure 4. The opening of the artificial crack results in stress concentrations and cracking in the repair layer.

Similar investigations have been performed by Kunieda et al. (2004). They were focused on the influence of the bond properties on the crack formation in repair layers.

3 RESULTS AND DISCUSSION

3.1 Strain hardening behavior under uniaxial tension

Figure 5 shows characteristic stress-strain curves as determined in uniaxial tension tests for the material composition specified in Table 1. The first cracks occurred at a stress of about 2.6 MPa, whereas the maximum stress was 2.8 MPa at the average.

It may be seen that the tensile stress does not decrease significantly before a strain of about 2.5% is reached. As stated before, the comparatively large strain capacity is caused by the numerous fine and closely spaced cracks. The individual crack opening displacements were not measured in these experiments. However, since the cracks were barely visible with the unaided eye it is assumed that the majority of the cracks had widths smaller than 40 μm. A characteristic crack pattern is shown in Figure 6.

3.2 Crack bridging behavior of SHCC layers on cracked concrete substrate

3.2.1 Crack bridging layers on precracked reinforced concrete beams

Figure 7 shows the curve of the total force versus load-line displacement for a beam with a 40 mm thick layer of SHCC. Initially, the beam exhibited a comparatively rigid behavior until the first

cracks in the SHCC layer occurred at a load of about 12 kN. Thereafter, the curve was less steep. Crack width measurements revealed that within this phase most of the cracks in the SHCC layer were formed. At about 50 kN, the load reached a plateau. Afterwards, an opening of the previously formed cracks could be observed. The failure of the beam was caused by yielding of the longitudinal reinforcement.

Of particular interest were the crack widths in the SHCC layer and the corresponding crack spacing which may also be expressed by the crack density. Because of the large number of individual cracks, the crack patterns were recorded photographically under monotonically increasing deflection by using an 8.0 megapixel camera (Nikon Coolpix 8800). Preferably, images of the regions underneath the previously formed cracks in the reinforced concrete beam were taken. Figure 8 shows

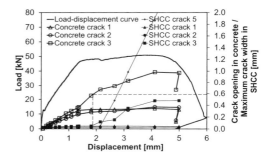

Figure 7. Force-displacement curve of a predamaged and repaired reinforced concrete beam (thickness of the repair layer 40 mm).

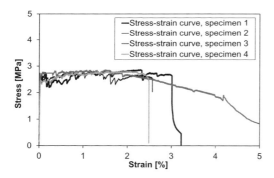

Figure 5. Stress-strain curves measured under uniaxial tension.

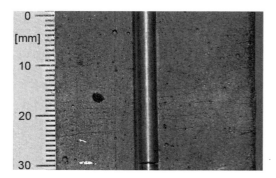

Figure 6. Crack pattern in SHCC under uniaxial tension.

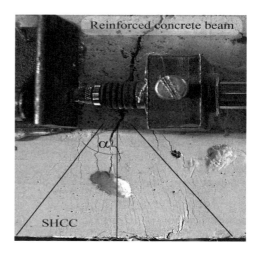

Figure 8. Crack pattern in the SHCC repair layer underneath a crack in the concrete beam.

one of these images. It may be seen that the wide opened crack in the substrate, i.e., in the reinforced concrete beam, did not "break through" the repair layer. The latter is also cracked, but numerous fine cracks were formed rather than a single crack.

The distribution angle α, see Figure 8, which describes the fan-out of the crack amounted to 22° on average.

Figure 7 also shows the crack opening values under increasing load-line displacement. With the help of the load-displacement curve it is possible to assign crack opening values to certain load levels. The label "concrete crack" is used for the initial cracks in the reinforced concrete beam, which existed before the application of the repair layer, and the term "SHCC crack" stands for newly formed cracks within the repair layer underneath the initial concrete crack with the same number. As stated before, the crack pattern in the SHCC repair layer is rather diffuse. For this reason, only the maximum crack width underneath the respective concrete crack is shown in Figure 7.

The crack pattern shown in Figure 8 belongs to concrete crack 3 and the SHCC layer underneath. A comparison of the crack widths reveals the crack bridging effect of the repair layer. While the discrete cracks in the concrete beam were opened continuously, numerous small cracks with widths less than 50 µm were formed in the SHCC.

The described crack bridging effect could be observed up to a crack opening displacement of about 0.6 mm in the reinforced concrete beams, see "concrete crack 3" in Figure 7. At this crack opening in the substrate, a single crack in the repair layer starts to open significantly as a result of damage localization in the SHCC. It could also be observed that with increasing displacement new cracks were formed in the reinforced concrete beams. The described four-point bending tests were performed with repair layers of thickness 3 cm and 4 cm, respectively. No essential differences in the cracking behavior were found.

3.2.2 Results of the zero-span elongation tests

The results of the four-point bending tests could be confirmed by the zero-span elongation tests. It was found that an SHCC layer of thickness 2.75 cm may bridge a crack opening displacement of about 0.6 mm without damage localization. Figure 9 shows for three specimens the average stress in the SHCC at the joint versus the joint opening, i.e., versus the artificial crack opening. The maximum crack widths at the outer faces of the SHCC layer are also shown in Figure 9. It may be seen that these crack widths were small (<100 µm) up to a joint opening of about 0.6 mm. Then, the crack width in the SHCC increased rapidly as a result of damage localization. Hence, the

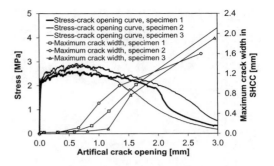

Figure 9. Average stress versus crack opening and maximum crack width in the SHCC layer, results of three zero-span elongation tests.

results of the three-point bending and zero-span elongation tests are in good agreement as far as the crack bridging capability of SHCC repair layers is concerned. The observed crack patterns were also consistent. As seen in the four-point bending tests, the existing discrete crack in the substrate fans out into numerous small cracks in the SHCC layer, see Figure 8.

The small crack widths at the SHCC surface will be advantageous when an additional coating is to be applied, for instance a polymeric coating. The technical requirements for such an additional layer would be less strict as far as its crack bridging capability is concerned. In addition, an improved durability of the repair system is expected.

4 PILOT APPLICATION

4.1 Initial situation and repair measure

The damaged concrete floor of the petrol filling station of a construction company has been chosen for a pilot application of SHCC repair layers. This floor is subjected to high loads due to heavy machinery (trucks, tracked vehicles, forklifts, etc.). Especially the areas near inspection shafts were damaged many times and conventional repair measures failed repeatedly, see Figure 10.

Probably, the damage is caused by both the settlement of the shafts and horizontal displacements due to temperature changes or braking forces. For this particular problem, SHCC was considered to be a suitable repair material. It is characterized by a large strain capacity and able to bridge comparable large crack opening displacements.

Three inspection shafts were repaired, i.e., the upper layer of the concrete floor surrounding these shafts was replaced by SHCC, see Figure 11. For one of the shafts (shaft 3), a polymer-modified cement mortar (PCC) was used as a reference material.

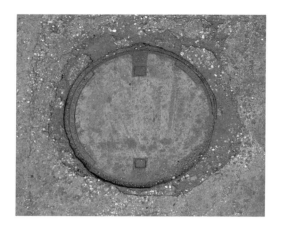

Figure 10. Damaged concrete surface in the vicinity of an inspection shaft prior to the repair measures.

Figure 11. Inspection shafts prepared for the application of the repair material.

In addition to the inspection shafts, another concrete surface had to be repaired, see Figure 12. This 2 m wide and 5 m long area was heavily damaged by wide opened cracks which were not tolerable for the floor of a petrol filling station. The surface has been milled off and, afterwards, a 40 mm thick SHCC layer was applied.

Table 2 contains the material composition for the SHCC used as repair material in the present study. As in the laboratory experiments, PVA fibers from Kuraray, Japan, with a length of 8 mm were used.

4.2 Results of the long-term observation

When comparing the two repair materials, i.e., the SHCC and the PCC, the same course of the crack paths could be observed. In both materials,

Figure 12. Cracked concrete surface prepared for the application of the repair material.

Table 2. Material composition for the pilot application.

Material	Content by mass
Cement CEM I 42.5 R	1.00
Fly ash	2.00
Quartz sand (0 ... 0.5 mm)	0.60
Water	0.90
Superplasticizer	0.02
Stabilizer*	0.002
PVA fibers (length 8 mm)	2.20% by volume

* Methylcellulose

predominantly tangential cracks were formed. Regarding the number of cracks and the crack lengths, however, the crack patterns differ significantly. Whereas in the PCC mortar only a single annular crack with comparatively large width could be found, in the SHCC expectedly numerous cracks with small widths occurred. The radial cracks in the PCC were also found to be wider than those in the SHCC. These differences in the crack pattern clearly point to a better durability of the SHCC repair layer. The resistance to the penetration of harmful substances should be significantly higher.

Currently, i.e., five years after the repair, only the area surrounding shaft 2 and the repaired concrete surface shown in Figure 12 are still existing. The other two shafts were completely replaced in the meantime. Therefore, the observations described in the following were made at the two remaining patches.

Figure 13 shows the surrounding of shaft 2 two days and five years, respectively, after the repair. The closely spaced cracks with small widths are visible with the unaided eye. However, because of their blunted edges they appear wider than the actually are. This could be proved by the inspection of drill cores. Furthermore, no spalling

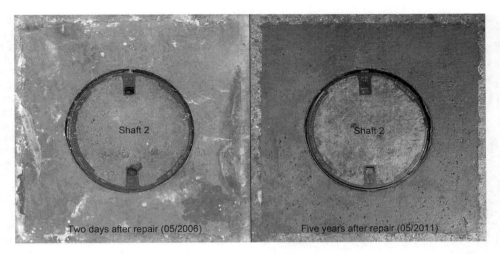

Figure 13. Repaired concrete surface surrounding an inspection shaft two days (left) and five years (right) after the repair.

could be observed at the SHCC surface and the bond to the surrounding concrete seemed to be undamaged. It has to be noted, however, that comparatively large air pores are visible. This may be attributed to imperfect compaction. In future projects, these flaws should be avoided by improving the material composition and the application method.

Prior to the documentation of the crack patterns, the SHCC surfaces were carefully cleaned. During the drying of the surface, the fine cracks became visible. Figure 14 shows the ring-shaped cracks around the shaft. The average crack spacing determined with the unaided eye amounts to 35 mm. This corresponds to a crack density of approximately 29 cracks/m. For the radial cracks, an average crack spacing of 27 mm and a crack density of about 37 cracks/m were observed. This means in total 66 cracks/m².

For the photographic documentation of the crack patterns, a 12 megapixel camera with macro lens was used, see Figure 15. Unfortunately, the blunted edges of the cracks did not allow for an exact crack width determination. In addition, some cracks were completely filled with dust which also hindered the measurement of their widths. Although the cracks could easily be detected in the photographic images, see Figure 16, an exact crack width measurement appeared to be impossible.

A resolution of approximately 12 μm per Pixel could be achieved. This allowed the detection of finer cracks than with the unaided eye. For the ring-shaped cracks, a crack density of 47 cracks/m was determined on the basis of the photographic images.

Figure 14. Crack pattern in the SHCC repair layer surrounding shaft 2 five years after the repair.

Five years after the repair measure, the adhesive bond strength between the SHCC layer and the concrete substrate was determined. In most pull-off tests, the concrete failed, although the average bond strength was only moderate. It amounted to 1.31 N/mm². In addition, drilled cores were taken from the SHCC repair layer. A dry density of 1570 kg/m³ and an average compressive strength of 74.5 N/mm² could be measured (core diameter 50 mm, height approximately 40 mm). The carbonation depth was less than 1 mm, however slightly larger at the edges of the cracks.

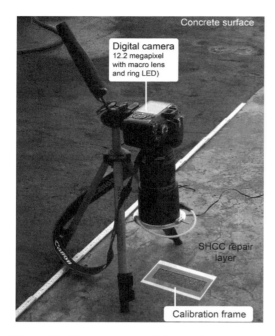

Figure 15. Documentation of the crack pattern in a SHCC repair layer.

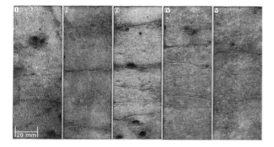

Figure 16. Images of a SHCC surface used for crack detection.

5 CONCLUSIONS

It was possible to produce a cement-based material with a tensile strain capacity of about 2.5%. The fracture behavior of this strain hardening cement-based composite (SHCC) is characterized by multiple cracking and small crack widths. Because of these properties, SHCC is a suitable material for crack bridging repair layers on damaged concrete surfaces.

In order to quantify the crack bridging capability of SHCC repair layers, two types of laboratory experiments were conducted, on one hand four-point bending tests of precracked concrete beams with SHCC layers on the tension face and on the other hand so-called zero-span elongation tests. Similar results were achieved. SHCC repair layers of thickness 3 cm may bridge crack opening displacements of up to 0.6 mm in the substrate. Higher crack opening displacements result in damage localization, stress relieve, and large crack widths at the surface. Below the aforementioned limit, discrete crack opening displacements in the substrate result in numerous fine cracks in the SHCC repair layer. The width of these fine cracks amounts to only about 50 μm. For this reason, the SHCC repair layers may significantly improve the durability of concrete structures.

The applicability of SHCC for patch repair has been proved under site conditions by a pilot application. A five-year observation of the patches has shown that the repair measure was successful.

REFERENCES

Kunieda, M., Kamada, T., Rokugo, K. & Bolander, J.E. 2004. Localized fracture of repair material in patch repair systems. In Li, V.C., Leung, C.K.Y., Willam, K.J. & Billington S.L. (eds.), *Proceedings of FRAMCOS-5, Vail, Colorado, USA*: 765–772.

Kunieda, M. & Rokugo, K. 2006. Recent progress on HPFRCC in Japan. *Journal of Advanced Concrete Technology* 4 (1): 19–33.

Lepech, M. & Li, V.C. 2009. Water permeability of engineered cementitious composites. *Cement & Concrete Composites* 31(10): 744–753.

Mechtcherine, V. & Schulze, J. 2005. Ultra-ductile concrete—material design and testing. In V. Mechtcherine (ed.), *Symposium on Ultra-Ductile Concrete with Short Fibres, Kaiserslautern, Germany*: 11–35.

Rokugo, K., Kunieda, M. & Lim, S.C. 2005. Patching repair with ECC on cracked concrete surface. *Proceedings of ConMat'05, Vancouver, Canada*: 22–24.

Wagner, C. 2007. *Nachverfestigendes zementgebundenes Material für die Sanierung gerissener Betonoberflächen (Strain hardening cement-based material for the restoration of cracked concrete surfaces)*. M.Sc. thesis, Leipzig University of Applied Sciences, Germany (in German).

Wagner, C., Slowik, V. & Waldenburger, K. 2008. Dehnungsverfestigendes zementgebundenes Material für die Sanierung gerissener Betonflächen (Strain hardening cement-based material for the repair of cracked concrete surfaces). *Bautechnik* 85(1): 49–56 (in German).

Wang, K.J., Jansen, D.C., Shah, S.P. & Karr, A.F. 1997. Permeability study of cracked concrete. *Cement and Concrete Research* 27(3): 381–393.

Concrete Solutions – Grantham, Mechtcherine & Schneck (eds)
© *2012 Taylor & Francis Group, London, ISBN 978-0-415-61622-5*

Flexural strengthening of RC-structures by textile reinforced concrete in practical application

S. Weiland
TUDALIT Markenverband e.V., Dresden, Germany

E. Lorenz
Faculty of Civil Engineering, Technische Universität Dresden, Dresden, Germany

Ch. Hankers
TORKRET AG, Essen, Germany

D. Matzdorff
planzwo GmbH, Hamburg, Germany

ABSTRACT: Textile Reinforced Concrete (TRC) represents an excellent alternative to existing techniques for strengthening of existing concrete structures, combining the benefits of lightweight fiber reinforced polymer strengthening with those of shotcrete with reinforcement. Strengthening by textile reinforced concrete noticeably increases both the ultimate load bearing behaviour as well as the serviceability. After very positive results from fundamental research, TRC has already been in use for strengthening rc-structures. Examples of the strengthening of concrete structures and the practical application of this new material are presented.

1 INTRODUCTION

Regarding sustainability, a significant increase in the lifespan of existing buildings is required. In consequence of this an appropriate care and maintenance regime is essential. Compared with new building activities existing structures, therefore, are more and more important.

Besides the adaptation to changing purposes, existing buildings often also show deterioration and even serious damage to the buildings, where measures to repair and reinforce the structures may be needed. Existing reinforced concrete structures have previously been strengthened by classic and established methods, such as shotcrete with reinforcement and glued strips of steel or with composite plastics such as carbon fibre and polyimide. In selecting the most appropriate measure structurally, building technology and economic concerns play a major role. Each method offers different advantages and disadvantages and exclusion criteria, which should be discussed by an experienced engineer.

Textile reinforcement represents an excellent alternative to existing means for strengthening of concrete structures, combining the benefits of lightweight fiber reinforced polymer strengthening with those of shotcrete with reinforcement.

The development of Textile Reinforced Concrete is based on the fundamentals of glass filament reinforced concrete with short filaments. Similar to ordinary reinforced concrete structures the filaments are aligned in the direction of the tensile stresses, which leads to an increase in their effectiveness. The load-carrying capacity increases compared to short filament concrete, (Curbach & Jesse, 2009). The reinforcement of concrete with technical textiles will definitely not replace steel reinforcements, but it extends concrete applications to completely new fields.

Because of the corrosion resistance of the textile materials, thick concrete covers as known in ordinary reinforced concrete are no longer needed. Thus, slender structural members with a wall thickness of 10 mm are possible. In addition, fine grain concrete matrices guarantee an even and sharp-edged high quality surface. A further advantage beyond that of lamellar strengthening methods is the two-dimensional load transfer. Textile reinforcements have mostly plane character but posses the necessary deformability to adapt themselves also to complicated and curved geometry. This was shown by a pedestrian bridge built of textile reinforced concrete, (Curbach et al., 2007). So also complex geometry such as shells, columns etc. can be strengthened by TRC easily.

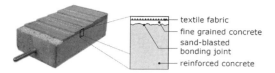

— textile fabric
— fine grained concrete
— sand-blasted
  bonding joint
— reinforced concrete

Figure 1. Textile reinforced concrete on RC-structure.

Low thickness may not only be helpful for new concrete elements, but also makes possible the strengthening of already existing concrete structures. The strengthening by textile reinforced concrete noticeably increases both the ultimate load bearing behaviour as well as the serviceability. The performance and even practical applications will be shown in the paper using experimental results of flexural strengthened slabs.

2 STRENGTHENING BY TEXTILE REINFORCED CONCRETE

Textile reinforcement represents an excellent alternative to existing techniques for strengthening of concrete structures, combining the benefits of lightweight fiber reinforced polymer strengthening with those of shotcrete with reinforcement. The combination of textile reinforcement and concrete results in a composite material with prime qualities—high tensile strength; minimal layer thickness; low weight; high corrosion resistance; and additional corrosion protection for existing concrete reinforcement.

The TRC-layers are applied by spraying or laminating. Before strengthening can be applied, the surface of the RC-member must be prepared, for example, by sandblasting. The surface must be rough enough so as to ensure a sufficient bond will form between the existing concrete and the strengthening layer (Ortlepp et al., 2006). The TRC-strengthening is then accomplished by applying alternating layers of fine-grained concrete and textile reinforcement to existing RC-members. This TRC-strengthening is suitable for nearly every acting force. Curbach et al. (2007) have shown that it is possible to strengthen for bending, shearing, torsion or axial forces. In all cases of textile reinforcement the following criteria must be taken into account:

- the load carrying capacity,
- the criterion of the minimum reinforcement,
- elastic/plastic ultimate mode (yielding of steel reinforcement),
- the necessary anchorage of the textile reinforced concrete layer.

The effectiveness of textile reinforced fine-grained concrete for general strengthening of concrete structures was proven by Curbach et al. within the context of investigations done by the Collaborative Research Centre 528 at the Technsiche Universität Dresden. Influential variables on the load-carrying capacity, as well as force transmission mechanisms into the reinforced layer, were characterised and described. Ongoing research projects deal with bond characteristics of textile reinforcements to the matrix (Lorenz & Ortlepp, 2009). Even for the case of fire loading on TRC-strengthened slabs Ehlig et al. (2010) achieved good results.

Jesse & Curbach (2009) give an excellent overview at the current state of knowledge on TRC-strengthening of concrete structures.

3 EXPERIMENTAL INVESTIGATION ON FLEXURAL STRENGTHENING

Using the example of flexural strengthening of the experimental investigation of rc-slabs the load bearing behaviour and the capability of the TRC-strengthening layer can be demonstrated.

3.1 Materials, specimen and test setup

A normal C20/25 concrete with a maximum aggregate size of 16 mm was used for the reference slab. The reinforcement consisted of 4 steel bars (BSt 500S) with an 8 mm diameter. The strengthening layer was comprised of several layers of different textile fabric, see Table 1, and a fine-grained mineral concrete matrix with maximum aggregate size of 1 mm.

The properties of reinforced concrete slabs with textile reinforcement for flexural strengthening were investigated in a static four-point-bending-test in order to avoid shear force influences within the range of the maximum bending moment, see Figure 2. The dimensioning and materials of the specimens were selected so as to be representative for the moment of support of a class of usual slabs of old multi-storey office buildings. The specimens had a length of 1800 mm, width of 600 mm and a thickness of 100 mm. The effective span between the supports was up to 1600 mm. Steel reinforcement ratio of the rc-slab-specimen was 0.34%.

The specimens were cyclically loaded on an incremental basis until failure (e.g., of the textile reinforcement in the tensile zone) in a displacement-controlled test. The load applied was measured by a load cell. Deflections at several points, as well as strain in the tensile zone, were observed in various locations using LVDT. The strain in the compression zone was measured by strain gauges. Additionally, the steel strain was taken with a strain gauge located on one of the reinforcing bars. The results were compared with non-strengthened reference slabs.

Table 1. Textile reinforcements for flexural strengthening.

	AR-Glass	Toho Tenax Carbon (12k)	SGL Carbon (50k)
	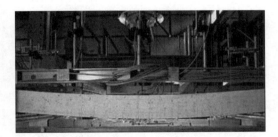		
Identifier	NMW3-004-04-p	NWM3-049-06-p2	NWM3-001-08-b1
Warp thread	AR-glass, 2400 tex	Carbon, 800 tex	Carbon, 3500 tex
Weft thread	AR-glass, 2400 tex	Carbon, 800 tex	Carbon, 3500 tex
Clearance warp/weft	10,8 mm/10,8 mm	10,8 mm/18,0 mm	10,8 mm/18,0 mm
Pattern /stitch length	full tricot/3,6 mm	full tricot/3,5 mm	full tricot/2,0 mm
Gramage	290 g/m²	149 g/m²	609 g/m²

Figure 2. TRC-strengthened slab in 4-point-bending-test.

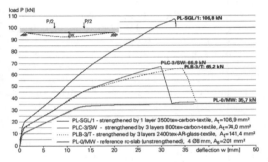

Figure 3. Test results for comparison of various textile reinforcements for flexural strengthening of RC-slabs.

3.2 *Experimental results*

The load-displacement-diagram in Figure 3 shows the typical behavior of reinforced concrete in states I (non-cracked), II (multiple cracking) and III (yielding of steel reinforcement) for all slabs, but the increase in the curves is diverse. In comparison to the non-strengthened slabs, the load-displacement-curve of the strengthened slab rises much more sharply and the first crack appears at a higher load. The reason for this is the larger moment of inertia than in the original, non-cracked state which results from the additional applied strengthening layer of reinforced concrete. A steeper rise of the curve, caused by the load carrying properties of the TRC-layer, after multiple cracking has already occurred can be observed. After yielding of steel reinforcement only the TRC-layer is responsible for bearing the additional loads until its bearing capacity will be reached. Rupture of the textile reinforcement in the bending tensile zone was the typical failure observed in all tests. Each test was aborted after rupture occurred, and therefore the force-displacement-line of the test specimen returned to the same level as that of the un-strengthened reference specimen. At this level

the steel reinforcement continued to yield, maintaining the ability to support loads in the same amount as the un-strengthened specimen until subsequent rupture of the steel or failure within the compression zone. The achieved ultimate load of the strengthened structure was almost four times higher than of the unstrengthened one. The bending capacity was only limited by other failure modes (e.g. shear) which the specimen had not been designed for. In comparison with the AR-Glass, the higher ductility and strength of carbon grids results in a higher ultimate load and better load bearing behaviour of the flexural strengthened slab.

The textile reinforcement improves both the load carrying capacity and also the properties of serviceability. The displacement of the strengthened slabs, related to the service load, is smaller than the displacement shown by the reference slab. This is caused by the fine crack pattern in the strengthening layer and the lower ultimate strain of the textile. Weiland (2010) gives more results of the experimental investigation and a detailed analysis of the bearing behaviour.

4 TRC IN PRACTICAL APPLICATIONS

With the excellent results of basic research and partners in the construction industry TRC-strengthening has already been applied in pilot projects on real structures. Due to the fact that the textile reinforced concrete is not a standardized building material, special approval and investigations by building authorities are necessary in each case. The following technically and economically successful practical applications demonstrate the capabilities.

The first practical application of the innovative strengthening method using textile reinforced concrete was carried out in October/November 2006 in the retrofit of a reinforced-concrete roof hypar-shell structure in Schweinfurt, Germany, (Weiland et al., 2007). To achieve the required increase in load bearing capacity 3 layers of carbon-textile NWM3-049-06-p2 were laid in fine grain concrete. The total thickness of the concrete layer was 15 mm, see Figure 4.

Another example was the alteration of the Engineering School Zwickau into an IRS Office Building in 2008. A more than one-hundred-year-old reinforced concrete roof construction was strengthened with TRC, see Schladitz et al. (2009).

The latest TRC-strengthening applications in an office building in Prague 2009/2010 and a production facility in Koblenz 2010 have shown the technical and economic potential. Especially with the pre-configured fine-grained concrete Pagel TF-10 the application was much easier and faster.

According to an investigation on large deformations of the slabs of the production facility in Koblenz 4–5 cm²/m of the necessary static steel reinforcement were missing in two areas of the slab. In order to ensure the structural safety under all loading conditions, structural strengthening was necessary. But due to the fact that the building was still in use any interruption of the production process by the building activity had to be avoided and the disturbance should be as the least possible.

The strengthening proposal recommended the use of TRC as the best solution with minimal effect on the production process. Within one week only and with minimal restrictions of the production process the missing static reinforcement was added by 3 layers 50k-Carbon-Textil, see cross-section in Figure 5. The TRC-strengthening was easily applied overhead, see Figure 6. Moreover the appearance of the slab and the dead load were almost not affected, see Figure 7.

The planning was executed by Planzwo GmbH in cooperation with the TUDAG and the

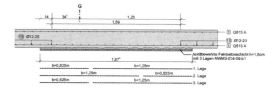

Figure 5. Cross section with TRC-strengthening-layer.

Figure 6. Overhead-application of TRC-strengthening-layer in the tensile zone of a rc-slab.

Figure 4. Thickness (15 mm) of TRC-strengthening layer on the hypar-shell in Schweinfurt.

Figure 7. Finished TRC-strengthening (20 mm thickness) during concrete curing and clearing of the construction site.

Technische Universität Dresden. The design and proof of structural safety of TRC-strengthening layer for the needed single case approval (ZiE) was based on experimental investigations. Moreover a special quality control concept was established as well as the manufacturing of on-site-specimens to ensure that the design values were reached. To assess the tensile behaviour of the composite textile reinforced concrete, special uniaxial tensile tests were performed.

5 SUMMARY

The results presented here show that Textile Reinforced Concrete (TRC) represents an excellent alternative to existing techniques for strengthening of concrete structures, combining the benefits of lightweight fiber reinforced polymer strengthening with those of shotcrete with reinforcement. With the mineral composite system the method is distinguished by its largely weather-independent and time-saving construction in the practical application and is therefore also from the economic point of view an excellent innovation, which will compete with common means of strengthening.

Remaining issues on design rules and interaction between reinforcing steel and textile reinforcement, especially the lack of official building regulations and technical approvals, are currently the largest barriers and obstacles for the practical application of Textile Reinforced Concrete (TRC).

These commitments include definitions and quality rules of the textile fabrics to be used as reinforcements, the concrete used, design rules and clear implementation rules for the strengthening system. Therefore, by early 2009, the TUDALIT® brand association was founded. In order to continue the development of textile reinforced concrete for reinforcement and repair parallel to the basic research, strongly supported by the German Research Foundation, a community over the whole value chain was gathered. Members of universities and even competitors of the industry cooperate to establish textile reinforced concrete in the building industry. The TUDALIT® brand association is currently working on a General technical approval for a method of strengthening rc-structures by TRC as an essential step on the way to practical application in the building industry. In the future the planners and contractors will be given a set of rules on which they can rely for textile reinforcements and design of the strengthening layer. Without the current required single case approvals in each individual case, practical application of textile reinforced concrete will become more efficient.

REFERENCES

Brückner, A.; Ortlepp, R.; Curbach, M. 2006. Textile Reinforced Concrete for Strengthening in Bending and Shear. In: *Materials and Structures* 39 (2006) 8, 741–748—doi: 10.1617/s11527-005-9027-2.

Curbach, M.; Graf, W.; Jesse, D.; Sickert, J.-U.; Weiland, S. 2007. Segmentbrücke aus textilbewehrtem Beton—Konstruktion, Fertigung, numerische Berechnung. In: *Beton- und Stahlbetonbau* 102 (2007) 6, 342–352—doi:10.1002/best.200700550.

Curbach, M.; Jesse, F. 2009. Eigenschaften und Anwendung von Textilbeton. In: *Beton- und Stahlbetonbau* 104 (2009) 1, 9–16—doi:10.1002/best.200800653.

Ehlig, D.; Jesse, F.; Curbach, M. 2010. RC Slabs with Textile Reinforced Concrete (TRC) Strengthening Under Fire Loading. *3rd International fib Congress, Washington, D.C., May 29 – June 2 2010*. Paper 307—DVD-Rom.

Jesse, F.; Curbach, M. 2009. Verstärken mit Textilbeton. In: Bergmeister, K.; Fingerloos, F.; Wörner J.-D. (Hrsg.): *Beton-Kalender 2010*. Berlin: Ernst & Sohn, 2009, 457–565.

Lorenz, E.; Ortlepp, R. 2009. Basic research on the anchorage of textile reinforcement in cementitious matrix. In: *9th International Symposium on Fiber-Reinforced Polymer Reinforcement for Concrete Structures (FRPRCS-9), Sydney, 13.–15.07.2009*. Book of Abstracts—ISBN 978-0-9806755-0-4.

Ortlepp, R.; Hampel, U.; Curbach, M. 2006. A new Approach for Evaluating Bond Capacity of TRC Strengthening. In: *Cement and Concrete Composites* 28 (2006) 7, 589–597—doi:10.1016/j.cemconcomp.2006.05.003.

Ortlepp, R.; Lorenz, A.; Curbach, M. 2009. Column Strengthening with TRC: Influences of the Column Geometry onto the Confinement Effect. In: *Advances in Materials Science and Engineering* 2009, Article ID 493097, 5 pp.—doi:10.1155/2009/493097.

Schladitz, F.; Curbach, M. 2008. Increase in the torsional resistance of reinforced concrete members using Textile Reinforced Concrete (TRC). In: *2nd International Conference on Concrete Repair, Rehabilitation and Retrofitting (ICCRRR), Cape Town, 24.-26.11.2008*. — Book of Abstracts pp. 391–392 and CD-ROM— ISBN 978-0-415-46850-3.

Schladitz, F.; Lorenz, E.; Jesse, F.; Curbach, M. 2009. Strengthening of a Barrel-Shaped Roof using Textile Reinforced Concrete. In: *33rd Symposium of the International Association for Bridge and Structural Engineering (IABSE), Bangkok, 9.-11.09.2009.*—Book of Abstracts, pp. 416–417 and CD-ROM—ISBN 978-3-85748-121-5.

Weiland, S. 2010. *Interaktion von Betonstahl und textiler Bewehrung bei der Biegeverstärkung mit textilbewehrtem Beton*. Dissertation, Dresden: Technische Universität Dresden, Fakultät Bauingenieurwesen, 2010, 207 S.—urn:nbn:de:bsz:14-qucosa-37944.

Weiland, S.; Ortlepp, R.; Hauptenbuchner, B.; Curbach, M. 2008. Textile Reinforced Concrete for Flexural Strengthening of RC-Structures—Part 2: Application on a Concrete Shell. In: Aldea, C.-M. (edt.): *Design & Applications of Textile-Reinforced Concrete. Proceedings of the ACI Fall Convention, Puerto Rico, 2007*. SP-251CD—3, 2008.

Concrete Solutions – Grantham, Mechtcherine & Schneck (eds)
© 2012 Taylor & Francis Group, London, ISBN 978-0-415-61622-5

Restoring the bearing capacity of circular tunnel linings with the help of high-strength carbon fibre mesh

A.A. Shilin, V. Gaponov, E.Z. Axelrod & S.S. Zalomov
ZAO "Triada-Holding", Moscow, Russia

ABSTRACT: This paper considers a new approach to repair and reconstruction of circular-shaped reinforced concrete tunnel linings based on reinforcing them with high-strength carbon fibre mesh embedded into a mineral matrix.

The core of the suggested technology is to supplement repair and waterproofing works with structural strengthening by creating a thin-wall inner shell composed of a carbon fibre mesh and a mineral matrix with high adhesion. The advantages and drawbacks of the mentioned technology are analyzed backed-up by the results of large-scale practical testing.

In conclusion the author estimates the efficiency of the proposed technology which has a good potential in terms of further development and application.

1 INTRODUCTION

The main criterion in structural state assessment of any underground structure as well as of its elements is deterioration, i.e. loss of their initial performance due to various factors.

When considering various options for restoration of tunnel lining bearing capacity, it must be noted that traditional steel reinforcement gives way gradually to up-to-date non-metal materials immune to corrosion, such as polymers reinforced with high-strength fibres. In the case of steel reinforcement, corrosion products expand thus leading to cracking of concrete with subsequent spalling of concrete cover, accelerated corrosion processes and—as a result—loss of structural bearing capacity due to the loss of bond between concrete and reinforcement as well as decrease of bar cross-section.

In the case of repair works if substitution or strengthening of steel reinforcement is used, corrosion can start again and the structure will need to be repaired within quite a short period of time (10–15 years).

During the last 30 years the market has been penetrated by so-called composite materials which have a number of advantages. They are light-weight (4–5 times lighter than steel); their tensile strength 4–5 times exceeds that of steel; they are insensitive to corrosion. The physical and technical data of such products are determined by the type and amount of fibres used, their direction and location with regard to the cross-section of the strengthened element. Polymers provide strain distribu-

tion between fibres and also protects them from any kind of exposure. Carbon Fibre Reinforced Polymers (CFRP) suit the purpose of concrete and reinforced concrete structures strengthening best of all. Reinforcing elements can be produced in various shapes: rods, meshes, sheets, and special prefabricated elements.

Beside the mentioned advantages there are certain limitations in the use of FRP products due to the properties of resins used as a system component:

- low thermal resistance (e.g. fire resistance): when temperatures are too high resins become fluid, the bond between the reinforcing element and the structure is lost and the system is no longer effective;
- cannot be applied on moist surfaces as moisture prevents resin polymerization;
- restricted temperature range (+10 ÷ +30 °C): when temperatures are lower than +10 °C resin cures too slow; temperatures higher than +30 °C make resin pot life too short;
- cured resin does not allow the structure to "breathe", which imposes restrictions on the size of structural area for gluing reinforcing elements.

The above mentioned considerations gave the authors the idea to investigate the possibility of substituting a polymer matrix for a matrix based on a hydraulic binder. Our investigations resulted in developing a strengthening system in which a high-strength fibre mesh is embedded into a mineral-based matrix. This matrix is property-wise compatible with cement substrates and after curing transfers loads into the mesh strands, thus securing the joint work of the whole system. Besides the fire-proof properties of the system become comparable to the similar properties of structural material; the matrix can be applied on a wet substrate allowing its surface to breathe; temperature range tolerances increase substantially.

We developed the procedure of strengthening circular reinforced concrete tunnel linings by way of creating a thin shell inside the tunnel formed by a carbon-fibre mesh and a matrix made of polymer-modified cement.

Depending on the required degree of strengthening, the shell might incorporate up to several layers of high-strength carbon-fibre mesh. Its general layout as well as work sequence is given in Figure 1.

We start with surface preparation (high-pressure water cleaning). Then a priming coat is applied to provide good bond between the matrix and the substrate.

On top of the priming coat a special mineral-based repair mortar with high adhesive properties is applied (layer thickness 5–10 mm). After this we lay a pre-treated mesh wound in a roll 1 m wide starting from the bottom of the tunnel along the inner surface of the lining ring and pressing it into the matrix. After 1 hour (required for matrix curing) the second layer of matrix is applied (layer thickness 15–20 mm) with the subsequent

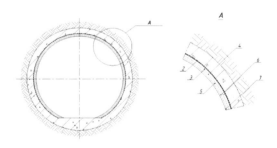

1. High-pressure water cleaning.

2. Application of priming layer.

3. Mineral-based matrix.

4. High-strength carbon-fiber mesh.

5. Second layer of matrix mortar.

6. Second layer of mesh.

7. Final layer of acrylic-based repair mortar.

Figure 1. General layout of circular tunnel lining strengthening.

laying of the second layer of carbon-fibre mesh. A finishing layer of the repair mortar is applied in an hour's time. The number of layers is defined with regard to the required bearing capacity of the structure.

Due to the fact that loads applied to tunnel linings along and across the axis of the tunnel differ, strains in the mesh taking up these loads are non-uniform. Our measurements show that the bending longitudinal forces are substantially higher than the compressive forces acting in the transverse direction. Based on this we can assume that the total area of mesh strands across the tunnel axis should by a minimum 1.5 times exceed the total area of the strands going in the direction of the tunnel axis.

2 TESTING

To determine optimum parameters of strengthening materials (both carbon-fibre mesh and mineral-based matrix) we carried out an extended study programme which comprised several stages.

2.1 Comparative testing

Comparative testing of high-strength carbon-fibre meshes produced by various manufacturers was carried out to select the type which suits the application best of all.

Testing was carried out as required by Russian national standards (GOST 25.601-80, 1987). The testing procedure implies a short-term tensile loading of a sample with a constant speed of load application. Testing was performed both for meshes with fibre strands embedded into an epoxy matrix (Fig. 2a) and for single strands with no matrix at all (Fig. 2b). For uniform distribution of testing load, additional pieces of fabric cloth were glued to the sample edges to allow them to be fixed in the testing machine grips. Tensile strength value taken per 1 m of mesh width was chosen as the criterion for comparison.

Samples consisting of 1, 3, and 5 strands were tested. The end value was taken as an average of 4 measured values.

The machine used for testing had a constant pre-set loading speed and an accuracy of <1% of the measured value (Fig. 2).

The results showed that for meshes from Germany and China the values stated in their technical data sheets and those tested were absolutely comparable, 15 t/m and 19 t/m, respectively The analysis of the test results showed that in meshes not embedded in an epoxy matrix strands work non-uniformly; this significantly influences

a)

b)

Figure 2. Testing of mesh samples: a) German mesh in an epoxy matrix, b) Chinese mesh with no matrix.

the choice of the number of mesh layers in the would-be shell as well as the future performance parameters of the whole system. Another important criterion was the price/quality ratio. Based on the test results combined with marketing researches we chose meshes of Chinese manufacture which we used afterwards for our large-scale testing. Table 1 shows the technical data of these meshes.

2.2 Development of the mineral matrix for strengthening tunnel linings

Part of our research was devoted to formulating a matrix with certain required properties, such as good bond to concrete; viscosity (suitable for mesh embedment); mechanical properties.

As a result we could formulate a mineral-based mortar with acrylic additives with the following properties: minimum bond to concrete 3 MPa compression strength 40 MPa. Depending on the consistency the mortar can be applied either by spray equipment or by hand.

Table 1. Technical data for meshes.

Property	Value
E-Modulus	>100 GPa
Tensile strength	>3 GPa
Surface density	570 g/m^2
Specific thickness	0.18 mm
Mesh cell size	13×21 mm

2.3 Testing of tunnel lining samples after strengthening

To be able to estimate the effectiveness of the strengthening shell, depending on its thickness and amount of reinforcement, for increasing the bearing capacity of the lining, we tested samples with and without the strengthening system (Fig. 1). Samples were taken from cast in-situ concrete linings with the following dimensions: outer diameter 500 and 2200 mm; wall thickness 500 and 2200 mm; length 270 and 600 mm respectively.

Samples Ø 500 mm were cut from a centrifuged non-pressure pipe reinforced by spiral reinforcement of Bp–1 grade, Ø 5 mm.

Standard manhole rings with low reinforcement amount were used as samples Ø 2200 mm (Fig. 3). Shells for samples Ø 500 mm incorporated 1 layer of carbon-fibre mesh. Mineral-based matrix mortar was applied by hand. Compression testing of a ring after reinforcement is shown in Figure 4.

The results of comparative testing of reinforced and non-reinforced samples are shown in Figure 5.

The maximum testing load for non-reinforced samples was 18 kN whereas for samples reinforced with a 1-layer shell the value amounted to 47 kN. The reinforcement factor was 2.45. It should be noted that after the peak value was reached the loading value went slowly down while the deformation increased thus eliminating the probability of brittle structural failure.

For samples Ø 2200 mm the following application procedure was introduced. First a layer of matrix mortar was wet-sprayed on the inner surface of each sample; then the high-strength carbon-fibre mesh was embedded into the matrix and finally another mortar layer was applied on top of it. To measure structural deformations strain gauges were glued both on the inner and outer surfaces of the samples in spots where maximum/minimum strain values were expected. Test results are given in Table 2.

Analysis of test results allows us to state that the load-bearing capacity of the reinforced lining samples became approximately 4 times higher. Structural deformations and strains are shown in Figures 6 and 7, respectively. For example, samples with a single mesh layer can resist the load of 3.60 t; double-layer reinforced samples are capable to withstand loads up to 3.82 t.

Mesh-reinforced samples which cracked during the first application of compressive load showed quite good results when loaded again, up to 93% of the initially applied load. It means that reinforced concrete linings with such kind of strengthening have a fairly high safety margin

a) Ring sample Ø 500 mm in a testing machine,

b) sample reinforced with 1 layer of mesh after testing.

Figure 3.   Test set-up for rings Ø 2200 mm.

Figure 4.   Testing of rings Ø 500 mm.

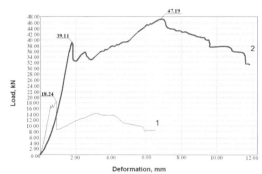

1 - non-reinforced sample

2 - sample Ø 500 mm with a reinforcing shell

Figure 5.   Relationship between loading force and structural deformation in samples.

Table 2.   Test results for circular samples Ø 2200 mm.

No	Sample	Max load t	Fracture mode	Max. load 2nd loading, t	Reinforcement factor
1	Non-reinforced	0.85	Brittle	–	–
2	Single layer of reinforcement	3.6	Gradual	3.54	3.85
3	Double layer of reinforcement	3.82	Gradual	3.01	4.09

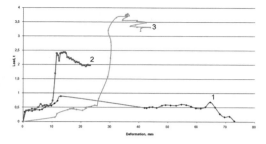

1 - Initial Sample
2 - sample strengthened with a single layer of carbon-fibre mesh
3 - sample strengthened with a double layer of carbon-fibre mesh

Figure 6. Relationship between a transverse deformation and vertical loading of reinforced and non-reinforced samples.

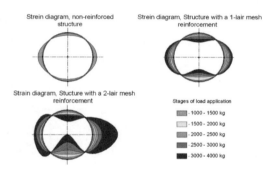

Figure 7. Strain diagrams for samples Ø 2200 mm obtained in the course of testing.

with regard to dynamic loading typical for transport tunnels.

3 CONCLUSIONS

The authors propose procedures for restoring the bearing capacity of circular reinforced concrete tunnel linings by way of creating a strengthening shell incorporating high-strength carbon-fibre mesh and mineral-based matrix.

- Carbon-fibre meshes should have the following properties:
  – E-Modulus—minimum 100 GPa;
  – breaking strength—minimum 3 GPa;
  – surface density—500–600 g/m^2.
- The mineral-based matrix after curing should meet the following requirements:
  – compressive strength—minimum 40 MPa;
  – bending strength—minimum 7 MPa;
  – tensile strength—minimum 4 MPa;
  – bond to concrete—minimum 3 MPa.
- When testing non-reinforced samples we registered brittle failure with an abrupt increase of deformation. Samples strengthened with a carbon-fibre mesh in a mineral-based matrix fail with a gradual deformation increase. No disintegration of fibre strands was noted. Such type of failure gives evidence of a higher safety margin of linings reinforced with a composite system. This is vitally important when we consider safe operation of underground facilities. Obviously, the second mesh layer increases the safety degree even further.
- The average reinforcement factor in case of a single-layer mesh reinforcement embedded into a mineral-based matrix for samples Ø 2200 mm was estimated as 3.79. A second layer of mesh adds to the structure the ability to resist loads only 30% higher as compared to a single-layer reinforcement. This can be explained by a comparatively low distance between mesh layers.
- If the reinforced samples do not fail completely at the first stage of testing, when loaded again they can withstand up to 93% of initial load, which confirms their high safety margin when subject to dynamic loading typical for transport tunnels.

Thus we can say that the proposed technique opens up vast possibilities for strengthening of underground structures, especially of those that cannot be accessed from the outside. However it needs to be extensively tested in field conditions to optimize material parameters, working sequence, time and labour expenses.

REFERENCES

GOST 25.601-80, 1987. *Strength Testing. Methods of Mechanical Testing of Composite Materials with Polymer Matrix. Tensile testing of Flat Samples at Normal, High, and Low Temperatures.* Russian Construction Committee, Moscow.
SNiP 32-02-2003, 2004. *Underground Tunnels.* Russian Construction Committee, Moscow.
SNiP 52-01-2003, 2004. *Concrete and Reinforced Concrete Structures*, Russian Construction Committee, Moscow.
Sapronov O., 2006. *Basic Principles and Estimation Procedure of Intervals between Repairs in Utility Tunnels*, Thesis, Dr. of Tech. Sciences, Moscow.
Shilin A., et al. 2007. *External Strengthening of Reinforced Concrete Structures with Composite Materials*, Moscow: Stroyizdat.

Concrete Solutions – Grantham, Mechtcherine & Schneck (eds)
© 2012 Taylor & Francis Group, London, ISBN 978-0-415-61622-5

UHPFRC composition optimization for application in rehabilitation of RC structures

Marijan Skazlić
Materials Department, Faculty of Civil Engineering, University of Zagreb, Croatia

Karla Ille
Laboratory for Materials, Institut IGH, Zagreb, Croatia

Mario Ille
Department for Rehabilitation, Institut IGH, Zagreb, Croatia

ABSTRACT: The aim of concrete rehabilitation is to prolong the useful service life of an existing structure and/or to restore its load-bearing capacity. Ultra High Performance Fiber Reinforced Concrete (UHPFRC) has a high durability in extreme environments and excellent mechanical properties; therefore it is suitable for use in rehabilitation of reinforced concrete (RC) structures. UHPFRC should be applied only in those zones where it is necessary (zones with extreme environmental loadings). This paper presents investigation work on the UHPFRC mechanical and durability properties, which are important for rehabilitation of deteriorated concrete structures. In addition, some testing of concrete model elements strengthened with UHPFRC in the tension zone is presented. Based on the investigation laboratory work, a program of site application of UHPFRC for rehabilitation of deteriorated concrete columns subjected to splashes from the adjacent road is presented. Results from this study suggested that there exists a great potential for application of UHPFRC for rehabilitation of deteriorated concrete structures especially in extremely aggressive environments.

1 INTRODUCTION

The aim of concrete rehabilitation is to prolong the useful service life of an existing structure and/ or to restore its load-bearing capacity. Highway bridges and overpasses are constantly subjected to the most severe exposure classes (chloride induced corrosion: XD2—direct contact, or XD3 splash zone) (Fig. 1). (Samaris 2006).

For that reason many bridge parts and whole bridges are losing their serviceability after only

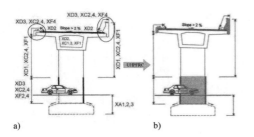

Figure 1. Exposure classes in highway structures and zones of most severe exposure (a); general concept of application of UHPFRC (b) (Samaris 2006).

20–30 years of service, which is a lot sooner than the expected design service life of 100–120 years. (Radić & Tkalčić 2006).

Today known products and systems for the protection and repair of reinforced concrete structures can only ensure protection for 10 to 20 years, and after that new repair must be done which is a heavy burden for society. In order to manage structures effectively and to reduce this burden to the minimum, the number and extent of interventions should be kept to the lowest possible level.

Over the last 10 years, considerable efforts to improve the deformational behaviour of cementitious materials by incorporating fibres have led to the emergence of Ultra-High Performance Fibre Reinforced Concretes (UHPFRC) characterized by a very low water/binder ratio and high fibre content. These new building materials provide the structural engineer with a unique combination of:

1. excellent rheological properties in a fresh state,
2. extremely low permeability,
3. high strength and tensile strain hardening in the range of the yield strain of construction steel (up to 0.2%). (Samaris 2006).

The extremely low permeability of UHPFRC associated with their outstanding mechanical properties makes them especially suitable to locally "harden" reinforced concrete structures in critical zones subjected to an aggressive environment and to significant mechanical stresses. Composite UHPFRC-concrete structures promise a long-term durability which helps to avoid multiple interventions on structures during their service life. (Samaris 2006).

2 MATERIAL SELECTION AND SUITABILITY OF UHPFRC FOR REHABILITATION

2.1 Material selection

Efficient construction rehabilitation depends mostly on proper material selection, therefore great attention must be dedicated to these phases during rehabilitation planning. During the selection of material for rehabilitation of reinforced concrete structure numerous factors must be respected that the selected material must satisfy (ability to approach structure, chloride and chemical ingress, material availability, ecological restriction ...).

The first step in this process is the definition of goals and project demands regarded the cause of damage, owner demand, usage and application conditions. The second step is the definition of requirements for material properties. Finally, the selected material must satisfy the required properties. (Radić et al., 2008).

2.2 Suitability of UHPFRC for rehabilitation

A well established principle for the application of a rehabilitation layer on an existing substrate is to try as far as possible to select a new material with mechanical properties close to those of the substrate. With this respect, UHPFRC with a high elastic modulus up to 55000 MPa might appear to be a bad choice. This argument is however wrong for several reasons:

1. In the elastic domain, the difference in elastic modulus of the UHPFRC with respect to normal concretes (on average 50000/35000 MPa) is largely compensated by the improved tensile strength of the UHPFRC (10 MPa for the matrix and up to 14 for the composite compared to 3 to 4 MPa for normal concretes).
2. UHPFRC exhibits a significant strain hardening, several times larger than its maximum elastic elongation, which is not the case for normal concrete.
3. UHPFRC exhibits significant viscoelasticity at an early age, comparable to high performance

concretes, (Habel 2004). Restrained shrinkage tests on UHPFRC specimens at an early age show that the development of stresses under full restraint remain moderate (45% of the tensile first crack strength) with respect to the uniaxial tensile characteristics of the UHPFRC tested, (Kamen et al., 2005).

The ultimate shrinkage of UHPFRC is not higher than that of usual concretes (in the range of 600 μm/m = 0.6 ‰ at 6 month). The driving force for this shrinkage is however different. In UHPFRC, with a very low water/binder ratio, drying shrinkage is negligible after 8 days of moist curing. The main source of deformations in UHPFRC is autogenous shrinkage, instead of drying processes in usual concretes. (Samaris 2006).

Strain hardening UHPFRC turns out to be an excellent compromise of density, high tensile strength and significant deformation capability, perfectly suited for combination with normal concretes, in existing or new structures.

2.3 Mechanical compatibility of UHPFRC and substrate

The successful rehabilitation of existing structures is a major challenge for civil engineers. When an existing concrete needs to be replaced, a new composite structure formed of the new material cast on the existing substrate will result from the intervention (Fig. 2).

Both the protective function and the mechanical performance of the composite system have to be guaranteed over the planned service life. More or less pronounced tensile characteristic stresses due to restrained shrinkage deformations at early age and long term are induced in a new layer applied on an existing one, (Bernard 2000). These characteristic stresses constitute a net loss of the performance in terms of potential tensile capacity. On the other hand, restrained shrinkage almost never

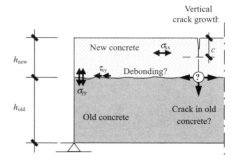

Figure 2. Composite cross-section and appearance of stresses between new layer of concrete and old concrete (Bernard 2000).

occurs under full restraint in structures. Both the deformability of the structure and the creep of the materials (new and substrate) contribute to a significant decrease of the induced stresses. It is thus very important to investigate the "mechanical compatibility" of a new material in terms of structural consequences: characteristic stresses compared to the tensile strength, and the evolution of these two parameters as a function of time.

A simple parameter that summarizes this interaction of material and structural properties is the so-called degree of restraint. Stresses due to restrained movements can principally be computed as the product of three factors according to the following equation:

Stress = stiffness × free strain × degree of restraint

Consequently, all three factors are equally important. The stiffness is dependent on the modulus of elasticity but also on creep or relaxation. The free strain is the strain that a completely free member would develop due to thermal or moisture changes, shrinkage, or any other internal or external source causing the volumetric change of the member material. The degree of restraint μ defines the conditions of restraint as the ratio between the actual stress σ_{real} taking into consideration the effective stiffness of the composite structure and the stress σ_{full} that would occur in a totally restrained composite structure.

The degree of restraint can be calculated for any structure from its geometrical characteristics and elastic material properties (modulus of elasticity). Simplified diagrams are available for simple geometries such as composite slabs with constant height. (Samaris 2006).

3 REHABILITATION TECHNOLOGY

The conventional approach to the repair of a corroding reinforced concrete structure comprises essentially the following operations: removing the deteriorated concrete up to 50 mm behind the affected bars; cleaning the bars and provision of additional reinforcement in cases where corrosion has significantly reduced the load bearing capacity of the bars; coating the exposed steel with cementitious or resin based materials; reinstatement of the concrete with repair mortar and adding supplemental cover as needed; finally, applications of coatings to the structure both for reasons and as a means of enhancing resistance to future ingress of water and aggressive agents. (Kenshel & O'Connor 2006).

As mentioned, products and systems for the protection and repair of reinforced concrete structures known today can only ensure protection

for 10–20 years. The basic conceptual idea is to use UHPFRC only in those zones of the structure where the outstanding UHPFRC properties in terms of durability and strength are fully exploited; i.e., UHPFRC is used to "harden" the zones where the structure is exposed to severe environmental and high mechanical loading. All other parts of the structure remain in conventional structural concrete as these parts are subjected to relatively moderate exposure. This concept (which is also applicable to new construction) necessarily leads to composite structural elements combining conventional reinforced concrete and UHPFRC.

The combination of the protective and load carrying properties with the mechanical performance of reinforcement bars provides a simple and efficient way of increasing the stiffness and load carrying capacity with compact cross sections. (Brühwiler & Denarié 2008).

For the example of UHPFRC layers applied on bridge deck slabs, the following geometries of application can be proposed, (Habel 2004) (Fig. 3):

1. Cross section (P) with a thin UHPFRC layer is designed for protection purposes. The tensile reinforcement in the existing concrete is situated near the interface between the two concretes. Such cross-sections are obtained when the tensile reinforcement of the existing RC structure (As, ct) is not or is only slightly deteriorated and the load carrying capacity is sufficient.
2. Cross section (PR) represents the case when additional tensile reinforcement is placed into the UHPFRC layer to replace and/or to complement the existing strongly deteriorated rebars. This configuration provides both an improved protection function and an increase in load carrying capacity.
3. Cross section (R) is designed primarily to increase significantly the load carrying resistance of the structural element. The cross-section consists of the original reinforced concrete section which is complemented by the reinforced UHPFRC layer which can be seen as an externally bonded additional reinforcement. Also, the UHPFRC provides the protection function for the structural element which is beneficial to durability of the element.

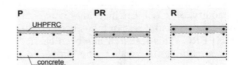

Figure 3. Basic configurations for composite structural elements combining UHPFRC and conventional structural concrete (Habel 2004).

The relatively high cost of these materials imposes using them only where they are "worth their money" and take the maximum benefit of their outstanding mechanical properties.

4 PROPERTIES OF UHPFRC

4.1 General properties

Increasing demands for construction of new, modern buildings and repair of deteriorated construction in the last few decades led to invention, development and application of new concrete types, such as ultra high performance fiber reinforced concrete (UHPFRC). (Nawy 2001).

UHPFRC, beside having ultra high compressive strength, also has improved tensile strength, stiffness and durability properties when compared to ordinary concretes. In comparison to ordinary concretes, UHPFRC is much more homogenous and less porous. Strength and other properties of UHPFRC grow with the higher number of contacts among particles, thus reducing porosity and defects within the structure. Considering that UHPFRC contains high quantity of binder, the size of maximum aggregate grain size should also be reduced. Reduction of porosity is achieved by using a low water/binder (w/b) ratio, adding superplasticizer (providing sufficient workability in a fresh state), and replacing a portion of cement with pozzolanic additives. (Skazlić 2003).

The reduction in water/binder ratio and the use of mineral additives have a positive effect on the improvement in the interface between cement matrix and aggregates as the weakest link in the concrete structure. The most efficient admixture to cement is silica fume. Because of its very small grains (about 10 times smaller than a cement grain) and large specific area, silica fume has a positive effect on the increase in density of the area surrounding cement particles and, because of higher reactivity, on accelerated hydration. Furthermore, silica fume reacts with free lime—the poorest component of cement—thereby making CSH gel. (Skazlić, 2003).

4.2 Tested properties of UHPFRC in fresh and hardened state

In the laboratory of the Materials Department at the Faculty of Civil Engineering, University of Zagreb, experimental research has been conducted on UHPFRC. This research has been carried out by investigating, in parallel, the properties and technology of concrete. The aim of the research was to get a new type of concrete that exhibits improved mechanical and durability properties in relation to other concrete types. At the same time,

they also needed to fulfill the condition that the obtained concrete types can be prepared at existing concrete production plants.

UHPFRC mix can be made with water-binder ratio of 0.16 to 0.25 and maximum aggregate grain size can be from 0.5 mm up to 2 mm. The UHP-FRC mix can contain 700–1200 kg/m^3 cement and addition of up to 15% of micro silica or metakaolin by cement mass. The reinforcement of this ultra compact matrix is provided by a mix of micro and macro steel fibers (2–13 mm in length). The amount of superplasticizer must be sufficient to ensure good workability in the fresh state for casting UHPFRC in molds or formwork (Fig. 4). It is important to emphasize that the UHPFRC material can be produced and placed with standard engineering tools.

After 28 days of water curing, mechanical and durability properties were tested. Values of numerous test results are presented in Table 1. (Skazlić & Bjegović 2005).

Figure 4. UHPFRC samples being prepared for flexural strength test.

Table 1. Test results for mechanical and durability properties of UHPFRC.

Item no.	Property	UHPFRC test results
1	Compressive strength HRN EN 12390-3	130 – 200 MPa
2	Flexural strength HRN EN 196-1	30 – 60 MPa
3	Static modulus of elasticity HRN U.M1.025	35000 – 50000 MPa
4	Coefficient of gas permeability EN 993-4	1.3×10^{-18} m^2
5	Coefficient of capillary water absorption HRN U.M8.300	$0.02 – 005$ kg $\cdot$ m^{-2} $\cdot$ h$^{-0,5}$
6	Diffusion of chloride ions NT BUILD 492	$< 0.5 \times 10^{-12}$ m^2/s

Figure 5 presents the fractured surface of UHPFRC with pull-out steel fibers after testing flexural strength.

5 PERFORMANCE REQUIREMENTS FOR STRUCTURAL REPAIR PRODUCTS

Before the application of material on a rehabilitated structure, initial performance tests on the repair products must be done. Test fields on structures with repair product must be done as well. Repair products must satisfy the requirements presented in Table 2 according to EN 1504-3. The presented UHPFRC characteristics are the results of numerous tests performed in the laboratory of the Department of Materials at the Faculty of Civil Engineering, University of Zagreb. UHPFRC characteristics that have not yet been tested according to standards required in specification standard HRN EN 1504-3, are marked with*. These characteristics will be tested within the experimental program presented in subparagraph 6 of this paper.

Specified requirements for structural mortar R4 are primarily based on the mechanical characteristics of mortar and bond strength between mortar and deteriorated substrate. Structural mortar R4 doesn't have sufficient durability properties to stop or even to minimize further deterioration of reinforced concrete structure caused by aggressive substances (i.e., chloride ions). A capillary absorption of less than $0.5 \, \text{kg} \cdot \text{m}^{-2} \cdot \text{h}^{-0.5}$ cannot prevent penetration of chloride ions in reinforced concrete structures.

Therefore it is not possible to use structural mortar R4 in rehabilitation as a single product. Application of a final coating or coating system on repair mortar will provide the required durability for a reinforced concrete structure. But final coating or coating system performances are decreasing in time with regard to environment conditions and their durability is approximately 10 years. After the exploitation period of 10 years, reparation of the final coating or coating system is necessary.

Figure 5. Fractured surface of UHPFRC with pull-out steel fibers.

Table 2. Performance requirements for structural repair mortar and comparison with UHPFRC properties.

Item no.	Performance characteristic	Requirement for structural mortar R4	UHPFRC
1	Compressive strength	≥ 45 MPa	> 130 MPa
2	Chloride ion content	≤ 0.05%	≤ 0.05%*
3	Adhesive bond	≥ 2.0 MPa	≥ 2.0 MPa*
4	Restrained shrinkage/expansion	Bond strength after test ≥ 2.0 MPa	Bond strength after test ≥ 2.0 MPa*
5	Carbonation resistance	d_k ≤ control concrete (MC(0,45))	–
6	Elasticity modulus	≥ 20 GPa	≥ 35 GPa
7	Thermal compatibility after freeze/thaw cycles	Bond strength after 50 cycles ≥ 2.0 MPa	Bond strength after 50 cycles ≥ 2.0 MPa*
8	Thermal compatibility after thunder shower	Bond strength after 30 cycles ≥ 2.0 MPa	Bond strength after 30 cycles ≥ 2.0 MPa*
9	Thermal compatibility after dry cycles	Bond strength after 30 cycles ≥ 2.0 MPa	Bond strength after 30 cycles ≥ 2.0 MPa*
10	Skid resistance	Class I: 40 units wet tested Class II: 40 units dry tested Class III: 55 units wet tested	
11	Coefficient of thermal expansion	Not required if tests 7, 8 or 9 are carried out, otherwise declared value	
12	Capillary absorption	≤ 0,5 kg·m^{-2}·h$^{-0,5}$	< 0,02 kg·m^{-2}·h$^{-0,5}$

UHPFRC has a capillary absorption of less than 0.02 kg·m⁻²·h⁻⁰·⁵, and together with its excellent mechanical properties, the material can provide long-term durability of reinforced concrete structures. Capillary absorption of UHPFRC is 25 times smaller than conventional repair mortar. The durability properties of UHPFRC are permanent in time, therefore interventions on reinforced concrete structures are minimized.

6 EXPERIMENTAL PROGRAM

After the collection of data on the mechanical and durability properties of UHPFRC, a program for research was made. The aim of this research was to evaluate the behaviour of concrete beams reinforced with UHPFRC in the tension zone under flexural stress.

Reference beams and beams used as a substrate were made with concrete class C25/30., and the tension zone was reinforced with UHPFRC. At the age of 24 h beams, were demoulded and part of the concrete cross-section was crushed and removed in order to prepare the surface before placing UHPFRC (Fig. 6). Specimens were then water cured for 28 days.

At 28 days of age, the surface of the specimens was coated with emulsion in order to have better adhesion between the base concrete beam and the repair material. The specimen was then placed back in the mould in which HPFRMC was poured (Fig. 7).

The reinforcing procedure of the concrete beams was performed in three different ways (Fig. 8):

A. The cross section of the concrete beam dimensions 120 × 150 mm was reinforced in the tensile zone with a 30 × 150 mm layer of UHPFRC,
B. The cross section of the concrete beam dimensions 90 × 150 mm was reinforced in the tensile zone with a 60 × 150 mm layer of UHPFRC,

Figure 6.   Removing part of the concrete cross section.

Figure 7.   Specimens prepared for applying UHPFRC.

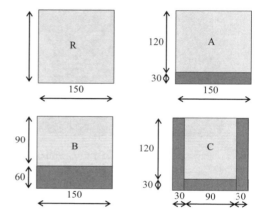

Figure 8.   Cross section of specimens.

C. The cross section of the concrete beam dimensions 120 × 90 mm was reinforced on the sides and in the tensile zone with a 30 mm thick layer of UHPFRC.

In order to evaluate the efficiency of the repair procedure and material, the bending behaviour of the specimens was tested. Testing was performed according to standard ASTM C 1609, with strain rate 0.05 mm/min up to the displacement of 4 mm.

The results of testing bending behaviour of specimens with different repair procedures are shown in Figure 9. In the diagrams shown in Figure 9, the area below the load versus displacement curve represents the ability of the specimen to absorb the energy produced during loading.

The presented results show that concrete beams that were reinforced with a 60 mm thick layer of UHPFRC had the highest tensile strength and the best behaviour under flexural loading. It can be concluded that this modus of reinforcing is the optimal one.

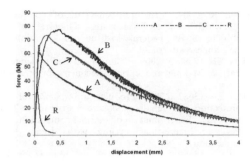

Figure 9. The results of flexural loading test of concretes at 28 days.

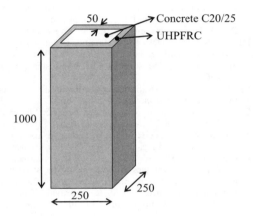

Figure 10. Cross section of column model.

After testing the mechanical and durability properties of the UHPFRC material, and its behaviour as reinforcement in the flexural zone, a new research program was done. The relatively high cost of UHPFRC imposes usage only where they are "worth their money" and take the maximum benefit of their outstanding durability and mechanical properties. On bridges, the most exposed tension elements are columns subjected to splashes from road. The aim of this research is to evaluate the durability of composite elements (ordinary concrete + UHPFRC) subjected to different durability and mechanical loading.

For this research a model of a repaired column will be made, dimensions 250 × 250 × 1000 mm. The substrate column will be made of concrete class C20/25. After 28 days of moist curing, concrete cover will be removed by hydrojetting and a 50 mm layer of UHPFRC will be placed on the outer side of the column (Fig. 10).

After placing a UHPFRC layer on the concrete substrate, two regimes of curing will be applied on column models:

1. water curing conditions: (20 ± 2)°C and > 95% r.h.
2. laboratory conditions: (20 ± 2)°C and (60 ± 10)% r.h.

By the end of the curing period the column models will be tested to determine the following mechanical and durability properties:

- mechanical properties:

  1. compressive strength of composite model according to HRN EN 12390-3,
  2. modulus of elasticity of composite model ISO 6784,
  3. bond strength between substrate concrete and UHPFRC layer according to HRN EN 1542,
  4. bond strength between the substrate concrete and the UHPFRC layer after compressive cycling load according to HRN EN 1542.
  5. shrinkage of reference concrete, UHPFRC and composite model according to ASTM C 341.

- durability properties:

  1. thermal compatibility after freeze/thaw cycles according to HRN EN 13687-1,
  2. thermal compatibility after thunder shower according to HRN EN 13687-2,
  3. thermal compatibility after dry cycles according to HRN EN 13687-3.

The durability properties of the composite column modeled are based on bond strength after different types of thermal stresses. UHPFRC is resistant to thermal stresses, but there remains a question what is happening at the connection of these two different materials. Compatibility between two materials is the most important property for quality rehabilitation.

By the end of the laboratory testing, on site application is planned. During reconstruction of a bridge on the Croatian highway test field, UHPFRC will be applied on central columns between road lanes. UHPFRC will be produced on site and poured into formwork with conventional concreting tools. To estimate the quality of on site made UHPFRC material and its application in the test field, bond strength will also be tested. Also, cores will be taken for laboratory testing of compressive strength and coefficient of capillary absorption.

7 CONCLUSION

The aim of concrete rehabilitation is to prolong the useful service life of an existing structure and/or to restore its load-bearing capacity.

Today known products and systems for the protection and repair of reinforced concrete structures can only ensure protection for 10–20 years, and after that new repair must be done which is a heavy burden for society. In order to manage structures effectively and to reduce this burden to the minimum, the number and extent of interventions should be kept to the lowest possible level.

Ultra High Performance Fiber Reinforced Concrete (UHPFRC) has a high durability in extreme environments and excellent mechanical properties; therefore it has a great potential for use in rehabilitation of reinforced concrete (RC) structures. The relatively high cost of UHPFRC imposes usage only where they are "worth their money" and takes the maximum benefit of their outstanding durability and mechanical properties.

The aim of this research is to determine mechanical compatibility between substrate (rehabilitated concrete) and UHPFRC as a material for rehabilitation. The behavior of composite elements (ordinary concrete + UHPFRC) subjected to different durability and mechanical loading will be tested.

An investigation program for rehabilitation of deteriorated concrete columns with UHPFRC subjected to splashes from roads is presented. The results of this study will provide a better knowledge of the mechanical compatibility of the ordinary concrete substructure and UHPFRC layer.

ACKNOWLEDGEMENTS

The test results presented above are a result of research projects (Modern methods of engineering materials testing, 082-0822161-2996, Project Leader Marijan Skazlić, PhD, Associate Professor) supported by the Ministry of Science, Education and Sports of the Republic of Croatia.

REFERENCES

ASTM C 341 2006. Standard Practice for Length Change of Cast, Drilled, or Sawed Specimens of Hydraulic-Cement Mortar and Concrete.

Bernard, O. 2000. Comportement à long terme des éléments de structure formés de bétons d'âges différents, Doctoral Thesis, No. 2283, Swiss Federal Institute of Technology (EPFL), Lausanne, Switzerland, (in French).

Brühwiler, E. & Denarié, E. 2008. Rehabilitation of concrete structures using Ultra-High Performance Fibre Reinforced Concrete, The Second International Symposium on Ultra High Performance Concrete, Kassel, Germany.

Habel, K. 2004. Structural behaviour of composite "UHPFRC-concrete" elements, Doctoral thesis n°3036, Swiss Federal Institute of Technology, Lausanne, Switzerland.

HRN EN 12390-3, 2009. Testing hardened concrete—Part 2: Making and curing specimens for strength tests.

HRN EN 13687-1 2002. Products and systems for the protection and repair of concrete structures—Test methods—Determination of thermal compatibility—Part 1: Freeze-thaw cycling with deicing salt immersion.

HRN EN 13687-2 2002. Products and systems for the protection and repair of concrete structures—Test methods—Determination of thermal compatibility—Part 2: Thunder-shower cycling (thermal shock).

HRN EN 13687-3 2002. Products and systems for the protection and repair of concrete structures—Test methods—Determination of thermal compatibility—Part 3: Thermal cycling without de-icing salt impact.

HRN EN 1542 2001. Products and systems for the protection and repair of concrete structures—Test methods—Measurement of bond strength by pull-off.

ISO 6784 1982. Determination of static modulus of elasticity in compression.

Kamen, A., Denarié, E. & Brühhiler, E. 2005. Mechanical Behaviour of Ultra High Performance Fibre Reinforced Concretes (UHPFRC) at early age, and under restraint, Proceedings Concreep 7, Nantes, France.

Kenshel, O.M. & O'Connor, A.J. 2006. Investigating rehabilitation strategies for concrete bridge structures in aggressive environments, Proceedings of the International Conference on Bridges, Dubrovnik, Croatia.

Nawy, E. 2001. Fundamentals of high-performance concrete. 2nd Edition, New York: John Wiley & Sons Inc.

Radić, J. & Tkalčić, D. 2006. Durability and service life of concrete bridges, Proceedings of the International Conference on Bridges, Dubrovnik, Croatia.

Radić, J. et al. 2008. Concrete structures rehabilitation—handbook.

Samaris D25b 2006. Sustainable and Advanced Materials for Road InfraStructure, WP 14: HPFRCC (High Performance Fiber reinforced Cementitious Composites) for rehabilitation, Guidelines for the use of UHPFRC for rehabilitation of concrete highway structures.

Skazlić, M. 2003. High performance hybrid fibre reinforcedconcrete. Master's Thesis, Zagreb: Faculty of Civil Engineering, University of Zagreb (in Croatian).

Skazlić, M. & Bjegović, D. 2005. Perspectives of Designing with New Concrete Types, Annual 2005 of the Croatian Academy of Enginering. 2.

Skazlić, M., Bjegović, D. & Serdar, M. 2008. Utilization of high performance fiber-reinforced micro-concrete as a repair material, Proceedings of the International Conference Concrete Repair, Rehabilitation and Retrofitting II, Cape Town, South Africa.

Surface protection methods and materials

Concrete Solutions – Grantham, Mechtcherine & Schneck (eds)
© 2012 Taylor & Francis Group, London, ISBN 978-0-415-61622-5

Quality control of hydrophobic coatings with an integrated marker element by Laser-Induced Breakdown Spectroscopy (LIBS)

K. Bienert, H. Schalk & A. Molkenthin
Specht, Kalleja und Partner GmbH, Berlin, Germany

G. Wilsch, S. Goldschmidt & E. Niederleithinger
BAM—Federal Institute for Materials Research and Testing, Berlin, Germany

ABSTRACT: Reinforced concrete structures are affected by damage, caused e.g., by freeze-thaw effects or corrosion. Most damage processes are triggered by moisture transport including soluble substances. Hydrophobic coatings can be used for prevention of such damage, but quantitative on-site quality assurance methods are so far missing. A way to overcome this problem is to integrate marker substances into the coating, which can be detected by spectroscopic methods. Different types of marker elements have been tested. It can be shown that transition metals are best suited for the task. Currently a LIBS (Laser Induces Breakdown Spectroscopy) system is developed for the measurement of penetration depth and content of the hydrophobic coating via the marker element in the peripheral zone of concrete.

1 INTRODUCTION

1.1 *Objective*

The cement paste between the aggregates in concrete is responsible for many important properties, such as strength, chemical resistance, porosity and permeability. Penetrating water with dissolved ions may cause damage. These processes are time dependent and of physical (freeze/thaw) or chemical (chloride induced corrosion) nature.

De-icing salts, which have been intensively used in the last decades, cause pitting corrosion on reinforcement due to penetration of chloride ions. Weathering as result of poor freeze-thaw resistance leads to damage of structures and calls for extensive reconstruction, or resurfacing much earlier than originally expected. For example the reconstruction of a concrete bridge pillar costs up to 150.000 €. An increasing number of reinforced concrete structures, mainly in transportation infrastructure, are affected by such damage.

To avoid damage resulting from penetrating moisture, protective systems are required. Hydrophobic coatings are obtained by applying a composition containing a water soluble organopolysiloxane or silane to the substrate. These hydrophobic agents are colourless and non film-forming. They soak in the pore-system in the near-surface region up to a few millimetres depth to achieve an effective prevention.

In spite of some verification methods for the evaluation of such protection areas, there is a lack of practicable methods for the determination of the efficiency and depth of penetration of these coatings. A broad application and a general acceptance are hampered by the nonexistence of a reproducible procedure for on-line and on-site quality assurance.

Nowadays this is normally done by taking a core and chemical analysis in a laboratory, which is time and cost consuming.

1.2 *State of the art—detection*

Hydrophobic coatings of cement based materials have been in the scope of extensive investigations in the last decade (Gerdes 2001). These results have led to a better understanding of the constitutive chemical processes and enabled the development of new concepts for the preventative protection of new and existing buildings. For the generation of a hydrophobic coating organo-silicon compounds are applied to the concrete surface, such as silanes. The silanes move into the near-surface concrete by capillary suction. During the transport, complex chemical reactions occur between the water-insoluble silanes and the water film on the surface. As a result ethanol and silanol are composed.

The activity of the chemical reaction is mainly influenced by the structure of the silane used (e.g., type of alkyl group and alkoxy group) as well as by the material properties of the concrete, e.g., porosity, moisture content, type of cement, contaminations, pH-value, etc.

With these parameters, the penetration depth and the concentration of the hydrophobic agent and thus the efficiency and durability of the coating are determined. Currently, the penetration depth of the hydrophobic coating is simply determined by taking cores 1–2 weeks after application. They are split vertically and then sprayed with an aqueous dye solution. The part which is affected by the hydrophobic coating is identified by its dark colour. The amount of coating substance can not be determined this way.

A procedure developed at the Federal Highway Research Institute (Bundesanstalt für Straßenwesen) measures the electrical resistance of the concrete near-surface region using a particular arrangement of electrodes (Hörner et al., 2002). Some days after application of the hydrophobic agent the surface is moistened and the electrical resistance is measured. If the hydrophobic coating is functional, the near-surface region remains dry and the resistance is high. If the coating is non-functional, moisture will penetrate into the concrete and the measured resistance is low. This way the effectiveness of the coating is qualitatively assessed, but the penetration depth, which is essential for the durability, cannot be determined.

For the determination of the penetration depth of the hydrophobic agent, two analytical procedures, fourier transform infrared (FTIR) spectroscopy and pyrolysis gas chromatography (GC), are used. For these procedures cores have to be taken ca. 10–14 days after application of the hydrophobic agent. Afterwards the cores are routed in fine steps (milimeter range) and the incoming drill dust has to be collected. After drying, the powder must be prepared with the KBr-method (FTIR-spectroscopy) or pyrolysed under air exclusion (pyrolysis-GC).

Using FTIR-spectroscopy the CH_2/CH_3-band in the measured spectrum gives, after calibration, quantitative values for the agent concentration in correlation to the distance from the sample surface.

With pyrolysis-GC the decomposition products of the hydrophobic agent at the end of the chemical reactivity (polysiloxan) will by identified and quantitatively estimated. Subsequently an ingress profile can be established (Herrmann 1997).

Both methods provide quantitative ingress profiles for the hydrophobic agent, but they are time and labour consuming. Also the results are obtained with a certain time delay.

The application is protected by a pending patent of the company Degussa AG (Hühls 1995).

1.3 Innovation

A combination of laser ablation and a spectroscopic detection method, the Laser Induced Breakdown Spectroscopy (LIBS), has the potential to overcome the limitations of the existing methods. LIBS is able to measure the penetration depth of the hydrophobic agent and to give quantitative values for content of the agent in the near-surface region. LIBS can be potentially used on-site and may deliver realtime results.

The elemental contrast of an aqueous soluble organopolysiloxane on concrete is low and thus difficult to detect (Wilsch et al., 2001, Goldschmidt 2007). Therefore a marker element which is easy to detect by LIBS and which is normally not a component of building materials, has to be integrated in the hydrophobic agent. The limit of detection (LOD) of the marker element for LIBS should be low to minimize the required quantity of the marker. To get quantitative values of the amount of applied hydrophobic agent a calibration function is necessary.

A validated LIBS system will detect the marker integrated in the hydrophobic agent and gives quantitative values for penetration depth and content of hydrophobic coating. The LIBS system will be developed into a mobile version, which will allow on-site measurements. The results will be obtained promptly. As LIBS needs direct access to the concrete to be investigated up to a depth of 15 mm, a special method of surface preparation will be developed, which is much less intrusive than coring.

An implementation of a mobile LIBS system for on-site quality control will improve the acceptance and the application of hydrophobic coatings on buildings. With successful application and effective quality control it is possible to avoid or delay extensive reconstruction, because damage occurs significantly later or can even be prevented.

2 IMPLEMENTATION

2.1 Hydrophobic agent

Aqueous soluble organopolysiloxane or silane are used as hydrophobic agents. These are compounds from the elements silicon, carbon, hydrogen and oxygen. The building material to protect is a heterogeneous material containing two phases: the cement paste and the aggregates. Cement paste is a mixture of water, cement, pozzolan, if any and air, which surrounds the aggregates in concrete. It is hardened due to hydration and contains silicon, carbon, hydrogen and oxygen in comparable concentrations.

A typical penetration depth of a hydrophobic agent is in the order of 6 mm to more than 10 mm.

2.2 Marker

Previous experiments have shown that the element contrast between concrete and the hydrophobic agent is low (Wilsch et al., 2001). An addition of a marker just by mixing has shown to be not effective due to chromatography effects (Goldschmidt 2007). The requirements for the marker are as follows:

- The marker element should not be present by nature in cements or aggregates.
- The chemical properties and functional capability of the hydrophobic agent must not change.
- The properties of the concrete (e.g., compression strength, serviceability) must not change.
- Time independent and high detection sensitivity by LIBS is required.
- The amount to be added should be minimised.
- The marker has to be chemically bonded to the hydrophobic agent to avoid chromatography effects.
- No complication in the production of the hydrophobic agent and no derogation in storage stability should occur.

The integration of the marker into the hydrophobic agent will be done in parallel to the development of the detection system and is not in the scope of this paper.

2.3 LIBS

Laser induced breakdown spectroscopy (LIBS) is an analytical tool which allows the quantitative measurement of element distributions on surfaces. Information about ingress of substances is gained by specific methods of surface preparation and the results are obtained directly after the measurement. The spatial resolution is in the millimeter range. All chemical elements are detectable by LIBS, but the limit of detection (LOD) depends on the element and the matrix: the LOD for LIBS is between some ppm and some tenths of a percent. The distance between consecutive measurements is in the sub millimetre scale.

At BAM, a laboratory setup is available. It is shown in Figure 1. A short laser pulse (ca. 10 ns) with energies in the range of 100 mJ to 400 mJ is focussed on the surface under investigation. Due to the high energy density in the focal point, plasma is formed. The plasma radiation provides information about the type and amount of a specific element in the evaporated mass. A translation stage is used to move the specimen in a plane perpendicular to the laser beam. To remove dust and enhance the signals, the volume around the plasma may be purged.

LIBS can be applied without extensive preparation directly on an optically accessible surface. A typical LIBS measurement covers only some tenth of a millimetre (see Figure 2). For the determination of depth profiles cores have to be taken. These cores are split in the cross section. The obtained depth resolution is one millimetre.

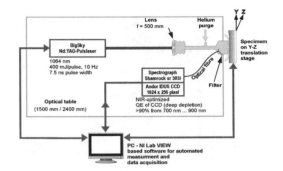

Figure 1. Typical LIBS setup.

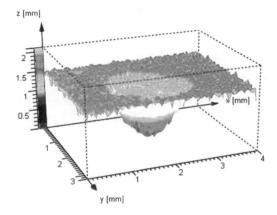

Figure 2. Ablation crater measured with confocal laser scanning microscope after 100 pulses on hardened cement paste (CEM III/A).

Practical examples for the application of LIBS for the investigation of building materials are the determination of the ingress profile of chloride, sulfate or alkali metals (Wilsch et al., 2005, Molkenthin 2008, Weritz et al., 2009).

For the detection of hydrophobic coatings with LIBS initially the necessary parameters, measuring sequences and calibration procedures are determined by the lab setup.

At a later stage, a mobile setup will be developed to be used on-site. The principle is shown in Figure 3. A pan-tilt-unit is used for surface scanning, ransport in a van should be possible and maximum setup time will be about 15 minutes.

To avoid coring, a special surface preparation method will be developed, which allows the determination of ingress profiles up to a depth of 15 mm with minimal effect of the surface.

A Labview (National Instruments) based software will control the measurement and deliver the depth profile in less than 5 minutes.

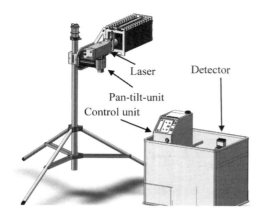

Figure 3. Schematic of mobile LIBS set-up under development.

Table 1. Overview of Markers (M), sample preparation methods (SPM), cement type used, and detection results.

SPM	M 1	M 2	M 3	M 4	M 5
a.	CEM III +	CEM III +	CEM III +	CEM III /	–
b.	CEM II / CEM I +	CEM II / CEM I +	CEM II +	CEM II /	CEM I +
c.	CEM I +	CEM I +	–	–	CEM I +

– = not applied; / = Marker not appropriate; + = Marker successfully detected

3 EXPERIMENTS

3.1 Marker—selection of elements

Due to the ongoing development, the selected elements cannot be listed at the current stage. In the following they are referenced as Marker 1 (M1)—Marker 5 (M5). The elements can be classified as follows:

3 Transition metals (M1, M2, M5)
1 Halogen (M4)
1 Alkali metal (M3).

The selection was made on the basis of the criteria listed in chapter 2.2.

3.2 Sample preparation types

The sample preparation has been carried out in three different ways:

a. Application of an aqueous solution including the marker to the surface of mortar specimen.
b. Cement and a well defined amount of marker (as powder) pressed to pellets.
c. Hardened cement paste—marker added as dissolved salt in water.

3.2.1 Surface application on mortar specimen (method a)

To find appropriate spectral lines for the selected marker elements, which are detectable by LIBS measurements, mortar samples were prepared. The surface of these specimens (made from CEM III, sand and water) was moistened by aqueous solutions of chemical compounds (salts) of the marker. Nitrate compounds were used because almost all inorganic nitrate salts are soluble in water at standard temperature and pressure. Different amounts of the salts were dissolved in deionized water to achieve concentrations of 10, 5, 1, 0.5 and 0.1%.

The results obtained on the moistened surface were compared with results on an unaffected surface.

3.2.2 Pellets (method b)

For the determination of the limit of detection (LOD) for the marker elements, pellets were pressed. The pellets were made by mixing dried cement (CEM II) and a milled amount of marker as the nitrate compound. The mixture was mixed for 5 minutes. Afterwards the mixture was pressed for 10 seconds with 5 tons and another 30 seconds with 10 tons using a mechanical press. The following concentrations were used: 1, 0.5, 0.1, 0.05, and 0.01%.

Because of the hygroscopic properties of the nitrates the obtained results were not satisfactory. Therefore oxides or carbonates were used as an alternative for the preparation of the pellets. Concentrations and preparation procedures were the same as described above, but CEM I was used.

3.2.3 Hardened cement paste (method c)

To investigate the behaviour of the marker in a more complex specimen, samples were produced from cement (CEM I) using water with dissolved marker. This was done for marker 1 and marker 2 by adding the respective nitrates to the water. Two series of samples with water/cement ratios 0.4 and 0.45 were made. After hydration the samples were stored for 28 days under a constant climate of 20° Celsius and 65% relative humidity. The following concentrations were used: 1, 0.5, 0.1, 0.05, and 0.01%.

3.2.4 Pellets—second generation (method d)

After obtaining good results for the pressed pellets made with the transition metal markers a second generation of pellets was produced using CEM I.

The added amounts of the marker were lower and had a finer gradation. The following concentrations were used: 1, 0.5, 0.4, 0.2, 0.1, 0.08, 0.06, 0.04, 0.02 and 0.01%.

3.3 Measurement of hydrogen distribution

The measurement of hydrogen distribution was done for two reasons:

a. To assess the heterogeneity of the concrete
b. To have an additional criterion for the estimation of penetration depth of the hydrophobic agent based on its hydrogen content.

Concrete is at least a two phase system. The cement paste and the aggregates have a percentage of some 30% and 70% by volume respectively. By mixing and pouring both, their heterogeneous distribution in the concrete can be achieved.

Transport and agglomeration of the hydrophobic agent occurs normally in the cement paste. Because of the heterogeneity of the concrete it is important to identify these zones of transport and agglomeration. The distinction may be done by determination of the hydrogen distribution. Other criteria have been presented in Molkenthin 2008.

As shown in the example of a concrete specimen (Figure 4), a clear separation is possible due to the measurement of the intensity of the hydrogen spectral line at 658.3 nm (H@656.3 nm). The aggregates are indicated by lower hydrogen intensities

(white) and thus distinguishable from the cement paste. This differentiation is caused by the water bonded in the cement paste. Major parts of the cement paste are hydrates.

The depth of carbonation and the water released during this process may be lightly seen in the upper and lower peripheral zone. An additional hydrophobic coating of this peripheral zone may lead to a significant increase of the hydrogen concentration in that zone.

4 RESULTS

The three transition metals (M1, M2, M5) and the alkali metal (M3) are identified by saturation of the surface of mortar specimens with aqueous solutions of different concentration (see 3.2.1), to have sensitive spectral lines which are detected by LIBS. For the halogen marker element (M4) no appropriate spectral line was observed. Thus this element was discarded from further investigation.

In the following sections the results obtained for the four left-over markers on pressed pellets and hardened cement paste specimen are presented.

4.1 Marker 1

Figure 5 shows the correlation between the content of marker 1 in pressed pellets and the measured LIBS signal for four different spectral lines. There is a clear correlation between a marker content of 0.01% and 1%.

4.2 Marker 2

Figure 6 shows the correlation between the content of marker 2 in pressed pellets and the measured LIBS signal for five different spectral lines (wavelength). There is an almost linear correlation between a marker content of 0.01% and 1%.

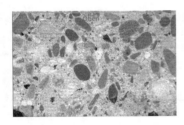

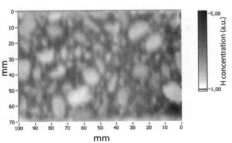

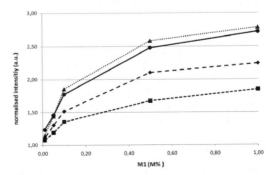

Figure 4. Top: Photo of cross section of the concrete specimen. Down: Hydrogen distribution in the concrete specimen via evaluation of H@656.3 nm used to differentiate the matrix from the mineral aggregate on a concrete sample.

Figure 5. Normalised intensity for five different spectral lines representing marker 1 measured on pellets (CEM I).

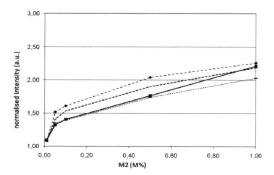

Figure 6. Normalised intensity for four different spectral lines representing marker 2 measured on pellets (CEM II).

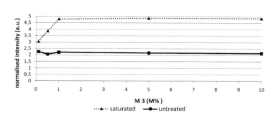

Figure 7. Comparison of normalised intensity of a spectral line from marker 3 measured on mortar specimens (CEM III) on a surface saturated with aqueous solution of salt and on an untreated surface.

4.3 Marker 3

The comparison of normalised intensities of a spectral line from marker 3 measured on mortar specimens (CEM III) on a surface treated with an aqueous solution of salt and on an untreated surface is shown in Figure 7. There is a clear difference between both measurements, but no correlation with the content of marker in the aqueous solution. That means that this treatment is not adequate to measure the element content.

4.4 Marker 5

Figure 8 shows the correlation between the content of marker 5 in pressed pellets and the measured LIBS signal for one spectral line (wavelength). There is a clear correlation between a marker content of 0.01% and 1%. Marker 5 has the best sensitivity of all tested markers (see Figure 9).

4.5 Factors of influence

The influence of the water/cement ratio for the production of samples of hardened cement on the LIBS intensity was investigated. The results are shown in Figure 10. There are higher intensities for

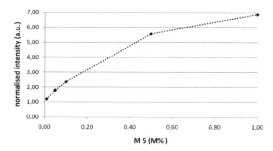

Figure 8. Normalised intensity for one wavelength of marker 5 measured on pellets (CEM I).

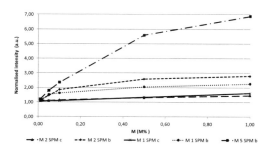

Figure 9. Comparison of normalized intensity measured on pellets containing additions of different markers.

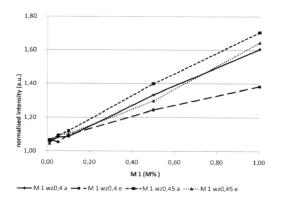

Figure 10. Comparison of normalized intensities of two spectral lines (a and e) measured on specimens of hardened cement paste produced with water/cement ratios of 0.4 and 0.45 and addition of marker 1.

both spectral lines (a and e) measured on the specimens produced with a water/cement ratio of 0.45.

5 CONCLUSIONS AND OUTLOOK

The investigations presented prove the feasibility of the concept. At least three elements were found (marker 1, marker 2 and marker 5) which are detectable with high contrast to the concrete constituent parts. There is a clear correlation of the normalized intensity of the measured LIBS-signal to the content of the marker. This correlation yields in the concentration range between 0.01% and 1.0%. The sensitivity of the three markers is different. The highest LIBS-signal (sensitivity) was reached using marker 5. It was shown that the sensitivity of LIBS is high enough to enable addition of the marker in concentrations which are economical.

The next step will be to improve the limit of detection for the selected markers by variation of LIBS measurement parameters (e.g., energy per pulse, surrounding atmosphere, size of focus area, time delay between laser pulse and measurement, width of time window for one measurement). The calibration will be done on more complex specimens and the routines for the consideration of material heterogeneity will be enhanced.

The parallel developed hydrophobic agents containing the integrated markers will be used to measure ingress profiles on concrete samples.

For the preparation of the surface under investigation currently different methods of surface treatment are under test. To measure ingress profiles up to a depth of 15 mm a mill seems to be optimal for producing a wedge. So the impact is minimized and an explicit advantage compared with coring is achieved.

A mobile LIBS system will be set up, tested and optimized, including measurements on real structures.

ACKNOWLEDGEMENTS

This work is funded by the German Federal Ministry for Education and Research (BMBF). The authors gratefully thank the BMBF for supporting this research work.

The cooperation with our partners in the frame of the project SILAMARK is deeply acknowledged.

REFERENCES

Gerdes, A. 2001. Transport und chemische Reaktion siliziumorganischer Verbindungen in der Betonrandzone. Building Materials Reports, Bericht No. 15, Institut für Baustoffe der ETH Zürich.

Goldschmidt, S. 2007. Ermittlung einer Tiefenhydrophobierung bei Zugabe eines Markers mittels der Laser Induced Breakdown Spectroscopy (LIBS). Diplomarbeit zur Erlangung des Akademischen Grades Dipl.-Ing., FHTW Berlin, 81 Seiten.

Herrmann, C. & Rotzsche, H. 1997. Bestimmung von organofunktionellen Silanen auf anorganischen Trägern mittels Pyrolyse-Gaschromatographie, in Bauchemie von der Forschung bis zur Praxis, GdCh-Monographie Band 11, GdCH-Fachgruppe Bauchemie (Hrsg.), Gesellschaft Deutscher Chemiker, Frankfurt a.M., 206–208.

Hörner, H.J., von Witzenhausen, N., Gatz, P. 2002. Messung der Hydrophobierungsqualität. BASt-Bericht B 37, Bundesanstalt für Straßenwesen, 24 Seiten.

Hüls AG, EP 0 741 293 vom 13.04.1995, Verfahren zur Untersuchung silanbehandelter, anorganischer Materilien.

Molkenthin, A. 2008. Laser-induzierte Breakdown Spektroskopie (LIBS) zur hochauflösenden Analyse der Ionenverteilung in zementgebundenen Feststoffen. Dissertation zur Erlangung des akademischen Grades Doktor der Ingenieurwissenschaften - Dr.-Ing., Universität Duisburg-Essen, 135 Seiten.

Oehmichen, D.S., Gerdes, A. & Nüesch, R. 2006. Reaktiver Transport in zementgebundenen Werkstoffen. Fachgruppe Bauchemie (Hrsg.); GdCH-Monographie 36: 281–288.

Weritz, F., Schaurich, D., Taffe, A. & Wilsch, G. 2009. Detailed depth profiles of sulfate ingress into concrete measured with Laser induced breakdown spectroscopy. Construction and Building Materials 23 (1): 275–283.

Wilsch, G., Schaurich, D., Wöstmann, J. & Wiggenhauser, H. 2001. Application of laser induced breakdown spectroscopy for detection of hydrophobic coatings. In Forde, M.C. (ed.), Proceedings of X. International Conference of Structural Faults & Repair, 4–6. July 2001, London, UK, Engineering Technics Press, CD-ROM.

Wilsch, G., Weritz, F., Schaurich, D. & Wiggenhauser, H. 2005. Determination of chloride content in concrete structures with laser-induced breakdown spectroscopy. Construction in Building Materials 19 (10): 724–730.

Concrete Solutions – Grantham, Mechtcherine & Schneck (eds)
© 2012 Taylor & Francis Group, London, ISBN 978-0-415-61622-5

Surface protection of high performance architectural concrete

V.R. Falikman
Moscow State University of Civil Engineering, Moscow, Russia

Yu. V. Sorokin & V.V. Deniskin
Scientific Research Institute for Concrete and Reinforced Concrete, Moscow, Russia

ABSTRACT: The performance of architectural concrete and architectural unit durability can be improved by surface treatment with special organic-silicate composition, contributing to partial or complete blocking of pores with high density air-silica-gel, which leads to a decrease of water absorption of 20–37% and an increase of freezing-thawing resistance by 20–50%. This paper reports on a laboratory study of the performance of such sealants, the factors that can influence successful impregnation and, by using electron microscopy, to study the nature of the pore sealing by the sealants.

1 INTRODUCTION

Modern concrete technology features, e.g., in making decorative façade elements, sculptural full relief, etc., a call for the use of highly workable and flowing mixes. Besides, the white and color cements are used as a rule to improve decorative properties, while the availability of a complicated surface texture and small pattern details require the use of aggregates with a limited maximum size. All these factors together lead to increasing of the cement mix water requirement that, in its turn, instigates the growth of shrinkage strains, increase in permeability and reduction in concrete freeze-thaw resistance. The features of cement chemical, mineralogical, and material composition (for example, increased content of C_3A, increased content of belite, introduction of bleaching mineral agents during grinding, e.g., diatomite, etc.) also contribute.

Applied methods of modifying the architectural concrete made on the basis of white cements or so called low water demand binder that are produced by controlled grinding of Portland cement clinker or Portland cement with chemical modifying agents and mineral additives provide an opportunity to control structure and properties of such concrete.

The important factor of increase in working life, conservation of ornamental properties and ease of maintainability of architectural concrete elements on the basis of white or colored cement, is their surface treatment. In real building practice, products from ornamental concrete are exposed to pollution to some extent even prior to the beginning of maintenance—during transportation, warehousing

and especially at installation which is carried out frequently without appropriate protection of the front face. It is difficult to remove pollution from the surface of the concrete articles having a capillary-porous structure. Use of intensive methods is accompanied by a surface damage and loss of ornamental properties. Architectural concrete in service pollution and staining or marking of the front face of ornamental elements occurs owing to absorbance of soiling microparticles from air, especially in industrial aerospheres, and also during scheduled operations of cleaning and repair of buildings, the roofing, adjoining territories, etc.

Elimination of contaminating impurities from the front face of ornamental elements, and upgrading of architectural concrete and architectural elements is attained by their treatment with various compositions reducing permeability to water and water absorption. Among the wide nomenclature of treating and coating compositions and systems (acrylic, urethane, epoxide, silicone, siloxanic, silaned, etc.) the greatest technical and economic efficienct possess silicate and organosilicate compositions combining comparative cheapness and accessibility of a raw-material base with a large-decrease of water absorption, and permeability to water, and increase of working life (Zhidkov et al., 1987, Terlikovsky et al., 1993). Nevertheless, a wide application of organosilicate penetrating sealant systems in building practice is restricted by their insufficient penetrating power at impregnating reference conditions (the mechanized or manual coating of protective composition at usual temperatures and an air pressure) that essentially reduces depth of impregnating and reduces its efficiency.

Advances in new generation organosilicate treatment compositions allows the elimination of the deficiencies specified above and to provide high performance of impregnation, both under normal conditions, and after intensive thermal or vacuum drying of the concrete surface (Bashlykov et al., 2001).

2 EXPERIMENTAL PROGRAM

2.1 Sealers

Penetrating sealant systems were developed on the basis of soluble sodium silicate in which the silica module (SiO_2/M_2O mole ratio) varies within 1,98 … 3,36. It is known that addition of some organic compounds to soluble silicates reduce their interfacial tension, reduce the interfacial angle of wetting and the strain rate of cured silicate systems (Charnoe, 1994). In the preliminary experiments we have carried out it has been found that technological parameters of organosilicate compositions for concrete impregnation can be essentially improved when surface active agents (SAA) of various natures were introduced to soluble silicate, including anionic and nonionic surfactants. These additives have a significant impact on the state of soluble silicates in an aqueous solution at low concentrations of SAA.

Small additions of SAA cause essential changes in the gelation processes. This has been used to develop highly effective organosilicate compositions for concrete impregnation. It is necessary to note that oxyethylated derivatives of fat alcohol represent a particular interest as SAA because oligoethylenoxide fragments can catalyze additional processes of gelation in soluble silicate. One such type of SAA was used to prepare sealing systems of optimum composition.

2.2 Materials and test methods

White cement of CEM I 32.5 grade, produced by Shchourovo cement plant in Russia, and standard siliceous sand according to GOST 6139 (ISC, 2003) were used for the tests. Washed crushed granite of 5–20 mm fraction in accordance with GOST 8267-93 was used as coarse aggregate for the concrete tests.

With few exceptions, the tests were performed in conformity with standards of the Russian Federation. Concrete samples for impregnation were made according to GOST 10180 (ISC, 1990) with mix designs in accordance with GOST 27006 (ISC, 1986). All experiments were executed according to GOST 26633 (ISC, 1991). The period between the first and second treatment was 20–24 hours, if necessary.

Fresh concretes were tested according to GOST 10181 (ISC, 2000), and hardened concretes—according to GOST 12730.0–12730.5 (ISC, 1978). The density, moisture content, water absorption and parameters of porosity of the concrete were defined in accordance with GOST 12730.0 … GOST 12730.4 (ISC, 1978). Frost resistance was determined according to GOST 10060.2 (ISC, 1995). Impermeability to water was estimated for a series of concrete samples according to GOST 12730.5 (ISC, 1978) by maximal water pressure, at which on four of six cylindrical samples water percolation was not observed.

The effect of sealant on the concrete void structure characteristics was explored studying the kinetics of their water absorption in conformance with the methods described in GOST 12730.4 (ISC, 1978). Parameters of the specimen porous structure were studied by the optical method using Gallery software.

According to GOST 12730.3 (ISC, 1978) a principle method of studying of characteristics of pore structures of concrete on the kinetics of their water absorption provides calculated-experimental definition of α and λ_2 parameters. The parameter α represents so-called uniformity coefficient of pores by sizes; parameter λ_2 is a parameter of mean value of pore coarseness (Shejkin et al., 1979).

2.3 Effects of various factors on sealer performance

Efficiency of organosilicate compositions for concrete sealing depends on many factors, including density and concrete porosity, moisture content of concrete, temperature of environments, and parameters of drying of concrete. In this context, the effect of organosilicate composition viscosity on depth of impregnation of concrete of different density; the effect of temperature and humidity concrete characteristics on the depth of impregnation at constant density of concrete; the effect of the residual moisture content of concrete on the depth of impregnation under conditions of constant temperature and viscosity of organosilicate compositions were studied. Besides, dependence of impregnation depth from porosity, age of concrete and impregnation factor was observed.

2.3.1 Effects of viscosity on sealer performance

The effect of viscosity of treatment systems on their efficiency with reference to concrete with various densities based on white cement was studied.

The effectiveness coefficient of surfacing on a parameter of strength K_3^R, equal to the relationship of strength of the processed concrete to the strength of unprocessed concrete, in %; and the effectiveness coefficient of surfacing on the parameter of water absorption K_3^B, equal to the relation of magnitude of water absorption of the processed concrete to water absorption of unprocessed concrete, %, have been accepted as criteria of efficiency of impregnation.

The obtained data on strength are corresponded, as shown below, with results of microscopic studies of structure, and also with results of definition of the characteristics of pore structures on water absorption kinetics.

2.3.2 Effects of temperature on sealer performance

Application of organosilicate compositions is not connected with use of special temperature control affecting a concrete surface at the time of coating. Nevertheless, a study was executed of concrete temperature effect on efficiency of sealing for the purpose of definition of an admissible temperature for works on impregnation of building structure surfaces. Reducing the temperature for sealer application and curing does not seem to have any major effect on the performance of sealers. The results showed that the sealer's application temperature had a little influence on their performance. Without more details on the analysis of the gained results, it has to be noted that an admissible temperature range from plus 5 to 40°C during application of organosilicate composition can be recommended.

2.3.3 Effects of residual moisture content on sealer performance

Moisture elimination from the concrete surface and the minimum dehumidification of the concrete surface were studied to improve the process of concrete impregnation.

2.3.4 Effects of concrete porosity on sealer performance

Depth and efficiency of impregnating of concrete with organosilicate compositions depend on such factors, as density, porosity and age of concrete. It is found that the efficiency of impregnation of concrete had no relation to age of manufacture though with increase in this age, efficiency of the secondary treatment decreased slightly, which can be connected with increase in relative volume of conditionally closed pores.

Parameters of pore structure of the concrete samples processed by sealant were studied by optical techniques using the «Gallery» software. Pores were visualized with luminophor capturing UV-light. The size of an analyzed field was 2×2 mm. Consistently fields were investigated lying directly under the processed surface at distances of 2–4, 4–6, 6–8 … 12–14 mm deep into the sample. In order to investigate further the structural changes

in the intrapore space additional investigations were carried out using an SEM microscope REM-100U equipped with a system of computer registration and image processing.

3 RESULTS AND DISCUSSION

On the basis of the studies it is possible to conclude that the sealing process at a surface of concrete occurs as follows: the sealer solution penetrates into pores thorough cracks and capillaries, forming a laminose coating on the surface of accessible hollows and transport channels changing sizes of these hollows. The filling of voids by sealer solution calls "turgescency" of concrete that results transformation of system of pores and capillaries existing in concrete before impregnation, and formation of new microcracks.

Moisture elimination from concrete surface and the minimum dehumidification of its surface (to the residual moisture content of 5%) allowed us to raise considerably the depth of impregnation (to 12.9 mm after single and to 14.3 mm after double treatment for concrete composition 2, viscosity organosilicate compositions—3.6 cpoise). Further drying of samples was accompanied by an increase in depth of impregnation to 14.0–18.5 mm which, however, was not much more significant. The gained results allow us to understand about limiting the moisture content of surface layer of the concrete which otherwise reduces the efficiency of concrete modification. Proceeding from the gained data, the mean of limiting moisture content may be accepted as 5%.

Data about the effect of viscosity of treating systems on their efficiency with reference to concrete with various densities based on white cement are presented in Table 1. Tests have shown that depth of impregnation increases as a natural result with viscosity decrease of organosilicate compositions, attaining the greatest values (21.8–27.0 mm) at the least viscosity (1.5 cpoise). Retreatment does not influence practically the depth of impregnation of concrete with a cement content of 450 kg/m³ (composition 1) that testifies to its dense structure with predominance of small pores and capillaries, sealing during first treatment. At the same time for concrete with a cement content of 225 kg/m³ (composition 2) double treatment allowed us to increase the depth of impregnation considerably. This can be connected with the more non-uniform structure of the concrete made at raised W/C, and also with presence in the structure of such material as the raised quantity of macropores and other defects which remain partly unsealed after treatment.

Comparison of concrete strength after impregnation shows (Table 1) that the greatest value

Table 1. Effect of viscosity of organosilicate compositions on depth and efficiency of concrete impregnation.

№	Composition. kg/m³					Surface treatment	Organosilicate composition viscosity. cpoise	Depth of impregnation. mm	Variation factor. %	Compressive strength. MPa	Water absorption			
	Cement	Sand	Coarse aggregate	Water	W/C						Mass. %	Vol. %	α*	λ_2*
1.	450	567	1152	203	0.45	–	–	–	–	48.2	4.3	10.0	0.54	1.02
						Single treatment	7.3	11.5	3.3	46.5	4.7	11.0	0.58	0.88
							5.5	14.2	3.5	48.0	4.5	10.6	0.66	0.63
							3.6	15.7	3.6	49.7	3.9	9.2	0.70	0.42
							2.6	17.0	3.4	49.3	4.1	9.5	0.69	0.58
							1.5	21.8	3.7	48.4	4.2	9.8	0.60	0.93
						Double treatment	7.3	11.7	3.0	47.0	4.6	10.7	0.73	0.90
							5.5	14.5	3.2	49.4	4.0	9.5	0.75	0.65
							3.6	16.1	3.3	52.6	3.4	8.7	0.83	0.31
							2.6	17.9	3.8	51.2	3.9	9.2	0.71	0.49
							1.5	23.5	4.0	48.6	4.0	9.4	0.66	0.76
2.	224	866	1059	195	0.87	–	–	–	–	19.8	10.4	23.6	0.32	2.74
						Single treatment	7.3	13.3	4.8	20.3	10.1	22.9	0.45	2.11
							5.5	15.8	5.5	20.9	9.6	21.8	0.49	1.60
							3.6	18.4	5.3	22.6	8.5	19.5	0.58	1.25
							2.6	19.6	5.5	22.4	8.8	20.0	0.55	1.59
							1.5	24.1	5.7	21.0	9.3	21.1	0.37	1.90
						Double treatment	7.3	14.8	4.3	20.8	8.9	20.2	0.52	1.88
							5.5	17.2	4.6	21.7	7.4	16.8	0.59	1.21
							3.6	19.8	5.0	24.8	6.7	15.2	0.69	0.87
							2.6	23.0	5.4	23.5	6.9	15.7	0.60	1.46
							1.5	27.2	5.5	22.2	7.3	16.6	0.45	1.80

* Parameter α—uniformity coefficient of open pores by sizes, λ_2—average diameter of open pores.

of strength was provided after application of a composition with mean viscosity over the range 2.6–5.3 cpoise, and maximum strength values were attained after impregnating by a composition with viscosity 3.6 cpoise. The strength reduction of the concrete impregnated by organosilicate composition with heightened viscosity is typical to the greatest degree for concrete of composition (1) with increased density and a predominance of small-sized pores and capillaries which creates conditions for their full sealing. The Result of impregnating of such concrete by a sealing system with raised (7.3 cpoise) viscosity was the strength reduction of the sealed concrete in comparison even to unprocessed samples. For concrete with more "coarse-pore" structure the specified effect did not appear, practically.

As a result of the sealing of concrete with composition (1) the uniformity coefficient of pores increased (Table 1), attaining the greatest values at a mean of viscosity of a treating composition (2.6–3.6 cpoise). Parameters of the mean value of pore coarseness λ_2 decreased to 0.42–0.58 simultaneously that corresponded to a fine-pored structure. The further decrease of viscosity of the treating system resulted in a pore structure uniformity decrease again and increased the mean coarseness of pores (the parameter λ_2 increased to 0.93) that is connected with incomplete sealing of large pores and capillaries in view of the downgraded quantity of an active component of organosilicate composition. Double treatment of concrete of composition (1) by organosilicate with viscosity 2.6–3.6 cpoise provided a microporous concrete structure of high uniformity ($\alpha = 0.71$–0.83, $\lambda_2 = 0.31$–0.49). Analogous regularity was observed for concrete of composition (2) also.

The analysis of the data on change of porosity of the processed sample of composition 1 for the strata lying at various distances from the surface of the concrete, showed (Figure 1) that the magnitude of the general porosity of concrete modified by an organosilicate composition decreased from the surface into the sample deep, attaining the minimum value at a distance of 8–10 mm from the surface. It is possible to assume that at this depth, the specific obstruction is formed when the sealant closes all overlying transport channels. The last circumstance makes difficult the further advance of organosilicate compositions into the sample depth.

One of the consequences of pore sealing with the specified composition was a significant decrease of the general relative area of pores— from 12.2% in unprocessed concrete to 7.9% in the concrete after single treatment and to 4.1% in the concrete with double impregnation. In the processed concrete a significant decrease in abundance of small and mean pores (to 0.01 mm and 0.01–0.03 mm) was observed that testifies to their partial or full sealing.

The microscopic analysis has shown that the structure of the superficial (0–2 mm) concrete layer is exposed to the lowest changes at impregnation with organosilicate composition. The bulk of the sealant passed deep into the sample using available large transport channels and pores in boundary layers, slightly reducing their sizes. In Figure 2a, b characteristic species of pore are shown, which are typical for the given layer of a sample, and oversized image patch of the pore is represented. The deposition of aerosilica gel was observed in a pore covering a spherical surface of pore in two layers that complied with a double impregnation of concrete.

When the depth of impregnation is higher (4–8 mm and more) the degree of filling of pores by sealing products increased. In Figure 3 a pore is shown, almost completely closed by aerosilica gel; the diameter of an open part of the pore (white line on a picture) is some four times less than the initial one (an arrow shows the old boundary line of the pore).

At depths over 12–14 mm the pores were observed to be unfilled by the sealing composition. In Figure 4, a spherical pore is shown, in which aerosilica gel beds are observed, the supply canal (A) is completely shut, and in its mouth the new closed pore (B) is visible formed by structured sealing composition.

Along with aerosilica gel formation, according to the microscopic analysis, growing crystals are revealed in partially filled pores with sealing composition whose nature requires additional study.

All other conditions showed equal efficiency of sealing of concrete with organosilicate composition which depended both on pore volume, and on the character of porosity. The increase in porosity due to the increase of absolute and relative volume of self-contained air pores, as occurs when air entraining agents are used, would not affect essentially on depth of surface impregnation or the water absorption decrease. At the same time, however, air entraining agents promote some increase in vapour permeability of the impregnated concrete. It is possible to explain this if we take into account that for concrete without admixtures open intercommunicated pores and capillaries are sealed with the organosilicate composition and do not participate in the process of mass transfer in drying whereas self-contained air pores, in concrete with the admixture, remain unfilled by aerosilica gel and under elevated temperature can serve as channels for air-steam mixture carryover.

The concrete surface treatment by organosilicate composition favors an increase of its working life that is caused by pore structure changes. The effect of formation of aerosilica gel as sealing and additional binding agent in pores and defects of concrete simultaneously revealed above allows

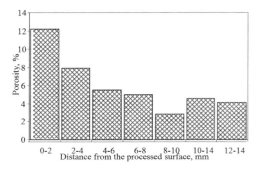

Figure 1. Porosity of concrete surface layers, impregnated with organosilicate composition, depending on distance from the processed surface.

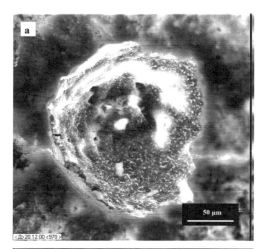

Figure 2. Formation of spherical depositions by aerosilica gel on inside surface of concrete pores after double treatment (beds of depositions are visible).

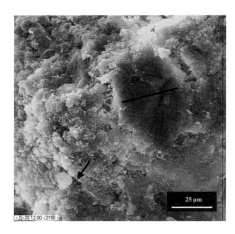

Figure 3. Partial pore filling with aerosilica gel in processed organosilicate composition concrete (black line—diameter of an open part of pore, the marksman—old boundary line of a pore).

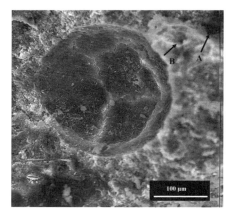

Figure 4. Partial filling of spherical pore of concrete with aerosilica gel as a result of full sealing of the delivering capillary (A). B—closed pore formed by structured aerosilica gel in a capillary mouth.

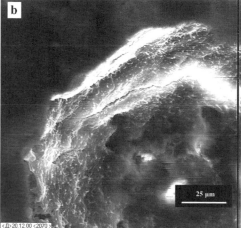

the possibility of a an increase of compressive strength owing to the so-called «hooping effect». This consists of blocking of structural defects by the polymeric buildup containing in the specified sealing systems, and deceleration of structural defect development under load. This view is confirmed by the results of experimental studies of concrete of various compositions with cement content over the range from 180 to 600 kg/m^3, impregnated by developed organosilicate composition.

The compositions and test results of fresh and hardened concrete are given in Table 2. The results show that the concrete surface treatment by organosilicate composition in a wide range

Table 2.   Effect of sealing on strength and water absorption of concrete.

№	Composition. kg/m³				Slump. cm	Concrete mix density. kg/m³	W/C	Treatment method	R_c. MPa *	Class of concrete	Water absorption. % mass.	Effectiveness ratio *	
	Cement	Sand	Corse aggregate	Water								K_3^R.%	K_3^B
1	178	786	1074	196	12.5	2234	1.1	–	8.57	B 5	13.5	–	–
								Single treatment	9.94		11.0	116	0.81
								Double treatment	10.9		9.3	127	0.69
2	239	774	1077	198	14.0	2288	0.83	–	16.6	B 12.5	11.2	–	–
								Single treatment	19.6		9.5	118	0.85
								Double treatment	22.1		8.0	133	0.71
3	295	721	1106	195	13.0	2317	0.66	–	23.1	B 15	9.3	–	–
								Single treatment	26.6		7.6	115	0.81
								Double treatment	29.1		5.9	126	0.63
4	363	652	1150	197	15.0	2362	0.54	–	31.5	B 25	7.6	–	–
								Single treatment	33.7		6.1	107	0.80
								Double treatment	35.9		4.3	114	0.57
5	422	627	1146	199	14.5	2394	0.47	–	39.5	B 30	4.5	–	–
								Single treatment	41.5		4.0	105	0.89
								Double treatment	45.4		3.6	115	0.80
6	485	575	1158	202	13.5	2420	0.42	–	43.6	B 35	4.2	–	–
								Single treatment	44.5		3.9	102	0.93
								Double treatment	46.7		3.4	107	0.81
7	541	541	1153	203	12.0	2438	0.375	–	50.4	B 40	3.9	–	–
								Single treatment	50.6		3.7	100	0.95
								Double treatment	51.9		3.5	103	0.90
8	598	488	1151	218	14.0	2455	0.365	–	56.4	B 45	4.0	–	–
								Single treatment	56.7		3.8	100	0.95
								Double treatment	57.5		3.5	102	0.88

* R_c—compressive strength; K_3^R—relationship of strength of the processed concrete to the strength of unprocessed concrete, in %; K_3^B— relationship of water absorption of the processed concrete to water absorption of unprocessed concrete, %.

Table 3. Effect of sealing on freeze-thaw resistance of concrete.

№	Cement consumption. kg/m³	W/C	Slump. cm	Class of concrete	Treatment method	Concrete strength. MPa/K_{fr} after freeze-thaw cycles									Freeze-Thaw resistance
						0	50	75	100	150	200	300	400	500	
1.	180	1.1	12.5	B 5	–	8.9/1.00	8.6/0.97	7.8/0.88	–	–	–	–	–	–	F 50
					Single treatment	10.2/1.00	10.7/1.05	11.5/1.13	10.0/0.98	8.7/0.85	–	–	–	–	F 100
					Double treatment	11.4/1.00	14.0/1.23	13.5/1.18	12.0/1.05	11.5/1.01	10.5/0.92	–	–	–	>F 150
2.	300	0.64	11.0	B 15	–	25.9/1.00	–	–	26.7/1.03	25.1/0.97	20.7/0.80	–	–	–	F 150
					Single treatment	29.1/1.00	–	–	–	32.0/1.10	30.0/1.03	24.7/0.85	–	–	F 250
					Double treatment	32.5/1.00	–	–	–	36.7/1.13*	35.4/1.09	32.8/1.01	–	–	>F 300
3.	450	0.43	13.5	B 30	–	43.3/1.00	–	–	46.3/1.07	–	44.6/1.03	37.2/0.86	–	–	F 250
					Single treatment	45.2/1.00	–	–	–	52.4/1.16	–	47.9/1.06	42.0/0.93	–	F 350
					Double treatment	50.5/1.00	–	–	–	56.1/1.11	–	56.6/1.12	48.5/0.96	–	F 400
4.	550	0.38	14.0	B 45	–	51.2/1.00	–	–	–	–	56.8/1.11	59.9/1.17	50.7/0.99	42.5/0.83	F 450
					Single treatment	51.8/1.00	–	–	–	–	–	64.8/1.25	58.5/1.13	52.3/1.01	F 500
					Double treatment	52.6/1.00	–	–	–	–	–	63.6/1.21	65.2/1.24	60.0/1.14	F 600

*–125 freeze-thaw cycles

of W/C-ratios, matching to strength classes of concrete from B5 to B45, is accompanied by an increase in strength, and with double impregnation this effect increases (Table 2). The greatest effect of strength raise (15–18% with single and 26–33% with double impregnation) is observed at W/C = 0.83 and 0.66 accordingly. At bigger or smaller W/C values the trend is observed to decrease in efficiency of sealing on strength parameters.

Similarly porous structure characteristics of concrete with various W/C ratios affect the efficiency of their sealing on a water absorption parameter. The data presented in Table 2 shows that unitary single surface treatment of concrete with W/C ratios over the range 0.54 … 1.1 results in a decrease in water absorption from 7.6–13.5% mass. to 6.1–11.0% mass. After double impregnation, the values of water absorption drop to 4.3–9.3% mass.

The data on frost resistance test results of concrete with the cement content of 180–550 kg/m^3 are shown in Table 3.

The results in Table 3 correspond to results of the above-stated studies and attests to the high performance of sealing concrete of low and medium classes made at raised W/C values. In all cases a higher strength of concrete corresponded to a smaller relative effect of improvement in frost resistance, and increase in degree of sealing gives raise to frost resistance. The effect of various parameters such as concrete W/C, sealers application temperature, etc. on the sealer effectiveness was also summarized herein above.

4 CONCLUSIONS

The obtained data confirms that the sealing composition of a new generation of sealers consisting of high-modulus sodium polysilicate solutions and containing additionally micro doses of organic components provides a rather effective organomineral sealing. The small organic additives control viscosity and wetting properties of system, and initiate polymerization-polycondensation processes in the cement matrix resulting in the formation of a high density aerosilicate gel. The surfacing of concrete by the specified sealing system improves essentially the physico-mechanical parameters of the impregnated concrete and raises considerably both operation reliability and durability in both new concrete products, reinforced concrete structures, and products and buildings which are under service conditions. With reference to architectural concrete it also raises the durability of the surface of ornamental elements to fouling and makes the process of their cleaning easier. The products also act as protective coatings while in service which has been confirmed by experience of practical application during restoration of some historical monuments and buildings in the City of Moscow.

Thus, the above mentioned method of the modification of the architectural concrete provides an opportunity to control its structure and properties. Thereby an optimum combination of construction and technical characteristics of concretes and decorative properties of products is achieved that should considerably expand the field of architectural concrete application and on the whole facilitate the growth of its social significance and attractiveness.

REFERENCES

Bashlykov, N.F., Falikman, V.R., Sorokin, Yu.V. & Deniskin V.V. 2001. Architectural Concrete: Integrated Control of Performance and Decorative Characteristics. *Proc. of 1st All-Russian Conference on Problems of Concrete and Reinforced Concrete.* M, v. 2: 1027–1042.
Charnoe, Z.P. 1994. Canadian Patent 2099426,—Publ. 31.12.1994.
GOST 6139. 2003. Sand for concrete testing. ISC.
GOST 8267. 1993. Crushed stone and gravel from solid rocks for construction works. ISC.
GOST 10060.2. 1995. Concretes. Rapid methods for determination of frost-resistance by repeated alternated freezing and thawing. ISC.
GOST 10180. 1990. Concretes. Methods for strength determination using reference specimens. ISC.
GOST 10181. 2000. Concrete mixtures. Methods of testing. ISC.
GOST 12730.0. 1978. Concretes. General requirements for methods of determination of density, moisture content, water absorption, porosity and watertightness. ISC.
GOST 12730.1. 1978. Methods of determination of density. ISC.
GOST 12730.2. 1978. Concretes. Methods of determination of moisture content. ISC.
GOST 12730.3. 1978. Concretes. Methods of determination of water absorption. ISC.
GOST 12730.4. 1978. Concretes. Methods of determination of porosity parameters. ISC.
GOST 12730.5. 1978. Concretes. Methods of determination of watertightness. ISC.
GOST 26633. 1991. Heavy-weight and sand concretes. Specifications. ISC.
GOST 27006. 1986. Rules for mix proportioning. ISC.
Shejkin, A.E., Chekhovsky, J.V. & Brusser, M.I. 1979. Structure and Properties of Cement Concretes. M, Stroyizdat, p. 344.
Terlikovsky, E.V. et al. 1993. USSR Inventor's Certificate No1787133.—Publ. 07.01.1993.
Zhidkov, Yu. N., Cheche, A.A., Chehovich, N.P., Kaberdin, R.V, et al. 1987. USSR Inventor's Certificate No1350165—Publ. 07.11.1987.

Concrete Solutions – Grantham, Mechtcherine & Schneck (eds)
© 2012 Taylor & Francis Group, London, ISBN 978-0-415-61622-5

Coatings and overlays for concrete affected by alkali-silica reaction

E.R. Giannini, A.F. Bentivegna & K.J. Folliard
University of Texas at Austin, Austin, Texas, USA

ABSTRACT: Alkali-Silica Reaction (ASR) affects numerous transportation structures, resulting in cracking that is unsightly and may create the appearance of a loss of structural performance. Extreme cases can lead to a loss of performance. Additionally, cracking provides easier access for aggressive agents such as chlorides to penetrate into the interior of the structure. The aesthetic and durability concerns caused by ASR may be mitigated through the use of coatings and overlays.

Field trials conducted by the U.S. Federal Highway Administration (FHWA) and the Texas Department of Transportation (TxDOT) to mitigate ASR in existing structures incorporated the use of breathable sealers. An outdoor exposure site at the University of Texas at Austin tested breathable sealers, waterproof membranes and pavement overlays on a variety of simulated field structures.

This paper will present the results of up to five years of post-treatment monitoring of field structures and over two years of exposure site testing.

1 INTRODUCTION

Alkali-Silica Reaction (ASR) is a leading cause of premature concrete deterioration. First discovered in California in the late 1930s and diagnosed by Stanton (1940), it has since resulted in deleterious expansion and cracking of numerous portland cement concrete transportation structures. The cracking is unsightly and can provide avenues of ingress for moisture and chlorides, which can lead to further deterioration of the structure. Expansion can lead to misalignment and crushing of adjacent elements.

The causes of ASR are now well understood and significant research has enabled the development of concrete mixture designs that will not result in expansive ASR. As a result, there should be few cases of ASR in new structures. However, there is a need for effective mitigation methods for structures already affected by ASR.

1.1 Alkali-silica reaction

ASR is a reaction that can occur between akali hydroxides (e.g. NaOH, KOH) in the concrete pore solution and certain forms of silica present in some aggregate particles. The reaction forms a hydrophilic alkali-silica gel that, in the presence of sufficient moisture, can expand with sufficient force to cause microcracking in the paste and aggregate. With sufficient expansion, this is manifested at the concrete surface as open macrocracking that may be accompanied by dark stains or white efflorescence.

Since expansive ASR requires a moist environment, transportation and hydraulic structures are particularly susceptible. Hydraulic structures such as dams are constantly exposed directly to moisture, while transportation structures experience wetting and drying cycles. Without sufficient moisture, the reaction can take place, but the gel will not be able to expand. Microclimate effects can often be observed, where portions of a structure that are more frequently exposed to rainfall show more severe signs of ASR, while unexposed portions show little, if any, signs of deterioration.

1.2 Mitigation methods

Research into mitigating ASR in existing structures has typically focused on either chemically inhibiting the expansive tendencies of the gel, providing mechanical restraint to the structure, or reducing the supply of external moisture. Lithium salts, particularly lithium nitrate, can be very effective in preventing further expansion (McCoy & Caldwell 1952, Stark 1992, Stokes et al. 1997). However, it is very difficult to introduce sufficient quantities into large concrete elements (Giannini 2009). Mechanical restraint can take the form of external prestressing (active restraint) or fiber-reinforced polymer wraps and steel frames (passive restraint). Reducing the supply of moisture can be as simple as improving drainage details; this should, in fact be performed wherever possible for ASR-affected structures. Other techniques include epoxy crack injection, the application of pavement overlays and coatings such as breathable sealers and waterproof elastomeric membranes.

Breathable sealers such as silanes have been studied extensively in recent years by the U.S. Federal Highway Administration (FHWA), the Texas Department of Transportation (TxDOT), and other agencies for their potential to prevent the ingress of external liquid moisture while allowing the passage of water vapor. Given sufficient dry periods, the net effect is to reduce the moisture content of the concrete (Fig. 1). Studies show that expansion is markedly reduced if the internal relative humidity is below 90%, and can be almost completely eliminated if reduced below 80% (Pednault 1996). Research by Jensen (2000) and Wehrle (2010) suggests that silanes are most effective if applied to thin concrete elements because the depth to which silanes can reduce relative humidity is limited. Experimental work and models by Kubo et al. (2000) suggests that the greatest effect is achieved within 10 cm of the treated surface. Silanes can also significantly reduce the aesthetic damage caused by ASR. Trial applications to sections of a highway median barrier near Québec City in 1991 were not only effective in reducing expansion (Bérubé et al. 2002), but also resulted in a much improved appearance compared to untreated control sections. Figure 2 shows a boundary between

a treated and untreated section of barrier as it appeared in 2009. Some breathable sealers are more effective than others, so it is important to test several (Bérubé et al. 2002).

Waterproof elastomeric membranes can effectively prevent the ingress of external moisture, but lack the breathability of silanes and therefore also prevent internal moisture for exiting the structure during dry periods. Therefore, it may be somewhat self-defeating with regard to its ability to prevent or slow future expansion. Any such coating must also be sufficiently ductile that it can accommodate additional expansion of the structure without cracking or debonding. Elastomeric coatings can also address the aesthetic damage of ASR-induced cracking by providing a fresh, uncracked surface.

Pavement overlays present some of the same issues as waterproof membranes. They can limit moisture ingress, but also effectively prevent egress as well. However, the overlay does provide a new, uncracked surface for traffic. Unbonded concrete overlays have a flexible layer between the overlay and the damaged substrate concrete so that additional expansion can be accommodated. This is often accomplished with a thin layer of asphalt concrete. Asphalt concrete overlays can also be used to provide a new riding surface. With bridge decks, it is important that any overlay is of minimal depth to prevent adding excessive dead load to the structure. Thicker overlays can be used for pavements constructed on-grade. (Harrington, 2008).

1.3 Research objectives

The objectives of the research presented in this paper are to assess the effectiveness of a variety of breathable sealers, membranes and overlays on several types of transportation structures. Field trials were conducted on highway median barriers in Massachusetts and large columns supporting an overpass in Texas. An exposure site containing scaled column, bridge deck and on-grade pavement elements was constructed at the University of Texas at Austin to allow testing in a more controlled environment. The mitigation methods will be assessed by their ability to reduce expansion due to ASR. Breathable sealer should also reduce the internal relative humidity of the structure, while membranes and overlays should be able to accommodate continued expansion of the ASR-affected substrate.

2 FIELD TRIALS

The field trials in Massachusetts and Texas tested several breathable coating formulations on structures believed to be affected by ASR. Petrographic

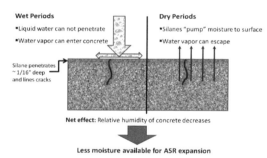

Figure 1. Mechanism of silanes.

Figure 2. Silane-treated (left) and untreated control (right) median barrier segments near Quebec City, Canada.

examination conducted prior to the field trials confirmed extensive signs of ASR in the Massachusetts median barriers and signs of developing ASR in the Texas overpass columns. The structures were instrumented and monitored for expansion and relative humidity for several years after the treatments.

2.1 Massachusetts field trial

Three silane treatments were applied to a total of 14 median barrier segments in October 2005. Each consisted of spray two applications at a rate 0.10 L/m². An isopropyl alcohol-based 40% silane sealer was applied to six barrier segments, designated T4-A/B/C and T5-A/B/C; three of these (T4-A/B/C) were in combination with a double spray application of lithium nitrate. Three segments, designated T6-A/B/C, were treated with an isopropyl alcohol-based 20% silane sealer. A water-based 20% silane was applied to five segments, designated T7-A/B/C, VB-1 and VB-2. Vacuum impregnation of lithium nitrate was also applied to VB-1 and VB-2.

The barriers were instrumented with embedded stainless steel gauge studs arranged in vertical and horizontal 500 mm gauge lengths. Expansions were measured using a DEMEC gauge with 0.001 mm precision. Sealed plastic tubes were embedded to a depth 50 mm to allow measurement of relative humidity as a function of depths using electrical probes. Instrumentation and initial measurements occurred at the same time as the treatments. Monitoring was conducted twice yearly through 2008 and data was also collected in May 2010.

Since the barrier segments were restrained horizontally by adjacent segments, the vertical expansion data was determined to be more significant. The average vertical expansions for each treatment type are shown in Figure 3. All silane-treated barrier sets experienced less expansion than the control sets.

Limited relative humidity data were obtained from this site, however data from May 2008 show that the silane-treated barriers had an average relative humidity of 85%, versus 88% for the control segments. Long-term humidity measurements are complicated by the difficulty of keeping the plastic sleeves sealed against external moisture between site visits.

2.2 Texas field trial

A single alcohol-based 40% silane sealer and a silane-siloxane blend were applied to a total of five columns in April 2006. Two untreated columns were selected as controls (columns 36 and 43). The columns were divided into moderate-severe damage (columns 32, 34 and 36) and low-moderate damage (columns 41 through 44), based on visual observations during initial site visits. In each set, one column was media blasted prior to silane application, while the other was left painted.

Columns 34, 42 and 43 were instrumented for expansion measurements in January 2006, while columns 32, 36, 41 and 44 were instrumented in May 2006, shortly after the treatments were applied. Expansions were measured over 500 mm horizontal and vertical gauge lengths on two of the four faces of each column. Plastic tubes for humidity measurements were installed at various times and embedded to depths ranging from 25 to 75 mm. The site was monitored approximately twice yearly from May 2006 to August 2009.

The horizontal expansions were determined to be most important because the columns were more heavily reinforced and bearing significant loads in the vertical direction, but restrained only by transverse reinforcement in the horizontal direction. Figures 4 and 5 show the horizontal expansion data for the moderate-severe damage columns and the low-moderate damage columns, respectively. With the exception of column 44, expansions were similar to the controls. Columns with silanes applied over paint experienced less expansion than those with silane applied on a blasted surface.

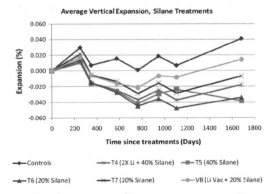

Figure 3. Vertical expansions of Massachusetts barriers.

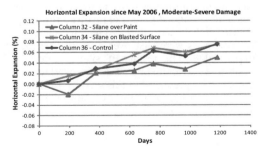

Figure 4. Horizontal expansion, moderate-severe damage columns.

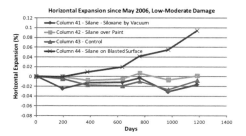

Figure 5. Horizontal expansion, low-moderate damage columns.

Relative humidity data was of limited usefulness. As with the Massachusetts field trial, it proved difficult to keep the plastic tubes free of water between site visits.

2.3 Need for exposure site

Although field trials offer the best opportunity for testing mitigation methods on full scale structures, they are limited by the need to travel to the site to take measurements, the time needed to obtain useful results and the lack of true control specimens. The latter is of greatest concern because it is difficult to evaluate a mitigation method if the treated specimen can not be compared to an identical untreated specimen.

An outdoor exposure site, however, can mimic field conditions while sets of nearly identical test specimens are monitored from the time of construction. Mixtures can be designed to yield more rapid results and ensure that ASR is the only deterioration mechanism present. Since there is no need to travel to the site, measurements can be taken in consistent climatic conditions.

3 EXPOSURE SITE TESTING

An exposure site was established at the University of Texas at Austin to study the effectiveness of various mitigation methods in a more controlled setting. This simulated field trial involved three types of structural elements and two reactive aggregates. All specimens were cast over a six day period in August 2008. The results of silane, waterproof membrane, concrete and asphalt overlay treatments will be presented in this section. Full details on the construction of the exposure site can be found in Bentivegna (2009).

3.1 Materials and specimens

Both reactive coarse and fine aggregates were included in this study, referred to as RCA and RFA, respectively. They consisted of a highly reactive natural sand from El Paso, Texas (RFA) and a moderate to highly reactive gravel from Bernallilo, New Mexico (RCA). The reactive aggregates were combined with local coarse and fine aggregates found to be non-reactive when tested in the ASTM C1293 concrete prism test. A high-alkali cement ($Na_2O_e = 0.80\%$) was used and sodium hydroxide was added to the mixtures to produce an alkali content of approximately 1.25% Na_2O_e. Table 1 shows the mixture proportions used for each of the reactive aggregates.

Specimen types included 20 unreinforced on-grade slabs, 22 reinforced bridge decks and 14 circular reinforced columns. The unreinforced slabs were $910 \times 910 \times 286$ mm in size. Reinforced bridge decks were $910 \times 910 \times 235$ mm and contained two layers of two-way steel reinforcement typical of bridge deck construction. The columns were 1219 mm in height by 610 mm in diameter and contained both primary vertical reinforcement and secondary spiral reinforcement. The sides of the slabs and bridge decks were sealed with epoxy paint to ensure that moisture ingress could only take place through the top or bottom of the specimen.

The specimens were instrumented for measuring expansions and for selected specimens, relative humidity. Visual inspection of the specimens was frequently conducted as well. Embedded stainless steel gauge studs were installed on 500 mm gauge lengths for most expansion measurements and monitored using a DEMEC gauge. For the slabs and bridge decks, three horizontal gauge lengths on two sides of the specimens, in addition to four gauge lengths on the top surface (Fig. 6). The gauge lengths on the sides of the slabs were located at depths of 64, 143 and 222 mm from the top surface, while those on the bridge decks were 51, 105 and 184 mm from the top surface. Two vertical gauge lengths were monitored on opposite sides of the columns (Fig. 7). Additionally, circumferential expansion of the columns was monitored using a stainless steel tape marked with a vernier scale with 0.03 mm precision (Fig. 7).

Monitoring was conducted under specific climatic conditions to minimize thermal and

Table 1. Mixture proportions for exposure site specimens.

Mix	w/cm	Water (kg/m³)	Cement (kg/m³)	Aggregate coarse	Fine (kg/m³)
RFA	0.42	176	420	1038	726
RCA	0.42	176	420	1038	751

*A water-reducing and retarding admixture was also used to provide sufficient workability.

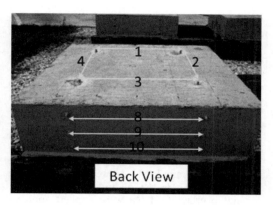

Figure 6. Expansion measurement locations on bridge deck specimen. A similar arrangement was used for the slabs. (Bentivegna 2009).

Figure 7. Column expansion measurements. 500 mm vertical gauge length (left) and circumference measurement (right). (Bentivegna 2009).

moisture effects on the data. An air temperature of 23 ± 1.5 °C with cloudy or mostly cloudy skies was required. Measurements were not taken during or immediately after rainfall events. Initial measurements were taken at an age of seven days. Several measurements were taken throughout the first year, with less frequent monitoring thereafter.

3.2 *Mitigation methods*

A number of mitigation methods were applied to the exposure site specimens. The specimens were allowed to expand and crack prior to application of the treatment to simulate the timing of mitigation measures in real field structures. Table 2 lists these methods and the number of specimens tested for each. They are described in greater detail below.

Table 2. Specimens selected for each mitigation method.

Method	Slabs	Decks	Columns
Control (untreated)	2 RFA	2 RFA	2 RFA
	2 RCA*	2 RCA	2 RCA
40% Silane	2 RFA	2 RFA	2 RFA
	2 RCA	2 RCA	2 RCA
100% Silane	2 RFA	2 RFA	2 RFA
	2 RCA	2 RCA	2 RCA
Membrane 1			1 RFA
			1 RCA
Membrane 1 + 50 mm concrete overlay		2 RFA	
		2 RCA	
Membrane 1 + 50 mm asphalt overlay		2 RFA	
		2 RCA	
Membrane 2		2 RCA	
50 mm asphalt overlay	2 RFA		
	2 RCA		
300 mm unbonded concrete overlay	2 RFA		
	2 RCA		

*Material variations in RCA slabs led to significant differences in the untreated control specimens. Where possible, comparisons were made to the appropriate control.

Two silane products were used: a water-based 40% silane and an isopropyl alcohol-based 100% silane. For the latter product, the MSDS lists the solvent as 2.0% by weight; the solids content is thus likely 98%, not 100%. Both silane treatments were applied at a rate of 0.33 L/m².

Two waterproof membranes were tested. Prior to membrane application, the surface of the bridge decks and columns were grit blasted. Membrane 1 was a methylmethacrylate (MMA) flexible waterproof membrane that was sprayed onto the specimens in two layers. No. 8 size angular aggregate was broadcast into the top layer to improve bond to subsequent overlays on bridge decks. A bituminous tack coat was also applied to the decks which would receive the 50 mm asphalt overlay. Membrane 2 was a combination waterproof MMA membrane and wearing course designed to seal and provide a new riding surface for damaged bridge decks that is much lighter than an asphalt or concrete pavement overlay.

Several overlays were also tested. All concrete overlays utilized a non-reactive mixture design and new gauge studs for top surface expansion measurements were installed. Concrete and asphalt overlays 50 mm thick were placed on selected bridge decks treated with Membrane 1. Asphalt overlays 50 mm in thickness were also applied directly onto the top surface of selected slabs. Unbonded concrete overlays 300 mm in thickness were applied to selected slab specimens; an asphalt layer 25 mm thick acted as a bond breaker between the overlay and substrate concrete.

3.3 Results

A new system for measuring relative humidity based on the work of Jensen (2000) is under development and has not yet been implemented on the exposure site. Therefore, the two criteria on which the mitigation methods will be evaluated are expansion since the time of treatment application and visual observation. When possible, a set of measurements was taken around the time of treatment. The most recent expansion measurements were taken between November 2010 and April 2011.

The 40% silane treatment was applied to the RFA specimens in January 2009 at an age of 143 to 145 days. Expansions were measured ten days after treatment and most recently in March and April 2011 for a total of over two years of post-treatment monitoring. Since that time, the slabs have expanded an average of 0.57%, compared to an average of 0.65% for the controls. The bridge decks have expanded an average of 0.22% compared to an average of 0.24% for the controls. The columns expanded 0.07% vertically and 0.30% in circumference compared to 0.11% and 0.33% for the controls.

The 40% silane treatment was applied to the RCA specimens in June 2009 at an age of 290 to 300 days. Expansions were measured approximately two months prior to the treatment and most recently in March and April 2011; nearly two years of post-treatment expansion data was recorded. The bridge decks have expanded an average of 0.02% compared to 0.10% for the controls. The columns expanded an average of 0.03% vertically and 0.06% in circumference, compared to 0.05% and 0.17% for the controls. Materials variations in several of the slabs selected for treatment made comparisons difficult.

The 100% silane treatment was applied to the RFA specimens at an age of 147 to 149 days. Expansions were measured six days after treatment and most recently in March and April 2011 for a total of over two years of post-treatment monitoring. Since that time, the slabs have expanded an average of 0.55%, compared to an average of 0.65% for the controls. The bridge decks have expanded an average of 0.17% compared to an average of 0.24% for the controls. The columns expanded 0.05% vertically and 0.30% in circumference compared to 0.11% and 0.33% for the controls.

The 100% silane treatment was applied to the RCA specimens at the same time as the 40% silane treatment; expansions were monitored on the same schedule as well. The bridge decks have expanded

an average of 0.02% compared to 0.10% for the controls. Figure 8 shows the average expansions for the treated and control bridge decks. Note the lack of expansion following treatment. The columns expanded an average of 0.00% vertically and 0.12% in circumference, compared to 0.05% and 0.17% for the controls. Materials variations in several of the slabs selected for treatment made comparisons difficult.

Membranes 1 and 2 were applied to RFA and RCA specimens in March 2009 at ages ranging from 214 to days. Concrete overlays of specimens that received Membrane 1 (M1+C) were applied in June 2009 at ages of 283 (RCA) and 287 (RFA) days. Asphalt overlays (M1+A) were applied approximately two weeks later. Since the installation of membranes and overlays destroyed the gauge studs used for top surface expansion measurements, only the side measurements will be compared. Reference measurements were taken shortly after installation of the membranes but prior to installation of the overlays. The most recent measurements were taken in March 2011.

During the post-treatment monitoring period, the RFA control specimens expanded an average of 0.14%. RFA bridge decks receiving M1+C and M1+A expanded 0.11% and 0.15%, respectively. RCA control specimens expanded 0.08% during this period while bridge decks receiving M1+C and M1+A both expanded 0.07%. RCA bridge decks receiving Membrane 2 also expanded 0.07%. The RFA and RCA columns receiving Membrane 1 could not be monitored adequately for expansion in the post-treatment period.

The expansions of the top surface of the concrete overlays (M1+C) were also monitored during this period. The overlays on the RFA bridge *decks contracted* slightly more than 0.02% after installation, while those on the RCA bridge decks showed no measurable expansion.

The 50 mm asphalt pavement overlays and 25 mm debonding layers were applied to the RCA

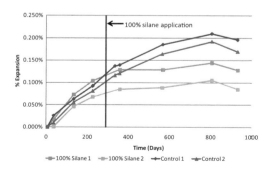

Figure 8. Expansions for 100% silane-treated and control RCA bridge decks.

and RFA slab specimens in June 2009 at ages of 296 and 300 days, respectively. The unbonded concrete overlays on the RFA and RCA slabs were placed in September 2009 at 385 and 386 days of age, respectively. As with the bridge deck overlays, only the side expansions of the substrate concrete were monitored after the overlay was installed. Reference measurements were taken in April and May 2009, for the RCA and RFA specimens, respectively. The most recent measurements were taken in March 2011 for the RFA slabs and November 2010 for the RCA slabs.

The RFA control slabs expanded an average of 0.58% during the post-treatment monitoring period. RFA slabs receiving the concrete and asphalt overlays expanded 0.48 and 0.53% during this period, respectively. The top surface expansion of the concrete overlays were also monitored and contracted less than 0.01%. The RCA control slab expanded 0.42%, while those with concrete and asphalt overlays expanded 0.28 and 0.30% during this period. The top surface of the RCA concrete overlays expanded 0.01%.

Qualitative visual inspection of the silane-treated specimens gave little indication of the performance of this method. The appearance was generally similar to the control specimens.

For the membrane- and overlay-treated specimens, visual inspection yielded some useful information. As seen in Figure 9, the expansion of the RFA bridge deck was sufficient to crack the first layer of Membrane 1, however the crack has not passed through the second layer or resulted in reflective cracking of the concrete overlay at this time. Figure 10 shows cracking that extended completely through Membrane 1 on an RFA column. The cracked area is above the top of the reinforcement cage and expansions in this region are likely higher than those measured in the central portion of the column. At the time of this writing, no

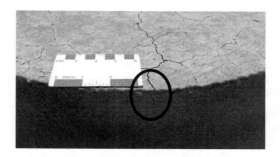

Figure 10. Crack (circled) that has passed completely through Membrane 1 on an RFA column.

Figure 11. RFA slab with 300 mm concrete overlay and 25 mm asphalt debonding layer.

failures of Membrane 1 have been observed on RCA bridge decks and columns. All asphalt and concrete overlays installed on the bridge decks appear to be in good condition. Some minor surface crazing is evident on the top surface of the concrete overlays, but no open cracks exist.

RCA bridge decks treated with Membrane 2 exhibit no signs of damage to the membrane at this time.

At the time of this writing, all asphalt and concrete overlays on the slab specimens appear to be in good condition, despite the continued and significant expansion of the substrate concrete. Figure 11 shows an RFA specimen with a 300 mm unbonded concrete overlay. The asphalt debonding layer is clearly visible and appears to have prevented reflective cracking of the overlay.

4 DISCUSSION

4.1 Field trials

In the Massachusetts field trial, all silane products were successful in reducing expansion relative to

Figure 9. Cracks (circled) in substrate concrete extending into the first layer of Membrane 1 on RFA bridge deck

the control barriers. The isopropyl alcohol-based silanes were slightly more effective than the water-based silane in this limited study. However, the expansions of the control barriers were still quite minimal over the course of the monitoring period. A slight reduction in internal relative humidity was measured, but the data are extremely limited.

In the Texas field trial, painted concrete columns treated with silane had similar or slightly less expansion relative to the untreated columns. Columns that were media-blasted prior to silane application had similar or significantly greater expansions than the untreated columns. This study was complicated by the lack of true control specimens. However, a comparison of blasted versus painted columns suggests that paint should not be removed from concrete prior to application of a silane.

4.2 Exposure site: Silane sealers

The 40% silane had minimal impact on the RFA specimens, but resulted in a significant reduction in expansion of the RCA specimens. In the case of the RCA bridge decks, expansion almost completely ceased following the treatment. The 100% silane resulted in a modest reduction in expansion of the RFA specimens relative to the controls and significant reduction in expansion of the RCA specimens. Expansion of the RCA bridge decks and vertical expansion of the RCA columns ceased or nearly did so.

Both silanes were more effective when used on reinforced specimens. It should be noted that vertical expansion was not measured on the bridge decks and may have been much greater than the horizontal expansions as no reinforcement was provided in this direction. Since the RFA control specimens exhibited greater expansions than the RCA specimens, it is unsurprising that the silane treatments were more effective in controlling expansion of the RCA specimens. Additional cracking caused by continued expansion after application of the silanes is likely to have provided avenues of moisture ingress so that the concrete was no longer waterproof; this has also been suggested by Kubo et al. (2000). Finally, since the bottom of the bridge decks were not sealed and the base of the slabs were exposed to ground moisture, moisture could still enter the concrete and contribute to expansion.

4.3 Exposure Site: Membranes and overlays

The waterproof membranes applied to the bridge decks were unsuccessful in significantly reducing expansion, however they do manage to cover the cracked surface and therefore mitigate the aesthetic damage caused by ASR. More importantly for bridge decks, they also provide a substantial barrier for chloride ingress and therefore could delay or

prevent the onset of corrosion in the reinforcement. The lack of expansion in the concrete overlays is an encouraging sign that Membrane 1 is able to accommodate expansion in the substrate concrete without transmitting this expansion to the overlay. However, the cracks observed to extend from the substrate through the first layer of Membrane 1 is cause for concern. Additional monitoring is required to determine how much expansion the membrane can tolerate without complete failure. The failure of Membrane 1 near the tops of the RFA columns should not yet be treated as a major cause of concern because the failure occurred in an unconfined region of the specimen.

The performance of Membrane 2 has been satisfactory, as it has fully accommodated the expansion of the substrate with no signs of distress. It should be noted that Membrane 2 was only tested on the less expansive RCA specimens and not the more expansive RFA bridge decks.

The asphalt and concrete overlays applied to the on-grade slabs have resulted in a small reduction in expansion relative to the control specimens. This is somewhat surprising considering that the membrane- and overlay-treated bridge decks saw no reduction in expansion. A significant amount of expansion still occurred in the substrate concrete of all slabs with overlays; the treatment was still unable to have a major impact on expansion. The debonding layer has been effective in preventing transmission of expansion and cracking of the substrate to the concrete overlays installed on both the RFA and RCA slabs.

A final concern with respect to overlays and impermeable membranes of any material is the total movement that must be accommodated when the substrate concrete is still expanding due to ASR. The pavement and bridge deck specimens could be considered full scale with respect to their depth, but not to their length and width. Even if the strain gradient can be accommodated locally, ASR can cause considerable damage if the structure runs out of room to accommodate movement. This can result in closing of and crushing at expansion joints. The impact of this can not be simulated with the specimens used in the exposure site study.

5 CONCLUSIONS

The following conclusions can be made from these studies:

- Breathable sealers such as silanes have the greatest potential for mitigating expansion due to ASR in existing structures.
- Some silanes are more effective than others. Testing or a database of past test results is needed to identify the most effective.

- Silanes can also mitigate the aesthetic damage caused by ASR.
- Continued expansion and uncoated surfaces can limit the effectiveness of silanes.
- Waterproof membranes and overlays are unable to significantly mitigate expansion due to ASR, but can mitigate some of the aesthetic damage.

ACKNOWLEDGEMENTS

The authors would like to acknowledge the support of our research sponsors, FHWA and TxDOT, as well as Transit Mix Concrete & Materials and Pumpco for their generous donation of ready mix concrete and pump truck services.

REFERENCES

Bentivegna, A.B. 2009. Development and monitoring of an outdoor exposure site to mitigate alkali-silica reaction in hardened concrete. MS Thesis. Austin: University of Texas at Austin.

Bérubé, M.-A., Chouinard, D., Pigeon, M., Frenette, J., Rivest, M. & Vézina, D. 2002. Effectiveness of sealers in counteracting alkali-silica reaction in highway median barriers exposed to wetting and drying, freezing and thawing, and deicing salt. *Canadian Journal of Civil Engineering* 29: 329–337.

Giannini, E.R. 2009. Field studies of mitigation strategies for alkali-silica reaction in hardened concrete. MS Thesis. Austin: University of Texas at Austin.

Harrington, D. 2008. *Guide to Concrete Overlays, 2nd Ed.* Ames, Iowa: National Concrete Pavement Technology Center.

Jensen, V. 2000. In-situ measurement of relative humidity and expansion of cracks in structures damaged by AAR. In M.-A. Bérubé, B. Fournier & B. Durand (Eds.) *Proceedings of the 11th International Conference on Alkali-Aggregate Reaction.* Québec City.

Kubo, Y., Hattori, A., Kurihara, S. & Miyagawa, T. 2000. Long term effect of silane treatments on expansion due to alkali-silica reaction by water control. In M.-A. Bérubé, B. Fournier & B. Durand (Eds.) *Proceedings of the 11th International Conference on Alkali-Aggregate Reaction.* Québec City.

McCoy, W. & Caldwell, A. 1951. A new approach to inhibiting alkali-aggregate expansion. *Journal of the American Concrete Institute* 22: 693–706.

Pednault, J. 1996. Development of testing and analytical procedures for the evaluation of the residual potential of reaction, expansion, and deterioration of concrete affected by ASR. M.Sc. Memoir. Québec City: Université Laval.

Stanton, T.E. 1940. Expansion of concrete through reaction between cement and aggregate. *Proc. of the American Society of Civil Engineers* 66: 1781–1811.

Stark, D. 1992. Lithium salt admixture—an alternative method to prevent expansive alkali-silica reactivity. *Proceedings of the 9th International Conference on Alkali-Aggregate Reaction.* London: The Concrete Society.

Stokes, D., Wang, H. & Diamond, S. 1997. A lithium-based admixture for ASR control that does not increase the pore solution pH. *Proceedings of the Fifth CANMET/ACI International Conference on Superplasticizers and Other Chemical Admixtures in Concrete: ACI SP-173:* 855–867. Skokie, Illinois: American Concrete Institute.

Wehrle, E.R. 2010. The effects of coatings and sealers used to mitigate alkali-silica reaction and/or delayed ettringite formation in hardened concrete. MS Thesis. Austin: University of Texas at Austin.

Whole life costing

Concrete Solutions – Grantham, Mechtcherine & Schneck (eds)
© 2012 Taylor & Francis Group, London, ISBN 978-0-415-61622-5

Life cycle cost analysis of reinforced concrete structures cast with self-compacting concrete and normally vibrated concrete

K.K. Sideris, A. Georgiadis, N. Anagnostopoulos & P. Manita
Democritus University of Thrace, Greece

E. Skarlatos
Tekton S.A Concrete Production Plant, Xanthi, Greece

ABSTRACT: Self Compacting Concrete (SCC), expresses different durability characteristics as compared with Normally vibrated Concrete (NC) of the same strength class mainly due to its advanced internal structure.

The main purpose of this research is to study the carbonation and chloride induced corrosion resistance of different SCCs of the strength classes C25/30 and C30/37. Based on the experimental results, the life cycle cost of reinforced concrete structures was estimated. It was found that SCC results to lower total life cycle cost as compared with the NC of the same strength class, especially when the carbonation resistance of the structure is of main concern.

1 INTRODUCTION

Self compacting concrete is considered as the most revolutionary development in concrete technology during the last century. The ability of the material to flow under its own weight and fill the formwork without any additional compaction results in different financial, technical and environmental benefits. However SCC still remains more expensive comparing with NC of the same strength class; The initial cost of SCC may be 5% to 25% higher than the initial cost of NC, depending on the strength class and the availability of fine materials. This difference is in many cases considered as the main disadvantage resulting in slower consumption of SCC by the technical market.

On the other hand SCC improves the quality of cast elements, resulting in increased durability (Sideris et al., 2003, RILEM TC 205, 2007). The initiation period during the service life of reinforced concrete structures cast with SCC is therefore increased, while the number or repairs needed for a specific structure to reach the initially scheduled life time is limited. These two factors reduce the overall cost of SCC.

The main purpose of this research is to study the carbonation and chloride induced corrosion resistance of different SCC of the strength classes C25/30 and C30/37 and to calculate their overall life cycle costs. Based on the experimental results, the life cycle cost of reinforced concrete structures was estimated. It was found that SCC results in a lower total life cycle cost as compared with the NC of the same strength class. When the carbonation resistance of the structure is the main concern, this reduction may be high up to 65%.

2 MATERIALS—EXPERIMENTAL PROCEDURE

The basic properties of SCC are the filling ability, the segregation resistance and the passing ability. Rheology of the cement paste is the crucial factor in order to fulfill the above requirements. Self compactibility is strongly connected with the dosage of fine materials. All materials passing the 0.125 mm sieve are considered as fine materials.

According to the European Guidelines for Self Compacting Concrete (Efnarc, 2005), the quantity of fine materials per cubic meter of concrete should be in the range of 380–600 Kg. A small quantity of Viscosity Modified Agent (VMA) may be also necessary to improve the segregation resistance of SCC in some cases, especially when the fine content of the mixture is close to the lower limits mentioned above.

A total of 6 concrete mixtures—four SCC and two normally vibrated concretes—were produced in this study. The mixtures were of the strength grades C25/30 and C30/37 as defined in the EN206-1 Standard. The cements used were of the type CEM II/A-M 42.5 N and CEM/IIA-M 32.5 N according to the EN197-1 Standard. The coarse

Table 1. Mix design (kg/m³) and rheological characteristics of concretes prepared.

	NCC 25/30	SCC25/30-1	SCC25/30-2	NCC30/37	SCC30/37-1	SCC30/37-2
CEM II42.5	50	51	51	130	130	130
CEM II32.5	300	305	304	305	305	305
Lim. Filler	–	101	50	–	50	–
Crushed lim. sand.	–	882	945	–	880	945
River sand	980	–	–	1110	–	–
Coarse aggregates	850	800	800	760	800	800
Water	191	193	189	187	188	182
Superpl/er	0.7%	1.60% (5.7 kg)	1.64% (5.81 kg)	1.1%	1.55% (6.74 kg)	2.3% (10 kg)
Retarder	–	0.45% (1.60 kg)	0.30% (1.06 kg)	–	0.30% (1.31 kg)	0.30% (1.31 kg)
VMA	–	–	0.30% (1.06 kg)	–	–	0.45% (1.96 kg)
w/c	0.54		0.53	0.43	0.43	0.42
w/p	0.54		0.47	0.43	0.39	0.42
Slump (cm)	18			16		
Flow (cm)		75	77		75	77
L-box (H_2/H_1)		0.80	0.95		1	1
V-funnel (sec)		17	7			

*** Superplasticizer lt/100 Kg cement.

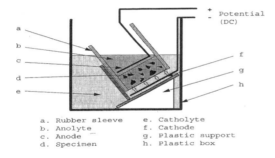

a. Rubber sleeve   e. Catholyte
b. Anolyte   f. Cathode
c. Anode   g. Plastic support
d. Specimen   h. Plastic box

Figure 1. Test device used for estimation of chloride diffusion coefficient De. (NT Built 492, 1999).

aggregates were of silicate origin with a maximum grain size of 16 mm.

The normally vibrated concretes were prepared with the use of natural river sand. In the case of self compacting concretes the sand used was of crushed limestone origin. Limestone filler was used as fine material. The amount of limestone filler was kept in low levels because of the limited availability of this in the construction site. A proper quantity of VMA was added in some mixtures due to the low content of fine materials. Mix design characteristics and rheological properties of all mixtures are presented in Table 1.

The compressive strength of all mixtures was assessed on 150 mm cube specimens cured in the curing chamber (T = 20°C and R.H. = 98%) until the age of the test. Carbonation depth was measured on cylindrical (Φ60/100 mm) specimens).

These specimens were initially cured for three days in the curing chamber and for 25 more days in the laboratory environment (T = 20 ± 2°C, R.H. = 55–65%). At the age of 28 days cylindrical specimens were moved to a carbonation chamber (CO_2 = 10%, T = 20 ± 2°C, R.H. = 65%) where they remained for six more weeks.

Chloride diffusion resistance of the concretes was also assessed on cylindrical specimens with a diameter of 100 mm and a height of 50 mm. These specimens were cured as above till the age of 28 days. The chloride diffusion coefficient D_e was then measured according to the procedure described in NT Built 492 (Figure 1).

3 EXPERIMENTAL RESULTS

3.1 Compressive strength

Compressive strength was measured for all mixtures al the ages of 7 and 28 days. These values are presented in Table 1.

3.2 Carbonation depth

Carbonation depth was measured by spraying the fresh broken surfaces of concretes with a phenol-opthalein indicator, according to the procedure described in the EN 14630 Standard. The relative carbonation depth d = d_i/d_{ref} (where d_i = carbonation depth of tested concrete, d_{ref} = carbonation depth of reference concrete) of all mixtures is plotted on Figure 2.

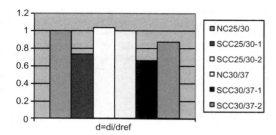

Figure 2. Relative carbonation depth of self compacting and normally vibrated concretes prepared.

Table 2. Chloride diffusion coefficients $D_C (10^{-12}$ m²/s) of self compacting and normally vibrated concretes prepared.

	NC 25/30	SCC 25/30–1	SCC 25/30–2	NC 30/37	SCC 30/37–1	SCC 30/37–2
D_C	44.53	35.88	52.39	28.3	22.10	32.79

3.3 Chloride diffusion coefficient

The chloride diffusion coefficient values D_e measured according to NT Built 492 are presented for all mixtures in Table 2.

4 DISCUSSION OF THE RESULTS

The compressive strength of all SCC mixtures prepared was increased as compared with those of the reference concrete mixtures of the same grade. This strength increase is mainly attributed to the better compaction achieved in SCC mixtures as well as to the improved interfacial transition zone.

The carbonation depth of SCC mixtures was in all cases equal to or lower than that of the reference NC. The improved performance of SCC mixtures against carbonation attack was also reported by other researchers (Trägardh: 1999, De Schutter et al., 2003, Heirman et al., 2006). This phenomenon is mainly attributed to the different pore size distribution formed in the case of SCC (Boel et al., 2007) and is more intense in mixtures with high w/c ratio as in this research.

Based on the experimental results the carbonation depth equations were set up for all mixtures prepared. (Figure 3).

Using the above formed equation the service life of reinforced concrete structures against carbonation induced corrosion was assessed. This is plotted in Table 3.

The following assumptions were made:

$t_L = ti + tp$

where t_L = the total service life of the structure, ti = the time for initiation of corrosion,

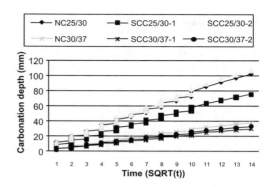

Figure 3. Carbonation depth of SCC and NC mixtures prepared.

Table 3. Service life of reinforced concrete structures due to carbonation induced corrosion.

	NC 25/30	SCC 25/30–1	SCC 25/30–2	NC 30/37	SCC 30/37–1	SCC 30/37–2
Time (years)	27	41	26	130	204	170
Increase (%)	–	52	–0,5	–	56	30

$$t_i = \left(\frac{x}{k}\right)^2,$$

k = carbonation coefficient of concrete
tp = the propagation period.
Exposure class: XC3, according to EN206-1.
Minimum clear cover of the reinforcement: 30 mm, according to the Greek Standards.
Propagation period tp: 10 years.

Reinforced concrete structures cast with SCC perform an increased service life up to 50% as compared with those of structures produced with NC. This is valid mainly for the mixtures with high dosages of limestone filler. VMA type SCC mixtures with small dosages of limestone filler do not perform with such an increase: the service life increase of SCC30/37-2 was30% instead of 56% in the case of SCC30/37-1, whereas SCC25/30-2 performed with roughly the same carbonation depth as reference concrete NC25/30. The different carbonation resistance behaviour is attributed to the lack of fine filler material of VMA mixtures.

Fine filler material is also the reason that differentiates the results when chloride diffusion coefficient is studied. However in this case the performance of SCC mixtures is not much improved, because of the different nature of the corrosion mechanism. Several researchers (Rougeau et al., 1999, Trägardh 1999) have also reported that the chloride diffusion coefficient is not significantly changed among normally vibrated and self compacting concretes produced with the same w/c ratio. Zhu and Bartos, (2003) produced SCC and NC concretes with compressive strength of 40 and 60 MPa at the age of 28 days. The SCC mixtures were of filler type (limestone filler or fly ash) and VMA type. They concluded that when only VMA was used for the production of SCC without incorporation of additional filler material the chloride diffusion coefficient measured was higher than that of the reference concrete, irrespective of the strength grade of the mixture.

Chloride diffusion coefficients measured in this study are presented in Table 2. The equation introduced by Tuuti was also used for the estimation of the service life of concrete structures against chloride induced corrosion as well. In this case the initiation time t_i was calculated by using the second Fick's law. Advanced P/C software was used (M.A. Ehlen, M.D.A. Thomas and E.C. Bentz, 2009). The following assumptions were made:

Exposure class: XS3, according to EN206-1.
Minimum clear cover of the reinforcement: 45 mm according to the Greek Standards.
Propagation period tp: 10 years.
Temperature conditions: Mediterranean zone.

The estimated service life values are presented for all mixtures in Table 4.

Using the data of Tables 3 and 4 the relative cost per cubic meter as well as per year of the structure's life for the SCC mixtures was calculated. The relative cost values of all mixtures are presented in Table 5.

Self compacting concretes have a higher production cost compared with the normally vibrated concretes of the same strength class. Increased quantities of chemical admixtures—superplasticizer and VMA- and fine materials required to achieve self compactability are the key factors responsible for this. It seems that the difference in production cost depends on the type of SCC—powder type, VMA type or mixed type—as well as on the strength grade; as we move to higher strength,

Table 4. Estimated total service life of reinforced concrete structures due to chloride induced corrosion.

	NC 25/30	SCC 25/30 -1	SCC 25/30 -2	NC 30/37	SCC 30/37 -1	SCC 30/37 -2
Service life (years)	34	36	33	37	40	36
Increase (%)	–	5.9	–2.9	–	8.1	–2.7

Table 5. Relative production and service life cost of SCC and NC produced.

	SCC 25/30–1	SCC 25/30–2	SCC 30/37–1	SCC 30/37–2
Relative production cost (% of relative NC, Euros/m³)	117	110	104	108
Difference in service life cost (relative cost per year of service life) (% of relative NC- CO_2)	–23.17	14.23	–65	–63
Difference in service life cost (relative cost per year of service life) (% of relative NC- Cl)	11	13	–2.7	12

the difference is smaller and is limited to only 4% for SCC30/37-1 (powder type SCC30/37). This is explained by the higher amount of cement and superplasticizer required by reference concretes as well.

It is also observed that the relative service life cost of SCC mixtures is reduced, due to the increased durability observed. When carbonation resistance is of main concern, the service life cost of SCC mixtures is in almost all cases reduced; this reduction may be up to 65% of the reference concrete's relative cost. This is, of course, depending on the type of SCC mixture.

In the case of chloride induced corrosion resistance, service life cost is once again lower in two SCCs. However, due to the different behaviour of SCC against chloride induced corrosion—their durability was improved but not as much as in the case of carbonation- this trend is not so clear while it is observed only in the powder type SCC produced.

5 CONCLUSIONS

The initial production cost of self compacting concretes is increased as compared with that of relative normally vibrated concretes of the same strength class. This is attributed to the increased quantities of chemical admixtures and fine filler materials needed for the production of SCC. The difference in production cost depends on the strength grade and the type of SCC.

SCC mixtures perform with different durability characteristics compared to the relative NC. The increased quantity of fine materials as well as the better compaction achieved are responsible for their refined pore structure which leads to improved durability resistance. Resistance against chloride induced corrosion was not as noticeable in the SCC mixtures produced in this research.

The improved durability of SCC has a significant effect on the service life cost of reinforced concrete structures. In spite their increased initial production cost, their service life cost, expressed as the production cost per year of service life, is usually lower as compared with the service life cost of normally vibrated concretes. This is depending on the strength grade and the type of the self compacting concrete produced.

REFERENCES

BIBM, CEMBUREAU, EFCA, EFNARC, ERMCO: European Guidelines for Self-Compacting Concrete: Specification, Production and Use, May 2005, *downlodable from www.efnarc.org*

Boel, V., Audenaert, K., De Schutter, G., Heirman, G., Vanderwalle, L., Desmer, B. & Bantomme, J.: "Transport properties of self-compacting concrete with limestone filler or fly ash", Materials and Structures, Vol. 40 (5), (2007), pp. 507–516.

Comite Européenne de Normalisation: « Concrete - Part 1: Specification, Performance, Production and Conformity », EN 206-1, (2000).

De Schutter, G., Audenaert, K., Boel, V., Vandewalle, L., Dupont, D., Heirman, G., Vantomme, J. & D'Hemricourt, J: (2003). "Transport properties in self consolidating concrete and relation with durability: Overview of a Belgian research project", Proc., Third Int. Symp. on SCC, RILEM, Reycjavik, Iceland, (Eds. Wallenik O. and Nielsson I), (2003), pp. 799–807.

EN 14630: Comité Européenne de Normalisation EN14630: Products and systems for the protection and repair of concrete structures—Test methods—Determination of carbonation depth in hardened concrete by the phenolphthalein method, (2006).

Heirman, G., Vandewalle, L., Boel, V., Audernaert, K., De Schutter, G., D'Hemricourt, J., Desmet, B. & Vantomme, J.: "Chloride penetration and carbonation in self-compacting concrete", International RILEM-JCI Seminar on Concrete Durability and Service Life Planning, March 14–16, (2006), Dead-Sea, Israel, pp. 13–23.

NT Built 492: Concrete, Mortar and Cement-based Repair Materials: Chloride Migration Coefficient from Non-Steady Migration Experiments, NTBuild, (1999).

RILEM TC205 Durability of self-compacting concrete, State of the Art Report, RILEM Publications S.A.R.L., Report 38, ISBN978-2-35158-048-6, (2007).

Rougeau, P., Maillard, J.L. & Mary-Dippe, C.: "Comparative study on properties of self-compacting and high-performance concrete used in precast construction", in Proc. 1st International RILEM Symposium on Self-Compacting Concrete, (1999), pp. 251–261.

Sideris, K.K., Kyritsas, S. & Haniotakis, E.: "Mechanical Characteristics and Durability of Self Compacting Concretes produced with Greek materials", Proceedings of the 14th Greek Concrete Conference, Kos Island, October 15–17, 2003, Vol. B', pp. 187–193 (in Greek).

Trägardh: "Microstructural features and related properties of self-compacting concretes", Proceedings of the First International RILEM Symposium on Self-Compacting Concrete, (Eds. Skarendahl A. and Petersson Ö), Sweden, (1999), pp. 175–186.

Zhu, M. & Bartos, P.J.M.: "Permeation properties of self-compacting concrete", Cement and Concrete Research, Vol. 33, 6, (2003), pp. 921–926.

Concrete Solutions – Grantham, Mechtcherine & Schneck (eds)
© 2012 Taylor & Francis Group, London, ISBN 978-0-415-61622-5

Epoxy-coated reinforcement—life cycle cost considerations

M. Zintel, C. Gehlen & B. Prust
Centre for Building Materials, Technische Universität München, Munich, Germany

ABSTRACT: To ensure the usability of German traffic infrastructure made of reinforced concrete, enormous annual expenditure is required. Unplanned high chloride loads due to de-icing salts are the ultimate cause of much corrosion damage and the resulting costs of repair. To achieve an improved durability of reinforced concrete structures, Epoxy-Coated Reinforcement (ECR) can be used. The assessment of the corrosion protection potential of such a system is the objective of a current research project. This paper presents a cost-benefit analysis of ECR by the means of realistic simulated scenarios (inter alia full probabilistic service life predictions, practical maintenance varieties) over the whole service life a structure. Just based on economic considerations the necessary extra service life by the use of ECR compared to normal black steel (uncoated) is calculated.

1 INTRODUCTION

About 40 years ago epoxy-coated reinforcement for concrete structures was developed and since then more and more used, particularly in North America (in 2009: already more than 60,000 bridges exist), although early corrosion damage e.g. in Florida became well known. Up-to-date, the technologies and know-how of resin syntheses and application appear to be significantly improved. Therefore this kind of protection against corrosion should be reconsidered (especially in Europe). The motivation for an ongoing research project is the quantitative assessment of the corrosion protection potential of such a product. Due to higher costs of application, a return of investment over the life cycle of a structure should be achievable. As a benchmark for upcoming findings regarding the effect of corrosion protection of ECR, the necessary extra service life through its application compared to uncoated rebars (black steel) can first be evaluated by economic considerations.

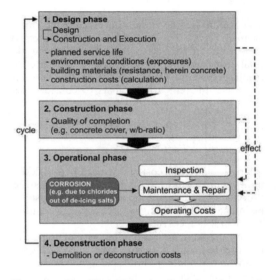

Figure 1. Simplified life cycle of reinforced concrete structures.

2 LIFE CYCLE OF REINFORCED CONCRETE STRUCTURES

Over the life cycle of traffic infrastructure made of reinforced concrete, four phases can be distinguished, see Figure 1. At first the "Design Phase" where fundamental decisions concerning the architectural design, the necessary construction, the planned service life and the cost budget have to be made; also detailed information about the location and orientation of exposed construction elements is essential (regarding environmental impacts,

e.g. chlorides). Because just based on the right assumption of real environmental conditions the most suitable building material (herein concrete: type of cement, w/b-ratio) can be selected and implemented in appropriate constructive designs (e.g. concrete cover).

Once the iterative design phase is successfully completed the structure can be built. In the so called "Construction Phase" the quality of execution (e.g. w/b-ratio) and the fulfillment of design specifications (e.g. concrete cover) are of importance.

After completion of the structure the third phase begins, the so called "Operational Phase". All considered parameters out of the first two phases have a major influence on the performance of the structure in operation. Costs for inspection strongly depend on size, execution, accessibility and should be adequate to the condition state of a structure (Schießl et al. 2011). The costs for maintenance and repair due to corrosion problems have a considerable correlation to the ratio of impact (environment) and resistance (concrete). Both arising costs over the service life of a structure determine the total operating costs.

When arriving at the end of the designated service life of a structure, costs for demolition and deconstruction have to be considered ("Deconstruction Phase").

With a novel "Design Phase" for a possible new structure a new life cycle starts again.

3 LIFE CYCLE COSTS

The objective of an optimized maintenance management regime is to guarantee structural integrity and unconditional usability by minimizing the total costs over the service life of a structure. As mentioned before, over the life cycle of a structure there are different arising costs to consider. See Equation 1 below:

$$C_{TOTAL} = C_{CON} + C_{INSP} + C_{M\&R} \atop + C_{FAIL\&DECON} \qquad (1)$$

where C_{TOTAL} = total cost of a structure from design until deconstruction; C_{CON} = design and construction costs; C_{INSP} = inspection costs; $C_{M\&R}$ = costs for maintenance and repair; and $C_{FAIL\&DECON}$ = failure and demolition costs.

In order to maintain the integrity of the structure up to a given future date, a cost-effective maintenance strategy should be applied, precisely because the total operating costs are dominated by the costs for maintenance and repair.

3.1 Costs for maintenance and repair

Symbolic for other European countries, the German federal highway network comprises 38,000 bridges, 90% of the bridges are reinforced or prestressed concrete bridges (BMVBS 2006). About 40% of the bridges display damage which needs to be repaired in the next years (status: 2007). Around 70% of the registered damage at bridges can be assigned to reinforcement corrosion which can be initiated by the carbonation of concrete or even more by the penetration of chlorides (de-icing salts) to the steel surface, see Figure 2.

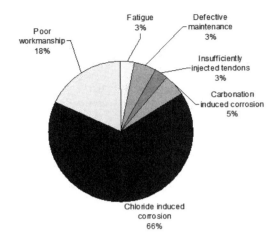

Figure 2. Causes of damage to bridge structures of the German motorway network (Schießl & Mayer 2007).

In 2005 alone, approx. 275 Mio. Euros had to be spent for maintenance and repair of bridges and civil engineering structures within the German motorway network. About 20% (approx. 54 Mio. Euro) of these expenditures were accounted to concrete repair actions. As damage caused by chlorides represents the most frequent damage in reinforced concrete structures, this paper concentrate on the mechanism, model and limit state for a durability design with respect to chloride induced reinforcement corrosion. A later transfer to carbonation induced corrosion will be possible without any problems.

4 PROBABILISTIC DETERIORATION MODELS

4.1 Process of deterioration

The actual life of traffic infrastructures (e.g. bridges and underground parking structures) mostly depends on the technical service life of the construction and thus also on the environmental impacts.

Normally the reinforcement in concrete is protected from corrosion by the high alkalinity of concrete's pore solution (high pH value). A thin iron oxide layer on the surface of the steel, the so called passive layer, protects the steel. This passive layer can be destroyed either by carbonation of concrete or by ingress of chlorides. Concrete structures that are exposed to de-icing salts or seawater may deteriorate from corrosion due to chloride attack.

In the process of degradation (chloride and carbonation induced corrosion) two periods can be distinguished, see Figure 3.

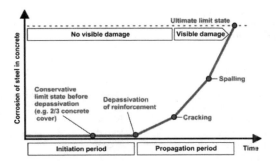

Figure 3. Time dependent development of reinforcement corrosion (Schießl et al. 2011).

During the first period, the so called "Initiation period", chlorides penetrate due to different transportation mechanisms from the element surface into the concrete. Damage of the reinforcement itself will not occur in this period. The "Initiation period" ends with the depassivation of the steel surface, once the chloride concentration at the steel surface exceeds a critical value (Breit 1997).

The actual reinforcement corrosion just appears in the subsequent "Propagation period". Crack formations and spalling of the concrete cover as first visual consequences of reinforcement corrosion just emerge in the advanced stage, when it's mostly already too late for an economic optimized intervention.

Approved full-probabilistic models for the depassivation of the reinforcement are available, see section 4.2.

4.2 Deterioration models

In general, design processes are based on the comparison of the resistance of the structure (R) with the applied load (S). Failure appears when the resistance is lower than the load. As the loads on a construction and the resistance are mostly variable (e.g. due to workmanship etc.), S and R cannot be compared in a deterministic way. The decision has to be based on maximum acceptable failure probabilities. The probability of failure p_f, describes the case when a variable resistance R is lower than a variable load S. This probability is required to be lower than the target probability of failure, p_{target}:

$$p_f = p\{R - S < 0\} \leq p_{target} \qquad (2)$$

With the limit state function $Z = R - S$ (R and S are distributed parameters with mean value μ and standard deviation σ) it is possible to calculate the reliability Z of the construction. If the variables S and R are normally distributed, the reliability of the construction Z itself is also normally distributed. Herein negative values define

the failure probability p_f. The reliability index β describes the distance of the mean value of variable Z to the abscissa in relation to its standard deviation. Therefore, a bigger reliability yields a smaller failure probability. This safety concept is shown in Figure 4 and Equation (3).

$$p_f = \int_{-\infty}^{\infty} f_S \cdot F_R \cdot dx = \Phi\left(-\frac{\mu_R - \mu_S}{\sqrt{\sigma_R^2 + \sigma_S^2}}\right) = \Phi\left(\frac{\mu_Z}{\sigma_Z}\right)$$
$$= \Phi(-\beta) \qquad (3)$$

The time and depth dependent chloride content can be modelled according to (FIB 34, Gehlen 2000):

$$p_f = p\{C_{crit} - C_{S,\Delta x} \cdot \left[1 - erf \frac{d_c - \Delta x}{2 \cdot \sqrt{k_e \cdot k_t \cdot D_{RCM,0} \cdot t \cdot \left(\frac{t_0}{t}\right)^a}}\right] < 0\} \qquad (4)$$

$$k_e = \exp\left(b_e\left(\frac{1}{T_{ref}} - \frac{1}{T_{IST}}\right)\right) \qquad (5)$$

This model is based on Fick's second law of diffusion presuming that diffusion is the dominant transport mechanism. As diffusion does not cover the transport mechanisms for an intermittent chloride penetration, Fick's second law is modified by neglecting the data until reaching the depth of the convection zone Δx and starting with a substitute surface concentration of $C_{S,\Delta x}$. This simplification provides good accordance to in situ analyses, but also leads to higher uncertainties when low concrete covers are present or calculations over short periods of time are conducted. The model input parameters are displayed in Table 1.

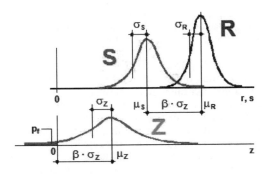

Figure 4. Safety concept for a full-probabilistic service life design.

843

Table 1. Input parameters of the chloride penetration model after (Gehlen 2000).

No.	Variable	Unit	Distribution/value	Description
1	$C_{S,\Delta x}$	[wt.-%/c]	Measurement/ literature	Substitute surface chloride concentration at depth Δx
2	Δx	[mm]	BetaD $0 \leq \Delta x \leq 50$ ($\mu = 8.9$; $\sigma = 5.6$)	Depth of the convection zone
3	$T_{IST}(k_e)$	[K]	ND ($\mu = 284.7$; $\sigma = 7$)	Element temperature
4	$D_{RCM,0}$	[mm²/a]	Measurement/ literature	Rapid chloride migration coefficient
5	a	[–]	Measurement/ literature	Ageing exponent
6	d_c	[mm]	Measurement/ literature	Concrete cover
7	C_{crit}	[wt.-%/c]	BetaD $0.2 \leq \Delta x \leq 2.0$ ($\mu = 0.6$; $\sigma = 0.15$)	Critical chloride content
8	$b_e(k_e)$	[–]	ND ($\mu = 4800$; $\sigma = 700$)	Regression variable
9	$T_{ref}(k_e)$	[K]	293	Reference temperature
10	k_t	[–]	1.0	Test transfer parameter
11	t0	[a]	0.0767	Reference time

The derivation of the input parameters can be found in (Gehlen 2000).

5 MAINTENANCE STRATEGIES

Structural integrity has to be guaranteed by considering the most extreme service conditions in order to ensure the safety of the structure and its users. Due to the deterioration, the relative structural performance decreases and can only be regained by intervention actions.

In most cases the decision for a single intervention is just made from an economical point of view and most often just considers the actual cost of work and neglects the durability of the repairs themselves (repetition of repairs). In order to investigate appropriate maintenance strategies, target safety levels (β_{target}: operator requirements) and optimum maintenance strategies must be formulated and resolved from the background of lifetime reliability and lifecycle cost.

The ability to model the deterioration of different kinds of concrete (type of cement) under different environmental exposure conditions and concrete covers (see table 1) allows, besides a reliable actual condition, assessment a forecast far into the future. Nowadays, this can be reflected in strategies for maintenance and repair.

Basic requirements for the selection of a standard intervention measure (e.g. concrete coating as an intervention action according to a preventive maintenance strategy or concrete replacement as

a reactive strategy) is the guarantee of minimum reliabilities (β_{min}: Serviceability Limit State (SLS), after (DAfStb 2008)) over the remaining service life of a structure.

In principle concrete coatings work as a barrier for chlorides present and preserve the actual condition state due to desiccation of the concrete. The replacement of the existing chloride-containing concrete leads to a recovery of the protective alkalinity and restores the original condition after construction.

Considering that intervention costs in practice have an impact on the relative reliability level, consequently previous maintenance expenditure also has a significant effect on the current reliability and maintenance costs in the future.

This correlation is illustrated schematically in Figure 5 for a reactive and a proactive maintenance strategy.

The proactive strategy usually requires frequent expenditure resulting in a structure that stays in good condition throughout its operational service life whereas the reactive strategy is accompanied by intense investment in rehabilitation as soon as the structure reaches poor condition.

In order to have detailed information about the current condition state of a structure, regular inspections are essential. Therefore the necessary effort of inspection should depend on the present condition state of the structure itself (Schießl et al. 2011).

When considering different strategies for maintenance a cost-benefit analysis over the remaining service life can mark out the "best" choice. In this

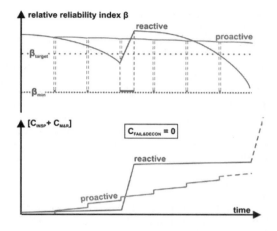

Figure 5. Relative costs of reactive and proactive structure management (Schießl et al. 2011).

technical-economic optimization, the discounting method to provide present day values of anticipated future costs can be used.

Besides the standard intervention measures according to a pro—or reactive maintenance strategy (concrete coating or replacement) various methods or systems for corrosion protection of reinforced concrete are available on the market. One promising option is the application of epoxy-coated reinforcement.

6 EPOXY-COATED REINFORCEMENT (ECR)

6.1 General

Since the 1970s, epoxy-coated reinforcement for concrete structures has been increasingly applied in North America to achieve an enhanced protection against corrosion of the reinforcement under aggressive environmental conditions, especially under chloride impact. Due to early corrosion damage of epoxy-coated reinforcement in the late-1980s at the Florida Key Bridges (USA) the coating technology of resins and application was further improved and developed significantly (Hartley 1994).

6.2 Corrosion protection potential

With the application of ECR at least one, rather several conditions for reinforcement corrosion should be eliminated:

- Depassivating media should be kept away from the steel (especially chlorides).
- Oxygen supply should be minimized

- The aqueous electrolyte (concrete) should be shielded from the steel
- The formation of potential differences should be prevented

All above-mentioned effects are closely linked to the impermeability of the epoxy coating itself. However, epoxy coatings like all other organic polymers are just marginally impermeable against water and oxygen. Therefore corrosion processes under such a marginally impermeable coating cannot be excluded totally. The corresponding transport mechanisms are generally diffusion controlled. Besides the transportation mechanism also knowledge about the storage mechanisms of encapsulated water (quantity of transported and embedded water and oxygen) are substantial for the durability assessment of epoxy coatings.

From this, significant requirements to guarantee the corrosion protection can be derived as follows:

- Quality of the material (water absorption, diffusion characteristics etc.)
- Quality of production (coatings thickness, number and size of defects etc.)
- Quality of adhesion (bond strength between reinforcement and coating)

In respect of treatment and endurance of ECR, additional requirements for a practical application are obligatory:

- Alkali resistance (in concrete: pH = 13)
- Bending capacity (no cracks, disbondment or squashing)
- Handling safety (operational demands on building site, e.g. transportation and installation)
- Possibility of repair (suitable patching material)
- Storage stability (to weather, UV radiation)
- Bond (sufficient bond strength: reinforcement/ coating and coating/concrete)
- Dynamic stress (no cracks, damages)
- Aging (load dependent and independent)

Besides all possible mastered challenges for a successful application, the process of production and the following installation on site cannot guarantee a completely defect-free product.

The question of the corrosion progress over time and in this case the modeling of existing degradation processes of such a system with no or a still tolerable number of defects is the subject of a current research project. A schematic illustration of the possible corrosion protection effect compared to black steel is displayed in Figure 6.

Anticipating future research results regarding an achievable extra service life due to the possible corrosion protection effect of ECR economic considerations can be conducted by cost-benefit analysis.

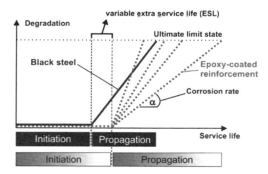

Figure 6. Possible corrosion protection effect of ECR compared to black steel.

7 COST-BENEFIT ANALYSIS OF ECR

7.1 General

An economic efficiency study is an assessment tool to identify the best option out of several possibilities. In this case, the study represents a decision support to select the maintenance strategy with the lowest investments over the entire service life of a structure (proactive or reactive,see section 5) out of a wide range of sceneries (see section 7.2).

In comparison to the most economical strategy an application of ECR with higher initial costs and additional costs of repair is considered. In this connection, the objective is to calculate a benchmark for the necessary corrosion protection effect of ECR simply based on economic aspects.

Fundamental variables in a cost-benefit analysis are estimates or plausible assumptions. On that account it is important to note that an anticipated economic feasibility study of ECR just can be used as a rough reference for upcoming quantitative test results regarding the real corrosion protection potential of such a system. This is the objective of a current research project.

7.2 Approach

Based on service life calculations (see section 4) under different parameters the point of time for intervention actions (constant intervention intervals at the same concrete compositions) can be calculated over the entire service life of a structure for a proactive and a reactive strategy. The necessary indicating Serviceability Limit States (SLS) for chloride induced corrosion are identical for both considered exposure classes:

– XD3 (alternately wet and dry condition)
– XD2 (wet, seldom dry)

In general the lowest safety boundary is $\beta_{SLS} = 0.5$ or $\beta_{SLS} = 1.5$ if the construction is hard

to access or regularly inspections are not possible (DAfStb 2008).

Regarding the proactive strategy (concrete coating) a higher safety level compared to the reactive strategy has to be guaranteed (no depassivation due to chlorides). This is realized by means of a fictive reduced concrete cover ($2/3\ d_c$), see figure 3. The intervention interval for renewing the concrete coating (after the initial intervention action) is set to a fixed value of 10 years. This conservative assumption fits to research results regarding the durability of concrete coatings (Raupach 2004) and should preserve the present condition state of the structure at a high safety level with minimal losses.

The calculated point of time (year before the limit β_{SLS} is reached) when the reliability index falls below the certain limit is called "$\Delta T_{REP,\ reactive}$" for the reactive and "$\Delta T_{REP,\ proactive}$" for the proactive strategy. This connection is displayed in the upper two illustrations of Figure 7 regarding the proactive and reactive strategies.

With additional information of real costs for single intervention actions, it is feasible to estimate the whole life cycle costs for both scenarios and mark out the most cost-efficient option (see e.g. sum of grey bars for each strategy over the planned service life, figure 7).

Taking the strategy with the lowest life cycle costs as a benchmark the minimal necessary extra service life of epoxy coated reinforcements (ESL in years) compared to black steel can be calculated as follows. With the knowledge of the higher initial investment due to the application of ECR and additional costs of repair (higher workload

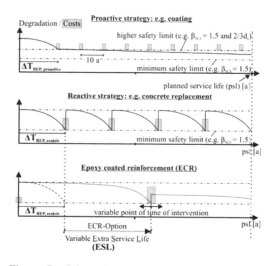

Figure 7. Schematic illustration of the developed approach.

due to manual patch repair of ECR) for a single intervention measure the fictive life cycle costs for varying intervention intervals (in one-year steps) can be calculated. The solution (ESL) is obtained from an iterative process where the length of the intervention intervals were scheduled in one-year steps up to a certain value (years) which barely leads to the lower deviation of the cost-benchmark. Taking this result as the necessary intervention interval (corresponds to the sum of $\Delta T_{REP, \text{ reactive}}$ + Extra Service Life (ESL), see figure 7) the necessary Extra Service Life (ESL) compared to black steel can be calculated by subtracting $\Delta T_{REP, \text{ reactive}}$.

To calculate and to compare all arising costs for each strategy (see grey bars in figure 7) the estimation of the present value is a common method in financial mathematics. The present value represents the cash-equivalent value future payments have in the present (herein referring to 2011). This value is determined by discounting future payments and a final add up (herein: interest rate = 3.0%). The whole economic calculation is based on the guideline for the execution of economic feasibility studies of the Federal Ministry of Transport Building and Urban Development (BMVBS 2004).

To conduct such a calculation additional practical boundary conditions e.g. regarding different scenarios (load/impact vs. material resistances), the construction costs of a fictional reinforced element, the area under repair, the annual maintenance expenses and the proper costs of a single repair, are necessary.

7.3 Boundary conditions

The time until the individual serviceability limit state (reactive and proactive) is reached obviously depends on different parameters, see section 4.2. To create different scenarios, several parameters were varied:

- Planned Service Life (psl): 50/100 years
- Serviceability Limit State (SLS): $\beta_{SLS} = 0.5/1.5$
- exposure classes: XD3/XD2 ($\approx$ XS3/XS2)
- binder: CEM I, CEM I + fly ash (FA), CEM III/A
- concrete cover: $d_c = 55/45$ mm, $2/3 \, d_c = 36.7$ mm
- w/b-ratio = 0.4 / 0.5

The chosen types of cement represent a good spectrum of practically relevant types. The two different concrete covers and w/b-ratios characterize the large range of an achievable quality of execution on site: for instance an optimal execution according to latest standards (e.g. XD3: $d_c = 55$ mm (DIN 1045-1 2008) and w/b = 0.4) and a possible case of execution deficiencies (e.g. XD3: $d_c = 45$ mm and w/b = 0.5). The difference of

the two exposure classes were taken into account with a variation of the substitute surface chloride concentration $C_{S,\Delta x}$ according to (Tang 1996). The information about the rapid chloride migration coefficient $D_{RCM,0}$ and the aging exponent a of the considered cement types are derived from different sources (DAfStb 2008; Gehlen 2000; Osterminski & Gehlen 2009) and partly changed after (Tang 1996) concerning different w/b-ratio. All selected parameters are described as stochastic values and listed in Table 2.

Using this information the calculation of the intervention intervals for each considered scenario is possible. With an additional combination of real costs for single intervention actions it is possible to estimate the whole life cycle costs for each scenario.

Taking the strategy with the lowest life cycle costs as a benchmark the minimal necessary extra service life of ECR (ESL in years) compared to black steel can be calculated (see section 7.2). Table 3 shows a summary of the individual assumptions adopted.

In general the assumptions indicated in table 3 are based on practical experience. For example the approach of 240 €/m² for construction costs fits to the average planning costs for construction of a ceiling of an underground parking garage. The exemplary area of 100 m² for the considered element can easily be extrapolated to any other size. In order to ensure comparability for the different strategies a constant area for every single intervention had to be established.

The constant area means in this case that 100% of the considered area of a construction element has to be restored (according to the three strategies) when a current condition state falls below the predefined safety limit ($\beta_{SLS} = 0.5$ or 1.5). This assumption is quite conservative as different achievable reliabilities β induce different probabilities of failure p_f, see section 4.2:

– $\beta = 0.5$ relates to $p_f \approx 6.7\%$
– $\beta = 1.5$ relates to $p_f \approx 30.8\%$

In practice this is normally expressed in areas of different sizes which have to be repaired because the serviceability limit state (depassivation of reinforcement) is already obtained and corrosion is obvious. Data about the real distributions of still passivated or depassivated surfaces could not be simulated until now and have to be investigated locally with different inspection techniques under real conditions. The details of the intervention costs for the three different approaches are displayed below in Table 4 a–b.

Possible saving of expenses due to reduced concrete covers (lower material costs) or different types of binders have not been taken into account. Equally cost advantages due to a smaller number

847

Table 2.   Selected parameters of the chloride penetration model for exposure class XD3 and XD2.

No.	w/b [–]	$C_{S,\Delta x}$ (XD3) [wt.-%/c]	$C_{S,\Delta x}$ (XD2) [wt.-%/c]	$D_{RCM,0}$ [mm²/a]	a [–]
CEM I					
1	0.4	LogN* (2.41; 1,08)	LogN* (1.82; 0.82)	ND* (280.7; 56.1)	BetaD* (0.30; 0.12; 0 ≤ a ≤ 1)
2	0.5	LogN* (2.73; 1.23)	LogN* (2.00; 0.90)	ND* (498.3; 99.7)	
CEM I + FA					
3	0.4	LogN* (2.67; 1.20)	LogN* (2.06; 0.93)	ND* (176.6; 35.3)	BetaD* (0.60; 0.15; 0 ≤ a ≤ 1)
4	0.5	LogN (2.99; 1.35)	LogN (2.27; 1.02)	ND* (283.9; 56.8)	
CEM III/A					
5	0.4	LogN* (2.47; 1.10)	LogN* (1.85; 0.83)	ND* (124.6; 24.9)	BetaD* (0.40; 0.16; 0 ≤ a ≤ 1)
6	0.5	LogN* (2.81; 1.26)	LogN* (2.06; 0.93)	ND* (131.2; 26.2)	

*LogN: log-normal size distribution, ND: normal distribution, BetaD: beta distribution.

Table 3.   Assumptions for the economic feasibility study on the example of a partial area of an underground parking ceiling.

No.	Description	Assumed costs Proactive	Reactive	ECR
1	Standard price for a fictional element (e.g. undergound parking ceiling)	240 €/m²		240 €/m² · 1.05*
2	Fictional area	100 m²		
3	Total construction costs	24,000 €		25,200 €*
4	Area of repair for every single intervention	25 m²		
5	Costs of a single intervention	5,900 € (factor: 0.25)	23,375 € (factor: 1.0)	31,125 € (factor: 1.31)
6	Annual maintenance costs	1.06%**	1.00%***	1.00%***

*incl. +5% due to the application of ECR (CRSI 1998); **higher maintenance costs due to a necessary installation and evaluation of a monitoring system (multiring electrodes (Schießl & Mayer 2007)) to ensure the sealing effect; ***according to (BMVBS 2004).

of intervention actions over the service life (e.g. reduced downtimes) were not included.

As another theoretical condition, the time-dependent degradation of the epoxy-coating wasn't considered; even the performance degradation of ECR over time is to be expected (especially if the corrosion protection effect of ECR is required at a late stage in the service life of a structure).

7.4   Results

The calculated present values for each scenario are displayed in the following four figures (Figures 8–11).

The diagrams are separated for different planned service lifetimes and minimum serviceability limit states β_{min}. For each scenery the same code of varied parameters is applied: "binder_w/b_d_c".

In addition the numerical values for the proactive and reactive strategy are integrated, see figures 8–11.

In the case of no stated value for the reactive strategy the estimated intervention interval is smaller than two years. Some scenarios like CEM I_05_45 are not considered in the calculations due to the fact that safety limits couldn't be met at any time.

Table 4a. Details for applied intervention costs separated for the reactive strategy and the usage of ECR.

No.	Position	Unit price	Comment
Reactive			
1	Site installation costs (without HPW*)	min. 5,000 €	Otherwise 3–5% of total costs of repair
2	Site installation costs (with HPW*)	min. 15,000 €	Otherwise 3–5% of total costs of repair
3	Soncrete removal by hand (removal depth on average: 8 cm)	490 €/m²	<24 m²: by hand is more economic
4	Concrete removal by HPW* (removal depth on average: 8 cm)	180 €/m²	>24 m²: HPW* is more economic
5	Surface preparation of exposed surface	15 €/m²	Underground treatment
6	Concrete replacement and curing (depth on average: 8 cm)	140 €/m²	Ready-mix concrete (horizontal surfaces)
Additional costs due to the application of ECR			
7	Abrasive blasting of reinforcement	60 €/m²	Release of corrosion products
8	Patch repair of epoxy-coated reinforcement	250 €/m²	Manual work

*HPW: high-pressure waterjet.

Table 4b. Details for applied intervention costs for the proactive strategy

No.	Position	Unit price	Comment
Proactive			
1	Site installation costs (renew coating)	min. 3,000 €	Otherwise 3–5% of total costs of repair
2	Removal of the old coating	15 €/m²	–
3	Surface preparation of exposed surface	10 €/m²	Underground treatment
4	Application of surface protection system	91 €/m²	Concrete coating

The theoretical lowest present value in all cases was an additional investment due to the use of ECR combined with guarantee of a full serviceability over the planned service life (condition: no additional interventions are necessary).

The following two examples serve to illustrate the base of the costs:

• The result of 50,800 € in the scenario "CEM I_04_55" in figure 8 demonstrates the present value of the arising life cycle costs over 50 years according to the proactive strategy: First coating application (5,900 € for 25 m², for details see table 3 and 4b) in the year before the reliability index falls below $\beta = 1.5$ (with 2/3

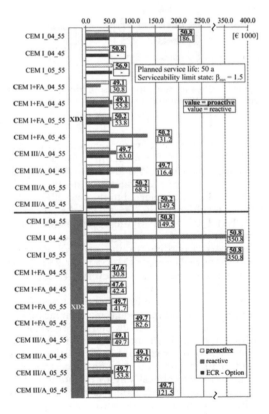

Figure 8. Present values for each scenario for a planned service life of 50a and $\beta = 1.5$.

849

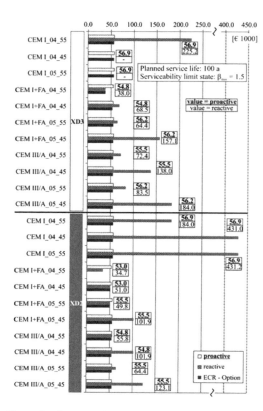

Figure 9.   Present values for each scenario for a planned service life of 100a and β = 1.5.

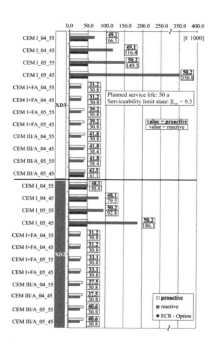

Figure 10.   Present values for each scenario for a planned service life of 50a and β = 0.5.

d_c = 36.7 mm), afterwards renewal in intervals of 10 years (5,900 € for 25 m²). Annual maintenance costs of 1.06% are on top. Finally all future costs were discounted with an interest rate of 3.0% and referred to the year 2011.

• The result of 186,100 € in the scenario "CEM I_04_55" in figure 8 demonstrates the present value of the arising life cycle costs over 50 years according to the reactive strategy: Concrete replacement (23,375 € for 25 m², for details see table 3 and 4a) every 14 years (see also $\Delta T_{REP, reactive}$ = 14a, Figure 12). That is the year before the reliability index falls below β = 5 (with d_c = 55 mm). Annual maintenance costs of 1.0% are on top. Finally all future costs were discounted with an interest rate of 3.0% and referred to the year 2011. Most of the results out of figures 8 and 9 show an expected trend: The most economical way to maintain a reinforced structure on a safety level of β = 1.5 is the application of a proactive strategy (concrete coating). The cost differences between the proactive and reactive strategy vary enormously

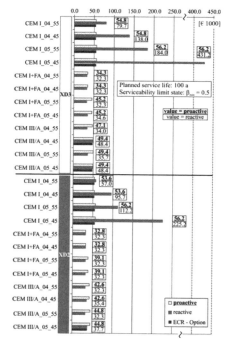

Figure 11.   Present values for each scenario for a planned service life of 100a and β = 0.5.

850

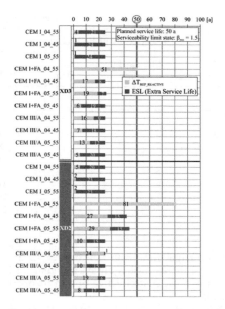

Figure 12. Necessary Extra Service Life (ESL) of epoxy-coated reinforcements (in years) for each scenario for a planned service life of 50a and β = 1.5.

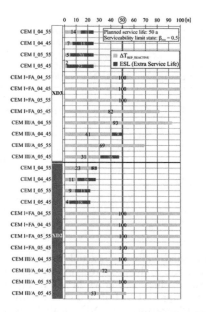

Figure 14. Necessary Extra Service Life (ESL) of epoxy-coated reinforcements (in years) for each scenario for a planned service life of 50a and β = 0.5.

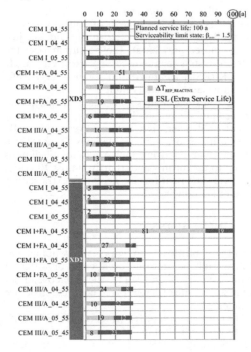

Figure 13. Necessary Extra Service Life (ESL) of epoxy-coated reinforcements (in years) for each scenario for a planned service life of 100a and β = 1.5.

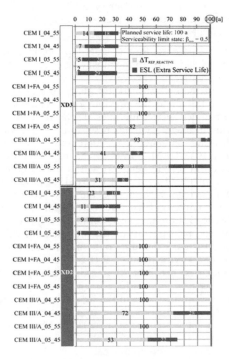

Figure 15. Necessary Extra Service Life (ESL) of epoxy-coated reinforcements (in years) for each scenario for a planned service life of 100a and β = 0.5.

851

Table 5. Statistical processing of the necessary extra service life of ECR depending on different parameters.

Planned service life	Exposition class after DIN EN 206	β	mean	Standard deviation	Min	Max
			Necessary extra service life of ECR (ESL)			
[a]	[–]	[–]	[a]			
50	XD3	1.5	16.2	6.6	7	24
		0.5	16.2	5.3	9	23
	XD2	1.5	15.5	7.7	1	28
		0.5	13.0	5.7	5	18
100	XD3	1.5	21.9	5.9	12	29
		0.5	19.0	9.3	7	31
	XD2	1.5	18.4	7.6	7	28
		0.5	21.8	6.4	10	28

and individually (e.g. partial more than +100% in relation to the proactive option). The highest present values are shown in scenarios with the cement type CEM I. The higher environmental load in exposure class XD3 leads to higher life cycle costs. In general, execution deficiencies (higher w/b and/or lower concrete covers at the same binder) result in higher present values. The only exceptions to this are some combinations with the binder type CEM I + FA. In certain cases even the reactive strategy would be preferable.

Presented costs for the ECR-Option have been iteratively adjusted to the most cost effective strategy (proactive or reactive).

The results illustrated in figures 10 and 11 are quite different to the previous ones. The considered planned service lifetimes are the same but the minimum reliability index is set to $\beta = 0.5$. Again, higher environmental loads increase the costs and binder type CEM I lead to the highest present values. But for all scenarios with a binder combination of CEM I + FA or CEM III/A (XD3 and XD2) the reactive strategy is the most economical way to maintain a structure. Once again, the costs for ECR-Option have been iteratively adjusted.

Based on the results of the present value calculations the corresponding outcomes for the necessary extra service life of ECR (ECR has to compete with the cost-benchmark) are displayed in the next four diagrams (figures 12–15).

The illustrated bars in the figures are separated into $\Delta T_{REP, reactive}$ (obligatory intervention interval regarding the reactive strategy) and ESL (necessary extra service life of ECR). The sum of both represents the required total service life of the system (individual concrete together with ECR) and indicates the required intervention interval for epoxy-coated reinforcement.

In principal the results of figures 12 and 13 show, that there is nearly always a chance for ECR to be the most cost effective option to operate a structure.

Only in the case of a planned service life of 50 years and using CEM I+FA (w/b = 0.4 and $d_c = 55$ mm) does ECR have no chance to be cost effective over the service life.

The analyses in Figures 14 and 15 demonstrate that the use of ECR at lower defined safety indices ($\beta = 0.5$) and especially under a limited planned service life (50 years) frequently has no possibility to be cost-effective in the end (see just single-colored grey bars). Table 5 summarizes the different results for the necessary extra service life of ECR (ESL) separated into planned service life, exposure class and safety limit β.

The statistical analysis in table 5 displays that the mean of the required extra life due to application of ECR mostly is less than 20 years, especially considering short service lifetimes. Taking into account that relatively high standard deviations belong to the mean values (partly almost 10 years) a general statement for one necessary extra service life is not conducive.

8 CONCLUSIONS

With the presented approach of an economic feasibility study, certain life cycle costs of different maintenance strategies can be calculated over a fictional service life of a reinforced concrete structure or element.

The combination of full probabilistic service life design with practical maintenance procedures and corresponding costs enables the planner or operator already in the design phase to choose the right building material (concrete) and also the most cost effective maintenance strategy or vice versa. Even increased costs associated with possible execution deficiencies can be considered in worst case scenarios. Stated advantages of different binders in the case of chloride induced corrosion (especially CEM III/A) have to be assessed on the background of existing disadvantages for corrosion due to carbonation.

The knowledge of the so called "best practice" also allows the comparison to other options or systems for an optimized maintenance (e.g. epoxy-coated reinforcement).

In general, the final results of the necessary extra service life of epoxy-coated reinforcement are promising. Especially among following boundary conditions the profitability analysis is possibly achievable:

- high environmental impacts (e.g. chlorides)
- low quality concrete (binders with low chloride penetration resistances)
- low concrete covers due to execution deficiencies or design specifications
- compliance of higher safety standards ($\beta > 0.5$)

It remains to be noted that an anticipated economic feasibility study of ECR just can be used as a qualitative orientation for future experimental results regarding the real corrosion protection potential of epoxy-coated reinforcement. This is the objective of an existing research project. At least the future research results must be judged on the presented theoretical results. Looking at it the other way round, if the experimental outcomes cannot guarantee or prospect the fulfillment of the conditions (necessary extra service life) the epoxy-coated reinforcement will not be a beneficial system from an economic point of view.

REFERENCES

BMVBS 2004. RI-WI-BRÜ—Richtlinie zur Durchführung von Wirtschaftlichkeitsuntersuchungen im Rahmen von Instandsetzungs-/Erneuerungsmaßnahmen bei Straßenbrücken. Federal Ministry of Transport Building and Urban Development, Berlin.

BMVBS 2006. Bericht über die Qualität, Dauerhaftigkeit und Sicherheit von Spannbetonbrücken. Federal Ministry of Transport Building and Urban Development, Berlin.

Breit, W. 1997. *Untersuchungen zum kritischen korrosionsauslösenden Chloridgehalt von Stahl in Beton.* Dissertation, Institut für Bauforschung der RWTH Aachen, Aachen.

CRSI 1998. Epoxy-coated rebar delivers cost effective value. Report, Concrete Reinforcing Steel Institute, Schaumburg, USA.

DAfStb 2008. Positionspapier des DAfStb zur Umsetzung des Konzepts von leistungsbezogenen Entwurfsverfahren unter Berücksichtigung von DIN EN 206-1, Anhang J. Berlin: Beuth-Verlag.

DIN 1045-1: 2008. Tragwerke aus Beton, Stahlbeton und Spannbeton. Teil 1: Bemessung und Konstruktion. Berlin: Beuth-Verlag.

FIB 34, 2006. Model Code for Service Life Design, fib Bulletin 34, The International Federation for Structural Concrete, Switzerland.

Gehlen, Ch. 2000. *Probabilistische Lebensdauerbemessung von Stahlbetonbauwerken.* Deutscher Ausschuss für Stahlbeton, Issue 510, Berlin: Beuth-Verlag.

Gehlen, Ch; Schießl, P; Schießl-Pecka, A. 2008. Hintergrundinformationen zum Positionspapier des DAfStb zur Umsetzung des Konzepts von leistungsbezogenen Entwurfsverfahren unter Berücksichtigung von DIN EN 206-1, Anhang J. *Beton- und Stahlbetonbau*, Vol. 103, Issue 12, pp. 840–851.

Hartley, J. 1994. Improving the performance of fusion-bonded epoxy-coated reinforcement. *Concrete*, Vol. January/February, pp. 12–15.

Osterminski, K. & Gehlen Ch. 2009. *Zuverlässigkeit Wasserbauwerke—Chlorideindringwiderstand.* Research Report, Centre for Building Materials, Technische Universität München, Munich.

Raupach, M. 2004. *Ergebnisse eines Forschungsprojektes zur Notwendigkeit und Dauerhaftigkeit von Parkhausbeschichtungen.*—Proceedings of the 16. Baupraktischen Informations-Seminar: Bauwerke instand setzen heute und morgen, Bad Nauheim, Germany.

Schießl, P. & Mayer, T.F. 2007. *Lebensdauermanagementsystem.* Deutscher Ausschuss für Stahlbeton, Issue 572, Berlin: Beuth-Verlag.

Schießl, P. et al. 2011. *Schlussbericht zum DAfStb/BMBF—Verbundforschungsvorhaben "Nachhaltig Bauen mit Beton": TP D Lebensdauer management system.* Issue 586, Berlin: Beuth-Verlag. (in press).

Tang, L. 1996. *Chloride Transport in Concrete—Measurement and Prediction.* Dissertation, Chalmers University of Technology, Gothenburg.

Author index

Abu-Tair, A.I. 585
Ahlborn, K. 427
Al-Ameeri, A.S.A. 3, 689
Alani, A.M. 95
Al-Baghdadi, H.M. 195
Al-Ghalib, A. 413, 575
Ali, M.K. 585
Ali, N.H. 689
Ali, O. 593
Al-Juborry, A. 503
Allahvirdizadeh, R. 435
Allam, H.M. 607
Allouche, E.N. 267
Al-Mahmoud, F. 705
Almosa, A.A. 251, 445
Almusallam, T.H. 251, 445
Al-Neshawy, F. 343
Al-Salloum, Y.A. 251, 445
Alsayed, S.H. 251, 445
Amir, A.M.A. 195
Anagnostopoulos, N. 835
Annerel, E. 487
Atkins, C. 133
Atta, A.M. 177
Austin, S. 141
Axelrod, E.Z. 789

Badr, A. 187
Barfield, M. 233
Behfarnia, K. 615
Belichenko, O.A. 313
Bentivegna, A.F. 123, 823
Berkowski, P. 9
Berthold, F. 427
Beushausen, H. 205
Bienert, K. 805
Bigaud, D. 593
Birtwisle, A. 419
Blanco, P.L. 631
Blanksvärd, T. 623
Boller, C. 397
Bonnet, S. 215
Bott, N. 15
Bouzelha, K. 45
Broomfield, J.P. 527
Brueckner, R. 133
Bruedern, A.-E. 741

Cai, X. 479
Castel, A. 705
Chen, X. 479
Chess, P. 25
Chilton, J. 575
Choinska, M. 215
Christodoulou, C. 141
Copuroglu, O. 307
Courage, W. 157

Dale, S. 325
Demski, D. 697
Deniskin, V.V. 813
Diawara, H. 233
Diaz-Loya, E.I. 267
Dmochowski, G. 9
Donchev, T. 491, 631, 765
Dousti, A. 105, 387, 435
Drewett, J. 15
Duber, A. 19
Dudkiewicz, J. 9

Eden, M.A. 497
Eftekhar, M.H. 387
Eghtesadi, Sh. 615
El shami, A. 215
El-Ashkar, N.H. 349, 749
Elrakib, T.M. 639
El-Shafiey, T.F. 177
Elzanaty, A.H. 607
Esteves, H. 25
Etman, E.E. 649

Falikman, V.R. 813
Faraji, F. 293
Faur, A. 227
Fawzi, A. 607
Flohrer, C. 661
Folliard, K.J. 123, 823
Foster, A. 133
Fraaij, A.L.A. 147
Francois, R. 705
Fyfe, E. 667

Gaponov, V. 547, 789
Garduno, A. 31
Ge, Y. 479

Gehlen, C. 841
Georgiadis, A. 835
Ghafoori, N. 233, 243
Ghassemzadeh, F. 293, 461
Giannini, E.R. 123, 823
Glass, G. 141
Goldschmidt, S. 805
Goodier, C. 141
Gralińska-Grubecka, A. 237
Gramegna, F. 557
Grantham, M.G. 39
Grünzig, H. 427
Gulikers, J.J.W. 535

Habeeb, G. 503
Hammer, U. 25
Hammoum, H. 45
Hankers, Ch. 783
Hannachi, N.E. 45
Hauser, S. 661
Heinemann, H.A. 55
Helmi, K.M. 749
Hold, S. 69
Holschemacher, K. 681
Homma, T. 467
Hou, B. 279
Hussein, M. 673

Ille, K. 795
Ille, M. 795
Ingham, J.M. 727
Ishiyama, S. 467
Iskhakov, I. 681
Islam, M.S. 233, 243

Jahn, H. 427
Javidmehr, S. 387
Jo, J.H. 423
Jones, S. 39
Jonkers, H.M. 331
Jurado Cabañes, C. 79

Kaminski, M. 697
Karantzikis, M. 667
Kew, H. 491
Khan, M.I. 251, 445
Khelidj, A. 215

Kobayashi, K. 369
Koenders, E.A.B. 307
Köhler, J. 427
Köliö, A. 541
Kolyvas, C. 667
Kreit, A. 705
Książek, M. 257
Kühnen, H.-C. 451
Kupwade-Patil, K. 267
Kurgansky, M. 547
Kurz, J.H. 397
Kusa, E. 697

Lahdensivu, J. 85, 541
Lam, E.S.S. 717
Lambert, P. 133
Lawley, D. 727
Lee, Y. 423
Leegwater, G. 157
L'Hostis, V. 377
Li, B. 717
Li, C.Q. 551
Li, H. 335
Li, W. 279
Lin, Y. 727
Lorenz, E. 783
Łukaszewicz, J.W. 237

Mahmoodian, M. 551
Majorana, C.E. 517, 557, 735
Manita, P. 835
Marie-Victoire, E. 377
Matsue, H. 405
Matzdorff, D. 783
Mayer, S. 25
Mazzucco, G. 735
Mechtcherine, V. 741
Meng, B. 451
Merola, R. 133
Minaii, Z. 461
Mircea, A.-T. 91
Mircea, C. 227, 511
Mizobuchi, T. 359
Moghadam, S.R. 387
Mohammad, F. 575
Mol, J.M.C. 147
Molkenthin, A. 805
Moradi-Marani, F. 105
Morsy, A.M. 749
Motamed, J. 95
Mounanga, P. 215
Mourad, S.M. 757
Mueller, T. 681
Müllner, F. 163

Nakamura, R. 369
Nakazawa, S. 369

Niederleithinger, E. 805
Nijland, T.G. 55
Nojima, J. 359
Nyknahad, D. 233

Okazaki, S. 405

Pacheco, J. 147
Park, J.H. 423
Patil, H.S. 287
Pavlov, S. 547
Pawlowski, A. 19
Pepenar, I. 101
Petkova, D. 765
Petkune, N. 491
Petrovay, Gh. 511
Piironen, J. 343
Pitchers, S. 39
Polder, R.B. 147, 157
Pomaro, B. 557
Prete, G. 557
Proust, A. 377
Prust, B. 841
Puttonen, J. 343

Rahman, M. 413, 575
Raijiwala, D.B. 287
Ramge, P. 451
Rashetnia, R. 105, 435
Raupach, M. 391
Razavizadeh, A. 461
Reichling, K. 391
Reyes, A. 31
Ribakov, Y. 299, 681
Rokugo, K. 369

Sajedi, S. 293, 461
Salomoni, V.A. 517, 557, 735
Satoh, A. 467
Sayah, A. 615
Sayed, M.M. 639
Schalk, H. 805
Schneck, U. 113, 427
Schrefler, B.A. 565
Schwarz, W. 163
Sciumè, G. 565
Scott, A. 727
Serre, D. 45
Shadhan, K.K. 689
Shah, A.A. 299
Shah, P.S. 631
Shannag, M.J. 757
Shekarchi, M. 105, 293, 387, 435, 461
Shilin, A.A. 789
Shinohara, Y. 467
Sideris, K.K. 835

Sisomphon, K. 307
Skarlatos, E. 835
Skazlić, M. 795
Slowik, V. 775
Soleimani, M. 293
Song, Y.C. 423
Sorokin, Yu.V. 813
Stoppel, M. 397

Taerwe, L. 487
Taffe, A. 397
Täljsten, B. 623
Tan, Y. 335
Tann, D.B. 585
Tian, H. 279
Tolmachev, S.N. 313
Tschötschel, M. 661

Ujike, I. 405
Urbonas, T. 741
Usman, M. 413
Utsi, V. 419

Vaidya, S. 267
Valipour, M. 387
Vallot, F. 377
van den Hondel, A. 163
van Hees, R.P.J. 55
Varjonen, S. 85
Vonau, W. 427

Wagner, C. 775
Wang, D. 279
Webb, J. 141
Weiland, S. 783
Wheat, H.G. 325
Wiggenhauser, H. 397
Wiktor, V. 331
Wilsch, G. 805
Woo, S.K. 423
Worm, D. 157
Wotherspoon, L. 727

Xie, Y. 335
Xotta, G. 517

Yamada, K. 467
Yamate, M. 405
Yang, W. 479
Yi, Z. 335

Zalomov, S.S. 789
Zijlstra, H. 55
Zintel, M. 841

856